Published by

Willmann-Bell, Inc.

P.O. Box 35025 • Richmond, Virginia 23235 • **www.willbell.com**

Published by Willmann-Bell, Inc.

Printed in the United States of America
First Printing 2003

Library of Congress Cataloging in Publication Data
Archinal, Brent A.
Star clusters / Brent A. Archinal, Steven J. Hynes ; foreword by David H. Levy.
p. cm.
Includes bibliographical references and index
ISBN 0-943396-80-8
1. Stars--Clusters, I. Hynes, Steven J. II Title.

QB853.A73 2003
523.8'5--dc21 2003045240

09 08 07 06 05 04 03 02 01 00 10 9 8 7 6 5 4 3 2

Preface

I have a memory of a long ago tropical night in Sri Lanka. The warm Indian Ocean laps gently on soft white sand. A gentle sea breeze stirs through the palm trees. The Sun, after a spectacular display of pink, red, gold and silver has set and darkness follows with incredible speed. Venus sparkles brilliantly above the horizon while I organize myself for a night's observing. I wait and watch the sky, hoping that the extensive veil of thin, high clouds will disperse. As the minutes pass the veil becomes fuller, transforming into a billowing mass of light and dark. Suddenly I realize my foolishness. Before my very eyes, the "clouds" of millions upon millions of stars in the direction of the center of the our galaxy—the Milky Way—have been finding their form. Through the middle of these starclouds, rivers of dark nebulae wind their way. As the darkness becomes complete the spectacle moves me to tears; that I should be privileged to see such splendor! Now, in addition to the starclouds and dark nebulae, I become aware of other features; here and there are scattered small, bright hazy spots of light. Reaching for my star atlas, I identify them; the brightest is clearly the star cluster M 7, to the north of the tail of Scorpius; nearby is the rather fainter spot of M 6. I can also clearly see the nebula and cluster complex of M 8, NGC 6231—the nucleus of the Sco OB1 Association, and among the fainter objects, the globular cluster M 22. Equipped with a 10.5-cm rich-field telescope, the clusters of Sagittarius and Scorpius are a joy to explore for the next two weeks.

I had always enjoyed viewing star clusters, but the Sri Lanka experience left me with a particular fondness for these most spectacular of deep-sky objects. Of course, many clusters, whether open or globular, are more obscure and can be quite challenging to find—and even more so to resolve! Moving beyond their sheer beauty clusters can reveal other fascinating features. Open clusters often contain variable stars and double stars, and sometimes have associated nebulosities. Globular clusters are good tests of resolution—can your telescope resolve the tightly packed stars? Globular clusters also contain variable stars, and some exhibit subtle morphological features, such as the M 13 "propeller."

Open clusters and globular clusters are particularly important from the astrophysical point of view. Open clusters are laboratories for students of stellar evolution because they all share a common heritage in their formation from a molecular cloud. Most are quite young as measured in cosmic time but others have spent many millions of years bound together by gravity as they orbit the hub of the Milky Way. If open clusters generally occupy the most recent epoch of cosmic time, then globular clusters reside at its farthest reaches. Unlike open clusters, these vast globes were formed from primeval material barely contaminated by heavy elements and contain up to perhaps a million stars. The stars in globular clusters are, therefore, highly evolved and have produced some exotic phenomena, such as the so-called "blue stragglers" and millisecond pulsars.

This book has several purposes. First, it provides historical and astrophysical background information about open and globular star clusters from the perspective of the visual observation. Second, we present a comprehensive catalog of objects, together with information about selected clusters of special interest. This catalog is augmented with photographs and notes again tailored for the observer. A large number of references is also given, to enable those with access to professional journals and the World Wide Web to pursue further research.

STEVEN HYNES

Have you ever looked for something in the sky and not found it? From my earliest experience as an amateur astronomer, it seemed there were a good number of objects that I sought, but was unable to find. Clearly, most of the problem initially was a lack of experience in observing, using a telescope, and simply seeing the sky.

But as time went by I became more and more aware that at least sometimes the problem was that the information I used to find the object was wrong or incomplete. The position might be a little off, or the size or other descriptive information would be off. And checking other sources of information didn't always help. Much as someone with a watch always knows what time it is but with two watches is never quite sure, two sources of information may only confuse the problem. The position, diameter, and even the name might be one thing in one atlas, and something else entirely in another atlas or catalog.

An outcome of encountering this sort of problem was an interest in tracking down and solving such problems. At first this was only a casual interest in checking data for deep-sky objects in general, such as those in the NGC. Eventually it led to some specialization, as I looked for star clusters that had been cataloged at some point but were now often nowhere to be found. And finally it has led to a good portion of what you see before you, a book on star clusters including the most complete catalog of such objects ever made.

I hasten to explain though that along the way there was more to it than this. The incredible beauty of the varied and luminous stars of a star cluster has always been a sight to behold. And when I recall some of my greatest observing experiences, indeed, some of the greatest experiences of my life, I find that star clusters are often in some way involved.

My earliest recollection as an amateur astronomer is as a teenager, trying to use my brother Bruce's telescope (a 3-inch Edmund Super Space Conqueror for those who can remember that model) to find objects in the sky. I can clearly remember the moment of discovery when I found a star cluster that looked something like a dipper of stars, and realizing it was the Pleiades. Just as clearly I can recall the interest of my parents who came outside on a cold early spring night in Ohio to take a look at my amazing find. And now in later years it is the Pleiades that I still look at with amazement, but also with the recollection of the support my parents have always given me, particularly as my interest in astronomy and science grew.

I recall trips to Arizona on vacation in the late 1970's and early 1980's, a place that to some extent I fell in love with and where I thought it might be nice to live someday—not realizing then that dream would come true sooner than I had thought. Certainly among the many spectacles of nature I saw here, I could count the clear dark skies of northern Arizona among the best. Among the objects observed in those skies were star clusters, whether with the unaided eye, through small telescopes, or even through the giant 72-inch Perkins reflector that a friend let us observe through briefly. For 30 minutes or so—while waiting for him to develop spectroscopic plates—I gazed at the core of the spectacular globular cluster M 13 using 1000 times magnification. I tried but failed completely to draw a portion of that core, lost in the utterly amazing view of star streams, lanes, and thousands upon thousands of stars.

My mind carries me forward to the winter of 1986, where from a cold hilltop in Ohio my new wife JoAnne and I managed our first reasonable view of the famous Comet Halley, then low on the meridian near the southern horizon. It had changed from the faint speck I had first seen in a 12.5-inch telescope the previous September—on the morning of my wedding day—to a respectable just naked eye object with a short tail. Perhaps just as interesting to me though was that in looking for the comet I had accidentally found the great globular cluster ω Centauri, which Halley was passing near. It did not have the wonderful appearance I was later to see from much more southern latitudes, but here it was reminding me that star clusters can come up in the most unexpected places.

Fast-forwarding another 10 years brings me to another memorable moment, another memorable comet, and another memorable star cluster. On the night of March 26–27, 1996, JoAnne and I and friends arrived about midnight at Big Meadows in the Shenandoah National Park in Virginia. The Moon was still in the sky, but the bright Comet Hyakutaki stood at a near standstill quite close to Polaris. We rested for a while until the Moon left the sky. Upon rising we were greeted with an absolutely amazing sight. Hyakutaki was still right were it had been earlier, except perhaps a little closer to Polaris. But with the Moon gone it was now nearly the brightest object in the sky. And the tail—oh, the tail!—crossed fully one third of the sky. The coma of the head of the comet blended in evenly into the long, long tail, that itself had a varying width. The tail passed right through the bowl of the Big Dipper (itself part of the Ursa Major moving cluster). Then it disappeared over 60° away—right in the middle of another "coma", the large, marvelous, and faintly sparkling Coma Berenices star cluster, now riding high almost overhead in one of the darkest skies I ever saw from Virginia.

There have been other star clusters, other observing sessions, other events with friends and family—and I hope there will be many more. I write these words only to remind you that these star clusters can be yours as well. They are there for all of us to understand, all of us to admire, and all of us to enjoy. I hope that what we have gathered together here will help to bring the star clusters to you.

BRENT ARCHINAL

Foreword

When John Louis Emil Dreyer published the *New General Catalogue of Nebulae and Clusters of Stars* in 1888, he tried to bring some sense and order to the lists of William and John Herschel. Dreyer's seminal work formed the basis of our understanding of the Deep Sky from that day to this. The book you are now holding—Archinal and Hynes' *Star Clusters*, is as seminal a work, deserving a place in every observer's bookshelf right next to the *NGC* itself.

The reason this new book is so important is that especially with star clusters and asterisms (physically unrelated groupings of stars), there has been a tremendous amount of confusion. Uncertain positions have resulted in many clusters being misrepresented, misplotted on atlases, or simply lost altogether. Archinal and Hynes have done a spectacular job carefully sifting through the *NGC* and many modern lists, trying to pinpoint the existence, and the positions, of these important deep sky objects.

The care involved in producing this book resulted in its taking years to put together. I remember talking with Brent on several occasions spread over years, getting a sense of the progress that the authors and their publisher were making. Even with the use of modern computers, telescopes, and assistance by several first-rate observers, the project took so long that even Dreyer would have been impressed with their perseverance and with the time and care that went into it.

Handsomely illustrated with images of the more striking of the objects, this book is beautiful as well as utilitarian. It has also placed its authors as the *de facto* arbitrators for the additions of new objects. I found that out while comet hunting a few years ago, and picking up a unique circle of stars I wanted to call Wendee's ring after my wife. The object, listed in the catalogue as Levy-Wallach J2204.3+4508 for its J2000.0 position in the sky, looks like a near-perfect ring of 11th magnitude stars. It is listed along with J2108.8+0620 (an S-shaped grouping of stars I call Equuleus S), and J2340.6+5618 (Nanette's River). I am honored that these three asterisms take their place in this momentous work.

I recommend a slow dipping into the pages of this book over many cloudy nights. You will learn about clusters and asterisms in our own galaxy, globulars in other galaxies, and deep sky objects within the Magellanic Clouds and M 31 that you never imagined to exist. Then when the sky clears, you'll be able to go out and observe some of these objects. Far more than a catalog, this book is a journey to fabulous places in distant parts of space.

David H. Levy

Table of Contents

Acknowledgments

Steven Hynes would like to acknowledge the help and ideas of Brian Skiff (Lowell Observatory). Other individuals whose contributions have eased the task include Owen Brazell, Murray Cragin, Steve Gottlieb, and Don Miles. Much of the research for the book was carried out at the library of the Nuffield Radio Astronomy Laboratories, Jodrell Bank, and he is indebted to the Director for permission to use these facilities and also to Sarah Jackson, the librarian, for her help and hospitality. Additional research was carried out at the library of Keele University and the Royal Astronomical Society where Peter Hingley, the RAS librarian, was very helpful.

Brent Archinal would like to thank several individuals who helped in the course of the cataloging work done for this book. Brian Skiff, in particular, has been of immense help. He has provided copies of both his list of open clusters with improved positions and other data, and of general information on Galactic globular clusters. Brian has continually provided updated information on star clusters gleaned from various publications and his own observations. He has also provided invaluable advice concerning various sources of data and answered many questions about star clusters in general. Murray Cragin, James Lucyk, the late Barry Rappaport and their publisher, Willmann-Bell, provided a machine-readable copy of their list of star clusters in the first edition of *The Deep Sky Field Guide to Uranometria 2000.0* (Willmann-Bell, Inc., 1993). S. George Djorgovski (Caltech) has provided machine readable copies of several data tables regarding Galactic globular clusters as originally published in Djorgovski and Meylan (eds.), *Structure and Dynamics of Globular Clusters, ASP Conf. Ser.* 50, 1993. William Harris (McMasters' University) and Hugh Harris (USNO Flagstaff) have also provided useful information concerning such clusters.

A number of individuals have graciously provided their own observations or other information on the identities of various star clusters and related objects. The accuracy of the cataloguing work done here owes a great deal to these individuals—although what errors may remain are certainly our own. Besides Brian Skiff, in particular, Alister Ling, Harold Corwin, Jr. (NASA/JPL/IPAC), Hugh Harris (USNO, Flagstaff, AZ), Jenni Kay, Steve Gottlieb, Barbara Wilson, Yann Pothier, Al Lamperti, Randall Poole, Dave Riddle, Susan French, Steve Mencinsky, Doug Snyder, Bruno S. Alessi, Joe Bergeron, Russell Lederman, Larry Sykara, Timo Karhula, Guy Mackie, Paul Markov, Glenn LeDrew, Mikkel Steine, Philipp Teutsch, Dana Patchick, and Robert Erdmann, Jr. have all provided such information. We also thank Gaspar Bakos for permission to reprint his superb drawing of M 13, shown in Figure 8.4 on page 263.

Brenda Corbin and Greg Shelton, USNO librarians, have been of tremendous assistance in tracking down references for this work. Even the most obscure references were found quickly and efficiently, either at the USNO library or in a few unusual instances, via a loan from other libraries. Steve Dick, USNO Historian, has provided useful information and assisted in obtaining the image of the USNO 40-inch telescope shown in Figure 4.1 on page 46.

Jenny Prennace and Donita Polly, USGS librarians in Flagstaff, AZ, have also assisted us in this work.

We would also like to express our gratitude to Tracy Knauss for her kind permission allowing us to reprint (in Chapter 7) the deep CCD images of faint Galactic globular clusters, taken by her and the late Mike Morton.

Keith Scollick of NASA/GSFC assisted with several questions in regard to the use of his marvelous SkyView utility. The SAOimage utility, written by Mike van Hilst and maintained by Doug Mink of the Smithsonian Astrophysical Observatory, has also proved very useful. Brian Cuthbertson and Emil Bonanno have provided copies of the *HyperSky* and *MegaStar* software, respectively, that have proven useful in helping to identify various star clusters.

As will be more fully explained later we have made extensive use of the Digital Sky Survey to confirm the existence of many clusters and to refine their positions which have been a longstanding problem.

The Space Telescope Science Institute has granted permission to reprint images from the Palomar Observatory Sky Survey, via the northern portion of the Digitized Sky Survey (DSS-N in this work). Lynn Kozloski provided assistance in obtaining this permission. Use of these images is courtesy of the Palomar Observatory and Digitized Sky Survey created by the Space Telescope Science Institute, operated by AURA, Inc. for NASA and is reproduced here with permission from AURA/STScI.

The Royal Observatory Edinburgh (ROE), the UK Particle Physics and Astronomy Research Council, and the Anglo-Australian Observatory have granted permission to reproduce images from the UK Schmidt survey, the southern portion of the Digitized Sky. Jason Cowen of ROE Media Services and Susan Tritton of the ROE Plate Library provided assistance in obtaining this permission. Use of these images is courtesy of the UK Schmidt Telescope (copyright is owned by the Particle Physics and Astronomy Research Council of the UK and the Anglo-Australian Telescope Board) and the Digitized Sky Survey created by the Space Telescope Science Institute, operated AURA, Inc, for NASA, and is reproduced here with permission from the Royal Observatory Edinburgh.

Ann Cowley and David Hartwick, co-editors of *Publications of the Astronomical Society of the Pacific,* and the Astronomical Society of the Pacific provided permission to reprint the photographs of Robert Trumpler and Heber Curtis.

Alison Doane, Curator of Astronomical Photographs, Harvard College Observatory, assisted in obtaining permission to use the photograph of Harlow Shapley.

The cataloging research has made use of the SIMBAD database operated at CDS, Strasbourg, France. Particular thanks is given to Gerard Jasniewicz of the CDS for much useful advice on accessing SIMBAD. This research has made use of the NASA/IPAC Extragalactic Database (NED) which is operated by the Jet Propulsion Laboratory, Caltech, under contract with the National Aeronautics and Space Administration. Special acknowledgement is also made to Göstå Lyngå, whose 1987 *Lund Catalogue* proved very useful.

Finally, we deeply appreciate the generosity of Bruno Alessi, Harold G. Corwin, Jr., Murray Cragin, Sue French, Jeff Medkeff, Mati Morel, Stephen O'Meara, Brian Skiff, Harold Suiter, and Philipp Teutsch who took the time to read and extensively comment on a near-final version of this work. Their comments have resulted in greatly improving the book you are now holding. However, any problems that remain in this text are the authors' alone.

From Brent Archinal, to JoAnne

From Steven Hynes, to my wife Julie and my children Carina and Anya

Chapter 1
The Discovery of Open Clusters

From a place deeply involved in stellar organizations we look out at the sidereal universe. Immediately around our minute association of sun and planets are the bright white stars of the Ursa Major cluster, with one of its members, Sirius, but a few light years distant. Much greater than such near-by groups is the local system, a star cloud that includes thousands of the surrounding bright stars and a million or so of the fainter. Still more inclusive is the Galaxy, which holds sun, clusters, and star clouds, and which, in turn, may be but one unit in a higher example of the gravitational clustering of sidereal bodies.

—H. Shapley, *Star Clusters* [1930]

1.1 Pre-telescopic Observations of Open Clusters

In centuries past, before the advent of artificial lighting, our ancestors had a greater familiarity with the night sky than is the case today. Knowledge of the stars was valuable; it gave power to the astrologers and priests and aided farmers and sailors. Observing from properly dark skies, they would have noted the seasonal changing of the constellations; the great arch of the Milky Way crossing the sky and the bright "wandering stars," the planets, making their way through the constellations of the ecliptic.

Observant ancients would have noticed more. In some parts of the sky, particularly along the plane of the Milky Way, were a number of small patches of enhanced brightness, such as that in the northern part of Perseus. Some of these patches could be resolved into faint stars, such as the Praesepe in Cancer, and others were more clearly composed of stars like the Pleiades (see Figure 1.1) and Hyades in Taurus.

The prominence of these last three objects resulted in them being featured in the starlore of many societies primarily because of the compactness of each group and the brightness of the individual members, together with the fact that they are visible from both northern and southern hemispheres. This is especially true of the Pleiades. This cluster seems to have found its way into the legends of almost all ethnic groups. A detailed account of these is given by Allen [1962] and Burnham [1978], where it is said that the name we use today is of ancient Greek origin. It is either derived from the word "to sail" indicating a heliacal rising heralding the start of the navigational season, or it may be a version of the Greek word "full" or "many." While the Pleiades would have been apparent even to primitive peoples, the first written mention of them is found in Chinese records, dating almost 4500 years ago. Certainly, they were known in Old Testament times and are specifically mentioned in the book of Job:

> It is God who moves mountains, giving them no rest, turning them over in his wrath; who makes the Earth start from its place so that its pillars are convulsed; who commands the Sun's orb not to rise and shuts up the stars under his seal; who by himself spread out the heavens and trod on the crests of the waves; who made Aldebaran and Orion, the Pleiades, and the circle of the southern stars... (*New English Bible* 1970)

Fig. 1.1 *"The Pleiads, rising thro' the mellow shade, glitter like a swarm of fire-flies tangled in a silver braid." Surely no star cluster has ever been described as well as the Pleiades are in these words by Tennyson (1809–1892) in his "Locksley Hall" [1842]. Photo by E. E. Barnard [1927, plate 4] covering a field of approximately 3°.*

In the centuries after the collapse of the Roman Empire and when European culture was at its nadir, arts and sciences flourished, and astronomical references are often found in Arabian literature. For example, in a poem written by Sadi in 13th century Persia, we find the line:

> The ground was as if strewn with colored enamel, and necklaces of Pleiades seemed to hang upon the branches of the trees....

In the legends of the Kiowa people of North America, the massive Devil's Tower rock formation in Wyoming was created by the Great Spirit to protect seven Indian maidens who were being pursued by bears. The maidens were subsequently placed in the sky as the Pleiades cluster. These stars were also important in the world system of the peoples of Mexico and Central America. The west face of the Great Pyramid of the Sun at Teotihuacan is oriented towards the setting point of the Pleiades.

All over the world, from Europe and Asia, through the Americas and among the people of the Pacific islands and Australasia, the Pleiades have a place in myth and legends. Often, they are considered to be female and almost always to be seven in number; in many traditions there is also a story about a "lost Pleiad." It has sometimes been suggested that variability in the shell-star Pleione may account for this latter aspect, but why the number seven should so often be quoted is a mystery. A person with average eyesight, at a fairly average site, can normally see between six and nine stars but some people with better eyesight, or a good observing location, can observe many more without optical aid. Maestlin, the tutor of Kepler, is said to have mapped eleven stars in 1579 prior to the invention of the telescope. Amateur astronomer William R. Dawes (1799–1868) once described as "probably the best astronomical observer in England in his day" and renowned for his keen eyesight, was clearly able to distinguish thirteen stars, and, from good sites, many modern observers have convincingly reported seeing between 12 and 14. Indeed, one of us [BA], can clearly recall making such observations himself in the days when his eyesight was better! Occasionally, some observers have claimed to be able to see as many as 18.

The star catalog of the great Greek astronomer Hipparchus (190–120 B.C.) is known to have included at least three clusters, the Double Cluster in Perseus and Praesepe (M 44), although these would have been thought of as nebulae rather than clusters. Unfortunately, no copies of this catalog have survived the passage of time. However, the revised and enlarged version compiled at Alexandria by Ptolemy (c. 83–161 A.D.) has survived as the *Almagest*, from the popular name of its Arabic translation. This catalog lists as nebulae, in addition to those recorded by Hipparchus, the Coma open cluster, M 7 in Scorpius, and the λ Orionis (= Collinder 69) group [Glyn Jones 1975].

In the 10th century, the Persian astronomer, Al Sûfi (903–986 A.D.), produced his *Book of the Fixed Stars* which included another important early star catalog based on the earlier work of Ptolemy. This included as nebulae those clusters already known, but also added the o Velorum (IC 2391) cluster and the asterism now known as "Brocchi's Cluster" (Collinder 399) in Vulpecula. The *Book of the Fixed Stars* also includes the first recorded observation of the "nebula" now known as the galaxy M 31 in Andromeda.

1.2 Galileo Examines the Nebulae

By the time the telescope was invented, around 1608, probably nine open clusters were known, of which about four could be more-or-less resolved without optical aid. It was not long afterwards that this remarkable invention was turned toward the night sky; Thomas Harriott used one to observe the surface of the Moon as early as the summer of 1609. The first person to make systematic astronomical observations, however, was the Italian mathematician and inventor, Galileo Galilei (1564–1642), who also observed the Moon and discovered the four major satellites of the planet Jupiter. Galileo also looked at the stars and "nebulae," and his discoveries were published in 1610 in his book *Sidereus Nuncius* (The Starry Messenger). Of the Milky Way he wrote:

> I have observed the nature and material of the Milky Way. With the aid of the telescope this has been examined so directly and with such ocular certainty that all the disputes which have vexed philosophers through so many ages have been resolved, and we are at last freed from wordy debates about it. The galaxy is, in fact, nothing but innumerable stars grouped together in clusters. Upon whatever part of it the telescope is directed, a vast crowd is immediately presented to view. Many are large and bright, while the number of smaller ones is quite incalculable.

Obviously, Galileo's statement that the galaxy can be resolved into stars "grouped together in clusters" is open to interpretation and his intention may have been lost in translation. He may certainly have meant to refer to the background clumpiness of the Milky Way; however, it is possible that he did observe some genuine clusters but did not think to record specific groups in his notes.

The latter is also suggested in the first part of the following paragraph where Galileo describes his observations of the nebulae:

> But it is not only in the Milky Way that whitish clouds are seen; several patches of similar aspect shine with faint light here and there throughout the aether, and if the telescope is turned upon any of them we are confronted by a tight mass of stars. And what is even more remarkable, the stars which have been called "nebulous" by every astronomer to this time turn out to be a group of very small stars arranged in a wonderful manner. Although each star separately escapes our sight on account of its smallness, or the immense distance from us, the mingling of their rays gives rise to that glow which was formerly believed to be some denser part of the aether that was capable of reflecting rays from stars or from the Sun.

Table 1.1 Hodierna's Categorization of Objects

Luminosae	Nebulosae	Occultae
1. Pleiades	1. Praesepe	1. "Preceding the two southern stars of Coma Berenices" (asterism)
2. Hyades	2. M 7	2. "The one following these stars, in the shape of an open rose, according to Ptolemy, and of an ivy leaf according to Copernicus" (asterism)
3. Coma star cluster	3. NGC 869 & 884	3. M 31
4. α Per cluster	4. M 6	
5. M 42	5. ν_1, ν_2 Sagittarii (asterism)	
6. λ Ori cluster	6. M 8	
7. ζ Sco & NGC 6231	7. M 36/M 37/M 38	
8. "In the water of Aquarius" (unknown object)	8. Cr 399	
	9. 88 Her	
	10. σ Cap.	

Galileo's opinion that all nebulae could be resolved into stars persisted for almost 200 years, until 1790, when William Herschel's observations of the planetary nebula NGC 1514 and its apparent central star dispelled the idea. In his 1791 paper, *On Nebulous Stars, Properly So Called*, Herschel described his observations and theories on this object and concluded that it could only be satisfactorily explained by some kind of "shining fluid," which was subsequently established by Huggins to be, in fact, gaseous.

1.3 Early Telescopic Discoveries of Open Clusters

The invention of the telescope gave an unprecedented impetus to the science of astronomy, bringing about many new discoveries. One of the first to appreciate the significance of Galileo's work was Giovanni Batista Hodierna (1597–1660), astronomer at the court of the Duke of Montechiaro in Sicily from 1637 until his death in 1660. In 1654, Hodierna published a booklet which included several observations of nebulae and clusters, some of the objects being his own discoveries [Serio 1985; Glyn Jones 1986]. He also seems to have been the first person to attempt some kind of classification system for deep-sky objects, dividing objects into three classes: *Luminosae*—nebulae containing some naked-eye stars, *Nebulosae*—nebulae which could be resolved into stars with a telescope, and *Occultae*—nebulae which could not clearly be resolved even when observed with a telescope. In each category, Hodierna listed the objects (using the present day identifications) in Table 1.1.

In addition to the above, Hodierna mentioned quite a number of other objects, some of which have been identified with M 47, M 41, NGC 2362, NGC 2451, and objects that are possibly M 33, M 34, M 79, NGC 2169, and NGC 2175. This makes him the first known observer of nine objects, and independent discoverer of two more, a most remarkable achievement not matched for a considerable number of years. Not unexpectedly, most of the objects found were some of the brighter star clusters.

During the following century, small numbers of nebulae (mostly clusters) were discovered by several observers; for example, Gottfried Kirch (1639–1710) found the open cluster M 11 in 1681 and the globular cluster M 5 in 1702, Edmond Halley (1656–1742) found the globular clusters ω Centauri and M 13 in 1677 and 1714 respectively, and Philippe de Cheseaux (1718–1751) found IC 4665, NGC 6633, M 16, M 25, M 35, M 4 and M 71, as well as M 6 independently. However, the next listing of any significance, following that of Hodierna, was published by Nicholas-Louis de Lacaille (1713–1762), and resulted from his expedition to the Cape of Good Hope in South Africa from 1751 to 1753. The most outstanding result of this trip was a catalog of 9,776 southern stars. In addition, he found 42 nebulae and star clusters, many of which were original discoveries. Lacaille is credited with first discovery of the great globular cluster NGC 104, the "Tarantula Nebula"—NGC 2070, the bright spiral galaxy NGC 5236 (= M 83) and NGC 3372—the great η Carinae nebula. As far as open clusters are concerned, Lacaille recorded what would later be known as NGC 2477, NGC 2516, NGC 2546, NGC 2547, NGC 3228, NGC 3532, NGC 3766, NGC 4755 ("Jewel Box" cluster), NGC 5662, NGC 6025, NGC 6124, NGC 6231, NGC 6242, IC 2395, IC 2488, IC 2602, and Tr 10, many of the finest sights in the southern sky.

The later years of the eighteenth century saw an almost exponential increase in the discovery of new telescopic deep-sky objects. Many of the brighter were recorded in the landmark catalog of Charles Messier (1730–1817) and Pierre Mechain (1744–1804), which was published in 1784. The scope and history of this catalog has been well covered in other publications [Glyn Jones 1968; Mallas and Kreimer 1979; O'Meara, 2000], and observation of the Messier objects can be recommended as an excellent introduction to the study of deep-sky astronomy generally. As far as open clusters are concerned, Messier included 30 objects in his list: M 6, M 7, M 8, M 11, M 16, M 17, M 18, M 20, M 21, M 23, M 24, M 25, M 26, M 29, M 34, M 35, M 36, M 37, M 38, M 39, M 41, M 42, M 44, M 45, M 46, M 47, M 48, M 50, M 52, M 67, M 73, M 93 and M 103; Messier himself discovered at least 9 of these.

1.4 Herschel's Classification System

Following the publication of the Messier catalog, a copy was obtained by Dr. William Watson, who sent it to his friend William Herschel (1738–1822). Herschel is one of the most remarkable figures in the history of astronomy. Born in Hanover Germany, he moved to England in November 1757; eventually settling in Bath, where he was joined by his sister Caroline. As a talented musician, Herschel soon became well established and prosperous, and was earning the not inconsiderable sum of £400 per year by 1771. Considering his subsequent distinguished career in astronomy, he did not take up a serious interest in this subject until about 1773 at the age of 35. His interest seems to have been sparked when, on buying a copy of Ferguson's *Astronomy*, he "read of the many charming discoveries that had been made by means of the telescope," and resolved to see the heavens and planets himself.

Herschel had a talent for telescope making and soon developed an international reputation for his instruments. After several years of telescope building and general observational work, Herschel set about a systematic search for double stars. He realized that, in the case of optical pairs where the components are greatly separated but along more-or-less the same line of sight, the distance of stars might be determined by trigonometric means. During this search, on March 13, 1781 he became the first person in modern times to discover a major planet and was subsequently honored by election to the Royal Society. He received an award of an annual stipend of £200 by King George III. This, together with a significant income from telescope making, enabled him to give up his musical career and concentrate full time on astronomy.

Watson sent Herschel the catalog recently published by Messier on December 7, 1781 the day of his election to the Royal Society. Herschel made a point of searching for every object on the list using a recently constructed 30-cm reflector. His enthusiasm for this work grew and with the completion of an even larger telescope (see Figure 1.2 on page 5) with a 48-cm diameter speculum mirror, he commenced a massive survey of the night sky, discovering some 2300 new objects within a period of seven years.

This significant database of observational material gave Herschel the means to classify the objects he had found. He separated them into eight categories:

I. Bright nebulae
II. Faint nebulae
III. Very faint nebulae
IV. Planetary nebulae
V. Very large nebulae
VI. Very compressed, rich clusters of stars
VII. Compressed clusters of small and large stars
VIII. Coarsely scattered clusters of stars.

Although now long superseded, the Herschel designations which resulted from this classification system proved sufficiently useful that they were often used by amateur astronomers until recent times. Indeed, Herschel's designations were used as the primary numbering system for deep-sky objects in *Norton's Star Atlas* until the 18th Edition was published in 1989.

Herschel also speculated on the origin of some of the morphological features he found in the nebulae and clusters that he discovered. In this he used the evidence of his extensive star count surveys, or gauges. Having gauged the Milky Way in various places, he concluded that the number of stars "constantly increase and decrease in proportion to its apparent brightness to the naked eye" and, supposing that the stars were of various sizes and brightnesses and almost equally distributed in space, made the following suggestions concerning the star clusters. First, in the case of a star considerably more massive than its neighbors, it would have the effect of attracting less massive stars close by, creating a globular cluster. He also suggested that open clusters (then called "irregular clusters") were formed when a group of similarly massive stars happened to lie within a certain distance of each other causing their mutual gravitational attraction to draw them together. The variations on these forms, he felt, could be explained by combining the effects described above, and that the occurrence of several clusters in the same region of space could be caused by the same principles on a larger scale—clusters being pulled together by their mutual gravitational attraction. As a result of these clusterings of stars and of star clusters, the dark spaces or "holes" which he had found in many Milky Way fields could be explained: they had been emptied by the stars being gravitationally attracted into clusters. Even if none of these theories is correct, Herschel's model was perhaps the first to be developed from a good observational base. In addition, he made [1785, 217] the following comment:

> These clusters may be the Laboratories of the universe, if I may so express myself, wherein the most salutary remedies for the decay of the whole are prepared.

There are prophetic elements in this statement, even if it is right for the wrong reasons!

To be fair to Herschel, his views did change as shown in a paper published in the *Philosophical Transactions* of 1814 where he drew attention to the common phenomenon of stars being found in association with nebulosities:

> The formation of these objects is extremely instructive, as it

manifests the affinity between the matter of which stars are composed and that of the most unshapen chaotic mass of nebulosity. For the vanishing chevelure of a star being equally connected, on the one hand, with the generally diffused nebulous matter, and on the other with the star itself, round which it is in a state of gradual condensation; this double union denotes the mutual gravitation of the whole mass of nebulosity and the stars towards each other; and unless this proof can be invalidated, we must admit the fact of the growing condition of stars, that are in the situation which has been pointed out.

This argument adds greatly to the probability of stars being originally formed by the condensation of the nebulous matter; for as it now appears that stars must receive an addition to their solid contents, when they are in contact with nebulosity, there is an evident possibility of their being originally formed of it. Moreover, the affinity between the nebulous and sidereal condition being established by these observations, we may be permitted to conceive both the generation and the growth of stars, as the legitimate effects of the law of gravitation, to which the nebulous matter, as proved by observation, is subject.

He clearly—and correctly—hypothesizes the likelihood of stars forming from nebulae, although he is referring to bright nebulae not dark nebulae, the existence of which had yet to be shown. It is also interesting to note his belief that after their formation, stars could continue to "grow" by absorbing material from the nebulosity.

Fig. 1.2 *The Herschels' "20-foot" telescope, with which most of the objects in the NGC were discovered. Of 48 cm (18¾ in.) aperture, it was used by William and John Herschel to survey the northern sky from England, and by John to survey the southern sky from Capetown, South Africa. In the Fall of 2001, the original tube was placed on display in Washington, D.C., USA, in a long term exhibit at the Smithsonian Institution's National Air and Space Museum, where it is on loan from the National Maritime Museum, the Royal Observatory Greenwich, in Greenwich England. Image from direct print of original copper-plate engraving, dated February 1, 1794.*

1.5 Open Clusters in the NGC

Following Sir William Herschel, the most important contributor to the discovery of deep-sky objects was William's son, John Herschel (1792–1871). John was a man of great talent himself and contributed to a wide range of mathematical and scientific studies. In this respect he benefited from his father's experience, knowledge and connections and in due course, his father's estate, when the older Herschel died in 1822. Not only did John inherit much of William's telescopic and other equipment, but also a substantial income. Furthermore, his mother, Lady Mary Herschel, had been the widow of a wealthy merchant when she married William in 1788, and when she died in 1832, John acquired the means to pursue his interests as he wished. In particular, he took his father's 48-cm (18¾-inch) reflector to South Africa, where he and his family stayed from 1834 to 1838, making extensive observations of southern sky nebulae, clusters and double stars. This was a significant and costly undertaking for the time. When he boarded the *Mountstewart Elphinstone* on November 13, 1833, he was accompanied by his wife, three children, a maid, a manservant and his mechanic, John Stone, together with three telescope mirrors, the telescope superstructure, an equatorial refractor, transit circle, clocks and other supporting equipment. On his return, it took him over eight years to write up and publish his observations in a monumental work entitled *Results of Astronomical Observations made during the Years 1834, 5, 6, 7 and 8 at the Cape of Good Hope* [Herschel 1847].

Later, he spent a great deal of time reducing his observations and updating and correcting his father's work to produce *A General Catalogue of Nebulae* containing 5,079 objects, which was published in 1864. However, John Herschel was by no means the only astronomer studying the deep sky. Many contemporary astronomers were also engaged on the search for new nebulae and clusters. For example, in the southern hemisphere, James Dunlop, using the observatory of Sir Thomas Brisbane at Paramatta, produced a catalog of 629 southern objects, which was published in the *Philosophical Transactions* of 1828. (Unfortunately, John Herschel was unable to find two-thirds of Dunlop's objects.) However, by far the greatest level of activity was in the northern hemisphere with observations by Barnard, Bond, Holden, Stone and Swift in the U.S.A.; D'Arrest in Denmark; Bigourdan and Stephan in France; Marth in Malta; Auwers, Hartwig and Schmidt in Germany; and Lord Rosse and his assistants in Britain.

Fig. 1.3 *John Louis Emil Dreyer (1852–1926). The author of A New General Catalogue of Nebulae and Clusters of Stars, being the Catalogue of the late Sir John F. W. Herschel, Bart., revised, corrected, and enlarged, more commonly known as the NGC. Photograph courtesy of the Armagh Observatory.*

William Parsons, the third Earl of Rosse (1800–1867), had constructed by far the largest telescope of its time, a 1.83-meter (72-inch) reflector, which was sufficiently complete for observations in 1845. He built it on the grounds of Birr Castle near Parsonstown in County Offaly, Ireland. Like large telescopes today, there was a great demand on its time and, in addition to the third Earl himself (and later his son), there was a series of resident astronomers who used it, primarily George and Bindon Stoney, William Rambaut, R.J. Mitchell, S. Hunter, Sir Robert Ball, Ralph Copeland and John Louis Emil Dreyer (1852–1926, see Figure 1.3). With all this activity astronomers soon found the need for a supplement to the *General Catalogue*; this was compiled by Dreyer and published in 1878. In 1886, he compiled a second supplement and submitted it for consideration by the Royal Astronomical Society:

> But considering the circumstance that Herschel's work is practically out of print, and that the simultaneous use of three catalogues and two copious lists of corrections would be very inconvenient, the Council proposed to me to amalgamate the three catalogues into a new General Catalogue.

Dreyer accepted the proposal and in 1888 *A New General Catalogue of Nebulae and Clusters of Stars* [Dreyer 1888] was published, covering all deep sky objects known to have been discovered up to 1887. This general compilation of deep-sky objects together with its supplements, the two *Index Catalogues* [Dreyer 1895, 1908], covering nebulae and clusters discovered up to 1907, remains the preferred reference list for observers of almost all types of deep-sky objects and is particularly useful for star clusters. Since many galactic clusters are comparatively conspicuous objects, they were readily picked out by the visual observers of this era. The selection was largely intuitive; therefore, the NGC and IC catalogs contain quite a few asterisms. Perhaps the most complete modern catalog of open clusters of recent years, the 5th Edition of the *Lund Catalogue of Open Cluster Data* [Lyngå 1987], contains information on 1152 objects, 541 of which are also listed in the NGC or IC.

Because of the rather subjective nature of the selection process, a number of NGC clusters have been omitted from some modern compilations, such as the RNGC [Sulentic and Tifft 1973]. The selection criteria are open to question, leaving doubt about the existence of some objects. This problem is addressed in more detail in Chapter 3.

The NGC was the last, complete, major catalog of deep-sky objects to be compiled by visual observers and to which amateur astronomers made a significant contribution. After this, the direction and techniques of astronomy changed. The science became more qualitative than quantitative as astrophysics developed to dominate the field, and photography supplanted visual observations. Indeed, the second *Index Catalogue* covering the objects IC 1530–IC 5386 was made up primarily of photographic discoveries. Using plates taken with the 41-cm (16-inch) Bruce refractor at Heidelberg Observatory, approximately 2800 new objects were found by Wolf and Schwassmann in the northern hemisphere. In the southern hemisphere, many plates were taken with the 61-cm (24-inch) Bruce refractor at the Arequipa station of Harvard College Observatory, and a detailed examination of these by Stewart and Frost added another 1130 objects.

1.6 Modern Classification of Open Clusters

Within an astonishingly short period of time, the combination of more sophisticated observational techniques and the application of new astrophysical understanding revolutionized the science and several major developments occurred in the study of star clusters.

As far as open clusters were concerned, several attempts were made to develop a satisfactory classification system. One was by P.J. Melotte [Melotte 1915a, b] who made a study of the Franklin-Adams plates (see Figure 1.4). This early all-sky survey was designed with exposures calculated to reach 16th–17th magnitude on a scale of 20mm to the degree. This enabled small clusters to be identified with a reasonable degree of certainty without large clusters losing the characteristic appearance by being presented at too large a scale. Melotte's study resulted in the discovery of several new open clusters and a four-tier classification system:

Fig. 1.4 *John Franklin-Adams (1843–1912). Shown with the 10-inch f/4.5 refractor (with a triplet objective by Cooke & Sons), he and his assistants ("Mr. Kennedy," "Mr. Mitchell," and "Mr. Wood") used to make the first photographic survey of the entire sky. The survey was reproduced after his death as the "Franklin-Adams Charts" [RAS, 1936]. From the Astronomer Royal [1915, plate 4].*

Fig. 1.5 *Harlow Shapley (1885–1972). Provided by and reprinted with the permission of A. Doane, Curator of Astronomical Photographs, Harvard College Observatory.*

Class I: Globular clusters, such as NGC 6205 (M 13).

Class II: Loose clusters having a regular well-defined outline. An example of this type was given as NGC 2287 (M 41).

Class III: Small, loose clusters, not well defined, and generally of a few stars only.

Class IV: Coarse clusters such as the Pleiades and Hyades.

Melotte himself acknowledged that there would be some difficulty in deciding to which class a cluster should properly belong, and apparently this system failed largely because of its vagueness. Certainly, it was never very widely used.

At Harvard, Harlow Shapley [1930] developed a classification system based on cluster "compactness" (the apparent number of stars and their concentration). It was intended to cover the entire range of stellar clusterings from multiple stars to globular clusters. The subdivisions of this system were as follows:

a. Field Irregularities: Shapley noted that star counts indicated a great many deviations from random stellar distribution. Often, this results in an excess over what would be expected. Shapley saw no immediate need for these to be cataloged or investigated but felt that a classification system should at least acknowledge their existence.

b. Star Associations: into this category were placed the "moving clusters," groups of sometimes distantly spaced stars sharing the same space motion, such as the Ursa Major group.

c. Very Loose and Irregular Clusters: Shapley suggested that this class was typified by the Pleiades and Hyades clusters, and perhaps even the α Persei group (although this might also be included in class b). Class c corresponds approximately to Melotte's class IV.

d. Loose Clusters: Shapley specified M 21 and M 34 as examples of this type, which he judged to be equivalent to Melotte's Class III.

e, f, g. Compact Clusters: roughly equivalent to Melotte's Class II where compact clusters were subdivided into three on the basis of their richness and concentration, (M 38, M 37 and NGC 2477 cited as examples of each type). Shapley placed globular clusters directly after open clusters of type g and noted that several of the most compact of this type appeared to be more like globular clusters than some of the loosest globular clusters classified by means other than appearance.

Shapley recognized that the above classification system was not really complete, since it was primarily dependent on the stellar density and distance of a group. He also divided open clusters into two groups on the basis of the spectra or colors of the component stars: (1) Pleiades type—where the stars are largely Main Sequence objects with the earliest spectral types being of type B and A, and (2) Hyades type—with a greater abundance of later spectral types.

The Shapley alphabetical sequence of open cluster classification was certainly more popular than that of Melotte and others of the period, and was used in Becvar's *Atlas Coeli Catalogue* (published in 1964, and one of the most popular amateur reference catalogs of its time).

Nevertheless, the open cluster classification system which has stood the test of time was developed by Robert J. Trumpler [1930] and published in his classic paper on the open cluster system of the Galaxy. This work is essential reading for anyone with an interest in open clusters, covering the determination and importance of the distances, sizes and space distribution of these systems.

Trumpler's study enabled him to devise a classification system which identified certain specific features of an open cluster, which could be ascertained independently of its distance. This removed the difficulty presented by most previous systems, such as that of Shapley, whereby a "loose cluster" might only appear to be loose because of its proximity. However, if placed at a uniform distance with other clusters, it might actually be more compact. The relevant features identified by Trumpler were: (i) degree of central concentration of the stars and the extent to which the cluster appears detached from the Milky Way background, (ii) the range of brightness among the component stars, and (iii) the overall number of stars contained within the cluster. For each characteristic, subdivisions were created and assigned Latin numerals, Roman numerals and lower-case letters respectively.

In the first instance, the clusters were placed in four groups according to the degree of concentration:

I. Detached clusters with strong central concentration.
II. Detached clusters with little central concentration.
III. Detached clusters with no noticeable concentration, in which the stars are more-or-less thinly but nearly uniformly scattered.
IV. Clusters not well detached but merging gradually into the background and appearing like a star field condensation.

After this, the clusters were divided into three groups according to the range of brightness within the stars:

1. Most of the cluster stars of nearly the same apparent brightness.
2. Medium range in the brightness of the stars.
3. Clusters composed of bright and faint stars.

The third component in the cluster classification system is the number of members contained in the cluster, indicated as follows:

p. Poor clusters with less than fifty stars.
m. Moderately rich clusters with 50–100 stars.
r. Rich clusters with more than 100 stars.

The three elements are put together in the above order; for example, M 11 (NGC 6705), the spectacular "Wild Duck" cluster in Scutum, is classified [Ruprecht, 1966, p. 37] as being of type I2r—a detached cluster with strong central condensation containing more than 100 stars of a medium range of brightness. Trumpler, using photographs showing fewer stars, classified this cluster as type II—little central condensation. (See Figure 1.7 on page 10.)

It is worth noting that during the early years of the 20th century, there were several changes in the description that these sort of clusters were given. In the previous century, they had been commonly called "irregular clusters"—which seems perfectly appropriate and descriptive—but later it became fashionable to describe them as "open clusters." In 1925, at the suggestion of Trumpler and others, the term "galactic cluster" was introduced on the grounds that almost all could be found close to the galactic plane and to obviate confusion with the open-structured type of globular clusters. In 1967 it was all changed yet again as "open cluster" once more became the preferred term on the grounds that "galactic" implied any object belonging to the Galaxy. Therefore, our own Galaxy's system of globular clusters is "galactic." Also, since star clusters were now being found in other galaxies, the term should be reserved to differentiate between the clusters of our own Galaxy and those of other galaxies. However, since it could well be argued that the term "open" implies "unbound" in the gravitational sense, which is not always the case, perhaps another change is due.

1.7 Trumpler and the Space Distribution of Open Clusters

In addition to the important function of setting out a useful open cluster classification system, Trumpler's 1930 paper provides an early attempt to learn something about the structure of the Galaxy from a study of the properties of open clusters. While his overall conclusions turned out to be incorrect, this is immaterial compared to the value of the other results which were produced from his remarkably comprehensive and intuitive analysis.

Trumpler knew that the dimensions of individual clusters must be quite small when compared with their distances from us; therefore, stars in a particular cluster were

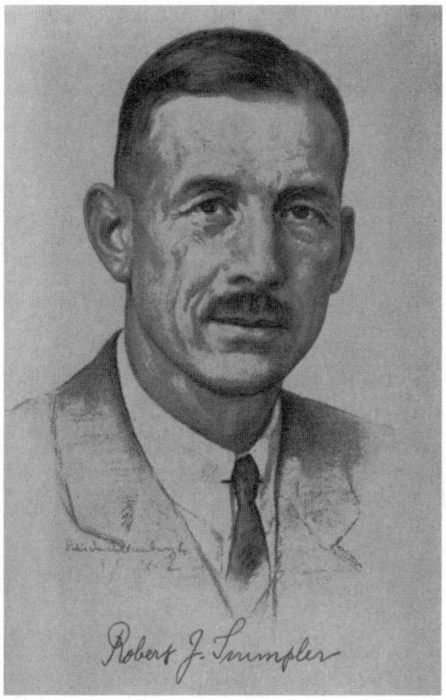

Fig. 1.6 *Robert J. Trumpler (1886–1956). This photograph originally appeared in the Publications of the Astronomical Society of the Pacific (Weaver and Weaver, 1957, PASP, 69, 304). Copyright 1957, Astronomical Society of the Pacific; reproduced with permission of the Editors.*

effectively at the same distances (i.e., the depth of the cluster could be ignored).

Also, there is an important relationship between the absolute magnitude, M, of a star (the magnitude it would have at a distance of 10 parsecs (pc)) and its apparent magnitude, m (the magnitude it appears to be as measured on Earth, with no correction made for distance). This relationship is calculated by means of the formula:

$$m - M = 5\log r - 5 \tag{1.1}$$

where r is the distance of the cluster in parsecs (pc). (The $m - M$ relationship is called the *distance modulus*, although to be strictly accurate, it also needs to include a term to correct for interstellar extinction. Trumpler was not aware of this at the time, however.)

To derive the absolute magnitude from this, the equation can simply be rewritten as:

$$-M = 5\log r - 5 - m \tag{1.2}$$

or, more conveniently:

$$M = m + 5 - 5\log r \tag{1.3}$$

To give a practical example, the star Sirius has an apparent magnitude of –1.44 and lies at a distance of 2.7 pc. Its absolute magnitude is therefore:

$$M = -1.44 + 5 - 5\log 2.7 \tag{1.4}$$

$$= 3.56 - 5 \times 0.4314 \tag{1.5}$$

$$= 3.56 - 2.16 \tag{1.6}$$

$$= +1.40 \tag{1.7}$$

Within recent years, the mean absolute magnitudes of various spectral types of stars had been determined from trigonometric and moving cluster parallaxes, or statistically from proper motions. Since most clusters are dominated by stars of type B and A, he carried out a program of observations to determine the apparent magnitude (hence, absolute magnitude) of the B and A stars in 100 selected clusters. With this information, he then calculated the distances of the clusters and worked out their true size from the apparent size on photographs.

Comparing the size of individual clusters against their distance, he came up with the remarkable result that those close to the Sun were only about half as big as the most distant ones. Such a correlation is extremely unlikely; it would be more plausible if the size distribution was fairly random across the distance range. Either the stars in the more distant clusters were not as bright (for the same spectral type, as those locally) or, more likely, their brightness was being diminished on the way. This would make them appear to be at a greater distance, and, therefore, larger than was really the case. Trumpler had shown the existence of interstellar dust. This was supported by another discovery; that the color of stars of the same spectral type became increasingly red with distance.

Making the appropriate corrections to compensate for this, Trumpler was able to plot the space distribution of his open clusters relative to the Sun. He found some evidence of spiral structure and made a comparison with other spiral galaxies such as M 31 and M 33, noting that they contain small "knots" in the structure of the spiral arms which could reasonably be open clusters. He also noted that most spiral galaxies have at their centers a small, bright nucleus. In this regard, he suggested that the bright and spectacular cluster in Carina, NGC 3532 (see Figure 1.8), might serve this function in our Galaxy, the reason being that this object (according to his work) lay close to the local system of open clusters. This formed a flattened disk-like system about 1000 parsecs thick and 10,000 parsecs in diameter.

These conclusions could not be reconciled with the recently published conclusions of Harlow Shapley based on the space distribution of globular clusters: that the Galaxy was a much larger system over 100,000 parsecs in diameter with a center situated in Sagittarius at a distance of 20,000 to 40,000 parsecs. Trumpler [1930, 185] discussed this significant discrepancy but discounted Shapley's findings:

> . . .there is no noticeable feature in the distribution of open star clusters which suggests a considerable extension of the Milky Way system in the direction of *Sagittarius.* A careful examination of Barnard's excellent Milky Way photographs of this region, which reach at least to the 17^m, did

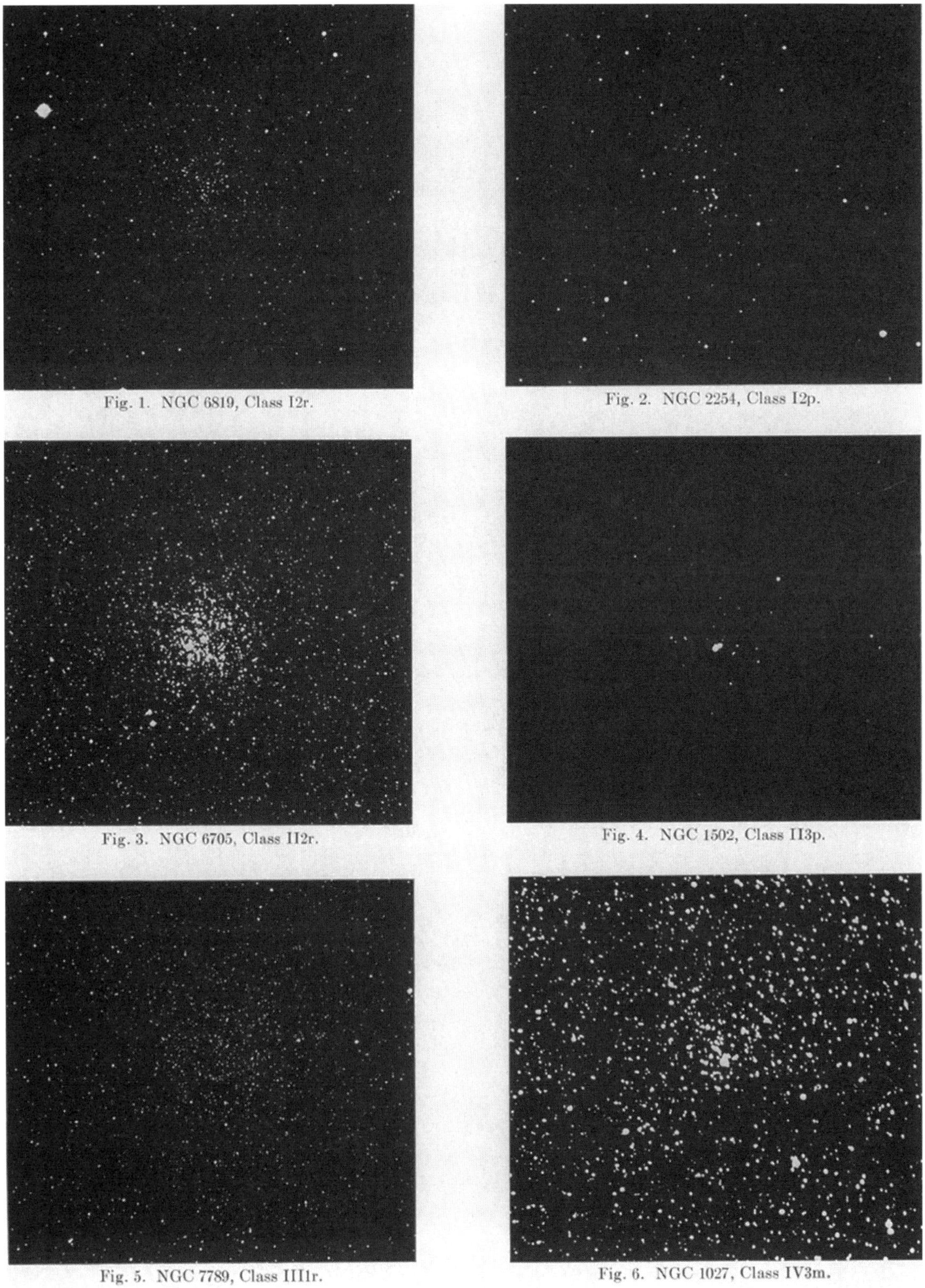

Fig. 1.7 *The prototypical Trumpler classes for Galactic open clusters. From Trumpler [1930, plate 5].*

Fig. 1.8 *NGC 3532 in Carina, shown here in a histogram equalization display of a 2° field of view DSS-S image. The bright star at left center is x Carinae (V=3.9 var, spectral type G0Ia0). © ROE.*

> not reveal any appreciable number of small distant undiscovered star clusters. It is hardly possible that every one of scores or hundreds of such distant clusters should be hidden from our view through absorption by dark matter. But even if we should admit such an assumption, we should still expect the visible parts of the open cluster system to show some arrangement concentric with the distant *Sagittarius* center.

Trumpler came to the conclusion that the globular clusters, like the Magellanic Clouds, while gravitationally bound to the Galaxy, should correctly be considered to be independent bodies. He pointed out that such a system of objects might be like some of the other clusters of extragalactic systems made up of "spiral nebulae, elliptical and globular nebulae." He was encouraged in this view by the similar conclusions of Lundmark.

There is a certain irony in that as the discoverer of interstellar absorption, Trumpler failed to appreciate its extent and significance. Nevertheless, his results from this paper are a considerable achievement, and he should be additionally credited with deriving a better estimate for the size of the Galaxy than did Shapley (even if the latter was correct about the implications of the distribution of the globular clusters).

1.8 Modern Listings of Open Clusters

Following the publication of the NGC and IC catalogs, open clusters continued to be discovered. For example, a list of 245 clusters was produced by Melotte in 1915. However, many of these are previously discovered objects in the NGC or IC: for example; Melotte 13 and 14 are NGC 869 and 884, the Double Cluster in Perseus, and Melotte 22 is the Pleiades. In fact, only 10 objects on the Melotte list had not been numbered before, the most conspicuous one being Melotte 111, the nearby cluster that is the namesake of the Coma Berenices constellation.

More significant in terms of original discoveries is the list produced by Trumpler and included in his classic paper of 1930. Thirty-seven objects were recorded here, and most were original discoveries found on the Franklin-Adams star charts by the author. However, a number were objects mentioned by previous observers in various papers, but not specifically cataloged as new discoveries. Most of these had been noted by Barnard [1927] on his *Atlas of Selected Regions of the Milky Way*. Some of the clusters in the Trumpler list are quite important, in particular Tr 15 and Tr 16, because of their association with the η Carinae Nebula (NGC 3372). One of us [SH] has a particular fondness for Tr 1 which is close to the cluster M 103 in Cassiopeia, as this was the first non-NGC/IC object that he independently "discovered."

Appendix B in, Shapley's *Star Clusters* [1930], contains an important list of clusters which has been a primary source of open cluster data until recent years. It was used extensively in Becvar's *Atlas Coeli*.

In January 1929, Clyde Tombaugh arrived at Lowell Observatory in Flagstaff, Arizona, to commence the search which would result in the discovery of the planet Pluto in just over twelve months. In the course of this search, Tombaugh examined a great number of plates taken with the 33-cm (13-inch) astrograph and inevitably came across many other new objects (mostly asteroids), but he also found 5 new open clusters.

These, together with many other clusters mostly from comparatively small listings, were brought together in the first "general catalog" of open clusters, the *Catalogue of Star Clusters and Associations*, published in 1958 (often referred to as the "Alter catalog" after its primary author [Alter, *et al.*, 1958]). At this time the advent of the computer database was some years away, and the catalog was produced in the form of a card-index. It contained identification information, positional data, size, distance, membership, magnitude, spectral characteristics, references and notes for each object. There seems to be an unwritten scientific law that the publication of any important database results in a flurry of activity in the same field; this catalog is no exception. New discoveries resulted in eight Supplements to the catalog being published [Alter *et al.*, 1959, 1960, 1961, 1962, 1963, 1964, 1965, 1966]. With the publication of the last Supplement, the total number of objects recorded was 1,017. Obviously, with a main catalog

Fig. 1.9 *The Herschels' "20-foot" telescope, at Feldhausen, John Herschel's estate near Capetown, South Africa, where it was in use from 1834 to 1838. Camera lucida drawing by J. Herschel, from Herschel [1847, frontispiece].*

and so many supplements, the system became rather unwieldy. Therefore, the entire catalog was revised [Alter *et al.*,1970], and a further revision and enlargement was published a decade later [Ruprecht,1981].

Another major catalog published in 1981 was the *Catalogue of Open Cluster Data* compiled by Göstå Lyngå Lyngå at the Lund Observatory. This is often referred to as the "Lund Catalogue" [Lyngå 1981]. This has now reached its 5th Edition and, in its computer readable form, is the primary data source for open clusters. This edition of the *Lund Catalogue* has been a primary reference source in the compilation of the catalog in this book. The computer readable form of the *Lund Catalogue* comprises six files, and the main catalog records information on approximately 1150 open clusters with information about identification, position (equatorial, galactic coordinates and Palomar Observatory Sky Survey (POSS) [National Geographic Society, 1955] chart X–Y coordinates), Trumpler class, membership, diameter, distance, reddening, age, metallicity, radial velocity, magnitude, earliest spectral class for a cluster member, magnitude of the brightest cluster member, galactocentric distance, numbers of stars of selected types (e.g. Be stars, WR stars, Cepheids, shell stars etc.) and comments on particular objects. Other files include cross-references between catalogs and 527 references (a valuable database). When printed out, the catalog occupies a significant volume of paper!

From the perspective of the amateur astronomer, there are several recent sources of data: the *Observing Handbook and Catalogue of Deep-Sky Objects*, by Christian B. Luginbuhl and Brian A. Skiff, published by Cambridge University Press in 1990 (reprinted in 1999); *The Deep-Sky Field Guide to Uranometria 2000.0*, by Murray Cragin, James Lucyk and Barry Rappaport, published by Willmann-Bell Inc. in 1993; and *The Night Sky Observer's Guide*, by George R. Kepple and Glen W. Sanner, published by Willmann-Bell, Inc. in 1998. Finally, we hope that the catalogs of clusters included in this volume, independently compiled by one of us [BA] from the most up-to-date sources available, will be found especially useful.

1.9 Extragalactic Open Clusters and Associations

The history of the discovery of extragalactic open clusters really goes back to John Herschel's expedition to the Cape of Good Hope during the years 1834 to 1838. Although other observers were active in the southern hemisphere at the time and before then, Herschel's observations were the first to combine high quality in both the observer and the

Fig. 1.10 *The field of the Large Magellanic Cloud (~13° square). From RAS [1936, plate 4].*

telescope. In the case of the latter, the large 48-cm speculum reflector (Figure 1.9 on page 12) was the same as that which had been used to such great effect by the Herschels in England. Great things were expected, and the astronomical community was not disappointed. The four-year trip resulted in the discovery of several thousand new double stars, clusters and nebulae; these were analyzed and published in 1847.

John Herschel was clearly impressed by his views of the Magellanic Clouds and devoted much observing time to them, cataloguing 1163 objects. He described the Clouds as follows:

> The general ground of both consists of large tracts and patches of nebulosity in every stage of resolution, from light irresolvable, in a reflector of 18-inches aperture, up to perfectly separated stars, like the Milky Way, and cluster-

Fig. 1.11 *The field of the Small Magellanic Cloud (~13° square). The globular cluster 47 Tucanae lies just to the upper right of the SMC. From RAS [1936, plate 2].*

> ing groups sufficiently insulated and condensed to come under the designation of irregular and in some cases pretty rich clusters. But besides these there are also nebulae in abundance and globular clusters in every state of condensation.

It was many years before the Magellanic Clouds were recognized as galaxies like the Milky Way in their own right, but Herschel was correct in his recording of its content. He was clearly able to resolve stars in some clusters, and many of the irresolvable condensed knots he found are in fact either open or globular clusters. Modern estimates suggest that the Large Magellanic Cloud (LMC, see Figure 1.10 on page 13) contains over 6000 star clusters, and the Small Magellanic Cloud (SMC, see Figure 1.11 on

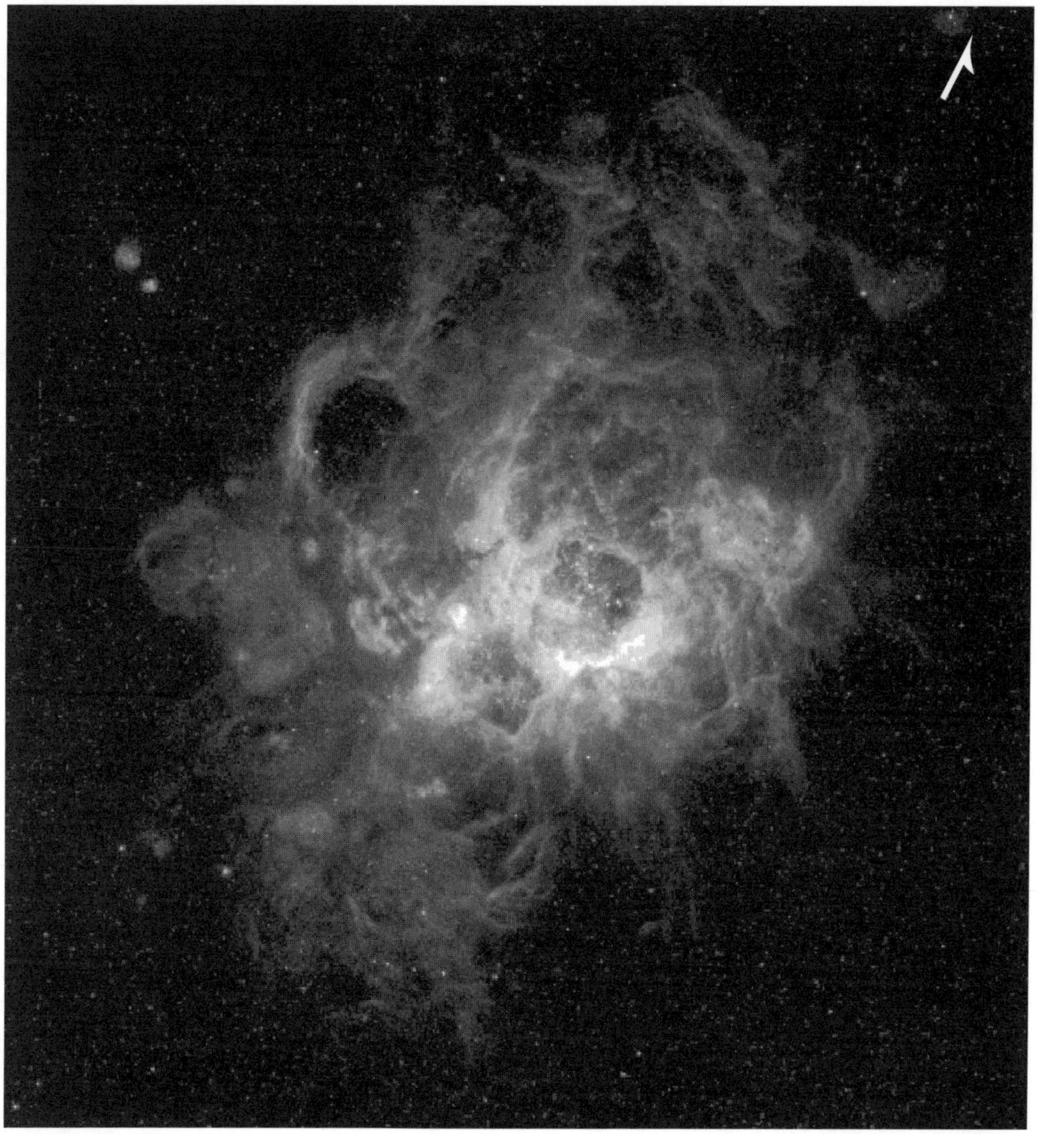

Fig. 1.12 *NGC 604, the largest association (approximate diameter 1500 light years) in the Pinwheel galaxy = M 33. WFPC2 HST image taken January 17, 1995. The field of view is 2', with north to the upper right and east to the upper left. Hui Yang (University of Illinois) and NASA.*

page 14) contains about 2000. To gain some idea of the complexity of the Magellanic Clouds and the number of clusters they contain, an examination of ESO(B) film copies #056 and #057 can be recommended, both taken with the 1.0-m. (40-inch) Schmidt camera at La Silla in Chile. Reference should also be made to the catalog of Kontizas, *et al.*, [1990]. For the amateur astronomer some charts showing the location and identification of clusters and other objects in the Magellanic Clouds can be found in *Webb Society Deep-Sky Observer's Handbook,* volume 7 [Hynes 1987]. Perhaps the best available charts for the amateur astronomer, however, are those produced by Mati Morel in Australia [Morel, 1993].

In addition to clusters found in the Magellanic Clouds, a small number of clusters and associations in other galaxies were observed by the visual astronomers who contributed to the compilation of the *New General Catalogue*. Perhaps the most conspicuous of these is the huge association NGC 206, which lies in one of the outer arms of the Local Group spiral, the Andromeda Galaxy (M 31 = NGC 224)—this should be visible in a 20-cm (8-inch) telescope. Also visible with a small telescope is NGC 604 (see

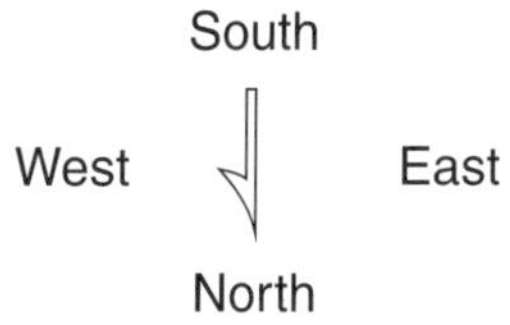

Fig. 1.13 *Throughout this work the orientation of illustrations is indicated by an arrow as shown in this illustration.*

Figure 1.12 on page 15), a massive nebulous association in the Local Group spiral galaxy M 33 (NGC 598). This galaxy also includes a number of other NGC/IC objects of a similar nature. Since then, as telescopes have increased in size and the type and quality of detectors have improved, it has been possible to search these and many other galaxies for fainter clusters and associations. Although comparatively rare in elliptical galaxies, which contain an older stellar population, they occur in great numbers in spiral galaxies which have a younger stellar population and are usually found involved with HII regions. Obviously, they are also found in larger numbers in the nearer spirals simply because they can be seen down to fainter magnitudes. About 200 associations have now been found in M 33 and a 1985 study by Hodge [1985], identified 88 stellar associations in the large nearby spiral NGC 2403; some of these can also be seen in medium-aperture amateur telescopes. At a somewhat greater distance is the beautiful spiral galaxy M 81 (NGC 3031) in Ursa Major; in this system a survey by Ivanov [1992] has produced a catalog of 180 associations. These nicely delineate the spiral arms and typically have a size of about 80 pc.

An interesting discovery [Jones 1993] is that And IV, normally classified as a dwarf galaxy of the Local Group, is almost certainly a large stellar association within the Andromeda Galaxy system. The CMD is consistent with a young stellar population, and at the distance of M 31, its size of 50 arc-seconds would indicate a real diameter of 180 pc (2 or 3 times smaller than the smallest dwarf irregular galaxies). Such a size, however, would not be unreasonable for a stellar association.

Chapter 2
The Astrophysics of Open Clusters

Notwithstanding a careful search, no variable stars of recognized type are yet available for the estimation of the distances of galactic clusters.

—Harlow Shapley, *Star Clusters* [1930]

2.1 Open Clusters and Associations: Some Definitions

Until the early years of the twentieth century, open clusters were cataloged primarily on the basis of the discoverer's intuition as to whether a particular grouping of stars was physically associated. In many cases the classifications were correct and a fairly good number of the clusters recorded in the NGC, compiled like this, are in fact still considered to be true clusters. Obviously, the reason for this is that many of those in the NGC are fairly rich and bright, or at least reasonably well detached from the background. The problems tend to arise with the more loosely arranged groups, which might be chance groupings of stars at greatly differing distances, of different types and with different space motions. These apparent clusters are called *asterisms*. To qualify as a genuine *open cluster* a group of stars needs to be physically related, i.e. gravitationally bound. This implies a common origin. In addition, the observed density should be sufficiently large as to render the group fairly stable against disruption, say, by the tidal effect of the Galaxy or passing interstellar clouds. This stable density is one solar mass per cubic parsec (or 1 $M_{\odot} pc^{-3}$ where $M_{\odot}$ is the mass of the Sun) or greater. But when is an open cluster so small as to be merely a multiple star? The dividing line is bound to be arbitrary but, for the purpose of deciding what objects are suitable for particular research projects, the minimum requirement for a group to be considered a cluster has been taken by some authorities as 10 stars [Lada and Lada 1991]. Open clusters can also be categorized according to their dynamical state; one can have either bound clusters or unbound clusters. In both cases, the space density of stars qualifies them to be normal open clusters; however, in the unbound clusters, the internal motions of the component stars are sufficiently high that the individual members cannot be constrained by the gravitational influence of the cluster as a whole.

What happens to open clusters over time as they orbit the center of the Galaxy? They will gradually "evaporate" to some extent as a result of the random velocities of stars within the cluster. The lowest mass stars will tend to leave first although they will all share some of the same space motion as the remaining cluster members. The result will be that the original cluster will be stretched out into a tube; if the Sun passes through such a system, the members will be identifiable by their space motion. About a dozen of these *moving groups* have been identified, the most significant being associated with the Hyades, Sirius, Arcturus, γ Leonis, σ Puppis, 61 Cygni and Wolf 630. The concept of moving groups was first introduced by Eggen [1959], and analysis of *Hipparcos* data seems to provide some confirmation of their existence [Skuljan *et al.*, 1997].

Within the young disk population near the Sun, several *superclusters* have been identified. These are groups and clusters of stars which, together with what appear to be field stars, have parallel space motions. Several such superclusters have been identified including the Hyades supercluster, which contains the Hyades and Praesepe clusters; the Sirius supercluster, which is centered on the moving group of stars which forms the Big Dipper in Ursa Major; the Pleiades supercluster, which contains the Pleiades, the α Persei moving group and IC 2602; and the most recently identified, the IC 2391 supercluster.

Finally, there are *stellar associations*, which are essentially unbound groups of primarily O-and B-type stars. Their sizes range from that of ordinary open clusters to a few hundred parsecs. The dividing line between open clusters and associations, as far as definition is concerned, is generally space density. Associations can be defined as a group of 10 or more physically related stars whose stellar space density is less than the tidal stability limit of 1 $M_{\odot}$ pc^{-3}. It is of interest that by this definition, the Hyades group of stars should actually be classified as an association rather than an open cluster.

2.2 The Origins of Open Clusters and Associations

Spectacular clouds of ionized hydrogen (H II regions) such as the Orion nebula have been known to astronomers for about 300 years, but it is only within this last century that astronomers have become significantly aware of the existence of clouds of cold, dark matter in the Galaxy. The first survey of real importance in this respect is that of E. E. Barnard [1927]. At first, it was only possible to study and delineate these dark nebulae by an analysis of painstaking star counts in and around the field [Bok and Cordwell 1973]. With the opening of the spectrum at radio wavelengths, the means arose to explore the general distribution of dark clouds within the Galaxy since radio waves penetrate the interstellar medium relatively unobstructed. Nevertheless, it was not until 1970 that observational evidence was found for the existence of massive interstellar clouds of molecular hydrogen [Robinson and McGee 1970]. The reason for this discovery being made so recently is that, although it is so abundant, molecular hydrogen itself does not emit any easily observable spectral line. However, its presence and distribution can be gauged from mapping the distribution of the carbon monoxide (CO) molecule, which is a trace constituent of molecular clouds with approximately one CO for every 10,000 H_2 molecules. The CO bands at 0.65mm and 2.6mm which are quite strong are believed to be the result of collisions between H_2 and CO. Since the abundance ratio is believed to be more-or-less constant, a measure of the column density of carbon monoxide will provide a direct measure of the hydrogen column density. (Column density is the concentration of atoms or molecules, in cm^{-3}, times the path length, in cm. It therefore has units of cm^{-2}.)

The mass of an individual cloud complex is often in the range of $10^5M_\odot - 10^6M_\odot$ (where $M_\odot$ is the mass of the Sun), and they typically occupy a space of diameter 40 pc or more; as a result, they are normally referred to as Giant Molecular Clouds (GMCs). Our own Galaxy is believed to contain over 4000 GMCs [Solomon and Sanders 1980], and their combined mass is so great that they represent the dominant form of matter in the interstellar medium.

Star clusters are born in molecular clouds, but during the early stages of their evolution, they are heavily shrouded by dust; and their development can only be effectively investigated at infrared wavelengths. In addition, it is only recently that infrared array cameras have been developed enabling high resolution observations to be made. For example, IRCAM, the prototype of such instruments which is in use with the 3.8-meter U.K. Infrared Telescope (UKIRT) on Mauna Kea, Hawaii, was commissioned in 1987. Originally, data from the 62x58 pixel array were digitized and sent to a remote pre-processor before transfer to a central computer for final storage and analysis. The principle of operation remains the same as 1024x1024 pixel and larger infrared array cameras have come into regular use.

Infrared (IR) surveys of the cold (about 10 Kelvin), dark clouds with such equipment (typically at 2.2-µm) have indicated the presence of many newly formed star clusters. For example, a survey of the LDN 1630 GMC (from the *Catalogue of Dark Nebulae*, by Lynds [1962]) in Orion has shown about 1000 sources, which are apparently young stars.

The average density of the material in a GMC is thought to be in the region of 300 atoms cm^{-3}, much too low for star formation to begin on its own; but IR observations of GMCs have shown that they are not of homogeneous density, having a "core-halo" structure. Unfortunately, little is known about the formation of massive, dense molecular cores within the clouds, nor the subsequent development of stars within the cores. However, observational evidence clearly points to a line of progression in which a dense core (or cores) form(s) in a GMC, and star clusters form within the cores. In the LDN 1630 cloud there are a number of distinct cores, the five most massive (having $M > 200M_\odot$) accounting for over half the mass in the entire cloud. It is, therefore, expected that the vast majority of the star formation here is occurring in a comparatively small number of regions. Near-IR surveys of stars within LDN 1630 confirm this to be the case; four of the molecular cores are associated with clusters. The clusters ([LDEG91] 1 to 4) in turn are the ionizing elements of the nebulae NGC 2023 (21 detected stars), NGC 2024 (309 stars), NGC 2068 = M 78 (192 stars) and NGC 2071 (105 stars). Why there should be such a difference in the star-forming efficiency of each of the cores is not clear, nor is it known why the fifth massive core (LBS 23) apparently has no associated cluster.

A molecular cloud with a newly formed embedded cluster is an extremely active region and is characterized by the presence of molecular outflows and H II regions. Together with the intense stellar wind from the infant stars, these can quickly disrupt the molecular cloud, particularly if the stars are of the massive type O variety, as will often be the case (the formation of low-mass stars, i.e., solar and below, involves a slightly different case). Until this time, the cluster has been in a stable condition, gravitationally bound together with the mass of the surrounding cloud. Once this cloud has dissipated the cluster will expand; if the original space density of the stars is high and the internal motions comparatively low, the cluster may well survive as a bound unit although a number of individual stars will have escaped. If the space density is less and the internal motions higher, the cluster stars may disperse to a greater extent and perhaps form the core of an unbound association.

A cluster forming in a core which is close to the edge of a molecular cloud will, of course, tend to "burn through" the material on the side adjoining empty space, forming an exit though which ionized gas will flow and expand into the interstellar medium. This is the "blister model" of H II regions [Zuckerman 1973; Zuckerman and Palmer 1974; Israel 1978] and observations have shown that the morphology of most can be explained by this means. The Orion Nebula is typical of such regions and its proximity (about 500 pc) has enabled it to be thoroughly studied at high spatial resolutions. The H II region itself is ionized by the partly embedded Trapezium cluster; behind this is the massive Orion MC-1 molecular cloud (see Figure 2.1 on page 19), weighing in at 200,000 $M_\odot$ and some 60 pc in

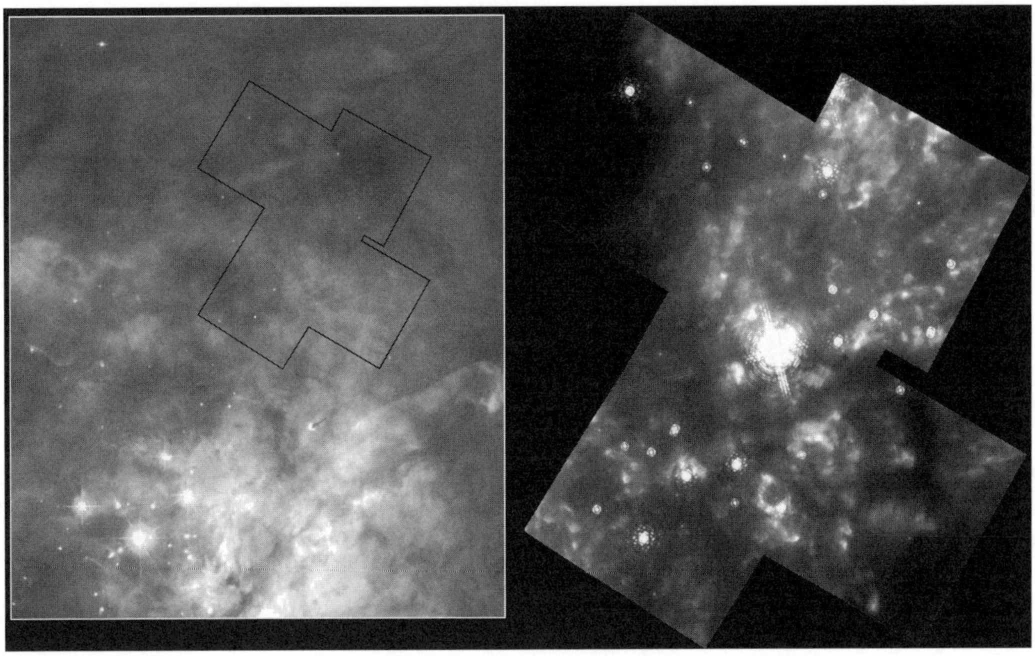

Fig. 2.1 *Orion Molecular Cloud (OMC 1). On the left is an HST image taken with the Wide Field and Planetary Camera 2 (WFPC2), covering a field of about 104 by 115 arc-seconds. On the right is an infrared HST image, taken with Near Infrared Camera and Multi-Object Spectrometer (NICMOS) instrument, about 50 arc-seconds in size (lower left to upper right) and showing the heart of the OMC cloud. The right image is from the region outlined in the left image. The bright "star" in the NICMOS image is the Becklin-Neugebauer object described in the text. NICMOS image: Rodger Thompson, Marcia Rieke, Glenn Schneider, Susan Stolovy (University of Arizona); Edwin Erickson (SETI Institute/Ames Research Center); David Axon (STScI); and NASA. WFPC2 image: C. Robert O'Dell, Shui Kwan Wong (Rice University) and NASA.*

extent—which is gradually being eaten away by the ionization front. This has broken through the molecular cloud on the side facing the Earth, revealing the beautiful and complex visible structure. Some remnants of the dark molecular matter still cross in front of the bright nebulosity forming what appears to be a dark lane separating M 42 and M 43.

Star forming activity is continuing in OMC 1. Not far to the north of the Trapezium, but a little more deeply embedded, is the Kleinmann-Low Nebula (KL), which was discovered at a wavelength of 22 mm in 1967. This contains a cluster which, with a total luminosity of about 100,000 times that of the Sun, is one of the brightest infrared sources in the sky. It is totally obscured at visible wavelengths, as the optical and ultraviolet radiation from the hot, young stars is quickly absorbed by the dense surrounding material. This is then heated and the energy re-emitted at infrared wavelengths. At the north end of this is the Becklin-Neugebauer object (BN), suggested to be a newly-formed star, perhaps only 10,000 years old, within a ring of warm dust left over from its formation. Alternatively, this may be a B-type main sequence star which just happens to be passing through the area. Images from the *Hubble Space Telescope* (HST) using the WFPC2 (Wide Field and Planetary Camera 2) and NICMOS (Near-Infrared Camera and Multi-Object Spectrometer) have clearly shown the presence of a number of new stars embedded in protoplanetary disks (proplyds), and knots of gas distorted by the outflow from newly formed massive stars.

It was believed for quite some time that stars in open clusters were all formed within a very short period of time. However, it now appears that, although the timescale is fairly short on the timeline of cosmic events, there is still a spread of several million years involved. This was discussed as long ago as 1983 in a paper by Adams, *et al.*, [1983]. More recently, a specific study of the open cluster NGC 4755 by Sagar and Cannon [1995] has shown that the star formation processes in the parent molecular cloud might have continued for more than 6 or 7 million years. It also seems that, in this case, the massive stars in the cluster formed about 4 million years before the bulk of the low mass stars.

2.3 Open Clusters, Associations and Galactic Structure

In helping to delineate the structure of the Galaxy, open clusters and associations are of value for several reasons. Primarily, it is possible to determine the distance of a cluster more accurately than that of a single star, and since they contain luminous stars, they can be studied at quite large distances. Because of their comparative youth, they also make ideal tracers for the youngest component of the galactic disk.

The first comprehensive study of the distribution of open star clusters was made by Robert Trumpler who published his results in 1930 (**see Section 1.7 starting on page 8**). Although some of his major conclusions were incorrect, his work provided some remarkable results indicating the Perseus arm of our spiral galaxy and also the Sagittarius and Carina features.

Trumpler's work was concerned solely with open clusters, and later Morgan, *et al.*, [1952] showed that H II regions and OB associations could also be used to delineate the spiral arms of a galaxy following their examination of the features in M 31. In addition, studies of Cepheid distribution, supergiants, and Wolf-Rayet (WR) stars have all been used with varying degrees of effectiveness to show the spiral structure of the Galaxy.

All these methods have their difficulties and uncertainties, and at times produce conflicting results. As far as open clusters and associations are concerned, one of the main complicating factors is establishing distance. In this respect, the Hyades cluster distance determination is of importance and will be discussed below.

2.4 The Hyades Cluster Distance

The Hyades star cluster is the nearest moderately rich open cluster, comprising perhaps 300 stars spread across about 20° of the sky and, from our vantage point, appears to be fairly well above the galactic plane. Because of these factors, it is little affected by interstellar reddening. In addition, there is no reason to believe that it is particularly atypical in any way; it might be surmised that results from studying this particular open cluster could be usefully applied to other clusters.

In fact, the Hyades have proven to be of fundamental importance in the study of open clusters, and astrophysics provides a starting point for cosmic distance calibrations on the Galactic and extragalactic distance scale. There have been many investigations to establish the Hyades cluster distance (see Table 2.1) and small revisions in the accepted distance can have far-reaching consequences for estimates of distances in the Universe.

The measurement of the trigonometric parallax of Hyades stars is the most direct way of determining its distance. However, a very high degree of precision is required, the mean parallax being only about 0.020″. The depth of the cluster is about 10% of its distance, so a distance scatter of about 0.002″ would be expected. Nevertheless, since ground-based measurement errors are typically of the same order, most of this would be swallowed up anyway! Several painstaking ground-based trigonometric surveys of Hyades stars have been undertaken, summarized by Hanson [1980]. The mean parallax determinations to that time resulted in a cluster distance modulus of m–M = 3.25±0.08 mag., which equates to about 44.5 pc (= 145 light-years).

Table 2.1
Hyades cluster distance determinations.

Year	Distance Modulus	Method	Reference
1952	3.03	Convergence	Van Bueren, H.G.; *Bull. Astr. Inst. Neth.*, Vol. XI, 385, 1952.
1963	3.26	Trigonometric	Jenkins, L.F.; *Gen. Cat. of Trig.Parallaxes*,Yale, 1963.
1965	3.03	Convergence	Wayman, P.A. *et al.*; *Royal Obs.Bull.* No.98, E33, 1965
1966	3.42	Various	Hodge, P.W. & Wallerstein, G; *PASP* 78, 411, 1966.
1967	3.23	Trigonometric	Eggen, O.; *Ann. Rev. Astron. Astrophys.* 5, 105, 1967.
1970	3.09	Convergence	Upton, E.; *Astron. J.* 75, 1097, 1970.
1972	3.66	Trigonometric	Argue, A. & Kenworthy, C.; *MNRAS* 159, 31, 1972.
1974	3.29	Trigonometric	Upgren, A.; *Astron. J.* 79, 651, 1974.
1975	3.19	Trigonometric	Klemola, A.R. *et al.*; *Astron. J.* 80, 642, 1975.
1975	3.19	Convergence	Corbin, T.E. *et al.*; *Bull. A.A.S.* 7, 337, 1975.
1977	3.18	Proper motions	McAllister, H.A.; *Astron. J.* 82, 487, 1977.
1977	3.27	Convergence	Carpenter, M.S.; *Neighbourhood Meeting on the Distance Scale*, Yale, 1977.
1980	3.25	Trigonometric	Hanson, R.B.; in *IAU Symp.* No. 85, "Star Clusters," p.71, 1980.
1982	3.30	Trigonometric	Eggen, O.; *Ap.J.* Supp. 50, 221, 1982.
1986	3.42	Proper motions	Lotkin, A.V. *et al.*; *Sov. Astron.* 31, 582, 1986.
1988	3.28	Convergence	Gunn, J.E. *et al.*; *Astron. J.* 96, 198, 1988.
1990	3.37	Convergence	Schwan, H.; *Astron. Astrophys.* 228, 69, 1990.
1991	3.40	Convergence	Schwan, H.; *Astron. Astrophys.* 243, 386, 1991.
1992	3.35	Convergence	Eggen, O.J.; *Astron. J.* 104, 1482, 1992.
1997	3.32	Trigonometric	van Altena *et al.*; *Baltic Astron.* 6(1), 27, 1997
1997	3.33	Various	Brown, A.G.A. *et al.*, *Proc. of the Hipparcos Venice '97 Symposium*, 1997.

Historically, the most important method of determining the Hyades distance has been the "convergent point," or "moving cluster" method which is illustrated in Figure 2.2 on page 21. The apparent movement of the cluster, or any other individual star or cluster across the 2-dimensional celestial sphere is the product of its movement perpendicular to the line of sight combined with its movement toward or away from us. In Figure 2.2, taking any cluster member, S as an example, the individual members will be moving together in some arbitrary direction relative to the observer with a common velocity, V. This motion is resolved into two components, known as the radial velocity (V_r), which is the motion either towards or away from us, and the tangential velocity (V_t), which is the movement perpendicular to the line of sight, at right-angles to the radial velocity. Both of these components can be measured by the terrestrial observer. V_r can be obtained from the Doppler effect on the spectral lines, while V_t can be seen in the proper motion, μ, of the star across the sky.

Because the Hyades are such a nearby group of stars, appearing to be quite scattered on the plane of the sky, the movement of the group as a whole means that the "tracks" of the individual members, projected forward, appear to converge on a particular point in the sky. This is the "convergent point" (see Figure 2.2) and is analogous to the apparent convergence at the horizon of straight railroad tracks. Once the radial velocity and proper motions of a cluster star, *S*, have been determined and the angular distance, θ, to the convergent point measured, then the distance to the star, *r* and therefore, the cluster, can be found as follows: by simple geometry, *V* can be calculated from θ and V_r, and once this parameter is determined, V_t can be calculated.

Using the convergent point method, van Bueren [1952] obtained a distance modulus of m – M = 3.03 mag.; and this value remained more-or-less the standard for around 20 years, with supporting evidence being provided by Wayman *et al.*, [1965]. However, doubt was cast on this figure by Hodge and Wallerstein [1966], who suggested an increase of 0.39 magnitudes on the basis of their work on the dynamical parallaxes of visual binaries, and taking into account the Wilson-Bappu effect [Wilson and Bappu 1957] on four giants in the Hyades cluster. The latter is a relationship between the K-line of calcium emission width and the absolute magnitude of a late-type star from which M_v, and therefore, parallax or distance, can be determined with a precision of half a magnitude, from the width of the K-line emission.

With two different methods of determining the distance to the cluster, each can be used as a check against the other. This is important since each has potential sources of error. In the case of trigonometric parallax exceedingly tiny angular measures have to be achieved. Not only this, from a ground-based location the Earth's atmosphere will distort the image size, and the effects of the Sun's own motion through space relative to the star in question has to be disentangled. The convergent point method is limited by the need to find a cluster which is reasonably well populated and sufficiently nearby in order that the members fill a significant solid angle on the sky. It is also based on the assumption that individual members of a cluster move through space on essentially parallel tracks. The cluster as a whole is dynamically simple, with little expansion, contraction, rotation and small random motions of individual stars compared to the center of mass of the cluster. Of course, in both methods, when looking at stars of increasingly faint magnitude, it becomes more difficult to separate those of the cluster from the other field stars, because of the vastly larger number of stars which need to have proper motions checked. For a specific star, the cluster membership cannot be determined from proper motions alone, but a figure for the probability of it being a cluster member can be worked out. With sufficiently precise proper motions, Hyades cluster members can be segregated from the field with better than 90% probability.

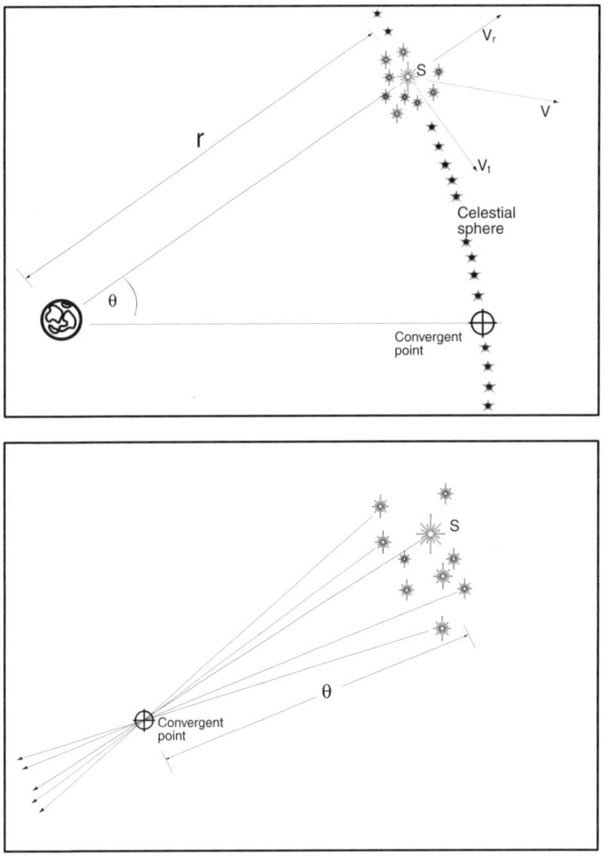

Fig. 2.2 *Determining the "convergent point." The motion (V) of a star (S) in a cluster can be resolved into two components, radial velocity (V_r) and transverse velocity (V_t). Measures for a series of stars will enable the apparent convergent point to be determined, and, combined with the angular distance (θ) to the convergent point, geometry will reveal the absolute distance (r).*

In a fairly recent analysis of ground-based observations, Schwan [1991] has derived distances for 145 Hyades members in an extended region around the cluster. The basis for this work is the proper motions published in the *Fifth Fundamental Catalogue* (FK5) [Fricke 1988] and the *Positions and Proper Motions Catalogue* (PPM) [Röser and Bastian 1989], which have a precision greater than that of the old AGK3 proper motions. A selection of 62 of the stars was used to determine the convergence point at $\alpha = 97.68°$ $\pm 0.42°$, $\delta = 5.98° \pm 0.18°$. Combining this with the mean cluster radial velocity of 39.1 km s^{-1} determined by Detweiler *et al.*, [1984], results in the following space velocities:

Equatorial coordinates:

$$V = (-6.19, +45.94, +4.86) \text{ km s}^{-1}$$

Galactic coordinates:

$$V = (-42.02, -20.12, -1.04) \text{ km s}^{-1}$$

With the cluster space velocity determined, the expected radial velocity has then been computed for each Hyades candidate star and then combined with the observed proper motion to produce the star's distance from the Sun.

Taking a subset of about 50 stars in the inner core of the cluster, Schwan has derived the following parameters for the Hyades:

Galactic coordinates:

$$X = -44.3 \text{ pc},\ Y = +0.5 \text{ pc},\ Z = -18.2 \text{ pc}$$

Distance of cluster center:

$$R_c = 47.9 \pm 0.8 \text{ pc}$$

Distance modulus of cluster center:

$$(m - M)_c = 3.40 \pm 0.04 \text{ mag.}$$

The mean errors are mainly caused by uncertainty in the determination of the convergence point.

The question of the Hyades cluster distance, and astrometry generally, has received a considerable boost from the results of the European Space Agency's *Hipparcos* satellite published in 1997. By using *Hipparcos* absolute trigonometrical parallaxes and proper motions of 5499 stars in the Hyades area, and radial velocities determined from ground-based observations, Brown, *et al.*, [1997] were able to select 1027 cluster candidates. From these 218 were identified with sufficient confidence to analyze in more detail. From the results, they have been able to obtain accurate positional and velocity data for the cluster and then construct a three-dimensional view of the Hyades structure. A 2.2 MB MPEG movie of this is currently available on the internet from the ESA web site (see Appendix E for web addresses). Thirteen new cluster members within 20 pc of the cluster center were also identified. The study showed that the cluster has a tidal radius of about 10 pc, within which is an inner core region of radius 2.7 pc. There seems to be no evidence for any systematic internal velocity structure, and instead the stars appear to be moving in a uniform way with an internal velocity dispersion of only about 0.3 km s^{-1}. The results point to the center of mass of the Hyades being at a distance of 46.34 ±0.27 pc (distance modulus m – M = 3.33 ±0.01 mag)

Once the distance to the Hyades has been determined, it is possible to plot its Hertzsprung-Russell (H-R) diagram.

In its original form, the H-R diagram consisted of a graph of the luminosities (or absolute magnitudes) of stars plotted against their spectral types (see Figure 2.3, which shows an H-R diagram in schematic form of stars in the solar neighborhood). It is important to note that the H-R diagram is like a single frame taken from a movie, a snapshot in time of a continuing dynamic process. (It would be interesting to see a computer-generated version of the entire "movie"!) The ideas which enabled its development were devised independently by Ejnar Hertzsprung (1873–1967) and Henry Norris Russell (1877–1957), although the work of the former, being published in rather obscure journals, was not at first given the recognition it deserved. Because of this, the graph was originally called the "Russell diagram"; the term "Hertzsprung-Russell diagram" was coined by Strömgren in 1933. On hearing this, Hertzsprung is quoted as having said wisely, "Why not call it the color-magnitude diagram? Then we would all know what it is about." However, the term Hertzsprung-Russell diagram has stuck and the term color-magnitude diagram (CMD) is used for a variant where, in the case of clusters, apparent magnitude is plotted against color index. The difference is primarily in terms of ease of application. A color index and spectral type are effectively measures of the surface temperature of a star. In clusters, since the stars are all at more-or-less the same distance, the apparent brightness of a star relative to other cluster members is a measure of its absolute luminosity compared to other stars in the cluster. In addition, because the stars in a cluster are born from the same interstellar cloud at about the same time (over a period of just a few million years) and have about the same chemical composition, they are all directly comparable except in mass and, therefore, rate of evolution.

2.5 Color-Magnitude Diagrams of Open Clusters

As a result of the comparative youth of many open clusters, it might be expected that a large number of the constituent stars will be found on the Main Sequence (that part of the CMD where most stars reside during the normal hydrogen-burning phase of their evolution) or towards the blue end of the color-magnitude diagram. In most cases this is indeed correct (Figure 2.3 on page 23). Most cluster stars are found in a fairly well-defined strip, contrary to the situation which exists in globular clusters (see Figure 6.1 on page 218). However, there are a number of complicating factors. Some open clusters have remained together over significant periods of time—and are no longer young; indeed, a very small number may be as old as the Galactic disk itself. These are characterized by a significant red giant population. The age of a cluster can

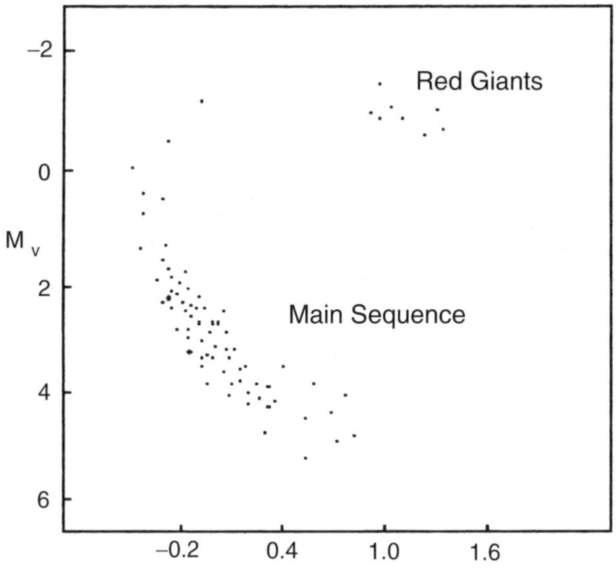

Fig. 2.3 *Schematic diagram of a typical open cluster Hertsprung-Russell (HR) diagram.*

be gauged from the luminosity of the main-sequence turn-off point. Using a variation on this method, the magnitude difference between the main-sequence turn-off and the red giant clump which is equivalent to the horizontal branch in globular clusters, Phelps, *et al.*, [1994] have found Berkeley 17 to be the oldest galactic open cluster, followed by Collinder 261 and NGC 6791. Altogether, they found 19 clusters to be as old, or older than M 67 (about 5 Gyr, where 1 Gyr is a billion years). More recently, it has been suggested that perhaps Palomar 1 might be the oldest known open cluster (see Chapter 7 on page 225).

A similar pattern exists in all open clusters, although it is more apparent in some than others. Uncertainties may exist in establishing the cluster membership of stars in the field of a particular object, particularly in the fainter and more distant objects. Some stars may be undetected close binaries and incorrectly plotted as single stars with characteristics different to those of the individual components. In addition, there may be doubts about the corrections which need to be made to compensate for interstellar absorption (not necessarily uniform over the face of the cluster).

Nevertheless, one can compensate for the uncertainties by statistical adjustments, and the distances to other clusters can be determined from a technique called "main sequence matching," using the accurately-known distance and H-R diagram of the Hyades as a reference frame. For example: if a CMD is plotted for the Pleiades, and then superimposed onto a plot of the Hyades CMD, it will be noted that the main sequence sections, which contain the bulk of the cluster stars, are separated from each other on the graph by a vertical distance called the "distance modulus." More widely extended, the relative distances of open clusters can be established, and from their distribution, some clues derived about the local structure of the Galaxy.

2.6 The Dynamics of Open Clusters

The dynamics of open clusters is probably the area with the greatest level of uncertainty. This is primarily the result of the comparatively small number of stars involved in each object, and the smaller the number of stars, the more difficult the calculations become. In addition to the motions of the open cluster members within the cluster (due to the mutual gravitational interactions), there are a number of other factors which can have a significant effect on its dynamics. Encounters with field stars as the cluster orbits the center of the Galaxy are inevitable; these affect the velocity distribution of stars within the cluster and, in the event of the cluster passing through a region densely populated with massive stars, the disruptive effects could be considerable. Also of major importance are the galactic tidal forces, which shape the size of the clusters by stripping away those stars less well bound. Added to this are the tidal effects from the presence of massive molecular clouds.

These might be considered as extrinsic influences on the dynamical development of a cluster; there are also intrinsic factors. In open clusters, particularly the younger ones, there is a population of extremely massive, short-lived stars. It has become clear that these stars lose mass at a considerable rate and as they do so, this mass is lost from the cluster. As a consequence of this, the coherency of the cluster as a gravitationally bound unit is reduced; therefore, the dynamical energy of the cluster has been increased. Furthermore, it is well known that the majority of stars are not single (like the Sun), but exist in pairs and multiple systems. In the context of the development of open cluster dynamics, these have an important part to play. Computer simulations show that over a period of time, many clusters will become dominated by massive binaries. These could add some stability to open cluster systems. Over a long enough period of time, stellar encounters will eject individual stars from a cluster, reducing their mass and thus causing the cluster core to contract. Therefore, those stars furthest from the core would also be lost, speeding up the contraction process. Lack of observation of this phenomenon suggests that there is some process which acts as sink of binding energy. It is entirely plausible that this could be caused by massive binaries; the energy transactions involved during encounters with other cluster stars could cause the binary to become more tightly bound and add energy to the other stars, inhibiting the contraction of the cluster as a whole.

Obviously, the galactic location, mass, stellar density, stellar numbers and other factors will combine together to make it necessary for each open cluster to have its own dynamical solution developed. At least, these factors make it extremely difficult to create any generalizations. And if this were not difficult enough, obtaining the observational data upon which dynamical investigations need to be based is greatly hampered by problems of separating out cluster stars from foreground and background Milky Way stars. There are some exceptions; in the case of clusters like the Hyades and Pleiades, the situation is a little easier because of their comparatively high Galactic latitude.

Theoretical considerations [Ambartsumian 1938; Spitzer 1940] have shown that a cluster is unlikely to evaporate completely, and that an open cluster remnant (OCR) of some description will be left. The question of the identifying characteristics of OCRs depends on the initial membership and also the Galactocentric distance. The nature of such remnants in the solar neighborhood has been considered by De la Fuente Marcos [1998], who points out that OCRs resulting from clusters with an initial population of less than about 100 would have to contain about 40% of their initial population in order to have a stellar density greater than that of the field. However, this reduces to only about 7% for clusters with an initial population of 750–1000. Of course, for any given Galactocentric distance, the evolution of an open cluster with a small initial population will differ from that with a large population. It turns out that OCRs derived from poorly populated clusters are likely to be those most easily detected because they contain luminous, early-type stars (OCRs from rich clusters will be dominated by faint, low mass stars, of spectral type K). These are difficult to detect at any significant distance, and De la Fuente Marcos suggests that large numbers of these OCRs in the disk of the Galaxy may be relevant in accounting for the apparent "missing mass." The basis for this is the assumption that stars form mainly in open clusters, and therefore, with a mean population of 300 stars for a typical open cluster, the number of possible remnants could be as high as 3×10^8 to account for the 10^{11} stars which the galactic disk is believed to contain. If the typical mass of an OCR is about $30M_\odot$, it is possible that the mass contained in them all is as large as $10^{10}M_\odot$, about one-sixth the mass of the entire disk.

Wielen [1975] has suggested that the Ursa Major moving group (Collinder 285) may be an OCR, and van Albada [1968] has indicated a number of observational candidates, including σ Ori, ρ Oph, 67 Oph, 1 Cas and 8 Lac. De la Fuente Marcos draws attention to the results of Stefanik, *et al.*, [1997] on the group Upgren 1, which consists of two groups of dynamically different sets of stars. The larger group consists of 5 stars including a long period binary and an unusual triple. The properties of this group match very well the properties of an OCR with an initial population of approximately 1000 stars, as derived in numerical simulations.

Fig. 2.4 *Gaseous pillars in the Eagle Nebula and Star Cluster, also known as M 16 or NGC 6611. The tips of these pillars are dense, compact pockets of interstellar gas called* evaporating gaseous globules *(EGGs), where stars are being formed. HST WFPC2 image. Jeff Hester (Arizona State University) and NASA.*

2.7 Recent Developments

The importance of accurate and detailed information on star positions, distances, and proper motions in open cluster investigations cannot be overemphasized. The last several years have seen numerous improvements in both the quality and quantity of this type of data.

We have already mentioned the *Hipparcos* catalog in connection with the important question of the Hyades distance. After its launch in 1989, an engine failure resulted in the *Hipparcos* satellite being placed in an incorrect orbit. However, it was possible to carry out most of the originally planned mission. The primary result was a catalog of 118,218 stars in 17 volumes, as described by Perryman [1997]. Included were accurate positional data, proper motions, magnitudes, color indices, and information about variability and multiplicity with a limiting magnitude of about $V \sim 12.4$ (although the completeness is only at the level of $V = 7.3$ to 9.0). Valid parallaxes (distances) and their uncertainties were also determined for approximately 20,000 (the nearest) of these stars.

Published along with the main *Hipparcos* catalog was the *Tycho* catalog [Egret and Fabricius 1997]. It included a survey of stars observed by the *Hipparcos* spacecraft brighter than magnitude 11.0 (and not included in the *Hipparcos* catalog itself). It was estimated that 99.9% of all stars brighter than $V = 10.0$ were included as well as a large proportion of the stars between magnitude 10.0 and 11.5.

Surprisingly, these catalogs have already become mostly of historical interest. The parallax information provided by *Hipparcos* is still of great use, e.g. for checking the relative distances of nearby stars in order to see if they are physically associated. However, the basic stellar position and proper motion information of both the *Hipparcos* and *Tycho* catalogs have been superseded by the *Tycho-2* catalog [Høg, *et al.*, 2000]. This catalog incorporated a re-reduction of the data collected by the *Hipparcos* satellite, in order to reach fainter magnitudes and to achieve better accuracy. It also incorporated the results of the great *Astrographic Catalogue* or *AC* [Urban and Corbin, 1998]. This project, begun in the late 19th century, involving a number of observatories around the world, was designed to photograph and measure the positions of all stars brighter than about magnitude 11. The U.S. Naval Observatory, during the 1990's, finally completed the *AC*. By combining the earlier star positions of this catalog with the star positions as measured by the *Hipparcos* satellite, quite accurate proper motion data could be generated. The result was the *Tycho-2* catalog, containing positions, proper motions, and two colors for the 2.5 million brightest stars. This catalog is estimated to be 99% complete down to a magnitude of V = 11.0 and 90% complete down to V = 11.5. This should serve as a gold mine of data from which to determine from their proper motions whether groups of stars in the sky are physically associated. The *Tycho-2* catalog is available from the CDS and can be accessed directly via the Vizier web utility (see Appendix E beginning on page 455 for web addresses).

For fainter stars, now available is the incredible *USNO-B2.0* catalog [Monet, *et al.*, 2003] of over 1 *billion* objects, more precisely containing 1,042,618,261 stars and nonstellar objects. This catalog has been generated from the digitization of most of the major photographic surveys of the sky and from the detection of 3,643,201,733 objects on those surveys. It includes objects down to a magnitude of $V = 21$, has 0.2 arcsecond positional accuracy at J2000.0. This is essentially an inventory of about 1% of the entire Milky Way. Proper motions and approximate magnitudes and colors (accurate to 0.3 magnitudes in up to 5 colors) of all the objects are included, based on their position and approximate magnitude on the photographic surveys taken at different epochs. This catalog is so large (over 80 Gigabytes) that is it not being generally distributed as catalogs have routinely been in the past, but is only accessible via various web interfaces, e.g. at the USNO Flagstaff web site or Vizier (Appendix E). The color information in this catalog is probably not of sufficient accuracy in general for use in definitely determining whether groups of stars are related. However, as with *Tycho-2*, the proper motion and perhaps the color information, with proper consideration of the uncertainties involved, can be used to determine whether stars appearing close to each other in the sky are physically related as a cluster.

The near future will see the creation of even more astrometrically and photometrically useful catalogs. Covering the intermediate magnitude range between the fairly bright stars of the *Tycho-2* catalog and the faint stars of the *USNO-B2.0* catalog will be the *USNO CCD Astrograph Catalog* (or *UCAC*), scheduled for completion sometime in 2004. This catalog is based on an all-sky CCD survey and is expected to contain 80 million stars between magnitudes V = 7.5 and 16.5. The proper motions are expected to be accurate at the 1 to 5 milliarcseonds/year level—far superior to any other source at this faint magnitude range.

The *USNO-B2.0* catalog itself is expected to be upgraded in September of 2003, incorporating the precise positional and photometric information from the infrared *2-Micron All Sky Survey* (or *2MASS*) [Skrutskie, *et al.*, 1997; Appendix E]. This survey will include observations of approximately 300 million infrared sources (including a catalog of over 1 million galaxies) and its use should result in substantial improvements to the USNO catalog.

There is also the *Sloan Digital Sky Survey* (*SDSS*) [Feder, 1998; Appendix E], begun in 1998 and continuing to map about one quarter of the sky. It is covering the areas away from the Milky Way and as visible from the *SDSS* Apache Point Observatory in New Mexico. The primary purpose of this survey is to obtain positions and redshifts of about 1 million galaxies and quasars, and thereby accurately map the distribution of galaxies through much of the known universe. However, the survey will also include the creation of a detailed catalog of the some 100 million objects (including mostly stars) observed. The positions of these stars will not necessarily be improved on, but the color information collected could become quite useful in examining relationships between groups of stars in the sky (i.e. whether they are likely physically associated as star clusters or not).

Clearly the situation as to the best star catalogs for a given purpose and given sky and magnitude coverage is a fast changing one. The U. S. Naval Observatory maintains a web site (Appendix E) that recommends what catalogs should be used for a particular purpose. This should be invaluable to those who wish to use the most current and accurate information but to do not wish to keep track of the details of all the available data sources.

However, other new sources of data—not necessarily related to specific catalogs—should not be forgotten. For several years, Jean-Claude Mermilliod has created a detailed database on the measurements of individual stars in open star clusters. This is available on the Web (Appendix E), and currently includes information on the stars in approximately 600 Milky Way and also Small Magellanic

Cloud clusters. The type of information collected and capabilities include: a) cross reference tables between the various numbering systems established for each cluster; b) active scanned maps and plotted charts where data for individual stars can be selected; c) positions, magnitudes, and other data for individual stars; d) plotting facilities; e) extensive bibliographic data; and f) extensive archives of published tables. This information should facilitate greatly the study of already known clusters.

Finally, the results from the (*HST*) and the many large telescopes that have come online in the last few years should be mentioned. There have been relatively few direct studies of open clusters with these instruments as they pursue research programs mostly related to cosmology. However, the incredible images of clusters and star forming regions have undoubtedly raised the profile of this area of astronomy. In particular, images of the Orion nebula and the pillars of gas and dust in the Eagle Nebula and cluster (NGC 6611 = M 16, see Figure 2.4) have captured the public imagination and appeared in popular books, newspapers, and even on T-shirts.

The *HST* and other large telescopes are also being used more and more to observe the open and globular cluster systems of nearby galaxies and the globular star cluster systems of many distant galaxies. In the early 1990's the total number of such systems that had been studied extensively at all was probably less than 10. Yet one can now find in the literature dozens, if not hundreds of such studies for most galaxies in the Local Group, and even some galaxies out to the Virgo cluster and beyond. The rate at which star clusters form is still a topic of discussion, but clearly the rate at which they are being discovered is increasing greatly, perhaps even exponentially.

Chapter 3
The "Missing" Star Clusters

When you have found growing older to be a process of the reconciliation of the spirit to life, it is decidedly uncomfortable to have some youngster come along and point out the irreconcilable things in the universe. Just as you have made a tacit agreement to call all things non-existent, it is highly discommoding to have somebody shout in strident tones that they are very real and significant.

—Randolph Bourne (1886–1918), *American Essays*

3.1 Introduction

Any set of data has a set of uncertainties associated with it. If it is data, it is measured information. All measurements have random and systematic errors associated with them. In many cases the process of measurement involves blunders, where the measurement is incorrect or assigned to some physical object incorrectly.

The collective human knowledge of star clusters is by no means a different case. For every measurement made of any astronomical object, many types of errors are possible. There is the random error involved in making even the best possible measurement. For star clusters this means an absolute position can never be determined. Its size can never be perfectly measured, and its total brightness can never be absolutely obtained. Further, such measurements are affected by systematic error. When measuring the position of a star cluster relative to some nearby star, it is quite possible, even likely for older measurements, that there is some offset in the reference star's position or the coordinate system from which its position was obtained. If the diameters of clusters are measured from a photographic plate, a scale error may cause the sizes obtained to be systematically too small or too large. If poor calibrator stars are used to determine the magnitude of a cluster, it may end up being measured brighter or fainter than it actually is. These are all actual problems that beset *all* star clusters to one degree or another.

But as with any form of measurement, blunders—just flat out mistakes—are also possible. The fainter and more obscure a star cluster is, the less measurements there are, and the more likely that what measurements exist may be grossly erroneous. This is not to say that bright, well-known star clusters are immune from the problem. As we shall see, many relatively famous star clusters have identification problems due to a simple mistake somewhere in the (often distant) past. The effect of such a mistake has propagated forward to the present day.

The most common and most obvious form of these mistakes becomes apparent in the case of the missing or, interchangeably what have come to be known as nonexistent star clusters. These are the clusters whose very existence is either in doubt, or for which at least one reference declares that the cluster does not exist at all.

Intuitively this seems completely contradictory. How could a visual observer or a researcher studying a photographic plate see a group of stars and consider it a newly discovered (or at least possible) star cluster—only to have later researchers claim the object does not exist at all?

This situation seems odd, and yet the problem is common enough to require a chapter to discuss it in detail. Also considered will be the related situation of star clusters often being assigned many names, the wrong name, or even no name at all. Obviously there is a connection between these two situations, since being assigned an incorrect designation is one way for a star cluster to end up missing.

One of us [BA] has in fact already discussed this in some detail in the book *The "Non-Existent" Star Clusters of the RNGC*, Monograph No. 1 of the Webb Society [Archinal 1993]. The specific case of the RNGC is considered there, where many NGC star clusters are listed as nonexistent. Details of how this could happen are described there, but more importantly a catalog of 229 such objects is given. Between the catalog and the many notes provided, it became clear that many of the nonexistent clusters do in fact exist, perhaps as a real cluster or only a group of stars.

This chapter will consider first the past work and references to the situation of the missing clusters that have called attention to the problem. Then follows a detailed look at the possible reasons that a star cluster became missing or its identity otherwise confused. We'll also list many of the actual cases where these reasons caused a problem and look at how these problems have been and still can be solved. Finally we take a look at what sort of practical problems these errors have caused, and speculate on how further work will be done to resolve these problems.

It should be added that many additional examples of errors relative to star cluster identification and basic data are listed under the various clusters highlighted in the Extended Notes sections of Chapters 4 (page 111) and 7 (page 232). The text in this chapter will concentrate on cluster identity problems.

Before proceeding it should also be emphasized that the present work in no way is meant to replace or revise the previous Monograph by Archinal. Rather, it is meant to review the subject generally, providing some additional background and historical details, and discussing the general reasons for the missing cluster problem. Likewise the general catalog of star clusters presented in Chapters 4 and 7 and in Appendix C is not meant to be a definitive source of information on such objects. The Monograph information has been incorporated into the new catalog, and several corrections have been made for some of the objects (as explained in the Extended Notes section of Chapter 4). However, the Monograph still stands on its own as the primary reference for information on many of these objects. Readers who are particularly interested in investigating or observing the objects listed there are encouraged to consult the Monograph directly. Copies are still available for sale from the Webb Society and Willmann-Bell, Inc. (See Appendix E on page 455 for Web and mailing addresses.)

3.2 The Discovery of the Missing Star Clusters

There is no single event or publication which can definitely be cited as the point where it was discovered that large numbers of star clusters were missing or even non-existent. Rather it appears that the idea gradually evolved during the latter half of the 20th century as modern catalogs of star clusters were generated and began to be used by both professional and amateur astronomers. Here we would like to review some specific cases where these problems were first raised. Much of this material is based on a letter by one of us to the *Webb Society Quarterly Journal* [Archinal, 1994].

The late Walter Scott Houston, who wrote the Deep-Sky Wonders column for *Sky & Telescope* magazine, surely deserves much credit for calling attention to these problems over many years. In the period 1947 to 1959, many of his columns described star clusters, including some whose very existence had been questioned. Archinal [1993] describes these comments in detail under entries for NGC 2234, 2318, 2413, 2932, 6561, and 7352.

The first modern professional references to this general problem appeared in the first edition of the *Catalogue of Star Clusters and Associations* [Alter, *et al.*, 1958]. While compiling that catalog, the fundamental question faced by all catalog compilers arose. What objects were eligible for catalog selection, and what objects were not? In particular they faced a definition question: just what is an open star cluster? They write [ibid, 10]:

> A photographic or visual inspection reveals a number of star condensations, which are distinguished more or less prominently from a more thinly populated background. Such differences in density may be due to the presence of an open cluster, to accidental star distribution, or to intervening absorbing matter which depopulates the surroundings; or to any combination of these three causes. Therefore, every cluster catalog based on such an inspection runs the risk of including star condensations which are not clusters, or excluding real clusters under the assumption of being only accidental condensations. This point of view was always taken by the compilers of cluster catalogs. Of the more than 600 clusters in the N.G.C. and I.C. only about half have been recognized in various later catalogs (usually augmented by new members), according to the structural qualities demanded by the various authors.

As an example of this, there is a discussion of several NGC and Collinder objects, which are rejected as star clusters even though earlier (and sometimes later) authors considered these groups of stars as real physical associations.

Alter *et al.*, [1958, 14–15] conclude:

> These examples ... make it quite clear that in many cases the question of cluster qualities is assessed very differently by different authors. It is therefore probable that a number of clusters contained in this Catalogue will, in fact, be no real clusters, while others, not yet recognized as clusters—either on account of the faintness of their stars or of their apparent inconspicuousness (here the Palomar Atlas may be a turning point)—will be included in due course: the character of this Catalogue offers every possibility of extension.

So here we see that Alter, *et al.*, [1958] freely admitted that their catalog omitted many objects that had been considered clusters by others, and that they also assumed there were many more clusters yet to be discovered. Unfortunately it is precisely this omission of possible (or even proposed and at one point refuted) star clusters that has caused problems later on—as astronomers began looking for these very objects or, even worse, discovered them anew.

Twelve years later, Alter, *et al.*, [1970] issued a new version of their catalog. During the intervening years, many new star clusters had been discovered. These discoveries were mostly due to searches of the still fairly new Palomar Observatory Sky Survey, and to new studies of the southern Milky Way. In addition, much new data had become available for already known clusters. Yet the situation was still much the same. Here Alter, *et al.*, [1970, 10] made a point of noting that, regarding open clusters, still "no precise definition of these clusters has been developed." They also repeated, in paraphrased form, their earlier statements about the inclusion of clusters in their catalog. So the problems caused by ignoring many objects previously cataloged as clusters continued. For that matter, the problems increased in number, as many objects discovered during the intervening 12 year period were not included in the catalog.

Also in 1970, Harold Corwin [1970a,b] noted that various clusters in Cygnus (NGC 6989, 6996, and 7150) could be considered missing. He even described NGC 7150 as "one of several hundred NGC objects that 'really isn't.'" Here was one of the first, if not the first, reference to these objects as truly being missing. This was also the first fairly clear indication that there were groups of stars in the sky that existed, had been cataloged, but were not being included in modern compilations.

The problem of missing clusters rose to a whole new level in 1973 with the publication of the *Revised New General Catalogue* (RNGC) by Sulentic and Tifft. Here all of the objects of the NGC (and many additional objects) had their type indicated by a combination of one or more of 10 code numbers. Objects that were coded type "7" (there were 799) were indicated to be simply "nonexistent" objects. It turned out that a good portion of these objects (212) had previously been listed in the NGC (by description) as something like star clusters.

Apparently, the first person to call attention to this situation in print was Walter Scott Houston, who pointed out in his February, 1974 column, a possible problem with NGC 2413 which had been designated "nonexistent" by the RNGC.

However, it fell to amateur astronomer Patrick Brennan to call attention to this as a much more general problem. Houston noted his correspondence with Brennan in his December, 1975 and January, 1976 columns, and pointed out that a number of obvious objects had been listed as nonexistent in the RNGC. These two columns, although perhaps not widely noticed at the time, led many later amateur astronomers to try to observe these objects and to verify their existence. See letters to the editor of the *Webb Society Quarterly Journal* [Pasterfield 1994; Archinal 1994] for comments in this regard.

A number of publications in the late 1970s and the 1980s continued to call attention to specific cases of groups of stars or even obvious clusters that had been listed as nonexistent in the RNGC. For example:

- Walter Scott Houston again brought up the subject of nonexistent clusters a number of times [Houston 1977, 1979, 1982, 1983, 1985, 1988a, 1989].
- The case of nonexistent clusters was covered in a special appendix to the Webb Society's book *Open and Globular Star Clusters* [Barker 1980]. Here some additional observations of Brennan's are presented.
- Brian Skiff wrote of specific problems in *Deep Sky Monthly* in 1981 and 1982, and in *Deep Sky* in 1983. He also noted the case of M 41 usually being given a bad position in a review of the first printing of *Uranometria 2000.0* in 1987. Although no one was questioning the existence of M 41, this brought attention to bare on the fact that much of the basic data regarding star clusters could be considered suspect.
- Jim Meketa wrote an entire article on the so-called nonexistent clusters of Cygnus in *Deep Sky* [1984].
- Alister Ling mentioned such clusters in the (U.S.) National Deep Sky Observers Society's publication *Betelgeuse* [1984, 1986] and in *Deep Sky* [1987].
- Phil Harrington wrote of this problem often in *Deep Sky* [1984–1988] and in his 1990 book on binocular deep sky observing.
- One of us [SH] also wrote of these problems in the *Webb Society Quarterly Journal* [Hynes 1986a,b].

As pointed out earlier what was hopefully a major leap forward in understanding this situation and in finding many of these so-called nonexistent clusters (or at least real groups of stars), was the publication of a complete monograph on the subject [Archinal, 1993]. The publication has now led to countless reports in the amateur astronomical literature of observations of many of these objects.

The Catalog data presented later also hopefully will go a long way toward further addressing this problem. It is not meant to serve instead of the Monograph or as a revision of it. That publication has detailed information for many objects that is not included here, and much further research is still needed for the more obscure objects. However, the catalog data given in the Monograph have been incorporated here. More significantly, a large number of errors related to cluster identifications and positions have been corrected, as described in detailed notes that accompany the catalog here. Many of these are non-NGC objects, which were generally not even considered in the Monograph.

3.3 Problems Caused by the "Missing" Star Clusters

One may wonder why all of this is important. What difference does it make if there are a few (or even many) clusters or other objects that have incorrect designations, positions, or other data, or are not listed in a given catalog? It turns out that there are many ramifications of such problems and errors. Some are rather obvious. Others are more obscure—but sometimes fairly serious.

For professional and amateur astronomers alike, more and more computer software is being developed to display astronomical data. Much of the software provides displays, i.e., maps, of portions of the sky. Examples of individual PC based software packages include *MegaStar*, *Guide*, *TheSky*, *HyperSky*, *RealSky*, etc. There are also a number of web sites that display maps of the sky in some form, such as the NASA/GSFC SkyView utility. See Appendix E on page 455 All of these have in common such features as displaying various types and catalogs of nonstellar objects. Many of them even key off an object name in order to determine a position and then display the sky at that position. Clearly, these tools are only as good as the data they include. Yet many of them rely on sources for star cluster information that have numerous identification and data problems or are notoriously incomplete.

In fact, many of these software and hardware manufacturers heavily advertise claims such as that they have "The Complete NGC" or "all the IC objects" or that you can "Select... all NGC objects...". Yet, obviously the identifications for many NGC and IC objects have never yet been definitively published, so these listings are incomplete at best. (Even worse, in the past some manufacturers have assigned *different objects* to the slots of the NGC numbers where an identification is in question—talk about confusing the issue.) Also, as we have indicated here, many identification and positional errors, and other incorrect basic data remain in even the best astronomical catalogs of the past.

To be sure, astronomers and these software and hardware devices also rely on other data that is sometimes far worse for other types of objects. Examples are data for planetary nebulae, diffuse nebulae (which have ill-defined shapes as well), galaxies (of which there are tens of thousands named), stars (of which there are millions formally named, and hundreds of millions identified), double stars, and variable stars (including many suspected variables that are not truly variable). And it should be realized that the producers of various astronomy software tools rarely, if ever, publish information so others can take advantage of the corrections. In the short run this may be because they feel that having software with more accurate data gives them a competitive advantage. However, in the long run, fixing identification and data problems and not announcing the changes to others only causes confusion, since the corrections are applied in only one place (e.g. one publication or software package). (The corrections listed in the various printings of first editions of *Uranometria 2000.0* and the *DSFG* are exceptions.) If only the effort and resources, etc. that go into developing these tools would even partially go into correcting the data and permanently making the corrected information available to all. Clearly there is also no (or at least extremely limited) funding for this sort of work by government sources (e.g. NASA or U.S. National Science Foundation). Understandably, this sort of work may not be considered leading edge or glamorous enough, e.g. in comparison to research on the creation of the universe. But the problems caused by all these identification and data errors continue to propagate.

Beyond simply finding and observing various objects, one of the leading examples of problems caused by identification errors is that various scientific papers and data on specific objects can not be cross-correlated. This is because the data is associated with different names for the same object. This is a common problem in the widely used astronomical database SIMBAD, which has entries for all astronomical objects mentioned in recently published scientific papers (generally back to the 1970s). See Appendix E on page 455 Although SIMBAD includes numerous alias names for many objects, duplicate entries for the same object can often be found where the names have not yet been associated as aliases. As one would guess, this often happens because an author is using an incorrect or incomplete name. It also even happens in the case where an object is "discovered" multiple times under different names. This is a particularly disturbing problem. It means that researchers may search for data on a particular object, and finding none, are either blocked from doing further work, or are forced to spend valuable time obtaining and reducing new observations—when an object (like a star cluster) has already been well studied but under a different name. It is also a problem in dealing with historical data, where very old observations may exist for a given object; but that data have become inaccessible since the object now has a different name and the equivalence is not known.

There are also important research problems caused by more poorly known objects (e.g. star clusters here) not having good known positions. Brian Skiff has reported the case of an elaborate scientific study and published paper [Aparicio, et al, 1991] that was done on the cluster NGC 6749 (= Berkeley 42). Photometric data was obtained for the cluster with great difficulty, and a color-magnitude diagram was published. However, an examination of their image of the "cluster" and analysis of the diagram shows that only background Milky Way stars were observed. In other words, apparently due to an incorrect position, it seems that the measurements were not made of the cluster stars themselves but rather only of nearby field stars—all for want of a single good star cluster position.

Another case where positions are important is in the field of lunar occultations of stars. Measurements of such occultations over the years have improved our knowledge of the Moon's orbit, the shape of the lunar limb (i.e., topography), and the size and shape of the Moon overall. In recent years, such information has been partially supplanted by Lunar Laser Ranging data, and artificial lunar satellite measurements (e.g. by the U.S. Department of Defense satellite *Clementine*, and by NASA's *Lunar Prospector*). However—particularly considering the current lack of funding for Lunar Laser Ranging operations—the information still proves useful for determining the overall shape and size of the Moon. This in turn is useful for determining the size of the Sun during past and present solar eclipses. Such information is quite useful in long-term studies of climate change. What is the connection to star clusters? Well obviously, if the Moon passes in front of a star cluster, many more occultations, including grazing occultations (where a star "grazes" the limb of the Moon, possibly disappearing and reappearing behind mountains) are visible than normal. Many tens, hundreds, or even thousands of such occultations can be observed in one night if the Moon passes in front of a star cluster. Much useful data about the cluster itself can also be obtained, as the occultations can help to improve star positions and proper motions, and reveal previously unknown double or multiple stars in the cluster. In recent years, most predictions of lunar occultations have relied on accurate star catalogs (such as those described in Section 2.7 on page 24), so having accurate star cluster positions is not as important as it once may have been for the general purpose of collecting occultation data. However for those looking to study a particular cluster, having an accurate position with which to predict an occultation of that cluster's stars is still important. And even some of the most complete star catalogs (e.g. USNO-B1.0) are incomplete within the confines of rich open or globular clusters due to crowding and overexposure of the original photographic material from which the catalog was derived. If one was seeking observations of large numbers of faint stars over a short time, then doing predictions with star cluster catalog positions may be preferable to using star catalog positions.

Finally, the most obvious use of good cluster positions and identifications is for planning and making observations of such clusters. For an amateur astronomer, one could argue that an incorrect position may result only in a little extra time sweeping the area of the cluster looking for it. However, not only do the poor positions and data that are often available for a given celestial object affect the locating of an object by an observer, but it often affects the finding of succeeding objects as well. This is especially true since many astronomers—amateur and professional—use digital setting circles, computer-controlled telescopes, or similar devices to locate objects. When an object does not immediately show up where the device says it should be, the observer (at best) may end up searching the surrounding area to see if it can be located. Or (at worst) the observer may give up looking for the object entirely and assume the equipment (for which he or she may have just paid a great amount of money) is faulty. If the object does happen to be found, the observer may then recalibrate his device; i.e., indicate that he or she is observing the "correct" position of the object in question. Then when one searches for the next object, its position will now also be off by the same amount that the previous one actually was. We have seen how this situation can potentially be extremely frustrating to observers, particularly amateurs who are just becoming familiar with their telescope. But this even happens to professional astronomers as they attempt to locate objects with large computer-controlled telescopes. Manufacturers of such hardware and software products should be very interested in getting the best possible data included in their catalogs of objects. Otherwise most observers likely assume it is the product that is not working—rather than assuming that the data itself is bad.

And for the professional astronomer searching for an object, or not even finding it, this means wasting valuable and expensive telescope time that could otherwise be used for obtaining data. In the case of the *Hubble Space Telescope*, an incorrect position may result in losing hours of precious observing time worth tens to hundreds of thousands of dollars. In practice *HST* and other large telescope target positions are checked (or should be) ahead of time, e.g. against the *Digitized Sky Survey*. However, the time of astronomers and other analysts may still be wasted while trying to find the correct position of a cluster. It is also still possible to incorrectly locate a cluster or even observe the wrong one (some other cases of which are noted later in the Extended Notes of Chapter 4). In any case, even if an observer always checks the positions of objects to be observed, having good identifications and values from a catalog will certainly help to provide verification and confidence in the planned observations.

3.4 Major Reasons for the Missing Star Clusters

So why are various star clusters considered missing or nonexistent? There are many reasons.

The most fundamental explanation was mentioned in the historical review above. Various catalogs of star clusters adopt different definitions for star clusters and, therefore, different criteria for the objects they include. If a possible cluster (or for that matter a definite asterism of stars—an apparent group of stars that are not physically associated) is not included in the catalog; by implication, the cluster is now missing. In other words, a reference to the cluster may now be found, e.g. in the NGC, but it has "disappeared" from one or more modern star cluster catalogs.

One outcome of this is the discovery of many new clusters, particularly during the 1960s and 1970s, of objects that had been discovered long before but were not included in the modern catalogs like Alter, *et al.*, [1958 and 1970], Ruprecht [1981], and Lyngå [1987]. A good example is a number of objects that van den Bergh and Hagen [1975] list as discoveries, which are in fact NGC objects. Apparently these and many other authors checked whether a new-found cluster of theirs was in a current star cluster catalog, but did not check the NGC and IC catalogs. This immediately resulted in objects being observed and data being collected under different star cluster names—a situation that persists for many clusters to this day (but which may be nearly ended with the publication of the catalog in this book).

It is helpful to consider a little further why a given object would not be included in a star cluster catalog. Clearly in many cases, some sort of judgement was made that the given object was too sparse in stars to be considered a true physical cluster (rarely in these cases were astrometric or photometric studies used to determine that a group of stars was definitely an asterism). Unfortunately, there appear to be a number of cases where the object was simply "not found," and, therefore, not included in a catalog. In this case the object was missing even for the catalog compiler(s). How could this happen, given for example that the *Palomar Observatory Sky Survey* (POSS) [National Geographic Society, 1955] became widely available after the mid 1950s?

One of the major problems appears to be that these objects were either larger or sparser in stars than the catalog compilers suspected. A substantial number of objects that went missing for some period of time are objects that are 30′ to 1° or even more in size, made up (often) of comparatively bright stars. Many of these were William Herschel discoveries, which Herschel in fact included in his "class VIII" of large, scattered star clusters. It appears that many catalog compilers relied on positions alone (and no other indications of size, number of stars, or description) to locate these more obscure objects. Expecting a small cluster of, say, 1′ to 15′ in size, nothing was found at the correct position; the object was considered nonexistent or just a few Milky Way stars, and ignored.

It has been speculated by some authors (e.g. Houston) that the modern reliance on the POSS may have automatically meant that many large sparse groups of stars and real clusters were ignored. The speculation appears to have been based on the assumption that such clusters are not at all visible on the POSS. However, work done by one of us [BA] to identify these objects on the digitized sky survey (DSS)—which includes the POSS—has shown that *all* of the large sparse clusters or groups of stars considered were visible on the POSS and other such surveys. The key was having a clear description from the original discovery including, when available, a description of size, brightness, and number of stars. This seems a clear indication that many modern compilers have not consulted such information.

This then is the key to identifying any star cluster, particularly those that have come to be considered missing or nonexistent. One must *check the original observations.* This should be the mantra, the slogan, the motto of anyone working in this field. Certainly there continue to be a few cases where this has not resulted in the original object being found unambiguously. However, in hundreds of other cases where an object was considered missing, it was relatively easily found by looking at the original discovery observations; e.g., position, description, and other data when available. It should be noted that the term "original" is important. Many astronomers, particularly earlier in this century, did in fact use the NGC and IC catalogs as their primary references for determining cluster identifications. Unfortunately, these publications—like any compilation of such a massive amount of data—have many errors. Many of the missing clusters have only been re-identified by examining the discover's observations, as cited in the NGC and IC. In fact, one should recall that the purpose of the NGC and, in particular, the IC was not to create an all encompassing catalog containing all data on nonstellar objects, but rather to serve as indices to such data, particularly the discovery data. This is the reason for the very name of the IC—the "Index Catalogue." Granted it may take some work in visiting or contacting a good library, or in checking with an observatory for the original observations. However, this is the only way to verify the identity of any of these clusters or asterisms.

There is one final special—and important—case to consider of why a cluster might be missing. That is the case of the type of a cluster being confused between being globular and open. Many open clusters have in the past been considered as globular clusters when they are now not accepted as such. This is because throughout the 19th century and a good part of the 20th, the definition of a globular cluster was in terms of a cluster's appearance. If it was "globular-like" in shape, it must be a globular cluster. But eventually it was realized that there really were two distinct classes of objects. The open clusters were relatively small, containing several to tens to hundreds—and maybe thousands—of stars. The globular clusters contained tens of thousands of stars to millions of stars and displayed a distinctive color-magnitude diagram. The case of an object once being considered a globular cluster and now being considered an open cluster is then not too surprising. However, there apparently have been at least a few objects classified as obscure (sometimes even missing) open clusters, which are in fact globular clusters. The cases of NGC 6540 and IC 1257 are specific examples of so-called NGC/IC open clusters having been identified as distant globular clusters in only the last few years. More details on these objects are given later in Section 7.2, beginning on page 232. However, it should be noted that globular clusters are critical to the study of our Galaxy, stellar and galactic evolution, and even the size and age of the universe itself. The more of these relatively rare objects that can be discovered in our Galaxy, the better. These recent cases have raised the question of whether there are other such objects—cataloged now as an open cluster or asterism, but in fact a globular cluster. Some such cases have in fact been noted in the course of the work on this book and are raised in Section 7.2. Only time will tell whether these or some other currently known objects will be identified as true Milky Way globular clusters.

3.5 Specific Examples of Missing Star Clusters

Having looked at the main reasons why a cluster may at some point be considered missing, it is possible to estimate how often these cases actually occur? To do this rigorously would require a great deal of work. Certainly it would be a job beyond the scope of this book, and just as certainly, the effort could be better expended in actually resolving more of the problems that currently still exist.

However, a brief look at a sample of such problems seems reasonable. The sample we will use here is of the 224 objects previously listed in Archinal [1993]. There will be no attempt to describe these problems in detail (e.g., object by object) as that is covered in the Monograph, or in some cases in the Extended Notes sections here in Chapters 4 and 7. The reader is referred to those sources if details are desired for specific cases.

For the 224 objects under consideration, the RNGC lists the following numbers of objects of each type:

2 type "0," unverified southern object
9 type "1," open cluster
2 type "2," globular cluster
2 type "5," galaxy
212 type "7," nonexistent

The objects listed as open or globular clusters, or galaxies, had some major error of identity, position, or object type.

As of the publication of the Monograph, what was the true status of the known existence of these objects?

- 99 objects (44% of the 224) existed in some form, either as real clusters, possible clusters or asterisms, groups of a few stars, or even as galaxies (e.g., NGC 305).
- 119 objects (53%) still required verification of their existence.
- Five objects (2%) existed (four of type "7," and one [NGC 2239] of type "1") for which there were duplicate entries in the NGC and RNGC, i.e., the object had two different NGC numbers.
- Only one object (less than 0.5%), NGC 1498, could not be found and was felt not to exist.

Let's look now at some of these classes of objects in more detail, citing examples of specific objects. Let us consider the cases where the object does exist, but where some fundamental data (position and/or object type) is significantly in error or (in the case of object type) at least unusual, or the object exists but is a duplicate entry. Remember, the Monograph lists 104 (99 "real" objects plus 5 duplicate entries) cases like this. Examples of these problems are:

- An object listed as nonexistent or missing in one or more catalogs (like the RNGC) does in fact appear to be a true cluster or at least very likely a cluster. There are an amazing 48 such cases (e.g. NGC 6840, NGC 6843, NGC 7093, NGC 7708).
- An object is indeed apparently not a true physical cluster but does in fact exist (while listed as nonexistent or missing somewhere, like the RNGC). Here there are 33 cases. In reality, these appear to be Milky Way patches, groups (or asterisms) of stars, or a few stars (e.g. NGC 2664 which is four stars near M 67; NGC 3520 which is about 6 stars in Crater; NGC 5571 a nice group of stars).
- The RNGC lists an object as of type "0," i.e., as an "unverified southern object"—which actually exists. The two objects in this situation are NGC 1252 and NGC 2348.
- An open cluster has, at least at one point, incorrectly been considered a globular cluster (NGC 2158) causing confusion about its identity.
- An object does in fact exist, but only as a part of a larger object. One such case is NGC 2226, the central part of NGC 2225.
- An object has been listed somehow as a cluster or like a cluster, and yet turns out to be a galaxy. The Monograph lists three cases like this (i.e., NGC 1520, NGC 6328, and NGC 6403).
- The reverse has also occurred. An object listed somehow as a galaxy turns out to be a cluster or asterism.
- A single star has been listed somewhere as "resolvable" and at some point may have been considered a star cluster. There are four such cases (e.g. NGC 2846, NGC 2847, NGC 4426, NGC 4427).
- An object is cataloged with a substantially incorrect position, thus raising questions of whether it exists. There are seven such cases. One such object which is often listed with an incorrect position is M 41. In this particular case it does not appear that the existence of such a cluster has seriously been questioned, but it is likely that many observers—e.g., those just using telescopes with setting circles—have had trouble centering on it. NGC 6380 is another case, where the given (e.g. RNGC) position is poor. Except here the position is so poor and the object faint enough, that many observers fail to locate it. The other cases are NGC 2351, NGC 6605, NGC 6682, NGC 6683, and NGC 6991. It should be noted that this "category" does not include many other cases (39) in the Monograph where a slightly improved position was given for the NGC object in question.

Besides these problems, there are also objects where the very name is in question or has become confused.

- Typographical errors in names sometimes cause problems, e.g. "M 41" is listed as "M 14" in the NGC).
- An object somehow is listed in the *same catalog* under two different entries. Among the NGC objects considered in the Monograph, there are 5 cases of this; e.g., M 47 has two NGC entries listed as NGC 2478 and NGC 2422. Also NGC 2239 is actually NGC 2244, the Rosette nebula cluster. Further NGC 2520 is NGC 2527, NGC 3218 is NGC 3183, and NGC 4409 is NGC 4420.
- Sometimes an object's name has somehow been incorrectly switched with that of another nearby object; e.g.

most modern sources reverse the identities of NGC 6996 and NGC 6997 in the North American Nebula. NGC 6997 is the obvious ("West Virginia") cluster within the main nebula itself, while NGC 6996 is a scattering of stars about 1° to the north (in "Canada"). (These are two more cases of objects that really exist.)

- Often an object is listed as a discovery in a new catalog, and thus becomes known under two different names. The data and even object type then often become confused. A good example is the globular cluster NGC 6749 = Berkeley 42. (See the Monograph and Section, 7.2, Extended Notes on Galactic Globular Clusters beginning on page 232 for more information.) Admittedly, the RNGC was one of a few references that correctly listed NGC 6749 as a globular cluster (even before this was unequivocally determined), but it did not note the equivalence with Berkeley 42.

Beyond the objects which exist, there is also the relatively unusual category of objects that may not in fact exist and truly are missing. As noted above, when the Monograph was written, only one object was found that fit this example, and that was NGC 1498. This object was observed by William Herschel only once (in February 8, 1784), as a star cluster in Eridanus, and up until the publication of the Monograph, no trace of it had ever been found. However, as can be seen in the Extended Notes section of Chapter 4, it has now been determined that this object is likely a group of three stars—and (mostly due to the mention of it in the Monograph) has even been independently observed twice.

But the largest category of all—at the time the Monograph was written—was the list of 119 objects whose existence had not yet been verified. The real problem was that no one had yet done a definite check to find out if the object existed or what it was. In the work done to create the catalog for this book many more of these objects were in fact identified (as belonging to one of the other cases listed above). Several amateur astronomers have also reported observations of many of these objects (e.g. in the *Webb Society Quarterly Journal* or the Webb Society's *Observing Section Reports*). But due to the number of objects, and the trail that must be followed, there are still a significant number of objects (dozens at least) where the object has still not been definitely identified. The trend—from all of the cases above—indicates that most of these objects do exist in some form, perhaps many still as real clusters of stars. But for now the work is not done. Indeed, it may be that it will be you, the reader, that finally determines what a number of these objects truly are.

3.6 Methods for Tracking Down Missing Star Clusters

Let's assume that one is faced with determining the true identity of a given object. How do you go about it? In this section we'll cover some of the steps that should prove useful in answering such questions. These are procedures and techniques that have proven useful to us in tracking down the identities and missing information on a number of objects. A number of examples of how these steps can be used exist both in Archinal's 1993 Monograph and in the Extended Notes in Chapters 4 and 7 in this book. The reader will note that many of the examples almost read like a detective story—and that is certainly no coincidence. Solving the identity of a nonstellar object is just like solving any other mystery. It takes research and perseverance, assisted by experience, and oftentimes by luck. But it is interesting, rewarding, and useful work.

3.6.1 Go to the Original Source

As noted in a previous section, the cardinal rule in all of this work is to go to the original source, i.e., the publication where the discovery of the object was first announced. This step is critical in order to once and for all identify any celestial object.

One may be tempted to use some summary catalog, such as the NGC, IC, (or their modern equivalents), or other modern compilation catalogs in order to identify an object. Obviously these catalogs must be used and trusted to some extent by the modern observer or no astronomical work would ever get done. But these catalogs can never be completely relied upon to give all the details (correctly) of the original discovery observations.

Therefore, for objects listed in any catalog, it's important to follow the catalog back to the original reference. For example, in the classic NGC and IC, for each object the discoverer information is given. In the introductions to these catalogs J. L. E. Dreyer describes the actual publications of each discoverer referred to. This is where the reader should look for more information. In other words the NGC and IC were not written as be-all and end-all catalogs of nonstellar objects, but were intended to refer the reader to other information on the objects.

The problem arises that these references are mostly to 19th century publications (although including earlier, and in the case of the second IC, early 20th century publications). These works are now obviously difficult to find—but not as difficult as one might at first believe. Almost all large college and research institution libraries (see e.g., Figure 3.4 on page 37) have many of these publications available, and large astronomical libraries have the great majority or nearly all of them. There are also plans (by the Astrophysics Data System, see Appendix E on page 455) to place various astronomical journals on-line (on the World Wide Web) going back well into the 19th century. This should soon be a valuable resource for many of the publications. Finally, there are many amateur astronomers who have now made photocopy sets of the critical publications (when copyrights have expired) and (for the cost of photocopying) freely exchange them. So it is possible to go back to these original references in most cases.

Although such an identification may not be truly definitive, it is still possible to make a reasonably accurate preliminary identification using only such catalogs as the NGC and IC. In some cases this is the only alternative, as some discoverers (notably E. E. Barnard) passed information on their discoveries directly to Dreyer, so the information is not published elsewhere.

Many star clusters and other nonstellar objects of scientific interest are now known that were not included in the NGC and IC. Here part of the situation is the same—the discovery publication should be consulted if at all possible. However, this work may be easier in that most such discoveries are more recent. It was particularly during the late 1950s and 1960s that there was an "explosion" of discoveries of star clusters and other nonstellar objects as astronomers first examined the Palomar Sky Survey (POSS) [National Geographic Society 1955] and other sky surveys in detail. Many of these papers are easily obtained from library shelves. Discoveries continue right up until the present. At this point there are already several years of recent journals on-line and accessible via the world wide web (e.g., via the Astrophysics Data System).

So, assuming one has found the original discovery publication for a specific object, what can be done next? The simplest thing is to check the object's position: precess it to 2000.0; check a star atlas, sky survey, or the sky itself; and see what's there. If you find something that matches the discover's description, chances are good that you're done—you've identified the object. If this sounds simple, that's because it is. As mentioned in the last section, there are many objects for which these steps have never been taken, and the object still remains unidentified. The work, of course, is in finding the publication, precessing a position, and checking the sky.

Many times, however, it will not be all that simple. No obvious object will appear at the 2000.0 coordinates. Then there are other steps to take:

- Take a closer look at the description and see if you can come up with a better match against the sky. In the case of a star cluster, maybe you're looking for something richer in stars than the real object, smaller or larger than the real object, or brighter or fainter than the real object.
- One may need to "re-reduce" the position of the object. For example, William Herschel always gives not the position of his object, but the offset position from a bright star. Sometimes the original reduction (usually by Caroline or John Herschel) was in error and the error has propagated to the present day. What should be done is to take the bright star's position for 2000.0, precess it back to the observation date, add on the offsets, and precess the resulting position forward again to 2000.0. This new 2000.0 position for the object in question should be checked—particularly if it is substantially different from those of later publications.

  One should resist the temptation to just add the offsets to the star's 2000.0 position and assume the resulting location is a good approximation to the object's 2000.0 position. If the offsets are particularly large, the objects are near the north or south celestial poles, or the time of the original observation (as with William Herschel's observations) was some time ago, the errors in using this method can be substantial. NGC 1798 is one object which has gone undetected partly because some researchers have used this latter imprecise method and come up with the wrong coordinates.
- Another step, while considering the positional information, is to take a "wider" look around the area; i.e., within a few tens of arcminutes or a few degrees, look to see if any other object fits the discovery description. Blunders in the originally recorded position; e.g., one minute of time in right ascension, or one degree in declination, are always possible. If you can make some object fit with some single digit offset to the original position, then perhaps you've solved the whole problem.
- Check to see if there's a drawing or even a photograph of the object. Many older references, even by William and John Herschel, have nice drawings of the object they've discovered; however, they are hidden in plates in the back of the publication. Likewise, many 20th century publications (e.g. Collinder 1931) have plates of photographs in the back. Several Collinder clusters are identified here in Chapter 4, for the first time since their discovery. Why? Because Collinder's photographs of the clusters were matched for the first time to photographs (the Digitized Sky Survey—see below) of the sky.
- Check to see what type of telescope the observer is using. The Herschels used telescopes ranging from small "comet seekers" through 20-cm (8-inch) reflectors, (most often) up to their 48-cm (18¾-inch) reflector. Many NGC objects were discovered with even larger telescopes. For example Lassell used a 122-cm (48-inch) reflector, and William Parsons (Lord Rosse) and his co-workers used the great 183-cm (72-inch) "Leviathan of Parsonstown" in Ireland. Others were found by E. E. Barnard observing from Tennessee with the equivalent of a modern richest-field telescope. A perusal of the introductions to the NGC and IC will reveal that there were dozens of observers and even more dozens of telescopes used to discover the objects

included. Therefore, one should have some idea of the size of the telescope used and its field of view. It will then become clear whether it was a large or small, bright or faint object that was seen—or possibly seen.

- Finally, do not forget to check for errata or notes by the author, a contemporary, or later observers. John Herschel provided some extensive notes in his GC—later reprinted in the NGC—about many of his discoveries. In 1912, J. L. E. Dreyer (the NGC and IC author) also published the Collected Works of William Herschel. There he includes many notes on the proper identity of a number of William's discoveries. There are also other researchers of the late 19th century and early 20th who have looked into the Herschels' and later NGC discoveries. These include: Auwers [1862], Astronomer Royal [1911], Bigourdan [1899–1917], Wolf [1926], Carlson [1940] (although Carlson made many errors, often repeated in the RNGC), and Cederblad [1946]. Lastly there are more modern publications discussed below that can also be consulted for such information.

3.6.2 Check a Sky Survey

As described above, once you have information on a given object (e.g a position), you should check the sky to see what's really there. Observing the sky is an option that will be discussed next. A far quicker and easier option has become to check the Digitized Sky Survey (DSS) or some other photographic survey.

The DSS is the complete digitization of the Palomar Observatory Sky Survey [National Geographic Society 1955] and the (southern sky) U. K. Schmidt Survey [SERC/PPARC and Anglo-Australian Observatory Board 1993–5]. It was completed at the Space Telescope Institute in the early 1990s and initially made available on a set of 102 CD-ROMs. Many astronomical institutions and libraries have sets of these where you can go to use the CDs directly. However, far more convenient is to access them on the World Wide Web. Currently the information from the CDs is available on-line at several locations. A partial list is given below.

SkyView
Goddard Space Flight Center,
Greenbelt, Maryland
http://skyview.gsfc.nasa.gov/

STScI Digitized Sky Survey
Space Telescope Science Institute,
Baltimore, Maryland
http://archive.stsci.edu/dss/

Canadian Astronomy Data Center
Dominion Astrophysical Observatory,
Victoria, British Columbia
http://cadcwww.dao.nrc.ca/dss/

CDS Aladin
http://aladin.u-strasbg.fr/java/nph-aladin.pl?-rm=14.1&-server=Aladin

ESO Online Digitized Sky Survey
European Southern Observatory,
Garching, Germany
http://archive.eso.org/dss/dss/

SkyEye
Instituto di Radioastronomia,
Bologna, Italy
http://terra.bo.cnr.it/skyeye/gb/

This list is based on a similar list maintained at

http://archive.stsci.edu/dss/sites.html

Other sites may now be available. The Skyview and Aladin sites seem to be the most useful of these sites in the opinion of the current authors, as they allow for the overlaying on the DSS and DSS II data from a large number of astronomical catalogues. It is also possible to survey data outside visible light.

The U. S. Naval Observatory (Flagstaff, AZ) maintains a web server, at http://www.nofs.navy.mil/projects/pmm/. The Precision Measuring Machine (PMM) Project there allows for access to their own scans of essentially all of the major photographic surveys of the sky, as well as to their USNO-B1.0 catalog [Monet, *et al.,* 2003].

When the coordinates of an object and some default field of view are specified, these web sites allow one to obtain a corresponding image of the sky, in .GIF or .FITS format. These images can be viewed immediately with a web browser or displayed with local software. There are also batch options to download larger numbers of images (at least with SkyView) at times when access is faster or cheaper.

Once such images are obtained, an object can sometimes be rapidly identified. With appropriate viewing software, coordinates and object sizes can be quickly measured since the .FITS files usually have coordinate information included in them. Positions from the DSS are usually on the *Guide Star Catalog* (GSC, see Appendix E on page 455) reference system, usually accurate to 1–2 arcseconds (not accounting for motions of the stars since the images were taken) relative to even the best reference frame.

It should also be added that a lower resolution version of the DSS is available in a package of 18 CD-ROMs; e.g., under the name RealSky from the Astronomical Society of the Pacific, see Appendix E on page 455. For users with limited or slow internet access or users who wish to display images in the field, this package is certainly an excellent option. However, the positional accuracy and image quality are not as good as the full resolution DSS.

After addressing all of these high-tech approaches to checking what is in the sky, something should also be said about the real photographic surveys that do exist and are still underway. The POSS and UK Schmidt Surveys that were used in the DSS have already been mentioned. However, there are other similar large Schmidt camera photographic surveys that have been performed during the 1960's to present, and most large astronomical libraries have copies of these. These images can still be more useful than the DSS. This is due to the higher resolution of such original prints or newer emulsions, coverage of the sky in some areas where the DSS is missing information or has joints between two images, better photometric information on the relative brightness of stars, and different epochs that may be useful in checking out changes due to the proper motion of nearby and cluster stars.

One older survey should also not be forgotten. This is the famous Franklin-Adams chart [RAS 1936], the first complete photographic survey of the entire sky. This was performed by John Franklin-Adams and others during the period 1903–1912. This is still a fairly good low resolution atlas of the sky. Most importantly, with respect to star cluster related work, the famous catalogs of Melotte, Raab, Trumpler, Shapley ("Harvard"), and Collinder relied heavily on the prints from this survey. As can be seen in some cases in the Extended Notes of Chapter 4, it is still necessary today to consult these charts in order to make a positive identification of many of the clusters discovered in the first part of this century.

3.6.3 Consult the Sky

And if all else fails, there is still another way to verify the existence of a particular cluster or nonstellar object. Observe it. This can be done photographically or, more likely nowadays, with a CCD; but there is also a lot to be said for doing this visually.

A large number of objects, almost all of the NGC and many of the IC objects, were discovered by visual observers. In cases where an identity is in doubt, it is useful to make visual observations that compare with those of the early observers. It may even be useful to try to match up the telescope in use with that of an earlier observer, using a small comet sweeper (20 to 25-cm (8 to 10-inch) telescope as William Herschel and other early observers did), or a moderate sized amateur telescope (say 25 to 46-cm, 10 to 18-inches in aperture) to try to match many of William and John Herschel's discoveries with their 18¾-inch telescope. (One should keep in mind that the Herschels' used speculum metal mirrors, which likely were 60–80% efficient in their reflectivity). There are also large amateur to professional sized telescopes that may be best to match the observations of Lassell (and his 48-inch) or Lord Rosse (72-inch).

Fig. 3.1 *An example of a large astronomical library. The rotunda of the U. S. Naval Observatory library, in Washington, D.C., one of the most complete astronomical libraries in the world. Photo by Perry W. Remaklus.*

As an example of this, much of the work in Archinal's Monograph in identifying lost objects, was undertaken just by observing the sky in the appropriate position with a 13 to 15-cm (5 or 6-inch) telescope. A number of amateur astronomers, as the acknowledgements in this book reveal, continue to observe and identify such objects. There are even cases where visual observations from different apertures appear to have been useful in trying to identify a specific object. See the case of NGC 6724 in the Extended Notes section of Chapter 4.

Clearly this is a case where the modern deep-sky observer, sometimes assailed for not doing "science" (whatever that really means) can contribute greatly to the identification of long-lost objects, information which can then be of good use to all astronomers—amateur and professional—to come.

3.6.4 Report the Results

Well, let's say that you've run across an object that you could not find while you were observing. You've gone to the local university's astronomy library; you've looked up the discovery reference, and found some useful information. You've checked the DSS, and you've even gotten a clear night and actually located the previously "missing" object in the telescope. Now what do you do?

Obviously, there is a certain pleasure in what you've already accomplished. You've done some detective work, and solved a (perhaps long) dormant mystery. Perhaps you've become the first person to see an object or even a likely star cluster—and identify it—since some early observer such as William Herschel. Well, you could stop here, but the obvious thing to do next is to let others know what you've found.

One way to do this is by e-mail, as there are a number of observers who exchange e-mail on this type of subject. A very useful place to post your information electronically is to the "amateur astronomy" or "amastro" e-mail list. Also available are Usenet newsgroups, such as sci.astro.amateur or sci.astro. These e-mail postings, particularly those on the "amastro" list, are widely read by those interested in object identifications. Submissions to groups like this achieve some level of permanence since the messages are archived and made available over the internet by the service provider. Another place to post observations (actually deep-sky observations of any sort) is at netastrocatalog.

However, in the long run it would be nice to see such useful information achieve a little better level of permanence. In this way others can more reliably see what you've found, now and in years to come. As amateur-astronomy oriented publications go, the best place to submit such work for publication is to the Webb Society (in the U.K.) for use in their *The Deep-Sky Observer* (for this and the following, see Appendix E on page 455). Another possibility is the U. S. oriented National Deep Sky Observer's Society publication *The Deep Sky*. However, for particularly useful or detailed work, one might also wish to submit something for publication in a professional journal, such as the *Publications of the Astronomical Society of the Pacific*. Such material will be refereed, but if published will have wide spread and permanent distribution in the astronomical community, including on-line availability, and the cataloging of references to any of the objects mentioned in the SIMBAD database [Egret, *et al.*, 1991].

Another way to distribute such information is as we are doing here—in a book or catalog format. We hope that the bringing together of an extensive database on star clusters (see Chapters 4 and 7), detailed notes on object identifications and errors in earlier catalogs, along with a discussion of other related subjects will provide users with a comprehensive reference that is affordable and capable of wide disseminated.

It is very important, however, to avoid the situation where identifications or problems are corrected in a specific publication, but the corrections and errata are not specifically cited. What often happens is that a catalog, atlas, or computer software developer over the years will run into these problems but not report them. This causes even further confusion about an object down the line as one compares the "corrected" product against uncorrected data. A significant exception are the first editions of *Uranometria 2000.0* [Tirion, *et al.*, 1988a, b] and *DSFG* [Cragin, *et al.*, 1993] where errors were not only corrected in succeeding printings, but also *listed* so that observers will be able to watch for these errors in other sources and be able to more easily resolve discrepancies when they run into them. We have attempted to follow this philosophy in this publication, since the Extended Notes sections of Chapters 4 and 7 also cite all known errors in the earlier Monograph by Archinal.

But, it can only be said that we hope that if you go to the trouble of tracking down an object's identification or solving a problem with some erroneous information attached to it, that you will report the results in some way.

3.7 The Future of the Missing Star Cluster Problem

What can be said of the future of the missing star cluster problem? For one thing we feel that the material in Archinal's Monograph and the catalog data and notes presented here (in Chapters 4 and 7) are collectively more complete and accurate than any other source regarding open star cluster and asterism identifications. However, this is in many ways a never ending-task and much work remains to be done.

- In particular, for all those objects still in question, the original discovery reference needs locating, and the object should be searched for on the DSS or (better in many cases) visually.
- There are several objects that have not been successfully re-located (e.g., some NGC, and vdB-Ha clusters). Further detailed follow-up work is needed to verify the existence of these objects, if possible.
- Identities, positions, and other basic information (diameter, number of stars, brightest V magnitude star, total V magnitude) for all star clusters need to be checked. Much work also must be done in the future to put this data onto standard scales; e.g., the magnitudes and numbers of stars should be down to a certain or at least specified limiting magnitude, and member and non-member stars need to be distinguished. As part of this work the definitive studies of each cluster should be identified.
- Star clusters and their individual stars need to be identified and cross-referenced to newer survey and star catalogs. See for example the list of catalogs given in Section 2.7 on page 24.

To summarize, it is clear that much is to be done in this area. We can only say that based on past experience, it will not be the professional astronomers who will do the work required. They understandably do not have the resources or immediate justification. If the body of information on star clusters is improved generally and if all the "missing star clusters" are ever found, it will likely be you, the reader, who will provide the information.

Chapter 4
General Catalog of Star Clusters and Asterisms

There is, however, a vast difference between cataloguing an object and recognizing its true character.

—Harlow Shapley, *Star Clusters* [1930]

....no one has ever satisfactorily defined to me where a multiple star ends and a cluster begins.

—Charles Worley, in Mermilliod [1996, 403] (1935–1997)

The irregular boundaries make difficult the determination of the diameters and forms of galactic clusters; they are not easily untangled from the rich and fortuitously irregular stars fields in which frequently they are embedded. Nevertheless, from star counts, studies of spectra, and measures of motion, it is possible to deduce the extent and form of a fair proportion of those now catalogued.

—Harlow Shapley, *Star Clusters* [1930]

4.1 Introduction

The creation of a catalog of star clusters has a long tradition. As described in Chapter 1, throughout history numerous catalogs of both stellar and nonstellar objects have been prepared by astronomers both well-known and comparatively unknown. The twentieth century saw the creation of a number of such compilations of star clusters. Often these were part of some larger study on the structure of the Milky Way or the Universe as a whole. At other times professional and amateur astronomers prepared these compilations for general reference. In any case, a truly complete general catalog of known star clusters has not been made in some time—if indeed it has ever been.

In this section we describe such a general compilation catalog of star clusters intended for very general use. It is a general catalog in that all known star clusters and asterisms in the Milky Way galaxy and many of the known extragalactic star clusters have been included. It is a compilation catalog in that it is a collection of data from several disparate sources. It is for very general use in that not just well known Galactic objects are included. Also covered are extragalactic clusters (listed separately), groups of stars whose existence as a true cluster is in doubt, and even objects that are known to be nothing more than *asterisms*—the latter being chance groupings of stars along the line of sight. Some galaxies and galaxy clusters are included, having been mistakenly cataloged as star clusters in the past. The generality of the objects included assures that the listings derived here will be of great utility. Both professional astronomers who desire the best possible data on well-known objects, and amateur (and professional) astronomers who wish to observe any and all reported possible clusters and asterisms will find much of value here. This generality should also help to assure that the more obscure of both real clusters and asterisms—not generally now cataloged—will not continue to be discovered again and again as new possible clusters.

For convenience and completeness, our overall catalog is actually broken into three different parts in this book. In Table 4.1 on page 49, we give a catalog of Milky Way star clusters, asterisms, and misidentified objects. Milky Way globular clusters and suspected globular clusters are included in that table. However, for convenience, we give a separate catalog of those objects in Table 7.1 on page 227, including some additional information (i.e., horizontal branch V magnitudes). The third part of the overall catalog is a listing of extragalactic star clusters, possible clusters, and objects misidentified as such clusters. It is included in Appendix C. Tables there list objects by external galaxy, moving outwards from the Milky Way. Table C.1 lists objects in the Large Magellanic Cloud. Table C.2 includes objects in the Small Magellanic Cloud. Table C.3 has globular clusters, globular cluster candidates, and objects previously misidentified as these for the Andromeda Galaxy; i.e., NGC 224 = M 31. Table C.4 includes the 5 known globular clusters and one asterism in the Fornax Dwarf galaxy.

We also provide a name and alias name listing and index as Table D.3. If the reader already knows the parent galaxy for an object and its preferred name and approximate right ascension, it can be looked up directly in the tables of Chapters 4 or 7 or Appendix C. However, if one only has the name of an object, it can be looked up in Table D.3 to find the parent galaxy (and hence the appropriate final table), preferred name, and right ascension, from which its entry can be found in the main tables. Table D.1 also includes such a name list for the Messier star clusters, and Table D.2 includes such a list for common (and e.g., informal) names of star clusters and asterisms.

Other information is presented in this Chapter, and in the other Appendices. The next section describes the content of the catalog Tables by column. Section 4.3 discusses the source of images used, particularly in this Chapter but also throughout the book. Section 4.4 includes Extended Notes on all objects—except for Milky Way globular clusters, where the Extended Notes are in Section 7.2.

Appendix A includes a list of nomenclature, acronyms, and abbreviations used in the catalog tables and throughout the book. Appendix B includes a lengthy description of how the catalog was assembled, describing in detail the various sources used. Appendix E, as has already been mentioned, contains World Wide Web and postal mail addresses for various resources mentioned in the catalog and throughout the book.

Following the Appendices are an index to terms, topics, and objects mentioned in the book— but *not* in the catalog, an extensive list of the references used throughout the book and catalog, and finally a bibliography of useful general references on star clusters and observing.

4.2 Description of the Catalog

The catalog is presented here in Table 4.1, in Chapter 7, and in Appendix C. Table 4.1 contains the listing of all Galactic objects (2,017 entries), including asterisms and objects previously misidentified as Galactic clusters. Section C.1 and C.2 list the clusters and misidentified objects of the Large and Small Magellanic Clouds, respectively (2,025 and 419 entries). Table C.3 lists globular clusters and misidentified objects in the Andromeda (M 31) galaxy (578 entries). Tables C.4 lists the 5 Globular clusters and 1 asterism of the Fornax Dwarf galaxy. In each of these sections objects are listed by 2000.0 right ascension order. There is a total, across all sections, of 5,045 separate entries.

Galactic globular clusters are included for completeness in the main catalog starting on page 49, but they are also listed separately (along with the horizontal branch V magnitudes) in the Globular Cluster Catalog, Table 7.1, starting on page 227.

The following material describes the various main columns of data in the catalog, including comments on units, data quality, etc. Note that not all of these columns are present in all the tables. In other words, some of these columns are not given for the listings of objects in the external galaxies, since the information may not be relevant or generally available.

Object name. This is, so far as can be determined, the original name of the given cluster (or other type of object), unless an NGC or IC designation is available which is given here instead (following IAU recommendations).[1] The origin of these names is discussed in Appendix A beginning on page 267. Table D.3 beginning on page 377 lists the various alias names for the names and IAU names.

Object type. This 4 character field indicates the type of object, so far as is known.

Possible object types are (total number of objects in parentheses, names given if 3 or fewer):

*	Star (19).
*?	Possible star (5).
**	Two stars (7).
**?	Possible pairs of stars (4).
***	Three stars (7).
***?	Possible group of three stars (1, i.e., KMHK 898 (in LMC)).
****	Four stars (2, i.e., Lodén 615 and NGC 6892).
***HII**	Star and/or HII region (1, i.e., NGC 2847 and NGC 6892).
2cl	Two open clusters (6).
2gal	Two galaxies (1, i.e., SL 6).
3cl	Three open clusters (1, i.e., NGC 2044 (in LMC)).
??	Object type is unknown, but at some point has been considered a cluster or "resolvable"(7).
MW	Asterism, either a rich Milky Way star field or obvious patch of bright Milky Way (17).
MW?	Same as MW, but some doubt remains (5).
MW??	Object type unknown, but MW type is suggested (1, i.e., NGC 6506).
MWcl	MW type or possible real cluster (2, i.e., NGC 5120, NGC 5269).
SNR	Supernova remnant (2, i.e., Bica 1 and NGC 6334).
as??	Object type unknown, but asterism is suggested (2, i.e., NGC 843, NGC 2653).
asMW	Asterism or MW type (3, i.e., NGC 2039, NGC 2063, and NGC 5299).
asgl	Asterism and galaxy (1, i.e., NGC 7833).
ass	Association (20 total, including 5 in LMC, 5 in SMC).
ast	Asterism (86 total, including 1 in Fornax and LMC).
ast?	Probable asterism, but possibly a real cluster (82 total, including 76 Galactic, 4 in the LMC, and 2 in the SMC).
cl	Open cluster (3513 total, including 1221 Galactic, 1958 in the LMC, 333 in the SMC, and 1 in M 31).
cl:	Probable open cluster, but considered by at least one reference to be an asterism (79).
cl?	Possible open cluster, not well differentiated from an asterism (312 total, including 233 Galactic, 4 in the LMC, and 75 in the SMC).
cl??	Type unknown, but possibly an open cluster (28).
clpn	Open cluster and planetary nebula (1, i.e., NGC 2818).
dne	Does not exist (3, i.e., Cr 429, Basel 11, Gri 1).
dup?	Is probably a duplicate of another object given here (1, i.e., NGC 2229 is probably a duplicate of NGC 2972).
dupl	This object has some other preferred name—see the comments. (Such an entry has usually been retained since the position associated with it is substantially incorrect.) (3, i.e., Bok 1, NGC 3218, and NGC 4409).
gal	Galaxy, once thought to be a star cluster (61 total, includes 20 Galactic and 41 in M 31).
gal?	Possible galaxy, once cataloged as a star cluster (1, i.e., HW 60).
galn	Galaxy nucleus, once thought to be a star cluster (1, i.e., [HS66] 356).

1. At the 1925 (Cambridge, UK) meeting of the IAU, it was resolved that "It is recommended that in all published work, Nebulae be uniformly designated by their numbers in the N.G.C. or Index Catalogue of Dreyer." Here "Nebulae" was meant to imply all nonstellar objects, including star clusters. [Jaschek and Pecker, 1979, p. 61]

gcl	Globular cluster (669 total, including 148 Galactic, 15 in the LMC, 1 in SMC, 5 in Fornax, and 500 in M 31).
gcl?	Suspected globular cluster (17 total, including 3 Galactic, i.e., 2MASS-GC 1, 2MASS-GC 2, and PWM78 2, and 14 in M 31).
gxcl	Galaxy cluster (3, i.e., Abell 1763, Abell 2141, Shk 1).
mc	Moving cluster (9).
mc?	Possible moving cluster (2, i.e., La 1 and La 2).
neb	Emission nebula (16 total, including 5 Galactic, 11 in the LMC).
neb*	Nebulous star (1, i.e., BRHT 7b (in LMC)).
nf?	Not yet found. Likely does not exist (8).
pass	A portion of a larger association (2, i.e., LH 24 and LH 26 in the LMC).
pn	Planetary nebulae (4).
ptcl	A portion of a larger open cluster (15 total, including 10 Galactic, 4 in the LMC, and 1 in the SMC).

Equatorial position in 2000.0 coordinates. These coordinates are given to the precision indicated by their source. For objects whose primary reference was the *Lund Catalogue*, the *DSFG1e*, or Archinal's *Monograph*, the positions were only available to 0.1^m and 1′, and the accuracy of these positions may be from a few to several arcminutes. For particularly small (e.g., < 5′) Galactic clusters the positions are likely to be less accurate than the size of the cluster. For objects whose primary reference is SIMBAD, the accuracy varies widely. Positions measured by Skiff and Archinal from the DSS are generally good to the few arcminute level or better (the position of individual stars are probably good to the few arcsecond level or better). For Galactic globular clusters, the accuracy is usually better than 1′, generally much better, often accurate to the few arcsecond level. The accuracy of positions for Galactic clusters is similar to that of the other references, but some are much worse and some are much better. Most of the extragalactic objects have higher precision positions, probably to the arcsecond level, at least relative to other nearby objects. As to the accuracy of these positions, no distinction has been made between the J2000.0 and B2000.0 epochs, although the 1979 IAU precession has been used to update all positions [Lieske *et al.*, 1977].

IAU Constellation abbreviation for the given position. Boundaries are as defined by Delporte [1930]. A name followed by "?" indicates the position is within 5′ of a constellation boundary, and depending on its size and the accuracy of the position, the object may lie partially or completely in another constellation. The constellation is not given in the listing of objects in the Fornax Dwarf galaxy and the Andromeda galaxy.

Trumpler type. Here the type of Galactic open clusters are specified using Trumpler's [1930] classification scheme. As described by Lyngå [1987], this is:

Concentration:

I. detached, strong concentration
II. detached, slight concentration
III. detached, no concentration
IV. not detached

Range of brightness:

1. most stars of nearly the same brightness
2. medium range in brightness
3. bright and faint stars in the cluster

Richness:

vp very poor
p poor
m medium
r rich
vr very rich

Nebulosity:

n cluster is involved in nebulosity

The Trumpler type is not available (and, therefore, not listed) for objects in external galaxies, since it is not really well-defined or necessarily useful for describing such clusters.

Diameter in arcminutes. This is an indication of the diameter of a cluster in arcminutes. Since these values are usually approximates, and are derived from widely varying photographic material, they should be considered rough estimates only. Diameters of Galactic globular clusters, where possible, are taken from values derived by Brian Skiff, based on the size of the cluster at the 25 magnitudes per square arcsecond isophote. For clusters where an estimate is not available at the 25 magnitude per square arcsecond level, but a value is available at the 22 magnitude level, the latter value is simply doubled. According to Skiff this closely approximates what the 25 magnitude level value should be. Diameters of objects listed in M 31 are not given, since they are generally unavailable, and in any case usually quite small (a few arcseconds or less).

Total V magnitude. This is the total visual magnitude of the cluster. For Galactic open clusters, Brian Skiff of Lowell Observatory has generally determined these values by summing the magnitudes of the brightest stars of the clusters. Most cases where a particularly bright involved or nearby star has been excluded from the total are indicated in the comments at far right. The values are as given in the *Lund Catalogue*. For clusters with no magnitude determined by Skiff, earlier, much less accurate (usually photographically determined) magnitudes are given. These and other values given, i.e., from SIMBAD, should generally be assumed to be rough values good to the 0.5 to 1.0 magnitude level. However, the relative magnitudes of extragalactic objects probably have a much higher precision than this.

Number of stars in clusters. This is the total (or at least minimum) number of stars in the cluster. For Galactic objects, values are obtained either from the *Lund Catalogue* or, if not available there, the *DSFG1e*, or from specific studies cited. Values from the *Lund Catalogue* are the larger of either the value given by Lyngå from his own examination of the POSS (his reference "320") or values obtained by Brian Skiff by counting stars in published references (reference "422"). Note that for infrared clusters, this is technically the number of infrared sources. Some of the sources may later be found to be multiple stars, protostars, etc. In this case they are likely not detectable in visible light. These numbers are not generally available, and, therefore, not included in the listings of extragalactic clusters. However, since these numbers can be derived from the OGLE-SMC catalog, they are included in the SMC listing.

V magnitude of brightest star. These values are obtained from either the *Lund Catalogue* or; if not available there, the *DSFG1e*; from specific studies cited; or from SIMBAD. Values from the *Lund Catalogue* are all originally from the "Bochum-Strasbourg" compilation. Comments here may indicate whether a brighter foreground (non cluster member) star may exist. These values are not given for objects in the LMC and M 31 listings since the values for only a few such objects have been incorporated into the main catalog.

Surface brightness (*SB*) of cluster (V magnitude per square arc-minute). This is an approximate surface brightness for the cluster, determined from the values given in the Total *V* magnitude column and the diameter column—if both of these are available. This is computed as:

$$SB = V + 5\log_{10}(A)$$

where *V* is the total V magnitude and *A* is the diameter in arc-minutes. Surface brightnesses are not given for LMC and M 31 objects, since they can be computed for only a small subset of objects, and since they are in any case usually quite similar to the total V magnitude.

Distance. This is the distance in parsecs (multiply by 3.262—or divide by 0.3066—for the distance in light years). For Galactic open clusters the value is that given by the *Lund Catalogue*, or specific studies cited. Values are from Lyngå's "jdl" [Janes, *et al.*, 1988] study (for 419 clusters) or selected other references (for 49 clusters) including Lyngå's references 50, 51, 64, 170, 359, 378, 434, and 505. Distances for C1722-343, PMG 1, and 2 are given from their discovery references; for Tr 32, C1819-146, and C1820-146 from Kharchenko and Schilbach [1995]. For Galactic globular clusters, the value is that given by Peterson [1993]. The distance for IC 1257 is from Harris, *et al.*, [1997] and that for the Pyxis globular cluster from its discovery reference [Weinberger 1995]. Distances have not been given in the lists of extragalactic objects, as they are so uncertain (and, therefore, would be listed as the same for all objects in a given external galaxy).

***SkyAtlas 2000.0* [Tirion, 1981] chart number.** For the given coordinates this is the chart number upon which the object would best appear. Note that there is no guarantee that the object is plotted on *SkyAtlas 2000.0* or that it is correctly identified. These numbers are not given for objects in external galaxies, since all objects for such galaxies are on a single chart (chart 18 for the Fornax Dwarf, chart 24 for the LMC and SMC, and chart 4 for M 31).

***Uranometria 2000.0 Deep Sky Atlas* (second edition) [Tirion, *et al.*, 2001a, b] and corresponding *DSFG* (second edition) [Cragin and Bonanno, 2001] chart number.** For the given coordinates, this column lists the chart number upon which the objects would appear in the *Uranometria 2000.0 Deep Sky Atlas* (i.e., the second edition of *Uranometria 2000.0*) or be listed in the (second edition) *Uranometria 2000.0 Deep Sky Field Guide*. Note that a preliminary (but nearly final) version of the catalog here was used as the primary source for the star cluster data used in this second edition of *Uranometria 2000.0* and the *DSFG*. So data (e.g., particularly positions and diameters) in the catalog here and those compilations should generally match completely. However, they contain only a selection of objects included in the current catalog, such as NGC, IC, and other definitely observable clusters, asterisms, and star clouds.

Source. This column indicates the primary source from which the data given have been taken. Possible values, their corresponding references, and the total number of objects (in parentheses) are:

1. *Lund Catalogue* [Lyngå, 1987] (40).
2. *DSFG1e* [Cragin, *et al.*, 1993] (1).
3. Archinal *Monograph* [1993] (15).
4. B. Skiff cluster measurements (568).
5. SIMBAD (as of February 2, 1996) (128).
6. Djorgovski and Meylan globular cluster catalog [1993] (49).
7. B. Skiff globular cluster catalog (1).
8. Misc. updates and corrections by Archinal (128).
9. Caldwell Catalog [Moore and Pepin, 1995] (5).
10. Information from B. Alessi (109).
11. KMHK [Kontizas, *et al.*, 1990] catalog (1,404).
12. Welch [1991] list of SMC cluster positions (132).
13. OGLE-CL SMC [Pietrzyński, *et al.*, 1998] catalog (212).
14. Clusters from list of Platais, *et al.*, [1998] (10).
15. Dutra and Bica [2000] list of possible infrared clusters (58).

16. Dutra and Bica [2001] list of possible infrared clusters near the Galactic center (42).
17. P. Teutsch [private communication 2001] list of possible clusters (30).
18. Barmby, *et al.* [2000] list of M 31 globular clusters (531).
51. Corrections to *Lund Catalogue* (51).
52. Corrections to *DSFG1e* (25).
53. Corrections to Archinal *Monograph* (32).
54. Corrections to SIMBAD (56).
55. Corrections to Djorgovski and Meylan globular cluster catalog (86).
56. Corrections to KMHK catalog (30).
57. Corrections to OGLE-CL SMC catalog (8).
99. Final corrections and additional clusters based on DSS images and other checking (1,326).

In the cases of "corrections," see the object's catalog comments, or the Extended Notes. The total number of corrections in the various categories should not be considered particularly significant, since many of them were changes or additions of a "housekeeping" nature. For example, most of the "corrections" to the Djorgovski and Meylan cluster list were made to add the Melotte alias names for globular clusters.

Comments and alias names. This column includes miscellaneous information concerning the object, its alias names, and names of objects associated with it.

Comments. Any Messier designation is given. Miscellaneous comments are given on identification, bright foreground stars, appearance, etc., as derived from the *DSFG1e*, SIMBAD, or other research done in the preparation of this catalog. A "center star," if mentioned, is one whose position was adopted for the cluster. (The term "central star" is not used. Such stars may not necessarily be in the geometrical center of the physical cluster.) For objects with particularly complex identification problems or other lengthy comments, an Extended Notes section is given. These are all identified by the phrase "See notes."

Comments can be prefixed by a name or other abbreviation, with the meaning shown in the nearby table.

Alias names and associated objects. Names prefixed by "Alias:" or "Aliases:" are alternate names for the given object. A number in parenthesis indicates that the name is not necessarily an alias name for the object, but the name of an associated object. A "(2)" indicates that the name of the object given *includes* the object listed. A "(3)" indicates that the name of the object given is *part of* the object listed here. A "(4)" indicates that the name of the object given is otherwise *associated* with the object listed (is a nebula in the given star cluster). A "(5)" indicates that the name given has been used as an alias, but its use should be *denigrated*. This means its use must be kept track of but should be avoided in the future. Such names are for some reason inappropriate usually (as explained in the Extended Notes or in Chapter 7).

Archinal	Comments resulting either from investigation of the particular object or from a final review of all the objects on the DSS.
[DB00] or [DB01]	Comments from the Dutra and Bica [2000; 2001] listings of infrared clusters.
DSFG1e	Comments from the original *The Deep Sky Field Guide* [Cragin, *et al.*, 1993].
KMHK	Comments from the LMC star cluster catalog by Kontizas, *et al.*, [1990].
Moore	Comments from the original Caldwell catalog by Moore and Pepin [1995].
OGLE	Comments from the SMC star cluster catalog by Pietrzyński, *et al.*, [1998].
Skiff	Edited comments from Brian Skiff's determination of better positions for these objects (see "Information from Brian Skiff on Galactic clusters and asterisms," Section B.4 on page 281).
Teutsch	Comments from Philipp Teutsch on his list of 32 suspected Galactic open clusters (described above).

A special case of an alias name often given is the "IAU Name" of the object. This name is in the form "Chhmm_ddd", where "hhmm" and "ddd" represent the *truncated* B1950.0 right ascension and declination of the object. The right ascension ("hhmm") is given in hours and minutes, and the declination ("_ddd") in tenths of degrees with the correct sign. These names have often been used heavily as the "official" name, particularly for Galactic objects (see e.g., the *Lund Catalogue*). It is important to note that once these names are assigned, they remain fixed and are not subject to change with improved cluster positions. In other words, care must be taken to consider these designations as just that—*names*, and not necessarily as good indicators of a cluster's position. Values given here are usually derived from the *Lund Catalogue* [Lyngå 1987], the SIMBAD database, or Peterson [1993]. Cases where more than one such name exists for a cluster have usually been noted in the Extended Notes section.

4.3 Star Cluster Images

In the remainder of this chapter, and for that matter throughout this book, we include a number of images of star clusters. These images are intended to serve several purposes. Primarily they act as a representative sample of images of star clusters (for comparison against each other), images in other sources, and their visual appearance in the sky itself. Secondarily in many cases they serve to identify particularly sparse or little known clusters, or clusters (or putative clusters or asterisms) that are not at all obvious either visually or in images. There are many occurrences where clusters or groups of stars have been misidentified and the images serve to identify them. Likewise there are many cases where extremely sparse clusters or possible clusters or asterisms do not stand out on the sky either under visual observations or in photographic or CCD images. Here again, the images serve to identify these objects, after having had their identifications carefully checked against original references.

Images of the sky are generally reproduced here with north up and west to the right. A north-point arrow, with a hook on its west side, has been added to most of the images. Where easily possible, we have rotated or flipped images to this orientation as necessary relative to their original source. For some few historical images and for very high resolution and/or infrared *HST* images the orientation is uncertain and is not marked.

The sources of the images included here are many. We have made a conscious effort to use a number of older images. This has partially been due to a desire to keep publication costs down by using (now) uncopyrighted material, but also since many of the illustrations (from John Herschel, E. E. Barnard, and P. Collinder) are the discovery drawings or images of the object in question and in essence *define* the given object.

We have also chosen to use a number of Digitized Sky Survey (DSS) images. These images have been chosen for their uniformity in appearance, the ability to reproduce them at similar scales, and to show sparse, faint, obscure, or previously incorrectly identified or unidentified clusters (for which there is no other obvious source of images). The northern celestial sphere DSS images originate from scans of the Palomar Sky Survey, and are identified here with the acronym "DSS-N". The southern celestial sphere DSS images originate from scans of various UK Schmidt surveys, and are copyright Royal Observatory Edinburgh (ROE), the UK Particle Physics and Astronomy Research Council, and the Anglo-Australian Observatory (AAO). These are all reproduced here with permission.

Two sources have been used to obtain the DSS images. For smaller, default resolution images (600 pixel square images, about 17′ on a side), the images were downloaded from the NASA/GSFC SkyView web site. For images covering a larger field of view, full resolution DSS images in FITS format were created from the U. S. Naval Observatory library's set of DSS CD-ROMS. These FITS format images were then converted to TIF format for use in publication here. No other type of processing of these images has been done, except in some cases, as noted, where a histogram equalization stretch or contrast enhancement of the image has been performed in order to bring out faint detail.

Other sources used for images are as follows (in chronological order):

- John Herschel's discovery drawings of a number of NGC objects, from his "Cape Observations" of 1847.
- E. E. Barnard's drawing of M 8, which appeared in *Astronomische Nachrichten*.
- Drawings of three bright clusters (M 13, M 20, and M 42) from Harvard College Observatory from the 1850's to the 1870's as printed in 1876 in the *Harvard Annals*, which show the visual appearance of these objects well. These images are also available on the Web.
- A photograph of ω Centauri, taken by E. C. Pickering and W. Fleming and published in 1897.
- Photographs of M 44 and Eta Carinae by Solon Bailey, which appeared in 1908 in the *Harvard Annals* as part of his "Catalogue of Bright Clusters and Nebulae."
- Photographs of M 8 and M 20 by James Keeler as published in a large collection of photographs of clusters and nebulae in the *Publications of Lick Observatory* of 1908.
- The Royal Astronomical Society's (1936 printing) of J. Franklin-Adams photographic charts of the sky. These include a number of images upon which Melotte and Collinder clusters were discovered.
- A photograph of M 35 by Raab [1922].

Fig. 4.1 *John Hall (1908-1991) and the U. S. Naval Observatory (USNO) 1-meter (40-inch) reflector, circa 1949. Originally built in Washington, D.C. in 1933, under the direction of George Ritchey, this telescope was the first large instrument (and the last such telescope built by Ritchey) of what came to be known as the Ritchey-Chrétien design, eventually used for a large number of reflecting telescopes, including the Hubble Space Telescope. Hall, as the head of the Astrometry and Astrophysics Division of USNO, oversaw the move of this instrument to the then new USNO site near Flagstaff, Arizona, in September, 1955. Hall himself went on in 1958 to become the director of Lowell Observatory. One of the first uses of the instrument in Arizona was to undertake the first large and precise photometric study of open clusters. This was published by Hoag, et al., [1961] and still forms the basis for much of the magnitude information (total cluster magnitude and magnitudes of the brightest stars) in the catalog given in this book. Figure 4.106 on page 192, NGC 7510 is from this instrument. The 40-inch telescope itself is still in operation at the Flagstaff station of USNO, being used today primarily for CCD photometry.*

- A number of photographic plates by E. E. Barnard, that appeared in his 1927 "Atlas of Selected Regions of the Milky Way," and upon which he and Collinder discovered a number of star clusters.
- Copies of several plates from P. Collinder's 1931 PhD dissertation, "On Structural Properties of Open Galactic Clusters and their Spatial Distribution."
- A photograph of NGC 7510 obtained by Hoag, *et al.*, [1961] at the U. S. Naval Observatory. See Figure 4.1 for a photograph of the telescope and more information.
- Numerous released photographs from the Hubble Space Telescope. These are available from the Space Telescope Institute Public Affairs Office on the Web.
- Several CCD images of faint globular clusters by Tracy Knauss and the late Mike Morton. See Section 7.3 on page 252 for further information.

Table 4.1: Catalog of Clusters and Asterisms in the Milky Way, and Objects Misidentified as Such

Name	Type	2000.0 R.A.	Dec.	Con.	Tr. Type	Diam. (′)	Tot. Vm	#str	Bt* Vm	V Sur	Dist. (pc)	S #	2U #	Ref	Comments and Aliases
Berkeley 58	cl	00 00 12	+60 56.5	Cas	II1m	5.0	9.7	39	15.0	13.2		1	18	4	Aliases: OCl 277.0; C2357+606
NGC 7801	cl??	00 00 23	+50 44.4	Cas								1	30	4	Skiff: Asterism, center defined as position of wide m12 pair.
Stock 18	cl	00 01 35	+64 37.4	Cas	IV2p	5.0						1	8	4	See notes. Skiff: Center star is AG+64 1262. Alias: C2359+643
Berkeley 59	cl	00 02 10	+67 25.2	Cep	I3m n	10.0		40	11.0			1	8	4	Skiff: Position = <BD+66 1674/75>. = NGC 7822? Aliases: Lund 3; OCl 286; OCl 286.0; C0000+671
Berkeley 104	cl	00 03 27	+63 35.5	Cas	II1p	3.0		15	16.0			1	8	4	Aliases: Lund 4; OCl 282; C0000+633
[PTB93] 8	cl	00 04.2	+68 39	Cep		60.0		6				1	8	99	Archinal: Infrared cluster. Not visible on DSS.
Blanco 1	cl	00 04.2	−29 56	Scl	IV3m	70.0	4.5	30	8.0	13.7	240	18	159	8	Zeta Scl cluster. Zeta (V=5.04, B4III) not a member? Cluster large and bright. Includes 13 HD stars. Aliases: Zeta Scl; EQ 0001−302; Zet Scl; C0001−302
Stock 19	cl	00 04 39	+56 04.9	Cas	III1p	2.0		6	8.0			1	18	4	Skiff: Center star is HD 240492. Aliases: Lund 6; OCl 274; C0001+557
NGC 7826	cl??	00 05 15	−20 42.9	Cet				12				18	141	4	Skiff: Asterism, center defined between HD 19/30.
[PTB93] 5	cl	00 05.3	+67 38	Cep		120.0		15				1	8	99	Archinal: Infrared cluster. Not visible on DSS.
NGC 7833	asgl	00 06 32.6	+27 38.8	Peg		2.5		4	14.1			4	63	53	See notes. Includes GSC 01735-01920, 01735-02056, 01735-01814, and faint galaxy on E side. Just NE of equal N/S double GSC 01735-01837.
Czernik 1	cl:	00 07 39	+61 28.7	Cas	I2p	3.0		12				1	18	4	Aliases: Lund 7; OCl 283; C0005+611
Alessi 20	cl?	00 09 23	+58 40.0	Cas		40.0						1	18	99	
Berkeley 1	cl	00 09 41	+60 28.7	Cas	III1p	5.0		10				1	18	4	Skiff: Sparse. Aliases: Lund 8; OCl 284; C0007+601
King 13	cl	00 10 10	+61 11.0	Cas	II2m	5.0		30	12.0			1	18	4	Aliases: Lund 9; OCl 285; C0007+609
NGC 32	**	00 10 53.2	+18 47 33	Peg		0.6						10	63	99	Archinal: Wide pair GSC 1182-00609 and GSC 1182-01510, confirmed against Schmidt's original obs. (DSS shows asteroid trail above.)
[PTB93] 7	cl	00 15.2	+68 16	Cep		72.0		10				1	8	99	Archinal: Infrared cluster. Not visible on DSS.
Berkeley 60	cl	00 17 42	+60 56.5	Cas	III1p	3.0		20	14.0			1	18	4	Aliases: Lund 10; OCl 288; C0015+606
[AO84] VIII	mc	00.3	−09.0	Cet		10000.	2.36	29	2.90	22.4		17	121	54	Moving cluster with very large angular size, hypothesized by Agekyan and Orlov [1984].
King 1	cl	00 21 52	+64 23.0	Cas	II2r	9.0		100	13.0			1	8	54	Aliases: Lund 11; OCl 290; C0019+641
Mayer 1	cl	00 21 54	+61 45.0	Cas	IV2p n	8.0		20				1	18	4	Skiff: Center star is BD+60 39. Aliases: Lund 1155; OCl 288.1; C0019+614
NGC 104	gcl	00 24 05.2	−72 04 51	Tuc		50.0	4.0		11.7	12.5	4600	24	204	55	See notes. Moore: 47 Tucanae. Aliases: 47 Tuc; Mel 1; EQ 0021−723; 1E 0021.8−7221; 2E 0021.8−7221; 2E 82; 1ES 0021−72.3; Ksi Tuc; Caldw 106; C0021−723
Berkeley 2	cl	00 25 15	+60 23.3	Cas	I1m	2.0		30	15.0			1	18	4	Aliases: Lund 12; OCl 289; C0022+601
Stock 20	cl	00 25 16	+62 37.8	Cas	II2p	1.0			13.0			1	8	4	Aliases: Lund 44; OCl 292; C0022+623
NGC 103	cl	00 25 18	+61 19.3	Cas	II1m	5.0	9.8	88	11.0	13.3	2858	1	18	4	Aliases: Cr 1; Lund 13; OCl 291; OCl 291.0; C0022+610
NGC 110	cl?	00 27 25.4	+71 23 26	Cas?	IV1p	19.0		100	9.71			1	8	99	Archinal: Confirmed against J. Herschel's position and description. Scattering of stars on DSS around GSC 4303-01643 (9.71 mag.). Aliases: h 22; C0024+711
NGC 129	cl	00 29 58	+60 12.7	Cas	III2m	12.0	6.5	193	11.0	11.9	1589	1	18	4	Skiff: Center star = DL Cas = HD 236429. Aliases: Cr 2; Lund 15; OCl 294; C0027+599
Stock 21	cl	00 30 28	+57 55.6	Cas	IV2p	4.7		10	12.0			1	18	99	Archinal: Confirmed against Stock's position and diameter (5′). About 20 stars (Stock says 10 A1 stars). Aliases: Lund 16; OCl 293; C0027+577
NGC 133	cl:	00 31 18	+63 21.2	Cas	IV1p	3.0	9.4	5		11.8		1	8	4	Aliases: Cr 3; OCl 296; C0028+630
NGC 136	cl	00 31 31	+61 30.6	Cas	II1p	1.5		20	13.0		4093	1	18	4	Aliases: Cr 4; Lund 18; OCl 295; C0028+612
King 14	cl	00 31.9	+63 10	Cas	III1p	7.0	8.5	186	10.0	12.7	2767	1	8	4	Skiff: Sparse, but looks okay. Aliases: Alter; Lund 19; OCl 297; C0029+628
NGC 146	cl	00 33.1	+63 18	Cas	II2p	5.0	9.1	132	11.56	12.6	3192	1	8	4	Skiff: Sparse, but looks okay. Aliases: Cr 5; Lund 21; OCl 299; C0030+630
King 15	cl	00 33 07	+61 51.2	Cas	IV2p	3.0		12	18.0			1	18	4	Aliases: Lund 20; OCl 298; (4) IRAS 00302+6134; C0030+615
NGC 189	cl	00 39 36	+61 05.7	Cas	III1p	5.0	8.8	90	10.95	12.3	752	1	18	4	Skiff: Diameter 3.7′ too small. Aliases: Cr 462; Lund 23; OCl 301; C0036+608
Stock 24	cl	00 39 50	+61 57.6	Cas	III1p	5.0	8.8	180	13.0	12.3	1762	1	18	4	Aliases: Be 3; Lund 22; OCl 302; C0036+616
Dolidze 12	ast	00 40.8	+60 51	Cas								1	18	99	Archinal: DSS shows slight condensation of Milky Way. Aliases: OCl 303; OCl 303.0; C0037+605
NGC 225	cl	00 43 36	+61 46.0	Cas	III1p n	15.0	7.0	76	9.26	12.9	614	1	18	4	Aliases: Cr 7; Lund 25; OCl 305; C0040+615

Table 4.1: Catalog of Clusters and Asterisms in the Milky Way, and Objects Misidentified as Such

Name	Type	2000.0 R.A.	Dec.	Con.	Tr. Type	Diam. (′)	Tot. Vm	#str	Bt* Vm	V Sur	Dist. (pc)	S #	2U #	Ref	Comments and Aliases
Czernik 2	cl	00 43 39	+60 12.0	Cas	IV2m	10.0		30				1	18	4	Skiff: Average of two independent determinations. Aliases: Lund 27; OCl 304; OCl 304.0; C0040+598
King 16	cl:	00 43.7	+64 11	Cas	I2m	5.0	10.3	71	11.0	13.8	2300	1	8	4	DSFG: Probably not a cluster. Skiff: Okay. Aliases: Lund 26; OCl 306; C0040+639
Berkeley 4	cl	00 45 13	+64 23.5	Cas	I2p	4.0	10.6	48	18.0	13.6		1	8	4	DSFG: Probably not a cluster. Skiff: Center star is BD+69 89. Aliases: Lund 29; OCl 307; C0042+641
NGC 188	cl	00 47 30	+85 14.5	Cep	I2r	15.0	8.1	550	10.0	14.0	1486	1	1	4	Aliases: Cr 6; Lund 28; Mel 2; OCl 309; Raab 1; OCl 309.0; Caldw 1; C0039+850
Berkeley 61	cl	00 48 10	+67 12.1	Cas	II1p	3.0		15	14.0			1	8	4	Aliases: OCl 308; C0045+669
Dolidze 13	cl	00 50.0	+64 08	Cas	IV1m	10.0		30				1	8	99	Archinal: DSS shows approximately 10′ diameter condensation of stars in Milky Way, just SW of HD 4776 (V=5.373v, B9.5V+...). Aliases: Lund 31; OCl 310; C0047+638
King 2	cl	00 50 57	+58 11.5	Cas	II2m	4.0		40	17.0			1	18	99	Archinal: Two thirds complete "stellar ring" visible on DSS at cluster center. Aliases: Lund 32; OCl 311; C0048+579
NGC 272	ast	00 51 26	+35 49.3	And		5.0	8.5	8	9	12.0		4	62	4	DSFG: L-shaped asterism. 7′ diameter heart-shaped asterism 15′ NW. Skiff: Asterism, position is for [L-shaped] circlet. Aliases: OCl 312; C0048+355
NGC 288	gcl	00 52 45.5	−26 34 51	Scl		13.0	8.1		12.6	13.7	8400	18	158	99	See notes. Archinal: Position measured from DSS. Aliases: Mel 3; EQ 0050−268; C0050−268
IC 1590	cl	00 52 49	+56 37.7	Cas	n	4.0	7.4		9.0	10.4		1	18	4	See notes. Involved in nebula NGC 281. Skiff: Center star is HD 5005, including nebula NGC 281. Aliases: Cr 8; OCl 313; Lund 34; (4) NGC 281; Mrk 1; OCl 313.0; Sh 2- 184; CTB 7; C0049+563
LeDrew 1	cl?	00 53.3	+49 32	Cas		40.0	7.8	22	9.8	15.8		4	44	99	See notes. Possible cluster, disk. 1999 Sept. by G. LeDrew in 10x50 binoculars. Associated with NGC 752? [LeDrew, 2001] Alias: Alessi 1
NGC 305	ast	00 56 21	+12 03.8	Psc				6				10	100	4	
Skiff J0058.4+6828	cl	00 58 24	+68 28.0	Cas	II2r	7.0		200	10.16			1	8	8	See notes. Discovered by B. Skiff while classifying galaxies on POSS-II. Includes TYC 4296 1455 1 (V=10.16) and IRAS 00551+6812. Alias: (4) IRAS 00551+6812
Berkeley 62	cl	01 01 12	+63 56.5	Cas	III2m	6.0	9.3	50	13.0	13.2	1897	1	8	4	Aliases: Lund 35; OCl 314; OCl 314.0; C0057+636
Czernik 3	cl:	01 03 07	+62 47.2	Cas	III2p	1.5	9.9	10		10.8		1	8	4	Aliases: Lund 36; OCl 315; C0100+625
NGC 362	gcl	01 03 14.3	−70 50 54	Tuc		14.0	6.8		12.7	12.5	8600	24	204	55	Aliases: Mel 4; EQ 0100−711; Caldw 104; C0100−711
NGC 358	cl?	01 05 11	+62 01.3	Cas		3.0		25				1	29	4	
NGC 366	cl	01 06 27	+62 13.7	Cas	II3m	4.0		30	10.0			1	29	4	Aliases: Cr 9; Lund 37; OCl 316; Mrk 2; C0103+619
PWM78 1	cl?	01 08 04.8	+65 38 51	Cas		1.5		35				1	8	8	Possible very reddened cluster. Alias: C0104+653
NGC 381	cl	01 08 18	+61 35.0	Cas	III1m	7.0	9.3	50	10.0	13.5		1	29	4	Aliases: Cr 10; Lund 38; OCl 317; OCl 317.0; C0105+613
HW 60	gal?	01 09 27.6	−72 22 19	Tuc		0.2						24	204	99	In SMC. Archinal: Appears to be a galaxy on DSS image. HW: Unresolved, 0.2′. NED has an infrared source here, 2MASXi J0109277-722220.
Stock 3	cl	01 12 03	+62 16.4	Cas	IV1p	5.0		8	11.0			1	29	4	Aliases: Lund 39; OCl 318; C0109+620
[PKL98] 1	cl?	01 13 50	+32 01.7	Psc		3.0		3			201	4	62	14	
NGC 433	cl	01 15 10	+60 07.5	Cas	III2p	4.0		15	9.0			1	29	4	Aliases: Lund 41; OCl 319; St 22; OCl 319.0; C0112+598
NGC 436	cl	01 15 58	+58 49.0	Cas	I2m	5.0	8.8	49	10.0	12.3	2109	1	29	4	Aliases: Cr 11; Lund 42; Mel 6; OCl 320; Raab 2; C0112+585
NGC 457	cl	01 19 33	+58 17.4	Cas	II3r	20.0	6.4	204	8.59	12.9	3053	1	29	4	See notes. φ_{1+2} Cas not included in magnitude total or as brightest star.; Moore: Phi Cas Cluster. Aliases: Cr 12; Lund 43; Mel 7; OCl 321; Raab 3; OCl 321.0; Caldw 13; C0115+580
Teutsch J0121.3+2507	ast?	01 21 18	+25 07.6	Psc	III1p	5.0		20	20			4	80	17	Teutsch: Asterism? Scattered group at galactic latitude b=-37.3°.
Alessi J01232-3330	ast	01 23.2	−33 30	Scl		8.0		6	7			18	176	10	
NGC 559	cl	01 29 33	+63 18.1	Cas	I1m	7.0	9.5	120	9.0	13.7	1141	1	17	4	Aliases: Cr 13; Lund 45; OCl 322; (4) IRAS 01259+6301; Caldw 8; C0126+630
NGC 581	cl	01 33 22	+60 39.5	Cas	II2m	6.0	7.4	172	9.0	11.3	2493	1	29	4	DSFG: M 103. Aliases: Cr 14; Lund 46; M 103; Mel 8; OCl 326; Raab 4; C0129+604
NGC 603	***	01 34 44	+30 13 58	Tri		0.2	14	3	14.3	-1.6		4	62	53	See notes. Stars are GSC 02293-00998, 02293-00972, 02293-00966.
Czernik 4	cl:	01 35 36.4	+61 28 35	Cas	IV2p	4.0		10				1	29	99	Archinal: Center is HD 9583 (V=8.57, K0III). Aliases: Lund 47; OCl 327; C0132+611
Trumpler 1	cl	01 35 40	+61 17.2	Cas	II2p	3.0	8.1	112	10.0	10.5	2319	1	29	4	See notes. Skiff: Cluster is BD+60 276. Aliases: Cr 15; Lund 48; OCl 328; Mrk 3; C0132+610
NGC 609	cl	01 36 24	+64 32.2	Cas	II3r	3.0	11.0	77	14.0	13.4	2831	1	17	4	See notes. Aliases: Cr 16; King 3; Lund 50; OCl 325; C0133+643
NGC 629	***	01 39 02.1	+72 52 06	Cas		0.5			12.2			1	17	99	Archinal: GSC stars 04318-02212 (12.2), 04318-01730 (13.4), and 04318-01602 (13.3). Alias: STF 2
NGC 637	cl	01 43 04	+64 02.2	Cas	I2m	3.0	8.2	55	8.0	10.6	2400	1	17	4	Aliases: Cr 17; Lund 51; OCl 329; C0139+637

Table 4.1: Catalog of Clusters and Asterisms in the Milky Way, and Objects Misidentified as Such

Name	Type	2000.0 R.A.	Dec.	Con.	Tr. Type	Diam. (′)	Tot. Vm	#str	Bt* Vm	V Sur	Dist. (pc)	S #	2U #	Ref	Comments and Aliases
NGC 657	cl	01 43 29.8	+55 52 30	Cas		7.0		40	7.1			1	29	8	See notes. Includes as brightest star, double HD 10495 on E side; other stars V=11 and fainter; circlet of 5 stars included on SW side. Aliases: Lund 52; OCl 337; C0140+556
NGC 654	cl	01 44 00	+61 53.0	Cas	II2r	6.0	6.5	83	10.0	10.4	1977	1	29	4	Aliases: Cr 18; Lund 53; Mel 9; OCl 330; Raab 5; OCl 330.0; C0140+616
NGC 659	cl	01 44 24	+60 40.2	Cas	I2m	6.0	7.9	186	10.0	11.8	2520	1	29	4	Aliases: Cr 19; Lund 54; Mel 10; OCl 332; Raab 6; OCl 332.0; C0140+604
Collinder 463	cl	01 45 45	+71 48.6	Cas	III2m	57.0	5.7	79	8.49	14.5	661	1	17	99	Archinal: Confirmed against Collinder [1931] plate 12 (where image is flipped east to west). Aliases: Lund 57; OCl 324; OCl 324.0; C0144+717
NGC 663	cl	01 46 17	+61 13.1	Cas	II3r	15.0	7.1	108	9.0	13.0	2217	1	29	4	Aliases: Cr 20; Lund 55; Mel 11; OCl 333; Raab 7; OCl 333.0; Caldw 10; C0142+610
Berkeley 5	cl	01 47 44	+62 56.4	Cas	IV1p	5.0		15	17.0			1	17	4	Aliases: OCl 331; C0144+626
Collinder 21	ast	01 50 12	+27 04.8	Tri	III3p	7.0	8.2	20		12.4		4	80	4	See notes. Skiff [private comm.] has shown this group of stars is not a true cluster. Aliases: Lund 58; OCl 371; C0147+270
Phoenix dwarf gal	gal	01 51 06.3	−44 26 47	Phe		5.0						18	191	99	See notes. Archinal: Upon discovery thought to be a distant globular cluster but later shown to be a dwarf galaxy. 4′ NNE of fairly bright star. Aliases: (5) Sch.-West; C0149–447
Berkeley 6	cl	01 51 12	+61 03.6	Cas	II2p	5.0		20	14.0			1	29	4	Aliases: Lund 59; OCl 335; C0147+608
IC 166	cl	01 52 22	+61 51.3	Cas	II1r	8.0	11.7	179	17.0	16.2	3076	1	29	4	Aliases: Lund 60; OCl 334; Tom 3; C0149+615
Stock 4	cl	01 52.7	+57 04	Per	IV1p	12.0		15	11.0			1	29	99	Skiff: Too sparse. Archinal: DSS shows group of brighter stars in rich Milky Way. Aliases: Lund 61; OCl 342; OCl 342.0; C0149+568
ESO 245-SC09	cl	01 53.7	−45 57	Phe	III1	12.0						18	191	99	Archinal: Sparse group of stars on DSS. Faint galaxy on N side (01 53 49.2 −45 52 34, not in NED or SIMBAD).
Berkeley 7	cl	01 54 12	+62 22.2	Cas	II2p	4.0		18	14.0			1	29	4	Aliases: Lund 62; OCl 336; C0150+621
Czernik 5	cl	01 55 40	+61 21.4	Cas	III1p	2.0		10				1	29	4	Aliases: Lund 63; OCl 338; C0151+610
NGC 752	cl	01 57 35	+37 50.0	And	II2r	75.0	5.7	77	8.0	15.1	361	4	62	4	Aliases: Cr 23; Lund 64; Mel 12; OCl 363; Raab 8; Caldw 28; C0154+374
NGC 744	cl	01 58 30	+55 28.5	Per	III1p	5.0	7.9	99	10.0	11.4	1393	1	29	4	Aliases: Cr 22; Lund 65; OCl 345; OCl 345.0; C0155+552
NGC 743	cl	01 58 32	+60 10.0	Cas	IV1p	7.0		12	10.0			1	29	4	Skiff: Sparse. Aliases: Lund 66; OCl 343; C0155+599
[PTB93] 10	cl	01 58.7	+68 04	Cas		120.0		9				1	17	99	Archinal: Infrared cluster. Not visible on DSS.
Berkeley 8	cl	02 01 05	+75 29.6	Cas	II2m	5.0		40	14.0		1490	1	7	99	Aliases: Lund 67; OCl 323; C0156+753
Czernik 6	cl	02 02 08	+62 50.8	Cas	II2p	2.0		12				1	17	4	Skiff: Brightest star is BD+62 338 (B3II). Aliases: Lund 68; OCl 340; C0158+626
WHI B0200-03	cl	02 02 56.8	−03 15 10	Cet		1.2						10	119	99	Dias, *et al.* [2002] call this "Whiting 1", but the discovery paper gives no suggestion for such a name. Alias: (5) Whiting 1
Czernik 7	cl:	02 03 01	+62 14.8	Cas	II1p	4.0		20				1	29	4	Aliases: Lund 69; OCl 341; C0158+620
Stock 5	cl	02 04.4	+64 23	Cas	III3m	24.0		25	4.90			1	17	8	Archinal: Large. Diameter approximately 24′ (vs. Stock value of 15′). Bright star is 53 Cas (V=4.90, on West side). Aliases: Lund 70; OCl 339; OCl 339.0; C0200+642
NGC 843	as??	02 11 08	+32 05.8	Tri				3				4	61	4	Skiff: Triple star.
Stock 2	cl	02 14 43	+59 29.1	Cas	I2m	60.0	4.4	166	8.18	13.3	303	1	29	99	Archinal: Large group of bright stars, confirmed against Stock's [1956] discovery paper. Aliases: Lund 71; OCl 348; OCl 348.0; C0211+590
h Per	**	02 16 49	+57 02.6	Per		1.7	6.1	2	6.499	7.3		1	29	99	See notes. O'Meara and Green [2003] have determined that this (h Per) is not NGC 869 but the wide pair of stars HD 13854 and HD 13841.
NGC 869	cl	02 19 04	+57 08.1	Per	I3r	18.0	5.3	317	6.55	11.6	2232	1	29	99	See notes. Perseus "Double cluster" with NGC 884. Skiff: Center star is HD 14134 (V=6.6, B3Ia). BA: Not in total magnitude. Aliases: Mel 13; Raab 9; Cr 24; Mrk 4; OCl 350; OCl 350.0; Lund 73; (3) Doub. cl; C0215+569
Berkeley 63	cl	02 19 27	+63 43.3	Cas	III1p	3.0		12	15.0			1	17	4	Aliases: Lund 74; OCl 346; C0215+635
Basel 10	cl	02 19 28	+58 18.0	Per	II1p	2.0	9.9	23	10.23	11.4	2602	1	29	4	Aliases: Lund 40; OCl 349.1; C0215+580
Double Cluster	2cl	02 20 40.6	+57 09 41	Per		60.0	4.3			13.2		1	29	99	See notes. Includes NGC 869 and NGC 884, which see. Aliases: Chi Per; (2) NGC 869; (2) NGC 884
Berkeley 64	cl	02 21 46	+65 53.5	Cas	II1m	2.0		30	14.0			1	17	4	Aliases: Lund 75; OCl 344; C0217+656
NGC 884	cl	02 22 05	+57 07.8	Per	I3r	18.0	6.1	303	6.39	12.4	2222	1	29	99	See notes. Perseus "Double cluster" with NGC 869. Brightest star (HD 14433, V=6.39) not in total. Aliases: Mel 14; Raab 10; Cr 25; Mrk 5; OCl 353; OCl 353.0; Lund 76; (3) Doub. cl; C0218+568

Table 4.1: Catalog of Clusters and Asterisms in the Milky Way, and Objects Misidentified as Such

Name	Type	2000.0 R.A.	Dec.	Con.	Tr. Type	Diam. (′)	Tot. Vm	#str	Bt* Vm	V Sur	Dist. (pc)	S #	2U #	Ref	Comments and Aliases
NGC 886	cl	02 23 28.1	+63 46 16	Cas	III2p	14.0		20	11.0			1	17	53	See notes. Aliases: h 214; St 6; OCl 347; Lund 77; C0219+636
NGC 917	ast	02 26 09	+32 13.5	Tri		1.0		6				4	61	99	Archinal: Forms semicircle with 2 stars NW and 2 stars NE as J.H. indicated. Triple and double stars on E and W sides. Alias: h 220
Lederman 1	ast	02 27 18	+42 18.5	And		14.0						4	43	8	See notes. 14′x9′ "Black Widow spider" asterism of GSC stars, noted by R. Lederman, 1997. Just north of NGC 911 galaxy group.
Tombaugh 4	cl	02 29 10.7	+61 47 06	Cas	II1m n	5.3		40	16.0			1	29	99	Aliases: Lund 78; OCl 349; C0225+615
Markarian 6	cl	02 29 40	+60 42.4	Cas	III1p	6.0	7.1	29	8.8	11.0	511	1	29	4	Aliases: Abt 1; Bi 4; Lund 79; OCl 351; St 7; C0225+604
NGC 956	cl	02 32 14.9	+44 38 48	And	IV2m	9.0	8.9	30	9.0	13.7		4	43	99	Skiff: Sparse field. Archinal: DSS shows 4 bright stars with some fainter background stars. Aliases: Cr 27; Lund 80; OCl 377; C0229+444
IC 1805	cl	02 32 42	+61 27.4	Cas	II3m n	20.0	6.5	62	7.86	13.0	2210	1	29	4	See notes. Skiff: Center star is HD 15558 [V=7.8, O5(f)III]. Aliases: Cr 26; Lund 81; Mel 15; OCl 352; Raab 11; Mrk 7; RAFGL 333; Sh 2- 190; NRL 15; C0228+612
Czernik 8	cl:	02 32 58	+58 45.8	Per	II2p	2.0	9.7	19	9.87	11.2	2466	1	29	4	Skiff: Center star is LS I +58 65. Aliases: Lund 82; OCl 359; C0229+585
NGC 957	cl	02 33 20	+57 34.2	Per	III2m	10.0	7.6	119	11.0	12.6	2032	1	29	4	Aliases: Cr 28; Lund 84; OCl 362; OCl 362.0; C0230+573
Czernik 9	cl:	02 33.6	+59 53	Cas	III2p	10.0		12				1	29	4	Skiff: Okay. Aliases: Lund 83; OCl 355; C0229+596
Czernik 10	cl:	02 33 55	+60 10.5	Cas	IV1p	4.0		15				1	29	4	Aliases: OCl 354; C0230+599
King 4	cl	02 36 02	+59 01.0	Cas	III1p	5.0	10.5	44	13.0	14.0	3397	1	29	4	Aliases: Lund 87; OCl 361; C0232+587
Czernik 11	cl:	02 36 36	+59 39.3	Cas	IV2p	5.0		20				1	29	4	See notes. Superposed on galaxy Maffei 1 = UGCA 34 = PGC 9892 = IRAS 02329+5926 = GSC 3699-2055 (nonstellar). Aliases: OCl 358; Lund 86; (4) Maffei 1; C0232+594
Trumpler 2	cl	02 36 53	+55 54.9	Per	II2p	17.0	5.9	109	7.38	12.1	560	1	29	4	Skiff: Center star is HD 16068. Aliases: Cr 29; Lund 88; OCl 365; OCl 365.0; C0233+557
Dejc 1	gal	02 37 28.3	+21 08 31	Ari		0.1	15.2			10.2		4	79	8	See notes. Incorrectly identified as a globular cluster by Dejc [1963]. = GSC 01222-00294. Listed in RC3 as galaxy MKN 369 = CGCG 462-36. Aliases: MKN 369; CGCG 462–36; II Zw 4; III Zw 50; PGC 9944; (5) GCl 4; EQ 0234+209; C0234+209
Berkeley 65	cl	02 39 06	+60 24.0	Cas	II3p	5.0	10.2	41	13.0	13.7	3311	1	29	4	Aliases: Lund 89; OCl 360; C0235+602
Czernik 12	cl	02 39 23	+54 55.1	Per	III1p	3.0		15				1	29	4	Aliases: Lund 90; OCl 367; C0235+547
NGC 1039	cl	02 42 08	+42 45	Per	II3r	25.0	5.2	60	9.0	12.2	446	4	43	4	See notes. DSFG: M 34. Skiff: Large. Aliases: Cr 31; Lund 91; M 34; Mel 17; OCl 382; Raab 13; C0238+425
NGC 1027	cl	02 42 36	+61 35.7	Cas	II3m n	15.0	6.7	152	9.0	12.6	1213	1	29	4	Skiff: Center star is HD 16626 (V=7.0, F0, nonmember). Aliases: Cr 30; Lund 92; Mel 16; OCl 357; Raab 12; C0238+613
Czernik 13	cl	02 44 27	+62 19.5	Cas	III2p	4.0	10.4	56	12.84	13.4	4345	1	29	4	DSFG: Probably not a cluster. Aliases: Lund 93; OCl 356; C0240+621
DoDz 1	ast	02 47 27	+17 15.3	Ari	III2p	7.5	7.1	8	8.53	11.5		10	99	99	See notes. B. Skiff has determined from their Tycho-2 proper motions that the 8 stars here are not physically associated. Aliases: Lund 596; OCl 287; C0244+169
IC 1848	cl	02 51 11	+60 24.1	Cas	I3p n	18.0	6.5	74	7.10	12.8	2289	1	29	4	See notes. Around BD+59° 552 (V=7.10, O6e), in western end of large nebular complex. Cr 34 at east end. Aliases: Cr 32; Lund 95; OCl 364; Cr 33; (5) OCl 368; (5) C0255+602; (5) Lund 96; Mrk 8; W 5; OCl 364.0; Sh 2- 199; CTB 11; OCl 368.0; C0247+602
Latysev 1	mc?	02 52	+27.5	Ari		330.0	5.45v	5	6.72	18.0	4.9	4	79	8	See notes. 5 faint nearby stars spread over 5.5°. May be part of larger moving group [AO84] III. Aliases: (3) AO84 III; C0249+272
NGC 1146	ast?	02 57 38	+46 25.6	Per								4	43	99	Skiff: Asterism, southeastern of two groups.
Collinder 34	cl:	02 59 23.2	+60 34 00	Cas	I3p	24.0	6.8		7.94	13.7		1	29	51	See notes. At east end of nebular complex. IC 1848 at west end. Position for brightest star, HD 18326 (V=7.94v, O7V). Aliases: Lund 97; OCl 369; OCl 369.0; C0257+602
Berkeley 66	cl	03 04 05	+58 44.5	Cas	I3m	4.0		30	16.0			1	28	4	Skiff: Stars very faint. Aliases: OCl 373; C0300+585
NGC 1193	cl	03 05 56	+44 23.0	Per	I2m	3.0	12.6	40	14.0	15.0		4	43	4	Aliases: Cr 35; Lund 99; OCl 390; C0302+441
Alessi J03091+2420	ast?	03 09 03.2	+24 20 52	Ari		8.0		20	11.1			4	79	8	Possible cluster, centered on GSC 1783-00820. Anon. galaxy on west side. D* Pou 248. disk. B. Alessi, November 2, 1997.
NGC 1252	ast	03 10 56	–57 45.7	Hor		9.0		18	6.7		470	24	202	99	See notes. Archinal: Eggen [1984] has shown that the brighter stars here do not comprise a true cluster. Aliases: (5) C0307–583; C0309–583
NGC 1220	cl	03 11 41	+53 20.9	Per	I1p	2.0	11.8	15	13.0	13.3		1	28	4	Aliases: Cr 37; Lund 100; OCl 380; C0308+531

Table 4.1: Catalog of Clusters and Asterisms in the Milky Way, and Objects Misidentified as Such

Name	Type	2000.0 R.A.	Dec.	Con.	Tr. Type	Diam. (′)	Tot. Vm	#str	Bt* Vm	V Sur	Dist. (pc)	S #	2U #	Ref	Comments and Aliases
Trumpler 3	cl	03 12 00	+63 11	Cas	III2m	15.0	7.0	30		12.9		1	17	4	Skiff: Sparse. Aliases: Cr 36; Ha 1; Lund 101; OCl 366; C0307+630
NGC 1261	gcl	03 12 15.3	−55 13 01	Hor		6.8	8.3		13.5	12.5	16000	24	202	55	Aliases: Mel 19; EQ 0310−554; Caldw 87; C0310−554
King 5	cl	03 14 40	+52 42.0	Per	I2m	6.0		40	13.0			1	28	4	Aliases: Lund 102; OCl 384; C0311+525
NGC 1245	cl	03 14 42	+47 14.3	Per	II2r	10.0	8.4	200	12.0	13.4	2239	4	43	4	Aliases: Cr 38; Lund 103; Mel 18; OCl 389; Raab 14; C0311+470
Stock 23	cl	03 16 10.8	+60 06 56	Cam?	II3p n	29.0		25	7.6			1	28	8	See notes. Named "Pazmino's cluster" by W. S. Houston, after John Pazmino [Houston, 1978]. Center and brt. star is HD 20040 (V=7.6). Aliases: Lund 104; OCl 375; Pazmino cl; OCl 375.0; C0312+598
Czernik 14	cl	03 16 57	+58 36.2	Cam	III1p	4.0		15				1	28	4	Skiff: Asterism. Aliases: Lund 105; OCl 376; C0313+584
Czernik 15	cl	03 23 13	+52 13.2	Per	IV2p	4.0		10				1	28	4	Skiff: Sparse. Aliases: Lund 107; OCl 386; C0319+520
[AO84] IV	mc	03.4	+04.0	Tau		11000.	3.83	20	4.80	24.0		10	118	54	Moving cluster with very large angular size, hypothesized by Agekyan and Orlov [1984].
Melotte 20	cl	03 24 19	+49 51.7	Per	III3m	300.0	2.3	50	3.0	14.7	164	4	43	4	Skiff: Center star is α Persei. Aliases: Alpha Per; Cr 39; Lund 106; OCl 392; Per m.c.; OCl 392.0; C0318+484
King 6	cl	03 28 00	+56 27.0	Cam	II2m	10.0		35	10.0			1	28	4	Aliases: Lund 108; OCl 381; C0324+562
[LAL96] 1	cl	03 28.9	+31 17	Per	n	3.0			10K		320	4	60	8	SW Infrared cluster in NGC 1333. Obscured by V=7 magnitudes. Contains Herbig-Haro 7 to 11. Aliases: (4) NGC 1333; (2) HH 7; (2) HH 8; (2) HH 9; (2) HH 10; (2) HH 11
[LAL96] 2	cl	03 29.2	+31 22	Per	n	6.0			10K		320	4	60	8	NE Infrared cluster in NGC 1333. Obscured by V=7 magnitudes. Contains Herbig-Haro 12. Aliases: (4) NGC 1333; (2) HH 12
Czernik 16	cl	03 31 02	+52 36.2	Per	IV2p	5.0		12				1	28	4	Aliases: Lund 109; OCl 387; C0327+524
NGC 1342	cl	03 31 40	+37 22.5	Per	III2m	17.0	6.7	99	8.0	12.9	535	4	60	4	Aliases: Cr 40; Lund 110; Mel 21; OCl 401; Raab 15; C0328+371
Berkeley 9	cl	03 32 38	+52 39.1	Per	II1p	4.0		20	15.0			1	28	4	Aliases: OCl 388; C0329+525
Palomar 1	gcl	03 33 20.8	+79 34 57	Cep		2.8	13.6		16.3	15.8	13700	1	7	99	See notes. Youngest Galactic globular cluster or oldest open cluster. Faint, not obvious on DSS or DSS-II. Archinal: Position measured from DSS. Aliases: (5) VII Zw 7; EQ 0325+794; C0325+794
NGC 1348	cl	03 34 09	+51 25.2	Per	III2m	6.0		30	8.53			1	43	4	Skiff: Brightest star is IRAS 03304+5114 not quite centered. Aliases: Lund 112; OCl 391; (4) IRAS 03304+5114; C0330+512
Berkeley 10	cl	03 39 37	+66 30.5	Cam	II2m	10.0		50	14.0			1	16	4	Skiff: Position including group to north. Aliases: Lund 113; OCl 370; C0334+663
Alessi J03435-2925	ast	03 43.5	−29 25	For		18.0		10	10			18	156	10	
NGC 1436	gal	03 43 36.9	−35 51 11	Eri		1.5			11.66			18	174	99	Archinal: This is also NGC 1437, having been mistakenly recorded twice by J. Herschel. Data here from NED. Aliases: Dunlop 562; h 2581; h 2582; NGC 1437
IC 348	cl	03 44 34	+32 09.8	Per	III2p n	8.0	7.3	21	10.0	11.8	327	4	60	51	See notes. The IC 348 name applies to the (Gingrich) cluster and nebulosity. *o* Persei on north side. Aliases: Gingrich; Cr 41; OCl 409; OCl 409.0; OCISM 99; C0341+321
Pleiades	cl	03 47 29	+24 06.3	Tau	I3r n	120.0	1.5	100	3.0	11.9	125	4	78	54	M 45. Skiff: Center star is Alcyone. Aliases: M 45; Mel 22; Cr 42; OCl 421; Lund 117; HEAO 0346+24; C0344+239
Tombaugh 5	cl	03 47 44	+59 05.4	Cam	III2r	15.0	8.4	102	14.0	14.3	1800	1	28	4	Aliases: Lund 118; OCl 385; C0343+589
NGC 1444	cl	03 49 27	+52 39.3	Per	IV1p	4.0	6.6	57	6.77	9.6	938	1	28	4	DSFG: Visual magnitude 8.8 without brightest star. Skiff: Center star is HD 23675. Aliases: Cr 43; Lund 119; OCl 394; Mrk 9; OCl 394.0; C0345+525
Czernik 17	cl:	03 52 20	+61 58	Cam	IV1p	4.0		15				1	28	99	Archinal: Includes two "arcs" of stars or partial "stellar rings". Aliases: Lund 120; OCl 378; C0348+618
AM 1	gcl	03 55 02.7	−49 36 52	Hor		0.5	15.8		18.2	14.3	125900	18	190	6	Aliases: E 1; ESO 201-10; E; C0354−498
Kemble 1	ast	03 57 25.3	+63 04 19	Cam	III2p	180.0		20	4.96			1	16	8	See notes. "Kemble's Cascade". 3° long NW to SE chain of 20 stars. NGC 1502 is by SE end. Brt. and center star is HD 24479 (V=4.96).
NGC 1520	ast	03 57 51.1	−76 48 20	Men		5.0		11	9			24	219	99	Archinal: DSS shows probable asterism of 12 stars, 5′ in diameter.
King 7	cl	03 59 10	+51 46.8	Per	I2r	8.0		80	16.0			1	28	4	Aliases: Lund 121; OCl 395; C0355+516
NGC 1498	***	04 00 19	−12 01.2	Eri		0.8		3	13.8			11	138	53	See notes. Stars are GSC 05308-00383, 05308-00193, and 05308-00229. Much fainter background stars also contribute.
NGC 1496	cl	04 04 32	+52 39.7	Per	III2p	3.0	9.6	10	12.0	12.0		1	28	4	Aliases: Cr 44; Lund 122; OCl 396; C0400+524
Dolidze 14	cl	04 06 41	+27 34.2	Tau	III1p	10.0		18				5	78	99	Archinal: Faint galaxy (IRAS 04035+2727, at 04 06 38.8 +27 32 24) on S side. Aliases: Lund 123; OCl 425; OCl 425.0; C0403+273

Table 4.1: Catalog of Clusters and Asterisms in the Milky Way, and Objects Misidentified as Such

Name	Type	2000.0 R.A.	Dec.	Con.	Tr. Type	Diam. (′)	Tot. Vm	#str	Bt* Vm	V Sur	Dist. (pc)	S #	2U #	Ref	Comments and Aliases
NGC 1502	cl	04 07 50	+62 19.9	Cam	I3m	20.0	6.9	63	7.0	13.4	813	1	28	4	At SE end of W. S. Houston's "Kemble's Cascade" [Houston, 1980, 1985]. Skiff: Center pair is HD 25638/39. Aliases: Cr 45; Lund 124; OCl 383; Mrk 10; OCl 383.0; C0403+622
NGC 1513	cl	04 09 55	+49 31.0	Per	II1m	12.0	8.4	50	11.0	13.8	783	5	42	4	Skiff: Sparse. Aliases: Cr 46; Lund 125; OCl 398; C0406+493
NGC 1557	cl?	04 12 55	−70 29.9	Hyi		22.0		20				24	212	99	Archinal: Irregular sparse cluster, with the brightest star HD 27346 (V=7.1, A9IV) (J. Herschel's "star 7 m") on N side.
NGC 1528	cl	04 15 19	+51 12.7	Per	II2m	18.0	6.4	165	10.0	12.7	745	1	42	4	Aliases: Cr 47; Lund 126; Mel 23; OCl 397; Raab 16; OCl 397.0; C0411+511
Teutsch J0416.8+4103	cl?	04 16 50	+41 03.9	Per	III1p	2.0		30	30			5	42	17	Teutsch: Cluster? Compact group.
NGC 1547	gal	04 17 12.4	−17 51 30	Eri		1.0	13.6			13.6		11	156	99	
Waterloo 1	ast?	04 18 36.4	+52 51 28	Cam?	n	1.6		9	11.0			1	28	8	Apparent asterism of stars including BD+52 805 (V=11.0, B). Involved in Sh 2-208. Alias: (4) Sh 2-208
IC 361	cl	04 18 51	+58 15.0	Cam	II2r	7.0	11.7	60	14.0	15.9	2559	1	28	4	Aliases: Cr 48; Lund 127; Mel 24; OCl 393; Raab 17; C0414+581
Mayer 2	cl	04 19 51	+53 09.5	Cam	III1p n	3.0		18				1	28	4	Skiff: Center star is GSC 3719-0546. S 207=PK 151+02 1= etc... Aliases: Lund 1156; OCl 396.1; C0415+530
Berkeley 11	cl	04 20 27	+44 55.2	Per	II2m	5.0	10.4	35	15.0	13.9	2188	5	42	4	Aliases: Lund 129; OCl 404; OCl 404.0; C0417+448
NGC 1545	cl	04 20 57	+50 15.3	Per	IV2p	12.0	6.2	65	9.0	11.6	759	1	42	4	Skiff: Center star is HD 27292. Aliases: Cr 49; Lund 131; OCl 399; OCl 399.0; C0417+501
NGC 1548	ast	04 21 20	+36 55.0	Per	IV1p	30.0						5	60	99	Skiff: Small sparse group. Archinal: Id? Perhaps 5′ asterism? Aliases: OCl 415; C0417+368
Eridanus	gcl	04 24 44.5	−21 11 13	Eri			14.7		17.6		80300	19	156	55	Aliases: (5) UGCA 91; ESO 551-01; EQ 0422.6−2118; EQ 0423−21; C0422−213
Hyades	cl	04 26.9	+15 52	Tau	II3m	329.0	0.5	380	4.0	13.1	40	11	97	9	Famous moving cluster. Aliases: Cr 50; Lund 128; Mel 25; OCl 456; Taurus cl; OCl 456.0; Caldw 41; C0424+157
Czernik 18	cl	04 27 48	+30 57.0	Tau?	IV1p	6.0		15				5	60	99	Archinal: Faint galaxy on W side (UGC 03050, at 04 27 30.0 +30 56 53). Aliases: Lund 132; OCl 426; C0424+308
Cl [BW88] 1	cl	04 30 14.3	+35 16 24	Per	n	4.0		100	10.6		800	5	60	8	Radio/Infrared cluster in NGC 1579 = Sh 2-222. Center star is LkHα 101. HD 279899 (V=10.6, G5) brightest. Aliases: (4) NGC 1579; (2) LkHA 101
NGC 1582	cl	04 31 39	+43 44.6	Per	IV2p	24.0	7.0	20	9.0	13.9		5	42	99	Archinal: Scattering of bright stars on DSS. One of three bright stars is HD 28502 (V=8.67, A3). Aliases: Cr 51; Lund 133; OCl 407; OCl 407.0; (4) IRAS 04287+4344; C0428+437
AM 0430-392	cl	04 32 24	−39 17.4	Cae		1.8						19	174	10	
NGC 1605	cl	04 34 53	+45 16.3	Per	III1m	5.0	10.7	40	12.52	14.2	2559	5	42	4	Aliases: Cr 52; Lund 134; OCl 406; OCl 406.0; C0431+451
SL 6	2gal	04 36 09.5	−65 46 28	Dor		0.6						24	212	99	Aliases: ESO 84-G25; PGC 15613; (4) NGC 1641
Berkeley 67	cl:	04 37 50	+50 46.4	Per	III1m	10.0		30	15.0			1	42	4	Skiff: Absorption hole? Sparse. Aliases: Lund 135; OCl 400; C0434+506
Teutsch J0438.2+4317	cl?	04 38 15	+43 17.0	Per	II2m	4.2		60	60			5	42	17	Teutsch: Likely cluster. Compact group. The brightest stars form a nearly closed ring in the center.
NGC 1624	cl	04 40 37	+50 27.7	Per	II1p n	3.0	11.8	12		14.2		1	42	4	Aliases: Cr 53; Lund 136; OCl 403; Mrk 11; OCl 403.0; C0436+503
[PKL98] 2	cl?	04 41 37	+71 14.2	Cam		2.0		3			161	1	16	14	
Teutsch J0443.8+3603	ast?	04 43 52	+36 03.1	Aur	III3m	8.2		70	70			5	59	17	Teutsch: Asterism? Irregular group with star streams, in field of similar density.
Berkeley 12	cl	04 44 24	+42 41.2	Per	II1m	4.0		30	16.0			5	42	99	Aliases: Lund 138; OCl 412; C0441+425
Berkeley 68	cl:	04 44.5	+42 04	Per	III1r	12.0	9.8	113	13.68	15.2	3200	5	42	4	DSFG: Fairly even distribution. Skiff: Not visible. Aliases: Lund 137; OCl 413; C0441+419
NGC 1647	cl	04 45 42.2	+19 07 09	Tau	II2r	40.0	6.4	200	9.0	14.4	524	11	77	99	See notes. Center star is PPM 120214. SZ Tau probably not a member. See Geffert, *et al.* [1996]. Aliases: Cr 54; Lund 139; Mel 26; OCl 457; Raab 18; OCl 457.0; C0443+189
Palomar 2	gcl	04 46 05.9	+31 22 51	Aur		2.2	13.0		18.8	14.7	26000	5	59	55	See notes. Has been listed incorrectly as a galaxy, with designations MCG +05-12-001 = PGC 15963. [Lederman and Gottlieb, 1996] Aliases: (5) MCG +05-12-001; (5) PGC 15963; EQ 0443+313; C0443+313
LeDrew 4	ast?	04 46.4	+55 13	Cam		15.0	7.0	10	8.5	12.9		1	28	99	See notes. Possible asterism or cluster discovered by G. LeDrew [Priv. Comm. Oct. 8, 2001]. Independently discovered by B. Alessi. Alias: Alessi 2

Table 4.1: Catalog of Clusters and Asterisms in the Milky Way, and Objects Misidentified as Such

Name	Type	2000.0 R.A.	Dec.	Con.	Tr. Type	Diam. (′)	Tot. Vm	#str	Bt* Vm	V Sur	Dist. (pc)	S #	2U #	Ref	Comments and Aliases
Ruprecht 148	cl:	04 46 35	+44 42.6	Per	IV1p	4.0	9.5	112	14.0	12.5	5500	5	42	4	Skiff: = Ba 9. Center star is IRAS 04429+4437, sparse group. Aliases: Bas 9; Lund 140; OCl 408; (4) IRAS 04429+4437; C0442+446
IC 2091	ast	04 46 40.1	−04 40 24	Eri		0.6		5				11	117	99	Asterism of 5 stars, matching Issac Roberts' position (MNRAS, March, 1903, p. 302) on DSS.
NGC 1662	cl	04 48 29	+10 55.8	Ori	II3m	12.0	6.4	59	9.0	11.8	378	11	97	4	Skiff: Center star is HD 30485. Aliases: Cr 55; Lund 141; OCl 470; C0445+108
NGC 1663	cl?	04 49 24.3	+13 08 27	Ori	IV2p	9.0		30				11	97	51	See notes. W. Herschel's (VIII.7) and other modern positions 1 minute too far west. Aliases: H. VIII.7; OCl 461; Lund 142; C0445+130
ESO 485-SC20	ast?	04 50 04.3	−25 57 52	Eri	II2	5.0		22				19	155	99	Archinal: Sparse group. Asterism? Several background galaxies.
NGC 1664	cl	04 51 06	+43 40.6	Aur	III1p	18.0	7.6	101	10.0	13.9	1126	5	42	4	Aliases: Cr 56; Lund 143; Mel 27; OCl 411; Raab 19; OCl 411.0; C0447+436
Teutsch J0455.7+3647	cl?	04 55 43	+36 47.0	Aur	II2m	3.2		50	50			5	59	17	Teutsch: Cluster? Fairly compact group.
Berkeley 13	cl	04 55 46.2	+52 49 12	Cam	II2m	8.0		130	15.0			1	28	8	See notes. Center star is GSC 03734-00518. Position from GSC, Tr. type estimated from DSS. 4′ SW of HD 31134 (V=5.6, A2Vs). Aliases: OCl 402; Lund 144; C0451+526
Czernik 19	cl	04 56 56	+28 47.6	Aur	II1m	15.0		50				5	77	99	Archinal: DSS shows two condensations to cluster, on NW and SE. Aliases: Lund 145; OCl 443; C0453+287
Skiff J0458.2+4301	cl?	04 58 11	+43 01.0	Aur		4.0			10.5			5	42	8	Discovered by Skiff [1995c]. Skiff: Dubious.
NGC 1707	ast?	04 58 21.1	+08 14 20	Ori		0.8		5	13.5			11	97	8	See notes. Includes brightest star GSC 00684-01125, and GSC 00684-00494. Aliases: h 338; IC 2107
Berkeley 14	cl	04 59 44	+43 28.9	Aur	III1m	6.0		30	16.0			5	42	4	Aliases: Lund 146; OCl 416; C0456+434
Berkeley 15	cl	05 02 05	+44 30.8	Aur	I2m	5.0		35	15.0			5	42	4	Aliases: Lund 147; OCl 414; C0458+443
NGC 1708	cl?	05 03 28	+52 51.6	Cam		20.0		10	10			1	27	99	Archinal: 20′ diameter loose cluster which stands out in 1° DSS image.
NGC 1724	ast	05 03 33	+49 29.5	Aur								5	42	99	Skiff: 1′ diameter, including GSC 3352-0890/-1096/-1031. Archinal: Verified against Rümker's original observations to the 1" level. Aliases: Lund 1121; OCl 405; C0459+494
NGC 1746	cl	05 03.6	+23 49	Tau	III2p	40.0	6.1	20	8.0	14.1	420	5	77	99	Contains C0500+235 = NGC 1750 and C0501+237 = NGC 1758. Skiff: Too large to check. Archinal: 40′ group of ~10 bright stars. Aliases: Mel 28; Raab 20; Cr 57; OCl 452; Lund 148; (2) NGC 1750; (2) NGC 1758; (2) OCl 454; (2) C0500+235; C0500+237
NGC 1750	ptcl	05 03.9	+23 39	Tau								5	77	51	Part of C0500+237 = NGC 1746. Aliases: H. VIII.43; OCl 454; (3) C0500+237; (3) Mel 28; (3) Cr 57; (3) OCl 452; (3) Lund 148; C0500+235
NGC 1758	cl	05 04.4	+23 47	Tau	III2p	40.0		20				5	77	99	Part of C0500+237 = NGC 1746. Archinal: Id? Probably clump on E side of NGC 1746 and NGC 1750 overall group. Aliases: Lund 150; OCl 453; C0501+237
Dolidze 15	ast	05 04.6	+34 50	Aur	IV1p	18.0						5	59	4	DSFG: Probably not a cluster. Skiff: Not visible in 0.5 degree field. Aliases: OCl 430; OCl 430.0; C0501+347
Skiff J0507.2+3050	cl?	05 07 13.8	+30 50 34	Aur		6.0		30	10.8			5	59	8	See notes. Center star (probably not member) is GSC 02389-00693. Involved in nebulosity LBN 809. Alias: (4) LBN 809
[PKL98] 4	cl?	05 07 22	+22 16.7	Tau		2.0		6			276	5	77	14	
NGC 1778	cl	05 08 06	+37 01.4	Aur	III2p	8.0	7.7	112	10.06	12.2	1479	5	59	4	Aliases: Cr 58; Lund 152; OCl 429; OCl 429.0; C0504+369
Teutsch J0508.2+4951	ast?	05 08 16	+49 51.3	Aur	II2p	2.4		40	40			5	42	17	Teutsch: Asterism? Some condensation in rich field. Elongated north-south.
King 17	cl	05 08 24	+39 05.0	Aur	II2m	5.0		25	14.0			5	59	4	Aliases: Lund 153; OCl 424; C0505+390
NGC 1802	ast?	05 10 13	+24 07.5	Tau		20.0		25	9.2			5	77	4	See notes. Position from W. Herschel. HD 241219 is brightest star. This may also be larger 12′ x 60′ (elongated N-S) group of some 80 stars. Alias: H. VIII.41
NGC 1807	cl	05 10 46	+16 30.8	Tau	II2p	12.0	7.0	37	9.0	12.4		11	97	4	DSFG: Probably not a cluster. Aliases: Cr 59; Lund 154; Mel 29; OCl 462; Raab 21; C0507+164
NGC 1790	ast?	05 11 02	+52 07.1	Aur		15.0		8	10			1	27	99	Archinal: Irregular group of brighter stars.
NGC 1798	cl	05 11 40	+47 41.7	Aur	I1m	5.0	10	50	13.0	4.5		5	42	4	See notes. Skiff: 3′ diameter. Aliases: Be 16; Lund 155; OCl 410; C0508+475
NGC 1817	cl	05 12 27	+16 41.0	Tau	IV2r	20.0	7.7	283	9.0	14.2	1813	11	97	4	Skiff: Sparse. Aliases: Cr 60; Lund 156; OCl 463; Raab 22; C0509+166
Collinder 464	cl	05 12 39.0	+73 58 29	Cam	III3m	120.0	4.2	50		14.6		1	7	99	Archinal: Large 2° scattering of about 7 bright stars. Aliases: Lund 164; OCl 372; OCl 372.0; C0516+732

Table 4.1: Catalog of Clusters and Asterisms in the Milky Way, and Objects Misidentified as Such

Name	Type	2000.0 R.A.	Dec.	Con.	Tr. Type	Diam. (′)	Tot. Vm	#str	Bt* Vm	V Sur	Dist. (pc)	S #	2U #	Ref	Comments and Aliases
NGC 1851	gcl	05 14 06.3	−40 02 50	Col		12.0	7.1		13.2	12.5	12200	19	173	6	Aliases: Caldw 73; C0512−400
Dolidze 16	cl	05 14.6	+32 43	Aur	IV2p n	6.0		10				5	59	4	Skiff: Not visible in 0.3 degree field. Aliases: Lund 157; OCl 435; OCl 435.0; C0511+326
ESO 252-SC14	cl	05 16.0	−45 14	Pic	III2	3.0						19	189	10	
ESO 486-SC45	cl	05 16.7	−24 02	Lep	I3	3.0						19	155	10	
NGC 1901	cl	05 17.8	−68 26	Dor	III3m	40.0		40			415	24	212	51	DSFG: Extremely faint. Aliases: OCl 791.1; Lund 1166; (5) Bok 1; (5) C1108−231; C0518−685
Melotte 31	cl?	05 18 10.5	+33 22 25	Aur	n	135.0		35	4.54			5	59	8	Covers 1° square, including 14, 16, and 19 Aur. Center star is 16 Aur. Involved in nebulosity, IC 405 to W and N, IC 410 to E.
NGC 1857	cl	05 20 06	+39 20.6	Aur	I3m	10.0	7.0	40	11.0	12.0	1900	5	59	99	Skiff: Center star is HD 34545. Aliases: Cr 61; Lund 159; Mel 32; OCl 428; Raab 23; OCl 428.0; (3) Cz 20; C0516+393
ESO 486-SC54	cl	05 20.2	−26 03	Lep	II2	5.0						19	155	10	
Berkeley 17	cl	05 20 30	+30 34.7	Aur	III1r	8.0		100	16.0			5	59	4	DSFG: Fairly even distribution. Aliases: Lund 160; OCl 447; C0517+305
Czernik 20	cl	05 20 32.5	+39 32 50	Aur	IV1p	36.0		30				5	59	99	Archinal: 36′ diameter group of about 30 bright stars, including NGC 1857 and Iss 206. (Czernik 20′ diameter is too small.) Aliases: Lund 158; OCl 427; OCl 427.0; (2) NGC 1857; (2) Iss 206; C0516+394
Collinder 62	cl	05 20 53.0	+41 04 51	Aur	IV3p	35.0	4.2			11.9		5	42	99	Archinal: 35′ (diameter used here) long E-W line of 3 bright stars, with about 6 others scattered nearby. Aliases: Lund 161; OCl 423; OCl 423.0; C0519+409
NGC 1891	cl?	05 21.3	−35 44	Col		27.0			9.73			19	173	99	
IC 2127	neb	05 21 58.7	−67 57 33	Dor		0.6						24	212	99	Archinal: Newly identified here as brightest nebula in large complex. (Not a planetary nebula as IC indicates). Alias: Fleming 91
IC 410	neb	05 22.0	+33 29	Aur		30.0						5	59	52	See notes. Nebula involved with the cluster NGC 1893. Name "C0519+334" should be denigrated (this is not a cluster). Aliases: CTB 17; LBN 807; LBN 173.58-01.75; Min 2- 59; (4) NGC 1893; (5) OCl 438.0; C0519+334
Berkeley 18	cl	05 22 12	+45 27.5	Aur	III1r	12.0		300	16.0			5	42	4	See notes. DSFG: Fairly even distribution. Skiff: Stars very faint. Aliases: King 22; OCl 419; Lund 162; (5) C0519+454; (5) OCl 420; C0518+453
Dolidze 17	ast	05 22.4	+07 07	Ori	IV2p	12.0						11	97	4	DSFG: Probably not a cluster. Skiff: 10′ diameter, only five bright stars. Aliases: OCl 482; C0519+070
NGC 1893	cl	05 22 46	+33 25.2	Aur	II3r n	25.0	7.5	270	9.31	14.5	3960	5	59	4	See notes. Involved with nebula IC 410. Skiff: Center star is HD 242935 (V=9.4, O8). [Nebulosity is IC 410.]. Aliases: Mel 33; Raab 24; Cr 63; OCl 439; Lund 166; (4) IC 410; OCl 439.0; C0519+333
DoDz 2	cl	05 23.2	+11 27	Ori	III2p	10.0		12				11	97	4	Skiff: Sparse group, position okay more-or-less. Aliases: Lund 169; OCl 477; C0521+114
Dolidze 19	cl	05 23.7	+08 10	Ori	IV1p	23.0						11	97	4	Skiff: Position ~okay. Aliases: Lund 168; OCl 480; C0521+081
Berkeley 19	cl	05 24 03	+29 34.2	Aur	II1m	4.0	11.4	150	15.0	14.4	4831	5	59	4	Aliases: Lund 171; OCl 450; C0520+295
Dolidze 18	cl	05 24 09	+33 23.6	Aur	IV1p n	6.0		15				5	59	99	See notes. Archinal: 6′ x 2.3′ rectangular group of about 10 stars, east of NGC 1893 and on the east edge of IC 410 nebulosity. Aliases: Lund 170; OCl 440; C0520+332
NGC 1904	gcl	05 24 10.6	−24 31 27	Lep		9.6	7.7		13.1	12.6	13000	19	155	55	M 79. Aliases: M 79; Mel 34; EQ 0522−245; 1E 0522.1−2433; C0522−245
Teutsch J0524.2+3329	ast?	05 24 17	+33 29.2	Aur	III2p	3.3		40	40			5	59	17	Teutsch: Asterism? Faint condensation of stars in rich field. Located near eastern edge of nebula IC 410, 5.5′ N of cl Do 18.
Berkeley 69	cl	05 24 21	+32 36.4	Aur	II2m	3.0		30	14.0			5	59	4	Aliases: Lund 172; OCl 444; C0521+326
NGC 1896	cl?	05 25 41.9	+29 19 42	Aur		20.0		25	8.51			5	77	4	See notes. Most references (e.g. NGC) have declination 9° too far south. Center at HD 243448. Bright star is HD 35348 (V=8.51, K5). S Aliases: H. VIII.4; h 353; GC 1104
Berkeley 70	cl:	05 25 48	+41 56.6	Aur	III1m	7.0		40	15.0			5	42	4	DSFG: Probably not a cluster. Aliases: OCl 422; C0522+418
NGC 1883	cl	05 25 55	+46 29.4	Aur	II1m	5.0	12.0	30	14.0	15.5		5	42	4	Aliases: Cr 64; Lund 175; OCl 417; C0522+465
Collinder 65	cl	05 26 05.7	+16 42 01	Tau	II3p	219.0	3.0			14.7		11	96	99	Archinal: Large ~4° group of bright stars, centered on 113 Tauri. Aliases: Lund 174; OCl 474; OCl 474.0; C0523+160
Czernik 21	cl:	05 26 40	+36 00.5	Aur	IV1m n	8.0		40				5	59	4	Skiff: Absorption hole? Aliases: Lund 176; OCl 432; C0523+359
NGC 1947	gal	05 26 47.5	−63 45 41	Dor		3.0	10.64			13.0		24	212	56	See notes. KMHK confuses this galaxy with an LMC cluster and along with J. Herschel give a position 1° too far south. RC3 data here. Aliases: h 2855; ESO 085-G087; IRAS 05264−6347; PGC 17296
Dolidze 21	cl	05 27.4	+07 04	Ori	IV2p	12.0						11	96	54	See notes. Skiff: Not obvious in 0.3 or 0.5 degree field. Aliases: OCl 483; Lund 177; C0524+070

Table 4.1: Catalog of Clusters and Asterisms in the Milky Way, and Objects Misidentified as Such

Name	Type	2000.0 R.A.	Dec.	Con.	Tr. Type	Diam. (′)	Tot. Vm	#str	Bt* Vm	V Sur	Dist. (pc)	S #	2U #	Ref	Comments and Aliases
Waterloo 2	ast?	05 28 01	+40 22.3	Aur		4.0		6	8.81			5	59	8	Apparent asterism, near, but not involved in Sh 2-225. [Moffat, *et al.* 1979] image is flipped left to right.
NGC 1907	cl	05 28 05	+35 19.5	Aur	I1m n	5.0	8.2	113	11.0	11.7	1330	5	59	4	Aliases: Cr 66; Lund 179; Mel 35; OCl 434; Raab 25; C0524+352
Stock 8	cl	05 28 07	+34 25.4	Aur	I3m n	15.0		40	9.0			5	59	4	See notes. Nebulosity is IC 417. Skiff: Center star is BD+34 1054 (V=8.9, B0IV). [Nebulosity is IC 417.]. Aliases: OCl 436; Lund 178; (4) IC 417; C0524+343
Dolidze 20	cl:	05 28 33	+33 40.6	Aur	IV3p	5.0		10				5	59	4	DSFG: Probably not a cluster. Skiff: Sparse. Aliases: Lund 180; OCl 442; C0525+337
NGC 1912	cl	05 28 43	+35 51.3	Aur	II2r	15.0	6.4	160	8.0	12.3	1234	5	59	4	DSFG: M 38. Aliases: Cr 67; Lund 181; M 38; Mel 36; OCl 433; Raab 26; OCl 433.0; C0525+358
NGC 1931	cl	05 31 26	+34 14.7	Aur	I3p n	6.0	10.1	20		14.0		5	59	4	Skiff: = BD+34 1074. Aliases: Cr 68; Lund 182; OCl 441; St 9; OCl 441.0; (4) IRAS 05281+3412; RAFGL 5144; Sh 2- 237; WB89 653; Ced 49; C0528+342
NGC 1963	cl	05 32 10.8	−36 22 50	Col	II2	14.0		32	11.			19	173	53	See notes. In form of a figure "3". Cusp (center) and brightest star is GSC 07067-01021. 32 other GSC stars included. Aliases: h 2861; ESO 363-SC05
Berkeley 20	cl	05 32 37	+00 11.3	Ori	II2p	2.0		20	15.0			11	116	4	Aliases: Lund 183; OCl 497; C0530+001
DoDz 3	cl	05 33.5	+26 31	Tau	IV2p	10.0		10				5	77	4	Skiff: Sparse. Aliases: Lund 184; OCl 459; OCl 459.0; C0530+264
[HS66] 356	galn	05 33 59.6	−71 45 24	Men		1.2						24	212	56	D. Riddle has noted that [HS66] and KMHK misclassify this as an LMC cluster. This is the nucleus of the 12′ diameter ESO 56-G154. Aliases: KMHK 1096; (3) ESO 56-G154
Collinder 69	cl	05 35.0	+09 56	Ori	III3p n	70.0	2.8	20		12.0	500	11	96	4	Skiff: = λ Orionis cluster. Aliases: Lund 185; OCl 479; Orion cl; Lam Ori; Mrk 12; OCl 479.0; C0532+099
NGC 1981	cl	05 35.2	−04 26	Ori	III3p n	28.0	4.2	20	10.0	11.4	400	11	116	4	Skiff: Okay. Aliases: Cr 73; Lund 187; OCl 525.0; C0532−044
NGC 1976	cl	05 35 16	−05 23.4	Ori	n	47.0					455	11	116	4	See notes. M 42, the "Trapezium" star cluster and Great Orion Nebula. Skiff: = θ-1 Orionis cluster. Aliases: M 42; Trapezium; OCl 528; Lund 188; Mrk 14; OCl 528.0; 2E 1366; 2E 0532.6−0526; 1ES 0532−05.4; The1 Ori; ADS 4186; STF 748; C0532−054
NGC 1977	cl	05 35.3	−04 49	Ori								11	116	99	Skiff: Okay. Archinal: Stars overwhelmed by nebulosity on DSS image. Aliases: Lund 1159; OCl 525.1; C0532−048
NGC 1980	cl	05 35 26	−05 54.6	Ori	III3m n	15.0	2.5	30		8.4		11	136	4	Skiff: = ι Orionis. Aliases: Cr 72; Lund 189; OCl 529; OCl 529.0; C0532−059
Collinder 70	cl	05 35.6	−01 05	Ori	III3r n	140.0	0.6	100		11.3	430	11	116	4	Skiff: = Orion's Belt. Aliases: Lund 186; OCl 503; Orion belt; Mrk 13; Ori belt; OCl 503.0; C0533−011
DoDz 4	cl	05 35.9	+25 57	Tau	IV2p	25.0		15				5	77	4	Skiff: Sparse group. Aliases: Lund 190; OCl 460; OCl 460.0; C0532+259
NGC 1960	cl	05 36 18	+34 08.4	Aur	I3r	10.0	6.0	60	9.0	11.0	1230	5	59	4	DSFG: M 36. Aliases: Cr 71; Lund 191; M 36; Mel 37; OCl 445; Raab 27; C0532+341
ESO 120-8	cl	05 36 21.8	−61 47 14	Dor								24	201	5	Aliases: E 2; C0535−618
Teutsch J0536.8+3112	cl?	05 36 49	+31 12.3	Aur	III2m	6.0		70	70			5	59	17	Teutsch: Cluster? Large little condensed group.
NGC 1996	cl?	05 38.2	+25 49	Tau		22.0						5	77	99	Skiff: Perhaps large group? Archinal: Rich scattering of stars on DSS.
Sigma Ori	cl	05 38 45	−02 36.0	Ori	III3p n	10.0		4				11	116	4	Skiff: = σ Orionis A = HD 37468. Aliases: Lund 1158; OCl 516.1; C0536−026
Stock 10	cl	05 39.0	+37 52	Aur	IV2p	25.0		15				5	59	4	Skiff: Sparse group. Aliases: Lund 192; OCl 431; C0535+379
[DB01] 24	cl?	05 39 12.5	+35 45 53	Aur		1.2						5	59	16	Infrared cluster. [DB01]: Partly resolved cluster in HII region Sh 2-233SE, pair with Sh 2-233SE IR Cluster.
NGC 2017	ast?	05 39 16	−17 51.0	Lep		10.0		8	8			11	155	4	DSFG: A scattered group of 8 stars, 4 bright and 4 faint; not a true cluster. Contains the multiple star h3780. Skiff: = HD 37643.
Teutsch J0539.4+3320	cl?	05 39 29	+33 20.6	Aur	I3p	1.9		40	40			5	59	17	Teutsch: Likely cluster. Compact group. Stars in streams.
Berkeley 71	cl	05 40 57	+32 16.0	Aur	II1m	5.0		30	15.0			5	59	4	Aliases: Lund 193; OCl 449; C0538+323
Teutsch J0541.3+3914	cl?	05 41 22	+39 14.4	Aur	II2p	1.4		30	30			5	59	17	Teutsch: Likely cluster. Compact group, V-shaped.
[LDEG91] 1	cl	05 41 43	−02 15.9	Ori	n	4.0		21			400	11	116	8	Infrared cluster in NGC 2023. Position is for cluster. Aliases: (3) LDN 1630; (4) NGC 2023
[LDEG91] 2	cl	05 41 44	−01 53.8	Ori	n	10.0		309			400	11	116	8	Infrared cluster in the "Flame Nebula," NGC 2024. Position is for cluster. Aliases: (3) LDN 1630; (4) NGC 2024
NGC 2026	cl?	05 43 08	+20 08	Tau		10.0		35	9			5	77	4	Skiff: Sparse.

Table 4.1: Catalog of Clusters and Asterisms in the Milky Way, and Objects Misidentified as Such

Name	Type	2000.0 R.A.	Dec.	Con.	Tr. Type	Diam. (′)	Tot. Vm	#str	Bt* Vm	V Sur	Dist. (pc)	S #	2U #	Ref	Comments and Aliases
NGC 2063	asMW	05 43 55	+08 39.8	Ori		9.0		10	10			11	96	99	Skiff: Not obvious in 0.4 degree field. Archinal: 9′ scattered group centered on small Milky Way patch. On W side of NGC 2039.
NGC 2061	ast?	05 44 06	−33 56.1	Col		10.0		11	13			19	173	53	See notes. Includes galaxy ESO 363-19 on NE side.
Teutsch J0544.3+2848	ast?	05 44 23	+28 48.9	Aur	II3m n	4.5		60	60			5	77	17	See notes. Teutsch: Asterism? Scattered group with fainter background stars, little condensed. Near NE-edge of SNR Simeis 147.
NGC 2013	cl??	05 44.4	+55 47.6	Aur				8	11			1	27	4	Skiff: Okay. Center given of sparse large (0.3 degree) field.
NGC 2039	asMW	05 46 13	+08 39.7	Ori		55.0						11	96	99	Archinal: Approximately 1° wide by 30′ high scattering of stars aligned on enhancement of Milky Way. FU Ori and nebula on NNW side. NGC
[LDEG91] 3	cl	05 46 40	+00 06.4	Ori	n	7.0		192			400	11	116	8	Infrared cluster in M 78 = NGC 2068. Position is for cluster. Aliases: (3) LDN 1630; (4) NGC 2068
Teutsch J0547.0-0506	ast?	05 47 00	−05 06.4	Ori	III1p	7.0		25	25			11	116	17	Teutsch: Asterism? Scattered group of triangular shape. Bright star HD 38636 (V=8.20) in southern part. Located 3 degrees east of M 42.
[LDEG91] 4	cl	05 47 08	+00 17.9	Ori	n	8.0		105			400	11	116	8	Infrared cluster in NGC 2071. Position from DSS for NGC 2071. Aliases: (3) LDN 1630; (4) NGC 2071
Collinder 74	cl	05 48 40	+07 21.5	Ori	III1m	6.0	14.4	40		18.3		11	96	4	Skiff: Absorption hole? Aliases: Lund 195; OCl 489; C0545+073
Teutsch J0548.8+0930	ast?	05 48 49	+09 30.1	Ori	III1p	5.5		40	40			11	96	17	Teutsch: Asterism? Loose group of brighter stars than background.
Basel 4	cl	05 48 54	+30 11.1	Aur	II1p	5.0	9.1	134	12.18	12.6	5675	5	59	4	Skiff: Low contrast against MW. Aliases: Cz 22; Lund 194; OCl 455; C0545+302
King 8	cl	05 49 17	+33 37.6	Aur	II2m	4.0	11.2	198	15.0	14.2	3354	5	59	4	Aliases: Lund 196; OCl 448; EQ 0546+336; C0546+336
ESO 424-SC25	cl	05 49.8	−32 28	Col	III3	8.0						19	173	10	
Czernik 23	cl	05 50 08	+28 53.6	Aur	III1p	5.0						5	77	4	Aliases: Lund 197; OCl 458; OCl 458.0; (4) IRAS 05463+2853; C0546+289
Berkeley 72	cl	05 50 12	+22 15.0	Ori	II1p	2.0		15	15.0			5	77	4	Aliases: Lund 198; OCl 464; C0547+221
Teutsch J0550.3+4142	ast?	05 50 23	+41 42.9	Aur	II2p	4.0		25	25			5	41	17	Teutsch: Asterism? Small group of (∼10) brighter stars.
Berkeley 21	cl	05 51 46	+21 48.6	Ori	I2m	6.0	11.1	194	6.0	15.0	3631	5	77	4	See notes. Skiff: Same as origin used by Tosi, *et al.*, MNRAS, 299, 834. Aliases: Lund 199; C0548+217
[DB01] 25	cl?	05 52 04.9	+27 23 32	Tau		3.5						5	77	16	Infrared cluster. [DB01]: Resolved cluster or dust window, related to IRAS 05489+2723?, partly optical.
NGC 2099	cl	05 52 19	+32 33.2	Aur	I2r	15.0	5.6	1842	11.0	11.5	1343	5	59	4	DSFG: M 37. Skiff: Center star is HD 39183. Aliases: Cr 75; Lund 115; M 37; Mel 38; OCl 451; Raab 28; C0549+325
Teutsch J0552.4+2954	ast?	05 52 24	+29 54.1	Aur	IV2m	5.0		60	60			5	59	17	Teutsch: Asterism? Moderately rich scattered group of mostly faint stars, but little different from background.
NGC 2112	cl	05 53 46	+00 24.6	Ori	II2m n	18.0	9.1	50	10.0	15.4	802	11	116	4	Skiff: = GSC 0117-0339 (GSC magnitude 11.7). Aliases: Cr 76; Lund 1122; OCl 509; C0551+003
NGC 2132	ast	05 55 09.1	−59 54 37	Pic		45.0		15	8.0			24	201	99	Archinal: Large group of 6 bright stars (and several just fainter), right at W. Herschel's position, i.e. on HD 40484 (V=8.0, K2III).
Czernik 24	cl:	05 55 26	+20 52.7	Ori	III1m	5.0		35				5	77	8	Archinal: Position from DSS. Aliases: Lund 200; OCl 472; C0552+208
Basel 11b	cl	05 58 10	+21 57.6	Ori	III1p	3.0	8.9	70	11.48	11.3	1500	5	77	4	See notes. Aliases: Lund 1209; OCl 469.1; Bas 11B; C0555+219
Berkeley 22	cl	05 58 27	+07 45.4	Ori	I2p	1.5		20	15.0			11	96	4	Aliases: Lund 201; OCl 490; C0555+078
NGC 2129	cl	06 01 06	+23 19.4	Gem	I3m	6.0	6.7	73	10.0	10.6	1989	5	76	51	Archinal+Skiff: Midpoint between HD 250290 and HD 250289. DSFG: Visual magnitude without the two brightest stars = 8.2. Aliases: Cr 77; Lund 293; OCl 467; OCl 467.0; C0558+233
NGC 2126	cl	06 02 34	+49 52.0	Aur	III2m	6.0	10.2	40	13.0	14.1	1400	5	41	4	Aliases: Cr 78; Lund 202; Mel 39; OCl 418; Raab 29; C0559+499
NGC 2141	cl	06 02 56	+10 26.8	Ori	I2r	10.0	9.4	365	15.0	14.4	4246	11	96	4	Aliases: Cr 79; Lund 203; OCl 487; C0600+104
NGC 2143	cl?	06 03 07.4	+05 43 42	Ori		11.0		12	10			11	96	99	Archinal: Sparse group centered on HD 41080 (V=9.1, F0), SE star of parallelogram of 4 stars.
ESO 121-3	***	06 03 19.7	−60 30 01	Pic		0.6						24	201	99	
ESO 425-SC06	cl	06 04.8	−29 11	Col	II2	5.0						19	154	10	
IC 2157	cl	06 04 49.8	+24 03 21	Gem	II1p	5.0	8.4	56	12.0	11.9	1879	5	76	8	See notes. Archinal: Position from DSS. Center star is GSC 1864-00819. IC 2156 6′ to north. Aliases: Cr 80; Lund 204; OCl 465; Tr 4; C0601+240

Table 4.1: Catalog of Clusters and Asterisms in the Milky Way, and Objects Misidentified as Such

Name	Type	2000.0 R.A.	Dec.	Con.	Tr. Type	Diam. (′)	Tot. Vm	#str	Bt* Vm	V Sur	Dist. (pc)	S #	2U #	Ref	Comments and Aliases
IC 2156	cl?	06 04 50.6	+24 09 37	Gem		3.5		40				5	76	8	See notes. Archinal: Position from DSS. IC 2157 6′ to south.
ESO 489-SC01	cl	06 05.0	−26 44	Lep	III3	10.0						19	154	10	
NGC 2158	cl	06 07 26	+24 05.8	Gem	II3r	5.0	8.6	973	15	12.1	3875	5	76	4	See notes. Aliases: Cr 81; Lund 205; Mel 40; OCl 468; Raab 30; C0604+241
NGC 2169	cl	06 08 25	+13 57.9	Ori	III3m	6.0	5.9	30	6.94	9.8	918	11	96	4	Aliases: Cr 83; Lund 206; OCl 481; OCl 481.0; (4) IRAS 06057+1358; WB89 751; C0605+139
[CSS95] Cl 4b	cl	06 08 25	+21 29.5	Gem?		0.8		11			2000	5	76	54	Infrared cluster near Sh 2-247, reported by Carpenter, *et al.* [1995]. Aliases: (4) Sh 2- 247; (4) IRAS 06056+2131
[CSS95] Cl 4a	cl	06 08 41	+21 30.8	Gem?		1.6		57			2000	5	76	54	Infrared cluster near Sh 2-247, reported by Carpenter, *et al.* [1995]. Aliases: (4) Sh 2- 247; (4) IRAS 06056+2131
[CSS95] Cl 2	cl	06 08 54	+21 38.4	Gem		1.0		23			2000	5	76	54	Infrared cluster near Sh 2-247, reported by Carpenter, *et al.* [1995]. Aliases: (4) Sh 2- 247; (4) IRAS 06058+2138
Teutsch J0608.9+2615	cl?	06 08 56	+26 15.6	Gem	II3p	2.4		40	40			5	76	17	Teutsch: Cluster? Sparse but compact group. Located 2 degrees N of cl M35.
NGC 2168	cl	06 09.0	+24 21	Gem	III3r	25.0	5.1	434	8.0	12.1	853	5	76	4	See notes. DSFG: M 35. Skiff: Very large. Aliases: Cr 82; Lund 207; M 35; Mel 41; OCl 466; Raab 31; OCl 466.0; C0605+243
[CSS95] Cl 1b	cl	06 09 06	+21 50.3	Gem		1.1		23			2000	5	76	54	Infrared cluster near Sh 2-247, reported by Carpenter, *et al.* [1995]. Aliases: (4) Sh 2- 247; (4) IRAS 06061+2151
[CSS95] Cl 1a	cl	06 09 17	+21 50.3	Gem		0.7		10			2000	5	76	54	Infrared cluster near Sh 2-247, reported by Carpenter, *et al.* [1995]. Aliases: (4) Sh 2- 247; (4) IRAS 06061+2151
Teutsch J0609.3+3113	cl?	06 09 20	+31 13.5	Aur	II2m	3.5		50	50			5	58	17	Teutsch: Likely cluster. Condensed group. Located 3.5′ SE of bright star HD 41889 (V=7.62, A2)= ADS 4734 A
[DB01] 26	cl?	06 09 28.2	+24 55 40	Gem		4.0						5	76	16	Infrared cluster. [DB01]: Resolved stellar group related to IRAS 06063+2456, partly optical.
[DB01] 27	cl?	06 09 31.0	+21 23 57	Ori?		2.0						5	76	16	Infrared cluster. [DB01]: Resolved stellar group related to IRAS 06065+2124.
[PKL98] 6	cl?	06 09 36	−22 09.1	Lep		3.0		6			272	19	154	14	
NGC 2180	cl?	06 09 37	+04 42.7	Ori		6.0		>20	12			11	116	4	Skiff: Okay, define cluster center better from visual observation?
Collinder 84	cl?	06 09 39	+20 29.3	Ori	III3r n	22.0	6.8	75	8.0	13.5	2704	5	76	54	See notes. Involved in nebula NGC 2175. Skiff: = HD 42088 (V=7.6, O6.5V). [Nebula is NGC 2175]. Aliases: OCl 476; Lund 208; OCISM 106; (4) NGC 2175; C0606+203
[DB01] 28	cl?	06 09 46.9	+20 54 44	Ori		2.5						5	76	16	Infrared cluster. [DB01]: Resolved stellar group related to IRAS 06067+2055.
[CSS95] Cl 3	cl	06 09 50	+21 37.9	Gem		1.0		16			2000	5	76	54	Infrared cluster near Sh 2-247, reported by Carpenter, *et al.* [1995]. Aliases: (4) Sh 2- 247; (4) IRAS 06067+2138
NGC 2175.1	cl	06 10 53	+20 36.6	Ori	II2p n	5.0		20				5	76	4	See notes. Skiff: = HD 252812 (magnitude 11.0, B5). Aliases: Lund 1182; NGC 2175s; OCl 475.1; C0607+206
NGC 2165	cl?	06 11 05	+51 40.6	Aur		6.0		15	10			1	27	4	Skiff: Okay, sparse group.
NGC 2184	cl?	06 11 41	−03 35.7	Ori		33.0		30	9			11	116	99	
NGC 2186	cl	06 12 08	+05 27.5	Ori	II2m	5.0	8.7	30	12.0	12.2	1828	11	116	4	Aliases: Cr 85; Lund 209; OCl 498; C0609+054
NGC 2189	nf?	06 12.3	+01 08	Ori					10			11	116	53	See notes. Nothing obvious on DSS. Supposedly two clusters, near GSC 00131-01117 and 00131-01065.
[DB01] 30	cl?	06 12 24.9	+17 59 28	Ori		0.9						11	76	16	Infrared cluster. [DB01]: Partly resolved cluster in HII region Sh 2-254.
[DB01] 31	cl?	06 12 36.6	+17 56 55	Ori		1.7						11	76	16	Infrared cluster. [DB01]: Mostly a resolved cluster in HII region Sh 2-256.
[DB01] 34	cl?	06 13 16.0	+15 22 30	Ori		1.3						11	96	16	Infrared cluster. [DB01]: Mostly a resolved stellar group related to IRAS 06103+1523, pair with cluster 33.
[DB01] 33	cl?	06 13 21.2	+15 23 56	Ori		1.0						11	96	16	Infrared cluster. [DB01]: Mostly an unresolved cluster related to IRAS 06104+1524A, pair with stellar group 34.
[DB01] 32	cl?	06 13 28.0	+17 55 27	Ori		2.0						11	76	16	Infrared cluster. [DB01]: Partly resolved cluster in HII region Sh 2-258.
Czernik 25	cl	06 13 41	+06 56.8	Ori	III1p	2.0		20				11	96	4	Aliases: Lund 210; OCl 493; C0610+070
NGC 2194	cl	06 13 46	+12 48.4	Ori	II2r	9.0	8.5	194	13.0	13.3	2655	11	96	4	Aliases: Cr 87; Lund 211; Mel 43; OCl 485; Raab 33; (4) IRAS 06108+1248; C0611+128

Table 4.1: Catalog of Clusters and Asterisms in the Milky Way, and Objects Misidentified as Such

Name	Type	2000.0 R.A.	Dec.	Con.	Tr. Type	Diam. (′)	Tot. Vm	#str	Bt* Vm	V Sur	Dist. (pc)	S #	2U #	Ref	Comments and Aliases
NGC 2198	nf?	06 13.9	+01 00	Ori					10			11	116	53	See notes. Nothing obvious on DSS. Supposedly a cluster between GSC 00131-01266 and 00131-00888.
ESO 425-SC15	cl	06 14.6	–29 22	CMa	III3	5.0						19	154	10	
[EC95] 1	cl	06 14 37.0	+13 49 32	Ori	n	1.3		79			4000	11	96	8	Infrared cluster involved with Sh 2-269. Alias: (4) Sh 2- 269
[DB01] 29	cl?	06 14 45.1	+19 00 28	Ori		2.5						11	76	16	Infrared cluster. [DB01]: Resolved cluster in nebula BFS52, related to IRAS 06117+1901.
Skiff J0614.8+1252	cl	06 14 49	+12 52.0	Ori	II2m	5.0		20				11	96	8	See notes. Discovered by Skiff. 10′ east of NGC 2194.
NGC 2192	cl	06 15 18	+39 51.3	Aur	II2m	5.0	10.9	45	14.0	14.4		5	58	4	Aliases: Cr 86; Lund 212; Mel 42; OCl 437; Raab 32; C0611+398
[PKL98] 8	cl?	06 15 26	+03 50.7	Ori		2.0		6			348	11	116	14	
NGC 2204	cl	06 15 33	–18 40.0	CMa	II2r	10.0	8.6	353	13.0	13.6	4333	11	154	4	Aliases: Cr 88; Lund 213; Mel 44; OCl 572; Raab 34; C0613–186
Teutsch J0616.3+3621	ast?	06 16 22	+36 21.3	Aur	III1m	6.0		50	50			5	58	17	Teutsch: Asterism? Scattered group in moderately rich background.
NGC 2202	cl?	06 16 51	+05 59.8	Ori		7.0		12	9			11	96	4	Skiff: = HD 43511 [double], sparse field.
Collinder 89	cl	06 18.0	+23 38	Gem	IV2p n	60.0	5.7	15		14.6	1300	5	76	8	See notes. Includes 9, 10, 11, and 12 Gem, and IC 444 about 12 Gem. IC 443 is to the south. Aliases: 9-12 Gem; Lund 214; OCl 473; (4) IC 444; OCl 473.0; C0615+236
Skiff J0619.3+1832	cl?	06 19 22	+18 32.5	Ori	III2m	20.0		50				11	76	8	See notes. Discovered by Skiff. Three clumps of stars over a 20′ area. Includes BD+18 1170 (V=8.9, F7IV).
NGC 2220	cl?	06 20 35	–44 40.7	Pup		22.0	7.0	20	7.5	13.7		19	188	99	Archinal: Sparse group of bright stars, with 3 brightest on SE side. Galaxy ESO 255-5 on E side.
NGC 2215	cl	06 20 50	–07 17.0	Mon	II2m	8.0	8.4	40	11.0	12.9	982	11	136	4	Aliases: Cr 90; Lund 215; Mel 45; OCl 550; Raab 35; C0618–072
Collinder 91	cl:	06 21 33	+02 20.3	Mon	IV2p	14.0	6.4	20		12.1		11	116	4	DSFG: Probably not a cluster. Aliases: Lund 216; OCl 519; C0619+023
Berkeley 73	cl	06 22 05	–06 19.1	Mon	I1p	2.0		15	16.0			11	136	99	Archinal: DSS image shows a tiny (1′ long), but impressive, N-S star chain at center. Aliases: Lund 217; OCl 546; C0619–063
Collinder 92	cl	06 22.9	+05 07	Mon		11.0	8.6			13.8		11	116	99	DSFG: Probably not a cluster. Skiff: Not obvious in 0.4 degree field. Archinal: Id? Scattering of stars on DSS. Aliases: Lund 218; OCl 504; C0620+051
Dolidze 22	cl:	06 23.3	+04 39	Mon	IV2p	8.0		10				11	116	4	DSFG: Probably not a cluster. Skiff: Scattered group, center not obvious. Aliases: Lund 219; OCl 508; (4) IRAS 06204+0442; C0620+046
NGC 2219	cl	06 23 42	–04 41.2	Mon		10.0		25	7.30			11	116	99	Archinal: Nice group, including likely non-member HD 44756 (V=6.67, A2V) on W, and HD 44841 (V=7.30, K0) near middle.
NGC 2218	ast	06 24 28	+19 21.6	Gem		1.2		20	11.5			11	76	53	See notes. Triangular asterism, including GSC 1336-00358 (mag. 12.0), 1336-01104 (13.1), and 1336-00698 (11.5).
Alessi J06245-3151	ast	06 24.5	–31 51	CMa		10.0		7	9			19	172	10	
Teutsch J0625.4+1351	ast?	06 25 24	+13 51.9	Ori?	II1p	2.1		35	35			11	96	17	Teutsch: Asterism? Small group of faint stars in rich background. 3′ from Gemini-border. Teutsch J0625.6+1336 nearby.
Bochum 1	cl	06 25 24.9	+19 46 00	Gem		26.0	7.93	8	8.42	15.0	4060	11	76	8	See notes. Not detectable without chart. See Stephenson and Sandeleuk [1971] chart A. Brightest star is LS 44, centered on LS 51. Aliases: Lund 1124; C0622+198
Teutsch J0625.6+1336	cl?	06 25 40	+13 36.2	Gem?	I2m	3.4		70	70			11	96	17	See notes. Teutsch: Cluster? Either coarse group rich in faint stars or faint cluster. Teutsch J0625.4+1351 nearby.
NGC 2225	cl?	06 26 37	–09 38.5	Mon				40				11	136	4	Skiff: [NGC 2225/6] Single well-defined object.
NGC 2226	ptcl	06 26 37	–09 38.5	Mon		0.8						11	136	4	See notes. Core of cluster NGC 2225. Alias: (3) NGC 2225
NGC 2232	cl	06 27 15	–04 45.5	Mon	III2p	53.0	4.2	20	5.03	12.8	363	11	116	99	See notes. Aliases: Cr 93; Lund 220; OCl 545; C0624–047
NGC 2224	cl?	06 27 32.0	+12 39 20	Gem		20.0		20				11	96	99	Archinal: Loose group centered on HD 257536 (B=10.4, G5, from HD catalogue), as W. Herschel indicated.
Teutsch J0628.8+1455	ast?	06 28 50	+14 55.1	Gem	IV2p	3.0		40	40			11	96	17	Teutsch: Asterism? Scattered faint group in similarly rich background.

Table 4.1: Catalog of Clusters and Asterisms in the Milky Way, and Objects Misidentified as Such

Name	Type	2000.0 R.A.	Dec.	Con.	Tr. Type	Diam. (′)	Tot. Vm	#str	Bt* Vm	V Sur	Dist. (pc)	S #	2U #	Ref	Comments and Aliases
NGC 2234	cl?	06 29 29.2	+16 43 08	Gem		35.0		50	11			11	96	99	Archinal: Large (35′) sparse cluster, centered on HD 258165, with brightest star HD 45688 (V=7.88, G5, double). HD 45951 to NE.
NGC 2243	cl	06 29 35	−31 16.9	CMa	I2r	8.3	9.4	368	11.79	14.0	4117	19	172	4	See notes. Aliases: Cr 98; Lund 222; Mel 46; OCl 644; Raab 36; C0627−312
NGC 2236	cl	06 29 40	+06 49.8	Mon	II2m	8.0	8.5	243	12.0	13.0	3327	11	96	54	Aliases: Cr 94; Lund 221; OCl 501; OCl 501.0; C0627+068
Collinder 96	cl	06 30.3	+02 52	Mon	IV2p	12.0	7.3	15	8.75	12.7	1127	12	116	99	Skiff: DSS overlap region. Archinal: Collinder plate 4 image is flipped east to west. Aliases: Lund 224; OCl 523; C0627+029
Alessi 14	cl?	06 30 27	+09 44.5	Mon		1.4		8				12	96	99	
Cl van den Bergh 80	cl	06 30 50	−09 39.3	Mon	I2p n	2.0		6				12	136	4	Skiff: (= HD 46060?). Aliases: OCl 553.1; C0628−096
Collinder 95	cl	06 30 51.2	+09 56 37	Mon	III2p n	27.0		10				12	96	99	Archinal: DSS shows a rich scattering of stars in nebulosity. Collinder plate 4 image is flipped left to right. Aliases: Lund 225; OCl 491; OCl 491.0; C0627+099
Czernik 26	cl	06 30 58	−04 11.6	Mon	III1m	5.0		35				12	116	4	Aliases: Lund 226; OCl 544; C0628−041
Collinder 97	cl	06 30 58.1	+05 49 30	Mon	IV2p	25.0	5.4	15		12.4		12	96	99	Archinal: DSS shows order 8 bright stars, trending E-SE to W-NW. Aliases: Lund 228; OCl 506; OCl 506.0; C0628+059
Teutsch J0631.9+1151	cl?	06 31 54	+11 51.8	Mon?	II1p	1.5		15	15			12	96	17	See notes. Teutsch: Cluster? Compact group, but not very rich. Fainter stars to SW look like irregular background.
NGC 2237	neb	06 31 55.5	+04 56 34	Mon		80.0						12	116	9	See notes. The Rosette Nebula (not a cluster). Contains C0629+049 = NGC 2244. Avoid use of C0627+050. Aliases: (5) OCl 511; (4) NGC 2244; (4) C0629+049; (4) NGC 2239; (4) Mel 47; (4) Cr 99; (4) OCl 515; (4) Lund 229; OCl 511.0; Caldw 49; C0627+050
NGC 2244	cl	06 32 19	+04 51.4	Mon	II3r n	30.0	4.8	100	7.0	12.2	1502	12	116	4	See notes. Cluster in Rosette Nebula (NGC 2237). DSFG: The brightest star is a non-member. Skiff: = 12 Mon = HD 46241. Aliases: NGC 2239; Mel 47; Cr 99; (5) OCl 512; OCl 515; Lund 229; (5) Lund 227; (4) NGC 2237; Mrk 15; OCl 512.0; Caldw 50; C0629+049
NGC 2240	cl??	06 33 11	+35 15.0	Aur								5	58	4	Skiff: Sparse group.
Berkeley 23	cl	06 33 15	+20 31.8	Gem	III1m	4.0		25	15.0			5	76	4	Aliases: Lund 231; OCl 478; C0630+205
NGC 2250	ast?	06 33 47	−05 05.3	Mon		10.0		25	8.74			12	116	99	Archinal: Oblong (E-W) 10′ x 5.5′ group, with HD 46576 (8.74, A0) on NE side (as J. Herschel indicated). Alias: h 394
Basel 8	cl	06 34.2	+08 05	Mon	IV3m n	30.0		50			1300	12	96	4	Skiff: Too sparse. Aliases: Lund 398; OCl 499.1; C0631+081
NGC 2252	cl	06 34 19.8	+05 19 22	Mon	III2m n	18.0	7.7	30	9.0	14.0		12	116	99	Archinal: DSS shows obvious N-S stream of bright stars, with large bright nebula involved on SW side. Aliases: Cr 102; Lund 233; OCl 514; (4) IRAS 06323+0527; C0632+054
NGC 2248	ast	06 34.6	+26 19	Gem				4				5	76	99	Skiff: Double star? Archinal: Id? Triple star?
NGC 2251	cl	06 34 39	+08 22.0	Mon	III2m	10.0	7.3	92	9.10	12.3	1556	12	96	4	Skiff: Sparse. Aliases: Cr 101; Lund 232; OCl 499; C0632+084
NGC 2254	cl	06 35 46.6	+07 40 15	Mon	I1m	6.0	9.1	93	12.0	13.0	2109	12	96	99	Aliases: Cr 103; Lund 234; OCl 500; C0633+077
[AO84] VII	mc	06.6	+09.0	Mon		10000.	-1.51	31	-1.47			12	95	54	Very large moving cluster hypothesized by Agekyan and Orlov [1984]. Includes Sirius (α CMa), and may be part of Cr 285. Alias: (3) Cr 285
ESO 426-SC26	cl	06 36.3	−30 51	CMa	II2	4.0						19	172	10	
Basel 7	cl	06 36 19	+08 20.4	Mon	IV1p	5.0	8.5	139	10.35	12.0	1578	12	95	4	Aliases: Lund 1125; OCl 499.2; C0633+084
Ruprecht 1	cl	06 36.4	−14 09	CMa	III1p	6.0		15	11.0			12	135	4	Skiff: Okay, sparse. Aliases: Lund 236; OCl 563; C0634−141
Collinder 104	cl	06 36.5	+04 50	Mon	IV2p n	20.0	9.6	15		16.1		12	115	99	Archinal: Appears mostly as loose 20′ long “integral sign” chain of stars. Aliases: Lund 235; OCl 517; OCl 517.0; C0633+048
Trumpler 5	cl	06 36 31	+09 28.9	Mon	III1r n	15.0	10.9	150	17.0	16.8	977	12	95	4	DSFG: Fairly even distribution. Aliases: Cr 105; Lund 237; OCl 494; C0634+094
Cl van den Bergh 1	cl	06 37 05	+03 03.8	Mon	III1p	5.0	9.5	39		13.0	1700	12	115	4	See notes. Skiff: = CV Mon = GSC 0150-0121. Aliases: Lund 238; OCl 527; CV Mon cl; C0634+031
Collinder 106	cl	06 37.1	+05 58	Mon	IV2p	35.0	4.6	20		12.3		12	95	1	Aliases: Lund 239; OCl 510; (4) IRAS 06346+0600; WB89 846; C0634+060
Collinder 107	cl	06 37.7	+04 45	Mon	IV2p	30.0	5.1	204	7.14	12.5	1738	12	115	52	DSFG: Probably not a cluster. Aliases: Lund 240; OCl 518; OCl 518.0; C0635+047
Berkeley 24	cl	06 37 47	−00 52.7	Mon	III1p	6.0		25	17.0			12	115	54	See notes. Aliases: OCl 539; Lund 241; WB89 848; (5) IRAS 06351−0055; C0635−008
NGC 2260	cl?	06 38 04	−01 28.4	Mon		20.0		50	8			12	115	4	

Table 4.1: Catalog of Clusters and Asterisms in the Milky Way, and Objects Misidentified as Such

Name	Type	2000.0 R.A.	Dec.	Con.	Tr. Type	Diam. (′)	Tot. Vm	#str	Bt* Vm	V Sur	Dist. (pc)	S #	2U #	Ref	Comments and Aliases
NGC 2259	cl	06 38 33.3	+10 52 57	Mon	II1p n	3.5	10.8	25	14.0	13.5		12	95	99	Aliases: Cr 108; Lund 244; Mel 48; OCl 492; Raab 37; C0635+109
Collinder 110	cl	06 38 39	+02 03.3	Mon	IV1r	18.0	10.5	70	11.04	16.8	1950	12	115	8	Skiff: Position from "study-area center" of [Dawson & Ianna, 1998]. Aliases: Lund 243; OCl 530; OCl 530.0; C0635+020
Collinder 111	cl	06 38.7	+06 55	Mon		3.2	7.0			9.5		12	95	99	DSFG: Probably not a cluster. Skiff: Not obvious in 0.3 degree field. Archinal: Id? DSS shows 2 bright stars, scattering of fainter stars. Aliases: Lund 245; OCl 505; C0636+069
NGC 2262	cl	06 39 38.7	+01 08 30	Mon	II2r	4.0	11.3	180		14.3		12	115	8	See notes. Has inner compressed part 2′ in diameter with ~80 stars. Aliases: H. VII.37; h 400; GC 1438; Cr 109; OCl 531; Lund 242; C0635+012
Cl van den Bergh 83	cl	06 40.0	−27 18	CMa	III2p n	25.0		10				19	154	4	Skiff: Not obvious in 0.4 degree field. Aliases: Cl vdB 84; Lund 1165; OCl 626.1; C0638−272
NGC 2264	cl	06 40 59	+09 53.7	Mon	III3m n	40.0	4.1	40	5.0	12.1	794	12	95	4	Skiff: = S Mon = HD 47839. Aliases: Cr 112; Lund 246; Mel 49; OCl 495; Mrk 16; C0638+099
Ruprecht 2	cl:	06 41 01	−29 33.0	CMa	IV2p	3.0		10	12.0			19	172	4	Aliases: Lund 248; OCl 643; C0639−295
Berkeley 25	cl	06 41 14	−16 28.9	CMa	I2m	7.0		40	16.0			11	135	4	Aliases: Lund 247; OCl 576; C0638−164
NGC 2265	cl??	06 41.5	+11 56	Gem?				30	12			12	95	4	Skiff: Not obvious in 0.4 degree field.
Ruprecht 3	cl	06 42 06	−29 27.2	CMa	III1p	3.0		15	11.0			19	154	4	Aliases: Lund 249; OCl 642; C0640−294
NGC 2253	cl?	06 42.6	+66 24	Cam		3.0		15				1	15	53	See notes. Identification of NGC 2253 is uncertain. Assumed here to be small group observed by A. Ling.
Alessi 15	cl	06 43 04	+01 40.3	Mon		0.9		11				12	115	99	
Dolidze 23	cl	06 43 05.7	+00 01 19	Mon	IV3p	10.0		20				12	115	99	Archinal: DSS shows pentagon shaped sparse group of stars. Aliases: Lund 251; OCl 538; OCl 538.0; C0640+000
NGC 2269	cl	06 43 16.8	+04 37 04	Mon	II1p	3.0	10.0	12	10.0	12.4	1439	12	115	51	Archinal: Position poor in most catalogues. Measured here from DSS. Aliases: Cr 114; Lund 252; OCl 524; C0641+046
NGC 2266	cl	06 43 20	+26 58.2	Gem	II2m	5.0	9.5	50	11.0	13.0	3400	5	76	4	Aliases: Cr 113; Lund 250; Mel 50; OCl 471; Raab 38; C0640+270
Alessi 16	cl	06 43 35	+02 10.4	Mon		0.5		9				12	115	99	Archinal: Tiny nebulous cluster on DSS.
NGC 2270	cl??	06 43.9	+03 26	Mon								12	115	3	
Teutsch J0643.9+0123	cl?	06 43 55	+01 23.9	Mon	II2p	1.6		30	30			12	115	17	Teutsch: Likely cluster, fairly compact, bright star HD 289038 (VT=9.99, Tycho-mag., A2) on south side (meteor on DSS image).
Dolidze 24	cl	06 44 44	+01 45.0	Mon	IV2m	15.0		40				12	115	4	Skiff: Sparse group. Aliases: Lund 253; OCl 533; OCl 533.0; C0641+016
Dolidze 25	cl:	06 45.0	+00 18	Mon	IV1m n	20.0	7.6	50	8.87	14.1	5248	12	115	4	Skiff: Large V-shaped group, position okay. Aliases: Lund 254; OCl 537; C0642+003
NGC 2287	cl	06 46.1	−20 46	CMa	I3r	39.0	4.5	80	8	12.5	642	19	154	3	See notes. M 41. Aliases: Cr 118; Lund 256; M 41; Mel 52; OCl 597; Raab 40; OCl 597.0; C0644−206
Collinder 115	cl	06 46 40	+01 46.7	Mon	IV2m	10.0	9.2	50		14.2		12	115	4	Aliases: Lund 255; OCl 535; C0643+018
Cl van den Bergh 85	cl	06 46 52	+01 18.9	Mon	I2p n	4.0		15				12	115	4	See notes. Nebulosity is NGC 2282 = IC 2172 = BFS 54. Skiff: [Star and nebula are:] = HD 289120 = vdB 85 = IC 2172 = [NGC 2282]. Aliases: OCl 535.1; Lund 1160; (4) NGC 2282; C0644+013
NGC 2286	cl	06 47 41	−03 08.9	Mon	III2m	15.0	7.5	80	9.0	13.4	1271	12	115	4	Aliases: Cr 117; Lund 257; OCl 548; C0645−031
NGC 2277	cl??	06 47.8	+33 26	Gem								5	58	4	Skiff: Not obvious in 0.4 degree field, = nearby double star?
NGC 2281	cl	06 48 18	+41 04.7	Aur	I3m	25.0	5.4	119	8.0	12.4	461	5	41	4	Skiff: = Center of trapezium. Aliases: Cr 116; Lund 259; Mel 51; OCl 446; Raab 39; C0645+411
Bochum 2	cl	06 48 50	+00 22.6	Mon	I1p	1.5	9.7	10	10.86	10.6	5370	12	115	4	Skiff: = BD+0 1617 (triple). Aliases: Lund 1126; C0646+004
Ruprecht 4	cl	06 48 57	−10 31.0	Mon	III2m	6.0		40	14.0			12	135	4	Aliases: Be 74; Lund 258; OCl 560; C0646−104
NGC 2298	gcl	06 48 59.2	−36 00 19	Pup		5.0	9.3		13.4	12.8	10100	19	172	6	Aliases: EQ 0647−359; C0647−359
Berkeley 75	cl	06 49 00	−23 59.8	CMa	II2p	4.0		25	16.0			19	154	4	Aliases: Lund 260; OCl 614; C0647−239
NGC 2284	??	06 49.1	+33 13	Gem								5	58	99	Skiff: Not obvious in 0.4 degree field. Archinal: Id?
NGC 2285	??	06 49.4	+33 21	Gem								5	58	99	Skiff: Not obvious in 0.4 degree field. Archinal: Id?
Biurakan 12	cl:	06 50 16	+05 43.7	Mon	III1m	4.0		30	17.0			12	95	4	Aliases: Be 26; Lund 261; OCl 520; C0647+058
ESO 309-SC03	cl	06 50.7	−42 23	Pup	II2	6.0						19	188	10	
NGC 2299	nf?	06 51.1	−07 00	Mon								12	135	4	Skiff: Not obvious in 0.4 degree field.

Table 4.1: Catalog of Clusters and Asterisms in the Milky Way, and Objects Misidentified as Such

Name	Type	2000.0 R.A.	Dec.	Con.	Tr. Type	Diam. (′)	Tot. Vm	#str	Bt* Vm	V Sur	Dist. (pc)	S #	2U #	Ref	Comments and Aliases
Biurakan 11	cl	06 51 21	+05 46.1	Mon	III1p	2.0		25	15.0		8000	12	95	4	Aliases: Be 27; Lund 262; OCl 521; C0648+058
NGC 2301	cl	06 51 46	+00 27.6	Mon	I3r	15.0	6.0	80	8.0	11.9	755	12	115	4	Skiff: = BD+0 1660. Aliases: Cr 119; Lund 263; Mel 54; OCl 540; Raab 41; OCl 540.0; C0649+005
NGC 2302	cl	06 51 54	−07 05.0	Mon	III2m	5.0	8.9	30	12.0	12.4	1076	12	135	4	Aliases: Lund 264; OCl 554; OCl 554.0; C0649−070
Biurakan 10	cl	06 52 07	+02 55.0	Mon	I1p	3.0	10.4	20	15.0	12.8	6194	12	115	4	DSFG: Probably not a cluster. Aliases: Be 28; OCl 532; C0649+030
Ruprecht 149	cl:	06 52.2	−23 36	CMa	III2p	5.0		25	13.0			19	154	99	Skiff: Not obvious in 0.4 degree field. Archinal: Id? One of groups just to N and just to E? Large ghost star images interferring on DSS. Aliases: Lund 266; OCl 613; C0650−235
Berkeley 29	cl	06 53 04	+16 55.7	Gem	I1p	2.0		20	15.0			12	95	54	Aliases: OCl 486; Lund 267; (5) MCG +03-18-002; (5) UGC 3583; (5) Z 85-13; (5) Z 0650.2+1659; C0650+169
NGC 2306	cl?	06 54.6	−07 21	Mon		20.0		27	8			12	135	99	Skiff: Not obvious in 0.4 degree field. Archinal: Id?
NGC 2304	cl	06 55 12	+17 59.3	Gem	II1m	3.0	10.0	30		12.4		12	76	4	Aliases: Cr 120; Lund 269; Mel 55; OCl 484; Raab 42; C0652+180
Ruprecht 5	cl:	06 55 24	−18 43.8	CMa	IV1p	2.0		10	13.0			12	154	4	Skiff: Sparse group. Aliases: Lund 270; OCl 591; C0653−186
NGC 2309	cl	06 56 04	−07 10.5	Mon	I2m	5.0	10.5	40	13.0	14.0		12	135	4	Aliases: Cr 122; Lund 272; Mel 56; OCl 557; Raab 43; C0653−071
Ruprecht 6	cl	06 56 05	−13 15.1	CMa	III1p	1.0		10				12	135	4	Aliases: Lund 271; OCl 569; C0653−132
Collinder 121	cl	06 56 20.0	−24 43 46	CMa	IV3p	50.0	2.6	33	3.79	11.1	628	19	154	99	See notes. Archinal: DSS shows 5 bright stars and a scattering of fainter ones over a 30′ to 50′ diameter field. Aliases: Lund 268; OCl 619; OCl 619.0; C0652−245
Biurakan 7	cl	06 57 37	+08 17.3	Mon	II1m	4.0		30	14.0		4000	12	95	4	Aliases: Be 31; Lund 273; OCl 513; C0654+083
Biurakan 9	cl	06 57 46	+03 13.7	Mon	II2m	3.0		30	15.0			12	115	4	Aliases: Be 30; Lund 277; OCl 534; C0655+032
NGC 2311	cl	06 57 48	−04 36.7	Mon	III2m	7.0	9.6	50	12.0	13.8		12	115	4	Aliases: Cr 123; Lund 276; OCl 553; C0655−045
Ruprecht 7	cl	06 57 50	−13 13.2	CMa	II2m	3.0		30	14.0			12	135	4	Aliases: Be 33; Lund 275; OCl 570; C0655−131
Biurakan 8	cl	06 58 07	+06 25.9	Mon	II2r	5.0		70	14.0		9000	12	95	4	Aliases: Be 32; Lund 278; OCl 522; C0655+065
NGC 2312	cl??	06 58 48	+10 17.7	Mon								12	95	4	Skiff: Sparse group.
NGC 2318	ast?	06 59 28	−13 41.9	CMa					8			12	135	4	Skiff: = HD 52133 (V=8.3, F0V), sparse group around it.
Alessi J06594-1027	ast?	06 59 29.9	−10 27 10	Mon		7.0		25				12	135	8	Alessi: Nice group of B stars. Like many ESO clusters. Somewhat elongated E-W. Easy.
Biurakan 13	cl	07 00 22	−00 14.1	Mon	IV1p	2.0		20	17.0			12	115	4	See notes. Aliases: Be 34; Lund 280; OCl 543; C0657−001
Tombaugh 1	cl	07 00 27	−20 34.2	CMa	III1m	6.0		45	14.0		1259	19	154	4	Aliases: Haf 1; Lund 279; OCl 603; C0658−204
NGC 2319	ast?	07 00 37	+03 06.1	Mon		16.0		12	8.93			12	115	99	Archinal: Scattered group of brighter stars just as J. Herschel (and mostly as W. Herschel) described it. HD 52377 (V=8.93, B8) brightest. Aliases: H. VIII.1B; h 423
Ruprecht 8	cl:	07 01 46	−13 32.7	CMa	IV1p	3.0		10	12.0			12	135	4	Skiff: Sparse group? Aliases: Lund 281; OCl 573; C0659−135
Ruprecht 9	ast	07 01.9	−21 55	CMa								19	154	99	Archinal: Id? DSS shows one brighter star and a scattering of others. Aliases: OCl 610; C0659−218
NGC 2323	cl	07 02 47.8	−08 22 33	Mon	II3r	15.0	5.9	80	9.0	11.8	1023	12	135	52	See notes. M 50. Skiff: Center star is BD −08°1700. Aliases: Cr 124; Lund 283; M 50; Mel 58; OCl 559; Raab 45; OCl 559.0; C0700−082
NGC 2348	cl?	07 03 02.7	−67 23 39	Vol		11.0		30	9.9			24	211	53	Center and brightest star is HD 54266. Anonymous galaxy located 7′ to north (at $07^h\,02^m\,54.0^s$ −67° 16′ 35″).
Tombaugh 2	cl	07 03 06	−20 49.1	CMa	I1m	3.0		50	16.0		13183	19	154	4	Aliases: Haf 2; Lund 285; OCl 605; C0701−207
Czernik 27	cl	07 03 19	+06 24.0	Mon	III1p	3.0		15				12	95	4	Skiff: Maybe. Aliases: Lund 284; OCl 526; C0700+064
Bochum 3	cl	07 03 28	−05 00.3	Mon	IV1p	4.0	9.9	25	11.19	12.9	1762	12	115	4	Skiff: = HD 296184. Aliases: Lund 112; C0700−050
Cl van den Bergh 92	cl	07 03 55	−11 34.5	CMa	IV2p	3.0		12				12	135	4	Skiff: = BD-11 1763 (V=9.0, Be). Aliases: Lund 1162; OCl 566.1; C0701−114
NGC 2324	cl	07 04 08	+01 02.7	Mon	II2r	8.0	8.4	133	12.0	12.9	3185	12	115	4	Aliases: Cr 125; Lund 287; Mel 59; OCl 542; Raab 46; C0701+011
Haffner 3	cl	07 04 08	−06 07.1	Mon	III2p	5.0		20	14.0			12	135	4	Skiff: Sparse group. Aliases: Lund 286; OCl 556; C0701−060
Auner 1	cl	07 04 15.3	−19 44 44	CMa	III2m	3.0		30			4400	12	154	99	Behind ghost reflection of Sirius on POSS. Aliases: Lund 379; (4) IRAS 07020−1939; ESO 558-SC8; C0702−196
Ruprecht 150	cl	07 05 55	−28 24.5	CMa	II2p	2.0		12	13.0			19	154	4	Skiff: Small group. Two galaxies in 9′ field. Aliases: Lund 288; OCl 648; C0703−283

Table 4.1: Catalog of Clusters and Asterisms in the Milky Way, and Objects Misidentified as Such

Name	Type	2000.0 R.A.	Dec.	Con.	Tr. Type	Diam. (′)	Tot. Vm	#str	Bt* Vm	V Sur	Dist. (pc)	S #	2U #	Ref	Comments and Aliases
Haffner 4	cl	07 06 04	−15 00.2	CMa	III1m	5.0		30	14.0			12	135	4	Aliases: Lund 289; OCl 583; C0703−149
ESO 427-SC32	cl	07 06.2	−30 10	CMa	III3	10.0						19	172	10	
Ruprecht 10	cl:	07 06 27.6	−20 06 32	CMa	III1p	7.0		40	12.0			19	154	51	Position, diameter, number of stars determined from DSS. Aliases: Lund 290; OCl 604; C0704−200
Berkeley 76	cl	07 06 40	−11 44.0	CMa	IV1m	5.0		40	16.0			12	135	4	Aliases: Lund 291; OCl 568; C0704−115
NGC 2335	cl	07 06 50	−10 01.7	Mon	III2m n	7.0	7.2	57	10.0	11.4	1022	12	135	4	Aliases: Cr 127; Lund 292; Mel 60; OCl 562; Raab 47; C0704−100
Collinder 465	ast	07 06 52	−10 32.3	Mon	IV2p	9.0	10.1p			14.9		12	135	4	DSFG: Probably not a cluster. Aliases: OCl 564; C0704−105
Collinder 466	cl	07 06 56	−10 42.9	Mon	IV1p n	4.0	11.1	25	11.1p	14.1		12	135	4	Aliases: Lund 296; OCl 566; C0704−107
NGC 2331	cl	07 07 01	+27 15.8	Gem	IV2m	19.0	8.5	30	9.0	14.9		5	76	99	Archinal: Includes 1′ oval asterism of 7 stars on SE (noted by J. Herschel) at 07 07 32 +27 11.2. Aliases: Cr 126; OCl 475; C0704+274
Ruprecht 12	cl:	07 07 10	−28 09.1	CMa	IV1p	5.0		20	14.0			19	154	4	Skiff: Nice galaxy in field (MCG -5-17-07). Aliases: Lund 297; OCl 647; C0705−281
Ruprecht 11	cl	07 07 23	−20 47.1	CMa	III2p	5.0		25	11.0			19	154	51	Position, number of stars determined from DSS. Aliases: Lund 298; OCl 607; (4) IRAS 07051−2042; C0705−207
NGC 2338	ast?	07 07 48	−05 43.2	Mon								12	135	4	Skiff: Identification uncertain. Nice small cluster.
Ruprecht 13	cl	07 08.0	−25 52	CMa	IV2p	6.0		15	13.0			19	154	4	Skiff: Sparse group. Aliases: Lund 299; OCl 631; C0705−257
NGC 2343	cl	07 08 07	−10 37.0	Mon	II2p n	6.0	6.7	55	8.0	10.6	870	12	135	4	Aliases: Cr 128; Lund 300; OCl 565; C0705−105
NGC 2345	cl	07 08 19	−13 11.6	CMa	II3r	12.0	7.7	70	9.0	13.1	1754	12	135	4	Aliases: Cr 129; Lund 301; Mel 61; OCl 575; Raab 48; OCl 575.0; C0706−130
[DB01] 35	cl?	07 08 39.0	−04 19 07	Mon		0.6						12	115	16	Infrared cluster. [DB01]: Mostly unresolved cluster in HII region IC 466=Sh 2-288.
Haffner 23	cl	07 09.5	−16 56	CMa	IV2m	11.0		40	13.0			12	135	99	Skiff: Not obvious in 0.4 degree field. Archinal: Several star chains appear on DSS image here. Aliases: Lund 302; OCl 590; C0707−168
Berkeley 35	cl	07 09 54	+02 43.8	CMi	IV1p	5.0		20	16.0			12	115	4	Aliases: Lund 305; OCl 541; C0708+028
NGC 2349	cl??	07 10.0	−08 37	Mon		10.0						12	135	99	Skiff: Not obvious in 0.4 degree field. Archinal: Id?
NGC 2314	gal	07 10 32.4	+75 19 38	Cam		1.7	12.19			13.3		1	6	51	See notes. This is a galaxy that has been incorrectly identifed as a cluster in the past. The use of "C0703+753" should be avoided. Aliases: UGC 3677; PGC 20305; (5) Mel 57; (5) Raab 44; (5) OCl 374; C0703+753
NGC 2351	ast?	07 13.5	−10 29	Mon								12	135	4	Skiff: Not obvious in 0.4 degree field.
NGC 2352	cl??	07 13.6	−24 06	CMa								19	154	99	Skiff: Not obvious in 0.4 degree field. Archinal: Id?
NGC 2354	cl	07 14 16	−25 41.5	CMa	III2r	18.0	6.5	297	9.13	12.8	1795	19	154	4	Aliases: Cr 131; Lund 306; OCl 639; OCl 639.0; C0712−256
NGC 2353	cl	07 14 31	−10 16.0	Mon	III3p	18.0	7.1	106	9.0	13.4	1038	12	135	4	Aliases: Cr 130; Lund 308; Mel 62; OCl 567; Raab 49; OCl 567.0; EQ 0712−1026; C0712−102
Ruprecht 14	cl	07 14 55	−31 21.6	CMa	IV1p	3.0		10	13.0			19	172	4	Skiff: Small group. Aliases: Lund 309; OCl 672; C0713−312
Collinder 132	cl	07 15 21.1	−30 41 00	CMa	III3p	80.0	3.8	25		13.3	411	19	172	99	Archinal: Centered on bright star HD 56342 (V=5.341, B3V). DSS shows large ghost reflection image over the SW side of this group. Aliases: Lund 307; OCl 671; C0712−310
Berkeley 36	cl	07 16 23	−13 11.6	CMa	III1m	3.0		40	17.0			12	135	4	Aliases: Lund 310; OCl 577; C0713−130
Alessi 3	cl	07 16 29	−46 41.1	Pup		72.0						19	187	99	
NGC 2358	cl??	07 16.8	−17 03	CMa								12	135	99	Skiff: Not obvious in 0.4 degree field. Archinal: Id? Possibly N-S group of stars W of this position?
NGC 2355	cl	07 17 00	+13 45.0	Gem	II2m	8.0	9.7	40	13.0	14.2		12	95	4	Aliases: Cr 133; Lund 311; Mel 63; OCl 496; Raab 50; (4) IRAS 07139+1351; C0714+138
ESO 367-SC10	cl	07 17.1	−35 17	Pup	III3	3.0						19	172	10	
Basel 11a	cl	07 17 08	−13 58.4	CMa	II3m	5.0	8.2	89	10.90	11.7	1514	12	135	4	See notes. Aliases: Lund 1163; OCl 584.1; Bas 11A; C0714−138
NGC 2356	ast?	07 17.2	+13 58	Gem				4	7			12	95	99	Skiff: Not obvious in 0.4 degree field. Archinal: Id?
Collinder 135	cl	07 17 24.5	−36 50 30	Pup	IV2p	49.0	2.1	77	2.71	10.6		19	172	99	DSFG: Without brightest star, visual magnitude = 3.0. Archinal: DSS shows this cluster includes a group of 5 bright stars over a 38′ area. Aliases: Lund 312; OCl 700; C0715−367
NGC 2360	cl	07 17 44	−15 38.5	CMa	I3r	14.0	7.2	91	10.36	12.9	1143	12	135	4	Aliases: Cr 134; Lund 313; Mel 64; OCl 589; Raab 51; Caldw 58; C0715−155
ESO 559-SC02	cl	07 18.1	−18 36	CMa	I3	1.2						12	154	10	
Haffner 5	cl	07 18.1	−22 39	CMa	II2m	7.0		50	15.0			19	154	4	Skiff: Not obvious in 0.2 or 0.4 degree field. Aliases: Lund 314; OCl 624; C0716−225

Table 4.1: Catalog of Clusters and Asterisms in the Milky Way, and Objects Misidentified as Such

Name	Type	2000.0 R.A.	Dec.	Con.	Tr. Type	Diam. (′)	Tot. Vm	#str	Bt* Vm	V Sur	Dist. (pc)	S #	2U #	Ref	Comments and Aliases
NGC 2362	cl	07 18 42	−24 57.3	CMa	I3r	6.0	3.8	60	8.0	7.7	1570	19	154	4	Skiff: = τ Canis Majoris.; Moore: Tau CMa Cluster. Aliases: Cr 136; Lund 315; Mel 65; OCl 633; Raab 52; Mrk 17; Tau CMa cl; OCl 633.0; Caldw 64; C0716–248
Ruprecht 15	cl	07 19 34	−19 37.6	CMa	II1p	2.0		20	12.0			12	154	4	Skiff: Small group. Aliases: Lund 316; OCl 609; (4) IRAS 07174–1935; C0717–195
Haffner 6	cl	07 20 01	−13 09.5	CMa	IV2r n	7.0	9.2	66	16.0	13.4	1122	12	135	4	Skiff: Low contrast against sky. Aliases: Lund 317; OCl 582; (4) IRAS 07176–1304; C0717–130
NGC 2367	cl	07 20 05	−21 53.0	CMa	II3m	5.0	7.9	30	9.39	11.4	2858	19	153	4	Skiff: = HD 57370AB. Aliases: Cr 137; Lund 318; OCl 621; C0718–218
Berkeley 37	cl	07 20 18	−00 59.8	Mon	III1p	4.0		25	15.0			12	115	4	Aliases: Lund 319; OCl 551; C0717–010
NGC 2364	cl?	07 20 47	−07 33.0	Mon								12	135	4	Skiff: Asterism, but real object.
SSWZ94 1	cl	07 20 56.3	+01 48 41	CMi		2.0						12	115	99	
NGC 2368	cl	07 21 02.2	−10 22 28	Mon	IV1p	3.0	11.8	15		14.2		12	135	99	Skiff: Not obvious in 0.4 degree field. Archinal: Appears on the DSS as small upside-down "Y" group of about 16 stars. Aliases: Cr 138; Lund 320; OCl 571; C0718–102
Berkeley 77	cl	07 21 28	−03 14.0	Mon	I2m	5.0		30	13.0			12	115	4	Aliases: Lund 321; OCl 555; C0719–032
Czernik 28	cl	07 21.8	−00 59	Mon	III2p	5.0		20				12	115	4	See notes. Czernik 28 name preferred over King 23 (discovered 1965 and rediscovered 1966 respectively). Skiff: Okay, sparse cluster. Aliases: King 23; OCl 552; Lund 322; C0719–008
Haffner 7	cl	07 22 54	−29 29.8	CMa	I2m	3.0		40	14.0			19	153	4	Aliases: Lund 323; OCl 661; vdB-Ha 1; C0721–294
Haffner 8	cl	07 23 03	−12 17.8	CMa	II2m	5.0	9.1	71	12.0	12.6	1632	12	135	4	Aliases: Lund 325; OCl 578; C0721–122
Ruprecht 16	cl	07 23 09	−19 28.7	CMa	IV1p	4.0		15	13.0			12	153	4	DSFG: Probably not a cluster. Skiff: Sparse group. Aliases: Lund 324; OCl 612; C0721–193
Ruprecht 17	cl	07 23 35	−23 11.3	CMa	II1p	3.0		15	12.0			19	153	4	Skiff: Sparse group. Aliases: Lund 326; OCl 627; (4) IRAS 07213–2307; C0721–231
Berkeley 78	cl	07 23 38	+05 22.4	CMi	II1p	5.0		12	16.0			12	115	99	Archinal: HD 57838 (V=8.0, K2) just to W. Aliases: Lund 329; OCl 536; C0721+054
NGC 2374	cl	07 23 57	−13 15.8	CMa	IV2p	12.0	8.0	73	10.74	13.4	1211	12	135	4	Aliases: Cr 139; Lund 328; OCl 585; C0721–131
Collinder 140	cl	07 24 26.7	−31 51 00	CMa	III3m	60.0	3.5	76	5.36	12.4	376	19	171	99	Archinal: DSS shows scattered E-NE to S-SW trending 55′ group of 8 or so bright stars, with more cluster stars in background. Aliases: Lund 327; OCl 679; vdB-Ha 2; C0722–321
Ruprecht 18	cl	07 24 39	−26 11.3	CMa	III1m	8.0	9.4	40	12.0	13.9	1028	19	153	4	Aliases: Lund 331; OCl 646; C0722–261
NGC 2383	cl	07 24 40	−20 56.9	CMa	II3m	5.0	8.4	40	9.76	11.9	1968	19	153	4	Aliases: Cr 141; Lund 332; OCl 616; C0722–208
Haffner 9	cl	07 24 42	−16 59.4	CMa	I1m	4.0		35	14.0			12	135	4	Aliases: Lund 330; OCl 600; C0722–169
NGC 2384	cl	07 25 12	−21 01.4	CMa	IV3p	5.0	7.4	15	8.58	10.9	3266	19	153	4	Skiff: = HD 58509 (V=8.6, B2III/IV). Aliases: Cr 142; Cr 143; Lund 333; OCl 618; C0722–209
Ruprecht 19	cl:	07 25.6	−21 30	CMa	IV1p	5.0		20	13.0			19	153	99	Skiff: Not obvious in 0.3 degree field. Archinal: Id? Aliases: Lund 334; OCl 622; C0723–214
Waterloo 7	cl	07 26 08.0	−15 05 39	CMa		1.3		13	9.24		2800	12	135	8	Brightest star is LS 402 (V=9.24, B2Ib/II). Also contains LS 397 and LS 399.
Melotte 66	cl	07 26 19	−47 40.8	Pup	II1r	15.0	7.8	821	11.41	13.7	2876	19	187	4	Aliases: Cr 147; Lund 336; OCl 739; Raab 53; C0724–476
Trumpler 6	cl	07 26 23	−24 12.7	CMa	III2p	6.0	10.0			13.9		19	153	4	Aliases: Cr 145; Lund 335; OCl 638; C0724–242
Ruprecht 20	cl	07 26 41	−28 49.9	CMa?	III2m	6.0	9.5	30	11.0	13.4	1208	19	153	4	DSFG: Doubtful cluster. Skiff: = HD 58959 (V=8.8, F0V), sparse group. Aliases: Lund 337; OCl 659; C0724–287
Ruprecht 21	cl	07 27.1	−31 10	Pup?	III1m	11.0			11.0			19	171	99	Skiff: Not obvious in 0.15 or 0.4 degree field. Archinal: Id? DSS shows a slight concentration of stars in a rich field. Aliases: Lund 339; OCl 675; C0725–310
NGC 2395	cl	07 27 13	+13 36.5	Gem	IV2m	15.0	8.0	53	9.96	13.9	1180	12	95	4	Skiff: Sparse irregular group. Aliases: Cr 144; Lund 338; OCl 502; C0724+136
Trumpler 7	cl	07 27 21	−23 58.0	Pup?	II3m n	5.0	7.9	30	10.0	11.4	1622	19	153	4	Skiff: Irregular structure. Aliases: Cr 146; Lund 340; OCl 635; C0725–239
Alessi J07279-5141	ast	07 27.9	−51 41	Car		20.0		30	12			24	200	10	
NGC 2396	cl	07 28.0	−11 43	Pup?	IV1m	10.0	7.4	30	11.0	12.4		12	135	4	Skiff: Sparse group. Aliases: Cr 148; Lund 344; OCl 579; C0725–116
Czernik 29	cl:	07 28 24	−15 23.7	Pup	II2m	5.0	10.3	40	12.22	13.8	2938	12	135	4	Aliases: Lund 341; OCl 595; C0726–153
Haffner 10	cl	07 28 36	−15 21.9	Pup	III2m	3.0	11.5	40	15.0	13.9	2938	12	135	4	DSFG: Probably not a cluster. Aliases: Lund 342; OCl 594; C0726–152
NGC 2394	cl??	07 28 37	+07 05.2	CMi								12	95	4	Skiff: Sparse group.
ESO 559-SC13	cl	07 28.7	−20 49	Pup	II2	10.0						19	153	10	
Haffner 24	ast	07 28.8	−18 21	Pup	I2p	2.2		11	16			12	153	51	See notes. Considered not to be a true cluster in modern references. Aliases: OCl 608; C0726–182
Ruprecht 22	cl:	07 29 17	−29 10.5	Pup	IV1p	3.0		15	12.0			19	153	4	Skiff: Sparse group. Aliases: Lund 345; OCl 664; C0727–291

Table 4.1: Catalog of Clusters and Asterisms in the Milky Way, and Objects Misidentified as Such

Name	Type	2000.0 R.A.	Dec.	Con.	Tr. Type	Diam. (′)	Tot. Vm	#str	Bt* Vm	V Sur	Dist. (pc)	S #	2U #	Ref	Comments and Aliases
NGC 2401	cl	07 29 25	−13 58.0	Pup	I1p	2.0	12.6	20		14.1		12	135	4	Aliases: Cr 149; Lund 346; OCl 588; C0727−138
NGC 2399	ast	07 29.9	−00 21	Mon				3				12	115	99	Skiff: Not obvious in 0.3 degree field. Archinal: Id?
NGC 2400	ast	07 30.0	−00 21	Mon				3				12	115	99	Skiff: Not obvious in 0.3 degree field. Archinal: Id?
Dolidze 26	cl	07 30 02	+11 57.3	CMi	IV1p	23.0						12	95	99	DSFG: Probably not a cluster. Archinal: Faint scattered group with (very bright) 6 CMi (V=4.547, K1III) just NW of center. Aliases: Lund 347; OCl 516; C0727+120
Mayer 3	cl	07 30 04	−18 32.2	Pup								12	153	4	Skiff: Not obvious in 0.3 degree field; = S 305? Aliases: Lund 1164; OCl 609.1; C0727−184
[FM80] 1	cl?	07 30 12	−15 50.0	Pup		12.0		12			2500.	12	135	99	Dias, *et al.* [2002] call this "Waterloo 8", but the discovery paper gives no suggestion for such a name. Alias: (5) Wa 8
Ruprecht 23	cl	07 30 40	−23 22.4	Pup	III1p	4.0		20	13.0			19	153	4	Skiff: Sparse group. Aliases: Lund 348; C0728−232
Czernik 30	cl:	07 31 11	−09 57.0	Mon	III1p	3.0		20				12	135	4	Aliases: Lund 349; OCl 574; C0728−098
NGC 2409	ast?	07 31 37	−17 11.4	Pup	II3m n	16.0	7.3	6	8	13.3	828	12	135	4	See notes. Position is that of dominating (but non-member) BD−16 1994. Skiff: = Bochum 4 = BD-16 1994 (V=9.1, k3iii?). Aliases: Bo 4; Lund 1128; C0728−168
Bochum 6	cl	07 31 45.1	−19 26 45	Pup	I3m n	10.0	9.9	40	10.65	14.9	3981	12	153	99	Archinal: DSS shows irregular group of 5 stars, and some fainter, with nebulosity around N-most star. Aliases: Lund 1130; C0729−193
Ruprecht 24	cl	07 31 51	−12 46.5	Pup	IV1p	9.0		15	11.0			12	135	99	Archinal: Ruprecht's (2′) diameter too small - this is a 9′ diameter group with HD 59884 (V=8.03, A2III) on W side. Aliases: Lund 350; OCl 586; C0729−126
Bochum 5	cl	07 32.1	−16 57	Pup	I2p n	5.0	7.0	50	7.78	10.5	2291	12	135	8	See notes. NGC 2409 = Bo 4 just to SW. Skiff: Wide group centered on HD 59986 = vdB 97 = S 302 = RCW 7. Aliases: Lund 1129; C0728−169
NGC 2414	cl	07 33 13	−15 27.2	Pup	I3m	6.0	7.9	35	8.21	11.8	4150	12	135	4	Skiff: = HD 60308 (V=8.2, B2Iab). Aliases: Cr 150; Lund 352; OCl 598; C0731−153
NGC 2413	ast	07 33 19.0	−13 07 09	Pup		10.0			9			12	135	99	Archinal: Position is for brightest and center star HD 60307 (V=8.75, B4III). DSS shows a condensation both N and S of this star.
ESO 429-SC02	cl	07 33.4	−28 11	Pup	I2	5.0						19	153	10	
Ruprecht 40	cl:	07 33 27	−20 31.1	Pup	IV1p	2.0		10	13.0			19	153	4	Skiff: Sparse group. Aliases: Lund 401; OCl 634; C0731−203
Haffner 11	cl	07 35 22	−27 42.3	Pup	II2m	5.0		35	16.0			19	153	4	Archinal: The DSS shows that this is superposed on the small galaxy AM 0733-273. Aliases: Lund 354; OCl 657; vdB-Ha 3; (4) AM 0733−273; C0733−276
Alessi J07354-1505	ast?	07 35 25	−15 05.5	Pup		2.6		60	9.2			12	135	99	About 40′ south of M 47. Elongated, 2.6′ x 1.0′ in size. Brightest star is HD 60741 (V=9.2, F3V), on north side. Alias: Alessi 17
Alessi J07356-2746	ast?	07 35 37	−27 46.5	Pup		2.5		80				19	153	8	Size 2.5′ x 1.3′ (elongated E-W). 5′ SE of Haffner 11.
NGC 2421	cl	07 36 12	−20 36.7	Pup	I2r	8.0	8.3	70	11.0	12.8	1862	19	153	4	Aliases: Cr 151; Lund 355; Mel 67; OCl 626; Raab 54; C0734−205
NGC 2422	cl	07 36 36	−14 29.0	Pup	I3m	25.0	4.4	117	5.0	11.4	474	12	135	4	See notes. DSFG: M 47. Includes approximate combined magnitude for ADS 6216, centrally located in the cluster. Skiff: = HD 60997/8. Aliases: Cr 152; Lund 356; M 47; Mel 68; OCl 596; Raab 55; NGC 2478; OCl 596.0; C0734−143
Ruprecht 25	cl:	07 36 47	−23 23.1	Pup	III1p	2.0		10	14.0			19	153	4	Aliases: Lund 357; OCl 641; C0734−232
Czernik 31	cl:	07 36 58	−20 31.7	Pup	III2m	5.0		40				19	153	4	Skiff: Sparse group, absorption hole? Aliases: Lund 358; OCl 625; C0734−203
ESO 429-SC05	cl	07 37.0	−32 12	Pup	III3	1.2						19	171	10	
NGC 2423	cl	07 37 07	−13 52.3	Pup	II2m	12.0	6.7	86	9.02	12.1	749	12	135	4	Skiff: = HD 61098. Aliases: Cr 153; Lund 359; Mel 70; OCl 592; Raab 57; C0734−137
Alessi J07372-2623	cl?	07 37 11	−26 23.2	Pup	II2p	0.9		15				19	153	99	Archinal: Very compact possible cluster. West side has an "arc" shape. Possible "stellar ring". Alias: Alessi 18
Ruprecht 26	cl:	07 37 13	−15 40.5	Pup	III1p	4.0		20	12.0			12	135	4	Skiff: Sparse group. Aliases: Lund 360; OCl 602; C0734−155
Melotte 71	cl	07 37 30	−12 03.1	Pup	II2r	8.0	7.1	216	10.18	11.6	2689	12	135	4	See notes. Also known as "Wilk's cluster". Aliases: Cr 155; Lund 362; OCl 587; Raab 58; Wilk; (4) IRAS 07349−1159; C0735−119
Ruprecht 27	cl	07 37.6	−26 30	Pup	IV2m	6.0		30	12.0			19	153	99	Skiff: Sparse group, identification uncertain. Archinal: DSS shows N-S elongated possible cluster. Aliases: Lund 361; OCl 654; OCl 654.0; C0735−264
vdB-Ha 4	cl	07 37 45	−36 03.8	Pup	II1p	2.0		20				19	171	4	Aliases: Lund 1055; C0736−359
NGC 2419	gcl	07 38 08.5	+38 52 55	Lyn		4.6	10.3		17.3	13.6	83500	5	57	6	Aliases: EQ 0734+390; Caldw 25; C0734+390

Table 4.1: Catalog of Clusters and Asterisms in the Milky Way, and Objects Misidentified as Such

Name	Type	2000.0 R.A.	Dec.	Con.	Tr. Type	Diam. (′)	Tot. Vm	#str	Bt* Vm	V Sur	Dist. (pc)	S #	2U #	Ref	Comments and Aliases
NGC 2425	cl	07 38 18	−14 52.7	Pup	II1m	5.0		30	14.0			12	135	4	Aliases: Haf 12; Lund 363; OCl 599; C0736−147
NGC 2420	cl	07 38 24	+21 34.4	Gem	I1r	6.0	8.3	304	11.0	12.2	1944	5	75	4	Aliases: Cr 154; Lund 364; Mel 69; OCl 488; Raab 56; C0735+216
Melotte 72	cl	07 38 29	−10 41.6	Mon	III1m	5.0	10.1	40		13.6		12	135	4	See notes. Also known as Cr 467. Aliases: Cr 156; Lund 365; OCl 581; Raab 59; Cr 467; (5) OCl 580; (5) C0736−104; (5) Lund 367; C0736−105
AM 2	cl	07 38 44	−33 50.4	Pup		3.0			16.3		12400	19	171	55	See notes. Ortolani, *et al.* [1995] have recently shown this to be an old open cluster (rather than a globular cluster). Position from DSS. Alias: ESO 368-SC7
NGC 2428	cl?	07 39 18	−16 31.0	Pup		13.0		50				12	135	53	See notes. Has 2 NW-SE streams of stars, extending 18′ long (including HD 61486, V=8.7, on NW). NGC 2430 adjacent to north. Alias: H. VIII.47
NGC 2430	ast?	07 39 30	−16 20.4	Pup		7.5		20	8.0			12	135	53	See notes. Includes (V=8.0) HD 61553 and (V=10.4) HD 61612. NGC 2428 is larger group to south. Alias: H. VIII.46
Ruprecht 28	cl:	07 39 36	−30 55.7	Pup	IV1p	5.0		20	14.0			19	171	99	Skiff: Sparse group, identification uncertain. Archinal: DSS barely shows rise in faint stars of Milky Way background. Aliases: Lund 366; OCl 680; C0737−308
ESO 493-SC03	cl	07 39.7	−27 18	Pup	I2							19	153	10	
Bochum 15	cl	07 40 15	−33 32.6	Pup	IV2p n	3.0	6.3	33	7.65	8.7	3767	19	171	4	Skiff: = Bran 61 = IRAS 07383-3325. Knot of three stars plus nebula. Aliases: Lund 113; C0738−334
Haffner 13	cl	07 40 26	−30 04.8	Pup	III3p	15.0		15	8.0			19	171	4	Skiff: = HD 61944. Sparse group. Aliases: Lund 368; OCl 678; vdB-Ha 5; C0738−300
Alessi J07405-5155	ast	07 40.5	−51 55	Car		10.0		15	11			24	200	10	
NGC 2408	ast?	07 40.5	+71 39	Cam					10			1	15	99	Skiff: Not obvious in 0.4 degree field. Archinal: Id?
NGC 2439	cl	07 40 46	−31 41.5	Pup	II3r	9.0	6.9	181	9.0	11.7	3563	19	171	99	Archinal: The DSS image shows this to be a "ring" shaped cluster. Aliases: Cr 158; Lund 370; Mel 74; OCl 688; Raab 61; vdB-Ha 6; C0738−315
NGC 2432	cl	07 40 54	−19 05.1	Pup	II2m	7.0	10.2	50		14.4		12	153	4	Aliases: Cr 157; Lund 369; Mel 73; OCl 620; Raab 60; C0738−189
Ruprecht 29	cl:	07 41.1	−24 19	Pup	IV2p	5.0		20	13.0			19	153	99	Skiff: Not obvious in 0.4 degree field. Archinal: Id? Aliases: Lund 371; OCl 650; C0739−242
ESO 429-SC13	cl	07 41.1	−30 44	Pup	II2							19	171	10	
Ruprecht 151	cl	07 41.3	−16 17	Pup	III2m	8.0		30	12.0			12	135	4	Skiff: Maybe sparse group. Aliases: Lund 372; OCl 606; OCl 606.0; C0739−161
NGC 2437	cl	07 41 47	−14 48.6	Pup	II2r	20.0	6.1	186	10.0	12.6	1637	12	135	4	DSFG: M 46. The planetary nebula NGC 2438 lies in front of this cluster. Aliases: Cr 159; Lund 373; M 46; Mel 75; OCl 601; Raab 62; OCl 601.0; C0739−147
Ruprecht 30	cl	07 42 22	−31 28.0	Pup	IV2m	6.5		30	11.0			19	171	99	Archinal: Sparse 6.5′ diameter group of brighter stars, on 24′ DSS image. Ruprecht's diameter of 4′ a little too small. Aliases: Lund 374; OCl 687; C0740−313
Ruprecht 31	cl	07 43 00	−35 35.4	Pup	III2p	5.0		15	11.0			19	171	4	Skiff: = HD 62540; asterism, identification uncertain. Aliases: Lund 375; OCl 711; C0740−354
ESO 368-SC11	cl	07 44.4	−34 39	Pup	III3	1.0						19	171	10	
NGC 2447	cl	07 44 30	−23 51.2	Pup	I3r	10.0	6.2	80	9.0	11.2	1091	19	153	4	DSFG: M 93. Aliases: Cr 160; Lund 376; M 93; Mel 76; OCl 649; Raab 63; OCl 649.0; C0742−237
NGC 2448	cl??	07 44 34	−24 40.4	Pup				18	11			19	153	4	Skiff: = HD 62747 = HR 3004, sparse 20′ group.
Haffner 14	cl	07 44 48	−28 22.8	Pup	III1m	10.0		50	14.0			19	153	4	Skiff: Sparse group. Aliases: Lund 377; OCl 674; vdB-Ha 7; C0742−282
Ruprecht 32	cl:	07 45 06	−25 31.6	Pup	II3m n	6.0	8.4	30	10.0	12.3	5346	19	153	4	Skiff: = Bran 66B = GSC 6544-0130. Aliases: Lund 378; OCl 651; BRAN 66A; OCl 651.0; (4) IRAS 07429−2523; WB89 1049; C0742−254
NGC 2451	ast	07 45.4	−37 57	Pup	II2m	50.0	2.8	153	6.0	11.3		19	171	8	See notes. Röser and Bastian [1994] have shown this is not a true cl., although there may be two cl. (PMG 1 & 2) surrounding it. Aliases: Cr 161; Lund 380; OCl 716; vdB-Ha 9; C0743−378
PMG 1	cl	07 45.4	−37 57	Pup		120.0		24	4.83		220	19	171	99	See notes. Puppis Moving Group. Discovered by Röser and Bastian [1994] around (asterism) NGC 2451. Probably not obvious visually. Aliases: [PKL98] 10; (5) NGC 2451B
PMG 2	cl?	07 45.4	−37 57	Pup				16	6.3		400	19	171	8	See notes. Possible cluster behind Puppis Moving Group. Discovered by Röser and Bastian [1994]. Probably not obvious visually.
Haffner 15	cl	07 45 30	−32 50.5	Pup	II2m	3.0	9.4	35	12.0	11.8	2489	19	171	4	Aliases: Lund 351; OCl 696; vdB-Ha 8; C0743−326
Ruprecht 33	cl	07 45.8	−21 57	Pup	IV1p	9.0		20	13.0			19	153	4	Skiff: Sparse group. Aliases: Lund 381; OCl 640; C0743−218
ESO 258-SC01	cl	07 45.8	−46 43	Pup	III3	10.0						19	187	10	
Ruprecht 34	cl	07 45 54	−20 22.5	Pup	II3m	7.0	9.5	35	12.0	13.7		19	153	4	DSFG: Probably not a cluster. Aliases: Be 38; Lund 382; OCl 628; C0743−202

Table 4.1: Catalog of Clusters and Asterisms in the Milky Way, and Objects Misidentified as Such

Name	Type	2000.0 R.A.	Dec.	Con.	Tr. Type	Diam. (′)	Tot. Vm	#str	Bt* Vm	V Sur	Dist. (pc)	S #	2U #	Ref	Comments and Aliases
Ruprecht 35	cl	07 46 14	−31 16.8	Pup	II1p	1.5		10	14.0			19	171	4	Aliases: Lund 383; OCl 689; vdB-Ha 10; C0744−311
Berkeley 39	cl	07 46 50	−04 40.5	Mon	II2r	8.0		120	16.0			12	115	4	See notes. Aliases: Lund 384; OCl 561; C0744−044
ESO 368-SC14	cl	07 47.0	−32 58	Pup	III3	4.0						19	171	10	
ADS 6366 cl	ast?	07 47 02.4	+00 01 05	CMi		4.5		8	8.32			12	115	8	See notes. Disc. by J. Herschel, 1827. Center and brt. star is triple ADS 6366 (V=8.32, 9.27, 12.33). Alias: (2) ADS 6366
NGC 2453	cl	07 47 35	−27 11.7	Pup	I3m	4.0	8.3	76	9.46	11.3	2126	19	153	4	Aliases: Cr 162; Lund 385; OCl 670; C0745−271
Ruprecht 36	cl	07 48 24	−26 17.9	Pup	IV1m	5.0	9.6	30	12.0	13.1	2109	19	153	4	Aliases: Lund 386; C0746−261
Haffner 25	cl:	07 48 40	−25 56.8	Pup	III1p	2.0		20	14.0			19	153	99	See notes. Identified as the correct object by P. Teutsch [Priv. Comm., 2002] Aliases: Lund 387; OCl 656; C0746−257
AH03 J0748.6-2656	cl?	07 48 40	−26 56.8	Pup		4.0		20				19	153	99	See notes. A previously unidentified cluster, at first confused with Haf 25, 1 degree to the north.
NGC 2455	cl	07 48 59	−21 17.9	Pup	III2m	15.0	10.2	50	12.0	16.1		19	153	4	Skiff: Sparse group. Aliases: Cr 163; Lund 388; Mel 77; OCl 636; Raab 64; C0746−211
ESO 311-SC14	cl	07 49.4	−42 42	Pup	III2	6.0						19	187	10	
Ruprecht 37	cl	07 49 47	−17 14.8	Pup	II2m	4.0		30	14.0			12	134	4	Aliases: Be 40; Lund 389; OCl 615; C0747−171
Haffner 16	cl	07 50 21	−25 27.1	Pup	I2m	5.0	10.0	30	12.0	13.5	3855	19	153	4	See notes. "Pismis" cluster (no Pismis number). Aliases: Lund 390; OCl 655; Pi; C0748−253
Czernik 32	cl	07 50 28	−29 50.9	Pup	II1m	3.0		30				19	171	4	Aliases: King 24; Lund 391; OCl 683; vdB-Ha 11; C0748−297
Ruprecht 38	cl:	07 50 31	−20 11.3	Pup	III2p	2.0		15	13.0			19	153	4	Skiff: Small group. Aliases: Lund 392; OCl 629; C0748−200
Haffner 17	cl	07 51 36	−31 48.9	Pup	I2p	2.5		20	15.0			19	171	4	Aliases: Lund 393; OCl 694; vdB-Ha 12; (4) IRAS 07495−3142; C0749−317
NGC 2459	ast	07 52 02	+09 33.4	CMi				2				12	94	4	Skiff: Five stars in knot, brightest star (GSC 0783-0827) taken as center.
NGC 2477	cl	07 52 10	−38 32.0	Pup	I2r	20.0	5.8	1911	12.0	12.3	1151	19	171	4	Skiff: Big. Aliases: Cr 165; Lund 395; Mel 78; OCl 720; Raab 65; vdB-Ha 13; Caldw 71; C0750−384
Ruprecht 39	cl	07 52 20	−22 26.5	Pup	III1p	2.0		15	14.0			19	153	4	Aliases: Lund 394; OCl 645; (4) IRAS 07498−2220; C0750−223
NGC 2467	cl	07 52 30	−26 25.8	Pup	I3m n	15.0	7.1	50		13.0	4018	19	153	4	Involved in Sh 2-311. Skiff: = HD 64315 (V=9.2, O6e). Aliases: Cr 164; Lund 396; OCl 668; BRAN 80A; OCl 668.0; Sh 2- 311; CTB 23; C0750−263
ESO 123-SC26	cl	07 52.5	−60 20	Car	III3	16.0						24	200	10	
Haffner 18a	ptcl	07 52 38.2	−26 22 56	Pup		1.5						19	153	8	Haffner 18b on SE, Haffner 18c on E, NGC 2467 5′ SW. Position measured from DSS. Alias: (3) Haf 18
Haffner 18ab	ptcl	07 52 39	−26 23.3	Pup		3.0						19	153	4	Haffner 18c on NE, NGC 2467 5′ SW. Aliases: (2) Haf 18a; (2) Haf 18b; (3) Haf 18
Haffner 18b	ptcl	07 52 43	−26 23.8	Pup		1.0						19	153	8	Haffner 18a on NW, Haffner 18c on NE, NGC 2467 5′ SW. Position measured from DSS. Alias: (3) Haf 18
Haffner 18	cl	07 52 44	−26 22.7	Pup	I2p n	5.0	9.3	25	11.0	12.8	6026	19	153	8	See notes. Position and diameter measured from DSS. Aliases: (2) Haf 18a; (2) Haf 18b; (2) Haf 18c; (2) Haf 18ab; C0750−262
Haffner 19	cl	07 52 46	−26 16.7	Pup	I1m n	2.0	9.4	39	14.0	10.9	6637	19	153	4	Aliases: Lund 400; OCl 662; C0750−261
Haffner 18c	ptcl	07 52 48	−26 21.6	Pup		3.0						19	153	4	Haffner 18a on W, Haffner 18b on SW, Haffner 19 5′ N. Alias: (3) Haf 18
Ruprecht 41	cl	07 53 48	−26 58.2	Pup	IV1p	2.0		20	14.0			19	153	4	Skiff: Sparse group. Aliases: Lund 402; OCl 673; C0751−268
Ruprecht 152	cl	07 54 29	−38 14.3	Pup	II1m	3.0		35	16.0			19	171	4	Aliases: Lund 403; OCl 719; vdB-Ha 14; (4) IRAS 07525−3809; C0752−381
NGC 2479	cl	07 55 06	−17 42.5	Pup	III1m	11.0	9.6	45		14.8		12	153	4	Skiff: Sparse cluster. Aliases: Cr 167; Lund 406; OCl 623; Tr 8; C0752−175
Waterloo 3	cl	07 55 06.4	−25 21 54	Pup	n	1.9		20	12.85			19	153	8	Figure in discovery paper [Moffat, et al, 1979] has N up (not to left). 9′ SSW of HD 65011 (V=8.0, G6/G8III). Alias: (4) BRAN 84
NGC 2482	cl	07 55 10	−24 15.5	Pup	IV1m	10.0	7.3	40	10.04	12.3	748	19	153	4	Skiff: Sparse cluster. Aliases: Cr 166; Lund 405; OCl 653; OCl 653.0; C0752−241
NGC 2483	cl	07 55 39	−27 53.2	Pup	III2m	9.0	7.6	45	9.26	12.4	3327	19	153	4	DSFG: Probably not a cluster. Skiff: Sparse group; DSS SERC-V short exposure field. Aliases: Lund 353; OCl 677.1; C0753−278
Trumpler 9	cl	07 55 40	−25 53.2	Pup	II2p	6.0	8.7	20	10.09	12.6	1666	19	153	4	Aliases: Cr 168; Ha 2; Lund 407; OCl 663; C0753−258
Haffner 20	cl	07 56 15	−30 22.4	Pup	II1p	3.0	11.0	33	14.0	13.4	2443	19	171	4	Aliases: Lund 409; OCl 692; vdB-Ha 16; C0754−302
NGC 2489	cl	07 56 16	−30 03.9	Pup	I2m	5.0	7.9	112	11.0	11.4	1164	19	171	4	Aliases: Cr 169; Lund 408; Mel 79; OCl 690; Raab 66; vdB-Ha 15; C0754−299
NGC 2464	cl??	07 57.3	+56 40	Lyn								1	26	99	Archinal: Id? DSS shows a galaxy and a close double (or star and galaxy) here.

Table 4.1: Catalog of Clusters and Asterisms in the Milky Way, and Objects Misidentified as Such

Name	Type	2000.0 R.A.	Dec.	Con.	Tr. Type	Diam. (′)	Tot. Vm	#str	Bt* Vm	V Sur	Dist. (pc)	S #	2U #	Ref	Comments and Aliases
Ruprecht 42	cl	07 57 37	−25 55.0	Pup	III2p	4.0		20	14.0			19	153	4	Aliases: Be 41; Lund 410; OCl 669; C0755–257
NGC 2516	cl	07 58.0	−60 45	Car	I3r	22.0	3.8	103	7.0	10.5	412	24	200	4	Skiff: Too large to check. Aliases: Cr 172; Lund 411; Mel 82; OCl 776; Raab 69; OCl 776.0; Caldw 96; C0757–607
Ruprecht 43	cl	07 58.8	−28 54	Pup	IV1p	7.0		25	12.0			19	153	99	Skiff: Not obvious in 0.25 or 0.4 degree field, DSS SERC-V short exposure field. Archinal: Id? Aliases: Lund 412; OCl 684; C0756–287
Ruprecht 44	cl?	07 58 50	−28 34.7	Pup	IV2m	5.0	7.2	84	12.0	10.7	4227	19	153	99	Archinal: Small (5′ diameter) sparse group, much more obvious on DSS II than DSS image (with histogram equalization display). Aliases: Lund 413; OCl 681; C0757–284
ESO 561-SC05	cl	07 59.3	−22 41	Pup	II2	7.0						19	153	10	
ESO 494-SC09	cl	07 59.3	−27 35	Pup	I2	3.0						19	153	10	
Ruprecht 45	cl:	07 59.6	−16 17	Pup	IV1m	9.0		35	13.0			12	134	4	DSFG: Probably not a cluster. Skiff: Okay, sparse group. Aliases: Lund 414; OCl 617; C0757–161
NGC 2506	cl	08 00 02	−10 46.2	Mon	I2r	12.0	7.6	807	11.0	13.0	3226	12	134	4	Aliases: Cr 170; Lund 415; Mel 80; OCl 593; Raab 67; EQ 0757–106; Caldw 54; C0757–106
Ruprecht 153	cl	08 00 18	−30 13.9	Pup	IV2p e	2.8			14.0			20	171	4	Skiff: Identification uncertain. DSS SERC-V short exposure field. Aliases: Lund 416; OCl 693; C0758–301
NGC 2509	cl	08 00 48	−19 03.0	Pup	I1r	12.0	9.3	70		14.7		12	153	4	Skiff: Okay. Aliases: Cr 171; Lund 417; Mel 81; OCl 630; Raab 68; C0758–189
Haffner 21	cl	08 01 11	−27 12.5	Pup	I1p	3.0	10.3	51	15.0	12.7	3251	20	153	4	Aliases: Lund 418; OCl 677; C0759–270
ESO 311-SC21	cl	08 01.7	−41 36	Pup	III3	4.0						20	187	10	
Ruprecht 154	cl	08 01.7	−44 25	Pup	III2p	3.0		10	13.0			20	187	4	Skiff: Measured by Archinal from the DSS. Aliases: Lund 419; OCl 738; C0800–442
Ruprecht 46	cl	08 02 10	−19 27.9	Pup	I2p	3.0	9.1	15	12.0	11.5	752	12	153	4	Skiff: = HD 66290 (V=9.4, G8III:). Aliases: Lund 420; OCl 637; C0759–193
Ruprecht 47	cl	08 02 18	−31 04.7	Pup	II1p	4.0	9.6	20	13.0	12.6	3006	20	171	4	Skiff: = GSC 7120-1160. DSS SERC-V short exposure field. Aliases: Lund 421; OCl 699; C0800–309
ESO 430-SC09	cl	08 02.4	−29 47	Pup		0.8						20	171	10	
Ruprecht 48	cl	08 02 42	−32 02.5	Pup	III1p	2.0		20	12.0			20	171	4	Skiff: DSS SERC-V short exposure field. Aliases: Lund 422; OCl 702; C0800–318
Ruprecht 49	cl	08 03 17	−26 46.2	Pup	II1p	2.0	9.6	10	13.0	11.1	1754	20	153	4	Aliases: Lund 423; OCl 676; C0801–266
Ruprecht 50	cl	08 03.4	−30 52	Pup	II2m	3.0		30	12.0			20	171	4	Skiff: Identification uncertain. DSS SERC-V short exposure field. Aliases: Lund 425; OCl 698; vdB-Ha 17; C0801–307
Collinder 173	cl	08 03.5	−46 16	Pup	IV2p	370.0	0.6			13.4	330	20	187	99	Skiff: Too large to check, sparse. Archinal: Too large to check on DSS (4d image used) as supposedly 370′ in size. Aliases: Lund 424; OCl 741; OCl 741.0; C0802–461
Ruprecht 51	cl	08 03.6	−30 37	Pup	IV1m	4.0		30	14.0			20	171	4	Skiff: Okay. DSS SERC-V short exposure field. Aliases: Lund 426; OCl 697; C0801–305
ESO 430-SC14	cl	08 03.6	−31 26	Pup	II3	5.0						20	171	10	
NGC 2527	cl	08 04 53	−28 08.3	Pup	II2m	10.0	6.5	45	8.59	11.5	567	20	153	99	Skiff: Lindoff center star adopted = GSC 6566-0092. Aliases: Cr 174; Lund 429; OCl 685; OCl 685.0; NGC 2520; C0803–280
Ruprecht 155	cl:	08 04.9	−31 46	Pup	IV1p	3.0		10	13.0			20	171	99	Skiff: DSS SERC-V short exposure field. Archinal: Id? DSS shows scattering of stars. Aliases: Lund 427; OCl 703; C0803–316
Ruprecht 52	cl	08 05.0	−31 56	Pup	III1p	3.0		15	13.0			20	171	4	Skiff: DSS SERC-V short exposure field. Aliases: Lund 428; OCl 705; (4) IRAS 08031–3151; C0803–318
ESO 430-SC18	cl	08 06.9	−30 50	Pup	III2	12.0						20	171	10	
NGC 2533	cl	08 07.0	−29 52	Pup	II2r	6.0	7.6	124	8.99	11.5	1345	20	171	4	Skiff: DSS SERC-V short exposure field. Aliases: Cr 175; Lund 430; OCl 695; vdB-Ha 18; C0805–297
vdB-Ha 19	cl	08 07 04.0	−32 21 30	Pup	III2p	3.0		12				20	171	99	Skiff: DSS SERC-V short exposure field. Aliases: Lund 1056; C0805–322
Gamma Vel cl	cl	08 09 32.0	−47 20 12	Vel		18.0		10	1.8		460.	20	187	99	Gamma-2 Vel (V=1.8, WCvar+) is brightest member. Listed as “Brandt 1” in Dias, *et al.* [2002].
NGC 2547	cl	08 10 11	−49 13.5	Vel	I3r n	25.0	4.7	112	7.0	11.7	436	20	187	4	Skiff: Large. Aliases: Cr 177; Lund 432; Mel 84; OCl 753; Raab 71; BRAN 115; OCl 753.0; C0809–491
NGC 2539	cl	08 10 38	−12 49.0	Pup	III2m	15.0	6.5	59	9.0	12.4	1247	12	134	4	Aliases: Cr 176; Mel 83; OCl 611; Raab 70; C0808–126
Ruprecht 53	cl	08 10 50	−27 00.0	Pup	IV3m	6.0		40	10.0			20	153	4	Skiff: Sparse. Aliases: Lund 433; OCl 682; C0808–268
Ruprecht 54	cl	08 11 23	−31 57.0	Pup	III2p	3.0		20	15.0			20	171	4	Skiff: DSS SERC-V short exposure field. Aliases: Lund 434; OCl 710; vdB-Ha 20; C0809–318
Ruprecht 55	cl	08 12 19	−32 34.0	Pup	III1p	6.0	7.8	36	11.0	11.7	4834	20	171	4	DSFG: Probably not a cluster. Skiff: Sparse group, DSS SERC-V short exposure field. Aliases: Lund 435; OCl 713; C0810–324

Table 4.1: Catalog of Clusters and Asterisms in the Milky Way, and Objects Misidentified as Such

Name	Type	2000.0 R.A.	Dec.	Con.	Tr. Type	Diam. (′)	Tot. Vm	#str	Bt* Vm	V Sur	Dist. (pc)	S #	2U #	Ref	Comments and Aliases
NGC 2546	cl	08 12.4	−37 37	Pup	III2m	70.0	6.3	40	7.0	15.5	986	20	171	99	Archinal: DSS shows 90′ group of bright stars, with 30′ group of fainter stars at center, all in nebulosity. DSS overlap region. Aliases: Cr 178; Lund 436; OCl 726; vdB-Ha 22; C0810−374
Haffner 22	cl	08 12.6	−27 52	Pup	II1m	7.0		30	15.0			20	153	99	Skiff: DSS SERC-V short exposure field. Archinal: Id? Rich field of stars, but no obvious cluster. Aliases: Lund 437; OCl 691; vdB-Ha 21; C0810−277
Ruprecht 56	cl:	08 12.6	−40 27	Pup	III2m	40.0		40	9.0			20	171	4	DSFG: Probably not a cluster. Skiff: Too large to check on DSS. Aliases: Lund 438; OCl 730; OCl 730.0; C0810−403
NGC 2548	cl	08 13 44	−05 45.0	Hya	I3r	30.0	5.8	80	8.0	13.2	628	12	134	4	DSFG: M 48. Aliases: Cr 179; Lund 439; M 48; Mel 85; OCl 584; Raab 72; C0811−056
Alessi J08141-1433	ast?	08 14 09.0	−14 33 41	Pup		7.0		22				12	134	8	Alessi: Nice elongated N-S group of B stars. Like many ESO clusters. Its brightest star is the southernmost one.
vdB-Ha 23	cl	08 14.4	−36 23	Pup	III2p	40.0		15				20	171	4	Skiff: DSS plate overlap region. Aliases: Lund 1057; C0812−362
Ruprecht 57	cl	08 14.8	−26 58	Pup	IV2m	5.0		30	12.0			20	153	99	Skiff: Not obvious in 0.3 degree field. Archinal: Id? Aliases: Lund 441; OCl 686; C0812−268
Ruprecht 58	cl	08 14 49	−31 56.2	Pup	IV1m	6.0		30	12.0			20	171	4	Skiff: Sparse group, DSS SERC-V short exposure field. Aliases: Lund 440; OCl 712; C0812−318
Haffner 26	cl:	08 15.4	−30 49	Pup	III2p	6.0		20	14.0			20	171	99	Skiff: DSS SERC-V short exposure field. Archinal: Id? DSS shows scattering of stars. Aliases: Lund 442; OCl 707; C0813−306
Alessi J08154-5808	ast	08 15.4	−58 08	Car		4.0		8	11			25	200	10	
Pismis 2	cl	08 17 54	−41 40.4	Pup	II1r	4.0		100	15.0			20	187	4	Aliases: OCl 733; vdB-Ha 25; OCl 733.0; C0816−414
NGC 2568	cl	08 18 19	−37 06.3	Pup	II2m	3.0	10.7	30	11.0	13.1	2094	20	171	4	See notes. DSFG: NGC 2568 = Pi 1. Skiff: DSS SERC-V short exposure field. Aliases: Pi 1; OCl 727; vdB-Ha 24; Lund 443; C0815−369
NGC 2567	cl	08 18 30	−30 38.7	Pup	II2m	11.0	7.4	117	11.0	12.6	1638	20	171	4	Skiff: Not UX. Aliases: Cr 180; Lund 445; Mel 86; OCl 708; Raab 73; vdB-Ha 26; (4) IRAS 08164−3029; C0816−304
NGC 2571	cl	08 18 57	−29 45.0	Pup	II3m	7.0	7.0	49	8.82	11.2	1223	20	171	4	Aliases: Cr 181; Lund 446; OCl 701; vdB-Ha 27; C0816−295
Ruprecht 59	cl	08 19 22.0	−34 28 51	Pup	III1p	3.0	9.0	21	12.0	11.4		20	171	99	DSFG: Probably not a cluster. Skiff: DSS SERC-V short exposure field. Aliases: Lund 447; OCl 717; C0817−343
Ruprecht 156	ast	08 19 28.8	−45 23 56	Vel	I1p	0.3		7	15.			20	187	51	Archinal: Position from DSS. Tiny (probable) asterism of 7 stars. Aliases: OCl 744; C0817−452
NGC 2579	ast?	08 20 53	−36 12.8	Pup	IV2p n	1.0	7.5	10	9.51	7.5	1033	20	171	99	See notes. DSFG: Probably not a cluster. Skiff: DSS SERC-V short exposure field. Archinal: Rich field only, with 1′ nebulous asterism. Aliases: Cr 182; Lund 449; OCl 724; (4) GUM 11; C0819−360
NGC 2580	cl	08 21 28	−30 17.5	Pup	II2m	8.0	9.7	50		14.2		20	171	4	Aliases: Cr 183; Lund 450; OCl 709; vdB-Ha 28; C0819−301
AH03 J0822.2-3624	ast?	08 22 12	−36 24	Pup		12.0		20	9.5			20	171	8	Listed in original ADC version of Lund Catalogue as NGC 2579. Includes HD 70679, HD 70697, and HD 70742 (V=9.5, B8/B9II).
NGC 2588	cl	08 23 10	−32 58.5	Pup	II1p	2.0	11.8	20		13.3		20	171	4	Skiff: DSS SERC-V short exposure field. Aliases: Cr 186; Lund 452; OCl 715; vdB-Ha 29; C0821−328
Collinder 185	cl	08 23 19	−36 20.1	Pup	III2m	10.0	7.8	30	10.08	12.8	1486	20	171	8	See notes. Collinder position 1ᵐ too far west, 10′ too far north. Aliases: Lund 451; OCl 725; C0820−360
NGC 2587	cl	08 23 25	−29 30.5	Pup	III2m	10.0	9.2	40		14.2		20	171	4	Skiff: Small group. Aliases: Cr 184; Lund 453; OCl 706; vdB-Ha 30; C0821−293
Collinder 187	cl	08 24 12	−29 10.2	Pup	IV1p	5.0	9.6	20		13.1		20	153	4	Skiff: Sparse. Aliases: Lund 454; OCl 704; C0822−289
Ruprecht 60	cl:	08 24 26	−47 12.7	Vel	II1m	3.0		30	13.0			20	187	4	Aliases: Lund 455; OCl 751; vdB-Ha 31; C0822−470
ESO 312-SC03	cl	08 24.5	−41 18	Pup	III3	2.0						20	187	10	
Ruprecht 61	cl	08 25 15	−34 08.7	Pup	II1p	2.0		25	14.0			20	171	4	Skiff: DSS SERC-V short exposure field. Aliases: Lund 456; OCl 718; vdB-Ha 32; C0823−340
SSWZ94 2	cl	08 25 25.2	−39 37 57	Pup		3.0						20	171	99	
ESO 312-SC04	cl	08 26.9	−41 15	Vel	II2	1.0						20	187	10	
ESO 370-SC13	cl	08 27.2	−34 42	Pyx	II1	2.0						20	171	10	
NGC 2609	cl?	08 29 30	−61 06.6	Car		6.0		10				25	200	4	Skiff: = HD 72425 (V=9.4, F5V), sparse group.
Ruprecht 157	cl	08 29 52	−19 05.8	Pyx	IV1m	7.0		30	11.0			12	153	4	Skiff: Sparse group. Aliases: Lund 457; OCl 652; C0827−189
vdB-Ha 34	cl	08 31 12	−44 29.9	Vel	IV2p n	25.0		20				20	187	4	Skiff: = HD 72453 (V=9.2, B4). Sparse group of brighter stars in Gum nebula region. Aliases: Lund 1058; C0829−443

Table 4.1: Catalog of Clusters and Asterisms in the Milky Way, and Objects Misidentified as Such

Name	Type	2000.0 R.A.	Dec.	Con.	Tr. Type	Diam. (′)	Tot. Vm	#str	Bt* Vm	V Sur	Dist. (pc)	S #	2U #	Ref	Comments and Aliases
Pismis 3	cl	08 31 21	−38 39.0	Vel	II1m	6.0		50	13.0			20	171	4	Aliases: OCl 731; vdB-Ha 33; C0829−385
Alessi J08317-3904	ast	08 31.7	−39 04	Vel		24.0		17	6			20	171	10	
ESO 313-SC03	cl	08 31.7	−41 47	Vel	II3	2.5						20	187	10	
ESO 370-SC17	cl	08 31.8	−36 12	Pyx	III3	3.0						20	171	99	Archinal: Id? DSS shows no 3′ cluster here.
Ruprecht 62	cl:	08 32 30	−19 39.8	Pyx	IV2p	7.0		20	11.0			12	153	4	DSFG: Probably not a cluster. Skiff: Sparse group. Aliases: Lund 460; OCl 658; C0830−194
Ruprecht 63	cl	08 32 40	−48 18.0	Vel	II1p	3.0		20	13.0			20	187	4	Aliases: Lund 459; OCl 758; vdB-Ha 35; C0831−481
Pismis 4	cl	08 34.6	−44 22	Vel	III3m n	25.0	5.9	45	8.0	12.9	550	20	187	4	Skiff: Large group in Gum nebula. Aliases: Lund 461; OCl 746; vdB-Ha 36; BRAN 159; C0832−441
vdB-Ha 37	cl	08 35 48	−43 36.1	Vel	II1m	3.0		40				20	187	4	Aliases: Lund 1059; C0834−434
NGC 2627	cl	08 37 15	−29 57.0	Pyx	II2r	9.0	8.4	60	11.0	13.2		20	171	4	Aliases: Cr 188; Lund 462; Mel 87; OCl 714; Raab 74; vdB-Ha 38; C0835−297
Ruprecht 64	cl	08 37.4	−40 05	Vel	II3r	70.0		80	9.0			20	171	99	Archinal: DSS shows large (80′) scattered grouping of stars involved in nebulosity. HD 74067 (V=5.20v?) E and CD -40° 4427 on SW. Aliases: Lund 463; OCl 740; OCl 740.0; C0835−399
Pismis 5	cl	08 37 39	−39 34.8	Vel	III2p n	2.0	9.9	10	11.0	11.4		20	171	4	See notes. DSFG: Probably not a cluster. Aliases: Lund 464; OCl 735; BRAN 165; OCl 735.0; C0835−394
NGC 2635	cl	08 38 27	−34 46.3	Pyx	II1p	3.0	11.2	15	13.0	13.6		20	171	4	DSFG: Probably not a cluster. Aliases: Cr 190; Lund 465; Mel 89; OCl 728; Raab 76; vdB-Ha 39; C0836−345
NGC 2645	cl	08 39 04	−46 13.6	Vel	II3p	3.0	7.32	12	9.0	9.7	1670	20	187	99	See notes. Position is that of nearly-central pair HD 73919/CoD−45 4352. Skiff: = Pi 6 = HD 73919/CoD-45 4352. Aliases: Pi 6; OCl 754; Lund 467; vdB-Ha 40; C0837−460
Ruprecht 65	cl:	08 39 22	−44 03.3	Vel	IV2p	5.0		20	13.0			20	187	4	DSFG: Probably not a cluster. Aliases: Lund 466; OCl 750; OCl 750.0; C0837−438
IC 2391	cl	08 40.3	−52 55	Vel	II3m	60.0	2.6	30	4.0	11.5	153	25	200	4	See notes. Skiff: = o Velorum = HR 3447 = HD 74195 (V=3.6, B3IV).; Moore: Omicron Vel Cl.. Aliases: Cr 191; Lund 469; OCl 767; Omi Vel; vdB-Ha 42; OCl 767.0; Caldw 85; C0838−528
Waterloo 6	cl	08 40 20.7	−46 07 25	Vel	II3p	2.0	8.4	30	9.18	9.9	1820	20	187	99	Skiff: = HD 74129 (V=9.1, A). Small group. Aliases: Lund 486; C0838−459
NGC 2632	cl	08 40 22	+19 40.2	Cnc	II3m	70.0	3.1	161	6.0	12.3	158	12	74	4	See notes. M 44. “Praesepe” or “Beehive cluster.” Skiff: = HD 73710 = HR 3428 (SIMBAD/Lynga center [= 39 Cnc = HD 73665] is too far N). Aliases: Cr 189; Lund 468; M 44; Mel 88; OCl 507; Praesepe; Raab 75; OCl 507.0; C0837+201
Ruprecht 66	cl	08 40 32	−38 04.6	Vel	II1p	2.0		20	15.0			20	170	4	Aliases: Lund 470; OCl 732; vdB-Ha 41; (4) IRAS 08387−3752; C0838−378
Pismis 7	cl	08 41 09	−38 42.1	Vel	II1m	3.0		35	13.0			20	170	4	Aliases: Lund 471; OCl 734; vdB-Ha 43; C0839−385
Pismis 8	cl	08 41 35	−46 16.3	Vel	II2p	3.0	9.5	25	10.0	11.9	1454	20	187	4	Aliases: Lund 473; OCl 755; vdB-Ha 44; C0839−461
Ruprecht 67	cl:	08 41 45	−43 22.5	Vel	III2m	7.0	9.1	35	12.0	13.3	1202	20	187	4	DSFG: Probably not a cluster. Skiff: Sparse group. Aliases: Lund 474; OCl 748; C0840−432
Eta Cha cl	cl	08 42.2	−78 56 37	Cha		32.0		12	5.455		97.	25	218	99	Discovered in X-ray by Mamajek, *et al.* [1999]. Large group of at least 12 stars around Eta Cha (V=5.455, B8V).
IC 2395	cl	08 42 31	−48 06.5	Vel	II3m	13.0	4.6	40	5.53	10.2		20	187	51	See notes. Aliases: Lac III-3; Raab 79; Cr 192; OCl 763; (5) C0839−480; vdB-Ha 47; Lund 472; Lund 1060; C0841−479
NGC 2659	cl	08 42 34	−45 00.0	Vel	III2r	15.0	8.6	80	10.0	14.5	1450	20	187	4	Skiff: Group extends to NE. Aliases: Cr 194; Lund 476; Mel 91; OCl 752; Pi 9; Raab 78; vdB-Ha 46; OCl 752.0; C0840−447
NGC 2660	cl	08 42 39	−47 12.0	Vel	I1r	3.0	8.8	381	13.0	11.2	2884	20	187	4	Aliases: Cr 193; Lund 475; Mel 92; OCl 759; vdB-Ha 45; C0840−469
ESO 432-SC03	cl	08 42.9	−27 52	Pyx	II2	8.0						20	152	10	
NGC 2658	cl	08 43 28	−32 39.4	Pyx	I2r	10.0	9.2	80	12.0	14.2		20	170	4	Skiff: Diffuse. Aliases: Cr 195; Lund 477; Mel 90; OCl 723; Raab 77; vdB-Ha 48; OCl 723.0; C0841−324
ESO 313-SC11	cl	08 43.7	−37 43	Vel	III2	4.0						20	170	99	Archinal: Id? DSS shows no 4′ cluster here, unless group of stars to NE is intended.
ESO 313-SC12	cl	08 43.9	−40 14	Vel	I2	10.0						20	170	10	
Ruprecht 68	cl	08 44.5	−35 55	Pyx	III1r	10.0		80	14.0			20	170	4	Skiff: Okay, large and diffuse. Aliases: Lund 480; OCl 729; vdB-Ha 49; C0842−357
Collinder 197	cl	08 44 40	−41 16.6	Vel	III3m n	25.0	6.7	40	7.35	13.7	991	20	187	4	Skiff: = HD 74804 (V=7.3, B4II). Stars spread mostly S of nebula, but no real cluster. Aliases: Lund 479; OCl 742; C0842−411
Bochum 7	cl	08 44.8	−45 58	Vel	IV3p	20.0	6.8	12	7.55	13.3	5754	20	187	99	Skiff: Check VM chart. Archinal: Id? Several bright stars running N-S on E side of field, otherwise only rich field. Aliases: Lund 1131; C0843−458

Table 4.1: Catalog of Clusters and Asterisms in the Milky Way, and Objects Misidentified as Such

Name	Type	2000.0 R.A.	Dec.	Con.	Tr. Type	Diam. (′)	Tot. Vm	#str	Bt* Vm	V Sur	Dist. (pc)	S #	2U #	Ref	Comments and Aliases
Ruprecht 69	cl	08 44 49.1	−47 36 04	Vel	IV1p n	2.0		10	14.0			20	187	99	Aliases: Lund 478; OCl 762; C0843−474
Collinder 196	cl:	08 45.1	−31 37	Pyx	IV2p	3.0	10.5	12		12.9		20	170	99	DSFG: Probably not a cluster. Skiff: Not obvious in 0.4 degree field. Archinal: Id? Aliases: Lund 482; OCl 721; C0843−314
Collinder 198	cl	08 45.4	−31 45	Pyx		5.0	11.2			14.7		20	170	99	DSFG: Probably not a cluster. Skiff: Not obvious in 0.4 degree field. Archinal: Id? Aliases: OCl 722; C0843−315
NGC 2670	cl	08 45 30	−48 47.5	Vel	III2m	7.0	7.8	30	13.0	12.0	955	20	187	4	Aliases: Cr 200; Lund 484; Mel 93; OCl 764; Raab 80; vdB-Ha 50; C0843−486
NGC 2671	cl	08 46 12	−41 52.6	Vel	I2m	5.0	11.6	40		15.1		20	187	4	Aliases: Cr 201; Lund 485; OCl 745; vdB-Ha 51; C0844−417
ESO 260-SC6	cl	08 46 15	−47 41.9	Vel	III2	2.0						20	187	99	Archinal: ESO incorrectly suggests this is Ru 69.
NGC 2669	cl	08 46 19	−52 56.1	Vel	III3m	14.0	6.1	90	7.69	11.8	1042	25	200	51	See notes. Includes Harvard 3. Brightest star is HD 75105 (V=7.69, B8III/IV). Aliases: h 3140; Cr 199; OCl 745; Lund 745; C0843−527
Harvard 3	ptcl	08 46.5	−52 54	Vel		7.0		40				25	200	51	See notes. Central condensation of NGC 2669. Includes no HD stars. Aliases: Cr 202; vdB-Ha 52; Lund 747; C0845−527
NGC 2664	ast	08 47 08	+12 36.3	Cnc				4	9			12	94	4	Skiff: Trapezoid of magnitude 10 to 11 stars.
ESO 211-SC01	cl	08 47.2	−52 04	Vel	III3	4.0						25	200	10	
Trumpler 10	cl	08 47 45	−42 30.0	Vel	II3m	30.0	5.0	40	6.42	12.4	415	20	187	4	See notes. Skiff: Small group of bright stars. Aliases: Cr 203; Lund 487; OCl 747; Lac II-6; vdB-Ha 53; OCl 747.0; C0846−423
ESO 260-SC7	cl	08 48 00	−47 01.8	Vel	III2	5.0						20	186	99	Archinal: ESO suggests this is Ru 70. However, the original Ru 70 position is about 1 minute farther east.
Ruprecht 70	cl	08 49.1	−46 49	Vel	IV2p	5.0			13.0			20	186	99	Skiff: Not obvious in 0.4 degree field. Archinal: Id? Aliases: Lund 488; OCl 760; C0847−466
Ruprecht 71	cl	08 49.5	−46 47	Vel	III2m	7.0		30	11.0			20	186	99	Skiff: Not obvious in 0.4 degree field. Archinal: Id? Aliases: Lund 489; OCl 761; C0847−465
vdB-Ha 54	cl	08 49 41	−44 21.2	Vel	II1p	4.0		20				20	186	4	Aliases: Lund 1062; C0848−442
NGC 2666	cl??	08 50.0	+47 03	UMa								6	39	99	Skiff: Not obvious in 0.3 degree field. Archinal: Id?
NGC 2678	ast	08 50 03	+11 20.3	Cnc				13	9			12	94	4	Skiff: Four magnitude 8 stars only.
[CV98] 1	cl?	08 50 07	+11 56.7	Cnc		5.0						12	94	99	Dias, *et al.* [2002] name this "Chupina 1".
[CV98] 2	cl?	08 50 30	+12 17.7	Cnc		2.1						12	94	99	Dias, *et al.* [2002] name this "Chupina 2".
NGC 2682	cl	08 51 24	+11 49	Cnc	II3r	25.0	6.9	324	9.0	13.9	791	12	94	4	See notes. DSFG: M 67. Skiff: Okay. Aliases: Cr 204; Lund 490; M 67; Mel 94; OCl 549; Raab 81; OCl 549.0; C0847+120
[CV98] 3	cl?	08 51 27	+11 23.7	Cnc		2.9						12	94	99	Dias, *et al.* [2002] name this "Chupina 3".
ESO 211-SC03	cl	08 51.6	−50 15	Vel	II3	2.5						25	186	10	
[CV98] 4	cl?	08 52 00	+12 22.7	Cnc		5.0						12	94	99	Dias, *et al.* [2002] name this "Chupina 4".
Ruprecht 72	cl	08 52 05	−37 36.1	Vel	IV1p	3.0		12	13.0			20	170	4	Skiff: Perfectly ridiculous cluster!. Aliases: Lund 491; OCl 737; C0850−374
Ruprecht 158	cl	08 52 23	−37 33.6	Vel	III2p	2.0		10	12.0			20	170	4	See notes. Skiff: Perfectly ridiculous cluster!. Aliases: Lund 492; OCl 736; C0850−373
ESO 371-SC25	cl	08 53.0	−35 29	Pyx	I2	3.0						20	170	10	
[CV98] 5	cl?	08 53 01	+11 51.7	Cnc		4.5						12	94	99	Dias, *et al.* [2002] name this "Chupina 5".
NGC 2653	as??	08 55.6	+78 25	Cam								2	6	99	Skiff: Not obvious in 0.3 degree field. Archinal: Id?
vdB-Ha 55	cl	08 56 10.9	−39 30 40	Vel	III1m	2.0		30				20	170	8	Archinal: Position from DSS. Aliases: Lund 1063; C0854−393
vdB-Ha 56	cl	08 57 08	−43 15.4	Vel	IV3m n	20.0		35				20	186	4	Skiff: Large circlet, position = HD 76838 is brightest star on S side (earliest spectral type). Aliases: Lund 1064; C0855−430
Muzzio 1	cl	08 57.2	−47 45	Vel	II2m	10.0		30			1700	20	186	99	Skiff: DSS plate overlap region. Archinal: Id? Nothing obvious on DSS, possibly due to being in overlap region. Aliases: Lund 496; C0855−475
[DB01] 36	cl?	08 58 05.0	−47 22 40	Vel		1.2						20	186	16	Infrared cluster. [DB01]: Partly resolved cluster in re ection nebula vdBH-RN 26, in RCW 38?
Markarian 18	cl	09 00 31	−48 59.1	Vel	I3m	5.0	7.8	30	9.32	11.3	1500	20	186	4	Skiff: = HD 77421 (V=9.3, B). DSS SERC-V short exposure field. Aliases: Cr 205; Lund 493; OCl 766; vdB-Ha 57; C0858−487
Ruprecht 73	cl	09 01 12	−50 54.5	Vel	IV1p	3.0		25	14.0			25	186	4	Skiff: DSS SERC-V short exposure field. Aliases: Lund 495; OCl 769; (4) IRAS 08599−5041; C0859−507

Table 4.1: Catalog of Clusters and Asterisms in the Milky Way, and Objects Misidentified as Such

Name	Type	2000.0 R.A.	Dec.	Con.	Tr. Type	Diam. (′)	Tot. Vm	#str	Bt* Vm	V Sur	Dist. (pc)	S #	2U #	Ref	Comments and Aliases
Pismis 10	ast	09 02.6	–43 38	Vel		2.5			10.0p			20	186	99	DSFG: Probably not a cluster. Skiff: Not obvious in 0.2 degree field. Archinal: Id? Aliases: OCl 757; C0900–434
ESO 260-SC17	cl	09 04.8	–46 02	Vel	III3	7.0						20	186	10	
ESO 165-SC09	cl	09 05.2	–55 57	Vel	II2	15.0		20				25	199	8	Archinal: Nice cluster on DSS, about 20 stars. Brightest star (on the southern side) is HD 78327 (V=9.2, K2).
Pyxis	gcl	09 07 57.8	–37 13 17	Pyx?		4.0	12.90		15.2	15.9	40000	20	170	54	See notes. Pyxis globular cluster. Discovered in 1995. May belong to LMC or SMC. See Weinberg [1995], and Irwin, Demers, and Kunkel [1995]. Alias: [W95] 3
[PKL98] 11	cl	09 09 30	–59 07.7	Car		9.0		11			132	25	199	14	
vdB-Ha 58	cl	09 10 28	–56 19	Vel	III1p	2.0		25				25	199	4	Skiff: Identification uncertain. Aliases: Lund 1065; (4) IRAS 09089–5605; C0908–560
ESO 166-SC04	cl	09 10.5	–53 53	Vel	III2	4.0						25	199	10	
ESO 261-SC03	cl	09 11.4	–47 02	Vel	III3	10.0						20	186	10	
NGC 2808	gcl	09 12 02.6	–64 51 47	Car		14.0	6.2		13.5	11.9	9200	25	210	6	Aliases: EQ 0911–646; C0911–646
[PKL98] 12	cl?	09 13 47	–43 44.4	Vel		3.0		6			174	20	186	14	
Pismis 11	cl	09 15 53	–50 00.7	Vel	I2p	2.5		20	12.0			25	186	4	See notes. Skiff: = CoD-49 4263 = CPD-49 2322 (V=11.0, B). Aliases: OCl 772; vdB-Ha 60; (5) C0914–498; Lund 498; Lund 1066; C0915–495
NGC 2818	clpn	09 16 10	–36 37.1	Pyx	III1m n	8.0	8.2	298	11.32	12.7	3221	20	170	4	See notes. The NGC 2818 designation applies to the cluster and planetary nebula. Aliases: Cr 206; Lund 497; Mel 96; OCl 743; Raab 82; Dunlop 564; h 3154; vdB-Ha 59; C0914–364
ESO 211-SC09	cl	09 16.7	–50 17	Vel	I2	2.0						25	186	99	Archinal: 1′ diameter cluster of faint stars on edge of DSS overlap region.
NGC 2849	cl	09 19 23	–40 31.2	Vel	I1m	3.0	12.5	40		14.9		20	186	4	Aliases: Cr 207; Lund 499; OCl 756; vdB-Ha 61; C0917–403
ESO 314-SC14	cl	09 19.7	–38 07	Vel	III2	10.0						20	170	10	
NGC 2846	*	09 19.9	–14 41	Hya				1				12	133	99	Skiff: = Star superposed on galaxy NGC 2848? Archinal: Id?
Pismis 12	cl	09 20 00	–45 07.0	Vel	III1p	5.0	9.7	20	12.0	13.2		20	186	4	DSFG: Doubtful cluster. Aliases: Lund 500; OCl 765; vdB-Ha 62; C0918–449
Ruprecht 159	cl	09 20 08	–60 24.2	Car	IV2p	2.0		50	15.0			25	199	99	Archinal: Faint and small, barely standing out from background on histogram equalization display of DSS image. Aliases: Lund 501; OCl 795; C0919–601
NGC 2847	*HII	09 20 08.7	–16 31 02	Hya				1				12	133	99	Archinal: Star and HII region 0.6′ NW of nucleus of NGC 2848.
vdB-Ha 63	cl	09 20 38	–49 13.3	Vel		1.5						20	186	4	Skiff: DSS SERC-V short exposure field. Aliases: Lund 1067; (4) IRAS 09183–4902; C0918–490
E 3	gcl	09 20 59.3	–77 16 57	Cha			11.4		17.0		7300	25	218	6	Alias: C0921–770
Ruprecht 74	cl	09 21.0	–37 07	Pyx	III1p	2.0		20	13.0			20	170	4	Skiff: Sparse group. Aliases: Lund 502; OCl 749; C0919–368
Ruprecht 75	cl	09 21 54	–56 18.7	Vel	II1p	2.0		20	12.0			25	199	4	Aliases: Lund 503; OCl 786; vdB-Ha 65; C0920–560
NGC 2866	cl?	09 22 06.5	–51 06 08	Vel		20.0						25	186	99	Includes the cluster Pismis 13. Diameter here from visual observation by B. Skiff. Alias: (2) Pi 13
Pismis 13	cl	09 22 06.5	–51 06 08	Vel	I2m	2.0	10.2	30	12.0	11.7	2805	25	186	99	Included in NGC 2866, and discovered along with it by J. Herschel. Aliases: Lund 504; OCl 774; vdB-Ha 64; (3) NGC 2866; C0920–509
ESO 261-SC07	cl	09 24.3	–44 42	Vel	III3	33.0						20	186	10	
Ruprecht 76	cl	09 24 18	–51 39.9	Vel	IV2p	5.0	10.8	20	13.0	14.3	1337	25	199	4	Skiff: = HD 81518 (V=9.3, B9III/IV). Sparse group. Aliases: Lund 505; OCl 775; C0922–515
vdB-Ha 66	cl	09 25 16	–54 43.1	Vel	III2p	1.5		20				25	199	51	See notes. Many references incorrectly identify this as a globular cluster. Aliases: Lund 1068; ESO 166-12; UKS 2; EQ 0923–545; UKS 0923-54.5; C0923–545
vdB-Ha 67	cl	09 26 43	–51 16.5	Vel	III1m	4.0		40				25	186	4	Skiff: Rich cluster. Aliases: Lund 1069; C0925–511
Ruprecht 77	cl	09 27 02	–55 07.3	Vel	II1m	5.0	10.4	58	14.0	13.9	4943	25	199	4	Aliases: Lund 506; OCl 784; vdB-Ha 68; C0925–549
IC 2488	cl	09 27 27	–56 57.4	Vel	II3r	18.0	7.4	70	10.0	13.7		25	199	4	Skiff: Sparse. Aliases: Cr 208; Lund 507; Mel 97; Raab 83; vdB-Ha 69; C0926–567
Ruprecht 78	cl	09 29 07.9	–53 41 57	Vel	II2m	3.0		30	15.0		3311	25	199	99	Aliases: Lund 508; OCl 782; vdB-Ha 70; C0927–534
Pismis 14	cl	09 29.3	–52 42	Vel	II2p	1.5		12	14.0			25	199	99	Skiff: Nothing small obvious in 0.25/0.4 degree field. Archinal: Id? Aliases: Lund 509; OCl 780; C0927–525
[AO84] VI	mc	09.5	+02.0	Hya		11000.	2.37	18	3.10	22.6		13	113	54	Moving cluster with very large angular size, hypothesized by Agekyan and Orlov [1984].
NGC 2910	cl	09 30 30	–52 54.8	Vel	III3m	6.0	7.2	59	9.25	11.1	1272	25	199	4	Aliases: Cr 209; Lund 510; OCl 781; vdB-Ha 71; C0928–526

Table 4.1: Catalog of Clusters and Asterisms in the Milky Way, and Objects Misidentified as Such

Name	Type	2000.0 R.A.	Dec.	Con.	Tr. Type	Diam. (′)	Tot. Vm	#str	Bt* Vm	V Sur	Dist. (pc)	S #	2U #	Ref	Comments and Aliases
vdB-Ha 72	cl	09 31 23	−53 02.2	Vel	III1p	2.0		25				25	199	4	Aliases: Lund 1070; C0929–527
vdB-Ha 73	cl	09 31 56	−50 13.2	Vel	II1p	1.5		20				25	186	4	Skiff: Rich cluster. Aliases: Lund 1071; C0930–499
NGC 2901	??	09 32.4	+31 07	Leo								6	56	99	Skiff: Double star: brighter component = GSC 2494-0616, 9 32 19 +31 07.1 (mG 13.7). Archinal: Id?
Basel 20	cl	09 32.5	−56 18	Vel		10.0					3873	25	199	99	Skiff: Not obvious in 0.4 degree field. Archinal: Id? Alias: C0931–561
NGC 2925	cl	09 33 11	−53 23.8	Vel	II3m	15.0	8.3	40		14.2	774	25	199	4	Skiff: Sparse. Aliases: Cr 210; Lund 511; OCl 783; OCl 783.0; C0932–532
Turner 5	cl?	09 33 50.9	−36 36 57	Ant					8.890			20	170	99	Turner and Berdnikov [2002] propose this possible cluster may be associated with the Cepheid variable T Antliae (V=8.89var).
vdB-Ha 75	cl	09 34 42	−54 40.9	Vel	IV2m	3.0		30				25	199	4	Skiff: Absorption hole? Aliases: Lund 1072; C0933–545
Pismis 15	cl	09 34 45	−48 02.1	Vel	II1m	5.0		35	14.0			20	186	4	Aliases: Lund 512; OCl 773; vdB-Ha 74; C0932–479
NGC 2932	MW?	09 35.3	−46 57	Vel								20	186	99	Skiff: Not obvious in 0.4 degree field. Archinal: Id?
ESO 315-SC14	cl	09 35.4	−39 32	Ant		3.0						20	170	10	
[AO84] II	mc	09.6	+16.0	Leo		10000.	-0.05	24	0.08			12	93	54	Moving cluster with very large angular size, hypothesized by Agekyan and Orlov [1984].
NGC 2972	cl	09 40 12	−50 19.3	Vel	II1p	5.0	9.9	25	11.40	13.4	1180	25	186	4	Aliases: Cr 211; Lund 513; OCl 778; vdB-Ha 76; (4) IRAS 09386–5006; C0938–501
Hogg 1	ast?	09 40 33	−50 34.7	Vel		7.0						25	186	99	Archinal: Scattering of 5 bright stars and some fainter ones. Confirmed at Hogg position. Aliases: OCl 779; C0938–503
Ruprecht 79	cl	09 41 03	−53 50.0	Vel	III2p	6.0	9.2	109	11.0	13.1	2420	25	199	4	Skiff: DSS SERC-V short exposure field. Aliases: Lund 515; OCl 787; vdB-Ha 77; C0939–536
NGC 2982	cl	09 42 01	−44 01.6	Vel	III1p	12.0			10			20	186	4	See notes. Skiff: = GSC 7705-1451, sparse group elongated E-W. Aliases: Ru 80; OCl 770; Lund 516; C0940–438
vdB-Ha 78	cl	09 43 48	−56 34.4	Vel	III1p	1.5		15				25	199	4	Skiff: DSS SERC-V short exposure field. Aliases: Lund 1073; C0942–563
vdB-Ha 79	cl	09 44.1	−53 18	Vel		2.5						25	199	99	Skiff: Not visible, DSS SERC-V short exposure field. Archinal: Id? Aliases: Lund 1074; C0942–530
NGC 2995	cl??	09 44.1	−54 47	Vel				20	11			25	199	99	Skiff: DSS SERC-V short exposure field. Archinal: Id? DSS shows nothing obvious (in 8′, 24′, and 48′ fields). Alias: h 3189
NGC 2999	dup?	09 45.2	−50 26	Vel								25	186	99	Duplicate identity for NGC 2972? Observations are needed to verify this. Skiff: Not obvious in 0.35 degree field. Archinal: Id?
Ruprecht 81	cl:	09 45 13	−44 06.3	Vel	IV3p	5.0			12.0			20	186	4	Skiff: Sparse group. Aliases: Lund 517; OCl 771; (4) IRAS 09433–4354; C0943–439
Ruprecht 82	cl	09 45 49	−53 59.7	Vel	IV2p	6.0	8.1	143	12.0	12.0	2455	25	199	99	Archinal: Only slight condensation in field, but confirmed against Ruprecht's position and description. Aliases: Lund 518; OCl 788; C0943–537
NGC 3033	cl	09 48 40	−56 24.7	Vel	II2m	12.0	8.8	50	10.59	14.2	1067	25	199	4	Skiff: = HR 3895 = HD 85250 (V=6.1, KOIII, nonmember). Aliases: Cr 212; Lund 519; C0947–561
Ruprecht 84	cl	09 49 04	−65 15.1	Car	III2p	4.0		20	11.0			25	210	4	Skiff: DSS SERC-V short exposure field. Aliases: Lund 521; OCl 814; C0947–650
Ruprecht 83	cl	09 49 15	−54 36.0	Vel	I2m	3.0	9.8	44	12.0	12.2	2168	25	199	4	Skiff: DSS SERC-V short exposure field. Aliases: Lund 520; OCl 791; vdB-Ha 80; (4) IRAS 09473–5420; C0947–543
NGC 3036	cl	09 49 16	−62 40.5	Car				20				25	210	4	Skiff: = GSC 8946-0802; asterism 4′ long elongated NE-SW; DSS SERC-V short exposure field.
Pismis 16	cl	09 51 14	−53 10.6	Vel	I3p	2.0	8.0	12	9.0	9.5	2218	25	199	4	Aliases: Lund 522; OCl 790; vdB-Ha 81; C0949–529
Hogg 2	cl:	09 51.5	−56 17	Vel	IV2p	7.0		20				25	199	99	Archinal: Confirmed against Hogg position and size. Faint, only visible on DSS with histogram equalization display. Aliases: Lund 523; OCl 797; C0949–560
Collinder 213	cl	09 55 00	−50 56.8	Vel	IV2p	17.0	8.7	21	8.7	14.9		25	186	8	Archinal: Position from DSS. Diam., no. stars from Collinder. Irregularly shaped. Includes HD 85911 (V=9.6) and HD 86113 (V=8.7). Aliases: Lund 524; OCl 785; OCl 785.0; C0952–504
ESO 435-SC09	cl	09 55.5	−28 59	Ant	II2	15.0						20	152	10	
Ruprecht 160	cl	09 55.5	−47 01	Vel	I3p	1.7			14.0			20	186	4	Skiff: Small group. Aliases: Lund 525; OCl 777; C0953–467
Hogg 3	cl?	09 57 40	−54 40.6	Vel	IV2p	2.0		10				25	199	8	Position measured from DSS. Scattered group with 3 brighter stars. May not be a cluster? Hogg 4 to NE. Aliases: Lund 526; OCl 794; C0956–544
Hogg 4	cl?	09 57 53	−54 36.6	Vel		4.0						25	199	8	Position measured from DSS. Scattered group. May not be a cluster? Hogg 3 to SW. Aliases: Lund 527; OCl 793; C0956–543
ESO 435-SC17	cl	09 58.8	−30 55	Ant	II1	4.0						20	170	10	

Table 4.1: Catalog of Clusters and Asterisms in the Milky Way, and Objects Misidentified as Such

Name	Type	2000.0 R.A.	Dec.	Con.	Tr. Type	Diam. (′)	Tot. Vm	#str	Bt* Vm	V Sur	Dist. (pc)	S #	2U #	Ref	Comments and Aliases
NGC 3105	cl	10 00 40	–54 47.3	Vel	I2p	2.0	9.7	97	12.36	11.2	6185	25	199	4	See notes. Skiff: DSS SERC-V short exposure field. Aliases: Cr 214; Lund 528; OCl 798; vdB-Ha 82; C0959–545
vdB-Ha 84	cl	10 01 19	–58 13.1	Car		4.5						25	199	4	Skiff: DSS SERC-V short exposure field. Aliases: Lund 1075; C0959–579
Ruprecht 85	cl:	10 01 26	–55 06.6	Vel	III1m	3.0		40	15.0			25	199	4	Skiff: DSS SERC-V short exposure field. Aliases: Lund 530; OCl 799; vdB-Ha 83; C0959–548
Ruprecht 86	cl	10 01 27.7	–59 30 41	Car	III2m	12.0			12.0			25	199	99	Archinal: DSS shows 3′ x 15′ E-W grouping of stars standing out slightly from Milky Way background. Confirmed against Ruprecht. Aliases: Lund 529; OCl 801; C1000–592
vdB-Ha 85	cl	10 02.0	–49 35.5	Vel	IV1m	5.0		50				20	186	8	Archinal: Group of 4 brighter stars with two included clumps (clusters?) NW and SE. All 5′ SE of HD 87120. Aliases: Lund 1076; C1000–494
NGC 3114	cl	10 02.7	–60 06	Car	II3r	35.0	4.2	171	9.0	11.9	908	25	199	4	Skiff: Too big to check on DSS, looks ~okay. DSS SERC-V short exposure field. Aliases: Cr 215; Lund 531; Mel 98; OCl 802; Raab 84; vdB-Ha 86; OCl 802.0; C1001–598
Loden 28	cl?	10 03 08.6	–58 08 38	Car		15.0						25	199	99	Archinal: Not obvious on DSS, but confirmed against Lodén chart.
ESO 092-SC05	cl	10 03.2	–64 45	Car	I2	5.0						25	210	10	
ESO 435-SC33	cl	10 03.9	–32 03	Ant	II1	3.0						20	169	10	
Loden 1	cl	10 04 25	–55 47.3	Vel		16.0		29	7.99			25	199	99	Archinal: Confirmed via Lodén chart. Brightest star is HD 87699 (V=7.99, Lodén). Includes position of Schuster 1 cluster.
vdB-Ha 87	cl	10 04 34	–55 23	Vel	II2m	3.0		30				25	199	4	Aliases: Lund 1077; C1002–552
Schuster 1	cl	10 04 39.0	–55 51 29	Vel	II1m	1.3		50				25	199	51	See notes. Very faint cluster. Not visible on the DSS, but appears on the DSS-II image. Possibly a globular cluster? Aliases: Lund 1210; Schuster; C1002–556
Trumpler 11	cl	10 04.9	–61 36	Car	II3m	5.0	8.1	6		11.6		25	199	99	Archinal: DSS shows 3′ clump, with a brighter star to N and S. Aliases: Cr 216; OCl 808; C1003–613
Palomar 3	gcl	10 05 31.4	+00 04 17	Sex		1.6	13.9		18.0	14.9	90800	13	113	55	Has been listed incorrectly as a galaxy, with designations UGC 5439 = MCG +00-26-017 = CGCG 08-35. [Lederman and Gottlieb, 1996] Aliases: (5) Sex C; (5) UGC 5439; (5) MCG +00-26-017; (5) CGCG 08–35; EQ 1003+003; C1003+003
Hogg 5	cl	10 06 09	–60 23.1	Car	I3r	3.0		20				25	199	99	Position from DSS. Appears as asterism there. This is NOT Tr 12, but Hogg suggests [1965, p. 11] it may be an extension of it. Aliases: Lund 533; OCl 804; C1004–601
vdB-Ha 88	cl	10 06 15	–51 36.8	Vel	III1p	4.0		20				25	199	4	Aliases: Lund 1078; C1004–513
Hogg 6	cl	10 06 28	–60 29.9	Car		3.0						25	199	8	Archinal: Position from DSS. Appears as asterism there. Hogg [1965, p.11] suggests this may be an extension of Tr 12. Aliases: Lund 535; OCl 805; C1004–602
Trumpler 12	cl	10 06.5	–60 18	Car	I3p	4.0	8.8	11		11.8		25	199	8	Aliases: Cr 217; Lund 534; OCl 803; vdB-Ha 89; C1004–600
NGC 3123	nf?	10 07.0	+00 04	Sex								13	113	99	Skiff: Not obvious in 0.3 degree field. Archinal: Id?
Leo I	gal	10 08 27.5	+12 18 27	Leo		9.8	10.18			15.1		13	93	8	Dwarf galaxy, mistaken for a globular cluster by Czernik (Cz 33). Data here from RC3. Aliases: UGC 5470; DDO 74; PGC 29488; CGCG 064–073; CGCG 1005.8+1233; MCG +02-26-027; RC2 A1005+12; (5) Cz 33
Ruprecht 161	cl	10 08.8	–61 11	Car	III2p	32.0			11.0			25	199	99	Skiff: Not obvious in 0.3 degree DSS SERC-V short exposure field. Archinal: Id? Aliases: Lund 536; OCl 810; OCl 810.0; C1007–609
ESO 435-SC48	cl	10 09.6	–28 21	Ant	I2	4.0						20	151	10	
Loden 27	cl	10 11.1	-56 35	Vel	III2p	21.0		30	10.72			25	199	99	Confirmed via Lodén chart. Three brighter stars and a scattering of fainter ones. Aliases: Lund 1167; OCl 800.1; C1009–563
vdB-Ha 90	cl	10 12 10	–58 04.2	Car		4.0	10.3	8	12.09	13.3	1426	25	199	4	Skiff: = Bochum 8. Aliases: Bo 8; Lund 1079; C1010–578
ESO 436-SC02	cl	10 14.0	–29 11	Ant	I2	5.0						20	151	10	
NGC 3167	cl??	10 14.6	+29 36	LMi								6	55	99	Skiff: Nothing in 0.4 degree field. Archinal: Id? Possibly star? (or unresolved double star, or galaxy at 10 14 34.9 +29 36 37?
ESO 92-SC18	cl	10 14 58	–64 36.8	Car	I2	5.0		1100	15.7		9500	25	210	8	Archinal: DSS position. Other data from [Kassis, *et al.*, 1996]. Aliases: ESO 92-18; ESO 092-SC18
Ruprecht 87	cl	10 15 30	–50 42.3	Vel	III2p	4.0		20	11.0			25	186	4	Skiff: Small group. Aliases: Lund 537; OCl 792; C1013–504
Alessi 4	cl	10 16 13	–34 21.0	Ant		40.0						20	169	99	
vdB-Ha 91	cl	10 17.3	–58 42	Car		5.0						25	199	4	Skiff: Sparse group, position okay. DSS SERC-V short exposure field. Aliases: Lund 1080; C1015–584
NGC 3201	gcl	10 17 36.8	–46 24 40	Vel		20.0	6.9		11.7	13.4	5000	20	186	55	See notes. Aliases: Mel 99; EQ 1015–461; Caldw 79; C1015–461

Table 4.1: Catalog of Clusters and Asterisms in the Milky Way, and Objects Misidentified as Such

Name	Type	2000.0 R.A.	Dec.	Con.	Tr. Type	Diam. (′)	Tot. Vm	#str	Bt* Vm	V Sur	Dist. (pc)	S #	2U #	Ref	Comments and Aliases
Ruprecht 88	cl	10 18 48	−63 08.2	Car	III1m	5.0		30	12.0			25	210	4	Skiff: Sparse group, DSS SERC-V short exposure field. Aliases: Lund 538; OCl 822; C1017–628
vdB-Ha 92	cl	10 19 04	−56 25.0	Vel	II2p	2.0		15				25	199	4	Skiff: = GSC 8608-1428 = IRAS 10172-5609. DSS SERC-V short exposure field. Aliases: Lund 1081; (4) IRAS 10172–5609; C1017–561
NGC 3228	cl	10 21 23	−51 43.4	Vel	II3p	5.0	6.0	23	7.90	9.5	499	25	199	4	Aliases: Cr 218; Lund 539; OCl 800; vdB-Ha 93; C1019–514
ESO 062-SC08	cl	10 21.7	−69 20	Car	II2	5.0						25	210	10	
Loden 46	cl	10 23 16	−54 42.7	Vel		27.0		50	7.78			25	199	99	Archinal: Confirmed via Lodén chart. Brightest star is HD 90049 (V=7.78, Lodén).
Trumpler 13	cl	10 23 48	−60 08.5	Car	II2m	5.0	11.3	40		14.8		25	199	4	Skiff: 3.5′ cluster of brighter stars, including very small (0.7′) cluster of faint stars. Aliases: Cr 219; Lund 541; OCl 815; vdB-Ha 94; C1022–598
NGC 3247	cl	10 24 01	−57 45.5	Car	IV1p n	1.1	10.5	25	11.44	10.7	5012	25	199	51	See notes. Also known as Westerlund 2. But this is NOT Cr 220. Includes nebula GUM 29 = RCW 49 = Bran 300B. Aliases: h 3250; GC 2106; OCl 807; We 2; vdB-Ha 95; ESO 127-SC18; (5) OCl 809; (5) C1024–576; (4) GUM 29; C1022–575
Collinder 220	cl	10 25 52	−57 55.6	Car	III1m	9.5		50				25	199	51	This is NOT NGC 3247 as Collinder and most later catalogues claim. Alias: ESO 127-SC19
NGC 3218	dupl	10 26.5	+74 39	Dra								2	5	53	See notes. This is a duplicate identity for NGC 3183.
NGC 3255	cl	10 26 32	−60 40.7	Car	I2m	2.0	11.0	30	12.44	12.5	1445	25	199	4	DSFG: Probably not a cluster. Skiff: DSS SERC-V short exposure field. Aliases: Cr 221; Lund 544; OCl 817; vdB-Ha 96; C1024–604
IC 2581	cl	10 27 27	−57 37.5	Car	II2p n	5.0	4.3	398	4.64	7.8	2308	25	199	4	DSFG: Without brightest star, visual magnitude = 5.9. Aliases: Cr 222; Lund 545; OCl 811; vdB-Ha 97; OCl 811.0; C1025–573
NGC 3231	cl?	10 27 29	+66 47.9	UMa		9.5		19	10			2	14	53	See notes. HD 90318 (V=7.9) is just to south. Alias: h 704
Loden 172	cl	10 27 51	−60 34.6	Car		22.0		17	8.97			25	199	99	Archinal: Confirmed via Lodén chart. Brightest star is HD 90836 (V=8.97, Lodén). Just NE (and associated with?) NGC 3255.
Ruprecht 89	cl	10 28.5	−58 10	Car	III1p	4.0		25	13.0			25	199	4	Skiff: Not obvious in 0.25 degree DSS SERC-V short exposure field. Aliases: Lund 546; OCl 812; C1026–579
Loden 143	ast?	10 28 44	−58 49.3	Car	IV3p	5.5		12	9.40			25	199	99	Archinal: Confirmed via Lodén chart. Mostly just three 9th magnitude stars. Lodén suggests association with Ru 90. Aliases: Lund 1170; OCl 814.1; C1027–585
Loden 89	cl?	10 28 47.6	−56 44 41	Vel		30.0		26	8.86			25	199	54	Brightest star is HD 91052, which was measured by Lodén [1979b] as V=8.86, B9-A0, but incorrectly identified (as HD 91226).
Hogg 7	ast?	10 29.1	−60 43	Car	III2p	4.0						25	199	99	Archinal: Hogg position confirmed. Very slight condensation, at center of larger (21′) "+" shaped group of faint stars. Aliases: Lund 547; OCl 820; C1027–604
Hogg 8	ast	10 29 09	−60 53 36	Car	II2p	3.0		22				25	199	51	See notes. Position from DSS for included asterism of 3 stars. Whole group is 1.5′ N-S, and 5′ E-W. Brt. star at W end. Not a true cl. Aliases: OCl 821; C1027–606
Loden 59	cl	10 30 22	−54 07.1	Vel		5.5		25	12.60			25	199	99	Archinal: Confirmed via Lodén chart. Lodén suggests this is associated with NGC 3330. Aliases: Lund 1168; OCl 801.1; C1028–538
Collinder 223	cl	10 30.4	−60 05	Car	II2m	8.0	9.4	35		13.9		25	199	8	See notes. Position from T. Karhula. Aliases: Lund 549; OCl 818; C1028–595
Ruprecht 90	cl	10 31.0	−58 27	Car	IV2p	5.0		15	12.0			25	199	8	See notes. Position from T. Karhula. Aliases: Lund 550; OCl 813; C1029–579
Loden 112	cl	10 32 40	−56 41.9	Vel		22.0		8	9.27			25	199	99	Archinal: Confirmed from Lodén chart. Mostly eight 9-10th magnitude stars. Aliases: Lund 1169; OCl 811.1; C1030–564
Loden 153	ast?	10 34 46.7	−58 09 21	Car		7.0		10	9.4			25	199	51	See notes. Northwest of NGC 3293. Position is of center and brightest star, HD 91824 (V=9.4, 06/07). Aliases: OCl 815.1; C1032–578
Bochum 9	cl	10 35.5	−60 10	Car	III3m n	16.0	6.3	30	7.87	12.3		25	199	99	DSFG: Doubtful cluster. Archinal: Obvious as group of Tycho-2 catalogue stars, extending NE to SW. Aliases: Lund 1146; C1033–598
NGC 3293	cl	10 35 49	−58 13.5	Car	I3r	5.0	4.7	93	8.0	8.2	2459	25	199	4	Lodén 153 is to the northwest. Skiff: = HD 91969 (V=6.5, B0Ib). Beautiful cluster. Aliases: Mel 100; Raab 85; Cr 224; OCl 816; Lund 551; Mrk 19; vdB-Ha 98; Lo 153; BRAN 316C; OCl 816.0; GUM 30; RCW 51; C1033–579
Loden 165	cl	10 35 56	−58 44.2	Car		11.0		30	11.20			25	199	99	Archinal: Confirmed via Lodén chart. A scattering of about 30 stars, 12th magnitude and somewhat fainter. Aliases: Lund 1172; OCl 816.1; C1035–584
[AO84] I	mc	10.6	−01.0	Sex		10000.	2.13	17	3.53	22.1		13	112	54	Very large moving cluster hypothesized by Agekyan and Orlov [1984]. Includes the solar system (but not in statistics here)!

Table 4.1: Catalog of Clusters and Asterisms in the Milky Way, and Objects Misidentified as Such

Name	Type	2000.0 R.A.	Dec.	Con.	Tr. Type	Diam. (′)	Tot. Vm	#str	Bt* Vm	V Sur	Dist. (pc)	S #	2U #	Ref	Comments and Aliases
Loden 213	cl	10 36 40	−61 53.0	Car		24.0		24	8.47			25	199	99	Archinal: Confirmed via Lodén chart. Brightest star is HD 92027 (V=8.47, Lodén).
NGC 3324	cl	10 37 19	−58 39.6	Car	I3r n	5.0	6.7	44	8.21	10.2	3116	25	199	4	Skiff: Position centered in nebula. Aliases: Cr 225; Lund 552; OCl 819; OCl 819.0; C1035–583
vdB-Ha 99	cl	10 38 45.0	−59 10 58	Car	III3m n	20.0		40				25	199	99	Archinal: Bright star HD 92397 (V=4.87, K4.5III:) with 8′ diameter group of faint stars around it. Aliases: Lund 1082; C1036–589
NGC 3330	cl	10 38 48	−54 06.9	Vel	III2m	6.0	7.4	39	8.78	11.3	1361	25	199	4	Skiff: = GSC 8601-3587. Aliases: Cr 226; Ha 4; Lund 553; OCl 806; vdB-Ha 100; C1036–538
ESO 062-SC11	cl	10 38.9	−69 02	Car	II3	6.0						25	210	10	
SSWZ94 3	cl	10 41 25.5	−55 16 56	Vel		3.0						25	199	99	
Melotte 101	cl	10 42 00	−65 06.0	Car	III1m	16.0	8.0	50	9.73	14.0	1995	25	210	4	Aliases: Cr 227; Lund 554; OCl 841; Raab 86; vdB-Ha 101; C1040–648
Bochum 10	cl	10 42 08	−59 08.6	Car	II3m n	20.0	6.2	40	8.59	12.7	3221	25	199	4	Skiff: Including circlet and triangle stars only. Aliases: Lund 1147; C1040–588
IC 2602	cl	10 42 57	−64 23.7	Car	I3r	100.0	1.6	60	3.0	11.6	151	25	210	4	See notes. Skiff: = θ Car (HR 4199, V=2.8, B0Vp).; Moore: Theta Car Cl.. Aliases: Mel 102; Raab 87; Cr 229; OCl 838; vdB-Ha 103; Lund 556; (5) C1042–640; Mrk 20; OCl 838.0; Caldw 102; C1041–641
Alessi 5	cl	10 43 08	−61 10.0	Car		33.0						25	199	99	
Trumpler 14	cl	10 43 57	−59 32.9	Car		5.0	5.5	44	6.97	9.0	2867	25	199	4	Skiff: = HD 93129A (V=8.8, O3Ia). Aliases: Cr 230; Lund 557; OCl 826; Mrk 21; vdB-Ha 102; C1041–593
Collinder 228	cl	10 44 00	−60 05.2	Car		14.0	4.4	98	6.28	10.1	2304	25	199	4	Skiff: = HD 93146 (V=8.5, O6.5V). Aliases: Lund 555; OCl 828; OCl 828.0; C1041–597
Collinder 232	cl	10 44 39	−59 33.6	Car		4.0	6.8			9.8		25	199	4	Aliases: Lund 559; OCl 827; C1042–593
Trumpler 15	cl	10 44 44	−59 21.4	Car	III2p n	15.0	7.0	39	8.36	12.9	1989	25	199	4	Skiff: = HD 93249 (V=8.4, O8). Aliases: Cr 231; Lund 558; OCl 825; Mrk 22; vdB-Ha 104; OCl 825.0; 1E 1042.6–5905; C1042–591
Trumpler 16	cl	10 45 10	−59 43.0	Car	n	10.0	5.0	90	6.18	10.0	2630	25	199	4	See notes. DSFG: Includes η Carinae. Aliases: Eta Car cl; Cr 233; OCl 829; Lund 560; (2) Cr 234; Mrk 23; vdB-Ha 105; OCl 829.0; C1043–594
Collinder 234	ptcl	10 45 12.9	−59 44 47	Car		3.0		18	9.5			25	199	51	See notes. Southern part of Trumpler 16. Identified by Lundmark, and listed as Collinder 234. Center and brightest star is HD 93343. Aliases: OCl 830; (3) Tr 16; OCl 830.0
[DB01] 37	cl?	10 45 54.0	−59 56 58	Car		1.5						25	199	16	Infrared cluster. [DB01]: Partly resolved cluster in re ection nebula vdBH-RN 43, in η Carinae Complex?
Bochum 11	cl	10 47 12	−60 05.8	Car	IV3p n	22.0	7.9	20	8.40	14.6	3631	25	199	4	Skiff: = HD 93632 [V=8.4, O4III(f)]. Aliases: Lund 1135; C1045–598
Ruprecht 91	cl	10 47 38.4	−57 28 02	Car	III2p	17.0		15	6.283			25	199	99	See notes. Archinal: Ruprecht had wrong diameter (should be 17′, not 1.7′!). Center star is HD 93662 (V=6.283v, M1II). Aliases: Lund 562; OCl 824; C1045–572
ESO 437-SC61	cl	10 48.0	−29 23	Hya	I2	4.0						20	151	10	
NGC 3382	cl??	10 48.5	+36 44	LMi								6	55	99	Skiff: Nothing in 0.4 degree field. Archinal: Id?
Loden 189	cl	10 50	−56.5	Vel								25	199	5	
NGC 3446	cl?	10 52 17	−45 09.6	Vel		6.5		26				20	185	53	See notes. Galaxy ESO 264-G047 (type (R)SB0/a, size 1.3′ x 1.0′) on east side. Alias: h 3301
vdB-Ha 106	cl	10 52 38.6	−54 16 00	Vel	IV1p	3.0		20				25	199	99	Skiff: Can't find, DSS SERC-V short exposure field. Archinal: 2.5′ group that barely stands out from background. Aliases: Lund 1084; C1050–539
Ruprecht 162	cl:	10 53.0	−62 16	Car	IV2m	6.0		60	12.0			25	199	99	Skiff: Not obvious in 0.3 degree DSS SERC-V short exposure field. Archinal: Id? Aliases: Lund 563; OCl 840; C1051–620
ESO 128-SC16	cl	10 53.7	−58 14	Car	III2	10.0						25	199	10	
Ruprecht 92	cl	10 53 49	−61 45.0	Car	IV1p	8.0	8.6	58	12.0	13.1	2979	25	199	4	Aliases: Lund 564; OCl 834; C1051–614
Shakhbazian 1	gxcl	10 55 06.0	+40 27 33	UMa								6	55	99	See notes. A cluster of 17 galaxies incorrectly listed as a globular cluster ("SAHB 1") by Hesser and Shawl [1985]. Aliases: EQ 1052+407; C1052+407
Trumpler 17	cl	10 56 24	−59 12.3	Car	II2m	5.0	8.4	44	10.30	11.9	1377	25	199	4	Aliases: Cr 235; Lund 565; OCl 831; vdB-Ha 107; C1054–589
Graham 1	cl	10 56 32	−63 00.8	Car	I2p n	5.0		20				25	209	4	Skiff: = CPD-62 1822 (V=9.9, early B). Small group. Aliases: Lund 1175; OCl 843.2; Graham; C1054–627
Collinder 236	cl	10 57 00	−61 07.0	Car	III2p	10.0	7.7	20		12.7		25	199	99	See notes. Improved position and diameter provided by P. Teutsch [Priv. Comm., 2002] Aliases: OCl 835; BRAN 333; OCl 835.0; C1055–607
Bochum 12	cl	10 57 18	−61 43.6	Car	III3p	10.0	9.7	20	11.43	14.7	2218	25	199	4	Skiff: Small group. Aliases: Lund 1136; C1055–614

Table 4.1: Catalog of Clusters and Asterisms in the Milky Way, and Objects Misidentified as Such

Name	Type	2000.0 R.A.	Dec.	Con.	Tr. Type	Diam. (′)	Tot. Vm	#str	Bt* Vm	V Sur	Dist. (pc)	S #	2U #	Ref	Comments and Aliases
Hogg 9	ast?	10 58 22	–59 03.5	Car	II1p	1.0	10.6	10	11.54	10.6		25	199	4	See notes. DSFG: Probably not a cluster. Skiff: Small group. Aliases: Lund 567; OCl 832; C1056–587
GT Car cl	cl	10 59 00.6	–59 29 58	Car		1.0		18				25	199	99	Small cluster 3′ WSW of GT Car. Close to possible GT Car association (11 stars). Discovered by Turner, *et al.* in 1993. Alias: Turner 6
NGC 3496	cl	10 59 34	–60 20.2	Car	II1r	7.0	8.2	110	11.78	12.4	1047	25	199	4	Aliases: Cr 237; Lund 568; OCl 836; vdB-Ha 108; C1057–600
ESO 265-SC01	cl	11 01.0	–45 21	Vel	III1	4.0						20	185	10	
Sher 1	cl	11 01 03	–60 14.0	Car	I2p	1.0	8.8	11		8.8	2965	25	198	4	Skiff: Large SIMBAD position error. Aliases: Lund 569; OCl 837; C1058–601
NGC 3503	cl	11 01 18	–59 50.8	Car	III2p n	1.5	9.4	9	9.0	10.3	4111	25	198	99	See notes. Skiff: = vdB-Herbst 46 = Pi 17. Aliases: Pi 17; OCl 833; Lund 570; C1059–595
NGC 3484	??	11 03.0	+75 49	Dra								2	5	99	Skiff: Not obvious in 0.4 degree field. Archinal: Id?
NGC 3519	cl	11 04 03	–61 22.1	Car	III2m	8.0	7.7	93	11.0	12.2	1542	25	198	53	See notes. J. Herschel's and Ruprecht's positions and descriptions confirm that NGC 3519 = Ru 93. Aliases: h 3314; Ru 93; OCl 844; Lund 571; OCl 844.0; C1102–611
Alessi J11046-3157	ast?	11 04 37	–31 57.5	Hya		3.3		8				20	169	8	Alessi: Poor, but distinctive "C"-shaped group of 8 B type stars.
Ruprecht 163	cl	11 04 47	–67 56.7	Car	III2p	2.0		10	12.0			25	209	4	Aliases: Lund 572; OCl 857; C1102–676
NGC 3520	ast	11 05 30	–17 55.1	Crt				4	11			13	151	4	Skiff: Four-star asterism, magnitudes 12 to 15.
NGC 3532	cl	11 05.5	–58 44	Car	II3r	50.0	3.0	677	8.0	11.5	478	25	198	4	Skiff: Very large. Aliases: Cr 238; Lund 574; Mel 103; OCl 839; Raab 88; vdB-Ha 109; OCl 839.0; Caldw 91; C1104–584
Shorlin 2	cl	11 05 34	–61 15.2	Car		1.8			15.6			25	198	99	Contains Wolf-Rayet stars WR 38 and WR 38a. In southern part of Loden 306. Alias: (3) Lo 306
Feinstein 1	cl:	11 06.0	–59 48	Car	IV3m	25.0	4.7	40	6.55	11.7	1159	25	198	99	Skiff: Too large to check/sparse. Archinal: Id? A large scattering of stars. Aliases: Lund 573; OCl 842; (4) IRAS 11038–5932; C1103–595
Loden 306	cl	11 06 00.7	–61 10 34	Car		23.0		27	7.62			25	198	99	Archinal: Confirmed via Lodén chart. Brightest star is HD 96264 (V=7.62, Lodén). A scattering of bright and faint stars. Aliases: (2) Shorlin 1; (2) Shorlin 2
Shorlin 1	cl?	11 06 19	–61 14.3	Car		0.8			14.78			25	198	99	Contains Wolf-Rayet stars WR 38b and WR 39. Dias, *et al.* [2002] give a position 33 time seconds too far west. Alias: (3) Lo 306
vdB-Ha 110	cl	11 07.3	–61 27	Car	I1p	2.0		20				25	198	99	Skiff: Not obvious in 0.2/0.3 degree DSS SERC-V short exposure field. Archinal: Id? Aliases: Lund 1085; C1105–612
ESO 502-SC19	cl	11 08.1	–26 44	Hya	I3	3.0						20	151	10	
Loden 280	cl	11 09.5	–59 05	Car								25	198	4	Aliases: Lund 1173; OCl 842.1; C1107–588
Loden 309	cl	11 09.5	–60 31	Car								25	198	4	Aliases: Lund 1176; OCl 845.1; C1107–602
vdB-Ha 111	cl	11 09.5	–63 50	Car	II2p	2.0		8				25	209	4	Skiff: Not obvious in 0.15/0.25 degree DSS SERC-V short exposure field. Aliases: Lund 1086; C1107–635
NGC 3572	cl	11 10 26.6	–60 14 38	Car	II3m n	7.0	6.6	35	7.0	10.8	2811	25	198	8	See notes. Part of Cr 240. Aliases: OCl 846; Cr 239; vdB-Ha 112; (5) NGC 3572b; (3) Cr 240; C1108–599
Basel 17	cl	11 10 32.9	–59 01 55	Car	III2p	10.0	7.7	20	9.56	12.7	1637	25	198	51	See notes. Also known as Lo 282. Skiff: Sparse group elongated SE-NW. Aliases: Lo 282; OCl 843.1; Lund 1174; C1108–587
Hogg 10	cl	11 10 42.1	–60 23 03	Car	I3p	3.0	6.9	23	7.11	9.3	2571	25	198	8	See notes. Part of Cr 240. Center star is HD 97253 (V=7.1, O6). Aliases: OCl 847; Lund 576; (3) Cr 240; OCl 954.0; C1108–601
Trumpler 18	cl	11 11.4	–60 39	Car	II3m	6.0	6.9	30	8.08	10.8	1299	25	198	4	Skiff: Okay, sparse cluster. Aliases: Cr 241; Lund 578; OCl 850; vdB-Ha 113; OCl 850.0; C1109–604
Hogg 11	cl	11 11 32.6	–60 22 37	Car	IV1p	2.0	8.1	10	8.3	9.6	2270	25	198	4	Part of Cr 240. Center star is HD 97381. Skiff: Six stars only. Aliases: OCl 849; Lund 579; C1109–601
Collinder 240	ast	11 11 40.2	–60 18 35	Car	III2m n	32.0	3.9	42	4.6	11.4	2559	25	198	8	See notes. Collinder's 32′ by 23′ scattering of stars. Includes y Car, NGC 3572, Hogg 10, Hogg 11. Position is for HD 97398. Aliases: (2) NGC 3572; (2) Ho 10; (2) Ho 11; (5) NGC 3572a; OCl 848.0; C1109–600
[PRT94] 1	cl	11 11 58	–61 18 42	Car	n	1.8		51	9.23		2400	25	198	8	Infrared cluster involved with NGC 3576. HD 97499 is brightest star in V (V=9.23).
ESO 570-SC12	cl	11 12.2	–21 19	Crt	I3	13.0						20	151	10	
Hogg 12	cl	11 12 15	–60 46.2	Car	III2p	2.0	8.8	11		10.3		25	198	4	Skiff: Small group. Aliases: Lund 580; OCl 851; OCl 851.0; C1110–604
NGC 3578	nf?	11 12.8	–15 57	Crt								13	132	4	Skiff: Not obvious in 0.4 degree field.
NGC 3590	cl	11 13 00	–60 47.3	Car	I2p	2.0	8.2	30	10.27	9.7	2061	25	198	4	Aliases: Cr 242; Lund 581; OCl 852; Mrk 24; vdB-Ha 114; C1110–605

Table 4.1: Catalog of Clusters and Asterisms in the Milky Way, and Objects Misidentified as Such

Name	Type	2000.0 R.A.	Dec.	Con.	Tr. Type	Diam. (′)	Tot. Vm	#str	Bt* Vm	V Sur	Dist. (pc)	S #	2U #	Ref	Comments and Aliases
Stock 13	cl	11 13.1	−58 54	Car	I3p n	5.0	7.0	23	10.0	10.5	2664	25	198	4	Skiff: Okay, sparse group. Aliases: Lund 582; OCl 845; C1110−586
Leo II	gal	11 13 29.3	+22 09 12	Leo		12.0	12.01			17.4		6	73	8	Dwarf galaxy, mistaken for a globular cluster by Czernik (Cz 34). Data here from RC3. Aliases: UGC 6253; DDO 93; PGC 34176; Leo B; CGCG 126−111; CGCG 1110.8+2226; MCG +04-27-005; RC2 A1110+22; (5) Cz 34
Trumpler 19	cl	11 14.3	−57 34	Car	IV2m	10.0	9.6	40		14.6		25	198	99	Skiff: Not obvious in 0.35 degree field. Archinal: Id? Aliases: Cr 243; Lund 583; OCl 843; OCl 843.0; C1112−573
NGC 3603	cl	11 15 07	−61 15.7	Car	II3m n	4.0	9.1	44	11.25	12.1	5152	25	198	4	Skiff: = HD 97950 (V=9.0, WN etc). Aliases: Cr 244; Lund 584; OCl 854; vdB-Ha 115; C1112−609
Hogg 13	cl	11 16.3	−60 15	Car	IV1p	3.0		15				25	198	99	Skiff: Not obvious in 0.2/0.3 degree DSS SERC-V short exposure field. Archinal: Id? Aliases: Lund 585; OCl 853; C1114−600
IC 2714	cl	11 17 18	−62 43.0	Car	II2r	15.0	8.2	100	10.0	14.1	1138	25	209	4	Skiff: Weak concentration. Aliases: Cr 245; Lund 586; Mel 104; OCl 855; Raab 89; vdB-Ha 116; C1115−624
Melotte 105	cl	11 19 41	−63 29.1	Car	I2r	5.0	8.5	73	11.13	12.0	2014	25	209	4	Aliases: Cr 246; Lund 587; OCl 856; Raab 90; vdB-Ha 117; C1117−632
ESO 93-SC8	cl	11 19 42	−65 13.1	Car		2.0			13.8		13700	25	209	54	See notes. Bica, *et al.* [1999] have shown this is a very old (4-5 Gyr) open cluster. Alias: ESO 093-SC?8
Loden 336	cl	11 19.8	−58 51	Car								25	198	4	Aliases: Lund 1177; OCl 852.1; C1117−586
ESO 129-SC19	cl	11 21.2	−58 14	Cen	II2	5.0						25	198	10	
vdB-Ha 118	cl	11 22.9	−58 31	Cen	II1p	2.0		20				25	198	99	Skiff: Not obvious in 0.25 degree field. Archinal: Id? Aliases: Lund 1087; C1120−582
NGC 3676	gal	11 25 37.5	−11 08 23	Crt								13	131	53	See notes. This is the galaxy MCG −02-29-029. The original discovery position by Muller at McCormick Observatory was 30′ too far north. Alias: MCG −02-29-029
NGC 3680	cl	11 25 38	−43 15.0	Cen	I2m	7.0	7.6	66	10.0	11.8	791	20	185	4	Aliases: Cr 247; Lund 588; Mel 106; OCl 823; Raab 91; C1123−429
Palomar 4	gcl	11 29 16.8	+28 58 25	UMa		1.3	14.2		18.0	14.8	97900	6	72	6	Aliases: UMa glb; EQ 1126+292; C1126+292
Ruprecht 94	cl	11 30.4	−63 25	Cen	III2r	20.0		60	10.0			25	209	4	Skiff: DSS SERC-V short exposure field. Aliases: Lund 589; OCl 859; C1128−631
Loden 372	cl	11 30 52	−58 29.0	Cen	III2p	6.0		15				25	198	4	Skiff: Sparse group. Aliases: Lund 1178; OCl 853.1; C1128−582
Ruprecht 164	cl	11 31.1	−60 47	Cen	IV1m	6.0		40	14.0			25	198	99	Skiff: Identification uncertain, DSS SERC-V short exposure field. Some small (~1′) clumps near. Archinal: Id? Aliases: Lund 590; OCl 858; vdB-Ha 119; C1128−605
Loden 402	cl	11 32 49	−60 43.2	Cen		25.0		35	7.23			25	198	99	Archinal: Confirmed via Lodén chart. Brightest star is HD 100276 (V=7.23, B1, Lodén). Mostly rich Milky Way field.
NGC 3766	cl	11 36 15	−61 36.6	Cen	I3r	15.0	5.3	137	8.0	11.2	1772	25	198	4	Aliases: Cr 248; Lund 591; Mel 107; OCl 860; Raab 92; Mrk 25; vdB-Ha 120; BRAN 360; OCl 860.0; Caldw 97; C1133−613
Collinder 249	cl	11 38 20.4	−63 22 22	Cen	III3m n	65.0	2.9	61		12.0	1932	25	209	51	See notes. The associated nebula (near Lambda Cen) is IC 2944. Centered on HD 101205 (6.45V, O8). Aliases: LamCen cl; OCl 862; vdB-Ha 121; (5) C1135−630; Lund 592; Lund 1088; (4) IC 2944; BRAN 362A; OCl 862.0; C1134−627
IC 2948	neb	11 38 58	−63 28 19	Cen		44.0						25	209	51	See notes. Nebulosity near cluster C1134−627 = Cr 249, and nebula IC 2944. The use of the name C1136−632 should be avoided. Aliases: Frost 790; (5) OCl 864; (5) vdB-Ha 122; OCl 864.0; C1136−632
[AO84] IX	mc	11.7	+05.0	Vir		10000.	4.22	18	5.47	24.2		13	111	54	Moving cluster with very large angular size, hypothesized by Agekyan and Orlov [1984].
Lynga 15	cl	11 42.4	−62 28	Cen								25	198	99	Skiff: Not obvious in 0.25 degree field. Archinal: Id? Discovery reference unknown. Maybe group at 11 42 02.8 -62 30 08? Alias: C1140−622
Ruprecht 95	cl	11 43 40	−61 08	Cen	III1m	4.0		30	12.0			25	198	4	Skiff: DSS SERC-V short exposure field. Aliases: Lund 594; OCl 863; C1141−608
Stock 14	cl	11 43 51	−62 32.0	Cen	III3p	8.0	6.3	20	10.0	10.8	2693	25	209	99	Includes Lodén 466 and 467 (not given separately here). Skiff: = HD 101947 (V=5.1, F9Ia) = V810 Centauri. Sparse group. Aliases: OCl 865; Lund 595; Lo 465; (2) Lo 466; (2) Lo 467; C1141−622
ESO 129-SC32	cl	11 44.2	−61 05	Cen	II2	4.0						25	198	10	
NGC 3909	cl?	11 49 30	−48 15.9	Cen		35.0		34	9			20	185	99	Skiff: = GSC 8220-1490. Widespread group. Archinal: ESO size (2′) too small. Dias, *et al.* [2002] mistakenly list ESO object separately. Alias: ESO 217-SC8
NGC 3960	cl	11 50 34	−55 40.6	Cen	I2m	7.0	8.3	317	11.50	12.5	1683	25	198	4	Aliases: Cr 250; Lund 597; Mel 108; OCl 861; Raab 93; vdB-Ha 123; C1148−554
Ruprecht 96	cl	11 50 53	−62 08.3	Cen	IV1p	5.0		15	13.0			25	198	4	Aliases: Lund 598; OCl 866; C1148−618

Table 4.1: Catalog of Clusters and Asterisms in the Milky Way, and Objects Misidentified as Such

Name	Type	2000.0 R.A.	Dec.	Con.	Tr. Type	Diam. (′)	Tot. Vm	#str	Bt* Vm	V Sur	Dist. (pc)	S #	2U #	Ref	Comments and Aliases
Loden 481	cl	11 51 06.6	−61 14 38	Cen		28.0		29	9.26			25	198	99	Archinal: Confirmed via Lodén chart. Brightest star is HD 102907 (V=9.26, K5, Lodén). Includes star semi-circle (opening N).
Loden 480	ast?	11 56 06	−58 25.1	Cen?		5.0		10	10.78			25	198	99	Archinal: Confirmed via Lodén chart. Three type A0 stars and about 7 (unmeasured) others. Aliases: Lund 1179; OCl 865.3; C1153−581
Ruprecht 97	cl	11 57 23	−62 42.3	Cru	IV1p	5.0	9.1	142	12.0	12.6	3086	25	209	4	Aliases: Lund 599; OCl 867; vdB-Ha 124; C1154−623
Ruprecht 98	cl	11 58.8	−64 34	Cru	III2m	10.0	7.0	40	9.0	12.0	348	25	209	99	See notes. Position from T. Karhula. Aliases: OCl 868; vdB-Ha 125; C1155−642
NGC 4052	cl	12 02 01	−63 13.6	Cru	III2r	10.0	8.8	80		13.8	1900	25	209	4	Skiff: Position measured by Gottlieb. Aliases: Cr 251; Lund 601; OCl 870; vdB-Ha 126; OCl 870.0; C1159−629
Ruprecht 99	cl	12 03 20	−63 52	Cru	III1p	5.0		15	12.0			25	209	99	Skiff: Identification uncertain, DSS SERC-V short exposure field. Archinal: 6′ long N-S group barely standing out from background. Aliases: Lund 602; OCl 872; C1200−635
Ruprecht 100	cl	12 05.7	−62 31	Cru	IV1m	7.0		30	12.0			25	209	99	Skiff: Not obvious in 0.3 degree field. Archinal: Id? Aliases: Lund 603; OCl 873; C1203−622
NGC 4103	cl	12 06 40	−61 15.0	Cru	I2m	6.0	7.4	45	10.0	11.3	1468	25	198	4	Aliases: Cr 252; Lund 604; Mel 109; OCl 871; Raab 94; vdB-Ha 127; BRAN 380; OCl 871.0; C1204−609
Loden 565	cl	12 08 24.4	−60 50 51	Cru	IV3p	11.0		10	10.01			25	198	99	Archinal: Confirmed via Lodén chart. Centered on brightest and non-member(?) star HD 105437 (V=6.225, K3.5II). Aliases: Lund 1180; OCl 873.1; C1206−606
Ruprecht 101	cl	12 09 40	−63 00	Cru	IV1r	15.0		60	13.0			25	209	99	Archinal: Appears as obvious increase in fainter stars in rich field. Aliases: Lund 606; OCl 875; C1206−626
NGC 4147	gcl	12 10 06.2	+18 32 31	Com		4.4	10.4		14.5	13.6	18800	13	72	6	Aliases: GCRV 7290; EQ 1207+188; CSI+18-12076; C1207+188
Stock 15	cl	12 10.5	−59 29	Cru	IV1p	12.0			10.0			25	198	8	See notes. Position from T. Karhula. HD 105820 on SE side. Aliases: Lund 605; OCl 869; C1204−592
Alessi J12130-6242	ast?	12 13 02	−62 42.4	Cru		0.8						25	209	8	See notes. Alessi: Extremely faint cluster(?) of very very faint stars in very rich MW field. [Globular cluster candidate?]
NGC 4182	cl??	12 13.4	+04 03	Vir								13	111	99	Archinal: Id? Star only?
NGC 4184	cl	12 13.6	−62 42	Cru	IV1p	2.0		20	13.0			25	209	4	See notes. Skiff: Absorption hole? = Ru 102. Aliases: Ru 102; OCl 877; Lund 607; vdB-Ha 128; OCl 877.0; C1210−623
SSWZ94 4	cl	12 14 03	−63 35.6	Cru		1.8			15.3		6190	25	209	99	See notes. Frinchaboy and Phelps [2002] have recently determined this to be an old (1.5 Gy) open cluster.
Ruprecht 103	cl	12 15.9	−58 23	Cru	III2p	3.0		20	13.0			25	198	99	Skiff: Not obvious in 0.3 degree field. Archinal: Id? Aliases: Lund 608; OCl 876; OCl 876.0; C1213−581
NGC 4230	cl:	12 17 16	−55 05.2	Cen	IV2p	5.0	9.4	15		12.9		25	198	4	Skiff: = HD 106826. Sparse group around very bright star. Aliases: Cr 253; Lund 609; OCl 874; C1214−548
Loden 615	****	12 20 37.2	−64 46 56	Mus		1.9		4	11.62			25	209	99	Archinal: Confirmed via Lodén chart. Mostly only a small "keystone" of four 11th magnitude stars. Aliases: Lund 1181; OCl 882.1; C1217−645
ESO 130-SC13	cl	12 22 49.6	−59 37 40	Cru	III3	10.0						25	198	99	
NGC 4347	??	12 23.9	−03 14	Vir								13	111	99	Skiff: Nothing notable in 0.3 degree field. Archinal: Id? Possibly one of several faint galaxies.
NGC 4337	cl	12 24 04	−58 07.4	Cru	II3p	3.5	8.9	16	10.53	11.6		25	198	4	DSFG: Probably not a cluster. Aliases: Cr 254; Lund 610; OCl 878; vdB-Ha 129; C1221−578
NGC 4349	cl	12 24 07	−61 52.2	Cru	II2m	4.0	7.4	204	11.0	10.4	859	25	198	4	Aliases: Cr 255; Lund 611; Mel 110; OCl 882; Raab 95; vdB-Ha 130; OCl 882.0; C1221−616
ESO 064-SC05	ast?	12 24.5	−68 28	Mus	II2	10.0		10				25	209	99	Archinal: Irregular likely asterism of about 10 stars.
Collinder 257	ast?	12 24 45.9	−60 53 12	Cru		5.0		12	8.5			25	198	51	See notes. Cr 257 IS NOT Harvard 5 and IS NOT Hogg's no. 74. Position is for NE and fainter star of two, HD 107978. Other star is HD 107980.
Ruprecht 104	cl	12 24 51	−60 25.9	Cru	III1p	3.6			13.0			25	198	4	Aliases: OCl 879; C1222−601
Melotte 111	cl	12 25.1	+26 07	Com	III3r	300.0	1.8	273	5.0	14.2	79	7	72	99	Skiff: Too big to check on DSS. Aliases: Com st. cl; Cr 256; Lund 613; OCl 558; OCl 558.0; C1222+263
NGC 4372	gcl	12 25 45.4	−72 39 33	Mus		5.0	7.2		12.2	10.7	5200	25	209	55	Aliases: Mel 112; EQ 1223−724; Caldw 108; C1223−724
vdB-Ha 131	cl	12 26 25.7	−63 24 51	Cru	III1p	6.0		20				25	209	99	Archinal: Slight condensation visible on stretched image, with star Acrux to N interfering. Aliases: Lund 1089; C1223−631
vdB-Ha 132	cl	12 26 58	−64 03.1	Cru	III1p	4.0		20				25	209	4	Aliases: Lund 1090; (4) IRAS 12242−6350; C1224−638
NGC 4409	dupl	12 26 58.6	+02 29 42	Vir		2.0						13	111	99	See notes. This is a duplicate identity for NGC 4420. Alias: NGC 4420

Table 4.1: Catalog of Clusters and Asterisms in the Milky Way, and Objects Misidentified as Such

Name	Type	2000.0 R.A.	Dec.	Con.	Tr. Type	Diam. (′)	Tot. Vm	#str	Bt* Vm	V Sur	Dist. (pc)	S #	2U #	Ref	Comments and Aliases
NGC 4426	**	12 27 10	+27 50 19	Com		0.2		2	16.2			7	72	53	See notes. NGC 4426 = NGC 4427 (according to Dreyer). Corwin has determined this is just two stars. Alias: NGC 4427
Harvard 5	cl	12 27 16.3	−60 46 44	Cru	II3p	5.0	7.1	25	9.01	10.6	1029	25	198	51	See notes. Ha 5 IS NOT Cr 257. Position is for central bright star HD 108353. Aliases: Cr 258; vdB-Ha 133; OCl 880; C1224–605; Lund 615; Lund 1091; C1226–604
Loden 624	cl	12 28 25.7	−61 47 41	Cru		40.0		45	6.22			25	198	99	Archinal: Confirmed via Lodén chart. Center has 5 stars in NNW-SSE line, with chains of fainter stars to SW and NE, over 40′ field.
NGC 4439	cl	12 28 27	−60 06.2	Cru	II1p	4.0	8.4	20	10.26	11.4	1371	25	198	4	See notes. Skiff: = GSC 8975-0281. Aliases: Cr 259; Lo 623; Lund 616; OCl 884; OCl 884.1; vdB-Ha 134; C1225–598
Hogg 23	ast?	12 28 31.6	−60 53 43	Cru		7.0		37	8.94			25	198	51	See notes. Archinal: Probable asterism. Hogg incorrectly thought this was Cr 258. Position is for HD 108544 from SIMBAD. Aliases: Lund 1183; OCl 884.2; C1226–606
Ruprecht 165	cl:	12 28.6	−56 26	Cru	II3m	20.0		35	7.0			25	198	4	DSFG: Probably not a cluster. Skiff: = HD 108570 = HR 4749 (V=6.1, K0.5III); large group of bright stars. Aliases: Lund 618; OCl 881; C1225–561
Hogg 14	cl	12 28 39	−59 48.0	Cru	II3p	3.0	9.5	11	10.49	11.9	912	25	198	4	DSFG: Probably not a cluster. Skiff: = CPD-59 4248 = GSC 8658-0949. Small group. Aliases: Lund 617; OCl 883; C1225–595
ESO 131-SC09	cl	12 29.6	−57 53	Cru		5.0						25	198	10	
NGC 4463	cl	12 29 56	−64 47.4	Mus	I3m	6.0	7.2	30	8.28	11.1	1180	25	209	4	Skiff: = HD 108719. Aliases: Cr 260; Lund 619; OCl 885; Mrk 26; vdB-Ha 135; C1227–645
NGC 4505	cl??	12 32.3	+03 59	Vir								14	111	99	Skiff: No star group in 0.4 degree field. Archinal: Id? Only a single star at this position.
Ruprecht 105	cl	12 34.0	−61 32	Cru	III2p	12.0			12.0			25	198	99	Skiff: Not obvious in 0.3 degree DSS SERC-V short exposure field. Archinal: Id? Aliases: Lund 620; OCl 886; C1231–612
ESO 442-SC04	cl	12 34.1	−29 25	Hya	II1	10.0						21	150	10	
Upgren 1	ast	12 35 00	+36 22.5	CVn	IV2p	18.0	6.3	10		12.6	140	7	54	99	See notes. Found not to be a true physical group by Gatewood, *et al.* [1988]. Aliases: Lund 621; OCl 379; C1232+365
Canali	ast?	12 35 44.1	−12 01 30	Crv		7.5		6	7.4			14	131	8	Asterism or possible cluster west of Sombrero Galaxy, M 104. Noted by Eric Canali [1997].
Harvard 6	cl	12 37 54	−68 23.0	Mus	II1r	9.0	10.7	100		15.5		25	209	4	Aliases: Cr 261; Lund 622; OCl 889; vdB-Ha 136; C1234–682
Ruprecht 106	gcl	12 38 40.2	−51 09 01	Cen		2.0	10.9		14.8	12.4	19800	25	184	6	See notes. Skiff: Nice globular cluster!. Aliases: OCl 887; Lund 623; (5) C1235–509; C1236–508
NGC 4590	gcl	12 39 28.0	−26 44 34	Hya		11.0	7.3		12.6	12.5	9300	21	150	55	M 68. Aliases: M 68; Mel 113; EQ 1236–264; C1236–264
Trumpler 20	cl	12 39 32	−60 37.5	Cru	II2m	7.0	10.1			14.3		25	198	4	Aliases: Cr 262; Ha 7; Lund 624; OCl 888; vdB-Ha 137; C1236–603
NGC 4604	gal	12 40 45.1	−05 18 11	Vir		1.0	14.4			14.4		14	110	99	Identified as a galaxy by H. Corwin [Priv. Comm., 2002] who indicates the NGC declination is in error by 10 degrees. Aliases: MCG −01-32-037; PGC 42489
NGC 4609	cl	12 42 20	−62 59.6	Cru	II2m	6.0	6.9	52	10.0	10.8	1276	25	209	4	Skiff: = CPD-62 2888 (V=9.8, A). Aliases: Coalsack cluster; Cr 263; Lund 625; OCl 890; vdB-Ha 138; Caldw 98; C1239–627
Loden 670	cl	12 42 48.6	−63 03 19	Cru		33.0		27	5.30			25	209	99	Archinal: Confirmed via Lodén chart. Brightest star is HD 110432 (V=5.30, B0, Lodén).
Hogg 15	cl	12 43 36	−63 06.1	Cru	II1p	2.0	10.3	21	12.10	11.8	4150	25	209	4	Skiff: = GSC 8992-0405. Aliases: Lund 626; OCl 891; vdB-Ha 139; C1240–628
Loden 682	cl	12 47 19	−60 38.1	Cru		28.0		31	8.25			25	198	99	Archinal: Confirmed via Lodén chart. Mostly a NW-SE group of about 20 faint stars.
ESO 065-SC03	cl	12 51.6	−69 44	Mus	III2	6.0						25	209	10	
vdB-Ha 140	cl	12 53.5	−67 10	Mus	III1m	5.0		50				25	209	4	Skiff: Identification uncertain. Aliases: Lund 1092; (4) IRAS 12498–6654; C1250–669
Loden 694	cl	12 53 31	−60 50.4	Cru		16.5		31	8.66			25	198	99	Archinal: Confirmed via Lodén chart. Brightest star is HD 112026 (V=8.66, B2, Lodén).
NGC 4755	cl	12 53 38	−60 21.4	Cru	I3r	10.0	4.2	218	7.0	9.2	1498	25	198	9	See notes. John Herschel's "Jewel Box". Skiff: = HD 111934 (V=6.9, B2Ib). Aliases: Cr 264; Kappa Crucis cluster; Lund 627; Mel 114; OCl 892; Raab 96; vdB-Ha 141; Jewel Box; Caldw 94; C1250–600
NGC 4815	cl	12 57 59	−64 57.7	Mus	I2r	5.0	8.6	100	9.63	12.1		25	209	4	DSFG: Probably not a cluster. Aliases: Cr 265; Lund 628; OCl 893; Mrk 27; vdB-Ha 142; C1254–646
NGC 4833	gcl	12 59 35.0	−70 52 29	Mus		14.0	8.4		12.4	14.1	5800	25	209	55	See notes. Aliases: Mel 115; EQ 1256–706; Caldw 105; C1256–706
NGC 4852	cl	13 00 05	−59 36.6	Cen	I3r	12.0	8.9	60		14.3		25	197	4	Aliases: Cr 266; Lund 629; Mel 116; OCl 894; Raab 97; vdB-Ha 143; C1257–593
Loden 757	cl	13 12.4	−65 17	Mus	IV2p	20.0		20				25	208	4	Aliases: Lund 1184; OCl 894.1; C1309–650
Danks 1	cl	13 12 26.8	−62 42 01	Cen	I1p	1.0		25			4000	25	208	51	See notes. Archinal: Basic data from DSS. With Danks 2 to NE, and HD 114515 just to SW. Discovered in infrared. Aliases: Lund 1211; C1309–624

Table 4.1: Catalog of Clusters and Asterisms in the Milky Way, and Objects Misidentified as Such

Name	Type	2000.0 R.A.	Dec.	Con.	Tr. Type	Diam. (′)	Tot. Vm	#str	Bt* Vm	V Sur	Dist. (pc)	S #	2U #	Ref	Comments and Aliases
Danks 2	cl	13 12 53.8	−62 40 48	Cen	I1p	0.6		80			4000	25	208	51	See notes. Archinal: Basic data from DSS. With Danks 1 and HD 114515 to SW. Discovered in infrared. Aliases: Lund 1212; C1310−624
NGC 5024	gcl	13 12 55.3	+18 10 09	Com		13.0	7.7		13.8	13.3	18500	14	71	55	M 53. Aliases: M 53; Mel 117; C1310+184
AL 1	cl	13 15 16	−65 55.3	Mus		1.3						25	208	4	Andrews and Lindsay, 1967, cluster 1: "faint stars, circular". This is also vdB-Ha 144, and ESO 96-SC 4. Aliases: vdB-Ha 144; ESO 96-SC4; Lund 1093; ESO 96-4; C1311−656
NGC 5053	gcl	13 16 27.0	+17 41 53	Com		10.0	9.0		13.8	14.0	16100	14	71	6	See notes. Aliases: Cr 267; OCl 970; EQ 1313+179; C1313+179
NGC 5043	ast?	13 16 40	−60 02.5	Cen		10.0		18	7			25	197	4	Skiff: Asterism. Alias: ESO 132-SC02
NGC 5045	MW	13 17.0	−63 25	Cen		60.0		>180				25	208	99	Archinal: 1° Milky Way star cloud at this position, not well separated from surrounding area.
Harvard 8	cl	13 18 12	−67 05.0	Mus	III2m	5.0	9.5	30	11.57	13.0	1738	25	208	4	Aliases: Cr 268; Lund 631; OCl 895; vdB-Ha 145; C1315−669
Stock 16	cl	13 18 38.4	−62 31 56	Cen	III3p n	20.0	6.9	83	6.9	13.4	1855	25	208	8	Position measured from (star on) DSS. Includes HD 115316 (V=9.32), HD 115345 (9.05), HD 115455 (7.97), and HD 115669 (6.9). Aliases: Lund 632; OCl 898; C1315−623
Ruprecht 107	cl	13 19 46	−64 56.8	Mus	III2p	3.0	9.7	20	12.0	12.1	1959	25	208	4	Aliases: Lund 633; OCl 896; vdB-Ha 146; C1317−646
Collinder 269	ast	13 22.6	−66 07	Mus	IV2p	15.0	9.2p			15.1		25	208	99	DSFG: Probably not a cluster. Skiff: Not obvious in 0.3 degree field. Archinal: Id? Aliases: OCl 897; C1319−658
Loden 821	cl	13 23 39	−59 44.0	Cen		26.0		26	8.73			25	197	99	Archinal: Confirmed via Lodén chart.
ESO 324-SC15	cl	13 23.7	−41 53	Cen	I2	4.0						21	184	10	
Loden 807	cl	13 24.9	−62 25	Cen	III3m	20.0	7.9	35		14.4		25	197	1	Aliases: Lund 1185; OCl 898.1; C1321−621
NGC 5120	MWcl	13 25 39	−63 27.5	Cen	II1m	4.0	10.8	30	12	13.8		25	208	53	See notes. DSFG: (identified as Ru 166) Probably not a cluster. Aliases: h 3496; Ru 166; OCl 899; ESO 96-SC11; Lund 635; C1322−631
NGC 5139	gcl	13 26 45.9	−47 28 37	Cen		55.0	3.9		11.5	12.6	4900	21	184	9	See notes. The great ω Centauri globular cluster. Aliases: Omega Cen; Mel 118; Caldw 80; C1323−472
NGC 5138	cl	13 27 16	−59 02.5	Cen	II2m	8.0	7.6	92	10.30	12.1	1406	25	197	4	Skiff: Very rich background. Aliases: Cr 270; Lund 636; OCl 902; OCl 902.0; C1324−587
Basel 18	cl	13 27 49	−62 18.7	Cen	III1p	3.0	8.2	154	10.99	10.6	1528	25	197	4	Skiff: Outline of cluster uncertain. Aliases: Lund 1137; C1325−621
Hogg 16	cl	13 29 11	−61 12.0	Cen	II2p	7.0	8.4	20	10.10	12.6	1136	25	197	54	Skiff: = CPD-60 4701 = GSC 8991-4621 (V=10.3, B). Aliases: Bas 19; OCl 901; Lund 637; (5) C1325−610; C1326−609
ESO 065-SC07	cl	13 29.3	−71 16	Mus	III2	4.0						25	208	99	Archinal: Galaxy (ESO 383-G008 at 13 31 20.0 −35 05 17) on SW side.
NGC 5155	MW	13 29.6	−63 25	Cen		60.0		>200				25	208	99	Skiff: Not definable. DSS SERC-V short exposure field. Archinal: Milky Way star cloud, broken by dark nebula at several places (the center).
Collinder 271	cl	13 30.0	−64 11	Cen	IV2p	5.0	8.7	20	9.50	12.2	1622	25	208	4	Aliases: Lund 638; OCl 900; C1326−639
Collinder 272	cl	13 30.5	−61 16	Cen	III2m	10.0	7.7	102	10.50	12.7	2729	25	197	4	Skiff: Sparse group. Aliases: Lund 639; OCl 904; C1327−610
NGC 5168	cl	13 31 08	−60 56.4	Cen	I2m	4.0	9.1	50	10.36	12.1	1312	25	197	4	Aliases: Cr 273; Lund 640; OCl 905; Mrk 28; vdB-Ha 147; C1327−606
ESO 383-SC10	cl	13 31.5	−35 04	Cen	II2	5.0						21	167	99	Archinal: Galaxy ESO 383-G008 on SW side at 13 31 19.8 −35 05 19.
Ruprecht 108	cl	13 32 12	−58 28.2	Cen	III3p	10.0	7.5	15	9.0	12.5	724	25	197	4	Skiff: = HD 117527 (B8/9III). Aliases: Lund 641; OCl 907; OCl 907.0; C1328−582
Trumpler 21	cl	13 32 14	−62 47.3	Cen	I2p	5.0	7.7	20	8.94	11.2	1112	25	208	4	Skiff: Nice object. Aliases: Cr 274; Lund 642; OCl 903; vdB-Ha 148; C1328−625
Loden 848	cl	13 33.1	−65 41	Mus	III3m	69.0		25	7.74			25	208	99	Archinal: Confirmed via Lodén chart. Very large N-S scattered group. Brightest star is HD 117670 (V=7.64, F5, Lodén). Aliases: Lund 1186; OCl 901.1; C1330−642
Loden 915	cl	13 33 44	−59 16.2	Cen		30.0		36	9.11			25	197	99	Archinal: Confirmed via Lodén chart. Nice NE-SW group of faint stars south of HD 117606.
Abell 1763	gxcl	13 35 20.1	+41 00 05	CVn		20.0						7	37	8	Galaxy cluster mistaken for a globular cluster (Cz 35). Position is of intersection of two galaxy streams. Other data from NED. Aliases: (4) 1ES 1333+412; (5) Cz 35
Collinder 275	cl	13 35.4	−60 11	Cen	III3p	11.0	10.2	20		15.4		25	197	8	See notes. Position from T. Karhula. Aliases: Lund 643; OCl 908; C1331−598
ESO 132-SC14	ast	13 36 31	−62 12.8	Cen		0.5		4				25	197	8	See notes. This is NOT IC 4291 = Pismis 18, as the ESO Catalogue indicates.
IC 4291	cl	13 36 55	−62 05.6	Cen	II2m	4.0	9.7	35	10.0	12.7		25	197	99	See notes. DSFG: Probably not a cluster. Aliases: Pi 18; OCl 906; Lund 644; ESO 132-SC15; vdB-Ha 149; C1333−619
vdB-Ha 150	cl	13 38 02	−63 20.8	Cen	III2p	3.0		15				25	208	99	Archinal: Small group of faint stars at given position. There is also a N-S group of brighter stars on W side. Aliases: Lund 1094; (4) IRAS 13342−6307; C1334−630
Loden 894	cl	13 39 44.3	−64 19 56	Cen		8.0		6	9.73			25	208	99	Aliases: Lund 1187; OCl 905.1; C1335−640

Table 4.1: Catalog of Clusters and Asterisms in the Milky Way, and Objects Misidentified as Such

Name	Type	2000.0 R.A.	Dec.	Con.	Tr. Type	Diam. (′)	Tot. Vm	#str	Bt* Vm	V Sur	Dist. (pc)	S #	2U #	Ref	Comments and Aliases
vdB-Ha 151	cl	13 40 12	−61 43.8	Cen	I2m n	5.0		30				25	197	4	Aliases: Lund 1095; C1336−614
NGC 5272	gcl	13 42 11.2	+28 22 32	CVn		18.0	6.3		12.7	12.6	10100	7	71	55	M 3. Aliases: M 3; Mel 119; EQ 1339+286; 1E 1339.8+2837; C1339+286
[PKL98] 15	cl?	13 43 28	−59 07.3	Cen		3.0		4			246	25	197	14	
Latysev 2	mc?	13 44.4	+53 30	UMa		300.0	3.67	7	4.66	16.1		2	23	8	See notes. Includes 81, 83, 84, 86 UMa, in line between Zeta UMa and M 101.
NGC 5269	MWcl	13 44 45	−62 55.0	Cen					12			25	208	4	Skiff: Sparse group at this position.
Loden 1010	cl	13 45.4	−60 15	Cen	IV3m	30.0		35				25	197	99	Archinal: Confirmed via Lodén chart. Large (30′) group of bright stars on rich Milky Way background. Aliases: Lund 1190; OCl 911.3; C1342−600
Loden 991	cl	13 45.4	−62 00	Cen	IV2p	5.0		20				25	197	1	Aliases: Lund 1188; OCl 911.1; (4) IRAS 13417−6148; C1341−617
NGC 5286	gcl	13 46 26.5	−51 22 24	Cen		11.0	7.4		13.5	12.6	9300	25	183	55	Aliases: Mel 121; EQ 1343−511; Caldw 84; C1343−511
NGC 5281	cl	13 46 36.7	−62 54 34	Cen	I3m	8.0	5.9	40	7.98	10.4	1294	25	208	52	Center and brightest star is HD 119699 (V=6.61, A1II); DSFG: Total magnitude without it is 6.8. Aliases: Cr 276; Lund 645; Mel 120; OCl 911; Raab 98; vdB-Ha 152; C1343−626
NGC 5284	MW	13 47.1	−59 13 39	Cen		20.0			10.6			25	197	53	See notes. Milky Way patch around HD 119837. Alias: ESO 133-?04
[PKL98] 16	cl?	13 47 57	−66 01.2	Mus		1.0		4			232	25	208	14	
Collinder 277	cl	13 48.4	−66 04	Mus	IV1m	15.0	9.2	30		15.1		25	208	99	Improved position and diameter from P. Teutsch [Priv. Comm., 2002]. Aliases: Lund 647; OCl 909; C1345−658
NGC 5288	cl	13 48 45.6	−64 41 11	Cir?	II1p	3.0	11.8	25		14.2		25	208	99	Aliases: Cr 278; Lund 648; OCl 910; vdB-Ha 153; C1345−644
NGC 5299	asMW	13 50.4	−59 56	Cen		30.0		23	9			25	197	99	Archinal: Id? DSS shows a very rich Milky Way here, but also severe diffraction rings from nearby Hadar.
[PKL98] 17	cl?	13 51 44	−63 27.2	Cen		1.0		8			402	25	208	14	
Loden 995	cl	13 52 21	−64 53.7	Cir		22.0		21	9.07			25	208	99	Archinal: Confirmed via Lodén chart. Not obvious on DSS.
NGC 5385	cl?	13 52.4	+76 11	UMi		10.0		9	10			2	5	3	
Loden 1095	cl	13 53.5	−59 44	Cen	IV2p	20.0		10				25	197	99	Archinal: Confirmed via Lodén chart. DSS shows scattering of stars in diffraction rings from Hadar. Aliases: Lund 1191; OCl 913.1; (4) IRAS 13500−5928; (4) IRAS 13503−5929; C1350−595
NGC 5316	cl	13 54.0	−61 51	Cen	II2r	15.0	6.0	129	11.0	11.9	1076	25	197	8	Aliases: Cr 279; Lund 649; Mel 122; OCl 913; Raab 99; vdB-Ha 154; OCl 913.0; C1350−616
Loden 1002	cl	13 54.3	−65 18	Cir	IV2p	15.0		20				25	208	99	Archinal: Confirmed via Lodén chart. DSS shows only rich Milky Way. Aliases: Lund 1189; OCl 911.2; C1350−650
ESO 445-SC74	cl	13 54 38.1	−31 57 13	Cen	II3	2.5						21	167	99	
AM 4	gcl	13 56 21	−27 09.7	Hya		3.0	15.9		20.5	18.3	30300	21	149	55	See notes. Position from Skiff. Archinal: Diameter approximate, estimated from DSS image. Aliases: AM 1353−265; C1353−269
vdB-Ha 155	nf?	13 57.5	−59 35	Cen		11.0						25	197	51	See notes. May not exist. Not visible in 8-inch telescope or on DSS image. Aliases: Lund 1096; C1354−593
Loden 1101	cl	13 58 40.6	−61 44 10	Cen	III2m	16.0		30	10.12			25	197	99	Archinal: Confirmed via Lodén chart. Seven brighter stars with 20-30 in background. Aliases: Lund 1192; OCl 913.2; (4) IRAS 13544−6132; C1354−615
Loden 1177	cl	13 59.4	−57 50	Cen								25	197	99	Archinal: Confirmed via Lodén chart. DSS shows mostly just two bright stars, one at given position and one E. Aliases: Lund 1195; OCl 915.2; C1355−576
Loden 1152	cl	13 59.5	−59 22	Cen	IV2p	9.0		10				25	197	99	Aliases: Lund 1193; OCl 914.1; C1356−591
Loden 1171	cl	13 59 31.4	−58 22 47	Cen	III2m	6.8		35				25	197	99	Aliases: Lund 1194; OCl 915.1; C1356−581
NGC 5359	cl?	13 59.8	−70 24	Cir		8.0		12				25	208	99	Archinal: Scattered group of stars here fits John Herschel's description.
Lynga 1	cl	14 00 02	−62 09.5	Cen	II2p	3.0		15				25	197	4	Aliases: Lund 650; OCl 914; (4) IRAS 13569−6156; C1356−619
NGC 5381	cl:	14 00.6	−59 33	Cen	II2m	11.0		50	12.0			25	197	52	DSFG: Probably not a cluster. Aliases: Lund 651; OCl 915; Ru 109; vdB-Ha 156; OCl 915.0; C1357−593
Loden 1202	cl	14 04.4	−58 41	Cen	IV2m	20.0		30				25	197	1	Aliases: Lund 1197; OCl 915.4; C1400−584
NGC 5466	gcl	14 05 27.3	+28 32 04	Boo		9.0	9.2		13.8	14.0	15800	7	70	55	Aliases: Mel 124; C1403+287
Loden 1194	cl	14 05.8	−59 42	Cen	IV3p	14.0		10				25	197	99	Archinal: Confirmed via Lodén chart. DSS shows mostly scattering of stars, with two bright stars on E side. Aliases: Lund 1196; OCl 915.3; C1402−594

Table 4.1: Catalog of Clusters and Asterisms in the Milky Way, and Objects Misidentified as Such

Name	Type	2000.0 R.A.	2000.0 Dec.	Con.	Tr. Type	Diam. (′)	Tot. Vm	#str	Bt* Vm	V Sur	Dist. (pc)	S #	2U #	Ref	Comments and Aliases
Ruprecht 110	cl	14 06.5	−67 34	Cir	III2m	18.0		35	10.0			25	208	99	Archinal: Id? Nothing obvious on 0.4′ DSS image. Aliases: OCl 912; C1402–673
NGC 5460	cl	14 07.6	−48 18	Cen	I3m	35.0	5.6	61	9.0	13.3	769	21	183	1	See notes. Aliases: Cr 280; Lund 653; Mel 123; OCl 925; Raab 100; OCl 925.0; C1404–480
Loden 1225	cl	14 09.2	−59 42	Cen	IV3m	20.0		30				25	197	99	Archinal: Confirmed via Lodén chart. DSS shows triangle of stars 3′ E of brighter one. Aliases: Lund 1198; OCl 915.5; C1405–594
ESO 097-SC15	cl	14 15.5	−64 37	Cir?	II3	12.0						25	208	99	Archinal: Scattering of stars just standing out some from Milky Way background.
Loden 1282	cl	14 15.9	−59 08	Cen	IV1m	15.0		30				25	197	1	Aliases: Lund 1199; OCl 915.7; (4) IRAS 14119–5855; C1412–589
ESO 021-SC06	cl	14 15.9	−78 30	Aps	III3	9.0						25	216	99	Archinal: Large "Z" shaped chain of bright stars.
Loden 1289	cl	14 16 56.9	−57 51 14	Cen	IV3r	14.0		15	10.40			25	197	99	Archinal: Confirmed via Lodén chart. Center, brightest, and non-member star is HD 124689 (V=7.45, A9/F0V) Aliases: Lund 1200; OCl 915.8; C1410–576
Ruprecht 167	cl	14 18.2	−58 57	Cen	III2m	15.0		40	11.0			25	197	99	Archinal: Position for brightest part; also extends > 10′ to N. Aliases: Lund 654; OCl 917; OCl 917.0; (4) IRAS 14147–5841; C1414–587
Loden 1256	cl	14 18.2	−61 25	Cen	IV3m n	12.0		30				25	197	99	Archinal: NE to SW chain of stars. Aliases: Lund 1201; OCl 915.6; (4) IRAS 14149–6112; C1414–612
ESO 175-SC06	cl	14 18.5	−56 55	Cen	III2	18.0						25	197	10	
Arcturus group	ast	14 19.5	+19 04	Boo		300.0			-0.04			14	70	99	See notes.
NGC 5571	ast	14 19 31.8	+35 09 04	Boo				4				7	52	99	Archinal: Several galaxies on SW side.
Lynga 2	cl	14 24 24	−61 21.0	Cen	II3m	10.0	6.4	104	7.68	11.4	1076	25	197	99	Skiff: Center star is HD 125852. Archinal: Independently discovered as Lo 1296, including a few more stars to the north and south. Aliases: Lund 655; OCl 916; vdB-Ha 157; Lo 1296; C1420–611
NGC 5593	cl	14 25 40	−54 47.8	Lup	III2p	6.0		20				25	197	99	Improved position provided by P. Teutsch [Priv. Comm., 2002]. Aliases: Lund 656; OCl 926; C1422–545
Loden 1378	cl	14 27 25	−58 06.2	Cen		30.0		25	8.89			25	197	99	Archinal: Confirmed via Lodén chart.
NGC 5606	cl	14 27.8	−59 38	Cen	I3p	3.0	7.7	15	7.89	10.1	1852	25	197	8	Aliases: Cr 281; Lund 657; OCl 922; vdB-Ha 158; C1424–594
NGC 5621	nf?	14 27.8	+08 15	Boo								14	89	99	Archinal: Id? Possibly asterism of 3 faint stars?
NGC 5634	gcl	14 29 37.3	−05 58 35	Vir		5.5	9.5			13.2	25000	14	129	55	Aliases: Mel 126; EQ 1427–057; C1427–057
NGC 5617	cl	14 29.7	−60 42	Cen	I3r	10.0	6.3	292	10.0	11.3	1558	25	197	8	Aliases: Cr 282; Lund 658; Mel 125; OCl 919; Raab 101; vdB-Ha 159; C1426–605
Pismis 19	cl	14 30 43	−60 53.1	Cen	I1r	3.0		60	12.0			25	197	99	Aliases: Lund 659; OCl 921; vdB-Ha 160; C1426–607
Trumpler 22	cl:	14 31.2	−61 09	Cen	III2m	10.0	7.9	68	12.0	12.9	1632	25	197	99	DSFG: Probably not a cluster. Archinal: Includes westward opening semi-circle of 7 stars (e.g. a "stellar-ring"?). Aliases: Cr 283; Lund 660; OCl 920; vdB-Ha 161; C1427–609
IC 1023	cl?	14 32 25	−35 48.0	Cen		4.5		18				21	166	8	See notes. Center star is CoD–35 9596. Was first cataloged along with that star (Cordoba Durchmusterung). Alias: ESO 385-SC39
Turner 7	ptcl	14 32 33	−56 53.2	Cen		20.0						25	197	99	Turner [1982] indicates these stars around V Cen are the outer corona of NGC 5662. Listed as a cluster in Dias, *et al.* [2002]. Alias: (3) NGC 5662
Loden 1339	cl	14 33.5	−61 59	Cen	IV3m	30.0		30	10.86			25	197	99	Archinal: Confirmed via Lodén chart. DSS shows scattering of stars with small triangle at given position. Aliases: Lund 1202; OCl 918.1; C1429–617
Hogg 17	cl	14 33 50.4	−61 21 51	Cen	IV2p	4.0	8.3	41	9.55	11.3	1578	25	197	99	DSFG: Without brightest star, visual magnitude = 8.7. Aliases: Lund 661; OCl 923; (4) IRAS 14295–6111; C1429–611
NGC 5662	cl	14 35 30.8	−56 39 46	Cen	II3r	30.0	5.5	280	10.0	12.9	624	25	197	99	Aliases: Cr 284; Mel 127; OCl 928; Raab 102; vdB-Ha 162; (2) Turner 7; C1431–563
Ruprecht 111	cl:	14 35.8	−59 56	Cen	III1m	8.0		40	13.0			25	197	99	Archinal: Id? E-S scattering of stars, barely rising above Milky Way background. Large diffraction ring on DSS. Aliases: Lund 663; OCl 924; C1432–597
ESO 447-SC29	cl	14 37.4	−29 25	Hya	II3	12.0						21	148	10	
NGC 5694	gcl	14 39 36.5	−26 32 18	Hya		4.3	10.2		15.5	13.4	32800	21	148	6	Aliases: EQ 1436–263; Caldw 66; C1436–263
Alessi 6	cl?	14 40 07	−66 07.0	Cir		48.0						25	208	99	
Collinder 285	cl	14 40.9	+69 34	UMi					2.0		25	2	12	54	See notes. Ursa Major cluster (not to be confused with the UMa galaxy cluster). Aliases: Lund 664; OCl 252; UMa cl; C1440+697
Loden 1373	ast?	14 41.7	−62 51	Cen?		7.0		8	10.69			25	208	99	Archinal: Confirmed via Lodén chart. Mostly NE opening 1/4 semi-circle of 8 faint stars. Aliases: Lund 1203; OCl 923.1; C1437–626

Table 4.1: Catalog of Clusters and Asterisms in the Milky Way, and Objects Misidentified as Such

Name	Type	2000.0 R.A.	2000.0 Dec.	Con.	Tr. Type	Diam. (′)	Tot. Vm	#str	Bt* Vm	V Sur	Dist. (pc)	S #	2U #	Ref	Comments and Aliases
NGC 5715	cl	14 43 39.0	−57 34 13	Cir	III2m	7.0	9.8	30	11.0	14.0		25	197	99	Aliases: Cr 286; Lund 665; Mel 128; OCl 929; Raab 103; vdB-Ha 163; C1439−573
vdB-Ha 164	cl	14 44.1	−66 22	Cir		29.0						25	208	99	Archinal: Id? Nothing obvious on 45′ DSS image. Aliases: Lund 1097; C1439−661
Loden 1375	ast?	14 44 33	−63 22.9	Cir		15.0		9	10.00			25	208	99	Archinal: Confirmed via Lodén chart. Appears as scattering of about nine 10-11th magnitude stars. Aliases: Lund 1204; OCl 923.2; C1440−631
Loden 1409	cl	14 44.7	−61 41	Cir	IV3m	30.0		35	9.65			25	197	99	Archinal: Confirmed via Lodén chart. E-W 30′ long chain of stars with one bright star to N and S. Aliases: Lund 1205; OCl 925.1; C1440−615
ESO 134-SC12	cl	14 44.8	−59 10	Cir	III1	4.0						25	197	10	
NGC 5749	cl	14 48 48.8	−54 29 37	Lup	II2m	10.0	8.8	30		13.8	836	25	197	99	Archinal: Irregular, difficult to determine center. Aliases: Cr 287; Lund 666; OCl 930; vdB-Ha 165; C1445−543
Hogg 18	cl	14 50 41.4	−52 15 51	Lup	III2p	5.0	8.0	34	8.84	11.5	1009	25	197	99	Aliases: Lund 667; OCl 933; vdB-Ha 166; C1447−520
NGC 5764	cl	14 53 31.8	−52 40 16	Lup	III1p	3.0	12.6	12		15.0	1000	25	197	99	Archinal: DSS overlap region. Aliases: Cr 288; Lund 668; OCl 934; vdB-Ha 167; C1450−524
ESO 008-SC06	cl	14 55.2	−83 25	Oct	II1	10.0						25	216	10	
Ruprecht 112	cl	14 57.0	−62 32	Cir	III1r	10.0		80	14.0			25	208	99	Archinal: Rich group (Milky Way patch?) of faint stars. About 10′ south of HD 131491 (V=6.385, B4III, double). Aliases: Lund 669; OCl 927; C1453−623
IC 4499	gcl	15 00 18.5	−82 12 49	Aps		8.0	10.1		14.6	14.6	19100	25	216	55	Aliases: Mel 129; EQ 1452−820; C1452−820
NGC 5800	cl??	15 02.0	−51 55	Lup								25	196	99	Archinal: Id? Asterism of 4 obvious stars, and some fainter?
NGC 5824	gcl	15 03 58.5	−33 04 04	Lup		7.4	9.1		15.5	13.4	32400	21	166	6	Aliases: EQ 1500−328; 1E 1500.7−3251; C1500−328
NGC 5822	cl	15 04 02.3	−54 20 21	Lup	II2r	35.0	6.5	150	9.06	14.2	728	25	196	99	See notes. Archinal: Position from DSS. Archinal: Brightest/center star is HD 132944 (9.06, K0III:, SIMBAD). Aliases: Cr 289; Lund 670; Mel 130; OCl 937; Raab 104; vdB-Ha 168; Lo 2104; C1501−541
NGC 5823	cl	15 05 26	−55 36.5	Cir	II2r	12.0	7.9	103	13.0	13.3	1052	25	196	99	Aliases: Cr 290; Lund 671; Mel 131; OCl 936; Raab 105; vdB-Ha 169; (4) IRAS 15020−5525; Caldw 88; C1502−554
Loden 2115	cl	15 05 53	−54 26.5	Lup		19.0			9.46			25	196	99	Archinal: Confirmed via Lodén chart. Brightest star is HD 133365 (V=9.46, G0/G1) on S side.
Loden 2045	cl	15 08 23.4	−58 41 51	Cir		39.0			8.80			25	196	99	Archinal: Confirmed via Lodén chart. Center and brightest star is HD 133682 (V=8.80, B6V, SIMBAD).
Pismis 20	cl	15 15 23.1	−59 04 24	Cir	I3p	4.5	7.8	12	8.20	11.1	2536	25	196	99	Aliases: Lund 672; OCl 932; vdB-Ha 170; C1511−588
Palomar 5	gcl	15 16 05.3	−00 07 14	Ser		8.0	11.8		15.5	16.3	23000	14	108	99	See notes. Archinal: Faint. Not obvious on DSS or DSS II, but visible as a 8.0′ faint cluster between two bright stars. Aliases: (5) UGC 9792; (5) MCG +00-39-016; (5) CGCG 21−61; (5) Ser Dwarf; EQ 1513+000; C1513+000
Lynga 3	cl	15 16 47	−58 22.7	Cir	III1p	5.0	12.58			16.1		25	196	4	Aliases: Lund 674; OCl 935; C1512−581
Pismis 21	cl	15 16 47.7	−59 39 41	Cir	I3p	2.0			13.0			25	196	99	Aliases: Lund 673; OCl 931; vdB-Ha 171; C1512−594
NGC 5897	gcl	15 17 24.5	−21 00 37	Lib		11.0	8.4		13.3	13.6	12600	21	148	55	Aliases: Mel 132; C1514−208
NGC 5904	gcl	15 18 33.8	+02 04 58	Ser		23.0	5.7		12.2	12.5	7600	14	108	55	M 5. Aliases: M 5; Mel 133; EQ 1516+022; C1516+022
ESO 329-SC02	cl	15 27.5	−41 03	Lup	III2	8.0						21	182	10	
NGC 5925	cl	15 27.7	−54 31	Nor?	III2r	20.0	8.4	120		14.9		25	196	8	Aliases: Cr 291; Lund 675; OCl 938; vdB-Ha 172; (4) IRAS 15236−5421; C1523−543
NGC 5927	gcl	15 28 00.5	−50 40 22	Lup		6.0	8.0		14.5	11.9	8000	25	182	55	Aliases: vdB-Ha 173; Mel 134; EQ 1524−505; C1524−505
Alessi 8	cl?	15 29 33	−51 14.0	Nor		24.0						25	182	99	
ESO 099-SC06	cl	15 29.8	−64 52	TrA	III2	8.0						25	208	10	
Loden 2158	cl	15 33 05.9	−58 11 42	Nor		49.0			8.61			25	196	99	See notes. Archinal: Confirmed against Lodén charts. Superposed on Lo 2159! Non-member HD 138168 and HD 138181 at center.
Loden 2159	cl	15 33 05.9	−58 11 42	Nor		28.0			8.61			25	196	99	See notes. Archinal: Confirmed via Lodén chart. Early A-type cluster superposed on Lo 2158! Non-member HD 138168 and HD 138181 at center.
Lynga 4	cl	15 33 20	−55 14.2	Nor	II2m	3.0	11.4	30	12.48	13.8		25	196	4	DSFG: Probably not a cluster. Aliases: Lund 676; OCl 941; vdB-Ha 174; C1529−550
Harvard 9	cl	15 33.8	−53 35	Nor	IV2p	3.0						25	196	99	Archinal: Id? 9′ DSS field shows only scattering of stars, with brighter ones on N side. Aliases: Lund 677; OCl 944; C1530−534
NGC 5946	gcl	15 35 28.5	−50 39 34	Nor		3.0	8.4			10.8	10500	25	182	55	Aliases: vdB-Ha 175; Mel 135; EQ 1531−504; C1531−504

Table 4.1: Catalog of Clusters and Asterisms in the Milky Way, and Objects Misidentified as Such

Name	Type	2000.0 R.A.	Dec.	Con.	Tr. Type	Diam. (′)	Tot. Vm	#str	Bt* Vm	V Sur	Dist. (pc)	S #	2U #	Ref	Comments and Aliases
vdB-Ha 176	gcl	15 39 07.3	−50 03 02	Nor		3.0	14.0		16.3	16.4	13400	25	182	55	See notes. Recently shown to very likely be a Galactic globular cluster by Ortolani, *et al.* [1995]. Aliases: ESO 224-SC8; ESO 224-8; C1535−499
Loden 2313	cl	15 40 44.5	−52 32 09	Nor		21.0			10.1			25	196	99	Archinal: Confirmed via Lodén chart. Brightest star (V=8.37) not a member.
Lynga 5	cl	15 41 57.1	−56 39 30	Nor	III1p	3.0		20				25	196	8	Position and diameter from DSS. HD 139739, HD 139685, and HD 139636 on NE side. Verified as vdB-Ha 177 (with poor position). Aliases: Lund 678; OCl 942; vdB-Ha 177; C1538−564
Loden 2326	cl?	15 43 33	−52 28.5	Nor		1.6		5	10.82		900	25	196	99	Archinal: Identification confirmed against original paper by Johansson [1980].
NGC 5986	gcl	15 46 03.5	−37 47 10	Lup		9.6	7.6		13.2	12.5	10300	21	165	55	Aliases: Mel 136; EQ 1542−376; C1542−376
Johansson 1	cl	15 46 20	−52 22.9	Nor		29.0		26	6.05			25	196	99	Archinal: Identification confirmed against original paper by Johansson [1980].
NGC 5998	ast	15 49 28	−28 35.8	Sco		3.5		10				21	147	99	Archinal: Almost certainly asterism of 10 stars here, but W. Herschel's "parallelogram" not found.
Collinder 292	cl	15 50.8	−57 39	Nor	IV2m	15.0	7.9	50		13.8		25	196	99	Archinal: Id? Aliases: Lund 679; OCl 943; C1546−575
NGC 5999	cl	15 52 14	−56 28.2	Nor	I2m	3.0	9.0	40	12.0	11.4		25	196	99	Aliases: Cr 293; Lund 680; Mel 137; OCl 946; Raab 106; vdB-Ha 178; C1548−563
ESO 275-SC01	cl	15 55.1	−46 01	Nor	II2	6.0						21	182	99	Archinal: Small group similar in shape to the constellation Lyra!
NGC 6005	cl	15 55 47.4	−57 26 37	Nor	I2m	5.0	10.7	35	11.77	14.2		25	196	99	DSFG: Probably not a cluster. Aliases: Cr 294; Lund 681; Mel 138; OCl 945; Raab 107; vdB-Ha 179; (4) IRAS 15519−5718; C1551−572
Ruprecht 113	cl	15 57.2	−59 27	Nor	IV2p	25.0		20	9.0			25	196	99	Archinal: Id? Scattering of stars over a 30′ field? Aliases: Lund 682; OCl 940; OCl 940.0; C1553−593
Abell 2141	gxcl	15 57 42.3	+35 30 28	CrB		14.0	14.7			20.4		7	51	8	Galaxy cluster, mistaken for a globular cluster by Czernik (Cz 36). Data here from NED. Alias: (5) Cz 36
ESO 389-05**	ast	15 57 50.2	−36 12 23	Lup		1.8		7				21	165	99	ESO catalogue indicates this is just a group of 6 or 7 stars.
Trumpler 23	cl	16 00 50.7	−53 31 45	Nor	III1m	9.0	11.2	40		16.0		26	196	99	Aliases: Cr 295; Lund 683; OCl 950; vdB-Ha 180; C1556−533
Moffat 1	cl	16 01 36.1	−54 08 38	Nor	IV2p	8.0		20				26	196	99	Aliases: Lund 1141; Moffat; C1557−540
NGC 6025	cl	16 03 18	−60 25.4	TrA?	II3r	15.0	5.1	139	7.0	11.0	766	26	196	99	Archinal: Scattering of stars just to W of a dark nebula. Aliases: Cr 296; Lund 684; Mel 139; OCl 939; Raab 108; vdB-Ha 181; Caldw 95; C1559−603
Lynga 6	cl	16 04 51	−51 57.3	Nor		5.0	9.5	60	10.68	13.0	1587	26	196	99	Skiff: Center star is HD 143795. Archinal: Includes arc of 7 stars. Aliases: Lund 685; OCl 955; vdB-Ha 182; C1601−517
Ruprecht 114	cl	16 06 31	−56 52.5	Nor	IV1m	15.0		50	12.0			26	196	99	Archinal: Large, loose group of faint stars. Aliases: Lund 686; OCl 947; C1602−567
NGC 6031	cl	16 07 34.4	−54 01 00	Nor	I3p	3.0	8.5	121	10.85	10.9	1559	26	196	99	Aliases: Cr 297; Lund 687; OCl 951; vdB-Ha 183; (4) IRAS 16039−5355; C1603−539
Palomar 14	gcl	16 11 00.3	+14 57 49	Her?		2.5	14.7		17.6	16.7	72400	15	88	99	See notes. Center is GSC 00957-00359. Aliases: AvdB gcl; Arp 1; EQ 1608+150; AvdB; C1608+150
Lynga 7	gcl	16 11 03.0	−55 18 52	Nor		2.2			16.3		7200	26	196	55	See notes. Recently shown to be a likely Galactic globular cluster by Tavarez and Friel [1995]. Aliases: Lund 689; OCl 949; vdB-Ha 184; C1607−551
Ruprecht 115	cl	16 12 51.1	−52 23 15	Nor	III1p	5.0			13.0			26	196	99	Aliases: Lund 688; OCl 956; vdB-Ha 185; C1609−522
NGC 6067	cl	16 13 09	−54 13.1	Nor	I3r	15.0	5.6	315	10.0	11.5	1716	26	196	9	See notes. (Mistakenly called the "S Nor cluster" by Moore [1995] - see NGC 6087 instead.) Aliases: Mel 140; Raab 109; Cr 298; OCl 953; Lund 690; vdB-Ha 186; C1609−540
Pismis 22	cl	16 14 07.9	−51 53 02	Nor	I2p	3.3		30	7.77			26	196	99	See notes. Brightest star is HD 145542 (V=7.77, Westerlund) on SW. Rediscovered by Westerlund in 1969. Aliases: Lund 691; OCl 957; vdB-Ha 187; We 3; C1609−517
Ruprecht 176	cl	16 14 45	−51 20.0	Nor								26	182	99	Archinal: E opening arc ("stellar ring"?) of nine stars 9′ to N at 16 14 54 −51 13.1 Aliases: Lund 1206; OCl 957.1; C1611−512
NGC 6093	gcl	16 17 02.5	−22 58 30	Sco		10.0	7.3		12.5	12.3	8400	22	147	55	M 80. Aliases: M 80; Mel 142; EQ 1614−228; C1614−228
NGC 6087	cl	16 18 51.8	−57 53 59	Nor	II2m	15.0	5.4	349	8.0	11.3	904	26	196	99	See notes. S Nor cluster Archinal: Irregularly shaped, center appears (with difficulty) to be at brightest star, the cepheid S Nor (V=6.54v, F9Ib). Aliases: Cr 300; Lund 693; Mel 141; OCl 948; Raab 110; vdB-Ha 188; OCl 948.0; Caldw 89; S Nor cl; C1614−577
Harvard 10	cl	16 19.9	−54 58	Nor	III3m	25.0	6.9p	30		13.9	1312	26	196	99	See notes. Archinal: Scattering of stars, elongated E-W, with one non-member bright star to south, on 48′ DSS field. Also known as Cr 299. Aliases: Cr 299; OCl 954; Lund 695; (5) C1614−550; (5) OCl 952; ESO 179-SC1; ESO 179-SC2; C1615−548
Lynga 9	cl	16 20 39	−48 31.4	Nor	III1m	5.0						22	182	4	Aliases: Lund 696; OCl 966; vdB-Ha 189; C1616−484
Lynga 8	cl	16 22 57.0	−50 10 55	Nor	III2m	1.0						26	182	8	See notes. Lynga's position is substantially off and is given correctly for the first time here (measured from the DSS). Aliases: Lund 694; OCl 962; C1615−501
Ruprecht 116	cl	16 23 24.3	−51 59 48	Nor	II2p	5.0			9.0			26	196	99	Aliases: OCl 958; OCl 958.0; C1619−518

Table 4.1: Catalog of Clusters and Asterisms in the Milky Way, and Objects Misidentified as Such

Name	Type	2000.0 R.A.	Dec.	Con.	Tr. Type	Diam. (′)	Tot. Vm	#str	Bt* Vm	V Sur	Dist. (pc)	S #	2U #	Ref	Comments and Aliases
Ruprecht 117	cl	16 23 30.7	−51 52 06	Nor	III1p	1.7			12.0			26	196	99	Archinal: Very weak condensation of stars on DSS. Aliases: Lund 698; OCl 959; OCl 959.0; C1619−517
NGC 6121	gcl	16 23 35.5	−26 31 31	Sco		36.0	5.4		10.8	13.2	2000	22	147	55	M 4. See notes. Aliases: M 4; Mel 144; EQ 1620−264; C1620−264
Grasdalen 1	cl	16 23.8	−24 25	Oph?	n	30.0		91				22	147	51	See notes. Infrared cluster involved in ρ Oph dark cloud (LDN 1680). See Comeron, *et al.* [1993] for map. Aliases: (4) LDN 1680; Gr; C1622−243
Pismis 23	cl	16 23 58	−48 53.5	Nor	III2m	1.0			15.0			22	182	99	Archinal: Id? DSS, with histogram equalization, shows only a small triangle-shaped group of stars here. Aliases: Lund 699; Lynga 10; OCl 967; vdB-Ha 190; ESO 226-SC5; C1620−488
ESO 226-SC06	cl	16 24.2	−51 09	Nor	III2	4.0						26	182	10	
ESO 137-SC23	cl	16 24.4	−61 44	TrA	II2	5.0						26	196	10	
NGC 6115	cl?	16 24 26.8	−51 57 12	Nor	I2p	3.4	9.8	20	11.0	12.5	1343	26	196	99	Archinal: This is Ru 118. Aliases: Lund 700; OCl 960; Ru 118; C1620−518
NGC 6124	cl	16 25 17.2	−40 40 01	Sco	I3r	40.0	5.8	100	9.0	13.8	470	22	182	99	Aliases: Cr 301; Lund 701; Mel 145; OCl 990; Raab 111; Caldw 75; C1622−405
NGC 6101	gcl	16 25 48.6	−72 12 06	Aps		5.0	9.2		13.5	12.7	14900	26	207	55	Aliases: Mel 143; EQ 1620−720; Caldw 107; C1620−720
Collinder 302	cl	16 26.0	−26 13	Sco	III3p	505.0	1.0			14.5		22	147	1	See notes. Aliases: Antares cluster; Lund 702; OCl 1011; OCl 1011.0; C1623−261
NGC 6144	gcl	16 27 14.1	−26 01 29	Sco		7.4	9.0		13.4	13.3	9900	22	147	55	Aliases: Mel 147; EQ 1624−259; C1624−259
DoDz 5	ast	16 27.4	+38 04	Her	III1p	27.0						8	51	1	Aliases: OCl 128; C1625+381
NGC 6139	gcl	16 27 40.4	−38 50 56	Sco		8.2	9.1		15.0	13.7	9100	22	165	6	Aliases: EQ 1624−387; C1624−387
NGC 6134	cl	16 27 43.6	−49 09 51	Nor	II3m	6.0	7.2	179	11.0	11.1	649	22	182	99	Aliases: Cr 303; Lund 703; Mel 146; OCl 968; Raab 112; vdB-Ha 191; C1624−490
Ruprecht 119	cl	16 28 09.3	−51 31 07	Nor	II1p	8.0	8.8	13	10.0	13.3		26	196	99	DSFG: Probably not a cluster. Archinal: Weak condensation of stars on DSS. Aliases: Lund 704; OCl 963; OCl 963.0; C1624−514
Terzan 3	gcl	16 28 40.1	−35 21 13	Sco			12.0		15.0		25200	22	165	6	Alias: EQ 1625−352
Hogg 19	cl	16 28 51.7	−49 07 25	Nor	IV2p	4.0						22	182	99	Aliases: Lund 705; OCl 969; C1625−490
NGC 6171	gcl	16 32 31.9	−13 03 13	Oph		13.0	7.8		13.0	13.4	6400	15	127	55	M 107. Aliases: M 107; Mel 148; EQ 1629−129; C1629−129
NGC 6152	cl	16 32.7	−52 37	Nor	III3r	25.0	8.1	70	11.0	15.1	1030	26	196	99	Archinal: DSS overlap region - position and size not checked. Aliases: Cr 304; Lund 706; OCl 961; OCl 961.0; C1628−525
NGC 6169	cl	16 34 05.0	−44 02 43	Nor?	III1m	12.0	6.6	40		12.0	1100	22	182	99	Archinal: μ Nor (V=4.914, B0Ia) at center. Aliases: Cr 306; Lund 707; Mu Nor cl; OCl 984; Mrk 29; C1630−439
NGC 6167	cl	16 34 35	−49 46.0	Nor?	II3m	7.0	6.7	218	7.44	10.9	598	22	182	99	DSFG: Probably not a cluster. Archinal: Lund Catalogue position is off, a cluster diameter or so, to NW. Aliases: Cr 305; Ha 11; Lund 708; OCl 971; vdB-Ha 192; Dunlop 400; h 3635; ESO 226-SC06; C1630−495
Ruprecht 120	cl?	16 35 12.2	−48 17 13	Ara	II3p	3.4		11	12.0			22	182	99	Archinal: "Y"-shaped group, with top to W. Aliases: Lund 710; OCl 974; C1631−482
Collinder 307	cl	16 35.3	−50 57	Ara	III2p	5.0	9.2	12	11.10	12.7		26	182	99	DSFG: Doubtful cluster. Archinal: DSS overlap region - position and size not checked. Aliases: Lund 709; OCl 965; vdB-Ha 193; C1631−508
NGC 6178	cl	16 35 50.8	−45 38 48	Sco	III3p	5.0	7.2	19	8.41	10.7	904	22	182	99	Aliases: Cr 308; Lund 712; OCl 980; C1632−455
Dolidze 27	cl:	16 36.5	−08 56	Oph	IV2p n	25.0		15				15	127	1	Aliases: Lund 713; OCl 25; C1633−088
Lynga 11	cl	16 38 10	−46 19.1	Ara	III2p	4.0		15				22	182	4	Skiff: Center star is GSC 8325-3510. Aliases: Lund 714; OCl 979; C1634−462
ESO 452-SC11	gcl	16 39 25	−28 23.9	Sco		1.2	12.0		15.3	12.4	10300	22	147	99	See notes. Aliases: ESO 452-11; C1636−283
NGC 6192	cl	16 40 20.8	−43 21 55	Sco	I2r	9.0	8.5	60	11.0	13.3		22	182	99	Aliases: Cr 309; Lund 715; Mel 149; OCl 988; Raab 113; vdB-Ha 194; C1636−432
ESO 277-SC04	ast?	16 40 33.3	−43 45 23	Sco	I3	1.5		10				22	182	99	Archinal: Probably an asterism, but appears as a nebulous cluster on small scale (e.g. 1°) DSS image.
NGC 6193	cl	16 41 20.3	−48 45 48	Ara	II3p	14.0	5.2	14	5.66	10.9	1331	22	182	99	Archinal: Center and brightest star is double, HD 150135 = MlbO 8 (V=5.66). Substantial bright and dark nebula on W side. Aliases: Cr 310; Lund 716; OCl 975; Mrk 30; vdB-Ha 195; Caldw 82; C1637−486
NGC 6205	gcl	16 41 41.5	+36 27 37	Her		20.0	5.8		11.9	12.3	7200	8	50	55	M 13. See notes. Aliases: M 13; Mel 150; EQ 1639+365; C1639+365
Ruprecht 121	cl	16 41 47.6	−46 09 13	Ara	IV1m	6.0		35	13.0			22	182	99	Archinal: Weak condensation of stars, with similar, but larger condensation of Milky Way to NW. Aliases: Lund 717; OCl 983; C1638−460
NGC 6200	cl	16 44 08.6	−47 28 11	Ara	II2m	15.0	7.4	40	9.20	13.3	2259	22	182	99	Aliases: Cr 311; Lund 718; OCl 978; C1640−473

Table 4.1: Catalog of Clusters and Asterisms in the Milky Way, and Objects Misidentified as Such

Name	Type	2000.0 R.A.	Dec.	Con.	Tr. Type	Diam. (′)	Tot. Vm	#str	Bt* Vm	V Sur	Dist. (pc)	S #	2U #	Ref	Comments and Aliases
Hogg 20	cl	16 44.4	−47 33	Ara	III1p	4.0						22	182	99	Archinal: DSS overlap region - position and size not checked. Aliases: Lund 719; OCl 976; C1640−474
DoDz 6	cl?	16 45 28.6	+38 21 21	Her	IV2p	3.5		5	8.8			8	50	8	Center at third brt. star. Brt. star is HD 151366 = SAO 65529. Aliases: Lund 404; OCl 129; OCl 129.0; C1643+383
Hogg 21	cl?	16 45 36.9	−47 44 08	Ara		4.0		12				22	182	99	Archinal: E-W elongated group of 12 or so stars. Aliases: Lund 721; OCl 977; C1642−476
Lynga 12	cl	16 46 03	−50 46.0	Ara	III2m	6.0		35				26	182	4	Aliases: Lund 722; OCl 973; C1642−507
NGC 6204	cl	16 46 07.9	−47 00 44	Ara	I3m	6.0	8.2	45	9.61	12.1	887	22	182	8	Brightest star is CPD−46° 8199. Incl. CPD−46° 8206 and CPD−46°8200. Disc. by Dunlop. Hogg 22 to SE. Aliases: Cr 312; Lund 723; OCl 982; Dunlop 442; h 3644; GC 4229; vdB-Ha 196; C1642−469
vdB-Ha 197	cl	16 46 30.3	−45 51 36	Ara	IV2p	4.0		15				22	182	99	Archinal: Slight condensation in Milky Way star cloud. Strong dark nebula to W of cloud. Aliases: Lund 1100; C1643−457
Hogg 22	cl	16 46 35	−47 04 57	Ara	IV3p	1.2	6.7	10	7.29	7.1	2780	22	182	8	Brightest star is HD 150958. Includes CPD−46° 8221. Discovered by J. Herschel along with NGC 6204 (to NW). Aliases: OCl 981; C1643−470
NGC 6229	gcl	16 46 58.9	+47 31 40	Her		4.5	9.4		15.5	12.7	31600	8	35	6	Aliases: EQ 1645+476; C1645+476
Westerlund 1	cl	16 47 04	−45 50.6	Ara	IV1p	3.0		20	14.5		1400	22	182	99	See notes. Faint (V>14.5 stars) heavily reddened cluster. Non-member HD 151018 (V=8.73, O+...) is on SW side. Aliases: Lund 724; OCl 985; C1644−457
ESO 518-SC03	cl	16 47.1	−25 49	Sco	I2p	5.0		25	11.5			22	146	99	
NGC 6218	gcl	16 47 14.5	−01 56 52	Oph		16.0	6.1		12.0	12.1	5600	15	107	55	M 12. Aliases: M 12; Mel 151; EQ 1644−018; C1644−018
ESO 137-SC43	cl	16 48.4	−61 46	Ara	II2	6.0						26	196	10	
Lynga 13	cl	16 48 54	−43 26.2	Sco	III1m	9.0		30				22	181	4	Skiff: Center star is CoD-43 11129. Aliases: Lund 725; OCl 995; C1645−433
NGC 6216	cl	16 49 23.6	−44 43 39	Sco	I2m	4.0	10.1	40	12	13.1		22	181	99	See notes. Aliases: Mel 152; Raab 114; Cr 314; OCl 989; Lund 726; vdB-Ha 199; C1645−446
NGC 6208	cl	16 49 25.8	−53 42 18	Ara	III2r	18.0	7.2	303	9.96	13.5	986	26	196	99	Aliases: Cr 313; Lund 727; OCl 964; vdB-Ha 198; C1645−537
vdB-Ha 200	cl	16 50.0	−44 12	Sco	II2p	4.0		20				22	181	1	Aliases: Lund 1101; (4) IRAS 16465−4408; C1646−441
NGC 6222	cl??	16 50.7	−44 45	Sco		20.0						22	181	3	See notes. Identification unclear, but almost certainly NOT equal to 4′ diameter NGC 6216. Aliases: Lund 728; C1646−446
NGC 6227	MW	16 51.5	−40 54	Sco					8			22	181	99	Archinal: Id? Nothing obvious in 8′, 30′, 60′, and 120′ DSS fields.
NGC 6235	gcl	16 53 25.4	−22 10 38	Oph		5.0	8.9		14.0	12.4	9600	22	146	55	Aliases: Mel 154; EQ 1650−220; C1650−220
NGC 6231	cl	16 54 09.8	−41 49 30	Sco	I3p	14.0	2.6	93	6.0	8.3	1853	22	181	8	See notes. Archinal: Position is that of center star, HD 152248 (V=6.11, O8). Aliases: Cr 315; Lund 729; Mel 153; OCl 997; Mrk 31; vdB-Ha 201; Caldw 76; C1650−417
ESO 332-SC8	cl?	16 54 43	−40 42.5	Sco	I2	10.0						22	181	99	Archinal: ESO incorrectly suggests this is Cr 316.
Lynga 14	cl	16 55 05	−45 14.8	Sco	II1p	3.0	9.7	15	11.16	12.1	2249	22	181	4	Aliases: Lund 730; OCl 992; (4) IRAS 16513−4515; C1651−452
Ruprecht 122	cl	16 55 08.3	−40 56 35	Sco		3.0						22	181	99	See notes. Aliases: vdB-Ha 202; Lund 1102; C1651−408
Collinder 316	cl	16 55.5	−40 49	Sco	I2m	105.0	3.4		14.0	13.5		22	181	99	Archinal: Large group of bright stars, superposed on Tr 24. May just be brighter stars of Tr 24? Aliases: Lund 731; OCl 998; vdB-Ha 203; OCl 998.0; C1652−407
NGC 6242	cl	16 55 30.6	−39 28 01	Sco	I3m	9.0	6.4	23	7.28	11.2	1099	22	164	99	Archinal: Dark nebula on E side. Aliases: Cr 317; Lund 732; Mel 155; OCl 1001; Raab 115; vdB-Ha 204; C1652−394
vdB-Ha 205	cl	16 56 11.3	−40 40 06	Sco		4.0		14	6.68			22	181	99	Archinal: Brightest star is HD 152623 (V=6.68, O8:) Aliases: Lund 1103; C1652−405
Trumpler 24	cl	16 57.0	−40 38	Sco	IV2p n	60.0	8.6			17.5	1878	22	181	99	Archinal: Large group of stars, with IC 4628 nebulosity involved on N side. Cr 316 is superposed on this. Aliases: Cr 318; Ha 12; OCl 999; Mrk 32; OCl 999.0; C1653−405
NGC 6254	gcl	16 57 08.9	−04 05 58	Oph		20.0	6.6		12.0	13.1	4300	15	107	55	M 10. Aliases: M 10; Mel 157; C1654−040
NGC 6249	cl	16 57 41.7	−44 48 17	Sco	II2m	6.0	8.2	30	9.78	12.1	1019	22	181	99	Aliases: Cr 319; Lund 734; OCl 994; C1654−447
NGC 6250	cl	16 57 55	−45 56.1	Ara	II3r	16.0	5.9	35	7.62	11.9	996	22	181	8	See notes. Center star is HD 152822. 6 brighter stars and ~30 fainter star, standing out on NE to SW trending dark nebulosity. Aliases: Cr 320; Lund 735; OCl 991; vdB-Ha 206; (4) IRAS 16545−4750; C1654−457
NGC 6253	cl	16 59 06.1	−52 42 57	Ara	II1m	4.0	10.2	30	13.0	13.2		26	196	99	Aliases: Cr 321; Lund 736; Mel 156; OCl 972; Raab 116; vdB-Ha 207; C1655−526
NGC 6256	gcl	16 59 32.6	−37 07 17	Sco		4.1	11.3		15.3	14.4	10200	22	164	6	See notes. Aliases: vdB-Ha 208; Lund 1104; EQ 1656−370; C1656−370

Table 4.1: Catalog of Clusters and Asterisms in the Milky Way, and Objects Misidentified as Such

Name	Type	2000.0 R.A.	Dec.	Con.	Tr. Type	Diam. (′)	Tot. Vm	#str	Bt* Vm	V Sur	Dist. (pc)	S #	2U #	Ref	Comments and Aliases
Palomar 15	gcl	16 59 50.9	−00 32 28	Oph			14.2		17.1		41100	15	107	55	See notes. Has been wrongly listed as galaxy UGC 10642 = MCG +00-43-006 = CGCG 25-16 = PGC 59400 = Kara 781. [Lederman and Gottlieb, 1996] Aliases: Zwicky 1; (5) UGC 10642; (5) MCG +00-43-006; (5) CGCG 25–16; (5) PGC 59400; (5) Kara 781; EQ 1657–004; C1657–004
NGC 6259	cl	17 00.7	−44 39	Sco	II2r	15.0	8.0	162	11.0	13.9	1879	22	181	8	Aliases: Cr 322; Lund 737; Mel 158; OCl 996; Raab 117; vdB-Ha 209; C1657–446
NGC 6266	gcl	17 01 12.6	−30 06 44	Oph?		15.0	6.4		13.2	12.3	5500	22	164	55	M 62. Aliases: vdB-Ha 210; M 62; Mel 159; EQ 1658–300; C1658–300
NGC 6268	cl	17 02 04.1	−39 43 16	Sco	II2p	6.0	9.5			13.4	1072	22	164	99	Aliases: Cr 323; Lund 738; OCl 1002; vdB-Ha 212; (4) IRAS 16592–3940; C1658–396
vdB-Ha 211	cl	17 02 07.9	−41 06 35	Sco		4.0						22	181	99	Archinal: Brighter stars of long E-W chain. Aliases: Lund 1105; C1658–410
NGC 6273	gcl	17 02 37.7	−26 16 05	Oph		17.0	6.8		14.0?	13.0	10800	22	146	55	M 19. Aliases: M 19; Mel 160; EQ 1659–262; C1659–262
Harvard 13	cl	17 03 57	−48 07.1	Ara	IV1r	15.0		70	12.			22	181	99	Archinal: Irregular in shape, stars faint and difficult to identify from Milky Way background on DSS. Aliases: Lund 740; OCl 986; (4) IRAS 17015–4808; C1701–481
ESO 043-SC13	cl	17 04.1	−74 20	Aps	III2	8.0						26	216	10	
ESO 587-SC04	cl	17 04 22.3	−19 27 25	Oph	I1	2.5						15	146	99	
NGC 6284	gcl	17 04 28.8	−24 45 53	Oph		6.2	8.9			12.9	11800	22	146	55	Aliases: Mel 162; C1701–246
NGC 6281	cl	17 04 47.2	−37 53 16	Sco	II2p	8.0	5.4	70	9.0	9.9	542	22	164	99	Aliases: Cr 324; Lund 739; Mel 161; OCl 1003; Raab 118; vdB-Ha 213; C1701–378
ESO 332-SC20	cl	17 04.9	−38 19	Sco	III3	7.0						22	164	10	
NGC 6287	gcl	17 05 09.4	−22 42 29	Oph		4.8	9.3		14.5	12.7	6800	22	146	55	Aliases: Mel 163; EQ 1702–226; C1702–226
vdB-Ha 214	ast?	17 05 50.3	−36 33 21	Sco	IV2p	4.0		6				22	164	99	Archinal: Appears to be asterism of just 6 stars. Aliases: Lund 1106; C1702–366
ESO 278-SC02	cl	17 06 06.4	−46 07 01	Ara	II3	2.0						22	181	99	Archinal: Id? Just three faint stars?
ESO 332-SC22	cl	17 07.5	−40 49	Sco	III3	7.0						22	181	10	
NGC 6293	gcl	17 10 10.4	−26 34 54	Oph		8.2	8.3		14.3	12.9	8500	22	146	55	Aliases: vdB-Ha 215; Mel 164; EQ 1707–265; C1707–265
Terzan N 5	ast	17 11 15	−27 11.6	Oph								22	146	54	See notes. Not a globular cl., Djorgovski & Meylan [1993, p. 333] have found this to be either an asterism or nebula with stars superposed. Alias: C1708–271
DoDz 7	cl	17 11 23	+15 28.6	Her	IV1p	6.0		6				15	87	99	Archinal: Confirmed as 6′ diameter group of 6 stars. Aliases: Lund 741; OCl 93; C1708+156
Terzan N 33	gal	17 12 36.2	−25 06 43	Oph								22	146	54	See notes. Originally thought to be a globular cluster, this object has been confirmed [Djovgovski, *et al.* , 1990] to be a galaxy. Alias: C1709–251
Terzan N 34	gal	17 13 15.4	−25 02 28	Oph								22	146	54	See notes. Originally thought to be a globular cluster, this object has been confirmed [Djovgovski, *et al.* , 1990] to be a galaxy. Alias: C1710–250
Terzan N 35	gal	17 14 01.5	−24 48 56	Oph								22	146	54	See notes. Originally though to be a globular cluster or planetary nebula, this has been confirmed [Djovgovski, *et al.* , 1990] as a galaxy. Alias: C1711–248
Teutsch J1714.3+1718	ast?	17 14 20	+17 18.1	Her	III2p	2.2		15	15			15	87	17	Teutsch: Likely asterism. Sparse group in field with stars of similar density. At galactic latitude b=+29.0°.
NGC 6304	gcl	17 14 32.5	−29 27 44	Oph		8.0	8.3		14.5	12.8	6000	22	146	55	Aliases: vdB-Ha 216; Mel 165; EQ 1711–294; C1711–294
NGC 6318	cl	17 16 13.4	−39 25 26	Sco	III1m	5.0	11.8	35	12.0	15.3		22	164	54	See notes. Both S. Gottlieb and J. Kay have independently noted that NGC 6318 = vdB-Ha 218. Aliases: Mel 166; Cr 325; Raab 119; OCl 1004; vdB-Ha 218; Lund 742; Lund 1103; (4) IRAS 17126–3922; (5) C1714–394; C1712–393
vdB-Ha 217	cl	17 16 20.4	−40 49 50	Sco	I2m	5.0		30				22	181	99	Aliases: Lund 1107; C1712–407
NGC 6316	gcl	17 16 37.4	−28 08 24	Oph		5.4	8.1		15.0	11.8	12800	22	146	6	Aliases: vdB-Ha 219; EQ 1713–280; C1713–280
IRAS 17136-3617	cl	17 17 02	−36 20.8	Sco		0.8		30			2000	22	164	8	Infrared cluster, associated with cometary nebula GM 1-24. See Tapia, *et al.* [1991a, 1991b]. Nothing visible on DSS. Alias: (4) GM 1-24
NGC 6341	gcl	17 17 07.3	+43 08 11	Her		14.0	6.5		12.1	12.2	7500	8	34	55	M 92. Aliases: M 92; Mel 168; EQ 1715+432; C1715+432
Bochum 13	cl	17 17 20.7	−35 32 55	Sco	III3m	15.0	7.2	35	8.04	13.1	1644	22	164	99	Archinal: Mostly two brighter stars, with a few fainter background stars. Aliases: Lund 1139; C1714–355
NGC 6325	gcl	17 17 59.2	−23 45 57	Oph		4.1	10.2		14.7?	13.3	6000	22	146	6	Aliases: EQ 1714–237; C1714–237
Terzan N 16	gal	17 18 29	−27 46.5	Oph								22	146	54	See notes. Originally thought to be a globular cluster, Djovgovski and Meylan [1993, p. 333] have determined this is an external galaxy. Alias: C1715–277

Table 4.1: Catalog of Clusters and Asterisms in the Milky Way, and Objects Misidentified as Such

Name	Type	2000.0 R.A.	Dec.	Con.	Tr. Type	Diam. (′)	Tot. Vm	#str	Bt* Vm	V Sur	Dist. (pc)	S #	2U #	Ref	Comments and Aliases
NGC 6322	cl	17 18.5	−42 56	Sco	I3m	5.0	6.0	38	7.50	9.5	1182	22	181	1	Aliases: Cr 326; Lund 743; OCl 1000; vdB-Ha 220; (4) IRAS 17141−4256; C1714−429
Terzan N 15	gal	17 18 31	−26 17.9	Oph								22	146	54	See notes. Originally thought to be a globular cluster, Djovgovski and Meylan [1993, p. 333] have determined this is an external galaxy. Alias: C1715−262
vdB-Ha 221	cl?	17 18 34	−32 22.1	Sco	IV2p n	10.0		20				22	164	99	Archinal: Very sparse 10′ group - not a real cluster? Even vdB-Ha marked it only "probably real". Aliases: Lund 1110; C1715−323
Terzan N 17	gal	17 18 41	−27 50.2	Oph								22	146	54	See notes. Originally thought to be a globular cluster, Djovgovski and Meylan [1993, p. 333] have determined this is an external galaxy. Alias: C1715−278
vdB-Ha 222	cl	17 18 47.1	−38 17 24	Sco	II1p	2.0		20				22	164	99	Aliases: Lund 1111; C1715−382
Havlen-Moffat 1	cl	17 19 00.5	−38 48 52	Sco	III2p	6.0		20				22	164	99	Archinal: Confirmed against discovery paper. Aliases: Lund 1142; HM; C1715−387
NGC 6333	gcl	17 19 11.8	−18 30 59	Oph		12.0	7.8		13.5	13.2	7500	15	146	55	M 9. Aliases: M 9; Mel 167; EQ 1716−184; C1716−184
vdB-Ha 223	cl?	17 20 42	−35 53.1	Sco	III3p n	7.0		16				22	164	99	Archinal: Sparse group, elongated NE-SW, with stream of faint stars continuing to SW. Aliases: Lund 1112; C1717−358
NGC 6334	SNR	17 20 58.3	−36 03 40	Sco		5.0					2300	22	164	99	Archinal: 5′ x 4′ nebula (SNR) just NE of HD 156738 (V=9.37, B7/B8Iab...). Aliases: h 3678; C1718−360
NGC 6342	gcl	17 21 10.2	−19 35 14	Oph		4.4	9.5		15.0	12.7	12000	15	146	6	Aliases: EQ 1718−195; C1718−195
[DB01] 38	cl?	17 23 23.4	−35 53 44	Sco		0.4						22	164	16	Infrared cluster. [DB01]: Mostly unresolved cluster in radio HII region G 351.6+0.2.
Ruprecht 123	cl	17 23.4	−37 55	Sco	III3m	10.0		50	10.0			22	164	99	Archinal: Sparse group, brightest star on S side. Aliases: Lund 744; OCl 1008; C1720−378
NGC 6356	gcl	17 23 35.0	−17 48 47	Oph		10.0	8.2		15.1	13.2	16700	15	146	55	Aliases: Mel 171; EQ 1720−177; C1720−177
NGC 6328	gal	17 23 41.2	−65 00 35	Ara		2.0	12.3			13.8		26	207	99	
NGC 6355	gcl	17 23 58.6	−26 21 13	Oph		4.2	8.6			11.7	7000	22	146	6	See notes. Aliases: Cr 330; OCl 1036; EQ 1720−263; C1720−263
Trumpler 25	cl	17 24 30.3	−39 01 16	Sco	II1m	4.0	11.7	40		14.7		22	164	99	Aliases: Cr 329; Ha 14; Lund 747; OCl 1007; vdB-Ha 225; C1721−389
IC 4651	cl	17 24.7	−49 55	Ara	II2r	10.0	6.9	102	10.0	11.9	734	22	181	8	See notes. Aliases: Cr 327; Lund 746; Mel 169; OCl 987; Raab 120; vdB-Ha 224; C1720−499
Pismis 24	cl	17 24 43.4	−34 12 23	Sco	III2p n	2.0	9.6	15	10.43	11.1	1995	22	164	8	See notes. The DSS shows a poor cluster (including 6 GSC stars), with the SNR? NGC 6357 to the N, and including the double HD 319718 (V=10.43). Aliases: Lund 748; OCl 1016; vdB-Ha 227; (5) NGC 6357; C1722−343
Bica 1	SNR	17 24 53.5	−24 18 23	Oph								22	146	8	See notes. A likely supernova remnant thought at one point to be a globular cluster. 4′ south-southwest of HD 157588 (V=6.2). Alias: (5) EQ 1721−2415
NGC 6360	MW	17 25.4	−30 00	Oph								22	164	99	Archinal: Identity (J. Herschel's h 3685) refers to general patches of Milky Way here. Alias: h 3685
NGC 6352	gcl	17 25 29.2	−48 25 22	Ara		9.0	7.8		13.4	12.6	6100	22	181	6	See notes. Aliases: Cr 328; Mel 170; OCl 993; vdB-Ha 226; EQ 1721−484; Caldw 81; C1721−484
AH03 J1725.5-3424	cl?	17 25 32	−34 24 20	Sco		2.6		10	11.90		1740	22	164	8	Involved in nebula G 353.1+06. Position and diameter from DSS. 5′ northeast of HD 157515 (V=6.8). This IS NOT Pismis 24.
DoDz 8	ast	17 26 24	+24 11.6	Her	IV2p	14.0	6.83	6	8.26	12.6		8	68	51	See notes. Skiff [1994] has shown this group of stars is not a true cluster. Aliases: Lund 750; OCl 104; C1724+242
ESO 392-SC13	ast	17 26 52	−34 41.2	Sco	II2	10.0		25				22	164	99	Archinal: Sparse group. Alias: C1723−346
IC 1257	gcl	17 27 08	−07 05.6	Oph		1.7	13.1		17.5	14.3	24000	15	126	99	See notes. This has been shown to be a distant globular cluster. = GSC 5079-0033. Aliases: OCl 51; Lund 751; (5) Ced 144; C1724−070
Terzan 2	gcl	17 27 33.4	−30 48 08	Sco		0.6	14.3			13.2	2100	22	164	6	See notes. Aliases: HP 3; vdB-Ha 228; Lund 1113; C1724−307
NGC 6366	gcl	17 27 44.3	−05 04 36	Oph		13.0	9.5		13.6	15.1	4000	15	106	55	Aliases: Mel 173; EQ 1725−050; C1725−050
Ruprecht 124	cl	17 27 55.9	−40 43 12	Sco	III1p	2.0		15	12.0			22	181	99	Aliases: Lund 752; OCl 1005; C1724−407
[DB01] 39	cl?	17 28 19.1	−35 04 15	Sco		0.3						22	164	16	Infrared cluster. [DB01]: Mostly unresolved cluster candidate in G 352.866-0.199.
Trumpler 26	cl	17 28 29.9	−29 29 50	Oph	II1m	7.0	9.5	40		13.7	2800	22	146	99	Aliases: Cr 331; Ha 15; Lund 753; OCl 1032; C1725−294
Antalova 1	cl	17 28.9	−31 33	Sco	IV2p n	35.0		24	7.00			22	164	99	Archinal: Brt. star is HD 158186 = V1081 Sco (V=7.00, O9.5V) in 35′ scattered group. 10′ long straggling group just to SW of center. Aliases: (4) Gum 68; C1725−315
Antalova 2	cl	17 29.7	−32 29	Sco	IV1p	3.0	8.8	8	9.69	11.2		22	164	99	DSFG: Probably not a cluster. Aliases: Lund 1140; OCl 1021.1; C1726−324

Table 4.1: Catalog of Clusters and Asterisms in the Milky Way, and Objects Misidentified as Such

Name	Type	2000.0 R.A.	Dec.	Con.	Tr. Type	Diam. (′)	Tot. Vm	#str	Bt* Vm	V Sur	Dist. (pc)	S #	2U #	Ref	Comments and Aliases
Ruprecht 125	MW?	17 29.7	−40 29	Sco	IV2m	20.0		30	11.0			22	164	99	Archinal: Id? Appears to be only a Milky Way star cloud here. Aliases: Lund 754; OCl 1006; OCl 1006.0; (4) IRAS 17261−4030; C1726−404
[DB01] 41	cl?	17 30 24.0	−33 11 15	Sco		1.0						22	164	16	Infrared cluster. [DB01]: Partly resolved cluster in radio HII region G 354.664+0.470.
[DB01] 40	cl?	17 30 28.2	−34 41 30	Sco		1.7						22	164	16	Infrared cluster. [DB01]: Mostly unresolved cluster in radio HII region G 353.4-0.4.
Antalova 3	cl	17 30 34	−32 12.5	Sco		21.0		14				22	164	99	Archinal: DSS shows 7′ concentration of fainter stars and brighter stars to NW and SE. Involved with Gum 67 = RCW 132.
Terzan 4	gcl	17 30 38.9	−31 35 44	Sco			16.0				16900	22	164	6	Aliases: HP 4; EQ 1727−315; C1727−315
Collinder 332	cl	17 30.8	−37 04	Sco	IV1p	2.0	8.9	12		10.4		22	164	1	Aliases: Lund 755; OCl 1010; C1727−370
Harvard 16	cl	17 31 03	−36 48.2	Sco	III2r	15.0		70	8.52			22	164	99	See notes. Archinal: Scattered group standing out some from Milky Way, with brightest star HD 158529 (V=8.52, F3IV/V) on NE. Aliases: Lund 757; OCl 1012; vdB-Ha 230; Cr 332; OCl 1010; Lund 755; C1727−370; C1728−368
Haute Provence 1	gcl	17 31 05.2	−29 58 54	Oph		1.2	12.5		16.0	12.9	9100	22	164	6	Aliases: vdB-Ha 229; Dufay 1; EQ 1727−299; C1727−299
Collinder 333	cl	17 31 31.3	−34 00 37	Sco	II2m	8.0	9.8	30		14.3		22	164	99	Aliases: Lund 756; OCl 1017; C1728−340
NGC 6362	gcl	17 31 54.8	−67 02 53	Ara		15.0	8.1		12.7	14.0	7700	26	207	55	Aliases: Mel 172; EQ 1726−670; C1726−670
vdB-Ha 231	cl	17 31 55.7	−31 54 36	Sco	III1p n	2.0		15				22	164	99	Aliases: Lund 1114; C1728−318
Gri 1	dne	17 31 58	−33 50.1	Sco								22	164	54	See notes. This supposed globular cluster has been shown not to exist. Alias: C1728−338
Antalova 4	cl	17 32 39	−32 57.4	Sco		3.5		9	10.19			22	164	99	Archinal: Originally called "NGC 6374" (quotes significant) by Antalová, named Ant 4 here for first time.
IRAS 17301-2917	cl	17 33 21.9	−29 19 42	Oph								22	146	99	Archinal: Id? Infrared only? Rich field, with group of stars on E side at 17 33 33 -29 19.1. Aliases: (4) IRAS 17302−2919; C1730−293
Liller 1	gcl	17 33 24.5	−33 23 20	Sco		0.3	15.8		20.5	13.2	10200	22	164	6	See notes. Aliases: Liller I; (4) IRAS 17302−3327; (4) IRAS 17298−3329; EQ 1730−333; C1730−333
Terzan N 20	ast	17 33.5	−29 19 28	Oph		2.5		9				22	146	8	Also known as Terzan-Ju 20. Data measured from DSS. HD 159089 is about 7′ to the NE.
NGC 6380	gcl	17 34 28.0	−39 04 09	Sco		3.6	11.5		17.0	14.3	4000	22	164	55	Aliases: Ton 1; Pi 25; vdB-Ha 233; C1731−390
NGC 6383	cl	17 34 42.2	−32 34 54	Sco	II3m n	20.0	5.5	40	10.19	12.0	1333	22	164	99	See notes. DSFG: Involved in nebulosity which might be a possible SN. Aliases: (5) h 3687; h 3689; (5) NGC 6374; (5) Cr 334; Cr 335; (5) OCl 1022; OCl 1026; Lund 759; (5) C1729−325; Mrk 33; vdB-Ha 232; OCl 1026.0; C1731−325
Ruprecht 126	cl	17 35 04.4	−34 18 33	Sco	IV2p	6.0		20	13.0			22	164	99	Archinal: Sparse group. Aliases: Lund 760; OCl 1019; C1731−342
Terzan 1	gcl	17 35 47.0	−30 28 46	Sco			15.9		18.5		5900	22	164	99	Aliases: vdB-Ha 235; ESO 455-23; HP 2; C1732−304
[DB00] 50	cl?	17 36 09.9	−32 24 05	Sco		2.2						22	164	15	Infrared cluster. [DB00]: Related to Sh 2-12?
Tonantzintla 2	gcl	17 36 10.5	−38 33 12	Sco			12.2				8200	22	164	6	Aliases: Pi 26; vdB-Ha 236; C1732−385; EQ 1733−390; C1733−390
Trumpler 27	cl	17 36 12.7	−33 29 19	Sco	III3m	7.0	6.7	82	8.39	10.9	1379	22	164	99	Aliases: Cr 336; OCl 1021; vdB-Ha 237; ESO 393-9; (5) C1733−335; C1732−334
NGC 6388	gcl	17 36 17.0	−44 44 06	Sco		10.4	6.8		14.8	11.9	11000	22	181	55	Aliases: vdB-Ha 234; Mel 174; EQ 1732−447; C1732−447
ESO 334-SC02	cl	17 36.9	−42 14	Sco	II2	2.0						22	181	10	
Trumpler 28	cl	17 36 59	−32 28.4	Sco	III2m n	6.0	7.7	85	9.84	11.6	1374	22	164	99	Aliases: Cr 337; Lund 762; OCl 1029; vdB-Ha 238; C1733−324
NGC 6402	gcl	17 37 36.1	−03 14 45	Oph		11.0	7.6		14.0	12.8	10100	15	106	55	M 14. Aliases: M 14; Mel 175; EQ 1735−032; C1735−032
NGC 6396	cl	17 37 38	−35 01.7	Sco	II3m	3.0	8.5	30	9.79	10.9	1318	22	164	99	Archinal: Compact cluster, with faint extensions well off to N and NE. HD 159651 (V=9.14, F5II) just to W. Aliases: Cr 339; Lund 765; OCl 1018; vdB-Ha 239; C1734−349
[DB01] 1	cl?	17 37 40.7	−25 15 03	Oph		1.9						22	146	16	Infrared cluster. [DB01]: Resolved cluster or dust window, related to LDN 74? partly optical.
ESO 139-SC13	cl	17 37.7	−58 08	Ara	III2	5.0						26	195	10	
Ruprecht 127	cl	17 37 50.4	−36 18 25	Sco	II2p	5.0	8.8	20	11.0	12.3	1535	22	164	99	Aliases: Lund 763; OCl 1015; C1734−362
Collinder 338	cl	17 38.2	−37 33	Sco	III2m	20.0	8.0	40		14.5		22	164	99	Archinal: Id? Scattering of bright stars in rich Milky Way. Aliases: Lund 764; OCl 1013; OCl 1013.0; (4) IRAS 17349−3730; C1734−375
NGC 6401	gcl	17 38 36.9	−23 54 32	Oph		4.8	7.4		15.5	10.8	6300	22	146	6	Aliases: EQ 1735−238; C1735−238
ESO 393-SC12	cl	17 38.7	−35 39	Sco	III2	2.0						22	164	10	
[DB01] 2	cl?	17 39 20.1	−23 41 00	Oph		1.0						22	146	16	Infrared cluster. [DB01]: Resolved stellar group, related to LDN 114? partly optical.

Table 4.1: Catalog of Clusters and Asterisms in the Milky Way, and Objects Misidentified as Such

Name	Type	2000.0 R.A.	Dec.	Con.	Tr. Type	Diam. (′)	Tot. Vm	#str	Bt* Vm	V Sur	Dist. (pc)	S #	2U #	Ref	Comments and Aliases
NGC 6404	cl	17 39.6	–33 14	Sco	III2m	6.0	10.6	50		14.5		22	164	8	Aliases: Cr 340; Lund 766; OCl 1024; vdB-Ha 240; (4) IRAS 17361–3315; C1736–332
NGC 6400	cl	17 40 10	–36 57.7	Sco	II2m	12.0	8.8	60	9.0	14.2		22	164	99	Aliases: Mel 177; Raab 121; Cr 342; OCl 1030; vdB-Ha 241; Lund 767; (5) C1736–369; C1737–369
NGC 6405	cl	17 40 17	–32 15.5	Sco	II3r	33.0	4.2	331	5.5	11.8	486	22	164	52	M 6. Variable in brightness. Brightest star is BM Scorpii = HD 160371, V= 5.5 to 7. Aliases: Cr 341; Lund 769; M 6; Mel 178; OCl 1030; Raab 122; vdB-Ha 242; OCl 1030.0; C1736–321
NGC 6397	gcl	17 40 41.3	–53 40 25	Ara		31.0	5.3		10.0	12.8	2200	26	195	55	Aliases: Mel 176; EQ 1736–536; Caldw 86; C1736–536
Trumpler 29	cl	17 41 36.4	–40 07 07	Sco	III2m	12.0	7.5	30		12.9		22	164	99	Aliases: Cr 343; Ha 17; Lund 768; OCl 1009; OCl 1009.0; C1738–400
[DB00] 29	cl?	17 42 14.1	–28 18 28	Oph		0.7						22	146	15	
Alessi 9	cl	17 42 25	–47 00.3	Ara		110.0						22	181	99	
[DB00] 52	cl?	17 42 28.1	–29 56 23	Oph		0.9						22	164	15	
[DB00] 19	cl?	17 42 40.9	–27 28 30	Oph		0.9						22	146	15	
[DB00] 18	cl	17 42 48.4	–28 06 28	Oph		1.6						22	146	15	Infrared cluster with some optical visibility. [DB00]: Open cluster.
NGC 6415	MW	17 42 54	–35 08.3	Sco		23.0						22	164	99	Archinal: Identity (J. Herschel's h 3701') apparently refers to patch ("projection") of Milky Way here. Alias: h 3701'
[DB00] 22	cl?	17 42 58.9	–28 02 09	Oph		0.9						22	146	15	
[DB00] 20	cl?	17 43 12.4	–27 55 04	Oph		1.0						22	146	15	
[DB00] 21	cl?	17 43 17.3	–27 53 45	Oph		0.8						22	146	15	
NGC 6403	gal	17 43 23.6	–61 40 57	Pav		1.0						26	195	99	
ESO 393-SC15	cl	17 43 35.2	–34 13 38	Sco	III3	5.0						22	164	54	Aliases: (4) IRAS 17402–3412; C1740–342
ESO 520-SC?20	cl??	17 43.6	–24 43	Oph?		0.7						22	146	99	Archinal: Id? No 0.7′ cluster (or possible globular cluster) visible here on DSS.
Palomar 6	gcl	17 43 42.2	–26 13 21	Oph?		1.2	11.6			12.0	5900	22	146	99	Aliases: ESO 520-21; EQ 1740–262; GCl 75; (2) JaFu 1; C1740–262
JaFu 1	pn	17 43 57.4	–26 11 52	Sgr?		0.1	18.			13.6	5900	22	146	99	See notes. Planetary nebula associated with Palomar 6. Discovered 1997 by Jacoby, *et al.* - see finder chart there. Alias: (3) Pal 6
[DB00] 23	cl?	17 44 05.2	–27 40 03	Sgr?		0.9						22	146	15	
[DB00] 54	cl?	17 44 06.2	–29 10 23	Sgr?		1.0						22	146	15	
[DB00] 53	cl?	17 44 13.4	–29 15 34	Sgr?		0.7						22	146	15	
NGC 6416	cl	17 44.3	–32 21	Sco	III2m	15.0	5.7	304	8.43	11.6	773	22	164	99	Archinal: Large scattered cluster, not obvious on DSS. Aliases: Cr 344; Lund 771; OCl 1031; OCl 1031.0; C1741–323
Ruprecht 128	cl	17 44 19.3	–34 53 12	Sco	IV1m	5.0		45	13.0			22	164	99	Aliases: Lund 770; OCl 1020; vdB-Ha 243; C1740–348
[DB00] 55	cl?	17 44 24.4	–29 12 13	Sgr		0.7						22	146	15	
Collinder 345	cl?	17 44 35	–33 52.0	Sco		4.8	10.9	30	9.4	14.3		22	164	99	See notes. Archinal: An elongated N-S group in Milky Way starcloud. TYC 7385 21 1 (V=9.4) is brightest star, on S end. Aliases: Lund 772; OCl 1027; (4) IRAS 17412–3346; C1741–337
[DB01] 42	cl?	17 44 52.7	–29 40 48	Sgr		2.0						22	164	16	Infrared cluster. [DB01]: Resolved cluster in radio HII region G 359.3-0.3, dust window?
NGC 6426	gcl	17 44 54.7	+03 10 13	Oph		4.2	10.9		15.2	14.0	17500	15	106	6	See notes. Aliases: Cr 346; OCl 81; EQ 1742+031; C1742+031
[DB00] 58	cl?	17 45 00.1	–28 51 37	Sgr		0.9						22	146	15	Infrared cluster with some optical visibility. [DB00]: In Sh 2-17.
Terzan N 23	pn	17 45 11	–32 46.3	Sco		0.8					500	22	164	99	See notes. Bica, *et al.* [1995] have shown that this one-time globular cluster candidate is an emission (and probably planetary) nebula. Alias: C1741–328
NGC 6421	MW	17 45 14	–33 41.2	Sco		45.0						22	164	99	Archinal: Confirmed against J. Herschel's drawing. Alias: h 3702
[DB00] 33	cl?	17 45 32.2	–26 41 48	Sgr		0.8						22	146	15	
[DB00] 37	cl?	17 45 38.0	–26 12 10	Sgr		1.1						22	146	15	Infrared cluster with some optical visibility. [DB00]: Related L 9.
Central cluster	cl	17 45 40.0	–29 00 28	Sgr								22	146	99	See notes. The Galactic Center, a massive infrared cluster, also known as SGR A*. Aliases: Gal. ctr.; SGR A*; GAL 000.0+00.0
[DB00] 36	cl?	17 45 41.7	–26 12 55	Sgr		0.7						22	146	15	Infrared cluster with some optical visibility. [DB00]: Includes bright star?, related to L 9.
[DB00] 35	cl?	17 45 48.6	–26 15 03	Sgr		0.8						22	146	15	Infrared cluster. [DB00]: Related to L 9.

Table 4.1: Catalog of Clusters and Asterisms in the Milky Way, and Objects Misidentified as Such

Name	Type	2000.0 R.A.	Dec.	Con.	Tr. Type	Diam. (′)	Tot. Vm	#str	Bt* Vm	V Sur	Dist. (pc)	S #	2U #	Ref	Comments and Aliases
[NHS93] 17	cl	17 45 50.5	−28 49 28	Sgr		0.2						22	146	99	See notes. The "Arches Cluster", a massive young infrared cluster near the Galactic Center. Aliases: GAL 000.12+00.02; GAL 000.121+00.017; Arches cl
[DB00] 17	cl?	17 45 57.7	−27 53 16	Sgr		0.8						22	146	15	
IC 4665	cl	17 46.2	+05 43	Oph	III2m	70.0	4.2	57	6.0	13.4	342	15	86	1	See notes. Aliases: Cr 349; Lund 774; Mel 179; OCl 85; OCl 85.0; C1743+057
RAFGL 2004	cl	17 46 13.9	−28 49 48	Sgr		0.8						22	146	99	See notes. The "Quintuplet Cluster", a massive young infrared cluster near the Galactic Center. Aliases: IRAS 17430–2848; MGM 5; Quint. cl
vdB-Ha 245	cl	17 46 14.4	−29 42 05	Sgr	I1p	1.0		12				22	164	99	Aliases: Lund 1116; C1743–296
Collinder 347	cl	17 46 18.9	−29 20 09	Sgr	II2m n	10.0	8.8	40	10.65	13.8	1514	22	146	99	Aliases: Lund 776; OCl 1039; vdB-Ha 244; C1743–292
[DB00] 56	cl?	17 46 24.2	−29 22 19	Sgr		0.8						22	146	15	Infrared cluster. [DB00]: Deeply embedded, in Sh 2-16.
[DB00] 44	cl?	17 46 34.9	−24 53 26	Sgr		0.8						22	146	15	Infrared cluster with some optical visibility. [DB00]: Related to RCW 143?
[DB00] 1	cl?	17 46 51.2	−29 03 47	Sgr		0.7						22	146	15	Infrared cluster. [DB00]: In RCW 139.
NGC 6425	cl	17 46 53	−31 37.0	Sco	II1m	10.0	7.2	73	10.15	12.2	843	22	164	99	This is Cr 348 (incorrectly listed as Cr 384 in the Lund Catalogue). Aliases: Cr 348; OCl 1033; Lund 777; vdB-Ha 246; (4) IRAS 17437–3128; (4) IRAS 17437–3131; C1743–315
[DB00] 4	cl?	17 47 05.7	−28 46 54	Sgr		0.6						22	146	15	Infrared cluster with some optical visibility. [DB00]: In Sh 2-20.
[DB00] 5	cl?	17 47 07.0	−28 46 04	Sgr		0.4						22	146	15	Infrared cluster with some optical visibility. [DB00]: In Sh 2-20 deeply embedded, compact few stars.
Ruprecht 129	cl	17 47 08.2	−29 36 05	Sgr	IV1p	4.0		10	12.0			22	164	99	Aliases: Lund 778; OCl 1037; C1744–295
[DB00] 6	cl?	17 47 09.6	−28 46 26	Sgr		0.8						22	146	15	Infrared cluster with some optical visibility. [DB00]: In Sh 2-20.
[DB00] 45	cl?	17 47 17.5	−24 53 13	Sgr		1.5						22	146	15	Infrared cluster with some optical visibility. [DB00]: NW heavily reddened, pair with optical concentration NGC 6432.
NGC 6432	ast	17 47 22.3	−24 53 16	Sgr		0.7		4				22	146	99	
Djorgovski 1	gcl	17 47 28.3	−33 03 56	Sco		0.8	13.6			13.1	8800	22	164	6	
Ruprecht 130	cl	17 47 32	−30 05.8	Sco?	II1p	3.0		20	14.0			22	164	99	Aliases: Lund 775; OCl 1034; vdB-Ha 247; C1744–301
[DB00] 2	cl?	17 48 01.4	−29 06 52	Sgr		0.8						22	146	15	Infrared cluster. [DB00]: In Sh 2-19.
Terzan 5	gcl	17 48 04.9	−24 46 47	Sgr		2.4	13.9		20.5	15.8	14600	22	146	55	See notes. Archinal: Position measured from DSS. Aliases: Terzan 11; C1745–247
Collinder 350	cl	17 48.2	+01 18	Oph	IV1p	40.0	6.1	20		14.1		15	106	99	Archinal: Scattering of bright stars over 35′ field. DSS overlap area. Aliases: Lund 779; OCl 75; C1745+013
[DB00] 26	cl?	17 48 41.5	−28 01 42	Sgr		0.7						22	146	15	
NGC 6440	gcl	17 48 52.6	−20 21 34	Sgr		4.4	9.3		16.7	12.5	7000	22	146	6	Alias: C1746–203
[DB00] 38	cl?	17 48 58.7	−26 21 10	Sgr		0.8						22	146	15	
NGC 6437	MW	17 49 00	−35 51.1	Sco		40.0						22	164	99	Archinal: Star cloud with dark nebulae on E, W, and SW sides.
Ruprecht 131	cl	17 49 06.9	−29 13 48	Sgr	IV1p	8.0		15	11.0			22	146	99	Aliases: Lund 780; OCl 2; C1745–292
LeDrew 8	ast?	17 49.3	+28 04	Her		12.0	10.0	12	12	15.4		8	68	99	Possible asterism or cluster discovered by G. LeDrew [Priv. Comm. Oct. 8, 2001].
[DB00] 51	cl?	17 49 29.2	−31 15 51	Sco		2.2						22	164	15	Infrared cluster with some optical visibility. [DB00]: At edge of Sh 2-15, in RCW 134.
NGC 6444	cl	17 49.6	−34 49	Sco	IV1p	12.0		50	11.0			22	164	99	See notes. Aliases: h 3706; OCl 1023; Ru 132; Lund 782; (4) IRAS 17460–3446; C1746–348
Collinder 351	cl	17 49 51	−28 46.2	Sgr	IV2m	8.0	9.3	30		13.8		22	146	99	Archinal: As Collinder says, a slight condensation in a Milky Way star cloud. Aliases: Lund 781; OCl 5; C1746–287
[DB00] 8	cl?	17 50 04.7	−28 52 40	Sgr		0.7						22	146	15	Infrared cluster with some optical visibility. [DB00]: At Sh 2-21 edge.
[DB00] 7	cl?	17 50 06.1	−28 53 13	Sgr		0.8						22	146	15	Infrared cluster with some optical visibility. [DB00]: At Sh 2-21 edge.
JaFu 2	pn	17 50 10.8	−37 03 25	Sco		0.0820					9100	22	164	99	See notes. Planetary nebula associated with NGC 6441. Discovered 1997 by Jacoby, *et al.* - see finder chart there. Alias: (3) NGC 6441
[DB00] 3	cl?	17 50 12.4	−29 12 21	Sgr		0.8						22	146	15	
NGC 6441	gcl	17 50 12.9	−37 03 04	Sco		9.6	7.2		15.4	12.1	10700	22	164	99	Aliases: vdB-Ha 248; Mel 180; (2) JaFu 2; C1746–370
[DB00] 12	cl?	17 50 16.4	−28 51 42	Sgr		0.8						22	146	15	Infrared cluster with some optical visibility. [DB00]: In Sh 2-21.
[DB00] 10	cl?	17 50 17.6	−28 53 40	Sgr		0.6						22	146	15	Infrared cluster with some optical visibility. [DB00]: In Sh 2-21.

Table 4.1: Catalog of Clusters and Asterisms in the Milky Way, and Objects Misidentified as Such

Name	Type	2000.0 R.A.	Dec.	Con.	Tr. Type	Diam. (′)	Tot. Vm	#str	Bt* Vm	V Sur	Dist. (pc)	S #	2U #	Ref	Comments and Aliases
[DB00] 11	cl?	17 50 24.1	−28 53 06	Sgr		1.0						22	146	15	Infrared cluster with some optical visibility. [DB00]: In Sh 2-21.
[DB00] 57	cl?	17 50 26.5	−29 45 24	Sgr		0.7						22	164	15	
NGC 6451	cl	17 50 41	−30 12.7	Sco	I2r n	8.0	8.2	80	12.0	12.7	560	22	164	4	Aliases: Cr 352; Lund 783; Mel 181; OCl 1035; Raab 123; vdB-Ha 250; C1747−302
[DB00] 42	cl?	17 50 43.1	−26 17 29	Sgr		0.8						22	146	15	
Terzan 6	gcl	17 50 46.4	−31 16 31	Sco		1.4	13.9		20.5	14.6	1500	22	164	6	See notes. Aliases: HP 5; vdB-Ha 249; Lund 1117; C1747−312
[DB00] 31	cl?	17 50 49.5	−27 47 07	Sgr		0.8						22	146	15	
NGC 6453	gcl	17 50 51.8	−34 35 55	Sco		7.6	10.2		14.3	14.6	10100	22	164	6	Aliases: vdB-Ha 251; EQ 1748−346; C1748−346
[DB00] 34	cl?	17 51 07.6	−27 08 51	Sgr		0.8						22	146	15	
NGC 6455	MW	17 51 48	−35 10.5	Sco		58.0						22	164	99	Archinal: Milky Way star cloud, with dark nebula on NE, SE, and SW.
[DB00] 15	cl?	17 51 56.8	−28 48 56	Sgr		0.7						22	146	15	
[DB00] 43	cl?	17 52 07.1	−26 28 18	Sgr		1.1						22	146	15	
Basel 5	cl	17 52 28.4	−30 06 23	Sco?	III2m n	5.0		30			766	22	164	99	Aliases: Lund 785; OCl 1038; C1749−300
Ruprecht 133	cl:	17 52 34.1	−28 40 38	Sgr	IV2p	5.0		20	12.0			22	146	99	Aliases: Lund 786; OCl 6; C1749−287
[DB00] 46	cl?	17 52 44.5	−25 25 17	Sgr		0.6						22	146	15	Infrared cluster with some optical visibility. [DB00]: Near optical concentration NGC 6465.
Ruprecht 168	cl	17 52.8	−28 27	Sgr	IV1p	4.0		20	12.0			22	146	99	Archinal: DSS overlap region - position and size not checked. Aliases: Lund 789; OCl 7; (4) IRAS 17495−2826; C1749−284
Ruprecht 134	cl	17 52.8	−29 33	Sgr	II1m n	5.0		30	12.0			22	164	99	Archinal: DSS overlap region - position and size not checked. Aliases: Lund 787; OCl 4; vdB-Ha 252; C1749−295
NGC 6469	cl	17 52 56.5	−22 18 43	Sgr	IV2m	8.0	8.2	50		12.7	1600	22	146	99	Aliases: Cr 353; Lund 788; Mel 182; OCl 21; Raab 124; C1749−223
AL 2	cl	17 53.0	−29 54	Sgr		0.8						22	164	8	Andrews and Lindsay, 1967, cluster 2: "faint, unresolved". Alias: ESO 456-SC05
[DB00] 41	cl?	17 53 02.8	−26 39 26	Sgr		0.6						22	146	15	
[DB00] 40	cl?	17 53 15.9	−26 46 52	Sgr		0.6						22	146	15	Infrared cluster with some optical visibility. [DB00]: Few stars.
Czernik 37	cl	17 53 16.4	−27 22 19	Sgr	II1m	3.0		35				22	146	99	Aliases: Lund 790; OCl 8; vdB-Ha 253; C1750−273
[DB00] 28	cl?	17 53 28.7	−28 20 52	Sgr		1.6						22	146	15	
NGC 6475	cl	17 53 46	−34 47.1	Sco	I3r	75.0	3.3	80	7.0	12.7	239	22	164	52	M 7. Brightest star is HD 162587, center star is HD 162678. 50′ diameter, 75′ diameter with outliers. Aliases: Cr 354; Lund 791; M 7; Mel 183; OCl 1028; Raab 125; vdB-Ha 254; OCl 1028.0; C1750−348
ESO 456-SC09	cl	17 53.9	−32 29	Sco	III3	6.0						22	164	99	Archinal: DSS overlap region.
[DB00] 16	cl?	17 53 58.0	−29 31 42	Sgr		0.7						22	164	15	
[DB00] 27	cl	17 54 11.6	−28 41 53	Sgr		1.6						22	146	15	Infrared cluster. [DB00]: Open cluster.
NGC 6476	MW	17 54 12	−29 07.2	Sgr		20.0						22	146	99	Archinal: A small Milky Way star cloud as described by J. Herschel (his h 3712). Dark nebula on E side. Alias: h 3712
UKS 1	gcl	17 54 27.2	−24 08 43	Sgr		2.0	17.3		22?	18.8	7400	22	146	55	See notes. Visible mostly in the infrared. Aliases: EQ 1751−241; UKS 1751-24.1; C1751−241
NGC 6480	MW	17 54 34.7	−30 26 29	Sco		17.0			12.			22	164	53	See notes. "V" shaped eastward pointing star cloud, with GSC 7378-01423 at apex. LDN 1788 dark nebula on eastern side.
[DB00] 14	cl?	17 54 38.9	−29 13 36	Sgr		0.8						22	146	15	
[DB00] 39	cl?	17 55 03.3	−27 08 42	Sgr		0.7						22	146	15	
[DB00] 13	cl?	17 55 20.9	−29 23 26	Sgr		0.7						22	146	15	
[DB00] 24	cl?	17 55 30.2	−29 01 39	Sgr		0.9						22	146	15	
Trumpler 30	cl	17 56.4	−35 19	Sco	IV1p	20.0	8.8	20		15.3		22	164	99	See notes. Archinal: Confirmed on Barnard [1927] Atlas plate 24 (Barnard discovery). DSS shows this as a 20′ condensation in rich Milky Way. Aliases: Cr 355; Ha 18; Lund 792; OCl 1025; C1753−353
[DB00] 9	cl?	17 56 37.5	−29 43 06	Sgr		0.8						22	164	15	
[DB00] 30	cl?	17 56 55.8	−28 37 21	Sgr		0.7						22	146	15	
NGC 6494	cl	17 56 56	−19 00.7	Sgr	II2r	25.0	5.5	150	10.0	12.5	637	15	146	52	M 23. Aliases: Cr 356; Lund 793; M 23; Mel 184; OCl 30; Raab 126; C1753−190

Table 4.1: Catalog of Clusters and Asterisms in the Milky Way, and Objects Misidentified as Such

Name	Type	2000.0 R.A.	Dec.	Con.	Tr. Type	Diam. (′)	Tot. Vm	#str	Bt* Vm	V Sur	Dist. (pc)	S #	2U #	Ref	Comments and Aliases
Markov 1	ast?	17 57.2	+29 29	Her		15.0		7				8	68	99	See notes. Likely asterism discovered by P. Markov on 2000 July 4-5.
Ruprecht 135	cl	17 58 03.3	–11 39 03	Ser	IV2p	4.0		20				15	126	99	Aliases: Lund 794; OCl 49; C1755–116
[DB00] 48	cl?	17 58 30.0	–26 10 04	Sgr		1.0						22	146	15	Infrared cluster. [DB00]: In Reflection Nebula Bernes 4, in LDN 133.
[DB00] 49	cl?	17 58 34.0	–26 06 55	Sgr		0.9						22	146	15	Infrared cluster with some optical visibility. [DB00]: Compact few stars, core of LDN 133, deeply embedded.
ESO 456-SC29	cl	17 58.6	–32 01	Sgr	III3	0.8						22	164	99	Archinal: Small faint object. Could be asterism, open or globular cluster, or even a galaxy.
PWM78 2	gcl?	17 58 39.4	–05 04 21	Oph		2.0						15	106	8	See notes. Very reddened possible cluster. Difficult to make out on DSS. 40" diameter probable plate defect at 17 58 52.1 –05 09 48. Alias: C1755–050
[DB00] 25	cl?	17 58 54.8	–29 23 40	Sgr		0.7						22	145	15	
NGC 6496	gcl	17 59 02.0	–44 15 54	Sco?		5.6	8.6		14.3	12.3	5700	22	181	55	Aliases: Mel 185; EQ 1755–442; C1755–442
[DB00] 47	cl?	17 59 17.5	–26 17 19	Sgr		0.7						22	146	15	
Ruprecht 136	cl	17 59 17.8	–24 41 30	Sgr	IV1m	3.0		40	13.0			22	146	99	Aliases: Lund 795; OCl 15; C1756–247
Ruprecht 169	cl	17 59.5	–24 46	Sgr	IV2p	3.0		10	14.0			22	146	1	Aliases: Lund 796; OCl 14; C1756–248
[DB00] 32	cl?	17 59 34.6	–28 33 19	Sgr		0.9						22	146	15	
ESO 229-SC02	cl	17 59.6	–51 41	Ara	III2	3.0						26	195	10	
Trumpler 31	cl	17 59.8	–28 10	Sgr	III2p	5.0	9.8	25		13.3	986	22	146	1	Aliases: Cr 357; Lund 798; OCl 9; OCl 9.0; C1756–281
NGC 6507	cl	17 59 50	–17 27.0	Sgr	IV3m	8.0	9.6	35	12.0	14.1		15	126	99	Improved position provided by P. Teutsch [Priv. Comm., 2002]. Diameter is from W. Herschel (his H. VIII.53). Aliases: Cr 358; Lund 797; OCl 32; OCl 32.0; C1756–174
NGC 6506	MW??	17 59.8	–24 39	Sgr								22	146	99	See notes. Archinal: Id? Scattering of stars here. Perhaps this is or includes Ru 136?
Ruprecht 138	cl	17 59.9	–24 40	Sgr	IV1p	6.0		20	13.0			22	146	1	Aliases: Lund 800; OCl 16; C1756–246
Ruprecht 137	cl	17 59.9	–25 10	Sgr	IV2m	5.0		30	13.0			22	146	1	Aliases: Lund 799; OCl 13; C1756–251
Melotte 186	cl	18 01.1	+02 54	Oph	IV3m	240.0	3.0			14.9	200	15	106	1	Aliases: Cr 359; Lund 801; OCl 84; OCl 84.0; C1758+029
Ruprecht 139	cl:	18 01.2	–23 32	Sgr	III2r n	12.0		80	12.0			22	145	1	Aliases: Lund 802; OCl 20; C1758–235
Terzan 9	gcl	18 01 38.8	–26 50 23	Sgr		0.2	16.0		17.2	12.5	13800	22	145	6	Aliases: EQ 1758–268; C1758–268
ESO 456-SC38	gcl	18 01 49.1	–27 49 33	Sgr		9.9	9.90		15.5	14.9	5500	22	145	55	See notes. Near NGC 6520 and Barnard 86. Aliases: Djorg 2; EQ 1758–278; E456-SC38
NGC 6517	gcl	18 01 50.6	–08 57 32	Oph		4.0	10.1		16.0?	13.1	6100	15	126	6	Aliases: EQ 1759–089; C1759–089
Bochum 14	cl	18 02.0	–23 42	Sgr	III1p n	2.0	9.3	11	10.25	10.8	1107	22	145	51	See notes. Between M 20 and M 8. Brightest star is LS 4565. Position (matching discovery value) and diameter from DSS. Aliases: Lund 1123; C1758–237
NGC 6525	cl??	18 02.1	+11 03	Oph								15	86	3	
ESO 589-SC26	cl	18 02.2	–21 55	Sgr	II1	2.5						22	145	10	
NGC 6514	cl	18 02 31	–23 00.7	Sgr	n	30.0	6.3	70	6.0	13.7	1600	22	145	52	See notes. M 20. Trifid nebula and cluster. Trifid double star (HD 164492) on west, HD 164514 on north. Aliases: M 20; Cr 360; Mrk 34; Trifid nebula cl; OCl 23; Lund 803; C1759–230
Terzan 10	gcl	18 02 58	–26 04.0	Sgr		1.5	14.90		19.7	15.8	4800	22	145	55	See notes. Alias: EQ 1800–260
NGC 6520	cl	18 03 25	–27 53.5	Sgr	I2r n	5.0	7.6	60	9.0	11.1	1614	22	145	4	Skiff: Center star is CoD-27 12315. Aliases: Cr 361; Lund 805; Mel 187; OCl 10; Raab 127; Mrk 35; vdB-Ha 255; C1800–279
Teutsch J1803.5-2207	ast?	18 03 30	–22 07.5	Sgr	II2p	1.8		30	30			22	145	17	Teutsch: Asterism? Small sparse group in field of similar density. Includes multiple star near S-edge. Located 24′ NNW of cl M 21.
NGC 6522	gcl	18 03 35.0	–30 02 02	Sgr		9.4	9.9		14.1	14.8	7200	22	163	55	See notes. Position measured from DSS. Aliases: vdB-Ha 256; EQ 1800–300; C1800–300
NGC 6535	gcl	18 03 50.7	–00 17 49	Ser		3.4	9.3		12.8	12.0	6900	15	106	55	Aliases: Mel 189; EQ 1801–003; C1801–003
NGC 6531	cl	18 04 13	–22 30.0	Sgr	I3r	16.0	5.9	100	8.0	11.9	1230	22	145	52	M 21. Center star HD 164883. Includes HD 164863. Aliases: Cr 363; Lund 806; M 21; Mel 188; OCl 26; Raab 128; Mrk 37; OCl 26.0; C1801–225
NGC 6523	cl	18 04 25	–24 23.2	Sgr	II2m n	15.0	4.6	113	6.0	10.5	1528	22	145	8	See notes. M 8, Lagoon Nebula and cluster. Position (that of HD 164906) and size for cluster only. 35 bright stars, > 100 stars total. Aliases: M 8; H. V.13; h 3722; h 3725; NGC 6530; NGC 6533; Cr 362; OCl 18; OCl 19; Lund 807; (5) C1800–243; Mrk 36; C1801–243
ESO 139-SC54	cl	18 04.7	–58 31	Pav	II3	6.0						26	195	10	

Table 4.1: Catalog of Clusters and Asterisms in the Milky Way, and Objects Misidentified as Such

Name	Type	2000.0 R.A.	Dec.	Con.	Tr. Type	Diam. (′)	Tot. Vm	#str	Bt* Vm	V Sur	Dist. (pc)	S #	2U #	Ref	Comments and Aliases
NGC 6528	gcl	18 04 49.6	−30 03 21	Sgr		5.0	9.6		15.5	13.1	6600	22	163	6	Aliases: vdB-Ha 257; EQ 1801−300; C1801−300
NGC 6539	gcl	18 04 49.8	−07 35 09	Ser?		7.9	8.9		15.9	13.4	4000	15	126	55	Aliases: Mel 190; EQ 1802−075; C1802−075
NGC 6529	MW?	18 05.5	−36 18	Sgr								22	163	3	
NGC 6540	gcl	18 06 08.6	−27 45 55	Sgr		1.5	14.6			15.5	3400	22	145	6	See notes. Aliases: Cr 364; OCl 11; Lund 808; Djorg 3; C1803−278
Collinder 468	ast?	18 06 35	−27 27 36	Sgr	IV1p	0.9	11.	8	11.19	10.8		22	145	8	See notes. Archinal: Identified from Lundmark photo [Collinder, 1931, plate 12]. Brightest star is TYC 6850-1266-1 (V=11.19). Aliases: Lund 809; OCl 12; C1803−274
NGC 6546	cl	18 07.2	−23 18	Sgr	II1r	15.0	8.0	150	10.62	13.9	1202	22	145	1	Aliases: Cr 365; Lund 810; OCl 24; C1804−233
NGC 6544	gcl	18 07 20.6	−24 59 51	Sgr		9.2	7.5		12.8	12.3	2500	22	145	6	See notes. Aliases: Cr 366; Mel 192; OCl 17; EQ 1804−250; C1804−250
NGC 6541	gcl	18 08 02.2	−43 42 20	CrA		15.0	6.3		12.1	12.2	6600	22	181	55	Aliases: Mel 191; EQ 1804−437; 1E 1804.4−4343; Caldw 78; C1804−437
2MASS-GC 1	gcl?	18 08 21.8	−19 49 47	Sgr		3.3						15	145	99	See notes. Discovered in infrared, but visible on DSS-II image.
Cl van den Bergh 113	cl	18 08.6	−21 26	Sgr	III3p n	15.0		20				22	145	1	Aliases: Lund 1148; OCl 26.1; C1805−214
2MASS-GC 2	gcl?	18 08 36.5	−20 46 44	Sgr		1.9						22	145	99	See notes. Discovered in infrared, only a few faint stars visible on DSS-II image.
DoDz 9	cl	18 08.8	+31 32	Her	III2p	28.0		15				8	49	1	Aliases: Lund 812; OCl 119; OCl 119.0; C1806+315
NGC 6554	ast?	18 08 55	−18 22.8	Sgr		20.0			10.3			15	145	53	See notes. Includes HD 165811 (V=10.3), HD 165890 (V=10.4), and HD 165969. AX Sgr = HD 165782 (V~7.7) is just off southwest edge.
ESO 280-SC06	gcl	18 09 07	−46 25.3	Ara?		1.4			14.0		21900	22	181	99	See notes. The Galaxy's most recently recognized globular cluster. See Ortolani, *et al.* [2000].
NGC 6553	gcl	18 09 17.3	−25 54 28	Sgr		9.2	8.3		15.3	13.1	3500	22	145	99	Archinal: Position measured from DSS. Aliases: Mel 193; EQ 1806−259; C1806−259
ESO 521-SC38	cl	18 09.4	−24 32	Sgr	I1	3.0						22	145	10	
Collinder 367	cl	18 09 51	−23 49.7	Sgr	III3m n	40.0	6.4	30		14.4		22	145	99	Archinal: Nebulous cluster of brighter stars. Confirmed against Barnard [1927] Atlas plate 29 (Barnard discovery). Aliases: Lund 813; OCl 22; OCl 22.0; C1806−240
NGC 6558	gcl	18 10 17.6	−31 45 47	Sgr			8.6				8800	22	163	99	See notes. Archinal: Position measured from DSS. Aliases: Cr 368; Mel 194; OCl 3; vdB-Ha 259; EQ 1807−317; C1806−317
NGC 6561	cl	18 10 25	−16 41.5	Sgr		17.0		100	9			15	126	99	Archinal: Rich cluster of 100 or so faint stars.
IC 1276	gcl	18 10 44.2	−07 12 27	Ser		8.0	10.3		15.7	14.8	8900	15	126	55	Also widely known as Palomar 7. Aliases: Pal 7; EQ 1808−072; C1808−072
Terzan 11	gcl	18 12 15.8	−22 44 31	Sgr			16.4		18.5?			22	145	6	See notes. Aliases: Terzan 12; EQ 1809−227
Alessi J18124-1523	ast?	18 12 26.4	−15 22 39	Ser		4.0		30	8.0			15	126	8	Possible cluster, reported by B. Alessi, October 30, 1997. Includes HD 166716 (SIMBAD, V=8.0, double, B1/B2II).
ESO 456-SC72	cl	18 12.5	−29 35	Sgr	III2	1.4						22	163	10	
NGC 6568	cl	18 12 45	−21 35.0	Sgr	IV1m	12.0	8.6	50		14.0		22	145	4	Aliases: Cr 369; Lund 815; OCl 28; OCl 28.0; C1809−216
ESO 522-SC05	cl	18 12.9	−24 22	Sgr	II2	4.0						22	145	10	
NGC 6569	gcl	18 13 38.9	−31 49 35	Sgr		6.4	8.4		14.9	12.4	8700	22	163	55	Aliases: vdB-Ha 260; Mel 195; EQ 1810−318; C1810−318
NGC 6573	cl?	18 13 50	−22 08.5	Sgr		6.0		40				22	145	99	Archinal: Three "mini-groups" of stars in a 6′ group, much as J. Herschel described it (his h 1999). Alias: h 1999
AL 3	cl	18 14 05.7	−28 38 08	Sgr	I1m	1.3		30				22	145	8	Andrews and Lindsay, 1967, cluster 3: "sparse, circular". Position here measured from DSS. Aliases: Lund 1118; vdB-Ha 261; (4) IRAS 18111−2837; C1811−286
LeDrew 7	ast?	18 14.5	+03 43	Oph		25.0	7.4	10	8.4	14.4		15	106	99	Possible asterism or cluster discovered by G. LeDrew [Priv. Comm. Oct. 8, 2001].
Kod 1	*	18 15 07	−12 03.2	Ser			15		15		3500	15	126	54	See notes. NOT a globular cluster, but likely a heavily reddened star of spectral type M5-8 III. See Kodaira, *et al.* [1995]. Alias: C1812−121
Markarian 38	cl	18 15 16.6	−18 59 33	Sgr	I1p	2.0					1000	15	145	99	Aliases: Bi 5; Lund 816; OCl 33; C1812−190
NGC 6583	cl	18 15 50	−22 08.2	Sgr	I2m	5.0	10.0	35		13.5		22	145	4	Aliases: Cr 370; Lund 817; OCl 27; C1812−221
NGC 6605	ast	18 16 06	−14 58.6	Ser		29.0	6.0			13.3		15	126	99	Archinal: Elongated E-W group of stars. Aliases: Lund 820; OCl 47; (4) IRAS 18141−1501; (4) IRAS 18143−1500; C1814−149
ESO 335-SC05	ast?	18 16 12	−41 02.2	CrA	III3	9.3		14				22	181	99	Archinal: Sparse 9-10′ diameter group. Perhaps only an asterism? ESO catalogue says 7.0′ x 1.0′, position angle 75°.

Table 4.1: Catalog of Clusters and Asterisms in the Milky Way, and Objects Misidentified as Such

Name	Type	2000.0 R.A.	Dec.	Con.	Tr. Type	Diam. (′)	Tot. Vm	#str	Bt* Vm	V Sur	Dist. (pc)	S #	2U #	Ref	Comments and Aliases
Collinder 469	cl	18 16 33.7	−18 18 42	Sgr	IV1p	2.6	9.1	51		11.2	1400	15	145	99	Archinal: Small group on the SW side of Barnard 93 (on the north side of M 24). Confirmed against Collinder photograph. Aliases: Lund 818; OCl 35; C1813–182
C1814-190	ast	18 16 51	−19 01.8	Sgr				35				15	145	54	See notes. Discovered by D. G. Turner in 1984 via star counts [see Turner, 1984]. Not a real cluster [Turner, *et al.* 1993, p. 128]. Alias: Turner 4
WZ Sgr cl	cl	18 16 59.6	−19 04 33	Sgr								15	145	54	See notes. C1814–191a, discovered by Turner, *et al.* in 1993 [also in Gieren and Fouqué, 1993]. Position is that of WZ Sgr. Alias: C1814–191a
IC 4715	MW	18 17	−18 36	Sgr		120.0	2.5			12.9		15	145	99	See notes. M 24, Small Sagitarius star cloud. About 120′ long by 60′ wide, SW to NE. Includes NGC 6603, B 92, B 93, B 304, B 307. Alias: M 24
Teutsch J1817.1+0722	cl?	18 17 07	+07 22.9	Oph	III1m	4.0		60	60			15	86	17	Teutsch: Cluster? Noticeable concentration of bright and faint stars in rich field.
Trumpler 32	cl	18 17 10.4	−13 20 39	Ser	I2m	12.0	12.2	50	11.84	17.6	1720	15	126	51	See notes. Center and brightest star is GSC 5689-00194. Diameter is approximate. Stellar ring Iss 690 on SW side. Aliases: Cr 372; Ha 19; Lund 822; OCl 55; (2) Iss 690; C1814–133
Collinder 371	cl	18 17 16	−19 44.5	Sgr	III3m n	20.0	7.0	30		13.5		15	145	51	See notes. Includes nebulosity, NGC 6589, NGC 6595=NGC 6590, IC 1283, and IC 1284. Centered on IC 1283, the nebulous star HD 167722. Aliases: OCl 31; Lund 819; (2) NGC 6589; (2) NGC 6595; (2) IC 1283; (2) IC 1284; C1814–199
C1814-191b	cl	18 17 24.6	−19 05 09	Sgr								15	145	54	See notes. Discovered by Turner, *et al.* in 1993. GSC 06273-00146 at center. Alias: Turner 3
NGC 6596	cl	18 17.5	−16 39	Sgr	II2m n	10.0		30				15	126	99	Archinal: Sparse cluster. Aliases: Lund 821; OCl 41; C1814–166
NGC 6604	cl	18 18.1	−12 13	Ser	I3m n	6.0	6.5	105	7.48	10.4	2071	15	126	8	Aliases: Cr 373; Lund 823; OCl 56; Mrk 39; CTB 50; NRL 17; C1815–122
NGC 6603	cl	18 18 28	−18 24.4	Sgr	I2r	4.0	11.1	100	14.0	14.1	2880	15	145	8	See notes. Cluster in M 24 (this is NOT M 24). Over 100 stars. Aliases: Mel 197; Raab 129; Cr 374; OCl 36; Lund 824; (2) M 24; C1815–184
LeDrew 5	ast?	18 18.6	+12 03	Oph		42.0	5.8	12	7.0	13.9		15	86	99	Possible asterism or cluster discovered by G. LeDrew [Priv. Comm. Oct. 8, 2001]. Independently discovered by B. Alessi. Alias: Alessi 19
NGC 6584	gcl	18 18 37.7	−52 12 54	Tel		6.6	7.9		13.5	12.0	9600	26	195	55	Aliases: Mel 196; EQ 1814–522; C1814–522
NGC 6611	cl	18 18 45	−13 47.9	Ser	II3m n	8.0	6.0	543	11.0	10.5	2754	15	126	52	M 16, the Eagle nebula and cluster. Includes HD 168137 and HD 168075. About 90 stars total. Aliases: Cr 375; Lund 825; M 16; Mel 198; OCl 54; Mrk 40; C1816–138
AL 4	cl	18 19 05.8	−27 07 51	Sgr		1.6						22	145	99	Andrews and Lindsay, 1967, cluster 4: "sparse, circular". Alias: ESO 522-SC16
NGC 6613	cl	18 20 00	−17 05.9	Sgr	II3p n	7.0	6.9	40	8.65	11.1	1202	15	126	52	M 18. 30 bright stars, about 80 stars total. Aliases: Cr 376; Lund 826; M 18; OCl 40; C1817–171
ESO 103-14**	cl?	18 20 33	−63 48.5	Pav		4.0		20				26	206	99	The ESO lists this as NGC 6588, but that identification is uncertain. Patch of 20 stars in SW to NE bar.
NGC 6618	cl	18 21 09	−16 10.6	Sgr	III3m n	27.0	6.0	660	9.28	13.2	1500	15	126	52	M 17, Omega (or Checkmark) cluster and nebula. Nebula on west central side. About 150 stars. Aliases: Cr 377; Lund 827; M 17; OCl 44; Mrk 41; C1817–162
Ruprecht 140	cl	18 21 49.8	−33 11 51	Sgr	IV1p	5.0		15	11.0			22	163	99	Aliases: Lund 1119; OCl 1; (4) IRAS 18185–3310; C1818–332
C1819-146	cl	18 22.5	−14 32	Sct		2.8		130			1990	15	126	8	Discovered by Kharchenko and Schilbach [1995]. Appears as possible "stellar ring" on DSS. C1820-146 to east.
NGC 6625	cl	18 23 12.8	−12 00 47	Sct	IV3m n	39.0	9.0	30		17.0		15	126	99	Archinal: Centered on HD 169033 (V=5.705, B5V). Aliases: Lund 829; OCl 58; C1820–120
C1820-146	cl	18 23.6	−14 34	Sct		8.0		139			2130	15	126	8	Discovered by Kharchenko and Schilbach [1995]. Not obvious on the DSS. C1819-146 to west.
NGC 6624	gcl	18 23 40.5	−30 21 40	Sgr		8.8	7.6		14.0	12.3	8100	22	163	55	Aliases: vdB-Ha 262; Mel 199; KOHX 13; C1820–303
NGC 6626	gcl	18 24 32.9	−24 52 12	Sgr		13.8	6.9		12.0	12.6	5900	22	145	55	M 28. Aliases: Mel 200; M 28; C1821–249
Trumpler 33	cl	18 24 38.8	−19 43 57	Sgr	II2p	6.0	7.8	74	9.74	11.7	1282	15	145	99	Aliases: Cr 378; Lund 830; OCl 34; C1821–197
Ruprecht 170	cl	18 25 10.7	−10 01 40	Sct	IV1m	7.0		30	13.0			15	126	99	Aliases: Lund 831; OCl 64; C1822–100
Dolidze 28	cl?	18 25 30.0	−14 38 41	Sct	IV1p	14.0		16				15	126	99	Archinal: Very sparse group centered on Wolf Rayet star WR 115 = HIP 90299 (V=11.84, WN...). Aliases: Lund 832; OCl 53; C1822–146
NGC 6631	cl	18 27 09.5	−12 01 35	Sct	II1m	7.0	11.7	30		15.9		15	126	99	Aliases: Cr 379; Lund 833; OCl 59; OCl 59.0; C1824–120
NGC 6633	cl	18 27 15	+06 30.5	Oph	III2m	20.0	4.6	159	8.0	11.1	312	15	86	4	Aliases: Cr 380; Lund 834; Mel 201; OCl 90; Raab 130; C1825+065
IRAS 18274+0112	cl	18 29 57	+01 14.8	Ser	n	5.0		51				15	106	8	Infrared cluster. See Eiroa and Casali [1992]. DSS shows a small double nebula here.
NGC 6638	gcl	18 30 56.2	−25 29 47	Sgr		7.3	9.2		14.2	13.5	8500	22	145	6	Aliases: EQ 1827–255; C1827–255

Table 4.1: Catalog of Clusters and Asterisms in the Milky Way, and Objects Misidentified as Such

Name	Type	2000.0 R.A.	Dec.	Con.	Tr. Type	Diam. (′)	Tot. Vm	#str	Bt* Vm	V Sur	Dist. (pc)	S #	2U #	Ref	Comments and Aliases
NGC 6639	cl	18 30 57.8	−13 10 14	Sct		5.0		25	11			15	126	99	Aliases: OCl 57; C1827–132
Ruprecht 141	cl	18 31.3	−12 18	Sct	IV1p	6.0		20	12.0			16	126	99	Archinal: Slight condensation in Milky Way star cloud. DSS overlap region. Aliases: Lund 836; OCl 60; C1828–123
NGC 6637	gcl	18 31 23.2	−32 20 53	Sgr		9.8	7.7		13.7	12.7	10100	22	163	55	M 69. See notes. Aliases: M 69; NGC 6634; Mel 202; EQ 1828–323; C1828–323
Dolidze 29	ast	18 31.4	−06 37	Sct		18.0						16	126	99	See notes. DSFG: Probably not a cluster. Archinal: Id? Rich Milky Way field with 4 bright stars. Aliases: Lund 837; OCl 70; C1828–066
NGC 6647	MW	18 31.5	−17 21	Sgr			9.0					15	126	99	See notes. Archinal: Milky Way star cloud, with dark nebula to E, running in thin line to SW. Aliases: Lund 838; OCl 45; C1828–173
IC 4725	cl	18 31 45	−19 07.2	Sgr	III3m	26.0	4.6	601	8.0	11.7	711	15	145	52	See notes. M 25. About 80 stars. Aliases: Cr 382; Lund 839; M 25; Mel 204; OCl 38; Raab 131; C1828–192
NGC 6642	gcl	18 31 54.3	−23 28 35	Sgr		5.8	8.9			12.7	8000	22	145	6	See notes. Aliases: Cr 381; Mel 203; OCl 29; EQ 1828–235; C1828–235
Ruprecht 171	cl	18 32 00.7	−16 02 30	Sgr	III1r	12.0		60	14.0			15	126	99	Archinal: Rich faint cluster or Milky Way star cloud. Aliases: Lund 842; OCl 50; C1829–160
Ruprecht 142	cl	18 32 14	−12 14.2	Sct	IV1p	5.0		15	13.0			16	126	99	Archinal: Slight condensation in Milky Way star cloud. Aliases: Lund 841; OCl 61; (4) IRAS 18295–1216; C1829–122
NGC 6645	cl	18 32 38	−16 53.0	Sgr	IV1m	15.0	8.5	40	12.0	14.4		15	126	4	Aliases: Cr 383; Lund 844; Mel 205; OCl 48; Raab 132; C1829–169
Ruprecht 143	cl	18 32 43	−12 08.3	Sct	IV1m	6.0		30	14.0			16	126	99	Archinal: DSS overlap region. Aliases: Lund 843; OCl 62; (4) IRAS 18296–1210; (4) IRAS 18297–1207; C1829–121
Dolidze 30	ast	18 32.9	−06 02	Sct		18.0						16	126	99	DSFG: Probably not a cluster. Archinal: Id? Nothing obvious in 24′ field. Aliases: OCl 73; OCl 73.0; C1830–060
NGC 6649	cl	18 33 28.3	−10 24 08	Sct	I3m	6.0	8.9	477	13.2	12.8	1553	16	126	51	See notes. Archinal: Position measured from DSS. Aliases: Cr 384; Lund 847; Mel 206; OCl 66; Raab 133; C1830–104
Ruprecht 144	cl	18 33 32.7	−11 25 11	Sct	IV1p	2.0		10	12.0			16	126	99	Aliases: Lund 846; OCl 63; C1830–114
NGC 6659	nf?	18 33 55.8	+23 34 01	Her								8	67	99	Archinal: Centered on HD 342450 (B=9.3, K5).
Dolidze 31	ast	18 34.9	−06 51	Sct		18.0						16	126	99	DSFG: Probably not a cluster. Archinal: Id? Nothing obvious in 24′ field. Aliases: OCl 71; C1832–068
Kemble 2	ast	18 35.0	+72 23	Dra		30.0		17	7			3	10	99	See notes. "Mini-Cassiopeia" asterism. Discovered by L. Kemble in 1994. Kemble 2 name used here for the first time. Alias: Alessi J18350+7223
NGC 6652	gcl	18 35 45.7	−32 59 25	Sgr		6.0	8.5		13.3	12.4	14300	22	163	55	Aliases: Mel 207; EQ 1832–330; C1832–330
IRAS 18333-2357	pn	18 36 23.1	−23 55 18	Sgr		0.2			14.3			22	145	8	See notes. GJJC 1, planetary in M 22. 10" x 7", centered on 1" pair of V=14.3/14.7 stars. See notes for NGC 6656 = M 22. Aliases: GJJC 1; (3) NGC 6656
NGC 6656	gcl	18 36 24.2	−23 54 12	Sgr		32.0	5.2		10.7	12.7	3000	22	145	55	M 22. See notes. Aliases: Mel 208; M 22; EQ 1833–239; 1E 1833.3–2357; C1833–239
NGC 6664	cl	18 36 30.6	−08 11 15	Sct	III2m	12.0	7.8	60	9.0	13.2	1368	16	125	99	Aliases: Cr 385; Lund 850; OCl 68; Mel 209; OCl 68.0; C1834–082
Stephenson 2	cl	18 36 39.6	−06 04 26	Sct		4.5		40	19.7		1500	16	125	8	See notes. Heavily reddened cluster detected mostly in infrared. Brightest star is V magnitude 19.7. Not visible on DSS.
Teutsch J1837.1-1014	ast?	18 37 07	−10 14.1	Sct	II2p	2.5		35	35			16	125	17	Teutsch: Likely asterism? Small group, in absorption hole? (W part of field has fewer stars, heavily obscured region 30′ S of B 314).
IC 4756	cl	18 38.9	+05 26	Ser	II3r	40.0	4.6	466	8.0	12.6	388	16	105	51	See notes. Also known as the Graff Cluster or Graff 1. Aliases: Cr 386; Graff clus; Lund 851; Mel 210; OCl 94; Raab 135; Graff 1; (5) C1832+051; C1836+054
NGC 6682	MW	18 39.6	−04 46	Sct		47.0						16	105	99	
Trumpler 34	cl	18 39.8	−08 28	Sct	IV2m	5.0	8.6	87	11.17	12.1		16	125	99	DSFG: Probably not a cluster. Aliases: Cr 387; Lund 852; OCl 69; C1837–085
ESO 281-SC24	cl	18 40.0	−44 12	CrA	II3	6.0						22	180	10	
Dolidze 32	cl	18 40.5	−04 05	Sct	II2m	8.0		40				16	105	99	Archinal: Id? Nothing obvious in 24′ field. Aliases: Lund 853; OCl 80; C1837–041
Dolidze 33	cl:	18 40.7	−04 23	Sct	III2m	6.0		30				16	105	99	Archinal: Id? Only two stars stand out in 24′ field. Aliases: Lund 854; OCl 79; (4) IRAS 18378–0429; C1838–044
Palomar 8	gcl	18 41 29.9	−19 49 33	Sgr		5.2	10.9		15.4	14.5	28500	15	145	6	Aliases: EQ 1838–198; C1838–198
Mackie 1	ast?	18 41 52	−20 03.4	Sgr		2.0		7				22	145	99	See notes. Likely asterism near Palomar 8, found by Guy Mackie. 5′ south of HD 172596 (V=9.35, K1III). Brightest star is B=12.2 (USNO A2.0).

Table 4.1: Catalog of Clusters and Asterisms in the Milky Way, and Objects Misidentified as Such

Name	Type	2000.0 R.A.	Dec.	Con.	Tr. Type	Diam. (′)	Tot. Vm	#str	Bt* Vm	V Sur	Dist. (pc)	S #	2U #	Ref	Comments and Aliases
Dolidze 34	cl:	18 42 03.1	−04 32 43	Sct	IV1p	5.0		15				16	105	99	Archinal: Apparently asterism of 4 stars. Aliases: Lund 855; OCl 78; C1839−046
NGC 6683	cl	18 42 12.7	−06 12 45	Sct	II1p n	3.0	9.4	20	11.71	11.8	1197	16	125	99	See notes. Archinal: Center star is GSC 05125-01649. Brightest star is GSC 05125-02853. Aliases: Lund 856; OCl 74; OCl 74.0; C1839−063
Trumpler 35	cl	18 43 00.5	−04 13 31	Sct	I2m	6.0	9.2	65	11.41	13.1	1786	16	105	99	Skiff: Refine? Aliases: Cr 398; Lund 857; OCl 83; C1840−041
NGC 6681	gcl	18 43 12.7	−32 17 31	Sgr		8.0	7.8		13.0	12.3	9200	22	163	55	M 70. Aliases: M 70; Mel 211; EQ 1840−323; C1840−323
AL 5	cl	18 44 19.1	−04 55 53	Sct		2.2						16	105	99	Andrews and Lindsay, 1967, cluster 5: "faint stars, circular".
Berkeley 79	cl	18 44 57.5	−01 08 36	Aql	II1r	7.0		60	15.0			16	105	99	Aliases: Lund 859; OCl 86; C1842−012
NGC 6694	cl	18 45 15	−09 23.1	Sct	II3m	10.0	8.0	120	11.0	13.0	1519	16	125	52	M 26. HD 173348 is brightest star, on southwest side. About 100 stars. Aliases: Cr 389; Lund 858; M 26; Mel 212; OCl 67; Raab 136; OCl 67.0; C1842−094
Iskudarian 1	cl?	18 48.0	+36 51	Lyr		120.0		26	15.8		250	8	49	51	See notes. Postulated cluster of white dwarfs. V(?)=15.8 to 20.2 stars, over a 2° x 1° area. Aliases: Lund 860; OCl 136; OCl 136.0; (4) IRAS 18461+3647; C1846+368
Apriamasvili 1	cl	18 48.1	−05 51 07	Sct	IV1p	5.5	8.9	94	12.58	12.6	1360	16	125	51	See notes. Known as Apriamasvili cluster by discovery priority. Also known as Basel 1. Aliases: Bas 1; OCl 77.0; Lund 861; Apr; C1845−059
NGC 6698	cl??	18 48.2	−25 55	Sgr								22	145	99	See notes. Archinal: Id? Possibly 10′ x 5′ slight concentration of stars here?
NGC 6684	gal	18 48 57.5	−65 10 26	Pav		4.0	10.39			13.4		26	206	54	See notes. This galaxy has been mistaken for a Galactic globular cluster. Data here from RC3. Aliases: (5) GCl 102; ESO 104-G016; PGC 62453; AM 1843−651; SGC 184402-6513.8; C1846−652
Czernik 38	cl	18 49 47.0	+04 58	Ser	I2r	10.0		80				16	105	99	Aliases: Lund 862; OCl 95; C1847+048
Ruprecht 145	cl	18 50 19.4	−18 12 19	Sgr	III1m	35.0			10.0			15	145	99	Aliases: Lund 863; OCl 52; OCl 52.0; (4) IRAS 18475−1809; C1847−181
NGC 6704	cl	18 50 45.8	−05 12 18	Sct	I2m	6.0	9.2	71	12.0	13.1	1939	16	105	99	Aliases: Cr 390; Lund 864; OCl 82; OCl 82.0; C1848−052
NGC 6705	cl	18 51 04	−06 16.2	Sct	I2r	11.0	5.8	682	11.0	11.0	1675	16	125	52	See notes. M 11, Wild Duck cluster. Very rich, much greater than 200 stars. Aliases: Cr 391; Lund 865; M 11; Mel 213; OCl 76; OCl 76.0; C1848−063
NGC 6709	cl	18 51.5	+10 20	Aql	IV2m	15.0	6.7	111	9.0	12.6	887	16	85	99	Archinal: Very irregular. No obvious center on DSS image. Aliases: Cr 392; Lund 866; Mel 214; OCl 100; Raab 137; OCl 100.0; C1849+102
Collinder 394	cl	18 52 16.3	−20 12 12	Sgr	IV2m	22.0	6.3	50	6.97	13.0	643	22	145	99	Archinal: Scattered group of bright stars, centered on HD 174651 (V=8.48, B8IV). Aliases: Lund 869; OCl 42; OCl 42.0; C1850−204
Ruprecht 146	cl	18 52 30	−21 04.9	Sgr	IV1p	4.0		20	12.0			22	145	99	Aliases: Lund 867; OCl 39; C1849−211
NGC 6712	gcl	18 53 04.3	−08 42 22	Sct		9.8	8.1		13.3	13.1	6800	16	125	6	See notes. Aliases: Mel 215; OCl 72; OCl 72.0; C1850−087
Berkeley 80	cl	18 54 20.6	−01 13 12	Aql	II1p	3.0		20	15.0			16	105	99	Aliases: Lund 871; OCl 87; C1851−013
Stephenson 1	cl:	18 54 30.6	+36 53 59	Lyr	IV3p	40.0	3.8	77	4.30	11.8	315	8	49	99	Archinal: δ Lyrae cluster, discovered by Gordon Grant. δ^2 is center and brightest star (V=4.30v, M4II). Aliases: Del Lyr cl; Lund 870; OCl 137; OCl 137.0; C1851+368
NGC 6716	cl	18 54 34	−19 54.5	Sgr	IV1p	10.0	7.5	38	8.28	12.5	612	15	145	99	Aliases: Cr 393; Lund 872; OCl 46; C1851−199
Archinal 1	cl	18 54 49.4	+05 32 56	Ser	II2p	1.5		24	13.4			16	85	8	See notes. First listed here, discovered by Archinal. Includes 4 GSC stars, brightest is GSC 00457-00629. Near IC 4756.
Poole J1855.0+1047	cl?	18 55 02.7	+10 47 21	Aql		6.0		40				16	85	99	See notes. First described in detail by A. Ling. Center is HD 230024. Involved in star cloud ("Poole J1857.0+1027").
NGC 6715	gcl	18 55 03.3	−30 28 42	Sgr		12.0	7.7		15.2	13.1	21200	22	163	55	See notes. M 54. This may be the nucleus of the Sagittarius Dwarf Galaxy as well as a Galactic globular cluster. Aliases: M 54; Mel 216; EQ 1851−305; C1851−305
NGC 6717	gcl	18 55 06.2	−22 42 03	Sgr		5.4	8.4		14.0	12.1	7300	22	145	6	See notes. This is also widely known as Palomar 9. It contains IC 4802, a clump of stars NE of the nucleus. Aliases: Cr 395; Pal 9; OCl 37; (2) IC 4802; EQ 1852−227; C1852−227
IC 4802	ptcl	18 55 07.1	−22 41 52	Sgr		0.2						22	145	8	See notes. Clump of stars, NE of nucleus of NGC 6717 = Palomar 9. Alias: (3) NGC 6717
Poole J1855.8+1046	ast?	18 55 53	+10 46 17	Aql		3.5		15				16	85	8	See notes. First described in detail by A. Ling. Involved in star cloud ("Poole J1857.0+1027").
ESO 524-SC01	cl	18 56 38.9	−26 58 11	Sgr	III2	6.0						22	145	99	
NGC 6724	cl?	18 56 45	+10 26 47	Aql		3.0	10	10	12	3.4		16	85	53	See notes. Identification not certain. NGC 6724 may also be the enveloping star cloud (here "Poole J1857.0+1027"). Alias: (3) Poole J1857.0+1027

Table 4.1: Catalog of Clusters and Asterisms in the Milky Way, and Objects Misidentified as Such

Name	Type	2000.0 R.A.	Dec.	Con.	Tr. Type	Diam. (′)	Tot. Vm	#str	Bt* Vm	V Sur	Dist. (pc)	S #	2U #	Ref	Comments and Aliases
Poole J1857.0+1027	MW	18 57 04	+10 27	Aql		20.0						16	85	8	See notes. Star cloud that includes NGC 6724 (or may be NGC 6724). Diameter 20′ to 40′.
NGC 6728	ast	18 57 31.4	−08 57 56	Sct		18.0						16	125	99	Archinal: Large E-W scattering of stars with Iss 662 (stellar ring) at center. Alias: (2) Iss 662
NGC 6723	gcl	18 59 33.2	−36 37 54	Sgr		13.0	6.8		12.8	12.4	8700	22	163	55	Aliases: Mel 217; EQ 1856−367; C1856−367
NGC 6735	cl	19 00 45.3	−00 27 21	Aql		8.0		35	12			16	105	99	
NGC 6738	cl	19 01.4	+11 36	Aql	IV2p	15.0	8.3			14.2		16	85	1	Aliases: Cr 396; Lund 874; OCl 101; OCl 101.0; C1859+115
NGC 6743	cl?	19 01 26.7	+29 17 14	Lyr		8.0		35	8.2			8	67	53	See notes. Includes HD 176970 as brightest (V=8.2) and center star.
Ling 1	ast?	19 01 29	+27 18.0	Lyr		5.0		12	8.1			8	67	99	Discovered by Alister Ling in 1995 while searching for NGC 6743.
Berkeley 81	cl	19 01 39.7	−00 27 22	Aql	II2r	5.0		80	15.0			16	105	99	See notes. Aliases: Lund 875; OCl 88; C1859−005
NGC 6737	ast?	19 02 10.0	−18 32 48	Sgr								16	145	99	
ESO 397-SC01	cl	19 04.1	−33 23	Sgr	III2	6.0						22	163	10	
NGC 6749	gcl	19 05 15.3	+01 54 03	Aql		4.0	12.4		16.5	15.4	7300	16	105	55	See notes. Aliases: Be 42; OCl 91; Lund 876; (5) C1902+017; EQ 1902+017; C1902+018
NGC 6755	cl	19 07 49	+04 16.0	Aql	II2r	15.0	7.5	157	11.0	13.4	1675	16	105	4	Aliases: Cr 397; Lund 878; OCl 96; Cz 39; (5) C1905+042; (5) OCl 97; (5) Lund 877; C1905+041
NGC 6756	cl	19 08 43	+04 42.3	Aql	I1m	4.0	10.6	40	13.0	13.6	1507	16	105	4	Aliases: Cr 398; Lund 879; OCl 99; C1906+046
NGC 6752	gcl	19 10 51.8	−59 58 55	Pav		29.0	5.3		10.5	12.6	4200	26	194	55	Aliases: Mel 218; EQ 1906−600; Caldw 93; C1906−600
NGC 6760	gcl	19 11 12.1	+01 01 50	Aql		9.6	9.0		15.6	13.9	6100	16	105	6	See notes. Aliases: Mel 219; OCl 92; C1909+009
Berkeley 82	cl	19 11 20.3	+13 06 42	Aql	III1p	2.5		20	14.0			16	85	99	Aliases: Lund 880; OCl 103; (4) IRAS 19090+1301; C1909+129
LeDrew 6	ast?	19 13.3	+36 20	Lyr		37.0	5.5	12	7.1	13.3		8	49	99	Possible asterism or cluster discovered by G. LeDrew [Priv. Comm. Oct. 8, 2001].
ESO 282-SC26	cl	19 13.9	−42 37	CrA	III3	20.0						22	180	10	
NGC 6773	cl??	19 15.0	+04 53	Aql								16	105	99	Archinal: Id? DSS shows 4 bright stars in rich Milky Way background.
Berkeley 43	cl	19 15 30	+11 16.5	Aql	II1m	5.0		35	15.0			16	85	99	Aliases: Lund 882; OCl 102; C1913+111
NGC 6774	cl	19 16.3	−16 19.5	Sgr	IV2p	45.0		40	9.0			16	125	99	See notes. From DSS, center star is HD 180228. 40-100 stars total, depending on cutoff magnitude. Aliases: Lund 883; OCl 65; OCl 65.0; h 2034; GC 4481; Ru 147; C1913−163
NGC 6775	cl?	19 16 30	−00 54.5	Aql		13.0		10				16	105	99	Archinal: Straggling group of stars running NW to SE, as J. Herschel and Smyth describe it. DSS overlap region.
NGC 6779	gcl	19 16 35.5	+30 11 05	Lyr		8.8	8.4		13.2	13.1	9800	8	49	55	M 56. Aliases: Mel 220; M 56; EQ 1914+300; C1914+300
ESO 231-SC30	cl	19 16.9	−51 29	Tel	III3	20.0						26	180	10	
Berkeley 44	cl	19 17 17	+19 32.7	Sge	III1m	2.0		30	16.0			16	67	99	Aliases: Lund 884; OCl 110; C1915+194
Terzan 7	gcl	19 17 43.7	−34 39 27	Sgr			12.0		15.0		21900	22	163	55	May also be a member of the Sagittarius Dwarf Galaxy as well as a Galactic globular cluster. Alias: EQ 1914−347
ESO 141-SC47	cl	19 18.0	−57 54	Pav	II2	7.0						26	194	10	
Palomar 10	gcl	19 18 02.1	+18 34 18	Sge		4.0	13.2		18 ?	16.2	10600	16	67	6	Alias: EQ 1916+184
Berkeley 45	cl	19 19 06	+15 43.3	Aql	II1p	2.0		20	15.0			16	85	99	Aliases: Lund 885; OCl 107; C1916+156
ESO 337-SC23	cl	19 19.2	−37 37	Sgr	III3	5.0						22	163	10	
NGC 6791	cl	19 20 52.7	+37 46 27	Lyr	I2r	10.0	9.5	380	15.0	14.5	4681	8	48	99	Archinal: Very rich cluster - appears as a sparse globular cluster on DSS image. Aliases: Be 46; Lund 886; OCl 142; OCl 142.0; C1919+377
NGC 6793	cl	19 23 12.6	+22 09 27	Vul	III2p	7.0		15				8	66	99	Aliases: Lund 887; OCl 115; C1921+220
King 25	cl	19 24.5	+13 42	Aql	III2m	5.0		40				16	85	51	See notes. Aliases: OCl 106; Lund 889; C1922+136
Dolidze 35	ast?	19 25 24	+11 39.5	Aql	IV2p	7.0		10				16	85	99	Archinal: Likely this group of stars, 35′ E of Dolidze original position, but matching supposed 8′ diameter. Aliases: Lund 891; OCl 105; C1924+115
NGC 6795	***	19 26 05.1	+03 31 11	Aql								16	105	99	Archinal: Three stars running E-W, in rich Milky Way, as J. Herschel (h 2040) described it. Just NE of δ Aql. Alias: h 2040

Table 4.1: Catalog of Clusters and Asterisms in the Milky Way, and Objects Misidentified as Such

Name	Type	2000.0 R.A.	Dec.	Con.	Tr. Type	Diam. (′)	Tot. Vm	#str	Bt* Vm	V Sur	Dist. (pc)	S #	2U #	Ref	Comments and Aliases
Collinder 399	ast	19 26 12	+20 05 53	Vul	III3m	90.0	3.6	40	5.19	13.4	130	8	66	52	See notes. "Al Sûfi's" or "Brocchi's" or "Coathanger". Position for center star of "hanger". Not a true cluster. Aliases: Al Sufi's; Brocchi's; Coathanger; 4-5 Vul cl; OCl 113; Lund 890; OCl 113.0; C1923+200
NGC 6800	cl	19 27 00	+25 05.6	Vul	IV1p	5.0		20	10.0			8	66	99	Aliases: Lund 892; OCl 123; C1925+250
ESO 525-SC08	cl	19 27.3	−23 35	Sgr	II1	5.0						22	144	10	
Berkeley 47	cl	19 28 27.3	+17 21 57	Sge	II2p	3.0		20	16.0			16	85	99	Aliases: Lund 893; OCl 109; C1926+173
Arp 2	gcl	19 28 44.1	−30 21 14	Sgr		2.3	13.0		15.5	14.8	28300	22	162	55	May also be a member of the Sagittarius Dwarf Galaxy as well as a Galactic globular cluster. Aliases: EQ 1925−304; C1925−304
King 26	cl	19 29.0	+14 52	Aql	II1p	2.0		15				16	85	1	Aliases: Lund 894; OCl 108; C1926+147
NGC 6802	cl	19 30 35	+20 15.8	Vul	I1m	5.0	8.8	201	14.0	12.3	1019	8	66	4	Aliases: Cr 400; Lund 895; OCl 114; C1928+201
Stock 1	cl	19 35 47	+25 10.5	Vul	III2m	52.0	5.2	19	7.10	13.8		8	66	99	See notes. Skiff: HD 184928 (V=8.1) is center star. True cluster diameter is 52′, but apparent group extends to 80′ diameter. Aliases: Lund 896; OCl 127; OCl 127.0; C1933+251
NGC 6811	cl	19 37 09.6	+46 22 32	Cyg	III1r	15.0	6.8	249	11.0	12.7	1075	8	33	52	DSFG: Walter Scott Houston's "Hole in a Cluster.". Aliases: Cr 402; Lund 897; Mel 222; OCl 185; Raab 138; C1936+464
Collinder 401	cl	19 38 21.7	+00 20 43	Aql	IV2m	1.0	7.0			7.0		16	105	99	Archinal: Centered on HD 185297 (7.27, A2, double). Aliases: Lund 898; OCl 98; C1935+002
SSWZ94 5	cl	19 39 31.2	+25 38 42	Vul		2.0						8	66	99	Archinal: Condensation in rich Milky Way, checked by comparison with SSWZ94 discovery chart.
NGC 6809	gcl	19 39 59.4	−30 57 44	Sgr		19.0	6.3		11.2	12.7	4800	22	162	55	M 55. Aliases: M 55; Mel 221; EQ 1936−310; C1936−310
NGC 6815	ast	19 40.9	+26 51	Vul								8	66	99	Archinal: Id? Only rich Milky Way field obvious on DSS. Aliases: OCl 131; C1938+267
NGC 6819	cl	19 41.3	+40 11	Cyg	I1r	5.0	7.3	929	11.0	10.8	2051	8	48	51	See notes. Aliases: Cr 403; Lund 900; Mel 223; OCl 155; Raab 139; C1939+400
Terzan 8	gcl	19 41 45.0	−34 00 01	Sgr			12.4		15.0		22800	22	162	55	May also be a member of the Sagittarius Dwarf Galaxy as well as a Galactic globular cluster. Aliases: EQ 1938−341; C1938−341
Skiff J1942.3+3839	cl?	19 42 24	+38 39.0	Cyg	II1p	3.0		12	12.			8	48	99	See notes. Discovered by Skiff. Possibly as large as 50 stars over 10′ diameter. HD 186506 (V=6.4) is bright star to east. Alias: Teutsch J1942.4+3839
Collinder 404	ast?	19 42 28	+23 05 16	Vul		0.8	14.9p	6		14.4		8	66	99	Asterism(?) of 6 stars, involved in nebula NGC 6820. Aliases: OCl 122; (4) NGC 6820; C1940+229
Czernik 40	cl	19 42 38	+21 09.2	Vul	II2m	4.0		30				8	66	99	Aliases: King 27; Lund 901; OCl 118; C1940+210
NGC 6823	cl	19 43 10	+23 18.0	Vul	I3m n	7.0	7.1	79	8.81	11.3	2623	8	66	4	Skiff: Middle of trapezium. Aliases: Cr 405; Lund 903; OCl 124; Raab 140; Mrk 42; W 55; OCl 124.0; Sh 2- 86; CTB 76; [HC69] 44; C1941+231
Mandushev 1	ast	19 43 30	+29 15.0	Cyg		18.0		33	10.05			8	66	99	See notes. Archinal: Position determined from Turner, *et al.* [1998] Figure 1 and DSS.
SU Cygni	ast?	19 44 48.6	+29 15 52	Cyg?					6.82v			8	66	99	See notes. Possible association or cluster of stars around Cepheid variable SU Cygni. Not seen in 6, 18, and 20-inch telescopes. Alias: Turner 9
Roslund 1	cl	19 45 06	+17 35.0	Sge	IV1p	3.0		15				16	66	99	Archinal: Confirmed against Roslund position and diameter. Condensation in rich Milky Way. Aliases: Lund 904; OCl 112; C1942+174
Palomar 11	gcl	19 45 14.4	−08 00 26	Aql		10.0	9.8?		15.5	14.8	13300	16	125	6	Aliases: EQ 1942−081; C1942−081
Turner 8	cl?	19 45 16	+27 50.5	Vul?		2.5						8	66	99	Dias, *et al.* [2002] list a cluster here in Lynds 810, but the cited papers [Turner, 1986a; 1986b] mention no cluster. Alias: (4) Lynds 810
Roslund 2	cl	19 45 24.4	+23 56 34	Vul	IV2p	45.0		20	7.07			8	66	99	Archinal: Confirmed against Roslund position and diameter. Center and brightest star HD 186745 (V=7.07, B8Ia). Aliases: Lund 905; OCl 126; C1943+238
Teutsch J1947.7+2415	cl?	19 47 43	+24 15.7	Vul	I2r	2.5		100	100			8	66	17	Teutsch: Cluster or absorption hole? Small concentration of stars in irregularly obscured field. Located 3′ NW of HD 187202 (V=8.17).
Levy-W. J1948.2+3743	ast	19 48 12.1	+37 43 31	Cyg		33.5		12	7.55			8	48	99	33.5′ straight line star stream, from 19 49 30.5 +37 58 50 (on NE) to 19 47 34.6 +37 34 23 (on SW), and faint curve to NW.
NGC 6832	ast?	19 48 15.5	+59 25 22	Cyg?		12.0		50	7			3	20	99	Archinal: Scattering of about 50 stars around brightest and center star, HD 187748 (V=6.658, G0).
NGC 6827	cl	19 48 53.2	+21 12 58	Vul	I1m	2.0		30	13			8	66	53	See notes. Archinal: Position is of central "clump" of stars. Aliases: Be 48; OCl 120; Lund 906; C1946+210
C1947+272	cl	19 49 04	+27 17.9	Vul	III3m	3.5		186	13.81		643	8	66	99	S Vul on southwest, but not a member. Discovered by Turner [1985b]. See also Turner, *et al.* [1986]. Alias: Turner 1

Table 4.1: Catalog of Clusters and Asterisms in the Milky Way, and Objects Misidentified as Such

Name	Type	2000.0 R.A.	Dec.	Con.	Tr. Type	Diam. (′)	Tot. Vm	#str	Bt* Vm	V Sur	Dist. (pc)	S #	2U #	Ref	Comments and Aliases
NGC 6828	cl?	19 50.4	+07 55	Aql								16	84	99	Archinal: Obvious possible cluster here, as W. Herschel describes it.
Czernik 41	cl:	19 50 50.8	+25 18 09	Vul	III2m	8.0		30				8	66	99	Aliases: Lund 907; OCl 130; C1948+250
NGC 6830	cl	19 51 00	+23 06.0	Vul	II2p	6.0	7.9	82	10.0	11.8	1696	8	66	4	Aliases: Cr 406; Lund 908; Mel 224; OCl 125; Raab 141; C1948+229
SSWZ94 6	cl	19 51 01.9	+32 14 35	Cyg		1.0						8	48	99	
NGC 6834	cl	19 52 13	+29 24.5	Cyg	II2m	6.0	7.8	128	11.0	11.7	2167	8	66	4	Skiff: Center star is HD 332843. Aliases: Cr 407; Lund 909; Mel 225; OCl 134; Raab 142; C1950+292
Harvard 20	cl	19 53 10.3	+18 21 24	Sge	IV2p	8.0	7.7	28	8.90	12.2	2716	16	66	99	Aliases: Cr 408; Lund 910; OCl 116; OCl 116.0; C1950+182
NGC 6837	cl	19 53.5	+11 41	Aql	IV1p	3.0	12	20		3.6		16	84	99	Archinal: Id? Not obvious on DSS image. Aliases: Lund 1149; OCl 108.1; C1951+115
NGC 6838	gcl	19 53 46.1	+18 46 42	Sge			8.4		12.1		3900	16	66	6	M 71. See notes. Aliases: Cr 409; M 71; Mel 226; OCl 117; GCRV 12241; EQ 1951+186; CSI+18-19515; C1951+186
NGC 6839	ast?	19 54 19	+17 53.3	Sge		4.0		12				16	66	99	Archinal: Located based on the Herschel's and Archinal's [1993, p. 86] description.
NGC 6840	cl?	19 55 16	+12 07.5	Aql		4.0		20	10			16	84	99	
NGC 6843	cl?	19 56.1	+12 09	Aql		4.0		<20	10			16	84	3	
NGC 6846	cl	19 56 28.1	+32 20 55	Cyg	II2m	0.8	14.2	40	12.8	13.7		8	48	8	See notes. Most references have declination too far south by 2°. Planetary K 4-41 2′ to NE. Aliases: Cr 410; Lund 912; OCl 139; C1954+302
NGC 6847	MW	19 57.0	+29 20	Cyg?								8	66	99	Archinal: Rich Milky Way here as described by W. Herschel, but unable to identity the particular patch he referred to.
Loiano 1	cl	19 58 14.4	+32 32 42	Cyg		6.5		40	11.9		2700.	8	48	99	Discovered by Bernabei and Polcaro [2001]. Faint cluster with 1WGA J1958+3232 (V=15.96) at center.
Roslund 3	cl	19 58 41.1	+20 31 25	Sge	IV1p	5.0		20				8	66	99	Aliases: OCl 121; C1956+203
NGC 6856	cl?	19 59.3	+56 08	Cyg				15				3	20	3	
Berkeley 49	cl	19 59 30.2	+34 38 34	Cyg	I1p	3.0		20	16.0			8	48	99	Aliases: Lund 914; OCl 144; (4) IRAS 19580+3429; C1957+344
Berkeley 83	cl:	20 01 25.1	+28 38 36	Vul	II1p	2.0		20	17.0			9	66	99	Aliases: Lund 915; OCl 135; C1959+284
ADS 13292	cl?	20 02 23.6	+35 18 35	Cyg	I1p n	1.0		8	9.38			9	48	99	See notes. Suggested by Skiff to be a likely cluster. Involved in Sh 2-101. Bright star is ADS 13292A (V=9.38, B2II). Aliases: (4) Sh 2- 101; Teutsch J2002.3+3518
Dolidze 36	ast	20 02.5	+42 06	Cyg	IV1p	14.0						9	32	99	DSFG: Probably not a cluster. Archinal: Group of about a dozen brighter stars. Aliases: OCl 172; C2000+419
Dolidze 37	ast	20 03.0	+37 41	Cyg		8.0						9	48	51	Group of about 10 brighter stars. Aliases: OCl 154; C2001+375
NGC 6858	cl?	20 03.1	+11 16	Aql		10.0		12	10			16	84	3	
NGC 6859	***	20 03 49.5	+00 26 40	Aql				3				16	104	99	
NGC 6866	cl	20 03 55	+44 09.5	Cyg	II2r	15.0	7.6	129	10.0	13.5	1285	9	32	4	Skiff: -10′ Lynga declination error. Aliases: Cr 412; Lund 917; Mel 229; OCl 183; Raab 143; C2002+438
Alessi J20046-1030	ast?	20 04.6	−10 31	Aql		20.0	7.5	20	8.85	14.0		16	124	99	B. Alessi has shown, via Tycho and PMM catalog proper motions, that these stars may be physically associated. Aliases: LeDrew 3; Alessi 10
Berkeley 84	cl	20 04 42.2	+33 54 25	Cyg	II1p n	2.0		20	16.0			9	48	99	Aliases: Lund 978; OCl 143; C2002+337
[DB01] 4	cl?	20 04 45.4	+29 15 05	Vul		0.5						9	66	16	Infrared cluster. [DB01]: Partly resolved stellar group in nebula BFS 2a, in complex IC 4954.
Roslund 4	cl	20 04 52	+29 12.9	Vul	II3m n	6.0	10.0	30		13.9	2655	9	66	99	Archinal: 3 patches of bright nebulosity on W side, including IC 4954 and IC 4955. Aliases: (4) IC 4954; (4) IC 4955; C2002+290
[DB01] 3	cl?	20 04 52.9	+29 11 45	Vul		2.0						9	66	16	Infrared cluster. [DB01]: Mostly a resolved cluster in nebula IC 4955=BFS 2c, in complex IC 4954.
ESO 461-SC38	cl	20 04.9	−30 21	Sgr	II1	4.0						23	162	10	
NGC 6863	ast	20 05 07.4	−03 33 13	Aql				8				16	104	99	
Alessi J20053+4732	ast	20 05.3	+47 32	Cyg		12.0		19	9			9	32	10	
DoDz 10	cl	20 05 35	+40 40.4	Cyg	IV2p n	24.0		40	7.1			9	32	99	Archinal: Scattered cluster in rich Milky Way and bright nebula. Bright star is HD 190812 (V=7.1, A5) on NW side. Aliases: Lund 920; OCl 166; OCl 166.0; C2004+403

Table 4.1: Catalog of Clusters and Asterisms in the Milky Way, and Objects Misidentified as Such

Name	Type	2000.0 R.A.	Dec.	Con.	Tr. Type	Diam. (′)	Tot. Vm	#str	Bt* Vm	V Sur	Dist. (pc)	S #	2U #	Ref	Comments and Aliases
Dolidze 38	ast	20 06 04	+41 11 17	Cyg	III2p	15.0						9	32	51	Position from DSS. 15′ N-S, 10′ E-W, "Y"-shaped group. Brightest star is HD 227663. HD 190916 (V=7.6) to NW. Involved in nebulosity. Aliases: OCl 170; OCl 170.0; C2004+410
NGC 6864	gcl	20 06 04.8	−21 55 17	Sgr		6.8	8.6		14.6	12.8	18500	23	144	55	M 75. Aliases: M 75; Mel 228; EQ 2003−220; C2003−220
NGC 6871	cl	20 06 27	+35 47.4	Cyg	II2p n	30.0	5.2	66	6.83	12.6	1746	9	48	99	Archinal: About a dozen bright stars over a 30′ field of rich Milky Way. Dark nebulae on SW side. Aliases: Cr 413; Lund 921; OCl 148; Mrk 43; OCl 148.0; C2004+356
Teutsch J2006.8+3518	cl?	20 06 53	+35 18.1	Cyg	II2p n	2.5		20	20			9	48	17	Teutsch: Cluster? Small group in bright nebula, similar to ADS 13292 = Teutsch J2002.3+3518. Located 4′ S of dark nebula B 147
Biurakan 1	cl	20 07.5	+35 41	Cyg	IV3p n	10.0		15				9	48	99	Archinal: Id? Rich field around bright star, but no obvious cluster on DSS image. Aliases: Lund 922; OCl 149; OCl 149.0; C2005+355
NGC 6873	ast?	20 07 44	+21 05 51	Sge		14.0		15	8.4			9	66	53	See notes. 14′ E-W chain of stars, with Struve 2631 = HD 191065 (V=8.1 and 9.8, separation 4.6") on W end. Alias: (2) STF 2631
NGC 6874	cl?	20 07.8	+38 14	Cyg	IV1m n	7.0	7.7	20	10	11.9	2100	9	48	3	See notes. Aliases: Bas 6; OCl 157.1; Lund 304; C2005+382
Dolidze 1	cl:	20 08.2	+36 33	Cyg	IV2p n	6.0		10				9	48	99	Archinal: Id? Mostly E-W scattering of brighter stars in rich Milky Way field. Aliases: Lund 923; OCl 153; C2006+364
Biurakan 2	cl	20 09 14.3	+35 29 03	Cyg	III2p	20.0	6.3	78	7.72	12.8	1500	9	48	99	Archinal: Centered on HD 191566 (V=7.72, B0.5IV). Aliases: Lund 924; OCl 150.0; C2007+353
Dolidze 2	cl	20 09.9	+41 22	Cyg	IV1p n	7.0		15				9	32	1	Aliases: Lund 925; OCl 174; OCl 174.0; C2008+412
Roslund 5	cl	20 10.0	+33 46	Cyg	IV2p n	50.0		15			300	9	48	99	Archinal: Scattering of bright stars over 50′ rich Milky Way field. Confirmed against Roslund information. Aliases: Lund 926; OCl 145; C2008+336
IC 1310	cl	20 10 01	+34 58.2	Cyg	II1p n	3.0		12	14.0			9	48	99	See notes. Archinal: Discovered by Espin [1894], and later rediscovered as Berkeley 50. Aliases: Espin 6; Ced 178; Be 50; OCl 147; C2008+347; Lund 927
Theta Sge group	ast?	20 10 05	+21 00 11	Sge		15.5		6	6.5			9	66	53	See notes. 6 brighter stars, ~20-30 fainter. Theta Sge (V=6.4/8.9, 12.0") on S side. Do not confuse with NGC 6873, 45′ W. Alias: (2) STF 2637
IC 1311	cl	20 10 47	+41 10 19	Cyg	I1r n	5.0	13.1	60	17.0	16.6		9	32	51	See notes. Aliases: Cr 414; Lund 928; OCl 173; Tr 36; OCl 173.0; C2008+410
NGC 6883	cl	20 11.3	+35 51	Cyg	IV2m n	35.0	8.0	30		15.7	1380	9	48	1	Aliases: Cr 415; Lund 929; OCl 152; OCl 152.0; C2009+357
Ruprecht 172	cl	20 11 34	+35 36.4	Cyg	III2p n	5.0		20	12.0			9	48	99	Improved position from P. Teutsch [Priv. Comm., 2002]. Aliases: Lund 930; OCl 151; C2009+354
Collinder 416	cl	20 11 35	+26 32 04	Vul		8.0	5.6p	40		10.1		9	66	51	See notes. Part of or associated with NGC 6885. Aliases: OCl 133; C2009+264
Berkeley 51	cl	20 11 53	+34 24.5	Cyg	I1p n	2.0		20	15.0			9	48	99	Aliases: Lund 932; OCl 146; C2010+342
AH03 J2011.9+2644	ast?	20 11 56.9	+26 44 08	Vul		4.5		9	7.6			9	66	51	See notes. There is a slight chance this asterism around HD 192043 (V=7.6) is W. Herschel's VIII.22 = NGC 6882.
NGC 6885	cl	20 12 01	+26 28.7	Vul	III2m	20.0		34	5.91		597	9	66	99	See notes. Contains 20 Vul (V=5.91) and Cr 416 on northwest side. Skiff: Center star is 20 Vulpeculae. Aliases: H. VIII.20; H. VIII.22; h 2071; NGC 6882; Cr 417; OCl 132; Lund 933; 20 Vul cl; OCl 132.0; Caldw 37; C2009+263
Berkeley 52	cl	20 14 30	+28 56.6	Vul	I1m	2.0		40	18.0			9	66	99	Aliases: Lund 985; OCl 140; C2012+288
Om-2 Cygni group	ast?	20 15 08	+47 34 26	Cyg		19.0		7				9	32	8	See notes. One of Webb's [1962, p. 112] "fine fields".
Melotte 227	cl	20 15 18	−79 17.4	Oct	III3m	70.0	5.3	40		14.5		26	215	99	Aliases: Cr 411; Lund 934; OCl 918; OCl 918.0; C2004−794
Dolidze 3	cl	20 15 27	+36 49.4	Cyg	III2m n	7.0		40				9	48	99	Archinal: Condensation in Milky Way. Aliases: Lund 936; OCl 156; OCl 156.0; C2013+366
Dolidze 39	cl	20 16 12	+37 55.1	Cyg	IV2m n	12.0		40				9	48	99	Archinal: Scattering of bright stars with many fainter stars in background and very rich Milky Way field (or nebulosity). Aliases: Lund 937; OCl 159; OCl 159.0; C2014+377
NGC 6895	MW?	20 16.4	+50 14	Cyg		15.0						3	32	99	
IC 4996	cl	20 16 31.7	+37 38 35	Cyg	II3p n	7.0	7.3	56	8.0	11.5	1563	9	48	99	Aliases: Cr 418; Lund 938; OCl 158; Mrk 44; OCl 158.0; C2014+374
NGC 6892	****	20 16 57.2	+18 01 11	Sge								16	66	99	Identified by H. Corwin [Priv. Comm., 2002] as just 4 stars.
Cl van den Bergh 130	cl	20 17 42.2	+39 20 59	Cyg	II2p n	7.0	9.3	15	10.30	13.5		9	48	99	Aliases: Lund 1150; OCl 167.1; C2015+391
P Cygni cluster	cl?	20 17 43.5	+38 02 04	Cyg		3.7		25	4.795			9	48	99	See notes. Faint group of stars around (mostly W of) P Cygni (V=4.795v). See photo on 1995 February JRASC cover. In ring Iss 274. Alias: (4) Iss 274

Table 4.1: Catalog of Clusters and Asterisms in the Milky Way, and Objects Misidentified as Such

Name	Type	2000.0 R.A.	Dec.	Con.	Tr. Type	Diam. (′)	Tot. Vm	#str	Bt* Vm	V Sur	Dist. (pc)	S #	2U #	Ref	Comments and Aliases
Dolidze 4	cl:	20 17 46.6	+36 45 05	Cyg	IV1p n	9.0		20				9	48	99	Archinal: Possible cluster involved with nebula Sh 2-104 = LBN 195. Aliases: Lund 939; OCl 157; C2015+365
NGC 6896	ast?	20 18.0	+30 39	Cyg								9	48	99	Archinal: Id? Large planetary nebula NGC 6894 to W.
Collinder 419	cl	20 18 07.0	+40 43 55	Cyg	IV2p	4.5	5.4			8.7		9	32	99	Archinal: Center star is HD 193322 (V=5.82, O9V, double). Aliases: Lund 940; OCl 177; C2016+405
Dolidze 40	cl	20 18.2	+37 51	Cyg	III1p n	5.0		12				9	48	99	Archinal: Id? Group of stars 4′ to NW? Aliases: Lund 941; OCl 162; C2016+376
Berkeley 85	cl	20 18 47	+37 45.3	Cyg	III1m	6.0		40	15.0			9	48	99	Aliases: Lund 942; OCl 160; OCl 160.0; C2016+375
Dolidze 41	cl	20 19.2	+37 45	Cyg	IV1p	11.0						9	48	99	Archinal: About 9 bright stars, with Be 85 on W side. Aliases: Lund 943; OCl 163; C2017+375
Dolidze 42	cl	20 19 39.7	+38 08 16	Cyg	III1p n	8.0		20				9	48	99	Archinal: Has prominent chain of 10 stars NNE to SSW. Aliases: Lund 944; OCl 164; OCl 164.0; C2017+379
Berkeley 86	cl	20 20 21.2	+38 42 01	Cyg	IV2m n	7.0	7.9	30	13.0	12.1	1112	9	48	99	Aliases: Lund 945; OCl 167; OCl 167.0; C2018+385
Dolidze 5	cl	20 20 29	+39 21.9	Cyg	III3m n	10.0		30				9	48	99	Archinal: DSS overlap region. Loose cluster of bright stars involved in nebulosity. Aliases: Lund 946; OCl 171; OCl 171.0; C2018+392
Dolidze 6	cl	20 20 38.0	+41 21 36	Cyg	IV2p n	6.0		12				9	32	99	Archinal: Involved in spectacular dark and light nebulosity. Aliases: BD+40°4124 grp; OCl 182; OCl 181.1; Lund 947; C2019+412
Berkeley 88	cl	20 21 16	+48 08.7	Cyg	IV1p	2.0		12	15.0			9	32	99	Archinal: Probably an "absorption hole" in the Milky Way. Aliases: Lund 948; OCl 195; C2020+479
Alessi 11	cl?	20 21 24	+18 21 36	Del		24.0						16	66	99	
Berkeley 87	cl	20 21 35	+37 23.5	Cyg	III2m	10.0		30	13.0		836	9	48	99	Aliases: Do 7; Lund 540; OCl 161; C2019+372
[DB01] 5	cl?	20 21 41.8	+37 25 50	Cyg		1.7						9	48	16	Infrared cluster. [DB01]: Cluster and/or IR nebula in radio HII region G 75.8+0.4,rel. to OH maser ON 2, backgr. of cluster Be 87.
Dolidze 43	ast	20 21.7	+39 57	Cyg	IV2p	20.0						9	48	99	DSFG: Probably not a cluster. Archinal: Scattering of stars, including 5 brighter ones on south side. Surrounded by bright nebulae. Aliases: OCl 175; OCl 175.0; C2019+397
NGC 6904	ast?	20 21 48.3	+25 44 22	Vul		3.0			8.6			9	66	53	See notes. Includes HD 340139 (V=8.6, M1) as brightest star, and HD 340140 (V=9.6, F0). Additional stars off up to 7′ to north.
NGC 6910	cl	20 23 12	+40 46.7	Cyg	I3m n	10.0	7.4	66	9.61	12.4	1507	9	32	4	DSFG: Visual magnitude = 6.6 if bright star on NW included. Skiff: Mean of bright end stars HD 194241/279. Aliases: Cr 420; Lund 950; OCl 181; Mrk 45; C2021+406
Collinder 421	cl	20 23.3	+41 42	Cyg	III1p n	8.0	10.1	22		14.6		9	32	1	Aliases: Lund 951; OCl 184; OCl 184.0; C2021+415
NGC 6913	cl	20 24 06	+38 29.6	Cyg	II3m n	10.0	6.6	81	9.0	11.6	1343	9	48	52	M 29. Position is for HD 229239. 30 bright stars, about 100 stars total. Aliases: Cr 422; Lund 952; M 29; OCl 168; Mrk 46; C2022+383
Dolidze 8	cl	20 24.4	+42 16	Cyg	I2p n	6.0		20				9	32	1	Aliases: Lund 953; OCl 189; C2022+421
Berkeley 89	cl	20 24 28.4	+46 02 24	Cyg	III1p	3.0		15	15.0			9	32	99	Aliases: Lund 954; OCl 193; C2023+458
Dolidze 9	cl	20 25 33.4	+41 54 25	Cyg	IV2p n	3.0		5				9	32	99	Aliases: Lund 955; OCl 188; C2023+417
Dolidze 10	cl:	20 26.3	+40 07	Cyg	IV1p n	3.0		8				9	48	99	DSFG: Probably not a cluster. Archinal: Id? Scattering of bright stars in strong nebulosity. Aliases: Lund 956; OCl 180; OCl 180.0; C2024+399
Dolidze 11	cl	20 26 24.7	+41 25 00	Cyg	IV3p n	6.0		15				9	32	99	Aliases: Lund 957; OCl 186; C2024+412
ESO 026-SC02	cl	20 26.6	−80 00	Oct	III3	8.0						26	215	10	
[DB01] 7	cl?	20 27 13.0	+39 26 56	Cyg		3.5						9	48	16	Infrared cluster. [DB01]: Resolved cluster in radio HII region DR 6.
[HR91] 1	cl	20 27 24	+37 23	Cyg	n	2.8		160			600	9	48	8	Infrared cluster involved in Sh2 106. See Hodapp and Rayner [1991]. Alias: (3) Sh 2- 106
[DB01] 11	cl?	20 28 09.7	+40 52 42	Cyg		3.5						9	32	16	Infrared cluster. [DB01]: Mostly a resolved cluster in Radio HII region DR 7, related to IRAS 20264+4042.
Roslund 6	cl	20 28 49	+39 19.6	Cyg	IV3m n	24.0		30				9	48	99	Archinal: Scattering of bright stars in strong nebulosity. DSS overlap area and star reflections so identification difficult. Aliases: Lund 958; OCl 178; C2027+392
[DB01] 6	cl?	20 29 36.9	+39 01 15	Cyg		3.0						9	48	16	Infrared cluster. [DB01]: Partly resolved cluster in radio HII region DR 9.
Dolidze 44	cl:	20 29.7	+41 43	Cyg	IV2p n	10.0		15				9	32	52	DSFG: Probably not a cluster. Aliases: Lund 959; OCl 190; C2027+415
[DB01] 12	cl?	20 30 28.0	+41 15 48	Cyg		1.8						9	32	16	Infrared cluster. [DB01]: Resolved stellar group in radio HII region DR 11, related to IRAS 20286+4105.

Table 4.1: Catalog of Clusters and Asterisms in the Milky Way, and Objects Misidentified as Such

Name	Type	2000.0 R.A. Dec.	Con.	Tr. Type	Diam. (′)	Tot. Vm	#str	Bt* Vm	V Sur	Dist. (pc)	S #	2U #	Ref	Comments and Aliases
NGC 6939	cl	20 31 30 +60 39.7	Cep	II1r	10.0	7.8	301	11.91	12.8	1202	3	20	4	Aliases: Cr 423; Lund 960; Mel 231; OCl 217; Raab 144; C2030+604
[DB01] 8	cl?	20 31 45.4 +38 58 00	Cyg		2.0						9	48	16	Infrared cluster. [DB01]: Partly resolved cluster in Radio HII region DR 13.
[DB01] 21	cl?	20 32 21.8 +43 41 05	Cyg		2.5						9	32	16	Infrared cluster. [DB01]: Resolved cluster in radio HII region G 82.0+2.3, related to radio HII region DR 16?
[DB01] 9	cl?	20 32 27.8 +38 51 26	Cyg		1.4						9	48	16	Infrared cluster. [DB01]: Partly resolved cluster related to IRAS 20306+3841, in radio complex W 69.
[DB01] 10	cl?	20 32 29.0 +40 16 30	Cyg		2.5						9	48	16	Infrared cluster. [DB01]: Mostly a resolved cluster in radio HII region G 79.306+0.282 in DR 15, related to IRAS 20306+4005.
NGC 6934	gcl	20 34 11.6 +07 24 15	Del		7.1	8.9		13.8	13.2	14900	16	84	55	Aliases: Mel 230; EQ 2031+072; Caldw 47; C2031+072
NGC 6940	cl	20 34 32.3 +28 16 49	Vul	III2r	25.0	6.3	170	11.0	13.3	813	9	66	99	Aliases: Cr 424; Lund 961; Mel 232; OCl 141; Raab 145; OCl 141.0; C2032+281
NGC 6938	cl??	20 34 46 +22 13.9	Vul								9	66	99	
Steine 1	ast?	20 35 13 +46 05.5	Cyg		1.5		6	9.47			9	32	99	Possible asterism, discovered 2001 October 14 by M.Steine. Four Tycho II stars and some fainter, 30′ N of Sh 2-112.
Berkeley 90	cl	20 35 16 +46 50.7	Cyg	II1p n	3.0		20	14.0			9	32	99	Aliases: Lund 962; OCl 196; C2033+466
[DB01] 15	cl?	20 35 23.0 +42 22 05	Cyg		2.9						9	32	16	Infrared cluster. [DB01]: Resolved cluster in radio HII region DR 17.
NGC 6941	gal	20 36 23.5 −04 37 16	Aql		2.0						16	104	54	Had been listed in SIMBAD as an open cluster. Data here from NED. Avoid use of the name "C2033-048". Aliases: PGC 65054; TXS 2033-047; (4) IRAS 20337−0447; C2033−048
[DB01] 16	cl?	20 38 29.0 +42 06 25	Cyg		2.3						9	32	16	Infrared cluster. [DB01]: Mostly a resolved cluster, in radio complex W 75, related to radio HII region G 81.5+0.6?
[DB01] 20	cl?	20 38 37.0 +42 39 24	Cyg		1.5						9	32	16	Infrared cluster. [DB01]: Mostly a resolved cluster in radio HII region W 75N, pair with W 75N IR cluster.
[DB01] 19	cl?	20 38 56.8 +42 22 45	Cyg		2.0						9	32	16	Infrared cluster. [DB01]: Partly resolved stellar group in radio HII region W 75, pair with W 75S IR cluster.
[DB01] 14	cl?	20 39 33.0 +41 18 46	Cyg		4.0						9	32	16	Infrared cluster. [DB01]: Resolved stellar group in radio HII region DR 22, includes cluster 13 and a compact nebula.
[DB01] 13	cl?	20 39 34.0 +41 19 05	Cyg		2.3						9	32	16	Infrared cluster. [DB01]: Resolved cluster in radio HII region DR 22, in stellar group 14.
NGC 6950	cl?	20 41 10.5 +16 38 55	Del		14.0		60				16	84	99	Archinal: Scattered group of 50-60 faint stars around brightest and center star, TYC 1634 779 1 (V=9.84).
[DB01] 17	cl?	20 41 15.9 +41 51 51	Cyg		1.7						9	32	16	Infrared cluster. [DB01]: Resolved cluster in radio HII region DR 23.
[DB01] 18	cl?	20 41 20.1 +41 58 22	Cyg		1.8						9	32	16	Infrared cluster. [DB01]: Resolved stellar group at the edge of radio HII region DR 23, related to DR 23?
Ruprecht 173	cl	20 41 41.2 +35 32 44	Cyg	II2p	40.0		20	8.0			9	47	99	Archinal: Center star is HD 197310 (V=7.43, G0). Aliases: Lund 963; OCl 165; OCl 165.0; (4) Turner 11; C2039+353
Dolidze 47	cl	20 41 44.2 +36 37 15	Cyg	III2p	5.0		15				9	47	99	Archinal: Center star is BD +36°4195 (V=8.23, K2). Aliases: Lund 1151; OCl 171.1; C2039+364
[DB01] 22	cl?	20 42 33.5 +42 56 50	Cyg		1.7						9	32	16	Infrared cluster. [DB01]: Partly resolved cluster in radio HII region G 82.6+0.4.
Turner 11	cl?	20 43 24 +35 35.3	Cyg		60.0						9	47	99	Turner [1998] proposes that Ru 175 and the southern portion of Ru 173 form a cluster here with the Cepheid X Cygni. Aliases: (4) Ru 173; (4) Ru 175
Ruprecht 174	cl	20 43 28.3 +37 01 49	Cyg	IV1p	2.0		10	14.0			9	47	99	Aliases: Lund 964; OCl 176; C2041+368
LeDrew 2	ast?	20 44.0 +23 45	Vul		47.0	5.8	24	6.9	14.2		9	65	99	Possible asterism or cluster discovered by G. LeDrew [Priv. Comm. Oct. 8, 2001]. Independently discovered by B. Alessi. Alias: Alessi 12
Ruprecht 175	cl	20 45 24 +35 31.0	Cyg	IV2m	15.0		30	11.0			9	47	99	Skiff: Turner 1998AJ 116,274 from starcounts. Aliases: Lund 965; OCl 169; (4) Turner 11; C2043+353
[DB01] 23	cl?	20 45 37.6 +44 15 21	Cyg		1.8						9	32	16	Infrared cluster. [DB01]: Partly resolved stellar group in radio HII region G 83.941+0.781.
DoDz 11	cl	20 51 04 +35 54.5	Cyg	IV2p	5.0		12				9	47	99	Archinal: DSS overlap region. Aliases: Lund 966; OCl 179; OCl 179.0; C2049+357
NGC 6973	??	20 52.1 −05 53	Aqr								16	124	3	
Roslund 7	cl?	20 52 08.5 +37 53 44	Cyg	IV2p	20.0						9	47	99	Archinal: Sparse 20′ group of brighter stars, smaller than Roslund listed it (35′). Roslund called this a "doubtful" cluster. Aliases: Lund 967; OCl 187; C2050+377
NGC 6980	??	20 52.8 −05 49	Aqr								16	124	99	Archinal: Id?

Table 4.1: Catalog of Clusters and Asterisms in the Milky Way, and Objects Misidentified as Such

Name	Type	2000.0 R.A.	Dec.	Con.	Tr. Type	Diam. (′)	Tot. Vm	#str	Bt* Vm	V Sur	Dist. (pc)	S #	2U #	Ref	Comments and Aliases
NGC 6981	gcl	20 53 27.9	−12 32 13	Aqr		6.6	9.2		14.2	13.3	18100	16	124	55	M 72. Aliases: M 72; Mel 233; EQ 2050−127; C2050−127
Baractova 1	cl	20 53.7	+46 02	Cyg	IV2p	20.0		122				9	32	99	Lund Catalogue diameter of 4′ is much too small compared to Barkhatova estimate of 14′ to 20′. Aliases: Lund 968; OCl 200; OCl 200.0; C2052+458
NGC 6989	MW	20 54.1	+45 17	Cyg		10.0		17	10.0			9	32	3	
h 2091	cl	20 54 43.1	+47 16 49	Cyg	III3p	6.0		12	8.33			9	32	51	See notes. Often incorrectly identifed as H VIII.76 = NGC 6991, which it is only a part of. Position is for center star, HD 199310. Aliases: OCl 202; Lund 969; (3) NGC 6991; C2055+472
NGC 6991	cl	20 54.9	+47 25	Cyg	III2m n	25.0		35	5.67			9	32	53	See notes. Just west of HD 199478 (V=5.67). Includes h 2091, and nebulosity IC 5076 and vdB 137. Identified by Archinal. Aliases: H. VIII.76; (2) h 2091; (2) IC 5076
Berkeley 53	cl	20 55 59	+51 04.6	Cyg	III2m	6.0		40	16.0			3	32	99	Archinal: Bright star on E side is HD 199578 (V=6.60, B5V). Aliases: Lund 971; OCl 207; C2055+508
NGC 6996	ast?	20 56.4	+45 28	Cyg		5.0						9	32	99	See notes. Archinal: Scattering group of moderately bright stars including many in a meandering E-W chain.
NGC 6997	cl	20 56.5	+44 39	Cyg	III2m n	8.0	10.0	40		14.5	500	9	32	3	See notes. Aliases: Cr 425; Lund 970; OCl 197; C2054+444
NGC 6994	ast	20 58 56	−12 38.0	Aqr	IV1p	1.4	9.7	4	10.4	10.4		16	124	52	See notes. M 73, which B. Skiff has recently shown is an asterism of 4 stars. Stars are GSC 05778-00802, -00492, -00509, -00594. Aliases: Cr 426; Lund 972; M 73; OCl 89; C2056−128
ESO 464-SC09	cl	20 59.6	−29 23	Mic	I2	4.0						23	143	10	
Collinder 427	cl	21 00 36.6	+68 09 35	Cep	IV1p n	4.0	13.8	6		16.8		3	9	99	See notes. Archinal: On W side of NGC 7023 reflection nebula. Note this is NOT NGC 7023 itself. Aliases: OCl 233; Lund 973; OCISM 50; C2058+679
NGC 7006	gcl	21 01 29.5	+16 11 15	Del		3.6	10.6		15.6	13.4	39100	16	83	6	Moore: Very distant. Aliases: GCRV 13202; EQ 2059+160; CSI+16-20591; Caldw 42; C2059+160
Collinder 429	dne	21 01 35.8	+68 10 03	Cep								3	9	99	See notes. Archinal: Thought by Collinder to possibly be a cluster involved with NGC 7023. Aliases: OCl 235; Lund 974; (4) NGC 7023; C2059+679
NGC 7023	neb	21 01 35.8	+68 10 03	Cep		18.0						3	9	99	See notes. Archinal: This is a reflection nebula (= vdB 139), NOT a cluster, but with the cluster Cr 427 just to the W. Aliases: (4) Cr 427; (4) Cr 429
NGC 7011	cl?	21 01 45	+47 20.9	Cyg		3.8		35				9	32	99	Archinal: Long NE opening "V"-shaped group of stars.
NGC 7005	ast	21 01 56.0	−12 52 39	Aqr		1.8		4				16	123	99	
Berkeley 54	cl	21 03 00	+40 26.2	Cyg	I2m	4.0		30	17.0			9	47	99	Aliases: Lund 977; OCl 194; C2101+402
Collinder 428	cl	21 03.2	+44 35	Cyg	IV1p n	10.0	8.7	20		13.7	480	9	32	99	See notes. Archinal: On "west coast" of the North American Nebula (NGC 7000) and overwhelmed by that nebulosity on the DSS. Aliases: Lund 975; OCl 201; C2101+443
NGC 7024	cl?	21 06 04.8	+41 29 47	Cyg		10.0		14	10			9	32	99	Archinal: Centered at W. Herschel's triangle of stars.
NGC 7031	cl	21 06 52	+50 50.6	Cyg	III2m	15.0	9.1	62	11.31	15.0	884	3	32	99	Archinal: Group of 10 brighter stars of this cluster all on NE side. Aliases: Cr 430; Lund 979; OCl 210; (4) IRAS 21055+5040; C2105+506
French 1	ast?	21 07 22	+16 17.9	Del		13.0			8.84			16	83	8	See notes. "Toadstool" shaped Asterism. Noted by Susan French [1997]. See also di Cicco [1997]. Includes galaxy NGC 7025. Aliases: Toadstool; Alessi J21075+1619; (2) NGC 7025
Levy-W. J2108.8+0620	ast	21 08 48.4	+06 20 27	Equ		22.0		25	9.304			16	83	99	See notes. "S"-shaped star stream, discovered 2000 December by D. Levy and W. Wallach, named by them the "Equuleus S".
Dolidze 45	cl	21 09.0	+37 36	Cyg	III2m n	18.0		35				9	47	99	Archinal: Scattering of a dozen or so bright stars over an 18′ field. Aliases: Lund 980; OCl 191; OCl 191.0; C2107+374
NGC 7036	cl?	21 10 12	+15 22.6	Peg		8.0		20				16	83	99	Identified by H. Corwin [Priv. Comm., 2002] as group of about 20 stars over an 8′ x 5′ area.
Basel 12	cl	21 10.5	+46 14	Cyg	III2p	4.0		20			1466	9	32	1	Aliases: Lund 1109; C2108+460
Berkeley 91	cl	21 10 51	+48 32.3	Cyg	II1p	3.0		20	16.0			9	32	99	Aliases: Lund 982; OCl 206; C2110+482
NGC 7037	cl?	21 10 57	+33 46.0	Cyg		7.0		10	12			9	47	99	Archinal: Slight condensation of stars on DSS image.
NGC 7039	cl	21 11.2	+45 39	Cyg	IV2m	15.0	7.6	185	11.26	13.5	813	9	32	99	Archinal: 7′ high by 14 wide group of stars. Brightest star on NNE side. Aliases: Cr 431; Lund 981; OCl 203; OCl 203.0; C2109+454
IC 1369	cl	21 12 07	+47 46.0	Cyg	II2m	5.0	8.8	152	12.14	12.3	1585	9	32	99	Aliases: Cr 432; Lund 983; OCl 204; C2110+475
NGC 7044	cl	21 13 08	+42 29.5	Cyg	I1r	7.0	12.0	60	15.0	16.2		9	32	4	Aliases: Cr 433; Lund 984; OCl 198; C2111+422
Basel 13	cl	21 13 11	+46 34.3	Cyg		10.0					1236	9	32	99	Aliases: Lund 614; C2110+463
NGC 7050	ast	21 15 16.8	+36 10 18	Cyg								9	47	99	

Table 4.1: Catalog of Clusters and Asterisms in the Milky Way, and Objects Misidentified as Such

Name	Type	2000.0 R.A.	Dec.	Con.	Tr. Type	Diam. (′)	Tot. Vm	#str	Bt* Vm	V Sur	Dist. (pc)	S #	2U #	Ref	Comments and Aliases
Basel 15	cl	21 15.9	+48 50	Cyg		6.0					1355	9	32	99	Archinal: Id? Not obvious in a 1° DSS field. Aliases: Lund 1133; C2114+486
Berkeley 55	cl	21 16 57	+51 45.5	Cyg	III1m	5.0		30	14.0			3	19	99	Aliases: Lund 986; OCl 212; C2115+515
Berkeley 56	cl	21 17 34.5	+41 49 36	Cyg	II1m	3.0		40	16.0			9	32	99	Archinal: Faint. Visible on DSS only with histogram equalization display. Aliases: Lund 987; OCl 199; C2115+416
NGC 7055	cl?	21 19 25.8	+57 35 25	Cep				10				3	19	99	Archinal: DSS overlap region.
Basel 14	cl	21 21 14.0	+44 48 10	Cyg	II3p n	5.0		15			964	9	32	99	Archinal: Center and brightest star is BD+44 3786 (V=8.81, G). Aliases: Lund 1134; C2119+446
ESO 236-SC07	cl	21 21.5	−51 49	Ind	II3	30.0						26	193	10	
NGC 7058	cl?	21 21 48.3	+50 49 28	Cyg		10.0	9	17		5.9		3	32	99	
NGC 7062	cl	21 23 27	+46 22.7	Cyg	II2m	5.0	8.3	85	10.10	11.8	1703	9	32	4	Aliases: Cr 434; Lund 988; OCl 205; OCl 205.0; C2121+461
NGC 7067	cl	21 24 12.3	+48 00 41	Cyg	II1p	3.0	9.7	47	11.17	12.1	3707	9	32	99	Aliases: Cr 436; Lund 989; OCl 208; OCl 208.0; C2122+478
NGC 7063	cl	21 24.5	+36 30	Cyg	III1p	9.0	7.0	66	8.89	11.8	625	9	47	1	Aliases: Cr 435; Lund 990; OCl 192; C2122+362
Berkeley 92	cl:	21 24 46.3	+57 32 20	Cep	III1p	2.0		15	15.0			3	19	99	Aliases: Lund 991; OCl 220; C2123+572
NGC 7071	cl?	21 26 40	+47 55.3	Cyg		4.0	10	15	12	4.0		9	32	99	
NGC 7082	cl	21 29 19	+47 07.8	Cyg	IV2p	24.0	7.2	182	9.90	14.1	1318	9	32	99	Aliases: Lund 992; OCl 209; OCl 209.0; C2127+468
NGC 7078	gcl	21 29 58.3	+12 10 01	Peg		18.0	6.3		12.6	12.6	10500	16	83	55	See notes. M 15. Contains planetary nebula Pease 1 = K 648. For chart, see Skiff [1992]. Aliases: M 15; (2) Pease 1; Mel 234; C2127+119
Anon Platais	cl	21 30 02	+48 58.6	Cyg		10.0			8.9		1568	9	32	54	See notes. Brightest star is V1726 Cygni (cepheid, V=8.892-9.079, period 4.237d). Alias: C2128+488
NGC 7086	cl	21 30 28	+51 36.0	Cyg	II2m	12.0	8.4	80	10.19	13.8	1180	3	19	4	Aliases: Cr 437; Lund 993; OCl 214; C2128+513
Teutsch J2130.9+5249	ast?	21 30 59	+52 49.9	Cyg	IV2p	1.8		30	30			3	19	17	Teutsch: Likely asterism? Slight condensation in rich field, including bright star HD 235530 (V=9.36) on W side.
NGC 7092	cl	21 31 52	+48 25.5	Cyg	III2m	31.0	4.6	25	7.0	12.1	292	9	32	52	M 39. Position is of HD 205210. 25 bright stars with rich Milky Way background. Aliases: Cr 438; Lund 994; M 39; Mel 236; OCl 211; OCl 211.0; C2130+482
NGC 7084	cl?	21 32 33	+17 30.5	Peg		18.0						16	65	99	Identified by H. Corwin [Priv. Comm., 2002] as 18′ x 16′ group (with a 10′ x 9′ core).
NGC 7089	gcl	21 33 27.0	−00 49 12	Aqr		16.0	6.6		13.1	12.6	11900	17	103	99	M 2. Archinal: Position measured from DSS. Aliases: M 2; Mel 235; EQ 2130–010; C2130–010
NGC 7093	cl?	21 34 35.8	+45 59 31	Cyg		6.0		23				9	32	99	
IC 1396	cl	21 39.0	+57 30	Cep	IV3m n	90.0	3.5	50	3.82	13.3	794	3	19	8	See notes. DSFG: Excluding μ Cephei, visual magnitude = 4.8. Aliases: Cr 439; Lund 995; OCl 222; Tr 37; Mrk 47; OCl 222.0; CTB 105; C2137+572
NGC 7099	gcl	21 40 22.0	−23 10 45	Cap		12.0	6.9		12.1	12.3	7400	23	143	55	M 30. Aliases: M 30; Mel 237; EQ 2137–234; C2137–234
[AO84] V	mc	21.7	+03.0	Aqr		9900.0	-0.24	25	0.03			17	103	54	Moving cluster with very large angular size, hypothesized by Agekyan and Orlov [1984].
Alessi J21426+1004	ast	21 42.6	+10 04	Peg		24.0		20	8			17	83	10	
NGC 7129	cl	21 42 59	+66 06.4	Cep	IV2p n	8.0	11.5	10		16.0		3	9	99	Archinal: Scattered group with bright nebula at center. Aliases: Cr 441; Lund 996; OCl 240; C2140+658
Alessi J21430+1027	ast	21 43.0	+10 27	Peg		18.0		11	9			17	83	10	
Baractova 2	cl	21 43 38	+51 04 17	Cyg	III1p	5.0	8.37	21	10.0	11.9		3	31	8	See notes. Corrected position, diameter here from DSS. Magnitudes are photovisual from Barkhatova. Brightest star is GSC 03603-01101. Aliases: Lund 999; OCl 216; C2142+509
NGC 7127	cl	21 43 52.9	+54 35 46	Cyg	IV1p	6.0		12			1300	3	19	99	Aliases: Lund 997; OCl 219; C2142+543
NGC 7128	cl	21 43 58	+53 42.9	Cyg	I3m	4.0	9.7	71	11.50	12.7	2312	3	19	4	Aliases: Cr 440; Lund 998; OCl 218; C2142+534
Alessi J21450+1647	ast	21 45.0	+16 47	Peg		48.0		32	9			16	83	10	
NGC 7142	cl	21 45 09	+65 46.5	Cep	I2r	12.0	9.3	186	11.0	14.7	2952	3	9	4	Aliases: Cr 442; Lund 1000; OCl 241; C2144+655
NGC 7122	**	21 45 47.8	−08 49 47	Cap				2				17	123	99	Identified by H. Corwin [Priv. Comm., 2002].

Table 4.1: Catalog of Clusters and Asterisms in the Milky Way, and Objects Misidentified as Such

Name	Type	2000.0 R.A.	Dec.	Con.	Tr. Type	Diam. (′)	Tot. Vm	#str	Bt* Vm	V Sur	Dist. (pc)	S #	2U #	Ref	Comments and Aliases
Palomar 12	gcl	21 46 38.8	−21 15 03	Cap		2.9	11.7		14.6	14.0	19300	23	143	55	Has been listed incorrectly as a galaxy, e.g. MCG −04-51-013 = RC2 A2143−21 = Cap Dwarf. [Lederman and Gottlieb, 1996] Aliases: Cap gcl; (5) MCG −04-51-013; (5) RC2 A2143−21; (5) Cap Dwarf; EQ 2143−214; C2143−214
NGC 7134	ast	21 48 56	−12 58 25	Cap		0.5	13.4	4	14.2	11.9		17	123	53	See notes. Consists of GSC 05796-01213, 05796-01241, 05796-01172, and 05796-01247. V=12, GSC 05796-01217 is just to north.
NGC 7150	ast	21 50.4	+49 45	Cyg				5				9	31	3	
Collinder 470	cl	21 53.5	+47 16	Cyg	III2p n	20.0	7.2	110	9.64	13.7	959	9	31	10	See notes. This is NOT IC 5146, but is involved in IC 5146, the "Cocoon Nebula". Aliases: OCl 213; Lund 1001; OCISM 43; (4) IC 5146; C2151+470
NGC 7160	cl	21 53 40	+62 36.2	Cep	I3p	5.0	6.1	61	7.04	9.6	809	3	9	4	Aliases: Cr 443; Lund 1002; OCl 236; OCl 236.0; C2152+623
Berkeley 93	cl	21 55 29	+63 56.4	Cep	IV1p	4.3		120	16.0			3	9	99	Archinal: Lund Catalogue position, diameter, and number of stars all off for this cluster. Aliases: Lund 1003; OCl 239; C2154+637
NGC 7161	cl??	21 57.0	+02 57	Peg								17	103	99	H. Corwin [Priv. Comm., 2002] identifies this as possibly 3 stars at 21 56 57.9 +02 54 58
NGC 7175	cl?	21 58 51.6	+54 49 01	Cyg		29.0		11				3	19	99	H. Corwin [Priv. Comm., 2002] identifies this as 29′ x 21′ scattered group around HD 235682 (V=9.60, K)).
NGC 7193	cl?	22 02 59	+10 49.1	Peg	III1m	20.0		25	9			17	83	99	Archinal: J. Herschel's no. 2145, an obvious group and possible real cluster. Galaxy NGC 7190 on N side. Alias: h 2145
Levy-W. J2204.3+4508	ast	22 04 23.3	+45 08 13	Lac		8.5		40				9	31	99	See notes. Stellar ring, found by David Levy and Wendee Wallach.
NGC 7209	cl	22 05 08	+46 29.0	Lac	III1m	15.0	7.7	98	9.0	13.6	899	9	31	4	Aliases: Cr 444; Lund 1004; Mel 238; OCl 215; Raab 146; OCl 215.0; C2203+462
Collinder 471	cl	22 07.1	+72 00	Cep	III2p	130.0						3	9	1	Aliases: Lund 1005; OCl 255; C2206+717
NGC 7226	cl	22 10 26	+55 24.0	Cep	I2m	2.0	9.6	83	10.80	11.1	2148	3	19	99	Aliases: Cr 446; Lund 1007; OCl 226; C2208+551
IC 1434	cl	22 10.5	+52 50	Lac	III2m	7.0	9.0	40	12.0	13.2		3	19	1	Aliases: Cr 445; Lund 1006; Mel 239; OCl 223; Raab 147; OCl 223.0; C2208+525
NGC 7235	cl	22 12 24	+57 16.4	Cep	II3m	6.0	7.7	98	8.80	11.6	3163	3	19	99	Aliases: Cr 447; Lund 1008; OCl 229; C2210+570
NGC 7234	cl?	22 12 28	+57 02.5	Cep		3.5		8				3	19	99	Archinal: Small group matching W. Herschel's and A. Ling's [Archinal, 1993, p. 97] description.
Cl van den Bergh 150	cl	22 12 52.8	+73 18 25	Cep	III3p n	35.0		20				3	9	99	Archinal: Centered on "vdB 150" star, i.e. HD 211300 (V=6.08, KOII-III+...). Aliases: Lund 1154; OCl 259.1; C2211+730
Cl van den Bergh 152	cl	22 13 24.5	+70 15 05	Cep	III3p n	25.0		15				3	9	99	Archinal: Centered on "vdB 152" star, i.e. BD+69 1231 (V=9.29, B9.5V). Aliases: Lund 1152; OCl 252.1; C2212+700
[PTB93] 3	cl	22 14.3	+70 09	Cep		60.0		7				3	9	99	Archinal: Infrared cluster. Not visible on DSS.
NGC 7243	cl	22 15 09	+49 53.9	Lac	II2m	30.0	6.4	40	8.0	13.8	759	9	31	4	Aliases: Cr 448; Lund 1009; Mel 240; OCl 221; Raab 148; OCl 221.0; Caldw 16; C2213+496
NGC 7245	cl	22 15 16	+54 20.2	Lac	II2m	5.0	9.2	169	12.75	12.7	1845	3	19	99	Improved position from P. Teutsch [Priv. Comm., 2002]. Aliases: Cr 449; Lund 1010; Mel 241; OCl 225; Raab 149; OCl 225.0; C2213+540
King 9	cl	22 15 31	+54 24.6	Lac	I1m	3.0		40	18.0			3	19	99	Aliases: Lund 1011; OCl 227; C2213+541
IC 1442	cl	22 15 59	+53 59.1	Lac	III1p	5.0	9.1	104	12.0	12.6	1738	3	19	99	Improved position from P. Teutsch [Priv. Comm., 2002] Aliases: Lund 1012; OCl 224; C2214+538
PMH79 1	cl?	22 19 00	+63 15.4	Cep	II2m n	9.3		21	7.75		900	3	9	8	Possible cluster involved in nebula Sh 2-140. See Pismis, *et al.* [1979]. Brightest star is HD 211880 (V=7.75, B0.5V). Aliases: OCISM 53; (4) Sh 2- 140
NGC 7261	cl	22 20 10	+58 06.6	Cep	II3m	6.0	8.4	62	9.61	12.3	2119	3	19	99	Aliases: Cr 450; Lund 1013; OCl 237; C2218+578
Berkeley 94	cl	22 22 53	+55 52.5	Cep	II3p n	3.0	8.7	12	13.0	11.1	2105	3	19	99	Aliases: Lund 1014; OCl 231; C2220+556
[PTB93] 2	cl	22 24.9	+71 33	Cep		120.0		5				3	9	99	Archinal: Infrared cluster. Not visible on DSS.
NGC 7281	cl:	22 24 55.7	+57 50 25	Cep	IV2p	12.0		20				3	19	99	DSFG: Probably not a cluster. Archinal: Loose scattering of stars, with 3 equal stars in E-W line at center. Aliases: Lund 1015; OCl 238; C2222+575
NGC 7295	ast?	22 27 52	+52 49.1	Lac		2.0		20	10			3	19	99	Archinal: Small group right at J. Herschel's position, although he may have intended to include more scattered stars in area.
NGC 7296	cl	22 28 01	+52 18.8	Lac	II2p	3.0	9.7	20	10.0	12.1		3	19	8	Skiff: GSC 3619-0835 at center. BD+51 3383 = GSC 3619-2026 = IRAS 22259+5203 is bright red star on west side, V=9.70. Aliases: Cr 451; Lund 1016; OCl 228; OCl 228.0; (4) IRAS 22259+5203; C2226+520

Table 4.1: Catalog of Clusters and Asterisms in the Milky Way, and Objects Misidentified as Such

Name	Type	2000.0 R.A.	Dec.	Con.	Tr. Type	Diam. (′)	Tot. Vm	#str	Bt* Vm	V Sur	Dist. (pc)	S #	2U #	Ref	Comments and Aliases
Berkeley 95	cl	22 28.3	+59 08	Cep	II2p	5.0		15	15.0			3	19	99	Improved diameter provided by P. Teutsch [Priv. Comm., 2002]. Aliases: Lund 1017; OCl 242; C2226+588
Berkeley 96	cl	22 29 51.2	+55 24 22	Lac	I2p	2.0		15	13.0		4943	3	19	99	Aliases: Lund 1018; OCl 232; C2227+551
[PTB93] 1	cl	22 38.0	+75 15	Cep		120.0		10				3	2	99	Archinal: Infrared cluster. Not visible on DSS.
Berkeley 97	cl	22 39 22.2	+59 00 58	Cep	IV2p	2.0		12	11.0			3	19	99	Aliases: Lund 1019; OCl 243; C2237+587
Czernik 42	cl:	22 39 35	+59 54.8	Cep	III1p	2.0		15				3	19	99	Aliases: Lund 1020; OCl 245; C2237+596
NGC 7352	cl?	22 39 44.2	+57 23 06	Cep		5.0						3	19	99	Archinal: Scattering of bright stars over a 45′ or so DSS field. Brightest star at center.
Berkeley 98	cl:	22 42 39.2	+52 24 15	Lac	III2m	15.0		50	15.0			3	19	99	Aliases: Lund 1021; OCl 234; C2241+521
NGC 7380	cl	22 47 21	+58 07.9	Cep	III2m n	20.0	7.2	125	10.0	13.7	2982	3	19	99	Archinal: Difficult to check position on DSS due to rich nebulosity. Aliases: Cr 452; Lund 1022; OCl 244; Mrk 48; OCl 244.0; C2245+578
NGC 7394	cl?	22 50 24	+52 08.8	Lac		10.0		19	11			3	19	99	See notes.
King 18	cl	22 52 08	+58 18.7	Cep	II2p	5.0		20	12.0			3	19	99	Aliases: Lund 1023; OCl 247; C2250+580
NGC 7419	cl	22 54 17	+60 48.8	Cep	I2m	6.0	13.0	40	10.0	16.9	1920	3	19	99	Aliases: Cr 453; Lund 1024; OCl 250; C2252+605
King 10	cl	22 55.0	+59 10	Cep	II1m	4.0		40	11.0			3	19	1	Aliases: Lund 1025; OCl 248; C2252+589
NGC 7423	cl	22 55 06.5	+57 05 41	Cep	II2m	5.0		40	15.0			3	19	99	See notes. Archinal: Also known as Be 57. Aliases: Be 57; Lund 1026; OCl 246; (4) IRAS 22534+5653; WB89 220; C2253+568
h 2191	MW?	22 55.1	+57 06	Cep								3	19	3	
NGC 7429	cl	22 55.9	+59 59	Cep	IV2p	15.0		15	11.0		1920	3	19	1	Aliases: Lund 1027; OCl 249; C2253+597
NGC 7438	cl?	22 57 03	+54 17.9	Lac?		20.0		30	11			3	19	99	
NGC 7453	***	23 01 25.4	−06 21 18	Aqr		0.3		3				17	122	99	Archinal: DSS shows three close stars, with a brighter one NW (as Peters indicates).
Reiland 1	cl?	23 04 45.3	+60 04 40	Cep		1.0		10				3	18	8	See notes. Possible cluster. Reported by Houston [1988] as "Reiland's Nebulous Cluster". Also Bergeron 1. In nebula BFS 15. Alias: Bergeron 1
Palomar 13	gcl	23 06 44.4	+12 46 19	Peg		0.7	13.8		17.0	13.0	24400	17	82	55	This globular cluster also has been listed incorrectly as a galaxy, with designation CGCG 430-61. [Lederman and Gottlieb, 1996] Aliases: Peg gcl; (5) CGCG 430−61; EQ 2304+124; C2304+124
PWM78 3	cl	23 08 10.8	+60 52 28	Cep	II3r	3.0		180			4000	3	18	8	See notes. Very reddened cluster. NGC 7510 and King 19 lie < 1° to the south. Aliases: (4) IRAS 23058+6032; C2306+606
King 19	cl	23 08.3	+60 31	Cep	III2p	5.0	9.2	52	12.0	12.7	1225	3	18	1	Aliases: Bas 2; Lund 1028; OCl 254; C2306+602
NGC 7492	gcl	23 08 26.7	−15 36 41	Aqr		4.2	11.2		15.5	14.3	25100	17	122	6	See notes. Aliases: Mel 242; OCl 111; EQ 2305−159; C2305−159
NGC 7510	cl	23 11 04.2	+60 34 08	Cep	II3r n	7.0	7.9	75	10.0	12.1	3104	3	18	8	See notes. Archinal: Position measured from DSS. Aliases: Cr 454; Lund 1030; OCl 256; Mrk 49; C2309+603
[AO84] III	mc	23.2	+00.0	Psc		9800.0	1.80	27	2.06	21.8		17	102	54	Moving cluster with very large angular size, hypothesized by Agekyan and Orlov [1984].
Markarian 50	cl	23 15 14	+60 26.7	Cep?	III1p n	2.0	8.5	39	9.83	10.0	3417	3	18	99	Aliases: Bas 3; Bi 3; Lund 1031; OCl 257; C2313+602
[PTB93] 4	cl	23 17.7	+69 59	Cep		120.0		8				3	8	99	Archinal: Infrared cluster. Not visible on DSS.
Berkeley 99	cl	23 21 16.9	+71 47 42	Cep	III2r	5.0		60	14.0			3	8	99	Aliases: Lund 1032; OCl 271; C2319+714
Dolidze 46	ast	23 21.9	+55 46	Cas	IV1p	12.0						3	18	99	DSFG: Probably not a cluster. Archinal: Id? Scattering of bright stars. Brightest is HD 220220 (V=8.18, F2) on SW side. Aliases: OCl 253; C2319+555
NGC 7654	cl	23 24 51	+61 36.0	Cas	II2r	16.0	6.9	173	11.0	12.9	1565	3	18	52	M 52. 12′ diameter condensed central portion with 16′ outer diameter. Rich, much greater than 100 stars. Aliases: Cr 455; Lund 1034; M 52; Mel 243; OCl 260; Raab 150; OCl 260.0; C2322+613
Czernik 43	cl	23 25.8	+61 18	Cas	III1p	7.0		15				3	18	1	Aliases: OCl 261; OCl 261.0; C2323+610
Berkeley 100	cl	23 25 58	+63 47.0	Cep	IV2p	2.7		100	16.0			3	8	99	Archinal: Compact rich cluster. DSS overlap region. Aliases: Lund 1036; OCl 264; C2324+634
NGC 7686	cl	23 30 07	+49 08.0	And	III2p	15.0	5.6	80	7.0	11.5	1000	9	30	4	DSFG: Probably not a cluster. Skiff: Center star is HD 221246. Aliases: Cr 456; Lund 1037; OCl 251; C2327+488
Skiff J2330.2+6015	cl?	23 30 12	+60 15.5	Cas	II2m	2.8		40				3	18	8	See notes. Found by B. Skiff on DSS while checking V582 Cas, non-member brt. star on N side, GSC magnitude 12.2.

Table 4.1: Catalog of Clusters and Asterisms in the Milky Way, and Objects Misidentified as Such

Name	Type	2000.0 R.A.	Dec.	Con.	Tr. Type	Diam. (′)	Tot. Vm	#str	Bt* Vm	V Sur	Dist. (pc)	S #	2U #	Ref	Comments and Aliases
Stock 11	ast?	23 30 55	+55 45.4	Cas	IV2p	10.0			8.0p			3	18	99	See notes. Archinal: Contains four HD stars, all of which are near type A0 as Stock indicated, although this is 1/2° NW of his position. Aliases: OCl 259; C2330+552
Berkeley 101	cl:	23 32 46.5	+64 12 16	Cep	III2p	2.0		10	16.0			3	8	99	Aliases: Lund 1041; OCl 267; (4) IRAS 23310+6354; C2331+639
King 20	cl	23 33 14	+58 28.8	Cas	II2p	5.0		20	13.0			3	18	99	Aliases: Lund 1039; OCl 262; (4) IRAS 23308+5811; C2331+582
Czernik 44	cl	23 33 33	+61 57.7	Cas	II2p	4.0		20				3	18	99	Aliases: Lund 1040; OCl 265; C2331+616
Stock 12	cl	23 36 20	+52 32.6	Cas	IV2p	35.0		9	8.18			3	18	99	Archinal: Nine near A0 spectral type stars over a 35′ (not Stock's 20′) field. Brightest member star is HD 222029 (V=8.18, A0). Aliases: Lund 1042; OCl 258; C2334+521
NGC 7708	ast?	23 36 30	+72 51.0	Cep		30.0		25	7.3			3	8	53	See notes. Includes HD 221774 as brightest star, on NW side.
Aveni-Hunter 1	cl	23 37 47	+48 33.6	And	IV2p n	47.0		16	8.55			9	30	99	Archinal: Group of bright stars with nebulosity and BM And (V=12.4-14.6). DSS overlap region. Aliases: Lund 1153; OCl 252.2; C2334+481
Berkeley 102	cl	23 38.7	+56 38	Cas	II1p	5.0			18.0			3	18	1	Aliases: Lund 1043; OCl 263; C2336+563
Levy-W. J2340.6+5618	ast	23 40 39.6	+56 18 13	Cas		72.0		40	8.110			3	18	99	See notes. Star stream discovered by D. Levy and W. Wallach, on 2001 April 29-30.
Alessi J23407+0757	ast	23 40.7	+07 57	Psc		15.0		9	8			17	81	10	
Stock 17	cl	23 43 47.0	+62 09 37	Cas	I3p	1.0			8.45			3	18	99	Archinal: Brightest star is BD+61 2509 (V=8.45, B0.5Ib). Fits Stock's description if one assumes a 50 year precession error. Aliases: Lund 1045; OCl 268; C2343+619
Berkeley 103	cl	23 45.2	+59 18	Cas	II1p	2.0		20	15.0			3	18	1	Aliases: Lund 1044; OCl 266; C2342+590
King 11	cl	23 47 36.6	+68 38 26	Cep	I2m	6.0		50	17.0			3	8	99	Aliases: Lund 1046; OCl 279; (4) IRAS 23455+6819; C2345+683
King 21	cl	23 49.9	+62 42	Cas	I2p	4.0	9.6	20	10.0	12.6		3	8	1	Aliases: Lund 1048; OCl 270; C2347+624
NGC 7762	cl	23 49.9	+68 01	Cep	II2m	15.0	10.0p	40	11.0	15.9	912	3	8	99	Archinal: DSS overlap region. Aliases: Cr 457; Lund 1047; Mel 244; OCl 280; Raab 151; C2347+677
[PTB93] 9	cl	23 50.0	+67 51	Cep		120.0		9				3	8	99	Archinal: Infrared cluster. Not visible on DSS.
Alessi J23506+4149	ast	23 50.6	+41 49	And		15.0		9	8			9	30	10	
PWM78 4	cl?	23 50 53.0	+62 19 25	Cas		1.3		40				3	18	8	Very reddened possible cluster. Alias: C2348+620
NGC 7772	cl:	23 51.8	+16 15	Peg	III1p	5.0	9.6	10		13.1		17	81	99	Alias: C2349+159
[PTB93] 6	cl	23 52.9	+68 25	Cep		60.0		9				3	8	99	Archinal: Infrared cluster. Not visible on DSS.
King 12	cl	23 53.0	+61 57	Cas	II1p	3.0	9.0	15	10.0	11.4	2489	3	18	1	Alias: C2350+616
Harvard 21	cl	23 54 17.6	+61 43 43	Cas	IV1p	3.0	9.0	6		11.4		3	18	99	See notes. DSFG: Probably not a real cluster. Aliases: Cr 458; C2351+614
Czernik 45	cl	23 55 44.9	+64 37 24	Cas	II2p	2.0		8				3	8	99	Alias: C2353+642
NGC 7788	cl	23 56 44	+61 24.0	Cas	I2p	4.0	9.4	20		12.4	2333	3	18	99	Aliases: Cr 459; OCl 275.0; C2354+611
Frolov 1	cl	23 57 26.5	+61 37 23	Cas			9.2	26	10.60			3	18	99	Archinal: Center and brightest star is LS I +61 110 (V=10.7, B). Alias: C2354+613
NGC 7789	cl	23 57 28.6	+56 42 52	Cas	II2r	25.0	6.7	583	10.0	13.7	1841	3	18	51	Archinal: Position measured from DSS. Well-known and impressively rich cluster. Aliases: Cr 460; Mel 245; Raab 152; OCl 269.0; C2354+564
NGC 7795	cl?	23 57 34.5	+60 01 25	Cas		16.0		17	7			3	18	99	
NGC 7790	cl	23 58 24	+61 12.5	Cas	II2m	5.0	8.5	134	10.0	12.0	2963	3	18	4	See notes. Aliases: Cr 461; OCl 276.0; C2355+609
Basel 11	dne		$ $											51	An erroneous entry. Valid entries are C0714−138 = Basel 11a, and C0555+219 = Basel 11b. Alias: C0556+215
Bok 1	dupl		$ $											51	Erroneous notation for C0518−685 = NGC 1901. Alias: C1108−231

4.4 Extended Notes on Catalog Objects

This section includes extended notes on various objects in the catalog of open clusters, asterisms, and extragalactic clusters. These notes clarify identifications that in the past were uncertain, clarify nomenclature that has been confused, and also report errata regarding catalogs. They also include some extended descriptive material, along with research and historical notes. Objects are presented in alphabetical and numerical order by preferred cluster name and number. In some cases where an object is commonly known under more than one name or under an incorrect name, a reference is given to the main entry. Brief comments are usually given alone in the main catalog.

A separate listing of such notes is presented for known Galactic globular clusters along with the catalog of such clusters in Section 7.3.

Cited references are listed in the References starting on page 459.

ADS 6366 cluster: This is an asterism or possible cluster about the triple star ADS 6366 (see Figure 4.2). It is important to note that this group is *not* ADS 6366 itself, but merely contains it. The triple star was first observed by John Herschel in 1827, but was first cataloged by (and its discovery credited to) F. G. W. Struve as a double star, his Σ1141.

What is quite surprising about this group of stars is that they were also discovered by Herschel, who noted [1871, 9] that the triple star was "In a small cluster." However, this cluster is unusual because it is not an h, GC, or NGC object, and has not appeared in any other catalog until now (except for a mention by Webb—see below). The reason would appear to be that Herschel reported his observations of this very late in life in a paper read in 1870 and published in 1871. He indicated that the measures in that paper would have been published in his third list of such stars (published in 1832). However, in the earlier list he left out observations of stars already known to be multiple (such as this one, discovered by Struve). The 1871 publication date was well past the time when Herschel had published his lists of nonstellar objects (in 1833, 1847, and in the GC). Since he did not call any particular attention to this possible cluster beyond this brief mention, it also escaped the notice of later compilers (e.g. Dreyer, whilc making up the NGC). In fact, the discovery by Herschel seems to have completely escaped notice until now.

The stars were next alluded to by Webb [1962, 176]. He gives information on Σ1141 (= ADS 6366), and then mentions it is "In a pretty group." He erroneously lists it as being in Monoceros rather than in Canis Minor, although this may be due to the use of pre-1930 IAU constellation boundaries.

Fig. 4.2 *ADS 6366 cluster. A star cluster, credited here for the first time as being discovered by John Herschel, including the triple star ADS 6366. The short streak above left center is an image artifact. 17′ field of view. Image courtesy the Palomar Observatory and Digitized Sky Survey created by the Space Telescope Science Institute, operated by AURA, Inc. for NASA. Reproduced with permission from AURA/STScI.*

Finally, this group was singled out as a possibly significant object to one of us [BA] by Brian Skiff [private communication, 1998]. He first observed it from Anderson Mesa, near Flagstaff, Arizona, on March 19, 1988 with his 15-cm telescope. His observation reads [with abbreviations spelled out]: "ADS 6366—Rich 2° field centered on small cluster. Eight stars in the main central group. The first bright star west of central pair has a faint companion in position angle 135°, magnitude 13.5, separation 15″. The main group is 2.5′ x 0.75′ elongated east-west." Skiff further reports that be believes that "the spectra by Lindroos [1985] showed that these were not related apart from maybe the main double star," so this may not be a physical group. In any case, Skiff's observation resulted in checking the trail back in time to Herschel's actual discovery of this group.

ADS 6366 is actually a triple star. The A component is also known as HD 63065. According to the *Washington Double Star Catalog* [Worley and Douglass 1996], discovery credit for the A (V = 8.32, B9) and B (V = 9.27, A2V) components is given to Struve (Σ1141). Credit for the C (V = 12.33, F5IV) component is given to John Herschel (V magnitudes and spectral types here are from SIMBAD). The WDS shows that the position angle and separation for the AB components remains unchanged between Struve's 1831 observations and 1970, at 9° and 17.4″. From 1914 to 1961, the AC component has shown no motion in position

Fig. 4.3 *ADS 13292 cluster. A possible compact star cluster first noticed by Brian Skiff, including the (at least) quadruple star ADS 13292. 17′ field of view. Image courtesy the Palomar Observatory and Digitized Sky Survey created by the Space Telescope Science Institute, operated by AURA, Inc. for NASA. Reproduced with permission from AURA/STScI.*

angle from 88°, and an increase in separation from 26.5″ to 25.5″.

DSS images and Skiff's visual observation of this area invite speculation that there may be a very loose cluster or association here that is much larger than the main group. An 18′ image has an obvious semi-circle or spiral of 8–10 bright stars going around the main group, from west through north to the east. A 1° field also shows a stream of possibly related stars going off to the south-southwest and ending up about 12′ south. There is also a stream of stars going southeast about 12′.

ADS 13292: This asterism or possible cluster (see Figure 4.3) was singled out as a significant object by Brian Skiff [private communication, 1998]. This was cited as another example (besides ADS 6366) of "trapezia" of stars around the Milky Way. Brian states: "This is also pretty conspicuous in a telescope. Unlike ADS 6366 this one is probably a physical group of young stars. The central star, HD 227247, is a luminous early-B star. Quite a small knot of stars, as you can see."

The DSS does show a tight unresolved group of stars here, including *at least* eight fairly bright stars inside a 1′ diameter, centered at $20^h\ 02^m\ 23.6^s$ +35° 18′ 35″. The primary star of the cluster, HD 227247 = ADS 13292A (V=9.38, B2II, emission lines) is to the northwest. There are also a number of other stars close by that are possibly associated, in a rich Milky Way field overall. This group appears to be involved in the HII region Sh 2-101. The WDS [Worley and Douglass 1996] shows that the multiple star or group was discovered by T. E. Espin in 1894 and is also ES 202. This group was also independently discovered in 1989 as a possible cluster by Philipp Teutsch (his Teutsch J2002.3+3518), while examining POSS prints.

Note that Cygnus X-1 = HDE 226868 = V1357 Cygni (V = 8.83, O9.7Iab) just precedes this group by about 4^m in right ascension.

AH03 J0748.6–2656: This is a possible cluster which was accidentally discovered while searching for Haffner 25, see page 132.

AH03 J2011.9 + 2644: This is an asterism at William Herschel's position for NGC 6882—see page 187—but by his description is likely *not* NGC 6882, which is probably the same object as NGC 6885.

Alessi J12130–6242: Bruno Alessi [private communication, 1998] has reported the discovery of this possible cluster. He describes it as a very faint possible cluster of extremely faint stars in a very rich Milky Way field, lying just east of NGC 4184 in Crux. He points out that its appearance on the DSS-II resembles that of the very faint cluster SSWZ94 4, and speculates whether it is an analogue of that cluster.

As indicated on page 200, SSWZ94 4 has the appearance of a distant Galactic globular cluster, although it was recently determined to be an open cluster. An examination of the DSS and DSS-II shows that this new object, Alessi J12130-6242, is not quite as obvious as SSWZ94 4. This field has a lot of Milky Way "mottling," so this could be just a fluctuation in the Milky Way background. Therefore, it is listed here with type "ast?" rather than "gcl?" However, a study of it probably should be done with a large telescope in order to ascertain its true type.

AM 2: Ortolani, *et al.*, [1995] have shown this object to be an old open cluster, similar to M 67. It has previously been listed as a Galactic globular cluster. Although it has a horizontal branch (at V = 17.75 ± 0.10), the turn-off magnitude is located at approximately V = 20.0 ± 0.15. The small magnitude difference between these two values is the key age indicator that shows it to be an open cluster in nature. They estimate a true distance modulus of 15.46 magnitudes, and therefore, a distance of 12.4 kpc from the Sun. The position given in the catalog here is measured from the DSS. The value given by Djorgovski and Meylan [1993] and by Ortolani, *et al.*, [1995] is about 30^s too far east.

Anon. Platais = C2128+488: Platais [1979] first reported the possible existence of this cluster, along with the discovery of V1726 Cygni as a cepheid variable—and a possible cluster member. A follow-up study by Platais [1986] unfortunately seemed to indicate that astrometrically this was not a real physical cluster. However, new pho-

Fig. 4.4 *Archinal 1. A previously unrecognized, likely star cluster in Serpens. 17′ field of view. Image courtesy the Palomar Observatory and Digitized Sky Survey created by the Space Telescope Science Institute, operated by AURA, Inc. for NASA. Reproduced with permission from AURA/STScI.*

Fig. 4.5 *Arcturus group. A grouping of stars around the bright star Arcturus, postulated as a possible star cluster by Mattison and Burritt in their famous 1856* The Geography of the Heavens *and shown here as it appeared in its companion "Atlas." The field size and orientation is unknown.*

tometric and astrometric data from Turner, *et al.*, [1994] confirms that there is indeed a real cluster here and that V1726 Cygni is a probable member. The data presented in the catalog here are taken from the Turner, *et al.*, paper.

Apriamasvili 1 or Apr 1 = C1845-059: This cluster in Scutum is more commonly (and incorrectly) known as Basel 1. It was first reported by Apriamasvili [1964], who has discovery priority for the name. Its name Basel 1 originates in Becker and Fenkart [1971]. The primary name and alias list should be changed in the *Lund Catalogue*. It was labeled as Basel 1 in the first edition of *Uranometria 2000.0* and the corresponding *DSFG1e* (at least).

Arches Cluster: This is [NHS93] 17, refer to "Central Cluster" on page 117.

Archinal 1: This likely cluster is listed here for the first time, having been discovered by one of us, see Figure 4.4 on page 113. It was found rather serendipitously while investigating the identity of Graff 1 (= IC 4756) nearby. When Collinder [1931] gave the reference for the Graff discovery paper [Graff 1922], he incorrectly gave the position (in the paper title) as "$18^h\ 50^m\ +5°.5$." Assuming this was a 1900.0 position (it turns out it was actually an 1855.0 position), the updated position for 2000.0 ($18^h\ 55^m\ +05°.6$) was examined on the DSS and a star cluster found there. Later, after checking the correct position in a copy of the actual Graff paper, it was realized that this was a previously uncataloged star cluster, and therefore, a new discovery.

The cluster itself contains about 24 stars in an area 1.5′ in diameter. There are 4 GSC stars included, the brightest of which is GSC 00457-00629 at magnitude 13.4. The center of the group was taken to be the northern component of GSC 0457-00615. The other two GSC stars are 0457-00095 and 0457-00642. The estimated Trumpler type is II2p. A histogram equalization display of the DSS image in this area shows a possible Milky Way star cloud (or large patch of bright nebulosity?) in an approximately 8′ diameter area just to the west of the cluster.

No check of the colors or proper motions of these stars has been made, so their existence as a cluster has yet to be proven. However, the appearance on the DSS is more "cluster-like" than many other groups cataloged as star clusters.

Arcturus group: There is a scattering of stars around Arcturus, first apparently described in 1856 by Mattison and Burritt in their famous book, *The Geography of the Heavens* and its companion *Atlas*. In their *Geography* (p. 88) they describe "A rich group of stars in the vicinity of Arcturus, and surrounding that star. May be seen with small telescopes." It appears in their atlas on map VIII, as figure 50, and is reproduced here as Figure 4.5.

A low power view of the area around Arcturus will indeed show a sprinkling of stars, although it is difficult to reconcile Mattison and Burritt's figure with the sky here. However, comparison with star plots (i.e., via the *MegaStar* program) of the area seems to indicate that their il-

Fig. 4.6 *Barkhatova 2. The position of this cluster has been off in all prior published references. It appears to have been little studied, perhaps just because no one could find it until now. 17′ field of view. Image courtesy the Palomar Observatory and Digitized Sky Survey created by the Space Telescope Science Institute, operated by AURA, Inc. for NASA. Reproduced with permission from AURA/STScI.*

lustration refers to a large 6° (east-west) by 4° scattering of stars, centered about 1 degree east of Arcturus. That position and a diameter of 5° is used in the catalog here. Arcturus's magnitude is assumed for the brightest star – thus giving this group the brightest star of any in the sky (well, other than the moving group [AO84] I, which includes the Sun).

Barkhatova 2 = C2052+458: After an inquiry by Yann Pothier [private communication, 1996], one of us [BA] looked into the identification of this object in detail. Using the original discovery reference by Barkhatova [1958a], which plots the cluster stars and provides magnitudes, this cluster was located on the DSS, see Figure 4.6 on page 114. The position given by Barkhatova is substantially off, at (1900.0) $21^h\ 40.7^m$ +50° 44.5′; for 2000.0 this is $21^h\ 44.3^m$ +51° 12.1′. The position from the DSS was measured as (2000.0) $21^h\ 43^m\ 32.8^s$ +51° 03′ 56” for a centrally located star, with measured diameter of 5.2′. Barkhatova's position was too far east by 45^s in right ascension and north by 8.2′ in declination.

The number of stars was estimated to be 21, all stars in the central part of the field measured by Barkhatova. Of these 21 stars, 13 are in the GSC. The total photovisual and photographic magnitudes, derived from Barkhatova's measurements, are 8.4 and 9.3 respectively. The magnitude of the brightest star (again from Barkhatova) is 10.0 photovisual (as opposed to 10.3 from the GSC).

Other than listings in Ruprecht, *et al.*, [1981] and the *Lund Catalogue*, (estimates of Trumpler type, size, and number of stars) there appear to be no other data or observations available for this cluster—perhaps because Barkhatova's poor position is repeated in these later references. In any case, the position should be corrected in the *Lund Catalogue* at least.

Some further details on this cluster are given in Pothier and Archinal [1998].

Basel 1: This is Apr 1, see page 113.

Basel 11a = C0714-138, and Basel 11b = C0555+219: The *Lund Catalogue* lists both of these clusters incorrectly (as Basel 11) in the “print” file.

Basel 17 = Lodén 282 = C1108-587: The equivalency of Basel 17 and Lodén 282 has been checked by comparison of the discovery photographs, in Steppe [1977, 427] and Lodén [1977, 43] respectively. However, it should be noted that the Lodén photo and photometry covers some brighter and fainter stars over a larger area than that of the Basel 17 photo. One might even argue that Basel 17 is part of Lodén 282. However, Lodén was only trying to show that possible clusterings exist. If there is any real cluster here it seems likely it is the “Basel 17” area only.

There are three stars near the center of the Basel 17 area (Steppe's stars 13, 14, and 15, Lodén's stars 13, 11, and 19 respectively), and the southeast of these is taken here for the cluster center (at 2000.0: $11^h\ 10^m\ 32.9^s$ –59° 01′ 55.5”). The brightest star is “Basel 17, no. 11” at G=9.90 (RGU system).

It also should be noted that both papers were printed in 1977, but Steppe's was printed in March vs. Lodén's in July, so the Basel 17 name has priority. Therefore, the Basel 17 name should be used as the primary name, e.g. in the *Lund Catalogue* files.

Bergeron 1: This is the same object as Reiland 1, see page 196.

Berkeley 13 = C0451+526: An examination of a DSS image showed there was nothing at the *Lund Catalogue* position of Be 13. It was also confirmed by checking Ruprecht, *et al.*, [1981] that this was essentially at the original Be 13 discovery position (from Setteducati and Weaver, [1960]). However, just to the NE of that position (see Figure 4.7), about 4′ southwest of HD 31134 (V = 5.6, A2Vs, SIMBAD) lies a substantial star cluster with a diameter of 8′. Be 13 was originally listed as being 8′ in diameter with 15 stars. Although this is a fairly rich cluster there are perhaps about 15 brighter stars here, and the diameter matches perfectly (so this is almost certainly the indicated

Fig. 4.7 *Berkeley 13. One of many clusters whose location was poorly known until publication of the catalog here. 17′ field of view. Image courtesy the Palomar Observatory and Digitized Sky Survey created by the Space Telescope Science Institute, operated by AURA, Inc. for NASA. Reproduced with permission from AURA/STScI.*

Fig. 4.8 *Berkeley 39. A distant rich open cluster, and the first open cluster known to contain close binary systems among its "blue straggler" stars. 17′ field of view. Image courtesy the Palomar Observatory and Digitized Sky Survey created by the Space Telescope Science Institute, operated by AURA, Inc. for NASA. Reproduced with permission from AURA/STScI.*

cluster). The *Lund Catalogue* diameter of 1.5′ is certainly misleading, as is the total magnitude of 15.0, and the Trumpler type of III 1 p (this information may have been meant to apply to the brighter stars only).

The position given here is for the center star, GSC 03734-00518, at the GSC position. The Trumpler type ("II 2 m") and number of stars (approximately 130) have been estimated from the DSS image.

Berkeley 18 (C0518+453) = King 22 (C0519+454): The *Lund Catalogue* alias list correctly indicates that Berkeley 18 and King 22 are one and the same object. The preferred "C" name should probably be (according to the correct position) C0518+453. The *DSFG1e* (chart 66) incorrectly lists this object twice, first as Be 18 and again as King 22. The *DSFG1e* King 22 entry should be deleted. *Sky Catalogue 2000.0* vol. 2 makes the same mistake. The Berkeley discovery was in 1960 while the King discovery was in 1961, so the Be 18 name does have priority. Observations by Kaluzny [1997] give a distance of 5.8 kpc for Be 18 and, with an apparent diameter of 26 arcmin, this corresponds to a linear size of about 44 pc. His data indicate it to be "one of the most populous objects in the whole sample of known galactic open clusters."

Berkeley 21 = C0548+217: In the *Lund Catalogue* main data file, several items are incorrect regarding this object. For the IAU name "548+217," read "0548+217." For the (apparently Ruprecht [1966, 35]) Trumpler type, for "2 3m" read "2 3 m." For the Lyngå Trumpler type, for "1 2m –" read "1 2 m –." For the "total magnitude" (columns 235–238), for "1.1" read "11.1." The 11.1 V magnitude is from the *DSFG1e* and SIMBAD. Some (the Trumpler type), but not all, of these items are corrected in the CDS version of February 20, 1995. In addition, the IAU name is corrected for this object in the "galactic" file from the CDS version (although no change in this file is listed in the CDS "ReadMe" file).

Berkeley 24 = C0635-008: In the *Lund Catalogue* main data file, the minus sign is missing for the declination in the 1950.0 and 2000.0 positions (it is present in the "print" file). The correct position, from B. Skiff's [private communication, 1995] measurement on the DSS, is (2000.0) 06^h 37^m 47^s −00° 52.7′. The declination is similarly corrected (but the position is not as good as Skiff's) in the CDS version of February 20, 1995. In addition, the *Lund Catalogue* alias list is missing the identity "OCl 539" for this object (see e.g. Ruprecht, *et al.*, [1981]).

Berkeley 39: Be 39 lies in the constellation of Monoceros, about two-fifths of the way between the large, bright open cluster NGC 2548 (M 48) and the star δ Mon (V = 4.15), see Figure 4.8. It is a rich cluster of faint stars about 12′ in diameter yet was first studied in any detail only recently by Kaluzny and Richtler [1989]. They presented positions, magnitudes and colors for 827 stars in the region of the cluster and derived a color-magnitude diagram from the observations. This shows a clearly defined main sequence turnoff point with well developed subgiant and giant branches from which an age of 8–10 Gyr was determined, comparable to that of NGC 188. This makes it one of the oldest known clusters in the Galaxy. The faintness of the stars—the brightest barely reach V = 13—is due to the distance of the cluster, which is about 4.0 kpc away, and, being roughly in the direction of the Galactic anticenter, it lies some 11.7 kpc distant from the center of the Galaxy. In view of the age of the cluster, and the possibility that W UMa-type contact binaries could have evolved, a further study of Be 39 was made by Kaluzny, *et al.*, [1993] to search for these objects. About 2100 stars with V < 20.5 were included in the survey field, and among this population, twelve variable stars were discovered. One is believed to be an ordinary eclipsing binary with a period of about 1-day; however, the light-curves of the remaining eleven are typical of the W UMa contact binaries, with periods between 0.2254d and 0.546d. Interestingly, four of these also appear to be "blue stragglers," making Be 39 the first open cluster known to possess close binaries among its blue stragglers.

Berkeley 50: This is IC 1310, see page 134.

Berkeley 81 = C1859-005: In the *Lund Catalogue* main data file, the minus sign is missing for the declination in the 1950.0 and 2000.0 positions (it is present in the "print" file). This has been corrected in the CDS version of February 20, 1995. However, a more precise position, measured from the DSS is given here (2000.0: $19^h\ 01^m\ 43^s$ –00 27′ 13").

BFS 15 = WB89 239 = IRAS 23026+5948: This is nebulosity around the possible cluster Reiland 1 (See page 196).

BFS 54 = NGC 2282 = IC 2172: This is nebulosity around Cl vdB 85 (See page 118).

Bica 1: This object, when first discovered, was thought to be a Galactic globular cluster [Bica 1994]. However, later observations [Bica, *et al.*, 1995] showed it to be an emission nebula and likely supernova remnant. This lies 4′ south-southwest of SAO 185274 (V = 6.2).

Biurakan 13 = C0657-001: Brian Skiff has noted [private communication, 1995] that the "–" declination sign is missing for this cluster in the *Lund Catalogue*. He also gives an improved position (derived from the DSS) for 2000.0 of $07^h\ 00^m\ 22^s$, –00° 14.1′. The declination has been similarly corrected in the CDS version of February 20, 1995, but Skiff's position is probably better and is used here.

Bochum 1: This object was first reported as a cluster in a paper by Moffat and Vogt [1975a]. However, it is difficult to identify on the basis of that paper since no image is given, and there is no obvious group of stars at the given position. Fortunately, Moffat and Vogt do identify this area as "SLS Region A," and identify the stars involved by the SLS number. The SLS catalog is now more commonly known as the LS (Luminous Stars) catalog, and was done by Stephenson and Sanduleak [1971]. With the help of their chart [ibid. Figure A] and the LS star numbers, it was possible to identify this area and the stars on the DSS.

Moffat and Vogt assume this group of only 8 stars of spectral type O is a cluster, based on their common reddening and spectral type. However, these stars do not have any appearance of association on a DSS image. The involved stars are LS 44, 45, 46, 47, 48, 51, 53, and 54. (LS 50 is also in this group but is rejected as being an evolved giant not physically associated with the other stars.) The approximate center of this group is at LS 51, at (SIMBAD, 2000.0) $06^h\ 25^m\ 24.9^s$ +19° 46′ 00″. The brightest star is LS 44 at V = 8.42, and the total magnitude of the 8 stars is V = 7.93. Measured from the DSS, the overall diameter of the group is about 26′. Moffat and Vogt estimate a total distance of 4.06 kpc, based on the star magnitudes, spectral types, and reddening.

Bochum 4: This is NGC 2409, see page 165.

Bochum 5 = C0728-169: This is near NGC 2409 = Bochum 4, see page 165.

Bochum 14: See NGC 6514 = M 20 on page 178.

Brück 31 = OGLE-CL SMC0019 = OGLE-CL SMC0175: Pietrzyński, *et al.*, [1998] list Brück 31 twice in their compilation of SMC clusters, once as the cluster OGLE-CL SMC0019, and a second time as the cluster candidate OGLE-CL SMC0175. The coordinates and images they present for these two entries show they are one and the same object.

C1814-190: Using star counts in the area, Turner identified this object as a likely star cluster in 1984. Turner's position for the cluster of (1950.0) $18^h\ 13^m\ 54^s$ –19° 02.9′ is used here, 2.9′ northwest of the Cepheid variable WZ Sgr. He indicated there are roughly 35 stars brighter than B = 16. However, in Turner, *et al.*, [1993, p. 128], it is stated "the increase in star counts northwest of the Cepheid can be traced to gaps in the veiling dust rather than to a suspected star cluster." Therefore, the object is listed in the catalog here as an asterism (it is apparently an "absorption hole" in the Milky Way).

Although Turner named this cluster "C1814-190," note that the 1950.0 coordinates should have been truncated to obtain a name; therefore, the correct name would have been C1813-190. However, Turner's original name is used here and should be maintained.

C1814-191a: This is the WZ Sgr cluster, see Figure 4.9. It was discovered by Turner, *et al.*, in 1993. It is also listed in Gieren and Fouqué [1993].

Fig. 4.9 *The field of C1814-191a or the WZ Sgr cluster. The individual stars of the likely cluster are identifiable only with reference to the discovery paper by Turner, et al., [1993]. 17′ field of view. Image courtesy the Palomar Observatory and Digitized Sky Survey created by the Space Telescope Science Institute, operated by AURA, Inc. for NASA. Reproduced with permission from AURA/STScI.*

Fig. 4.10 *RAFGL 2004 = Quintuplet cluster. A massive cluster near the Galactic center, recently heavily studied at infrared wavelengths with the HST and Keck I telescope. This cluster contains the "Pistol Star," thought to be the most massive star in our Galaxy. The "Quintuplet" name originates from the 5 massive stars at its center (running diagonally from lower left to upper right), the only stars clearly seen in early images of the cluster. HST NICMOS camera image. The field of view is not specified but is less than the 51.2 arcsecond maximum field of the NICMOS camera. Don Figer (Space Telescope Science Institute) and NASA.*

C1814-191b: This cluster is part of the Sgr OB4 association. It was discovered by Turner, *et al.*, in 1993. The position in the catalog here was measured by one of us [BA], with the star GSC 06273-00146 at the center.

C2306+606: This is PWM78 3, see page 196.

Central Cluster= SGR A*, [NHS93] 17, and RAFGL 2004: These are the three extremely massive, young, infrared star clusters at the center of our Galaxy. They are also known as the Galactic Center, the Arches Cluster, and the Quintuplet Cluster, respectively.

A large number of papers have been written regarding these clusters during the 1990's, as infrared observing techniques progressed so these unusual objects could be further studied. Spectacular images of the Arches and Quintuplet clusters have also been obtained using the NICMOS (infrared) camera on the Hubble Space Telescope. Some of these images are reproduced here as Figures 4.10 and 4.11.

A fairly complete review regarding these clusters has been presented by Figer, *et al.*, [1999]—who obtained the NICMOS images. These clusters are the most massive young clusters in the Galaxy, and contain more hot Wolf-Rayet stars than any other starburst regions in the Local Group of galaxies. They are, therefore, considered the best examples of so-called "super" star clusters, and provide the best location for the investigation of the Wolf-Rayet star phenomena. Each of these clusters has a mass estimated at greater than 10,000 solar masses, and luminosities greater than 10 million times that of the Sun. The Central Cluster is known to contain at least 30 stars with masses over 20 times that of the sun. Keck I telescope images have shown that the Arches Cluster contains over 100 O stars within its central 0.6 pc region. It is one of the densest massive clusters, more so even than most globular clusters, with about 300,000 solar masses per cubic parsec. The Quintuplet Cluster also contains about 30 stars that are more than 20 times as massive as the Sun, including more Wolf-Rayet stars than any other Galactic cluster. Figer, *et al.*, further report that all three clusters are quite similar, except for their ages. They estimate the Central and Quintuplet clusters to be 3–5 million years old, while the Arches cluster is substantially younger, at less than 2 million years. They also present results of N-body gravitation simulations, which show that these clusters must be short-lived, implying a star formation rate of about 0.5 stars per century in the Galactic Center.

However, there is some question whether the Central Cluster does have similar characteristics and origin as the other two clusters. Kim, *et al.*, [1999] point out that "because of its unusual location at the bottom of the Galactic gravitational potential well, and in the immediate vicinity

Fig. 4.11 *[NHS93] 17 = Arches cluster. This large cluster, perhaps the most dense massive cluster in our Galaxy, lies near the Galactic center and has recently been heavily studied at infrared wavelengths with the HST and the Keck I telescope. The "Arches" name apparently originates from the appearance of the cluster on early images. HST NICMOS camera image. The field of view is less than the 51.2 arcsecond maximum field of the NICMOS camera. Don Figer (Space Telescope Science Institute) and NASA.*

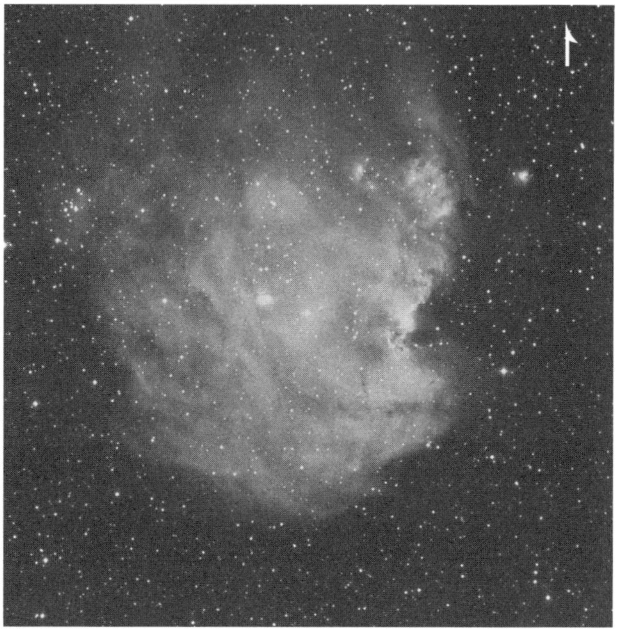

Fig. 4.12 *The emission nebula NGC 2175 and the involved possible cluster Collinder 84. 45′ field of view. Image courtesy the Palomar Observatory and Digitized Sky Survey created by the Space Telescope Science Institute, operated by AURA, Inc. for NASA. Reproduced with permission from AURA/STScI.*

of the postulated central supermassive black hole, it may have had quite a different origin."

These clusters have been included here because of their importance and for general completeness. However, as with a few other objects in the catalog presented, it should be remembered that these clusters have thus far only been observed in the infrared, with some of the largest telescopes available. Due to the extreme obscuration toward the center of the Milky Way, these objects will likely never be observed at visual wavelengths.

Chi or χ Persei: Although long considered to be the eastern component (NGC 884) of the Double Cluster, this has recently been shown to be the entire Double Cluster itself. See the entry below for the Double Cluster on page 130.

Cl Skiff clusters: See entries beginning with Skiff starting on page 198.

Cl vdB 1: This cluster should not be confused with the reflection nebula vdB 1, with which it has no connection. The Cl vdB 1 cluster was announced by van den Bergh in 1957, and his reflection nebula list (including a nebula vdB 1) was published in 1966. According to SIMBAD, Cl vdB 1 is also apparently known as the "CV Mon cluster" and the "Anonymous vdB cluster."

Cl vdB 85 = C0644+013: The "print" version of the *Lund Catalogue* has an incorrect OCl number. It should read "535.1" (not "535"). The alias file has the correct OCl number. Also note that the nebulosity in this cluster is NGC 2282 = IC 2172 = BFS 54 [private communications from B. Skiff and S. Gottlieb, 1995]. BFS refers to Blitz, *et al.*, 1982.

Collinder 21 = C0147+270: Brian Skiff has shown [private communication, 1997; Skiff 1998b] that by the color-magnitude diagram and the proper motions of the involved stars, this object is an apparent asterism rather than a true open cluster.

In addition, the declination given in the *Lund Catalogue* and other sources is about 10 minutes too far north. This was noted by comparison with the *DSFG1e* which has an essentially correct position. Skiff earlier [private communication, 1995] gave a 2000.0 position of $01^h\ 50^m\ 12^s\ +27°\ 04.8'$ which is used here.

Since the *Lund Catalogue* was intended to include only true Galactic open clusters, this object should be removed from that catalog.

Collinder 32 = Collinder 33 = IC 1848, and Collinder 34: See IC 1848 on page 134.

Collinder 84 = C0606+203: This possible cluster has in the past often been known as NGC 2175 (see Figure 4.12). However, the NGC description makes no mention of a star cluster here. NGC 2175 was discovered by someone named "Bruhns" and apparently first reported by Auwers as his no. 21 [Auwers 1862, 226]. The description there is only "Stern 8^m mit Nebel." This was translated into the NGC as "*8m in neb." (which more correctly should read "8th magnitude star with nebula"). So clearly the name NGC 2175 should be assigned to the nebula only. According to SIMBAD, the nebula is also called or is part of W 13, Sh 2-252, (including NGC 2174 and NGC 2175), LBN 854, LBN 190.10+00.58, and [KCW94] 189.876+0.516.

The possible cluster was discovered by Collinder [1931] and should, therefore, be known as Collinder 84. He incorrectly assigned this the NGC 2175 name [Collinder 1931, B6, B27]. Most modern references repeat the incorrect designation, including (at least) the *Lund Catalogue*, *Sky Catalogue 2000.0* (vol. 2), *Uranometria 2000.0 (first edition)*, the *DSFG1e*, and *NGC 2000.0*.

The reality of the cluster itself is in some doubt. An examination of it visually or on the DSS shows a fairly low star density and no obvious cluster involved with the NGC 2175 nebula. Therefore, it is listed here with type "cl?." The center star of the group is HD 42088 (V = 7.6, O6.5V).

Collinder 89 = C0615+236: The second part of the *Lund Catalogue* alias list entry for this object is missing the "89" (e.g. it currently reads "9–12 Gemini = C0615+236 Collinder"). Also note that this is a large group of bright stars (9, 10, 11, and 12 Geminorum) about 1° in diameter. An alternate size of 35′ given in the *Lund Catalogue*, in the *DSFG1e,* and shown on *Uranometria* chart 137 (first edition), is too small. Note the nebulae IC 443 about 1° to the south.

Collinder 121 = C0652-245: This object was first found by Collinder [1931] to be a scattered cluster of some 20 stars in a field with a diameter of about 1°. However, the first significant study was that of Feinstein [1967], who derived a distance of 0.63 kpc and extended the cluster membership to about 40 stars within 10° of the cluster center. A study by Eggen [1981] suggested that Cr 121 could more appropriately be considered as two separate objects, an open cluster of 13 identifiable stars lying at a distance of about 1.17 kpc, and a foreground OB association of 18 stars at 0.74 kpc. A recent analysis of *Hipparcos* data [Hoogerwerf, *et al.*, 1997] finds no clear difference in the parallax of stars selected from the two different groups identified by Eggen, and the distance of Cr 121 is derived as 0.546±0.03 kpc. The Wolf-Rayet star EZ CMa is identified as a member, and its parallax actually places it in the middle of the cluster.

Collinder 185 = C0820-360: The CDS February 20, 1995 version of the *Lund Catalogue* contains a slightly different position than the ADC version. The DSS does not show a likely candidate at either position. However, one of us [BA], via the DSS, has determined this cluster to be at (2000.0) $08^h\ 23^m\ 19^s$ −36° 20.1′. This position should be used for the *Lund Catalogue*. The position originally given by Collinder is about 1^m too far west and 10′ too far north (with nothing at Collinder's position). The *DSFG1e* (charts 362, 363) position should also be corrected, as it too lists this cluster at the incorrect Collinder position.

Fig. 4.13 *Collinder 223. Identified by T. Karhula apparently for the first time since Collinder's discovery. 17′ field of view SkyView/DSS-S image.*

Collinder 220: See NGC 3247 on page 171.

Collinder 223 = C1028-595: The position of this cluster in the *Lund Catalogue* and *DSFG1e* is about 16′ too far north. T. Karhula has provided the position used in the catalog here (see Figure 4.13). This identification has been confirmed by comparing the DSS image with Collinder's original description [1931, B11] and his note that this object has "Straight star-chains." [ibid, B33] which are visible on the south side of the cluster.

Collinder 234: See Trumpler 16 on page 205.

Collinder 236 = C1055-607: With assistance from P. Teutsch [private communication, 2002], this cluster was located on the DSS (see Figure 4.14) at the position of (2000.0) $10^h\ 57^m\ 00^s$ −61° 07.0′, with an estimated diameter of 10′. This has been confirmed using Collinder's photograph of this cluster [Collinder, 1931, plate 5; see Figure 4.15 on page 120] as it appears on the Franklin-Adams (F-A) charts, and also the F-A chart no. 18 itself. The diameter roughly matches Lundmark's and Collinder's [1931, p. B16] sizes of 8 'x 6' and 7' x 5' respectively.

Fig. 4.14 *Collinder 236. A 10′ diameter poor cluster or asterism identified by comparison to Collinder's illustration (Figure 4.15). 17′ field of view SkyView/DSS-S image © ROE.*

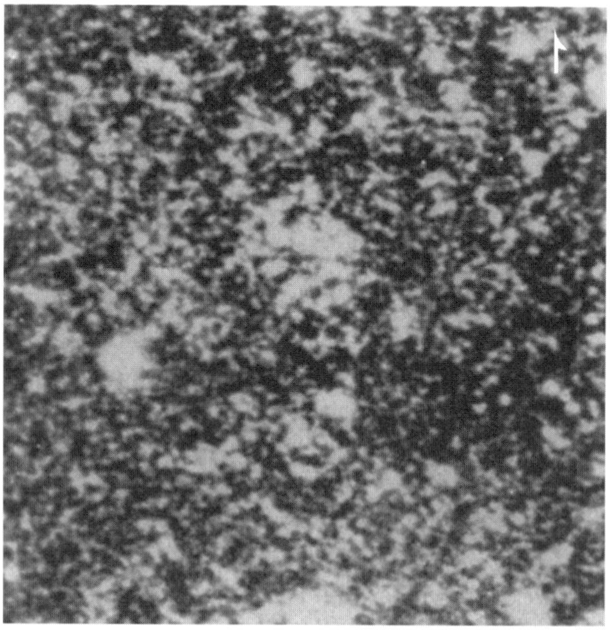

Fig. 4.15 *Collinder 236. Collinder's rather poor quality original illustration [1931, plate 5] of this group covering about a 56′ field, centered about 10′ south of the group, and derived from the Franklin-Adams Chart no. 18 shown in Figure 4.17. Collinder reproduced the photo with east to the right (and north up), but it is shown here with east to the left and north up.*

Note that SIMBAD (at least currently) gives a different position of 10^h 59^m 14.1^s 61° 19′ 15″, but there is no obvious cluster at that position.

Collinder 239 = NGC 3572: see page 173.

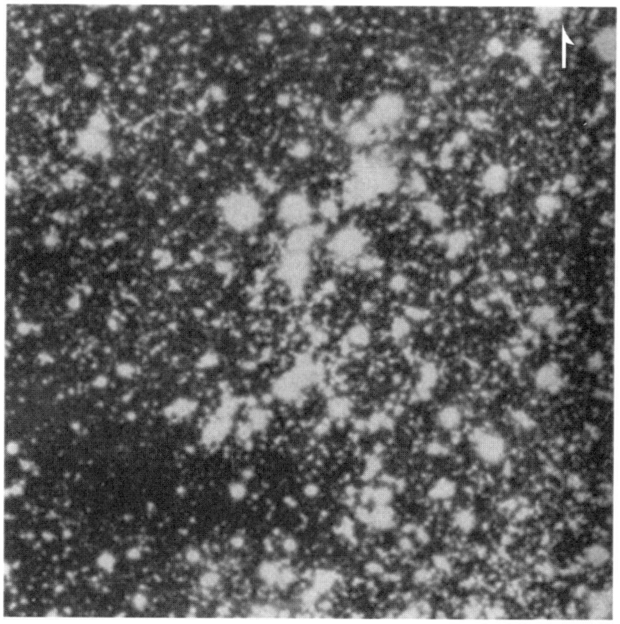

Fig. 4.16 *Collinder's illustration [1931, plate 5] of the area of Collinder 240, a reproduction from a Franklin-Adams chart [RAS, 1936]. Collinder reproduced the photo with east to the right (and north up), but it is shown here with east to the left and north up. Collinder 240 is the large overall group just above center, the brightest condensation in this group on the right side is NGC 3572, and the condensations below center are NGC 3590 (left) and Trumpler 18 (right).*

Collinder 240 = C1109-600: This is Collinder's [1931, B12] 32′ by 23′ scattering of stars (see Figures 4.16 and 4.19). Its identity and the identity of NGC 3572 have sometimes been confused since he unfortunately labeled this large object "NGC 3572a." It includes y Car and the clusters NGC 3572 (called "NGC 3572b" by Collinder) Hogg 10, and Hogg 11. The position is that of the bright star HD 97398, the diameter is Collinder's maximum, and the brightest star V magnitude is the SIMBAD value for y Car.

Collinder 249 = λ Centauri cluster = C1134-627: The nebula IC 2944 = Frost 789 is associated with this cluster. However, since there is no indication of the cluster in the IC, the IC 2944 designation should be not used for the cluster itself. Collinder [1931] and Lundmark apparently first discovered the cluster, so it should be known as Cr 249. The name should be changed in the *Lund Catalogue* alias list and main data files. The alias list should indicate the association with the IC 2944 nebula. In addition, this cluster is equivalent to vdB-Ha 121. It does not just "contain" it, as noted in the *Lund Catalogue* alias list. So the separate entries for vdB-Ha 121 should be removed from that list and main data files, and it should be indicated as equivalent to Cr 249 in the alias list. Brian Skiff first noted [private communication, 1995] the IC designation applies only to the nebula, and one of us [BA] has confirmed the other information here. Collinder calls this the λ Centauri cluster, al-

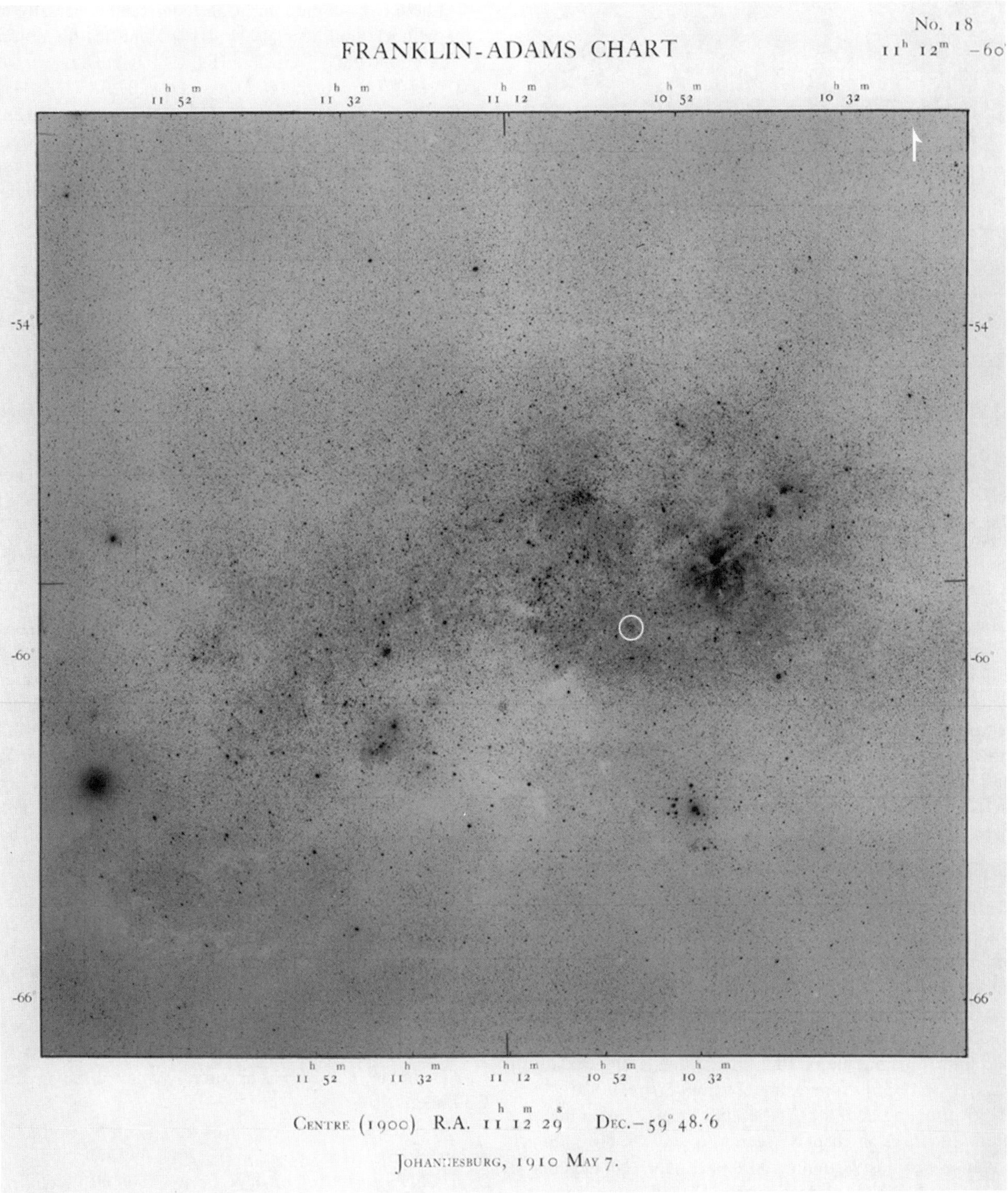

Fig. 4.17 *The region of western Crux, southern Centaurus, and northern Carina, as shown on Franklin-Adams Chart no. 18. The bright star at left is Acrux (α Crucis). The bright triangle of stars, just left of center and down includes NGC 3766, and below it is λ Centauri, involved in the IC 2944 nebulosity and the brightest star of the Collinder 249 cluster. The huge complex at center right includes the η Carinae region on its right side and NGC 3532 at the upper left. The sparse cluster Collinder 236, originally identified from this chart, is shown circled. Tick marks and the plate center position are shown for epoch 1900.0. This is a photographic projection. Therefore, lines of equal declination are not straight but substantially convex upward across the photograph. Overlays showing an approximate coordinate grid were supplied with the original charts. From RAS [1936, plate 18].*

Fig. 4.18 *Collinder 275, another Collinder cluster identified by T. Karhula, apparently for the first time since Collinder's discovery. 24′ field of view DSS-S image © ROE.*

though SkyView reveals it is centered on HD 101205 (V=6.45). The IC 2944 name should also be changed to Cr 249 in the *DSFG1e* (chart 450).

The first printing of the Caldwell Catalog lists this cluster as its object 100, but also repeats the incorrect IC identification. It also gives a position that is about 2^m too far east, and incorrectly calls this the "Gamma Cen Cl." when in fact it is the Lambda Centauri cluster. These errors have been corrected by O'Meara [2002] in his Caldwell book.

Collinder 257: See Harvard 5, *et al.*, (on page 132)

Collinder 275 = C1331-598: There is nothing at Collinder's original position (updated to 2000.0: 13^h 34.6^m −60° 08′) for this cluster. However, T. Karhula has provided the position (13h 35.4^m −60° 11′) of a scattered cluster. On the DSS (see Figure 4.18), this appears to match Collinder's description of being 8′ by 6′ in size, with 20 stars, and a total magnitude of 10.2. In addition, Collinder also says [1931, B35] "Interesting absorption streak 8′ x 0.7′, E130°, running across cl." The DSS image, with a histogram equalization display, seems to show such a faint streak of nebulosity running north-south through the cluster, strengthening this identification. Therefore, this group has been accepted as the correct identification of Cr 275 in this catalog. Note that the position is also incorrect in the *Lund Catalogue* and the *DSFG1e*.

Collinder 285 = C1440+697: This is the "Ursa Major Moving Cluster." Because of its size, any position or diameter for this cluster would be rather arbitrary. The position given here is from the *Lund Catalogue* (and is actually in Ursa Minor). Collinder [1931, B14] identifies his object 285 as the "U.maj." cluster. His 1900.0 position is 14^h 36.0^m +70° 00′ (for 2000.0, this is 14^h 37.3^m +69° 34′), which he notes is the direction of the actual geometric center of the cluster in space [Collinder 1931, B36) according to Rasmuson [1921]. It is apparently the only cluster for which Collinder gives no diameter. The *Lund Catalogue* also gives no diameter, so none is given here.

Collinder 299 = Harvard 10: See page 133.

Collinder 302 = Antares cluster = C1623-261: The "302" is missing from this entry in the second part of the *Lund Catalogue* alias list (i.e., it currently reads "Antares clster = C1623-261 Collinder").

Collinder 332 = Harvard 16: See Harvard 16 on page 133.

Collinder 345 = C1741-337: This object was at first not obvious on DSS images of the area. Collinder [1931, B38] noted that this was "Not on FAC 62, but on BAP 24.", meaning this was not visible on the Franklin-Adams charts, but was visible on the Barnard [1927] Atlas Plate no. 24. A comparison of that plate (reproduced here as Figure 4.20 on page 124) with the DSS shows that this is in fact an obvious north-south elongated condensation in a Milky Way star cloud. The position, diameter (4.8′), and number of stars (about 30) included in the catalog here were all determined from a 24′ DSS image. The brightest star is TYC 7385 21 1 = GSC 07385-00021, at V = 9.4 (according to SIMBAD), at the south end of the group. Since it is not clear if there is a true cluster, the type is listed as "cl?." The *DSFG1e* also indicates this is "probably not a cluster." The *Lund Catalogue* and *DSFG1e* positions, however, are about 7–8′ too far north.

Collinder 371 = C1814-199: Alister Ling has noted [private communication, 1996] that this cluster (see Figure 4.21 on page 125) is commonly incorrectly called NGC 6595, as in the *Lund Catalogue*. One of us [BA] has determined that the incorrect identification was first made by Collinder [1931, B17], where NGC 6595 is listed as Cr 371. In fact, Cr 371 was apparently a new discovery by Collinder.

However, some of the information given by Collinder is misleading. At his position of (2000.0) 18^h 16.9^m −19° 53′ is only a scattering of stars. Fortunately, also included is a photograph (his plate 9, shown here as Figure 4.22 on page 126) by Barnard, which shows that the cluster *includes* the area of the NGC 6589, NGC 6595 = NGC 6590, IC 1283, and IC 1284 stars and nebulosity. (Collinder's figure caption incorrectly says that "IC 1348" is included). The position for this overall group, measured from the DSS, is (2000.0) 18^h 17^m 16^s −19° 44.5′ (centered on IC

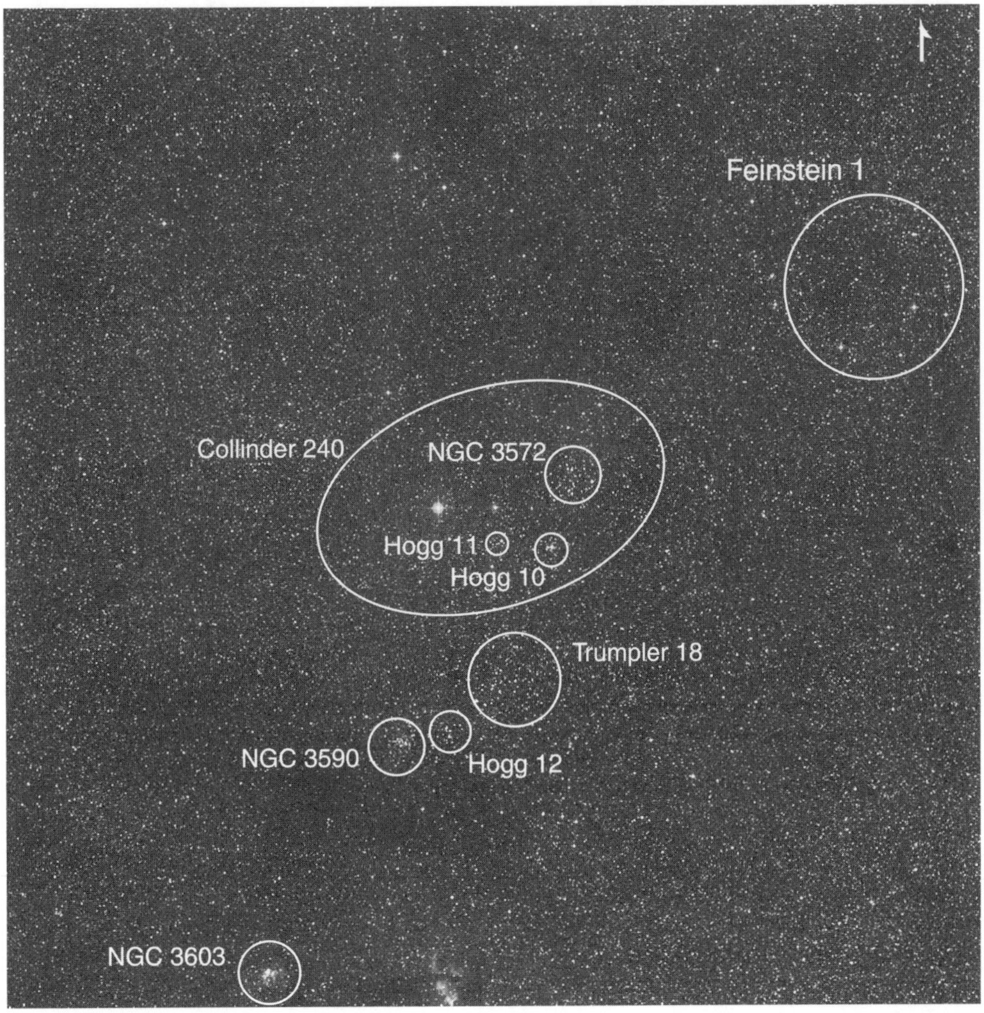

Fig. 4.19 *Collinder 240, a large (32′ x 23′) group covering the center one-third of this 2° image, containing the clusters NGC 3572, Hogg 10, and Hogg 11. The bright star just left of center is y Car. The concentrated group to the right (west) of it and slightly up (north) is NGC 3572. Hogg 10 appears here as a "double star" just south of NGC 3572. Hogg 11 is a tiny cluster (or asterism?) just south of the star between y Car and NGC 3572 (i.e., just east of Hogg 10). Also visible in this image is the large sparse group Feinstein 1 at the upper right, Trumpler 18, the slight condensation of stars just below the Cr 240 group; NGC 3590, the concentrated group just to the east of Trumpler 18; and NGC 3603, the bright nebulous cluster at bottom left. Circles here are for identification only and may not indicate the true cluster's size. DSS-S image © ROE.*

1283, the nebulous star HD 167722). The area covered is roughly 17′ in diameter. This fairly matches Lundmark and Collinder's size estimates of 15′ x 7′ and 16′ x 9′ respectively [ibid.]. The DSS image shows about 20 brighter stars, compared to 10 and 12 for Lundmark and Collinder. The difference in star counts is probably due to the fact that several star images on the Collinder illustration are merged due to overexposure. Used in the catalog here are the *Lund Catalogue* diameter of 20′ and star count of 30.

Regarding the NGC designations in this area, Ling has also pointed out that in the first IC [283] Dreyer corrected the position of NGC 6589 and noted that NGC 6590 = NGC 6595, based on information from Barnard (A.N. 3101). As an interesting aside, Collinder says [1931, B40] that in Dreyer's personal copy of the NGC, then in Lundmark's library, Dreyer had handwritten the correction "NGC 6595 = NGC 6590." It would be interesting to know if Dreyer's copy of the NGC is still extant.

Collinder 399 = C1923+200: This is the famous grouping of stars, also known as "Al Sûfi's Cluster," "Brocchi's Cluster," the "4-5 Vulpeculae Cluster," and the "Coathanger," the latter name due to its quite distinctive appearance (see Figure 4.23 on page 126). This group is a fairly obvious naked-eye object under dark skies, and lies in Vulpecula just northwest of the stars of the constellation of Sagitta.

This was discovered as a nebulous object by the Persian astronomer Al Sûfi (903–986 AD) where it was called (after translation) ". . . a little cloud situated to the north of the two stars of the notch of Vulpecula." [Glyn Jones 1975, pp.

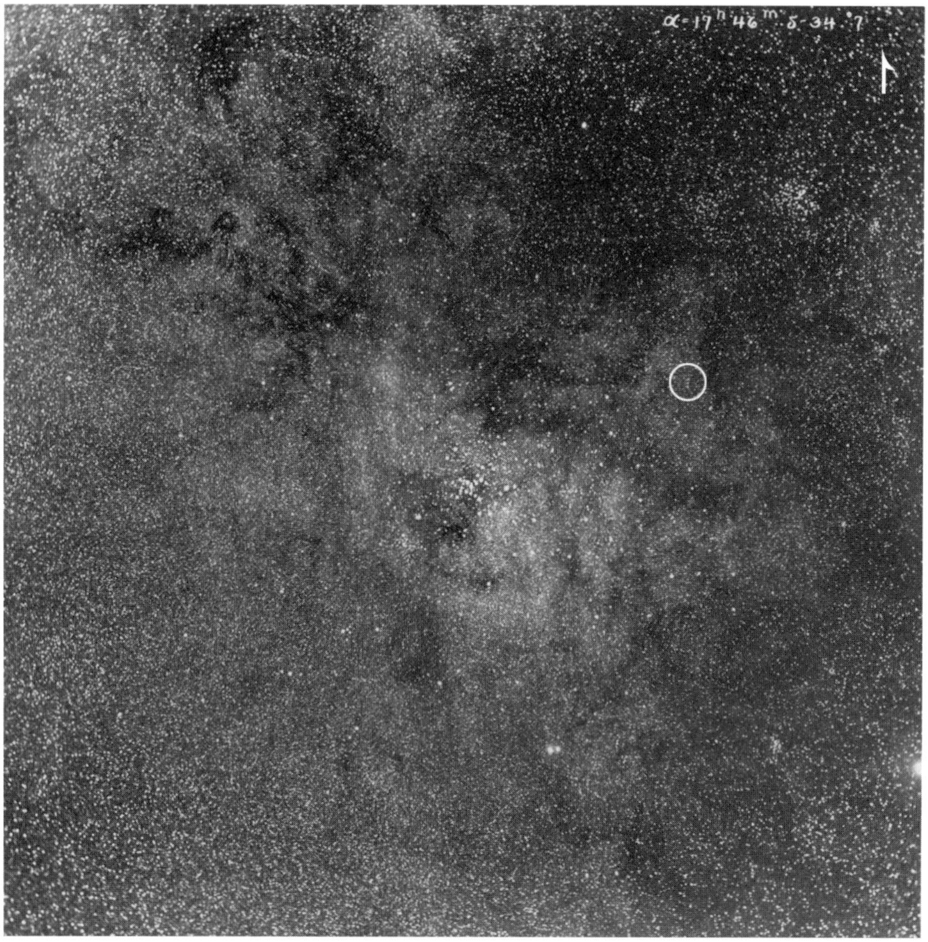

Fig. 4.20 *The region of M 7 (= NGC 6475) in a photo by E. E. Barnard [1927, plate 24] covering an 8° field. M 7 is the rich group at the center, and included in this field are M 6 (= NGC 6405) at upper right, many other open clusters, and Barnard dark nebulae. Barnard discovered a cluster on this image, on the lower left (southeast) side of M 7, which came to be known as Trumpler 30. Collinder discovered a possible cluster on this image, Cr 345, which is shown circled here.*

8-9]. It was also independently discovered by Hodierna [Serio, *et al.*, 1985, 12, 14].

This group has also come to be most commonly known as Collinder 399, based on Collinder's yet one more possible independent discovery and listing of it in his 1931 compilation. In the catalog here we use that name based on its widespread usage and recognition. The Al Sûfi's Cluster name should possibly be used based on historical preference, although the discovery by Al Sûfi was not widely known until Glyn Jones' 1975 publication.

Dalmiro F. Brocchi, who for many years drew the AAVSO charts for variable stars, later independently discovered this grouping at some point during the 1920s or 1930s [Houston 1975]. However, we have been unable to find any publication that explains the circumstances or date of Brocchi's discovery. In any case, his name has also come to be associated with it.

This group has also come to be most commonly known as Collinder 399, based on Collinder's yet one more possible independent discovery and listing of it in his 1931 compilation. In the catalog here we use that name based on its widespread usage and recognition. The Al Sûfi's Cluster name should possibly be used based on historical preference, although the discovery by Al Sûfi's was not widely known until Glyn Jones' 1975 publication.

Brian Skiff has shown [1998a] that by the colors, magnitudes, and proper motions of the involved stars, this object is an apparent asterism rather than a true open cluster. Skiff notes that an earlier paper [Hall and van Landingham 1970] is wrong in considering this a cluster and giving a distance and age. He cites problems in the poor proper motions available at that time and in the photometry reported in that paper.

Since the *Lund Catalogue* was intended to include only true Galactic open clusters, this object should be removed from that catalog.

The very faint and difficult to observe globular cluster Palomar 10 lies quite close to this group.

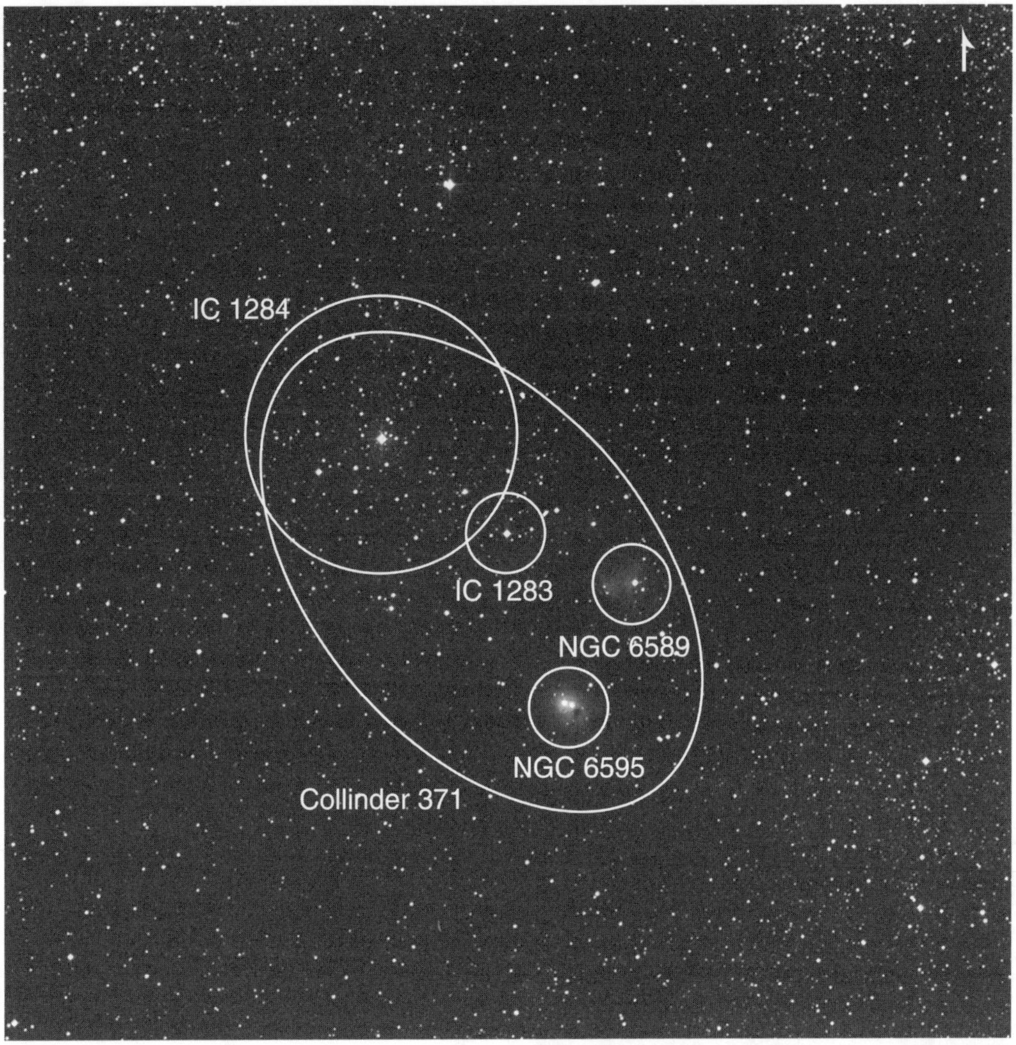

Fig. 4.21 *Collinder 371 is the central group of stars here, including the nebulae NGC 6589, NGC 6595 = NGC 6590, IC 1283, and IC 1284. Of these, only NGC 6595 and NGC 6589 are visible here as a nebulous spot around the double star at bottom center. NGC 6589 is a nebula around the fairly bright star north-northwest of NGC 6595. IC 1283 (not visible here) is a nebula around the star of similar brightness to the northeast of NGC 6595. IC 1284 (not visible here) is a large (15′ or so diameter) nebulosity covering the northeast part of Cr 371. Circles here are for identification only and may not indicate the true object diameter. 45′ field of view DSS-S image © ROE.*

Collinder 416 = C2009 + 264: This is with NGC 6885, see page 187.

Collinder 427 = C2058+679, Collinder 429 = C2059+679, and NGC 7023: NGC 7023 is a large reflection nebula, with a star cluster, Collinder 427, on its west side (see Figure 4.24). Unfortunately the identifications of the nebula and the cluster have often been confused, dating back to Collinder's incorrect cataloging of not one, but *two* clusters in this area. Collinder cataloged a second cluster here, Collinder 429, which he equated with NGC 7023. Unfortunately, there is no cluster in NGC 7023, so Collinder 429 does not exist. NGC 7023 is a William Herschel discovery, H IV.74. Herschel and the NGC ("*7 in eF, eL neby") describe this as a large nebulosity around a 7th magnitude star. Although Herschel mentions there are many stars, there is no indication in either source that there is a star cluster here. This is in fact a reflection nebula (also known as vdB 139), and has no cluster in it at all. Even Collinder says [1931, B43] "... there may be some doubt as to its cl. character, but probably it should be included." He gives no data himself for it, supplying only information from Lundmark. Even if there was a cluster here, it should not be called NGC 7023.

Another problem with Collinder's data is that he gave positions for *both* Collinder 427 and Collinder 429 that were 1 minute of right ascension too far west. The result is that his position for Collinder 429 (which was supposed to fall on the center of NGC 7023) falls precisely on the actual location of the real cluster here, Collinder 427. And Col-

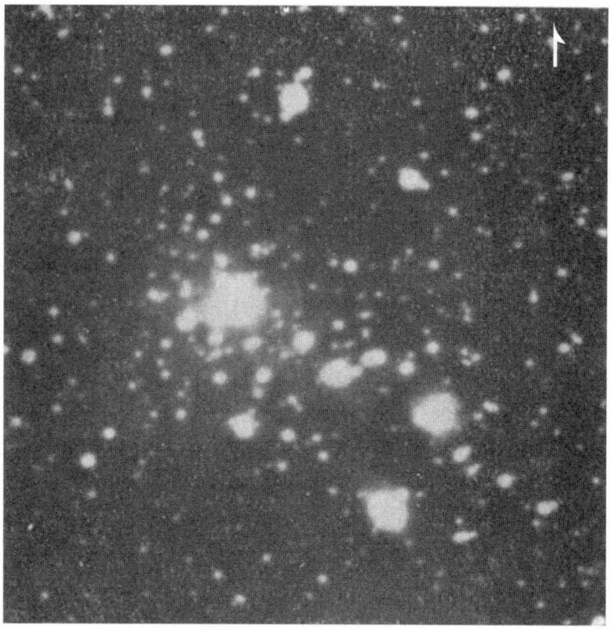

Fig. 4.22 *Collinder 371, as originally shown by Collinder [1931, plate 9] in a reproduction of an unidentified Barnard photo (but probably plate 31 from Barnard [1927], shown on page 139 as Figure 4.43). Compare to Figure 4.21. Here (among the large star images) the large IC 1284 nebulosity on the northeast side of the cluster is visible.*

Fig. 4.23 *"The Coathanger," or more formally, Brocchi's Cluster or Collinder 399. A famous naked-eye grouping in Vulpecula with a distinctive appearance, and recently shown by Brian Skiff to be an asterism. NGC 6802 is on the east (left) end of the group. Approximately 3.5° field of view DSS-N image, stretched using histogram equalization. Image courtesy the Palomar Observatory and Digitized Sky Survey created by the Space Telescope Science Institute, operated by AURA, Inc. for NASA. Reproduced with permission from AURA/STScI.*

Fig. 4.24 *The reflection nebula NGC 7023 (at left) and the scattered cluster Collinder 427 (at center). A supposed cluster of stars in NGC 7023 identified by Collinder, known as Collinder 429, does not appear to exist. 17′ field of view. Image courtesy the Palomar Observatory and Digitized Sky Survey created by the Space Telescope Science Institute, operated by AURA, Inc. for NASA. Reproduced with permission from AURA/STScI.*

linder's position for the real cluster falls 1 minute to the west of it on comparatively empty sky.

So later catalogs have assumed there is a cluster that is part of the NGC object and incorrectly called it NGC 7023, while giving the wrong position for it and the real cluster, Collinder 427. The *Lund Catalogue* in particular has this problem. The *DSFG1e* on the other hand, gives the correct position of the cluster, but incorrectly labels it "NGC 7023" and says "Involved in nebulosity which also carries the same designation." Collinder 427 is involved in the western part of the NGC 7023 nebula, but as indicated, it does not share the NGC name. The RNGC and *NGC 2000.0* also incorrectly list NGC 7023 as a star cluster. Among references examined, only the *Caldwell Catalog* [Moore 1995; O'Meara, 2002] correctly indicates that NGC 7023 is a reflection nebula only. OCISM [Leisawitz 1988] also incorrectly assumes that Collinder 429 is real, and that it is the same as NGC 7023. The data it presents (under its object 50) appears to apply mostly to Collinder 427 and partially to the NGC 7023 nebula.

It should be added that SIMBAD currently indicates "Cl vdB 139" as an alias name for this cluster. This name should be denigrated, as van den Bergh [1966] gives no indication there is a star cluster around his reflection nebula vdB 139 = NGC 7023.

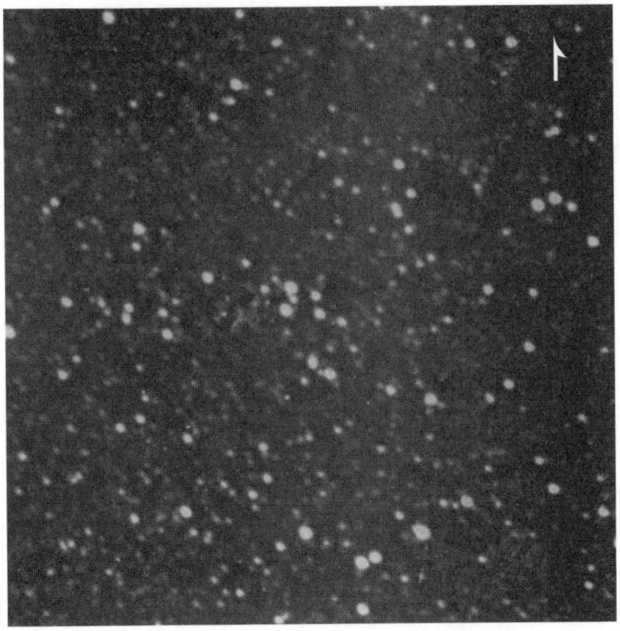

Fig. 4.25 *Collinder 468, as originally shown by Collinder [1931, plate 12] in an approximately 5′ field of view image from Lundmark.*

Collinder 428 = C2101+443: This cluster is on the "west coast" of the North American nebula (NGC 7000). E.g. see the plot of it on the cover of *Uranometria 2000* (first edition), Volume 1. On the DSS, it is overwhelmed by the bright nebulosity of the North American nebula itself. However, its identity was confirmed by comparing a plot of the GSC or (the brighter) USNO A2.0 stars in this region with the image of this cluster on Collinder's [1931] plate 11.

Collinder 467: This is Melotte 72, see page 146.

Collinder 468 = C1803-274: One of us [BA] has positively identified this tiny (55″) group of stars from a photograph by Lundmark [Collinder 1931, plate 12 and shown here as Figure 4.25]. The DSS (shown here as Figure 4.26) shows 7 or 8 stars here, including 5 GSC stars, with perhaps a few fainter stars. The brightest star is TYC 6850-1266-1, listed with V magnitude 11.19. The *Lund Catalogue* indicates a total magnitude of 13.4, which seems too faint and is changed here to 11. From the DSS image it appears likely that this object is nothing but an asterism, so its type is listed as "ast?." Indeed Collinder says [ibid. page B44] "The object is situated in the dense star cloud in Sagittarius. It is not a very good specimen but has been included on account of [its] appearance as forming a beginning of a condensation in the star cloud.

Collinder 470 = C2151+470: Most modern sources appear to identify this cluster as IC 5146 (see Figure 4.27 on page 127). However, there is no mention of a star cluster in

Fig. 4.26 *Collinder 468. This tiny (55″) group of stars was identified by comparison of this image to the original discovery photograph by Lundmark, from Collinder [1931, plate 12]. See Figure 4.25. The group is the small group of 3–4 stars at the center of this image. (The bottom of the image is darker due to this being a DSS image overlap region.) 17′ field of view SkyView/DSS-S image © ROE.*

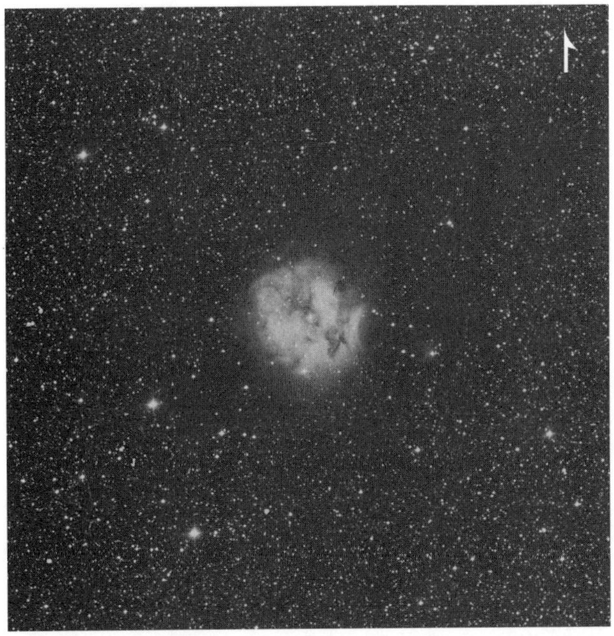

Fig. 4.27 *The Cocoon Nebula or IC 5146, and the involved star cluster Collinder 470. 45′ field of view. Image courtesy the Palomar Observatory and Digitized Sky Survey created by the Space Telescope Science Institute, operated by AURA, Inc. for NASA. Reproduced with permission from AURA/STScI.*

Fig. 4.28 *The nearby galaxy Sh 2-191 = Maffei 1, upon which is superimposed the possible cluster Czernik 11 (circled). In some references the galaxy has been misidentified as nebulosity in the cluster. 17′ field of view. Image courtesy the Palomar Observatory and Digitized Sky Survey created by the Space Telescope Science Institute, operated by AURA, Inc. for NASA. Reproduced with permission from AURA/STScI.*

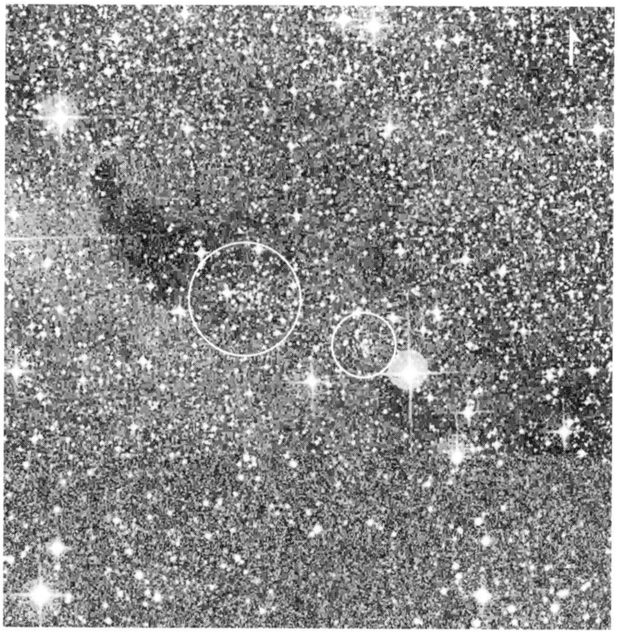

Fig. 4.29 *Danks 1 and 2. These two clusters, discovered in the near-infrared, are faintly visible on this DSS image (stretched using histogram equalization). Danks 1 is the small group just to the upper left of the bright star at right center (HD 114515), and Danks 2 is the group at center, slightly left. 17′ field of view DSS-S image © ROE.*

the IC description, which reads "pB, vL, iF, *9.5 in M." Its independent discoverers, Espin [1900 ("New Nebulae" number 6)] and Wolf [1904], also make no mention of the cluster. In fact IC 5146 is a nebula in Cygnus, now known as the famous "Cocoon Nebula."

The star cluster appears to have been discovered by Collinder, who listed it as his number 470 [1931, B21 and B44]. Unfortunately it was Collinder who incorrectly labeled this cluster IC 5146 (which it is involved with) and the incorrect designation apparently passed on to many later catalogs. The *Lund Catalogue*, *Uranometria 2000.0 (first edition)*, *NGC 2000.0*, and the *DSFG1e* (for example) all fail to indicate the correct designation for the cluster. It has been corrected to Collinder 470 in the catalog here.

Czernik 11 = C0232+594: See Figure 4.28. Brian Skiff has noted [private communication, 1995] that the "nebulosity" supposedly contained in this cluster is in fact the galaxy Maffei 1 (with alternate names: Sh1-137 = Sh2-191 = UGCA 34 = PGC 9892 = IRAS 02329+5926 = GSC 3699-2055 (nonstellar)). Therefore, since the cluster is also very sparse (see Figure 4.28), the Trumpler type should be changed from "I2p n" (i.e., Lyngå's—*Lund Catalogue* reference 320) to "IV2p" (IV2p is also given as an alternate Trumpler type, apparently originating from Ruprecht [1966, 34].) Skiff notes the position of the galaxy and the cluster is (GSC, 2000.0) $02^h\ 36^m\ 35.5^s$ +59° 39′ 18″. The cluster is about 5′ in diameter.

Czernik 28 = King 23 = C0719-008: The preferred name for this object should be Czernik 28, as Czernik discovered it in 1965 as opposed to its rediscovery by King in 1966. So the *Lund Catalogue* incorrectly lists this as King 23. In addition, the minus sign is missing for the declination in the 1950.0 and 2000.0 positions in the main *Lund Catalogue* data file as well as the 1950.0 position in the print file. The correct position, from B. Skiff's [private communication, 1995] measurement on the DSS, is (2000.0) $07^h\ 21.8^m$ –00° 59′. The declination is similarly corrected in the CDS version of February 20, 1995. However, Skiff's position is used here as it is a little better.

Danks 1 = C1309-624: This cluster was listed as cluster number 2, C1309-624, in Danks, *et al.*, [1983]. However, it was named Danks 1 in Lundström and Stenholm [1984].

Although discovered in the near-infrared, this cluster and Danks 2 (see below) are visible on the DSS (see Figure 4.29 on page 128). The positions and diameters given in the catalog here were measured and the number of stars estimated from a DSS image. The star HD 114515 lies adjacent, just to the southwest of this cluster. Danks, *et al.*, [1984] estimate a distance to these apparently young clusters of between 3.3 and 4.6 kpc (4 kpc is used).

Danks 2 = C1310-624: This cluster (see Figure 4.29) was listed as cluster number 1, C1310-624, in Danks, *et al.*, [1983]. However, it was named Danks 2 in Lundström and

Fig. 4.30 *Dejc 1 and NGC 992. Dejc 1, the nearly stellar object at the center of this image, was originally thought to be a Galactic globular cluster, but was later shown to be a galaxy. NGC 992 is the bright galaxy below center. The galaxy at right center is anonymous, having no current entry in either SIMBAD or the NASA Extragalactic Database (NED). It is however listed as the nonstellar object GSC 01222-00806. 17′ field of view. Image courtesy the Palomar Observatory and Digitized Sky Survey created by the Space Telescope Science Institute, operated by AURA, Inc. for NASA. Reproduced with permission from AURA/STScI.*

Stenholm [1984]. See Danks 1 just above for additional information.

This is also the last entry in the *Lund Catalogue* main data file, but is missing entirely from the alias list. It should be added to the Lund alias list as "C1310-624 = Danks 2; Number on Lund disk: 1212."

Dejc 1: This object was announced as a possible intergalactic globular cluster by A. N. Dejc [1963] and "confirmed" as likely to be such an object by Karimova and Kholopov [1963]. Dejc cited this object as being discovered earlier as a possible galaxy in [Pulkova 1955]. In the latter publication is it listed as on plate(**?**) no. 21, near NGC 992, with offsets x = +39′ and y = –10′. The latter coordinates place it 1′ east and 3′ north of NGC 992.

A check of the DSS at this location (see Figure 4.30) shows a tiny, possibly slightly oval object—perhaps an elliptical galaxy, which now has the designation GSC 01222-00294. The GSC coordinates are (2000.0) $02^h\ 37^m\ 28.25^s$ +21° 08′ 31.1″ and the magnitude is 14.45 ±0.40. However, it is listed as a stellar (as opposed to nonstellar) object in the GSC.

This is almost certainly the correct object, as it matches the offset position from NGC 992. It also is a good match for the original position from Dejc (1950.0: $02^h\ 34.6^m$ +20° 56′) (only one other star and a faint, possibly spiral galaxy match this position reasonably well). Further the small size and slight oval shape of the object in the DSS image appears to match the general description by Dejc [1963] and the size measured by Karimova and Kholopov [1963]. The only major discrepancy in this identification is that Karimova and Kholopov indicate (loosely translated) "The diameter of the object equals the diameter of the galaxy NGC 992 (4″ on the first photo, and 6″ on the second), and the brightness is a few times higher than the brightness of NGC 992." On the DSS image, the object is definitely smaller and fainter than NGC 992. Perhaps Dejc 1 is variable in brightness, or even just a variable star and not a galaxy at all? Or perhaps NGC 992 did not show up well on the photographs for some reason.

In any case, Ruprecht, *et al.*, [1981] noted that Dejc 1 is probably an elliptical galaxy, by private communication from Kukarkin. And it is certainly not a Galactic globular cluster, as listed in Hesser and Shawl [1985, 471 and 473].

The identification of Dejc 1 as a galaxy was clinched when B. Wilson [private communication, 1997] noted that this object is listed as a galaxy in the RC3 and *MegaStar*. It is listed there at (2000.0) $02^h\ 37^m$ 27.8s +21° 08′ 25″, with alternate names of MKN 369, CGCG 462-36, II Zw 4, III Zw 50, and PGC 9944. The V magnitude is 15.2 and the diameter is 0.1′. This position and magnitude are quite similar to those from the GSC, as given above. Since the DSS shows only one 15th magnitude object here, clearly these are one and the same object. The GSC position and RC3 magnitude are used in the catalog here.

It should be noted that the various references (mentioned earlier), depending on the transliteration and cluster naming convention in use, label this object Deutsch's object [Karimova and Kholopov 1963], GCL 4, AN (DEJCH) [Ruprecht, *et al.*, 1981, 2563], DEJC, 0234+209 [Hesser and Shawl 1985], Dejc 1, C 0234+209, and Cl Deje 1 [SIMBAD]. The "Deje" name appears to originate via a typographical error in reading the Hesser and Shawl paper.

Dolidze 18 = C0520+332: P. Teutsch [private communication, 2001] has pointed out a refined position for this possible cluster. It appears on the DSS as a roughly 6′ (east-west) by 2.3′ (north-south) rectangular group of about 10 brighter (than the general background) stars, involved on the east side of the IC 410 nebulosity (which includes the cluster NGC 1893). The position of the center of the rough rectangular shape is (2000.0) $05^h\ 24^m\ 09^s$ +33° 23.6′. This is about 5.5′ north of Dolidze's original position.

Dolidze 21 = C0524+070: This should not be confused with Harvard 21, see page 133.

Dolidze 29 = C1828-066: Although listed as "cancelled" in the *Lund Catalogue* alias list, this cluster is still included in the main catalog and its entry should, therefore, be removed.

Fig. 4.31 *The famous Double Cluster, NGC 884 (left) and NGC 869 (right). Approximately 105′ by 79′ field of view. Image courtesy the Palomar Observatory and Digitized Sky Survey created by the Space Telescope Science Institute, operated by AURA, Inc. for NASA. Reproduced with permission from AURA/STScI.*

Dolidze-Dzimselejsvili 1 = C0244+169: Brian Skiff has shown [private communication, 2000] using Tycho-2 catalog proper motions that the 8 stars in this group are not physically related. It is listed as an asterism in the catalog here, using a position, diameter, and brightest V magnitude from Skiff. The brightest star is HD 17334 (V = 8.53, spectral type A0). The total group V magnitude has been computed from the sum of the individual star V magnitudes also extracted by Skiff from the Tycho-2 data.

Dolidze-Dzimselejsvili 8 = C1724+242 : Brian Skiff has shown [Skiff 1994; private communication, 1997] that by the colors, magnitudes, and proper motions of the involved stars, this object is an apparent asterism rather than a true open cluster. The total magnitude, brightest V magnitude, and position given in the catalog here are those measured by Skiff.

Since the *Lund Catalogue* was intended to include only true Galactic open clusters, this object should be removed from that catalog.

Double Cluster: This is the famous pair of clusters, NGC 869 and NGC 884 (see Figure 4.31 on page 130). It is occasionally incorrectly listed (e.g. in the Caldwell Catalog, object 14) as a single cluster, while in fact it clearly consists of two independent open clusters.

These two clusters have also sometimes been known by the names of h and χ Persei respectively. However, quite recently O'Meara and Green [2003] have shown that these identifications are incorrect, having evolved through various confused references since Bayer showed two objects labeled h and χ in his *Uranometria* atlas of 1603. It now appears clear that χ in fact was meant by Bayer to represent the combined light of the two clusters. So χ is the double cluster itself. The identification of what h Persei is remains uncertain, although it seems likely that it is in fact a V = 6.1 magnitude wide (with 1.7′ separation) double star 20′ west of the core of NGC 869. It consists of HD 13854 (V = 6.499) on the north and HD 13841 (V = 7.39) on the south.

EQ 1052+407: This is Shk 1, a galaxy cluster, see page 198.

ESO 93-SC8 (or ESO 093-SC?8): There has been some speculation in the literature that this object is a Galactic globular cluster and for some time its nature was unclear. For example, S. Djorgovski and G. Meylan noted

[1993, p. 333] that this "is probably just a chance grouping of stars."

However, Bica, *et al.* [1999] have obtained high-resolution images and color-magnitude diagrams which show fairly conclusively this is in fact an old (4–5 billion years) open cluster, at a distance of approximately 13.7 kpc in the outer disk of the Milky Way.

ESO 132-SC14: Lauberts [1982] incorrectly associates this name with IC 4291 (see page 138) = Pismis 18. The DSS shows that at the position given is a previously unidentified asterism of 4 or so (not quite resolved) stars, about 30″ in size.

French 1: This is a probable asterism named here for the first time. It is also known as the "Toadstool" asterism due to its distinctive shape (see Figure 4.32). It was first discovered by Susan French [1997, 107], but unfortunately with an incorrect published position. Further information on this object was given by di Cicco [1997]. However, French [private communication, 1997] notes: "[The] position for the Toadstool is correct this time. However, the [published sketch] does not trace it out correctly. It's more obvious to the eye than in the photo, but the bright star [HD 201095] on the extreme right of the inset is part of the cap, and the star next to the galaxy is part of the stem. It's not a stick figure stem as drawn." The position and diameter here are measured from the DSS. NGC 7025 is the galaxy located by the "stem" of the "Toadstool." HD 201095 (V = 9.3), HD 201117 (V = 9.1), and HD 201195 (V = 8.8) are the three brighter stars of this 13′ diameter asterism.

B. Alessi, who independently discovered this group [private communications, 1997] points out that the proper motions of the brightest stars are somewhat similar, so it remains to be determined whether or not this is a physical association of stars or an asterism. The type is listed as "ast?" in this catalog.

Galactic Center: See the "Central Cluster" on page 117.

Graff Cluster or Graff 1: This is IC 4756, see page 140.

Grasdalen 1 or Gr 1 = C1622-243: This is a cluster of stars visible only in the infrared, discovered by Grasdalen, *et al.*, [1973]. It is associated with (inside) the so-called ρ Ophiuchi molecular cloud, and is, therefore, often (in recent professional publications) called the ρ Ophiuchi cluster. However, note that ρ is some distance away in the sky (to the northeast) from the cloud and cluster.

Comeron, *et al.*, [1993] has mapped a total of 91 infrared sources in this cluster (see their figure 1 and list of sources in their table 1). The sources are located in the cloud, which is about 30 arcminutes in length and oriented northwest to southeast. The rough position, number of stars, and size for this object given in the catalog here are derived from the Comeron, *et al.*, information.

Fig. 4.32 *The probable asterism French 1, also known as "The Toadstool." The toadstool figure is outlined as specified by S. French [private communication, 2003]. The galaxy NGC 7025 is on the left side of the group. 30′ field of view. Image courtesy the Palomar Observatory and Digitized Sky Survey created by the Space Telescope Science Institute, operated by AURA, Inc. for NASA. Reproduced with permission from AURA/STScI.*

The *Lund Catalogue* gives a position, diameter, and Trumpler type for this cluster, apparently based on Lyngå's 1983 examination of the POSS. However, this information should be considered incorrect as none of it applies to the real infrared cluster.

Grindlay 1 or Gri 1 = C1728-338: This supposed globular cluster has been shown not to exist. Djorgovski and Meylan note [1993, 333–334] that "Deep CCD and IR imaging by one of us (S.D.), and independently by Grindlay (priv. comm.), and by van Paradijs and Isaacman [1989] failed to reveal any cluster, inconsistent with the original measurement by Grindlay and Hertz [1981]."

[H86] 134 and OGLE-CL SMC0212: The OGLE-CL SMC catalog incorrectly lists *both* its objects no. 0212 and 0213 as [H86] 134. Comparing the Hodge [1986, 1116] figure 3 showing [H86] 134 with those of Pietrzyński, *et al.*, [1998, 259–260] showing the OGLE-CL SMC possible clusters indicates that [H86] 134 is only the eastern of these, i.e., [H86] 134 = OGLE-CL SMC0213.

However, it should be noted that there is an unresolved mystery here, since Hodge's given position for [H86] 134 is substantially off (e.g. about ¾° too far south). The same is true for several other nearby clusters listed by Hodge and the reason is unclear.

h Persei: Although long considered to be the western component (NGC 869) of the Double Cluster, this has recently been shown to be a wide double star about 20′ west of NGC 869. See the entry for the Double Cluster on page 130.

Haffner 16 = Pismis = C0748-253: There is no Pismis cluster number for this object, as this apparently was the first cluster discovered by Pismis. However, Ruprecht, *et al.*, [1981] notes the discovery reference for this cluster is Pismis [1957] as opposed to the discovery reference for the numbered Pismis objects [Pismis 1959]. In any case, the Haffner 16 name has priority of discovery for this particular cluster, so the use of the name "Pismis" should be avoided. This cluster should also not be confused with NGC 2568 = Pismis 1 (see page 167).

Haffner 18 = C0750-262: This is a likely cluster, which Haffner [1957] actually listed separately in parts, as his nos. 18a, 18b, and 18c.

Haffner 24 = C0726-182: Modern references do not consider this to be a true cluster. Even Haffner [1957, 90, footnote 13] called this a "Sehr schwaches Objekt" (very faint object). The position here is from Ruprecht, *et al.*, [1981], updated to 2000.0. The DSS does show a scattered grouping of bright and faint stars at these coordinates.

Haffner 25 = C0746-257 and AH03 J0748.6-2656: B. Skiff, while searching for the cluster Haffner 25, in 1995 located an object matching its description on the DSS at the position (2000.0) $07^h\ 48^m\ 40^s\ -26°\ 56.8$. Haffner 25 was listed at that location in preliminary versions of the catalog here. However, P. Teutsch [private communication, 2002] pointed out that he believed that position was incorrect and that the real Haffner 25 cluster lay at a position of $07^h\ 48^m\ 40^s\ -25°\ 56.8'$. That is precisely 1° to the north of our original position. It turns out that there are similar looking star clusters at *both* positions. The true Haffner 25 cluster is indeed at the position cited by Teutsch, while at the southern position there is a previously unknown possible cluster, which we list here under the name AH03 J0748.6-2656. Its diameter and number of stars have been estimated from the DSS and included in the catalog here.

Harvard 3 = C0845-527: See NGC 2669 on page 168, which this is part of.

Harvard 5, Cr 257, and Hogg 23: The identities associated with and near these objects (see Figure 4.33) are among the most confused of any clusters in the sky. This is due to various errors in position and description by Shapley [1930], Collinder [1931], Hogg [1965], van den Bergh and Hagen [1975], Seggewiss [1971], Lyngå [1987], and the *DSFG1e* [1993].

Harvard 5 = Cr 258 = vdB-Ha 133 = C1226-604: This was discovered by Shapley [1930], who gave a position for

Fig. 4.33 *Harvard 5, Collinder 257, and Hogg 23. The positions and identities of these objects are incorrect in a number of sources. Harvard 5 is the cluster at center, Collinder 257 is an asterism consisting mostly of the double star at lower right, and Hogg 23 is a likely asterism just off the lower left corner of this image (including the star at the lower left edge). 48′ field of view SkyView/DSS-S image © ROE.*

it that was slightly too far east. The correct position as measured from the DSS is given here (2000.0, $12^h\ 27^m\ 16.3s$ $-60°\ 46'\ 44''$). This is the position of HD 108353, the brightest star and at the cluster center. Collinder [1931, B13] indicates his object 258 is the same as Harvard 5, but also gave what turned out to be poor positions for this and his object 257. An examination of the Franklin-Adams chart 19 [by BA], using the relative offset between Collinder's coordinates for Cr 257 and Cr 258 confirms Collinder's identities. This cluster is also no. 74 in Hogg's [1965] list (but should not be called "Hogg 74" as only new clusters in that list received Hogg numbers) where it is incorrectly called Cr 257. One of us [BA] has also noted that the cluster was later discovered again as vdB-Ha 133 = C1224-605. It is incorrectly listed twice in the *Lund Catalogue*, under both the Harvard 5 and vdB-Ha 133 entries. The V magnitude of the brightest star given here is for no. 4 on the south side of the cluster [Seggewiss 1971]. This is actually not the brightest star of the cluster, but the brightest measured star.

Collinder 257: The examination of the Franklin-Adams chart also confirmed that Collinder 257 is *not* Harvard 5 (as the *Lund Catalogue* and other references state). It is instead an asterism consisting of two stars surrounded by several fainter ones. The position given here for Cr 257 is for the NE (and fainter) of these two stars, HD 107978 (the other star is HD 107980). The number of stars given is that cited by Collinder and the diameter is from an estimate from the DSS image. The V magnitude of the star is from Lundmark (via Collinder). Note that no "C" style name has yet been assigned to this cluster.

Hogg 23 = C1226-606: Hogg listed an object no. 75 which was supposed to be identical to Cr 258 but, clearly from Collinder's description and relative positions, is not. Seggewiss suggested this object be called Hogg 23 (the 23rd new object in Hogg's list). A position is given here measured from the DSS and is that of HD 108544. Hogg's original position is about 1^m farther east, at (1900.0, 12^h 23.5^m –60° 22′) 12^h 29.1^m –60° 55′. The object appears to be an asterism. The diameter and number of stars given here are from Hogg.

Surprisingly, *Uranometria 2000.0* (first edition) chart 450 shows all three of these "objects" reasonably well, although the "H5" symbol is plotted too far east (at Shapley's position). The three stars to the west are the real Harvard 5, with the "double' at the center. The group to the south is Hogg 23, and the pair beyond the real Harvard 5 to the SW is Cr 258. α Crucis (Acrux) is only 2° to the south. Therefore, in *Uranometria 2000.0* (first edition) and the *DSFG1e* (charts 428, 429, 450), at least the position of Harvard 5 should be corrected.

Harvard 10 = Collinder 299 = C1615-548: Harvard 10 is the preferred name of this cluster, which the *DSFG1e* (chart 432) lists as Cr 299.

Harvard 16 = Collinder 332 = C1728–368: P. Teutsch has pointed out [private communication, 2002] that at the commonly given (e.g., *Lund Catalogue*) position for Collinder 332 there is no obvious cluster. He suggested that one or the other of two nearby groupings of stars might be the supposed cluster. However, one of us [BA], while examining a DSS image of this region, noticed that the cluster Harvard 16 (in Scorpius) lies only about 15′ north of Collinder's original position for Collinder 332 and matches his description [Collinder, 1931, page B16] quite well. Collinder does not otherwise include any of the Harvard clusters (which were announced in H. Shapley's *Star Clusters* book, published in 1930). So it seems obvious that the Harvard 16 cluster is what he had independently discovered. The catalog here considers these objects to be one and the same. Collinder's poor position seems to have kept this association unknown until now, 73 years after the discovery of this cluster.

Harvard 21 = C2351+614, and Dolidze 21 = C0524+070: Harvard 21 should not be confused with Dolidze 21. Harvard 21 is listed in the second part of the *Lund Catalogue* alias list as "Collinder 458 = C2351+614," and yet in the first part Collinder 458 is listed as equal to Dolidze 21 = C0524+070. Ruprecht, *et al.*, [1981] and even Collinder [1931, B20] also list Harvard 21 = Collinder 458, so apparently it is the listing of Collinder 458 as Dolidze 21 that is incorrect and should be struck from the alias list. The confusion apparently arose as the cluster number is "21" in both cases.

Hogg 8 = C1027-606: Position from DSS for included asterism of 3 stars. This entire group is 1.5′ N-S, and 5′ E-W in extent. There is a bright star (HD 91024, V = 7.61var, B7Iab/Ib) at the W end. The Trumpler type, diameter, and number of stars given here is from Ruprecht, *et al.* [1981]. This is generally not considered a true cluster.

Hogg 9 = C1056-587: The *Lund Catalogue* incorrectly lists this as "globular?" in the alias list. It is not included in the globular cluster list of Djorgovski and Meylan [1993]. The *DSFG1e* (chart 427) notes this is "probably not a cluster" (i.e., it is a probable asterism).

Hogg 10 (C1108-601) and Hogg 11 (C1109-601): The HD identifications of the center stars given here were obtained via the DSS. The positions and brightest star (V) magnitudes are from SIMBAD. Note that for Hogg 11, the brightest star magnitude (8.3) is brighter than the listed total cluster V magnitude of 8.8 from Brian Skiff. Both of these objects are contained in Collinder 240 (see page 120).

Hogg 23: See Harvard 5, *et al.*, on page 132.

[HS66] 51: This is a tiny possible cluster in the LMC, on the NW side of NGC 1731, see page 153.

[HS66] 104: This is a small cluster in the LH 24 portion of the NGC 1845 association, see with NGC 1833, *et al.*, on page 155.

IC 348 = C0341+321 = Gingrich: IC 348 is a nebulous cluster discovered by Safford [1887] (his no. 70), and listed in an appendix to the NGC [Dreyer, 1888, p. 236], and as IC 348. Although the NGC and IC listings make no mention of the cluster, Safford called this "A loose cluster with nebula.."

Curtis [1915] found no evidence of a cluster here while looking for common proper motion stars that might be members of the Hyades. However, in 1922, Gingrich determined through parallax, proper motion, and color studies the existence of the cluster. Gingrich's name also came to be associated with the cluster due to this work.

Collinder [1931], the *Lund Catalogue*, and the DSFG1e give a position that is a little too far north, closer to the bright star, *o* Persei (V = 3.82, B1III). The catalog here gives a position centered on the cluster itself.

Both entries for this cluster in the DSFG1e (charts 94 and 95) fail to note the cluster is involved or associated with nebulosity—although there are separate listings for IC 348 as a bright nebula.

Fig. 4.34 *IC 1023. This sparse group was originally listed as a new discovery in the* Cordoba Durchmusterung *around CoD –35°9596 and was only recently re-identified as such by Brian Skiff. 17′ field of view SkyView/DSS-S image © ROE.*

IC 410: This is the nebulosity around NGC 1893, see page 157.

IC 417: This is the nebulosity around Stock 8, see page 202.

IC 1023: This has been identified by B. Skiff [private communication, 1997] as a group of stars around CoD –35° 9596 (see Figure 4.34 on page 134). Its entry in the IC originates from its entry on and in the CoD (Cordoba Durchmusterung) charts and catalog. The position here is the CoD position, updated to 2000.0 and rounded to 0.1′ precision. The size (4.5′) and number of stars (approximately 18) was measured by one of us [BA] on the DSS. B. Alessi [private communication, 1997] had originally drawn attention to this object, pointing out that it is also listed as ESO 385-SC39.

IC 1310 = C2008 + 347 = Berkeley 50: This cluster was discovered by T. E. Espin [1894] as his object no. 6, although described by him only as a "faint nebulosity." Since he was using a small telescope, this object probably was unresolved for him, similar to several of the other objects he discovered at that time (now known as ICs 1299, 1304-1307, 1310, 1311, 1314, 1363, 1369, 1378, 1400, 1402, 1434, and 1442). There is a faint background nebula here, but this is probably far too faint for Espin to have seen.

Updating his position to 2000.0 shows that it falls precisely on the DSS position of the cluster Berkeley 50, revealing that these objects are the same (see Figure 4.35). The name should be changed from Berkeley 50 to IC 1310 in the *Lund Catalogue*. The *DSFG1e* properly lists this as IC 1310. Both catalogs give positions that are substantially off. Espin's original position (updated to 2000.0) is used in the catalog here.

IC 1311 = C2008+410: The *Lund Catalogue* incorrectly lists this as "globular?" in the alias list. It is not included in the globular cluster list of Djorgovski and Meylan [1993]. In addition the *Lund Catalogue* position is off by 5′. A position measured from the DSS is given in the catalog here and essentially matches that given in the *DSFG1e*.

IC 1396 = C2137+572: Trumpler [1930] mistakenly considered this a previously unknown cluster (his "An. 37") and it became known as Tr 37. Some later authors (e.g. Markarian [1951] as Mrk 47), therefore, incorrectly list it under this designation.

IC 1590 = C0049+563: NGC 281 is incorrectly listed in the *Lund Catalogue* as a cluster and identical to IC 1590. NGC 281 was a Barnard discovery and is the nebula associated with IC 1590, a later Bigourdan discovery. In any case, Bigourdan [1899–1917] clearly stated these two were not the same object. Therefore, the correct name for the cluster is IC 1590, and the NGC 281 designation should be dropped from the *Lund Catalogue* alias list (unless noted that it is only the nebulosity). The *DSFG1e* (chart 36) incorrectly lists *both* NGC 281 and IC 1590 as clusters. The NGC 281 entry should be renamed to IC 1590 (with a comment added that the nebulosity is NGC 281), and the current IC 1590 cluster entry should be deleted. *Sky Catalogue 2000.0* vol. 2 also incorrectly lists NGC 281 as a cluster. Its entry for NGC 281 should also be renamed to IC 1590. H. Corwin [private communication, 2002] also notes that NGC 281 is probably also the same nebula as IC 11.

IC 1805 = C0229+612: This is the preferred name of this cluster, which the *DSFG1e* (charts 17, 37, 38) lists as Melotte 15—although it is listed separately in the *DSFG1e* as a bright nebula. The position given here is from Skiff, who has noted that the center star is HD 15558 at (SIMBAD value) V = 7.86. A check via SkyView/DSS shows his position and identification to be correct, and that this is the brightest star of the cluster. Therefore, the *Lund Catalogue* magnitude for the brightest star (V = 9.0) is incorrect.

IC 1848 = Collinder 32 = Collinder 33, and Collinder 34: IC 1848 = C0255+602 = Collinder 32 is a star cluster centered on the star BD+59° 552 = HD 17505 (V = 7.10, O6e, SIMBAD), and is the main cluster of a large nebular complex in Cassiopeia (see Figure 4.36). It is listed in the Second IC as a discovery by E. E. Barnard, apparently via private communication from Barnard to J. L. E. Dreyer. After Barnard's death, a beautiful photograph of

Fig. 4.35 *IC 1310 = Berkeley 50. Our work shows that this object, described by Espin in 1894 as a "faint nebulosity," is the same object as the cluster Berkeley 50, independently discovered in the early 1960's. 17′ field of view. Image courtesy the Palomar Observatory and Digitized Sky Survey created by the Space Telescope Science Institute, operated by AURA, Inc. for NASA. Reproduced with permission from AURA/STScI.*

Fig. 4.36 *IC 1848, a sparse open cluster, involved in nebulosity of the same name. 45′ field of view. Image courtesy the Palomar Observatory and Digitized Sky Survey created by the Space Telescope Science Institute, operated by AURA, Inc. for NASA. Reproduced with permission from AURA/STScI.*

Fig. 4.37 *The "IC 1848 complex," including the cluster IC 1848 on the right center, and the possible cluster Cr 34 at left center. Cr 34 was discovered by, and this photo is by, E.E. Barnard [1927, plate 2], showing an approximately 8.7° field.*

Fig. 4.38 *IC 1848 and Collinder 34. This pair of clusters is as shown on the photograph Collinder used to identify them [1931, plate 2], which had been reproduced from Barnard [1927, plate 2] (shown here as* ***Figure 4.37****). Approximately 1.5° field of view image. Collinder listed IC 1848 as Collinder 32, but also mistakenly listed it again as Collinder 33.*

this region was included in Barnard's (and Calvert's) 1927 *A Photographic Atlas of Selected Regions of the Milky Way*. This appears as Atlas Plate 2, shown here as Figure 4.37. The description there reads: "In the center of this plate are a number of clusters, or masses of brighter stars with many smaller ones, covering nearly 2° in right ascension. This whole group is immersed in a bed of very feeble nebulosity which seems to conform in extent and position with the two or three groupings of stars, but it is really greater in all directions. Although the nebulosity covers their full extent, it more strongly affects the western portion. There seem to be only one or two places in which it condenses about the individual stars." The "western portion" here is in fact the nebulous cluster IC 1848, while the rest of this complex could be considered as having one or more additional clusters, as Barnard notes.

Four years later, in 1931, Collinder cataloged three objects in this region, including his IC 1848 = Cr 32, and Cr 33 (= C0255+602) and Cr 34 (= C0257+602). One might reasonably assume that the two additional clusters are simply the other possible groups that Barnard discussed, and that may have partially been what Collinder intended. However, until now, the precise identities of Cr 33 and Cr 34 have not been particularly clear. Since Collinder's listing of these supposed clusters, all catalogs and atlases mentioning or showing them have been ambiguous as to their position and nature. Most references have chosen to assume that Cr 33 and Cr 34 are the same object, a possible star cluster involved in nebulosity at the eastern end of the "IC 1848 complex." The *Lund Catalogue* in its alias list indicates that Cr 33 contains Cr 34, while noting that the existence of both clusters was considered doubtful by Alter, *et al.*, [1970]. Indeed, Collinder gives positions and diameters for Cr 33 and Cr 34 that are quite similar, so it would be easy to assume they are either part of each other, or the same object.

However, a careful reading of Collinder's descriptions of Cr 32, 33, and 34 [Collinder 1931, B24-B24] will reveal the true identities of these groups. Collinder lists Cr 32 *and* Cr 33 as including the *same* bright star, BD+59° 552. There are also similarities in the descriptions, sizes, total magnitudes, etc. between these two clusters. He also shows a photograph of Cr 32–34 on his plate 2, shown here as Figure 4.38 on page 135. This is marked a "Barnard photo", and appears to be a reproduction (with south at the top) of part of Barnard's plate. Yet, there are still only two truly obvious groups here, the IC 1848 cluster on the west, and the less condensed grouping on the east. Therefore, Collinder's position for Cr 33 notwithstanding, it appears that IC 1848 = Cr 32 is the same cluster as Cr 33. One can only speculate that Collinder investigated the IC 1848 cluster at a different time than when he worked on the "Cr 33" and Cr 34 clusters, never noticing the similarities—particularly since he had somehow erroneously derived a position for Cr 33 substantially to the east of IC 1848.

Fig. 4.39 *The sparse clusters IC 2156 and IC 2157. Although not well differentiated here from the background Milky Way, IC 2157 is the group at lower center, while IC 2156 is the group at upper center. 17′ field of view. Image courtesy the Palomar Observatory and Digitized Sky Survey created by the Space Telescope Science Institute, operated by AURA, Inc. for NASA. Reproduced with permission from AURA/STScI.*

As to Cr 34, this can continue to be assumed to be the loose group of stars in the eastern end of the "IC 1848 complex"—apparently the group Collinder had in mind. On the DSS though, except for the nebulosity involved, this particular group does not stand out, so the possibility certainly exists that there is no cluster here at all. It is listed here with type "cl?."

To summarize, IC 1848 is *both* Cr 32 *and* Cr 33, a cluster in the western end of this complex. Cr 34 is a possible (but not proven) cluster in the eastern end of this complex. Barnard essentially discovered both.

IC 2111: This is the nebula in the northern part of NGC 1722, see page 152.

IC 2114: This is the nebula associated with NGC 1748, near NGC 1737, see page 153.

IC 2156 and IC 2157: Although IC 2157 is often listed in star cluster catalogs, no modern references appear to exist for IC 2156. By their IC coordinates these objects are close in the sky, so one of us [BA] has undertaken an investigation as to their precise identity.

IC 2156 was originally listed as "New Nebulae" no. 1 in Espin, T. E. [1900, 141]. It is given as at (1855 Jan. 11) $5^h\ 55^m\ 56^s$ +24° 09′, with remark "coarse cluster, a nebulous object on photographic plate." IC 2157 is object no. 2, at (same date) $5^h\ 55^m\ 59^s$ +24° 02′, with remark "Cl., triangular in shape, stars 9.5–14." These positions update to (2000.0):

IC 2156 $06^h\ 04^m\ 48^s$ +24° 09′
IC 2157 $06^h\ 04^m\ 51^s$ +24° 02′

A SkyView/DSS image shows a single brighter star (GSC 1864-0561) right on the IC 2157 position, with a scattering of bright stars over a 4′ diameter to the north. There is also a band of fainter stars stretching to the northwest. Any triangular shape is not obvious, but there is a big range of brightness in the stars as Espin's "9.4–14" implies. B. Skiff gives a position (from the DSS) for this cluster of $06^h\ 04^m\ 47^s$+24° 04.3′. This is fairly good if one includes some of the stars to the northwest. If only the brighter 4′ group is included, one obtains a position of $06^h\ 04^m\ 49.8^s$ +24° 03′ 21″ for a brighter center star (GSC 1864-00819).

Only about ½′ northeast of Espin's IC 2156 position (and 6′ to the north of the position just given) is a group of 5 stars, which probably would look nebulous on a low-resolution photograph. However, this does not quite match Espin's description of "coarse." Examining the DSS image again shows that there is a slight concentration of stars around this smaller group. There are about 40 stars total (of which about 15 stand out) in a 3.5′ diameter. A good position, the brightest (northeast) star of the central clump, is (2000.0) $06^h\ 04^m\ 50.6^s$ +24° 09′ 37″.

So it would appear that along with the fairly well known IC 2157, there is an asterism or possible separate cluster just to the north—which is IC 2156.

IC 2172 = NGC 2282 = BFS 54: This is nebulosity around Cl vdB 85, see page 118.

IC 2391 = C0838-528: Just to the North of the V = 1.95 star δ Vel is a small, hazy patch of light surrounding the star o Velorum. A small pair of binoculars or RFT will show a rather nice cluster, IC 2391. With larger instruments the effect is lost, because the cluster is not actually that rich. Because of its southerly location, it was not seriously studied until the mid-1960s. Perry and Hill [1969] carried out multicolor photometry on 42 stars in the area, and in conjunction with an analysis of previous data, concluded that IC 2391 had a membership of about 25 stars and lay at an unreddened distance of 0.15kpc; an age of about 30 million years was derived. The few more recent studies have not added anything else of great significance to this analysis, however, Jones and Page [1991] have reported the detection of 10 flare stars in the region of this grouping. About 1° east of IC 2391 is the much smaller and fainter grouping NGC 2669 (including Harvard 3). Of greater interest is the discovery by Eggen [1991] that IC 2391 is actually the core of a supercluster of stars, the members of which have at least 95% of their space motion directed toward R.A. $05^h\ 82^m$, Dec. −12° 44′. In addition to the stars in IC 2391, 63

Fig. 4.40 *The impressive cluster IC 2391, including o Velorum as its brightest star. The lines and darker area on the upper part of the image are artifacts from the original UK Schmidt plate. 2° field of view DSS-S image © ROE.*

field stars have been found to belong to the supercluster; included among these are RS CVn. The latter star is an eclipsing binary which is also variable because of the presence of large "starspots," (analogous to sunspots on the surface of the brighter component). Also included are α Pic and β Leo (which were discovered by IRAS to be involved with particulate discs) and β CMi (an unstable Be star with light variations of about 0.1 mag.). o Vel itself is involved in an expanding shell and is a Wolf-Rayet variable with a visual range of about 0.1 mag. over a period of about 2.779 days [Kholopov, *et al.* 1998]. Like the Pleiades supercluster the IC 2391 cluster appears to contain stars of two discrete ages, in this case 80 and 250 million years.

IC 2395 (C0839-480) = vdB-Ha 47 (C0841-479) = Lac III-3: One of us [BA] has determined that the IC 2395 and vdB-Ha identifications are clearly for the same object (see Figure 4.41). Both Bailey's (in the IC) and the vdB-Ha positions are fairly good, but are substantially different from the incorrect *Lund Catalogue* position for IC 2395. Skiff [private communication, 1995] gives a correct position, derived from a DSS examination, of (2000.0) $08^h\ 42^m\ 31^s$, −48° 06.5′. Jenni Kay [private communication, 1995] has confirmed the visual appearance of IC 2395 = vdB-Ha 47, and further confirmed there is nothing at the *Lund Catalogue* IC 2395 position. The *Lund Catalogue* diameter for vdB-Ha 47 (from vdB-Ha) is slightly off as it should read 13′ (instead of 12′). The *DSFG1e* (chart 397) also incorrectly lists both IC 2395 and vdB-Ha 47. The vdB-Ha 47

Fig. 4.41 *The cluster IC 2395, identified here for the first time as the same cluster as vdB-Ha 47, and (by Brian Skiff) as Lacaille's class III, number 3 object. 30′ field of view DSS-S image © ROE.*

Fig. 4.42 *IC 2602, whose brightest star is θ Carinae, at V=2.78. The stars in the southern portion of IC 2602 form the more distant cluster Melotte 101. This is a contrast enhanced view of approximately 2° field of view DSS-S image. © ROE.*

entry should be deleted, and the position and size of IC 2395 should be corrected as above.

Brian Skiff [private communication, 1998] has independently noted that IC 2395 is also unambiguously Lacaille's class 3, number 3 object (Lacaille star no. 3492). This identification of Lac III-3 has apparently not been made by previous researchers of Lacaille's work (e.g. Gingerich 1960; Glyn Jones 1975; Evans 1992). Gingerich and Glyn Jones apparently noted the equivalence with the brightest star of the cluster, GC 11988 (= HX Vel = HD 74455, V = 5.5) but for some reason did not realize the cluster IC 2395 was here. Perhaps they were relying on a poor cluster position that has only finally been corrected here.

IC 2602 = C1041-641: In the southernmost part of the Milky Way in Carina can be found the large, bright open cluster IC 2602, a fine object for binoculars or an RFT with over 30 stars visible (see Figure 4.42). It is centered on the V = 2.78 star θ Carinae, which is of type B0V. Photoelectric photometry of stars in IC 2602 by Braes [1961] and Whiteoak [1961] found that the cluster was fairly near, at a distance of about 0.15kpc, and also fairly poorly populated; the study made by Whiteoak found 29 probable and 40 possible members. From the estimated age and distance of IC 2602, Whiteoak also made the suggestion that the cluster was a local condensation in the extensive Sco-Cen Association. A subsequent investigation, by Hill and Perry [1969], confirmed many of the earlier findings, particularly the distance, and showed that the cluster has a minimum membership of 31 stars. However, a discrepancy was found concerning the age of the stars within the group which suggested that star formation was not coeval, but had occurred over a period of at least 16 million years. A small telescope will show a small, hazy patch among the stars in the southern part of IC 2602; this is the more distant cluster Mel 101.

IC 2944 = Frost 789: See Collinder 249 on page 120.

IC 2948 = Frost 790: This is not a cluster, but the nebulosity near the cluster C1134-627 = Cr 249, and nebula IC 2944. Since it is not a cluster, the use of the name C1136-632 (as in the *Lund Catalogue*) for this object should be avoided. The position and diameter given here are measured from a DSS image.

IC 4291 = C1333-619: The *Lund Catalogue* and the *DSFG1e* incorrectly call this Pismis 18. It should be known as IC 4291 by discovery priority. R. Innes's (IC) discovery position [Gill 1902] has been confirmed. The original Pismis 18 position is a little too far southwest, but the diameter and number of stars make it clear this is the correct object. This is also ESO 132-SC 15, although it is *not* ESO 132-SC 14 (see page 131), as the ESO incorrectly indicates. In any case, the name should be changed appropriately in the *Lund Catalogue* files, the *DSFG1e*, and *Uranometria 2000.0* (first edition).

In addition, the *DSFG1e* comment "Probably not a cluster" appears incorrect (and is not used in the catalog here), as the DSS shows this to be a relatively rich obvious star cluster.

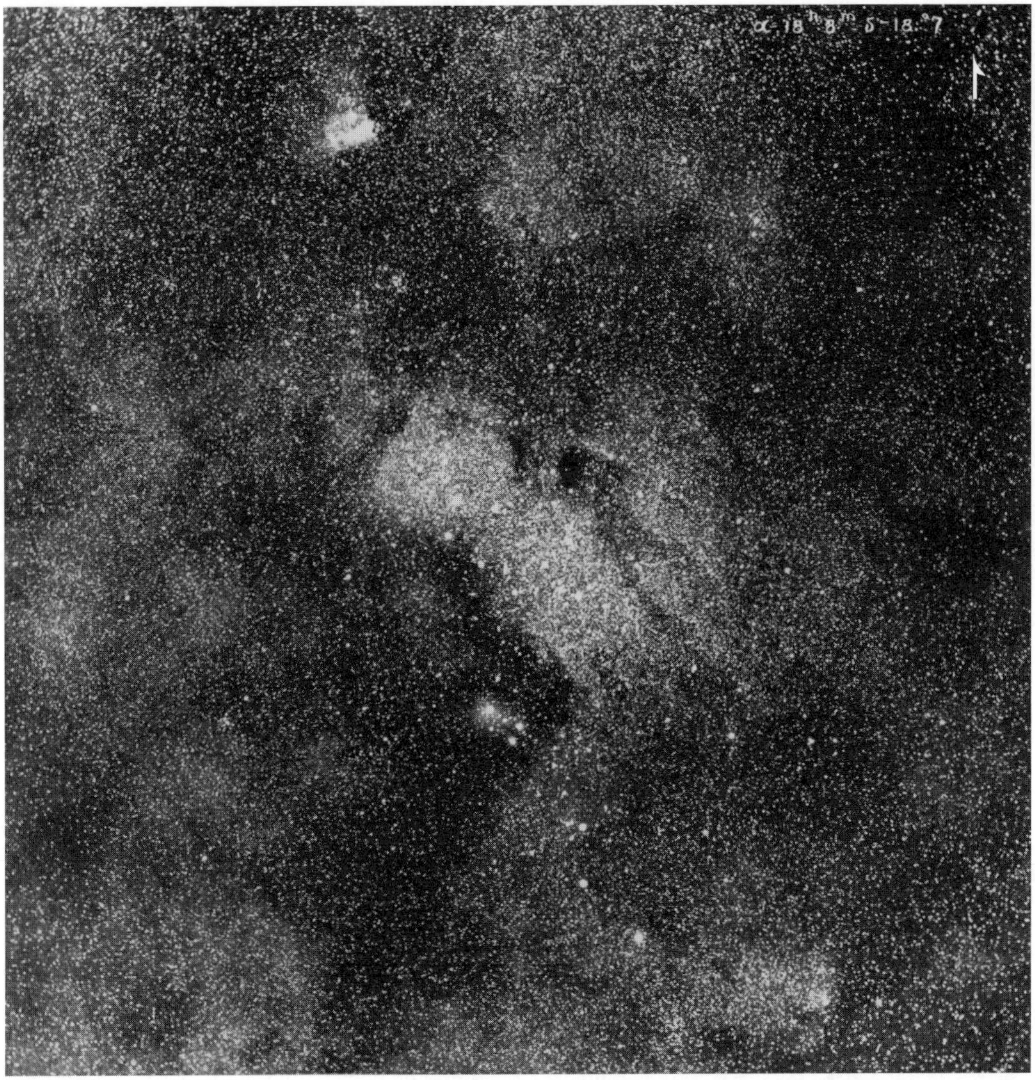

Fig. 4.43 *The Small Sagittarius Star Cloud, IC 4715, better known as M 24, one of the most spectacular areas of the Sagittarius Milky Way. The image here is from Barnard [1927, plate 31], covering an approximate 6.4° field of view. NGC 6603, a cluster in M 24 is visible as the small bright spot at the bottom of the upper left part of M 24. The two obvious dark nebulae on the north side of M 24 are B 93 (left) and B 92 (right). B 307 is the smaller dark nebula to the left of B 93, and B 304 is the dark nebula which streams down in two places to the lower right of B 92. B 297 is the large dark nebula at the right center edge of this photo. The obvious bright patch at upper left is NGC 6618 = M 17, while the smaller bright patch between it and M 24 is NGC 6613 = M 18.*

IC 4651 = C1720-499: van den Bergh and Hagen [1975, 15] list this as their number 224, but incorrectly indicate this is IC 4451.

IC 4665 = C1743+057: IC 4665 is a large (>40′) but rather obscure open cluster which lies just north, and slightly east of the V = 2.77 star β Oph (see Figure 4.44 on page 140). It is of interest for several reasons but mostly because it lies at a relatively large distance from the Galactic plane (+17°) and has also appeared to be fairly young, about 30–40 million years old, thus representing a link between the older clusters (such as the Pleiades and Hyades) and the very young associations. Hogg and Kron [1955] carried out multicolor photometry of stars in the cluster down to V = 11.58 and derived a distance of 0.43 kpc. The first comprehensive membership survey, by proper motion measurement, was carried out by Vasilevskis [1955]; among the stars in the vicinity brighter than V = 11.0, he found 26 probable and 18 possible members. Some early studies suggested that IC 4665 might have an unusually large population of spectroscopic binaries, but this result has now been discounted. A combined astrometric, photometric and spectroscopic program has been presented by Prosser [1993] who found more than 50 new proper motion/photometric candidate members, and from among a sample of fainter photometric candidates, 23 M dwarfs

Fig. 4.44 *IC 4665, a large (~70′ in diameter) open cluster north and slightly east of β Ophiuchi. 3.9° field of view. Image courtesy the Palomar Observatory and Digitized Sky Survey created by the Space Telescope Science Institute, operated by AURA, Inc. for NASA. Reproduced with permission from AURA/STScI.*

Fig. 4.45 *IC 4725 = M 25, a moderately rich cluster spread over a diameter of about 26′, shown here in a histogram equalization display of a 1° field of view DSS-S image. © ROE.*

with Hα emission. A reanalysis of the age of the cluster, using different methods, yielded conflicting results but rather suggests an age nearer to that of the Pleiades.

IC 4715 = M 24: This is a large Milky Way star cloud (the "Small Sagittarius Star Cloud") which contains the star cluster NGC 6603 and the dark nebulae B 92, B 93, B 304, and B 307 (see Figure 4.43). The position ($18^h17.0^m$ −18° 36′) is a rough estimate from the DSS, where the cloud appears to be about 120′ long by 60′ wide, oriented SW to NE. This agrees with the 2° size given in the catalog here, as given and shown by Barnard [1927, plate and chart 31]. The total magnitude is from O'Meara [1998]. Many references (the *Lund Catalogue*) incorrectly indicate that M 24 and NGC 6603 are one and the same object.

The identity of M 24 with IC 4715 does not appear to have been widely known until recently. The first modern use of it (since the Second IC was published in 1908) appears to have originated on the *Millennium Star Atlas* [Sinnott, *et al.,* 1997], chart 1368.

IC 4725 = M 25 = C1828-192: The Trumpler type ("I3m") estimated by Lyngåin the *Lund Catalogue* appears to be incorrect. This cluster is in no way "strongly detached" (type "I") from its surroundings (see Figure 4.45 on page 140). A better estimate (by one of us [BA] from the DSS) would be "III3m" and is used here. Trumpler himself [1930] gave "IV3r."

IC 4756 = C1836+054: This cluster is also known as the "Graff cluster" or "Graff 1," since it was independently discovered by Graff [1922]. Unfortunately over the years there have been a number of mistakes made in various sources when referring to this cluster.

For example, Collinder [1931], apparently understood that these objects were the same since he only included IC 4756 (= Cr 386) in his catalog. However, he did not explicitly note the equivalence, and in his notes section under Cr 386 he cites the wrong paper by Graff. Further, the position of the cluster given in the title of Graff's paper (which is listed, but not cited) is garbled (serendipitously for one of us—see "Archinal 1" on page 113).

These errors may have led Alter, *et al.*, [1958] to list the Graff cluster as a separate object. Later Supplements to the Alter, *et al.*, work continued this error.

The error was corrected in the Alter, *et al.*, [1970] and Ruprecht, *et al.*, [1981] compilations, where "ANON (Graff)" was listed as an alias name for IC 4756. (Although the name is incorrectly given in Ruprecht, *et al.*, 1981 as "IC 4656," at least in the machine readable version.)

The 1987 *Lund Catalogue* alias list is correct in listing the "Graff cluster" as an alias for IC 4756. Unfortunately the overall problem is re-introduced again since Graff 1 = C1832+051 is also listed as a separate cluster. This is still definitely the same object as IC 4756, since the same position is given as that given for the incorrect entry for the Graff cluster in Alter, *et al.*, [1958]. The separate entry for Graff 1 should be removed from all the *Lund Catalogue* files. The 5′ diameter cited in the *Lund Catalogue*, with Collinder [1931] given as a reference, also appears to be spurious. There is no indication by Collinder that this is a 5′ diameter cluster.

IC 4802: Harold Corwin has determined that this is a clump of stars just northeast of the nucleus of the Galactic globular cluster NGC 6717 = Palomar 9. For more information on this identification, see the Extended Notes entry for NGC 6717 in Chapter 7 (page 232). The position and diameter (0.2′) given have been measured from the DSS.

IC 5146 = Cederblad 198: This is the Cocoon Nebula, which is associated with the star cluster Collinder 470, see page 127.

Iskudarian 1 = C1846+368: This cluster, alternately transliterated to the name Iskudarjan 1, was postulated by Iskudarian and Saakian [1961] as a possible cluster of white dwarf stars in Lyra. They suggest it consists of 26 stars, with V(?) magnitudes of 15.8 to 20.2, spread over an area of 2° by 1°. The *Lund Catalogue* position for this is retained here, as it approximately matches Iskudarian and Saakian's position. However, the Lund's diameter of 110′ appears to be incorrect—a value of 120′ is used here.

On the surface, the physical existence of a cluster of white dwarf stars seems unlikely, but it is not clear if sufficient research was done on these stars to demonstrate its existence. Clearly due to its size, faintness, and the existence of much brighter field stars, this object cannot be "observed" (visually) in the way that a normal star cluster can.

Isserstedt 690: This is a "stellar ring," apparently associated with the cluster Trumpler 32, see page 206.

Kemble 1: This is "Kemble's Cascade" or "the Kemble Cascade," so named by W. S. Houston [1980 and 1985] after the late Fr. Lucian J. Kemble. This apparent asterism is an impressive 3° long chain of some 20 stars (mostly HD stars), running NW to SE (see Figure 4.46). The brightest and center star is HD 24479 (V = 4.96). The cluster NGC 1502 lies just north of the SE end of this chain. Czernik 17 lies about 1° to the south. Houston [1980] quotes Kemble as describing this in 7 x 35 binoculars as "a beautiful cascade of faint stars tumbling from the northeast down to the open cluster NGC 1502." It appears obvious on the lower left of *Uranometria 2000.0* (first edition) chart 18.

Kemble 2 = Alessi J18350+7223: This apparent asterism has come to be known as "Mini-Cassiopeia" due to its likeness to the constellation (see Figure 4.47). Fr. L. Kemble wrote to Arild Moland (formerly Arild Mikalsen) on August 31, 1994, describing his discovery:

> Do you want something really neat to observe? Yesterday, as I was preparing my night's observing, I was checking out some stuff on page 30 of *Uranometria*, I noticed a won-

Fig. 4.46 *Kemble 1, better known as "Kemble's Cascade." NGC 1502 is the small (at this image scale) cluster just northeast of the east (left) end of the chain of stars. Approximately 220′ by 135′ field of view. Joints between DSS overlap areas are visible. Image courtesy the Palomar Observatory and Digitized Sky Survey created by the Space Telescope Science Institute, operated by AURA, Inc. for NASA. Reproduced with permission from AURA/STScI.*

Fig. 4.47 *The probable asterism Kemble 2, also known as the "Mini-Cassiopeia" due to its shape. 36′ field of view. Image courtesy the Palomar Observatory and Digitized Sky Survey created by the Space Telescope Science Institute, operated by AURA, Inc. for NASA. Reproduced with permission from AURA/STScI.*

derful cluster of bright stars in Draco centered at about R.A. 18 35, Dec. +72 24. Within my 100x, 24′ field, there are 7 stars of 6–8 mag, and a number of fainter ones. Very charming asterism [my research so far indicates it is not a true Open Cluster]. High enough for your skies.

The brackets in the above quote are Kemble's [private communication, Moland 2000]. Kemble also provided a *MegaStar* chart of the stars of his discovery. In a reply dated September 21, 1994, Arild gave this group the "Mini Cassiopeia" nickname:

By the way, the asterism in Draco you've mentioned and charted for me, really caught my eye (at least on paper, as I haven't had a chance to see it for real yet) as quite a Cassiopeia in miniature. Save for the 8 mag star close to the center of the field on that map you sent me, the other brighter stars form something conspicuously similar to that all-too familiar constellation.

Kemble first wrote about this object in (a possibly unpublished?) article [Kemble, 1995] about clusters and asterisms in Draco. He mentions there that the cluster was independently named "Mini Cassiopeia" by a third unnamed person.

Independently of all this, Bruno Alessi, a Brazilian amateur astronomer, also discovered this same asterism on star plots (with the HyperSky program), and reported it to one of us [private communication, 1997]. The connection to the prior discovery by Kemble was made after examining information on star clusters on a web site maintained by M. Steine, and receiving further information from Steine and Moland on this object.

Both the "Kemble 2" and the "Alessi J18350+7223" names appear here in print for the first time.

P. Teutsch, after reviewing a partial draft of this book, has also reported [private communication, 2001] his independent discovery of this group, while observing the area visually at 70 power with a Celestron 8 telescope, on July 30, 1992.

King 22 = Berkeley 18: see page 115.

King 23 = C0719-008 = Czernik 28: see page 128.

King 25 = C1922+136: The "OCl 106" identity for this object is missing from the *Lund Catalogue* alias list.

KMHK 171 = BRHT 1a: This is either a separate star cluster or a portion of a star cluster, but either way the southern portion of NGC 1722, see page 152.

KMHK 173 = BRHT 1b: This is a possible LMC cluster in the nebula IC 2111, and the northern part of NGC 1722, see page 152.

KMHK 211 and KMHK 212: These are clumps of stars in NGC 1731, see page 153.

KMHK 878: This is a very faint LMC cluster that has been confused with NGC 1947, see page 158.

KMHK 1131: This is a possible cluster in the LMC association NGC 2042, see page 160.

KMHK 1260: This is *not* NGC 2094, see page 161.

Kodaira 1 = C1812-121: This supposed Galactic globular cluster apparently does not exist, at least as a cluster. Djorgovski and Meylan [1993, 334] note "It was only suggested as an obscured globular in a brief IAU Circular note. Deep CCD and IR imaging by one of us (S.D.) failed to reveal any cluster at the published coordinates." Kodaira, *et al.*, [1995] have now shown that this object is likely a star of spectral type M 5-8 III that is heavily reddened by (an E(V-K) of) approximately 7 to 8 magnitudes.

Latyshev 1: This is a possible moving cluster of only five stars, first suggested by Latyshev [1972]. It was identified by considering the space motion of several nearby (GJ, or *Gliese Catalogue*) stars in this area. These 5 stars are spread over an area of 5° by 6°, and are GJ 112 = HD 17190, GJ 113 = HD 17382, GJ 113.1 = VY Ari, GJ 118.2A = HD 18143 (one of three components), and GJ 120.2 = 51 Ari. The magnitude range is from V = 6.72 (51 Ari) to V = 7.81 (GJ 112), summing to V = 5.45 and B = 6.21. The position given in this catalog was computed from the vector average of the positions of the five stars, and the diameter was determined from the maximum arc distance between those stars. Positions and magnitudes used here were taken from SIMBAD. From the parallaxes cited by Latyshev, the average distance of the five stars is 4.9 pc.

It is interesting to note that three of these stars, GJ 112, GJ 113.1 and GJ 120.2, were also identified as members of a possible moving cluster "[AO84] III," in a later study by Agekyan and Orlov [1984]. Therefore, if both of these groups are considered as real physical groups, Latyshev 1 should probably be considered a part of [AO84] III.

Latyshev 2: This is a possible moving cluster of seven stars, first suggested by Latyshev [1977]. It was identified by considering the space motion of several nearby (GJ, or *Gliese Catalogue*) stars in this area. The stars cover an area of 3° by 3.5°, including primarily the line of four bright stars between ζ UMa (Mizar and Alcor) and the galaxy M 101. These are 81, 83, 84, and 86 UMa. The other 3 stars are HR 5169, HD 234064, and HD 234073. The magnitude range is from V = 4.66 (83 UMa) to V = 10.3 (HD 234073), summing to V = 3.67 and B = 4.05. The position given in the catalog here was computed from the vector average of the positions of the seven stars, and the diameter was determined from the maximum arc distance between them. Positions and magnitude used here were taken from SIMBAD.

Fig. 4.48 *The probable asterism Lederman 1, also known as the "Black Widow" due to its shape. This group is apparently more obvious visually than on this reproduction of a 30′ field of view. The galaxy NGC 914 is at lower right. The black spots at left center and lower center are image artifacts. Image courtesy the Palomar Observatory and Digitized Sky Survey created by the Space Telescope Science Institute, operated by AURA, Inc. for NASA. Reproduced with permission from AURA/STScI.*

Mysteriously, this cluster was not included in the *Lund Catalogue*, although Latyshev 1 (above) is given there.

Lederman 1: This is an apparent asterism of stars, reported by Russell Lederman [private communication, 1997], who named this the "Black Widow." The asterism is a fairly obvious group of GSC stars in the form of its namesake spider, just north of the NGC 911 galaxy group (see Figure 4.48). Using his 20-inch telescope, Lederman describes this as a 14′ x 9′ asterism in a 30′ field of view. He agrees that "...it sort of disappears on the DSS...," but that in his 20-inch "...it was fairly striking and provided geometrical patterns of stars with very small magnitude differences that separated them from the field."

LeDrew 1: This is likely a Galactic cluster, which was discovered by Glenn LeDrew in September of 1999. LeDrew was observing from "Teeple's Hill," a dark sky location about 100 km west of Ottawa, Canada. Using mounted 10 x 50 binoculars, he was searching for NGC 147 and NGC 185, but instead found a "curious knot of faint stars near the galaxies' general position." LeDrew later confirmed its existence as a likely physical cluster by comparisons of the proper motions and colors of the involved stars in the Tycho-2 catalog. He also noted that the motion and colors of the stars are similar to those of NGC 752, with which it may be related [LeDrew, 2001].

LeDrew also reports [private communication, 2001] seven other groups of stars that he ran across, many of which may also be physical clusters, given the available Tycho-2 data. These have been included in the catalog as possible asterisms (of type "ast?") pending further investigation of these groups. The groups are numbered (1 to 8) in decreasing order of confidence that they are real open clusters. Bruno Alessi has also reported his independent discovery of the group as Aless 1 [private communication, 2002]

After seeing a draft version of this text, Philipp Teutsch reported [private communication, 2001] that he independently discovered this object in 1997 while examining this area on *Atlas Stellarum*. Bruno Alessi has also reported [private communication 2002] his independent discovery of the group as Alessi 1.

LeDrew 4: Philipp Teutsch has similarly reported his independent discovery of this group, having observed it on 1993 February 17. He described it as "a charming group of 20 stars, diameter 20′, looks like a flower (a bloom on a stem)," although he had also included the two brighter stars 10′ SSE in this group, beyond what is cataloged here as LeDrew 4. And again Bruno Alessi [private communication 2002] has reported his discovery of this as Alessi 2.

Levy-Wallach J1948.2+3743: This star stream was found by David H. Levy and Wendee Wallach in November of 2002 while comet searching [private communication, 2002]. It appears as a 33.5′ long stream of about 12 stars in a near straight northeast (from TYC 3136-343-1, V = 10.6) to southwest (to TYC 3136-261-1, V = 11.8) line, roughly centered on the V = 7.55 K2 spectral type star HD 187374. Levy notes that a faint curve of stars can also be traced from the southwest end up toward the northwest, making a "cane" or "L"-shaped group of stars overall.

Levy-Wallach J2108.8+0620: This star stream was noticed by David H. Levy and Wendee Wallach in December of 2000. They called this the "Equuleus S" due to its location and appearance as a sinuous "S"-shaped stream of stars. The brightest and center star is HD 201331 = TYC 539-674-1 (V magnitude 9.3), with the stream extended east and west about 22′ and including about 25 stars of similar brightness. The stream starts to the NE at the star TYC 539-180-1 (12.1), curves south to TYC 539-1873-1 (10.2), heads west to HD 201331, and then NW to TYC 539-376-1 (10.3), and hooks south, ending at TYC 539-834-1 (12.0). This is included in the catalog since it is so impressive on the DSS and probably visually. However, since star streams have in general never been shown to be physically associated, this is almost certainly an asterism.

Levy-Wallach J2204.3+4508: While conducting a routine photographic, comet-hunting search, this apparent ring-shaped asterism—but impressive object—was discovered by David H. Levy and Wendee Wallach [private communication from D. Levy, 2000; Levy, 2001, p. 116], and informally named by them "Wendee's Ring." Two photographs were taken with their Schmidt camera, about 25 minutes apart, and the object noticed in the course of the normal comparison of the images. Using the original negatives, one of us [BA] confirmed this object on the DSS. This appears to be a 8.5′ diameter ring (similar to one of Isserstedt's "stellar rings") of about 40 mostly 14th magnitude stars.

Levy-Wallach J2340.6+5618: This long star stream was found by David H. Levy and Wendee Wallach [private communication, 2001] while observing with their 41-cm telescope on the night of April 29–30, 2001. It was described as "a beautiful chain of stars in Cassiopeia" and given by them the informal name "Nanette's River" in honor of their daughter.

The star stream consists of two parts. The entire stream is centered on the star TYC 4008-949-1 (with V magnitude 12.0). There is a brighter eastern part, which starts at TYC 4004-252-1 (10.3), hooks slightly east through TYC 4004-129-1 (11.0), and TYC 4008-301-1 (11.9), then heads west through the brighter stars TYC 4008-983-1 (8.9), TYC 4008-1003-1 (8.6), and TYC 4008-955-1 (8.1, the brightest star of the stream), and TYC 4008-1117-1 (9.1). The western part is a less obvious stream of fainter stars, continuing on through TYC 4008-961-1 (10.5), TYC 4008-1219-1 (11.9), the already mentioned TYC 4008-949-1 at the stream's center, and then through several more faint stars including TYC 4004-456-1 (10.1), TYC 4004-468-1 (11.6), TYC 4004-1163-1 (11.9), (the brighter) TYC 4004-797-1 (9.6), TYC 4004-486-1 (11.6), TYC 4008-1139-1 (12.2), TYC 4004-737-1 (12.0), and ending at TYC 4004-525-1 (11.2). There are approximately 40 stars along this entire stream.

As described under Levy-Wallach J2108.8+0620, such streams of stars have never been shown to have a real physical connection, so this overall stream is listed as an asterism in the catalog. It is included since it is an interesting and observable group of stars, with the eastern end seen easily in 25-cm binoculars by one of us [BA] at the 2001 (May) Texas Star Party.

LH 5: See NGC 1737, *et al.*, on page 153.

LH 15: This is NGC 1787, see page 155.

LH 24: This is the southwestern portion of NGC 1845, which see with NGC 1833, *et al.*, on page 155.

LH 26: This is the northeastern portion of NGC 1845, which see with NGC 1833, *et al.*, on page 155. Note that it is *not* the same object as NGC 1845, which Lucke and Hodge [1970, 173] indicate.

Fig. 4.49 *The sparse group Lodén 153, with the cluster NGC 3293 at lower left. 17′ field of view SkyView/DSS-S image © ROE.*

LH 37: This is part of NGC 1869, see page 157.

Lodén 153 = C1032-578: The *Lund Catalogue* alias list identifies this as "Identical to C1033-579," i.e., NGC 3293. However, a comparison of the photograph of this object in the Lodén discovery paper [1973] with the DSS indicates this is a loose group of stars (probably an asterism) northwest of NGC 3293 (see Figure 4.49). It is centered on HD 91824, whose position (from SIMBAD 2000.0) is $10^h\ 34^m\ 46.65^s$ –58° 09′ 21.7″. Lodén gives a V magnitude of 9.4 for this star, which is used in the catalog here, although SIMBAD gives a much brighter magnitude of 8.16. The diameter is approximately 7′, including 10 obvious stars. The *Lund Catalogue* alias list entries for Lodén 153 and NGC 3293 should be changed to indicate that these are separate objects. In addition, the Lodén object possibly should be added to the *Lund Catalogue* main data file if it is felt to be a real cluster.

Lodén 282 = Basel 17: see page 114.

Lodén 2158 and Lodén 2159: According to Lodén [1979a], Lo 2159 is an early A-type cluster superimposed on a separate cluster Lo 2158. There is a pair of bright non-member stars at center, HD 138168 (8.74, F3IV0) and HD 138181 (8.61,F3/F5V, SIMBAD).

Lyngå 8 = C1615–501: The position given by Lyng [1964] for this cluster originally and by him in the *Lund Catalogue*, is about half a degree too far west. We were originally unable to locate the cluster on the DSS. Fortunately, this cluster was shown on a plate in Lyng and Hansson [1972, 397], and it could then be found by com-

Fig. 4.50 *The small sparse cluster Lyngå 8, identified here with the correct position apparently for the first time. Note that several stars in this group appear to form a "stellar ring." 17′ field of view SkyView/DSS-S image © ROE.*

parison with the DSS (see Figure 4.50). Its identity was confirmed against a photograph of it in Lyngå's 1964 paper. The correct position, as given here is (2000.0) $16^h\ 22^m\ 57.0^s\ -50°\ 10'\ 55''$. The position should also be corrected in the *Lund Catalogue*.

Note that this cluster has a distinct arc of at least 8 stars, looking much like one of Isserstedt's "stellar rings."

Mackie 1: This is an irregular group of 7 stars of about equal brightness, and 9–15 fainter background stars, about 2′ in diameter (likely an asterism). It was first noted by Guy Mackie in his 32-cm telescope, while observing Palomar 8 in the same field the night of August 3–4, 2000. This information was reported to the "amastro" e-mail list by Alan Whitman and is described in Whitman and Mackie [2000] and Mackie [2001]. (See Appendix E.) Information on the cluster in the catalog was derived from the DSS, SIMBAD, and the USNO A2.0 catalog by one of us [BA], who posted similar information to the amastro list.

Mandushev 1: See the SU Cygni group on page 203.

Markov 1: This is a single (likely) asterism, discovered by Paul Markov of Toronto, Canada, on 2000 July 4–5 [private communication, 2001; Markov, 2001; also see Appendix E for web information]. Markov found it while observing the DoDz clusters in Hercules. The Tycho-2 proper motions and colors of the 7 or so involved stars appear to show they are physically unrelated and, therefore, just an asterism. However, as with many of these types of objects, better data are needed in order to confirm this.

Fig. 4.51 *The cluster Melotte 71, also known as "Wilk's cluster." 17′ field of view SkyView/DSS-S image © ROE.*

While reviewing a draft of this text, P. Teutsch [private communication, 2001] has noted his independent visual discovery of this group on July 28, 1992, and adds that probably other visual observers must have noticed this before.

Melotte 15 = IC 1805: see page 134.

Melotte 71 = C0735-119 = Wilk's Cluster: In the very northern part of Puppis, close to its boundary with Monoceros, lies the open cluster, Mel 71 (see Figure 4.51). Its discovery was announced by Melotte in his 1915 publication, and it was also independently discovered by Wilk in 1928 (known as "Wilk's cluster in Puppis" [Schüller 1931]). No significant studies of the cluster were made until that of Hassan [1976], who published some photometry suggesting that the cluster was 10′ in diameter and lay at a distance of 2.82 kpc. The most surprising result was that despite the distance and a fairly low galactic latitude of 4° 51′, the level of reddening appeared to be zero. This attracted the attention of Pound and Janes [1986] who carried out a more comprehensive photometric survey, covering 584 stars, and published a color-magnitude diagram of the cluster. They found a number of differences to the results obtained by Hassan and concluded that Mel 71 lies at a distance of 2.38 kpc and is reddened by about 0.32 mag. Also, it was estimated to have a membership of about 340 stars brighter than V = 18 and has a noticeable clump of red giant stars lying away from the main sequence. The red giant population indicates a considerable age for the cluster; Pound and Janes have arrived at a figure of 0.93 Gyr.

Melotte 72 = Collinder 467: A search of the DSS in the area of Collinder's cluster no. 467 failed to reveal any obvious cluster as described by Collinder. This is not surprising since even he noted that "This object can not, with absolute certainty be identified on the FAC [Franklin Adams Chart] copy in Lund." However, Collinder does cite the original reference for this cluster as being a note by Schüller [1931] in the *Bureau Central Astronomique Circular* (now the *IAU Circular*) no. 316. At the position given by Schüller—noticeably different from that of Collinder—there is also nothing obvious on the DSS. However, only 30^s west is the impressive cluster Melotte 72. Could it be that this is the intended cluster? The answer is almost certainly yes. Schüller describes his cluster as "1.3° southwesterly from α Monocerotis. It is a small, rich, and very compressed open cluster, 3′ in diameter, composed mainly of stars of sixteenth magnitude; it is connected with a 5′ long stream-like condensation of relatively bright stars." Melotte 72 is a small, rich, compressed cluster, with its core about 3′ in diameter, and with a 5′ long stream extending to the north between the two bright stars HD 61277 (V = 7.05, K5, SIMBAD) and HD 61401 (V = 8.49, B9, SIMBAD). It is also about 1.3° southwest of α Mon. Further, and quite significantly, Schüller *does not even mention* Melotte 72, which would have been a noticeable "companion" cluster to his if it had existed anywhere near. Schüller also seems to be unaware of the Melotte listing, since in this same note he reports the supposed discovery of a new cluster by Wilk, which is clearly Melotte 71 (see page 145) just to the south.

Therefore, Schüller's cluster = Collinder 467, is the same object as Melotte 72. The separate entry for Collinder 467 in the *Lund Catalogue* should be deleted, and Collinder 467 and its associated names added to the Melotte 72 entry in the *Lund Catalogue* alias list.

M 8 = NGC 6523 = NGC 6530 = NGC 6533: see page 179.

M 11 = NGC 6705: see page 182.

M 20 = NGC 6514: see page 178.

M 24 = IC 4715: see page 140.

M 25 = IC 4725: see page 140.

M 34 = NGC 1039: see page 150.

M 35 = NGC 2168: see page 161.

M 41 = NGC 2287: see page 164.

M 42 = NGC 1976: see page 159.

M 44 = NGC 2632: see page 168.

Fig. 4.52 *The Pleiades, or M 45, in this photo from Barnard [1927, plate 4], covering about a 3.6° square field. See Figure 8.1 on page 255 for the magnitudes of some of the brighter stars. Barnard indicated that this photograph was intended to illustrate the distribution of the various areas of nebulosity around the Pleiades. In a study of a number of photographs of this region he wrote in 1900 "One startling fact brought out by the study of these photographs is that the Pleiades and their involved nebulosities are but the central condensation of an enormous nebula, intricate in details, and covering at least 100 square degrees of the sky."*

M 45: The position given here is that of Alcyone (see Figure 4.52 on page 146 and Figure 8.1 on page 255). Note that the Pleiades cluster has no NGC or IC designation.

M 47 = NGC 2422: see page 165.

M 50 = NGC 2323: see page 165.

M 67 = NGC 2682: see page 169.

M 73 = NGC 6994: see page 189.

NGC 220, NGC 222, and NGC 231: There are three obvious clusters in the Small Magellanic Cloud, running SW to NE in this area of the sky (see Figure 4.53). These are best shown on chart 1 of [Morel 1989]. Most modern references assign these (in order) the names NGC 220, NGC 222, and NGC 231. However, according to Jenni Kay [private communication, 1995], the positions given for these objects are usually poor. Furthermore, based on John Herschel's original observations of this area [Herschel 1847, 52], the identities of two of these objects are somewhat uncertain.

The positions and sizes presented in the catalog here were obtained via an inspection of the area on the DSS. Further information follows here on the actual identities of these objects.

Fig. 4.53 *NGC 220, NGC 222, and NGC 231, shown from center lower right to center upper left, in the Small Magellanic Cloud. NGC 231 is assumed to be the concentrated cluster at the west (right) end of a larger scattered group, although it is possible that John Herschel originally intended the larger group to be the specified object. 17′ field of view SkyView/DSS-S image © ROE.*

Fig. 4.54 *NGC 241, a scattered association of approximately 60 stars, in the Small Magellanic Cloud. This object is correctly identified here for perhaps the first time since its discovery, using J. Herschel's original position. An incorrect position was given in the GC and NGC, and all later authors until now have erroneously identified this as the same object as NGC 242. 17′ field of view SkyView/DSS-S image © ROE.*

For NGC 220, the match with Herschel's three observations of h 2338 seems fairly reasonable by position, and fairly good by description. Therefore, there appears to be no problem with the identity of this object.

Regarding NGC 222, for this to be h 2339 Herschel must have been off in right ascension (which is likely in this case, considering his comments with this and other observations made the same night) and made a 5′ error in north polar distance (NPD). However, his single observation of h 2339 also matches his h 2338 (NGC 220, with only a 4′ NPD error), and there is no explanation why he did not see both h 2338 and h 2339 together. Therefore, the modern identification of NGC 222 with h 2339 is inconclusive. However, since there is an obvious cluster, separate from NGC 220, in this catalog it retains the NGC 222 name.

As to NGC 231, Herschel's position and description for h 2340 seem to indicate that this is a large scattering of stars, extending E-W, and including a cluster on its western end. The "modern" definition is that NGC 231 is the cluster itself (not the entire object that Herschel intended). Although his position (as usual) is quite poor, Dunlop appears to have observed the "modern NGC 231" as his object no. 2 [Dunlop 1828, 114]. Since the NGC [19] indicates that NGC 231 is both h 2340 and possibly Dunlop 2 (it says "Δ 2??"), this again leaves the strict identity of the object questionable. In the catalog here, the "modern" definition is used, with the obvious cluster being referred to as NGC 231. Although it is clear that NGC 231 is only contained in Herschel's h 2340, at least this name follows Dunlop's discovery priority. Finally, it should be noted that the diameter given here (18″) is of the inner portion of the cluster. The cluster continues loosely out to a diameter of 100″ or more, thus matching Dunlop's diameter of 90″ quite well.

NGC 241 and NGC 242: J. Herschel [1847, 52] discovered both NGC 241 and NGC 242 (his h 2342 = GC 127 and h 2343 = GC 128 respectively). He observed NGC 241 only once in his sweep 482 of August 12, 1834. His description reads: "a v F, R nebula or group [e.g. a very faint, round nebula or group] (We are now fairly in the Nubecula Minor, and the field begins to be full of a faint perfectly irresolvable nebulous light)." Located precisely at his observed position on the DSS (see Figure 4.54) is a faint scattered group of about 60 stars, approximately 7.5′ in diameter. This group, a likely association in the SMC, is assumed to be NGC 241 in the catalog here, using Herschel's position.

Herschel observed NGC 242 three times, and in his most detailed observation, gives the description "A binuclear nebula, or two, v S, R, running together." The DSS clearly shows a "binuclear" cluster right at Herschel's position; this object too seems to be clearly identifiable. This object has also been listed as Kron 22 and Lindsay 29, in both cases being properly identified as NGC 242. Kron also notes that this is a "double cluster."

However, it appears that all modern catalogs and references that mention NGC 241 confuse it as being part of (or equivalent to) NGC 242. NGC 241 does not appear to be listed anywhere (but here) as the association it likely is. This error can be traced to Herschel himself, who gave the wrong north polar distance for NGC 241 in the GC, a value about 10′ too far north—pretty much right at the position of NGC 242. This error propagated into the NGC position as well. Later investigators appear not to have checked the original observation information from Herschel, but relied on the NGC position. For example:

- Shapley and Wilson [1925, 3] not only make this error, but also assume the object in question is a nebula. They include NGC 242 in their catalog of nebulae in the Magellanic Clouds, and remark that "Nos. 241 and 242 may be parts of the same nebula." In their defense, J. Herschel did indicate that both NGC 241 and NGC 242 were nebulae.
- Lindsay [1963] writes of NGC 241 and NGC 242 that "These seem to be the same. A slight appendage of two or three unresolved stars SE of and attached to NGC 241 may give the impression of two objects." Lindsay is correct in noting that the "appendage" is the lesser of the two parts of NGC 242. However, it appears that a reliance on the NGC position of NGC 241 causes the assumption that it could be part of NGC 242. What is also odd here is that in Lindsay's [1958] actual catalog, this object is correctly listed as NGC 242= Lindsay 29, with no reference to NGC 241.
- Lauberts [1982], under ESO 29-SC6 (the actual NGC 242), incorrectly says this is "N 241 = N 242."
- Morel [1989] erroneously lists NGC 241 as being "= 242" and lists its class as "Nonexistent."
- Hatzidimitriou and Bhatia [1990] in their paper on "Cluster pairs in the Small Magellanic Cloud," list the pair here as being "N 242" and "BH 1." The pair itself is NGC 242, not one of the components. However, if one assumes they intended the main and larger component to be NGC 242, then their BH 1 component must be the southeastern portion of NGC 242. This appears to be the first time this component was named, although the origin of the BH acronym is not entirely clear. It obviously originates from the authors' names, but they indicate that BH is a reference to an earlier paper on the LMC—which had no information on SMC clusters. The name [HB90] 1, based on their 1990 paper, is used in the catalog here instead.
- Bica and Schmitt [1995], in their SMC and Magellanic Bridge cluster catalog, list the NGC 242 double cluster as two objects, i.e., NGC 241 = K 22w, L 29W, ESO 29-SC6w and NGC 242 = K22e = L29e = ESO 29-SC6e = BH 1 (where the "e" and "w" suffixes denote the east and west components of objects having the primary name), thereby again misusing the NGC 241 name.
- Pietrzyński, *et al.*, [1998], in their OGLE SMC cluster catalog, also list two objects at the NGC 242 location, with identifications OGLE-CL SMC0017 = NGC 241 = K 22 = L 29 and OGLE-CL SMC0018 = NGC 242 = K 22 = L 29. Clearly in both this and the Bica and Schmitt [1995] case, the groups being considered are all part of NGC 242 and have no relation to NGC 241. Both miss the identification of the southeastern object as Hatzidimitriou and Bhatia's [HB90] 1. Further, the listing of both of the OGLE objects as being *the same* as Kron 22 and Lindsay 29 is obviously in error—they are only the components of the overall group, which is NGC 242 = Kron 22 = Lindsay 29.

In summary, NGC 241 is a previously unrecognized association and has no direct connection with NGC 242. NGC 242 is a double cluster, with two components; one was named OGLE-CL SMC0017, while the southeastern one was listed as BH 1 (or here, [HB90] 1). NGC 241 has no alternate names, having not been identified (until now) since J. Herschel's discovery of it in 1834. NGC 242 has the alternate names Kron 22, Lindsay 29, and ESO 29-SC6. OGLE-CL SMC0017 has no alternate name, while [HB90] 1 is also known as OGLE-CL SMC0018.

NGC 281 = IC 11: See IC 1590, on page 134.

NGC 376: This is a star cluster in the Small Magellanic Cloud, discovered by John Herschel (his h 2378). However, J. L. E. Dreyer, in the Second IC [367] mistakenly indicated that this was a double star. *NGC 2000.0* [Sinnott 1988, 11] repeats this erroneous identification. This cluster is also incorrectly listed as a globular cluster by the RNGC. It may appear as a globular cluster because of its distance, but NGC 121 is the only true globular cluster in the SMC.

NGC 457 = C0115+580: Located in a rich Milky Way field to the south of the V= 2.68 star δ Cas, NGC 457 is a most distinctive open cluster in the form of a "stick-man" with the 'head' being represented by the V= 4.98 F0Ia star ϕ Cas (see Figure 4.55 on page 149). The first significant study of NGC 457 was that of Pesch [1959] who made UBV observations of 78 stars in the field. Forty-eight were judged to be members, with about 9 more possible. The color-magnitude diagram of the cluster was found to be similar to that of the Perseus Double Cluster, making it a fairly young object, with a distance of 2.88 kpc. One of the brighter stars in the cluster (No. 4) was found to be a red supergiant of type M0Ib, B – V = +1.65. Additional photometry of NGC 457 has been carried out by Moffat [1972], who obtained a distance of 3.2 kpc and an age of about 10 million years. More recently, CCD Strömgren *uvby* pho-

Fig. 4.55 *NGC 457, with it's distinctive "stick-man" shape, has been given numerous appellations related to its shape, including the "Dragonfly Cluster'", the "ET Cluster", and the "Owl Cluster" (see Appendix C.2 for such common names). The star V=4.98 star ϕ Cas is usually taken to form the head or one of the eyes, while the stick figure extends off to the northwest (upper right). 45′ field of view. Image courtesy the Palomar Observatory and Digitized Sky Survey created by the Space Telescope Science Institute, operated by AURA, Inc. for NASA. Reproduced with permission from AURA/STScI.*

tometry has been obtained by Fitzsimmons [1993] who derives a distance of 2.5 kpc, slightly closer than previous estimates, and an age of between 10–30 million years. More interestingly, star No. 7, which was classified as a non-member by Pesch on the basis of its colors, is found to be a probable 'blue straggler' cluster member (these stars are described in more detail in Chapter 6).

NGC 460: Jenni Kay [private communication, 1995] noted that a number of modern catalogs give an incorrect position for this object. Her corrected position is (2000.0: 01^h 14^m 37.9^s −73° 18′ 28″). Morel [1989] lists this object at an incorrect position, but plots it correctly on his chart 9. S. Gottlieb has also noted [private communication, 1995] that this object is listed correctly in the ESO catalog. Its designation there is ESO 011316-7332.3 or ESO 29-SC39.

The source of some of the confusion in the position of this object may trace back to Lindsay [1958] who gives a declination for this (Lindsay 97) 1° too far north.

NGC 603: As noted in Archinal [1993, 50], Harold Corwin determined some time ago (in 1976 or earlier) that this is nothing more than a group of 3 stars. It is superimposed on the outlying area of the Pinwheel galaxy, M 33 (NGC 598), having at least once been mistaken for part of that galaxy (the RNGC repeats Zwicky's incorrect assumption that this is a "knot in NGC 598").

However, it appears that the determination that this is nothing more than three stars has been made independently a number of times. S. Gottlieb points out [private communication, 1996] that this is listed as a "Cl of 3 st 14" magnitude in Reinmuth [1926]. Mayall and Aller [1942, 8, footnote 19] also report that "NGC 603 appears to be a small group of three faint stars." Lortet [1985] has pointed out the correct identification of this object. Dave Riddle [private communication, 1995] observed this object visually with a 51-cm (20-inch) *f*/4.5 reflector. He reports that it appears "as a tiny triangle of 13th–14th magnitude stars" and that under poor seeing, it appeared as a "nebulous unresolved hazy patch at 90X." A. Ling [private communication, 1996] also reported an observation of this (from February 4, 1995) as "a small nebulous just nonstellar smudge" through his 32-cm (12.5-inch) *f*/5.6 reflector.

The three stars are included in the *Guide Star Catalog* as GSC 02293-00998, 02293-00972, and 02293-00966. A magnitude of 14.35 is given for the first, while that of the second two stars are incorrect. The total size of the group (calculated from the GSC positions) is 15″. The position given here (2000.0: 01^h 34^m 44^s +30° 13′ 58″) is a central one determined from the DSS.

NGC 609 = C0133+643: The *Lund Catalogue* incorrectly lists this as "globular?" in the alias list. It is not included in the globular cluster list of Djorgovski and Meylan [1993].

NGC 657: Although this object is listed as a cluster in both the *Lund Catalogue* and the *DSFG1e*, there appear to be very few modern professional or amateur observations of this object. One problem may be the rather nondescript description in the NGC, which fails to mention the most important feature of the cluster, a fairly bright double star. John Herschel's original observation of this (his h 146) mentions the star prominently, "A D * (h 2070), the chief of a p rich loose cl; st 12 m." Why this description did not make it into the NGC is a mystery. The double star is STT 35 = HD 10495 = ADS 1353 A = IDS 01373+5522. The Washington Double Star Catalog (WDS) [Worley and Douglass 1996] lists this as a 7.2 and 10.4 magnitude pair, with position angle decreasing and separation increasing slowly (at 99° and 12.8″ respectively in 1958).

Y. Pothier has reported [private communication, 1996] an observation of this from December, 1992 with a 20-cm (8-inch) Schmidt-Cassegrain at 145x. He describes it as "a poor and sparse cluster of about 10 stars" between 11.5 and 12.0 visual magnitude in an area 2.8′ in diameter. However, a DSS image reveals about 40 brighter stars in a rough diameter of 7′. This larger number of stars and diameter is used in the catalog here as it matches Herschel's descrip-

Fig. 4.56 *NGC 1039 = M 34, a large beautiful cluster in Perseus. 1° field of view. Image courtesy the Palomar Observatory and Digitized Sky Survey created by the Space Telescope Science Institute, operated by AURA, Inc. for NASA. Reproduced with permission from AURA/STScI.*

tion of a "p rich loose cl." The position here is from the DSS and for the SW star of a pair just W of HD 10495.

NGC 869 and NGC 884: These two clusters comprise the famous "Double cluster," see page 130.

NGC 886 = C0219+636: Alister Ling [letter of December 18, 1988] has pointed out that in the *Lund Catalogue* this cluster is identified as Stock 6 = C0219+636 = OCl 347. NGC 886 should be the preferred name for this and added to the alias list. The name should be changed from Stock 6 to NGC 886 in *Sky Catalogue 2000.0* (vol. 2) as well. See [Archinal 1993, 50] for more information.

The *Lund Catalogue* and *DSFG1e* (probably originating from Stock's position) give a position that is several arcminutes too far north. John Herschel's original position (his object h 214) is used in the catalog here. On the DSS, this position is quite close to that of a star-like object at $02^h\ 23^m\ 28.6^s$ +63° 45′ 12″. This object appears to be a plate defect, since unlike other stars of similar brightness, it has no diffraction spikes.

NGC 1039 = M 34 = C0238+425: The center of M 34 is difficult to determine due to the large cluster size (see Figure 4.56). Found by Charles Messier on August 25, 1764, NGC 1039 (M 34) is a fairly bright and rich cluster which might be detected with the naked eye under good conditions. The first serious study of the cluster was that of Brüggemann [1937] who obtained positions and proper motions of 190 stars in the vicinity, concluding that 86 were likely members. Johnson [1954] subsequently carried out UBV photoelectric photometry of 57 stars in the area and found 42 to be cluster members, deriving a distance of 0.525 kpc. More recent investigations have suggested a somewhat smaller distance; typically, Cester, *et al.*, [1977] found 0.47 kpc and Canterna, *et al.*, [1979] found 0.44 kpc. The largest recent study of stars in NGC 1039 is that of Ianna and Schlemmer [1993], who have determined proper motions and membership probabilities for 354 stars in the region of the cluster, using astrographic plates taken since 1927. This survey found that 89 stars were probable cluster members, including all of the six visual binaries listed in the *Index Catalogue of Visual Double Stars (IDS).* A distance of about 0.455 kpc was derived and a comparison of theoretical isochrones to the CMD of probable members gave an age of around 2.5×10^8 years.

NGC 1252 = C0309-583: Eggen [1984] has apparently (there is some doubt—see comments just below) shown that this is not a true physical cluster, so it can be classified as an asterism. Although listed as "canceled" in the *Lund Catalogue* alias list, this cluster is still included in the main file and its entry should, therefore, be removed. (It is not listed in the "print" version of the catalog.) In addition, it is listed as "C0307-583" in the alias list and "C0309-583" in the main file. Given the position of this asterism, the later name would seem to be the preferred one.

S. Gottlieb has also pointed out [private communication, 1995] that the position given for this group in most catalogs is incorrect. The position that John Herschel gave is that of HD 20037, at magnitude 6.7 the brightest star of this group. This is some 20′ north of the position given in the *Lund Catalogue*. The position (2000.0: $03^h\ 10^m\ 56^s$ –57° 45′ 40″) and diameter (9′) given here have been measured from a DSS image of the group.

This position discrepancy raises the question of whether Eggen [1984] actually measured the stars of the cluster or instead measured field stars. This is particularly true since the primary star of interest in that study (TW Hor) is not particularly near the corrected position. For now this will still be assumed an asterism but a check would be desirable.

NGC 1498: As discussed in Archinal [1993, 50], this is one of a very few NGC objects that has resisted identification by multiple investigators (see Figure 4.57). Even J.L.E. Dreyer himself reported [1912, 1, 303] that "There is no very pronounced cluster near this place."

William Herschel discovered this (as his H.VII.3) on February 8, 1784 and described it as "A S. Cl. of com. st. some pL.." His class VII indicates that this is a "pretty much compressed cluster of large and small stars." He made only one observation, $72^m\ 30^s$ preceding and 30′ south of the star 3 Lep. Using a modern (SIMBAD) posi-

Fig. 4.57 *NGC 1498. This is William Herschel's long lost Class VII object 3, which consists mainly of the three stars at center and possibly some of the fainter background stars. The faint galaxies in this image all appear to be anonymous with no entries in NED or SIMBAD. There does appear to be a short linear image artifact just left (east) of the three stars. The star BD –12°769 (V=9.8) is the bright star at the bottom of the image. 17′ field of view SkyView/DSS-S © ROE.*

Fig. 4.58 *NGC 1647, a large bright cluster in Taurus, with approximately 200 stars. 60′ field of view. Image courtesy the Palomar Observatory and Digitized Sky Survey created by the Space Telescope Science Institute, operated by AURA, Inc. for NASA. Reproduced with permission from AURA/STScI.*

tion for the star, this gives a position of (2000.0) $03^h\ 59^m\ 54^s$ –12° 01.1′.

An examination of the DSS shows a small (45″) triangle of stars of equal brightness very close to this position, at $04^h\ 00^m\ 19^s$ –12° 01.2′. These stars are GSC 05308-00383, 05308-00193, and 05308-00229. There are some faint background stars here (which stand out with a histogram equalization display), so presumably Herschel somehow thought this was a cluster. Normally it is possible to check Herschel's positions by checking the positions of other objects he observed on the same night, but unfortunately there do not appear to be any other objects discovered by him on that night.

So although this triangle of stars and their surroundings do not have the appearance of a cluster, it can only be assumed that this is the correct object. This object was discovered before Herschel had gained much experience observing, so perhaps his confusion with this object is understandable. The slight discrepancy in position can also be explained by the long period of time (72.5 minutes) between the observation and when the reference star (3 Lep) was seen.

The identification of these three stars with NGC 1498 was first suggested by Y. Pothier [private communication, 1996]. He observed this group in the summer of 1993 with a 61-cm (24-inch) *f*/15 Cassegrain telescope at *f*/3.4 with an image intensifier coupled to a video-camera—thus reaching visual magnitude 17.

S. Gottlieb has reported [private communication, 1998] that Harold Corwin also independently suggested that these three stars comprise NGC 1498.

Finally, J. Kay, of Lobethal, S.A., Australia, reported [private communication, 1998] a visual observation of this group on 24 December 1997 with a limiting naked eye magnitude of 6.1. With a 32-cm (12.5-inch) *f*/5 Newtonian at 151 power, she reports that a "neat little triangle of three stars of similar brightness, 13 mag, catch the eye and draws it to them. The surrounding field is star poor, therefore, this dainty little triangle stands out well, and appears impressive enough to me. The group is about 1′ in size."

This visual observation appears to confirm that the (then) inexperienced William Herschel probably did observe this group. It is, therefore, included in the catalog here. The magnitude of the brightest star is given as 13.8, but this is the GSC magnitude of the brightest star and not necessarily visual (or correct). The GSC magnitudes of the other stars are 13.9 and 14.5. Note that although listed here as simply three stars, the surrounding faint background stars probably should also be considered part of this "object."

NGC 1647 = C0443+189: NGC 1647 is a fairly large, bright cluster of perhaps 200 stars in Taurus (see

Figure 4.58). It is just visible to the unaided eye, an easy binocular object, and a fine sight in a telescope, but rather overshadowed by its near neighbor, the Hyades. Despite being a seemingly easy target for photometric and other observations, it has been little studied. The first photoelectric UBV measurements were reported by Hoag, *et al.*, [1961], and the first major proper-motion study to determine cluster membership was that of Francic [1989]. The most comprehensive general survey of NGC 1647 has been conducted by Turner [1992] and is primarily concerned with the association of the cluster and the 3.15-day Cepheid variable SZ Tau. Obviously, in the determination of such matters, accurate photometry, spectral classifications, radial velocities and proper motions are critical; and the Turner paper provides new measurements and comparisons with previously published data. A distance for the cluster of 0.542 kpc is derived, together with an age of 1.9 x 10^8 years. It is concluded that SZ Tau is very likely a member of the cluster and, from its luminosity, that the Cepheid is pulsating in the first overtone mode. However, contradicting this, Geffert, *et al.*, [1996] have determined from a visual inspection of the POSS that the center star of this cluster is very near the star PPM 120214, at (2000.0) 04^h 45^m 42^s +19° 07′ 07″. They have also made a preliminary determination that SZ Tauri is not likely a member of this cluster.

NGC 1649 and NGC 1652: J. Kay [private communication, 1996] has noted that a number of references do not list NGC 1649 or list it as "nonexistent" (see [Morel 1983, 23]). However, John Herschel describes two objects in this vicinity of the sky, including his h 2660 (NGC 1649) and h 2661 (NGC 1652). His positions and descriptions match fairly well two close clusters, including KMHK 22 [Kontizas, *et al.*, 1990] and NGC 1652 (KMHK 23). Therefore, the KMHK 22 cluster should be known as NGC 1649. This object is just 2′ north of the 8.1 magnitude star SAO 249073.

The positions and magnitude given here are from the nonstellar objects GSC (09154-01699 and 09154-01135). Diameters were measured from the DSS (23″ and 60″ respectively). Lauberts [1982] also lists these objects as ESO 55-SC31 (NGC 1649) and ESO 55-SC32 (NGC 1652) (the latter of which is incorrectly labeled as "N 1652 = N 1649").

NGC 1663 = C0445+130: This is William Herschel's H.VIII.7. One of us [BA] has determined that Herschel's position was 1 minute of time too far west. Most modern catalogs (such as the *Lund Catalogue* and the *DSFG1e*) repeat the incorrect position. The type, position, size, and number of stars given were all estimated or measured from the DSS. It should also be pointed out that although listed as "canceled" in the *Lund Catalogue* alias list, this cluster was still included in the main file; and its entry should, therefore, have been removed. Now it appears to have been "canceled" simply because investigators were looking in the wrong place.

NGC 1707 = IC 2107: John Herschel's original description and position can be used to unambiguously locate this object. The position (2000.0: 04^h 58^m 21.1^s +08° 14′ 20″), size (48″) and number of stars (5) are from the DSS. Both Bob Erdmann, Jr. [private communication, 1996] and Yann Pothier [private communication, 1996] have reported consistent observations of this small group. Both the RNGC and Erdmann note that NGC 1707 and IC 2107 are the same object. The brightest star is GSC 00684-01125 at GSC magnitude 13.5, and GSC 00684-00494 (magnitude 14) is also included.

NGC 1722, IC 2111 and KMHK 171 = BRHT 1a, and KMHK 173 = BRHT 1b: An examination of the original discovery references and the DSS has shown that NGC 1722 is a large cluster (or association) in the LMC. It contains the nebula IC 2111 on its north side. The south portion of NGC 1722 contains the cluster KMHK 171 = BRHT 1a, while IC 2111 contains a group of stars or possible cluster KMHK 173 = BRHT 1b. Some modern sources (such as KMHK and BRHT) mistakenly identify these objects and other possible involved clusters.

John Herschel made three observations of this area, and listed them as his h 2689. Surprisingly, the position and description, "A knot of clustering stars", he lists first is clearly of the nebula and group of stars, IC 2111 and KMHK 171. His second and third listed observations identify the whole overall cluster. This is the overall identification he used in the GC, was used in the NGC, and has come to be accepted for NGC 1722.

IC 2111 was (re-)discovered by W. Fleming [Pickering 1901; Harvard College Observatory 1908] and described by her as a "gaseous nebula" (her number—actually the "Harvard Number"—85). Note that Dreyer, in the second IC, incorrectly gave the description for this object as "planetary, stellar." It is possible that since a lot of Fleming's other discoveries were stellar planetary nebulae, Dreyer just assigned that description to this object, too. Fleming's position ends up being slightly east of Herschel's "knot", but since she must have been using reasonably small-scale plates, and she specifically identified a nebula (presumably by its spectrum), this is likely the nebulous part of the "knot" itself.

The southern part of the NGC 1722 cluster or association was apparently first identified as a separate possible cluster in the KMHK catalog as their object no. 171. However, it is incorrectly identified there as being the same object as NGC 1722, rather than only part of it.

In essentially the same way, the "knot" in IC 2111 was apparently first identified as a "compact" star cluster in the

KMHK catalog, as no. 173. Another problem is that it is incorrectly identified as being equivalent to the IC 2111 nebula rather than as just associated with it. It is also not clear from its appearance on the DSS that this object is a real separate cluster. It appears there as only three stars, with maybe 5 much fainter stars, all involved in nebulosity. Therefore, it is listed in the catalog here as type "cl?."

Bhatia, *et al.*, [1991] list the southern and northern possible clusters here (i.e., KMHK 171 and KMHK 173 respectively) as a pair of clusters. The southern object is their BRHT 1a; the northern is their BRHT 1b. They unfortunately also repeat the incorrect identifications that KMHK makes, calling the southern object NGC 1722 (when it is only the southern part of NGC 1722) and the northern object IC 2111 (when it is only the possible cluster in the IC 2111 nebula). Their figure 1 also incorrectly identifies NGC 1722 and IC 2111, although it does show IC 2111 in the correct location.

Finally, it should be noted that some modern sources do list the identification of at least IC 2111 correctly. The MOL correctly calls it an "HII REGION IN THE LMC." *NGC 2000.0* identifies it as a nebula, using the MOL as its source. Morel, in his many publications on the LMC, also correctly identifies this nebula.

NGC 1731, KMHK 211, KMHK 212, and [HS66] 51: NGC 1731 = LH 4 is a John Herschel discovery (h 2691), an approximately 8′ diameter LMC cluster. Kontizas, *et al.*, [1990] are clearly wrong in claiming that this is their 0.7' diameter KMHK 212. KMHK 212 is a clump of stars forming a pair with KMHK 211, which is another clump of stars at the center of the cluster (a "double star" used by Herschel for the cluster position). From the DSS image it is not clear whether the KMHK objects are even clusters, so they are listed with type "ptcl" in the catalog here.

[HS66] 51 = KMHK 190 is a small very faint 15″ diameter cluster at the northern end of a chain of stars running north-south and on the northwest side of NGC 1731.

NGC 1737, NGC 1743, NGC 1745, NGC 1748, IC 2114, SL 87, LH 5, and Hen N 83: The identifications of objects in this area have become quite confused over time. The only way to properly identify them is to look in detail at all the discoveries made in this vicinity (see Figure 4.59 on page 154).

The first object discovered here was Δ114, which Dunlop (Δ) called "A small round nebula, about 20″ diameter, bright at the center" (2 observations; 1827 position of $4^h54^m18^s$ SPD 20° 36′). Dunlop's position is not particularly good (as usual), but since he only describes one object (which here I'll call "A"), it must be the bright nebula at 04^h $54^m03.4^s$ −69° 11′ 57″ (a position measured from the DSS for 2000.0).

John Herschel (h) saw 4 objects here, which he described as being arranged in a "trapezium" or "lozenge" form. When the DSS image is stretched with histogram equalization, there are indeed 4 patches here in such a shape. These objects are (with his 1830.0 positions):

	h m s			[d] ′ ″
(NGC 1737 =) h 2698	4 54 42	+/–	NPD	159 27
(NGC 1743 =) h 2699	4 54 58.8		NPD	159 28 0
(second obs.)	4 54 60.5		NPD	159 28 14
(NGC 1745 =) h 2702	4 55 18	+/–	NPD	159 26
(NGC 1748 =) h 2704	4 55 24.0		NPD	159 27 54

	h m s			[d] ′ ″
(NGC 1737 =) h 2698	4 53 58.8	-	-	– 69 10 19
(NGC 1745 =) h 2702	4 54 20.9	-	-	– 69 09 35
(NGC 1748 =) h 2704	4 54 24.7	-	-	– 69 11 00

Herschel also points out that h 2699 is Δ114, object "A" here, and estimates that it is 2′ in size. His description and position matches that of the bright object quite well. The last object, h 2704 is fairly obvious on the DSS. The first and third objects are small loose groups of stars, possibly involved in nebulosity, just north preceding h 2699 and h 2704, respectively. Herschel's description implies that all of these objects are unresolved, *except* that one of his two observations of h 2699 says "resolvable." The measured positions from the DSS for the other objects (for 2000.0) are:

	h m s	[d] ′ ″
(NGC 1737 =) h 2698	4 53 58.8	– 69 10 19
(NGC 1745 =) h 2702	4 54 20.9	– 69 09 35
(NGC 1748 =) h 2704	4 54 24.7	– 69 11 00

These are not great matches with Herschel's positions (which he notes are approximate for the two "±" positions), but the descriptions allow the objects to be positively identified.

Dreyer, in the NGC, lists Δ114 and h 2699 as the same object (now NGC 1743), just as Herschel did. This seems reasonable since Dunlop, observing with his 23 cm telescope, described this object as a nebula. Herschel, observing through his larger 48 cm telescope, called it a "resolvable" object. Both gave the same position. Therefore, it can be assumed this designation applies to a nebulous cluster, object "A." The other three Herschel objects were assigned NGC numbers as given above. From the DSS appearance and his general descriptions, they could be called nebulous clusters or, at least, nebulous groups of stars.

IC 2114 is Fleming (or HN) 86, another of Fleming's IC discoveries (from her Harvard College Observatory Circular 60 paper, "Objects Having Peculiar Spectra") that Dreyer incorrectly described in the IC as a stellar planetary.

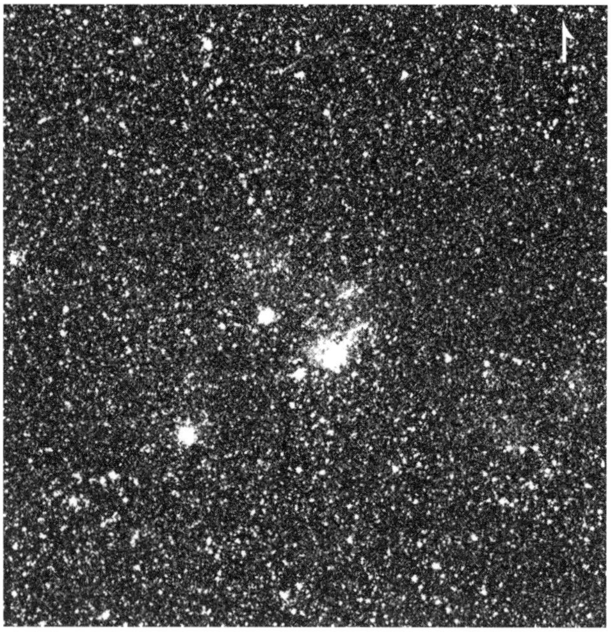

Fig. 4.59 *The Large Magellanic Cloud association LH 5, including a number of other objects, is shown centrally in this image. NGC 1743 is the bright nebulous cluster or group of stars at the center, with the cluster itself also known as SL 87. NGC 1737 is the smaller nebulous group or cluster just above it. NGC 1748 is the small, bright nebulous group just to the upper left (northeast) of NGC 1743, while IC 2114 is its involved nebula (also known as Hen N 83C). NGC 1745 is the larger faint cluster (or patch of stars here) just above NGC 1748. Hen N 83 is the overall nebulosity associated with this area, while Hen N 83A and Hen N 83B are the nebulosities associated with NGC 1743 and NGC 1737 respectively. Hen N 83D is the nebulosity in the middle of the triangle formed by NGC 1737, NGC 1743, and NGC 1748. NGC 1756, not part of LH 5, is the obvious cluster on the lower left. Shown here using contrast enhancement of a 17′ field of view SkyView/DSS-S image. © ROE.*

She listed this as at (1900.0) 4^h 55.1^m –69°21′, with description "Gaseous nebula." This updates to a 2000.0 position of $04^h54.6^m$ –69° 12′. There is no nebula at this position, although it is close to NGC 1748 = h 2704. Unfortunately, it is also at about the same declination and reasonably close to NGC 1743 and just north preceding NGC 1756. We can eliminate NGC 1756 as the likely object, since it is a normal, intermediate-age LMC cluster and does not have a peculiar spectra, [Corsi *et al.*, 1994]. NGC 1743 probably can not be totally eliminated as the likely object, but here we'll assume IC 2114 is the nebula in NGC 1748 because it is closer.

Henize [1956] listed 5 objects, including his (table 2) nos. 83 and 83A—83D. Updating his 1950.0 coordinates to 2000.0 and comparing to the DSS shows that his identities are:

- Hen N 83—Overall nebulosity in this area.
- Hen N 83A—Nebulosity involved with NGC 1743.
- Hen N 83B—Nebulosity involved with NGC 1737.
- Hen N 83C—Nebulosity involved with NGC 1748, i.e., this is IC 2114.
- Hen N 83D—Nebulosity in the middle of the triangle formed by NGC 1737, NGC 1743, and NGC 1748.

Shapley and Lindsay [1963] only list one object here, their no. 87. They give a diameter of 20″, and description "NGC 1743, few stars condensed in dense nebulosity," with a (1975.0) position of 4^h 54.1^m –69° 14′. We've seen that NGC 1743 is the nebulous cluster, so strictly speaking the cluster SL 87 is not precisely NGC 1743 but instead the cluster in it.

Next, we come to the Lucke and Hodge [1970] identification LH 5 which supposedly includes NGC 1737, 43, 45, 48, IC 2114, and Hen N 83. This is supposed to be a 6′ x 4′ association with at least 10 stars involved in nebulosity. It is listed at (1975.0) $4^h54.2^m$ –69° 15′, which converts to (2000.0) $04^h54.1^m$ –69° 13′. This is just southeast of NGC 1737. Clearly there is a large association here (maybe even bigger than listed by Lucke and Hodge) that does contain NGC 1737, 43, 45, and 48 (and its involved nebula, IC 2114). The overall nebulosity associated with it is Hen N 83.

Finally, there is KMHK 235. This object is listed at the position of object "A" with a size of 26.1 pc. This converts to an angular size of 1.8′. This matches the position and general description of Dunlop's and Herschel's object; so SL 87, as with KMHK 235 is the *cluster portion* of NGC 1743—in other words, SL 87 = KMHK 235. There is a discrepancy in size (SL saying 20″ and KMHK 108″), but these sizes obviously are dependent on the plate material used and on the observer. However, there really can be only one (possible) "cluster" here.

Therefore, it appears that NGC 1737 has to be accepted as a nebula and possible cluster, and SL 87 = KMHK 235 is that possible cluster. Still it is important to note that SL 87 = KMHK 235 is *not* strictly equivalent to the NGC 1743 designation, since it is not the name of the nebula. One ends up with the following identifications:

- NGC 1737 = h 2698—nebulous cluster or group
- NGC 1743 = Δ114 = h 2699—nebulous cluster or group
- NGC 1745 = h 2702—nebulous cluster or group
- NGC 1748 = h 2704—nebulous cluster or group
- IC 2114 = Fleming (or HN) 86 = Hen N 83C—nebula associated with NGC 1748.
- SL 87 = KMHK 235—cluster in NGC 1743.
- Hen N 83—Overall nebulosity in this area.
- Hen N 83A—Nebulosity involved with NGC 1743.
- Nen N 83B—Nebulosity involved with NGC 1737.
- Hen N 83D—Nebulosity in the middle of the triangle formed by NGC 1737, NGC 1743, and NGC 1748.
- LH 5—Association, including all of the above.

NGC 1783, NGC 1787 = LH 15, and SL 178 : Some modern references (LH [Lucke and Hodge 1970, 173], ESO, KMHK, Morel [1983, 2]) confuse the identities of these objects in the LMC. NGC 1787 = LH 15 is clearly (by John Herschel's description and position) a large (23′ diameter) association. It includes a number of clusters, including NGC 1783, SL 152, SL 178, [HS66] 84, and LW 100. In particular, it should not be confused with SL 178. Positions and diameters given in this catalog for NGC 1783, NGC 1787, and SL 178 have been measured from the DSS.

NGC 1785: There is a typographical error regarding the position of this object in Archinal [1993, 52]. John Herschel's (1830.0) discovery position should read 4^h 59^m 21^s NPD 159° 6′ 15″. The value in the table there [Archinal 1993, 22] is correct. This is his no. 147 in a list of objects in the Large Magellanic Clouds [Herschel 1847, 157].

Updating this position to 2000.0 gives 04^h 58^m 33^s –68° 51.3′. On the DSS just north of this position, there is a 4′ diameter group of stars, including nine in a NE-SW line (as well as a large plate defect in the same line about 7′ SW). Stretching the image in various ways does not show any nebulosity here so this would appear to be an asterism. However, since some physical association may be possible, the type in the catalog is given as "ast?." This group includes HD 268840 (V = 12.6), HD 268845 (V = 12.4), and HD 268856 (B = 11.4).

M. Morel, in his various publications, confirms this identity. In his *Catalogue of LMC Clusters and Nebulae* [1992] he lists this at (1950.0) 04^h 58^m 46^s, –68° 55.7′ (which is exactly the same as Herschel's position), and describes it as "Asterism; no cl.." He also (in his *Identification Charts for Some NGC Objects*, [private communication, 1995]) shows a chart of this same area and highlights the line of stars. He adds that this is one of several "finder charts for NGC objects not correctly identified in Hodge and Wright Atlas of LMC."

NGC 1798 = C0508+475: The *Lund Catalogue* alias list incorrectly calls this cluster "NGC 1789" (line 216, also line 1755: "Berkeley 16 = C0508+475 NGC 1789"). There is further information on this cluster where this problem was originally noted in [Archinal 1993, 52].

NGC 1802: This is W. Herschel's VIII.41. It was observed only once by him on December 7, 1785, sf 98 (k) Tauri (by 12^m 11^s, 0° 54′): "A co. Cl. of st. or projecting point of the m. way" [Dreyer 1912, 1, 363]. This area has now been recently observed visually a number of times. A. Lamperti in 1990 [mail of September 2, 1993], R. Poole [Hynes 1994], one of us [BA] in 1994, and D. Riddle in 1995 [private communication, 1995] all report observations. Unfortunately, Poole and Riddle point out a larger group of stars than the one described by Lamperti and BA.

Here the smaller group is favored due to a good match with Herschel's position (reduced to 2000.0: 05^h 10^m 09.6^s +24° 05.6′), but the identification should not be considered conclusive. Lamperti gives an observation (of October 21, 1990 in the Pocono Mountains) with a 33.3-cm (13.1-inch) *f*/5.17 at 70x, as "about 11 stars in a "dipper shape." This group was seen by one of us [BA] at the Warren Rupp Observatory, Mansfield, Ohio, using 79-cm *f*/7 Newtonian and described as about 10 stars with maybe 15 fainter ones in a 15–20′ field following 103 Tauri. The group includes its brightest star HD 241219 (V = 9.9), and just preceding the group is 103 Tauri (V = 5.5).

The observation of the larger group by D. Riddle is repeated here:

> "I observed the area of NGC 1802 with a [25-cm *f*/6] reflector on the evening of Dec. 20 and made the following notes. A rather large scattered group of ~80 stars, about 60′ X 12′ with the major axis running North to South, closely following the star 103 Tauri. Not as rich or as condensed as NGC 1746–50–58 which precedes this area. NGC 1802 appears more like an 'island' of stars in a rather barren field. LDN 1540–42–44 are to the NW and the LDN complex of 1547–48–49 is to the NE. These areas are very star poor regions and make the area of NGC 1802 seem quite rich by comparison. This area seems to match Herschel's description of a 'projecting point of the m. way.'"

Poole's observations [Hynes 1994] were made with a "20-cm, *f*/6 reflector under urban skies with a limiting magnitude of about 4.5, and seeing Ant. II—III." His description is:

> "NGC 1802 Long stream of stars, 8′ wide and 50′ long distantly curling about 103 Tau. The stream begins E. and slightly N. of 103 Tau at a triple and a wide double. It then flows S.E., S., and S.W. to another wide double [apparently duplicate line deleted here] with a faint comes to the W. From this double, another curving arc proceeds E, then S.W. for about 12′, terminating near a reddish mag 9 star. Overall, this double-hump star stream has a population of 30 stars of mag 9 and below. Although probably too wide and sparse to be a true cluster, it is fairly well detached and a pretty scene."

NGC 1833, NGC 1837, NGC 1845, SL 232 = KMHK 545, [HS66] 104, LH 24, and LH 26: A careful comparison of J. Herschel's original observations of NGC 1833 (h 2765), NGC 1837 (h 2769), and NGC 1845 ("h 2070") has been made with the DSS (see Figure 4.60). Positions and diameters given here were measured from the DSS. NGC 1833 and NGC 1837 could be identified from Herschel's positions and descriptions. For NGC 1845 Herschel has two observations listed under his name "h 2070", which—when carefully read in conjunction with his second observation of NGC 1837, identifies this object as the very large association here. In fact, NGC 1845 contains

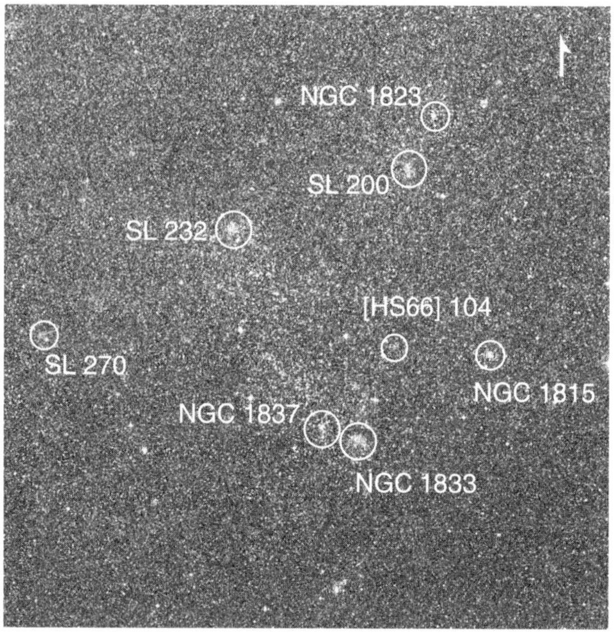

Fig. 4.60 *The Large Magellanic Cloud association NGC 1845, including the "sub-associations" LH 24 (the southwest portion of NGC 1845) and LH 26 (the northeast portion of NGC 1845). NGC 1833 is the obvious cluster at the bottom center, while NGC 1837 is the smaller cluster just to the upper left (northeast) of NGC 1833. SL 232 is the cluster at the upper left of the overall NGC 1845 association (upper left center in this image). The tiny [HS66] 104 (<15" in size) is the second nearly stellar object up from NGC 1833 (e.g. on the right side of the NGC 1845 association). Outside of the NGC 1845 association, NGC 1815 is the small cluster just below right center, SL 200 is the bright cluster at upper right center, and NGC 1823 is the cluster just above and right of it. SL 270 is the group at the left center edge. Shown here using histogram equalization of a 45' field of view DSS-S image. © ROE.*

NGC 1833, NGC 1837, another cluster farther to the northeast (which came to be known as SL 232), and a cluster to the northwest ([HS66] 104).

Unfortunately, most modern catalogs confuse the identity of NGC 1845. For example:

- Shapley and Lindsay [1963, 79] clearly identify their cluster no. 232 by its position and diameter, but mistakenly call it "NGC 1845, condensation in a rich field." In fact, the rich field here is the NGC 1845 association itself.
- Hodge and Wright [1967], following Shapley and Lindsay, also incorrectly assume in their atlas that NGC 1845 is the same object as SL 232.
- Lucke and Hodge [1970, 173], in their catalog of LMC associations, list *two* such objects in this area. Rather than catalog only the one large group seen by Herschel (NGC 1845), they chose to consider this as both a 16' x 10' association on the southeast (LH 24) and a (overlapping or adjacent) 17' x 10' association on the northeast (LH 26). Given this definition, they are correct in noting that NGC 1833, NGC 1837, and [HS66] 104 are in LH 24. However, they incorrectly indicate that LH 26 is the same object as NGC 1845—it is only the northeast portion of it.
- The RNGC, although citing *both* the conflicting SL and LH identifications, by its given position assumes that NGC 1845 is the SL 232 object only. *NGC 2000.0* made the same mistake, following the lead of the RNGC.
- Kontizas, *et al.*, [1990] (as KMHK 545) incorrectly follow the Shapley and Lindsay identification and list NGC 1845 as SL 232.

The only sources that have consistently identified NGC 1845 correctly until now are those by Morel [1983; 1990; 1992]. In any case, this catalog indicates NGC 1845 is the large (20′) association, LH 24 and LH 26 are two (approximately 10′ diameter) portions of that association, and the other objects are further parts of LH 24 or LH 26.

In a different problem, this time with respect to NGC 1833, Henize [1956] incorrectly says this is a nebula, his Hen N 190. In fact, J. Herschel makes no mention of a nebula here, so the NGC 1833 designation applies only to the cluster.

Similarly, *Uranometria 2000.0* (first edition) plots (and the *DSFG1e* lists) both NGC 1833 and NGC 1837 as bright nebulae (chart 444). However, both were identified by Herschel as clusters and not nebulae. In fact, no nebulosity is visible on a DSS image of the area so it seems unlikely that Herschel could have seen any nebulosity. Of course, Henize's Hα survey does show that NGC 1833 is involved in nebulosity, although he does not list any nebulosity in and around NGC 1837.

The KMHK catalog (KMHK 510) lists NGC 1833 as a "loose cluster."

NGC 1840: The identity of this cluster is difficult to establish, but in the catalog here it is assumed to be the cluster KMHK 529 (agreeing with the KMHK catalog). When John Herschel observed this object, he noted that his determined right ascension could be off, probably being 1 time minute too low. When his position is corrected and updated to 2000.0, it is $05^h05^m 40.6^s$ −71°45′ 24″. This is in between the clusters KMHK 529 and KMHK 551, but it is closer and at the same declination (which was apparently not in doubt) as KMHK 529. Unfortunately Herschel's description reads only (with abbreviation expanded) "Faint, round, brighter toward the middle, resolvable. Hardly visible through a thick haze." This is not enough to differentiate between the two clusters. However, since the position is closer and it appears slightly more obvious on the DSS, KMHK 529 is assumed to be the correct object.

This implies that the *DSFG1e*, which gives a position close to KMHK 551 is not correct in its identification, or, at least, position of this object.

NGC 1869, NGC 1871, NGC 1873, and LH 37: J. Kay has pointed out [private communication, 1996] that J. Herschel described NGC 1869, his h 2798, as a large cluster (e.g. "Cluster of 7th class, a fine L cluster of sc st which fills field. The point taken is the middle of 3 groups in the most condensed part."). This description does not match the cluster identified as NGC 1869 in Lauberts [1982], *NGC 2000.0*, and Morel [1983; 1990, chart 12]. There are 3 clusters (h's 3 groups) which are from north to south NGC 1873 = LH 36, LH 37, and NGC 1871 = LH 38 (see Morel's chart). However, clearly by h's description, NGC 1869 is the large star cloud, or association, containing all three groups and not the middle cluster, LH 37. The positions and sizes given here were measured from the DSS. Note that NGC 1869 and LH 37 still have the same position. LH 37 is also KMHK 671, which the KMHK catalog incorrectly identifies as NGC 1869.

NGC 1874 and NGC 1880: Some sources (e.g., SIMBAD and BRHT) list these objects as star clusters. M. Morel [1992, 4] correctly notes that both are *nebulae*. NGC 1874 is a nebula at (1950.0) $05^h\ 13^m\ 31^s$, –69° 26.0′, and NGC 1880 is a nebula at (1950.0) $05^h\ 13^m\ 58^s$ –69° 26.6′. Both lie in the association SL 320 in the LMC. These identities and coordinates have been confirmed by comparison of DSS images with the original observations, positions, and a drawing, all by John Herschel [1847].

Also, by comparing the coordinates of the BRHT 7a and BRHT 7b objects, it is clear that BRHT 7 is NGC 1874. Contrary to the BRHT publication, BRHT 7a and 7b are not clusters, but more likely just the two nebulous stars of NGC 1874 (and BRHT 7b is clearly not NGC 1880, as listed in the BRHT catalog). The positions given in the catalog here were measured from the DSS, the diameters are from BRHT, and the V magnitudes of the stars are from Morel [1990].

NGC 1893 = C0519+333 and IC 410: The *Lund Catalogue* alias list indicates that IC 410 is a part of the cluster NGC 1893. What is not clear is that IC 410 is only the *nebulosity* associated with NGC 1893. The nebula was discovered by Max Wolf [1892]. Although Wolf noted that there were involved stars, he mainly described the large diffuse nebula, and the cluster here already had the name NGC 1893. Therefore, the "cluster" style names for IC 410 (such as C0519+334 and OCl 438) should be denigrated.

The *DSFG1e* (chart 97) comments for NGC 1893 should indicate more clearly that IC 410 is the associated nebulosity. The separate IC 410 entry as an open cluster should be removed—the entry that this is a bright nebula can be left unchanged.

NGC 1896: This group of stars or possible cluster was listed with a –9° error in position in the GC and subsequent catalogs (the NGC and RNGC). Archinal [1993, 22] also lists the incorrect position (copied from the RNGC).

However, Alister Ling [private communication, 1994] has now observed this group, and Steve Gottlieb [private communication, 1994], Larry Sykora [private communication, 1997), and Harold Corwin [private communication, 1997] have apparently independently confirmed this identity. These confirmations are based on William Herschel's original observation of January 16, 1784 (his H.VIII.4) and offset position from β Tauri.

The DSS image shows a 20′ diameter scattered group of about 25 brighter stars (including 10 HD stars) over a rich Milky Way background. The brightest star of the group is at the southwest extreme. This is HDE 35348 (V = 8.51, K5). The group is centered on HDE 243448 which measured from the DSS is at (2000.0) $05^h\ 25^m\ 41.9^s$ +29° 19′ 42″ (the HD/HDE catalog position is poor). Although not an extremely obvious grouping, it is apparently striking enough visually and on the DSS that possibly this is a physical cluster, so it is listed with type "cl?."

NGC 1910: J. Kay [private communication, 1996] has pointed out that this designation has been applied to two different objects. One is a large loose cluster NE of S Doradus, and the other is a small cluster N of S Doradus. Lauberts [1982] and Morel [1990, chart 14; 1993] assign the NGC 1910 to the former object, while *NGC 2000.0* and the *DSFG1e* assign it to the latter.

The confusion would appear to trace back to J. Herschel's four original observations, which he listed under the designation h 2827. An examination of these observations leaves the question of which cluster is NGC 1910 since Herschel describes both clusters. Fortunately, the GC (also by Herschel) and NGC are clear on the subject, since they equate NGC 1910 (GC 1117) with Δ 129. Dunlop described this as "A pretty large and very ill-defined nebula, of an irregular round figure, with several small stars in it.." Further the GC and NGC give the same description, "Cl, L, pRi, iR, st 11...16," again of a large cluster.

To summarize, the large cluster is NGC 1910 = GC 1117 = Δ 129 = LH 41. The small cluster is SL 360. The identity of h 2837 is ambiguous, although it could be argued that Herschel had the larger cluster in mind since this was his identification in the GC. In any case, Dunlop discovered the large cluster (NGC 1910), and Herschel, the small one (SL 360). The LH and SL identifications here are from Morel [1983], the NGC 1910 position is from Kay, and the SL 360 position and the diameters have been measured from the DSS.

NGC 1925 = LH 45 and SL 415: John Herschel's original observation and position of NGC 1925 (his h 2837) has been checked against a DSS image of this area. It has been verified that it is a large (approximately 11′ diameter) association of scattered stars in the LMC. It was later cataloged as an LMC association (no. 45) by Lucke and Hodge [1970]. It is *not* a nebula as indicated by the *DSFG1e* and as plotted on *Uranometria 2000.0* (first edition) (chart 444).

Shapley and Lindsay [1963] describe their object no. 415 as "NGC 1925, small condensation in bright star region.", with diameter 15″. Clearly by its size this object could not be NGC 1925. M. Morel [private communication, 2002] has pointed out that SL 415 is a small 10″ diameter cluster at the position 05^h 22^m 01.9^s -65° 50′ 05″, and is also listed as the nonstellar object GSC 8890-00068″.

NGC 1932 and NGC 1933: Jenni Kay [private communication, 1996] has noted that NGC 1932 is a LMC star cluster, and NGC 1933 is an apparent stellar object preceding it. These objects were observed together by John Herschel (his h 2841) as a "A double neb; pos. 260°; dist 80″." Unfortunately, Herschel listed these out of right ascension order in the GC, and Dreyer repeated this listing order in the NGC. This was due to an error by Herschel in his description, where he used "first" and "second," rather than "larger" and "smaller" in the relative descriptions of these objects. Herschel recorded this in the notes to the GC (p. 19—and later the NGC notes, 215) but did not correct the catalog. H. Corwin [private communication, 1996] has suggested that, due to their right ascension order, the NGC names should be reversed. However, the identifications here are following the order of the actual NGC descriptions.

The position and diameter for NGC 1932 given in the catalog here were measured from the DSS. Other identities have also been noted including HD 271203, SL 420, and KMHK 825 (the later identity, thanks to M. Morel [private communication, 1996]). The SL (Shapley-Lindsay) compilation incorrectly indicated that no. 420 is "NGC 1922, 1923", when in fact it is the cluster NGC 1932. Some other modern compilations (Hodge and Wright [1967, 32], Morel [1992, 5; 1993, 24] incorrectly state that NGC 1932 and NGC 1933 are the same object.

The position and magnitude for NGC 1933 given here are from the GSC, since this is identifiable on the DSS image as the nonstellar object GSC 08890-00548. High-resolution observations or images are needed in order to determine the nature of this star-like object.

NGC 1947 and KMHK 878: Morel [1993, 27] noted that Hodge and Wright [1967] misidentify this galaxy as an LMC cluster. Similarly, R. Erdmann [private communication, 1995] noted that this galaxy is incorrectly listed as an LMC cluster in the catalog of Kontizas, *et al.*, [1990] (or KMHK 878). In J. Herschel's original observation of this (h 2855) he gave a position 1 degree too far south. This error was repeated in the KMHK catalog (and presumably by Hodge and Wright [1967]). S. Gottlieb [private communication, 1995] and B. Skiff [private communication, 1995] have confirmed that there is nothing at the KMHK position. The galaxy is listed here along with related data from the RC3 catalog.

There apparently is a cluster at the given position of KMHK 878, but it is very faint—visible only using histogram equalization while viewing the DSS image.

NGC 1963: D. Riddle [private communication, 1995] has identified and observed (38-cm telescope, 120x) this object as a "3"-shaped group of stars, 11th to 13th magnitude, about 10′ in size. S. Gottlieb has independently provided a similar identification, noting in particular that Vicker's CCD atlas [Vickers 1994b, 39] incorrectly associates NGC 1963 with the nearby IC 2135.

This identification and appearance is confirmed on the DSS. The "*8" described by J. Herschel is apparently GSC 07067-01021, at GSC magnitude 11. It is located just 10″ from Herschel's position updated only for precession, although his magnitude is a little too bright (if the GSC value is correct). There are 32 total GSC stars in the "3" figure. The DSS image shows these all to be fairly bright stars and part of a likely real star cluster. The diameter (14′) given here is from the DSS, and the position and magnitude of the brightest star are that of the above-mentioned GSC star.

NGC 1965 and NGC 1970: Although the *DSFG1e* (charts 444, 445) lists these as *both* clusters and bright nebulae at the same coordinates, they are indeed different objects (both are only nebulae). A check of John Herschel's original observations and drawing of this area [1847, h 2869, page 76, and plate VI, fig. 20, shown here as Figure 4.61 on page 159] verifies these identifications. In addition, it has been found that Morel's identification for NGC 1970 [1990, chart 19; 1992, page 7] is incorrect, being too far east. This whole area is involved in the cluster SL 476 = LH 58 (Morel's identification). As Herschel noted, the whole area of nebulosity involved with this cluster is Δ136 [Dunlop 1828, 119].

NGC 1974 = NGC 1991: There is no obvious star cluster in the LMC at J. Herschel's position (his h 2884) of NGC 1991. However, he clearly called this object "4th of a great line of rich clusters", observed in his sweep no. 760 on January 2, 1837. They were, from west to east: a) one whose position was "not taken" by Herschel (when observing h 2863 next), but which is clearly SL 456; b) Δ211 = h 2863 = NGC 1955; and c) h 2870 = NGC 1968. However, the fourth of these objects is Δ213 = h 2877 = NGC 1974, observed by Herschel in his earlier sweep no. 512 (November 23, 1834). He stated that this is part of the collection of clusters observed in his later sweep 760. Clearly, by his description, his h 2884 (NGC 1991) must be the same object as his h 2877 (NGC 1974). Further, if 1 minute of time is

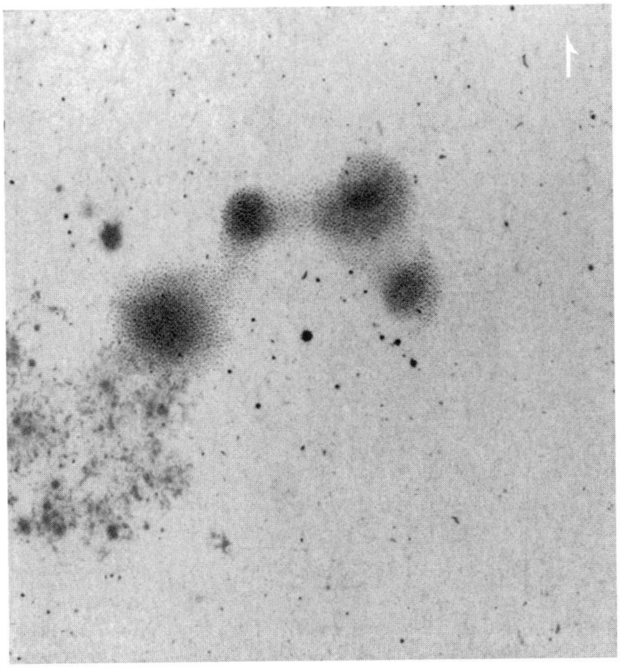

Fig. 4.61 *From left to right are shown here the nebulae NGC 1970, NGC 1966, NGC 1965, and NGC 1962, in J. Herschel's discovery drawing of this region (covering approximately a 20′ field of view—south was up in the original printing). Although this whole area is part of an association SL 476 = LH 58 and has many stars involved, clearly Herschel only discovered the 4 patches of nebulosity. From Herschel [1847, plate VI, fig. 20] (where it was printed with south down). Note that a number of the "dots" on this image and the black spot at right center are defects in the paper, and that the "splotchy" area on the upper right is also some sort of defect (perhaps mold) in the paper since it extends well off the plate itself.*

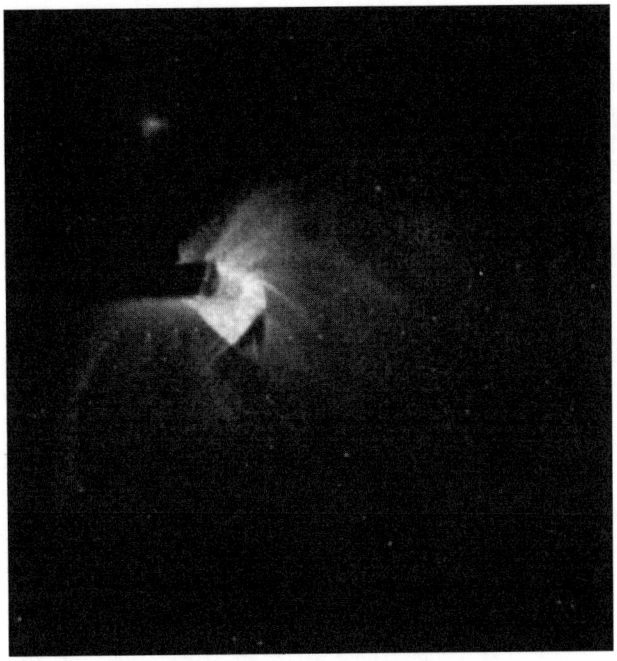

Fig. 4.62 *The Great Orion Nebula or NGC 1976 = M 42, including the Trapezium star cluster. Drawn by G. P. Bond from observations in 1859 to 1863 and engraved in 1864. Shown here with north up and east to the left (north was to the right in the original printing) and covering an approximate 0.5° field of view. From the* Harvard Annals *8 (1876), part 2, chapter 1, plate 27.*

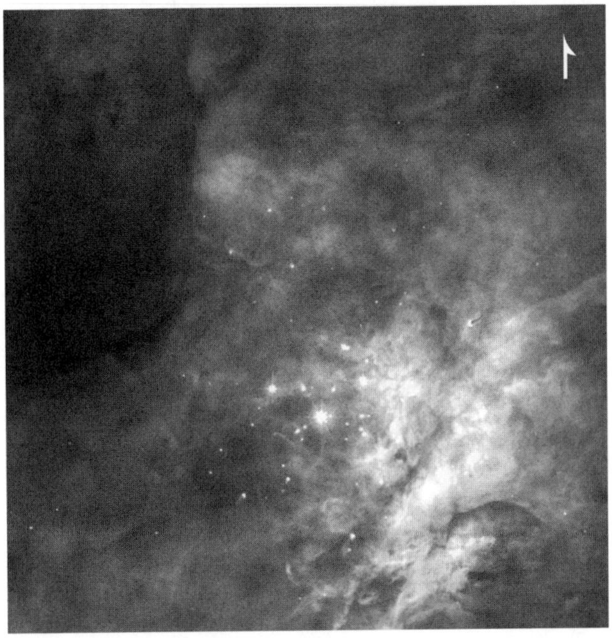

Fig. 4.63 *The central portion of the Great Orion Nebula or NGC 1976 = M 42, including the Trapezium star cluster, covering an approximate 7.3′ field of view. From WFPC2 HST images taken in 1994 and 1995. C.R. O'Dell and S.K. Wong (Rice University), NASA.*

subtracted from his measured right ascension for h 2884, the resulting position falls right on the 4th cluster here, i.e., NGC 1974.

Therefore, NGC 1991 is the same object as NGC 1974, with J. Herschel simply having recorded its position off by 1 minute of time.

NGC 1976 = M 42 = Trapezium cluster = C0532-054: Messier's original observations and the NGC note that M 42 = NGC 1976 consists of Theta-1 Orionis (Messier noted the four stars) involved in nebulosity (see Figures 4.62 and 4.63). Therefore, in terms of object type, M 42 should be considered a cluster involved in nebulosity.

There are also other problems regarding the name of this object in various catalogs. In the *Lund Catalogue* alias list, the primary name for this cluster is given as "NGC 1976." Yet in the main catalog and print file it is given as "Trapezium 1" (actually "30 1" in the main catalog). The primary name should probably be given as just NGC 1976 in all three files. In addition, the number "1" should be dropped from the Trapezium name in the *Lund Catalogue* files. Following the normal convention of the

DSFG1e, this should be listed there (charts 225, 226, 270, 271) both as a bright nebulae and open cluster. The name should be changed from "Trapezium" to NGC 1976 in *Sky Catalogue 2000.0* vol. 2.

NGC 1991: This is NGC 1974, see page 158.

NGC 2042, SL 601, and KMHK 1131: John Herschel [1847, 79] described a large "L" shaped irregularly figured or hooked cluster of stars, his h 2922, at the position of a 9th magnitude star. Clearly his description and position match that of a 9′ by 4′ LMC association known as LH 89. This association includes the nebulosity Hen N 135.

SL 601 = KMHK 1130 = BRHT 16a is a 70″ diameter cluster that lies in the northern part of NGC 2042. However, both the SL and BRHT catalogs incorrectly call this object NGC 2042.

Herschel's "star" is a possible LMC cluster cataloged as KMHK 1131 = BRHT 16b. The KMHK catalog incorrectly calls this NGC 2042. It actually lies at the center of the NGC 2042 association, and its position has been used here for that object. The KMHK and BRHT catalogs list this as a cluster, as does the catalog here, but the DSS shows the object as being nearly stellar in appearance.

NGC 2050 and NGC 2055: M. Morel [private communication, 2002] has pointed out that these LMC objects have often been misidentified in the past. He reports that NGC 2055 has been determined by J. Kay to be a very large star cloud, rather than a specific cluster or small association of stars. He also notes that J. Herschel's description of h 2928, which came to be known as NGC 2050, is consistent with a smaller association within NGC 2055, and these objects are so listed in the catalog here. He more specifically suggests that NGC 2055 includes 3 objects noted by Herschel: a) the cluster SL 609, b) a group of stars or possible cluster (known as BRHT 54b) 44″ south of [HS66] 371 = BRHT 54a, and c) an anonymous cluster (here called AH03 J0537.3–6919) at the position of GSC 9163-00556. Although Herschel's description is not complete enough to verify that these are the included objects, Herschel does mention [1847, p. 164, object 628] that he included this and other objects based on a drawing he made of the area of 30 Doradus. If this drawing could ever be located these identities could be completely confirmed.

NGC 2061: J. Herschel [1847, 79] observed this as his h 2924. He gives a position of $05^h\ 37^m\ 44.1^s$, 124° 01′ 59″ NPD (1830.0) and description "Cluster, 8th class; coarse, loose, and filling the field; stars 10...13m. Place, that of a double star in a vacant part."

D. Riddle [private communication, 1996] reports an observation of this cluster from Panacea, FL on March 19 and 20, 1996. His observation is as follows:

> In the same field following Alpha Columbae with my 18″ [46-cm] reflector and a 35 mm Panoptic eyepiece. A sparse, loose cluster of about 15 stars, 15 arc minute on a north to south axis, double star of equal magnitudes on the west side. The brightest member is plotted on the Uranometria charts. A "trapezium." Not a very impressive sight.

Fig. 4.64 *RCW 136, the inner core of the Tarantula Nebula star cluster, i.e., 30 Doradus. Planetary Camera 2 HST image of an approximate 6.5″ field. NASA/STScI.*

Particularly, in regard to the double star, this matches Herschel's description well. The DSS shows a group of 11 or so brighter stars with about 15 fainter background stars, all in a diameter of 10′. The group's center, relatively devoid of stars, is at (2000.0) $05^h\ 44^m\ 06^s$ −33° 56.1′. There is a faint edge-on galaxy on the NE side of the group, ESO 363-19 (or ESO 054237-3355).

NGC 2070: This is the famous Tarantula nebula and cluster, also known as the 30 Dor cluster (which contains RCW 136, shown here as Figure 4.64). The NGC does not clearly state that the NGC designation applies to the 30 Dor star cluster. Lacaille, the original discoverer (his "class 1, no.2"), considered this a nebula [Glyn Jones 1975, 46]. However, both the Δ142 and h 2941 observations, drawings, and (in the case of Herschel) actual catalog of stars involved imply that this object is a nebulous cluster. The *DSFG1e* agrees with this identification, listing this as both a nebula and cluster (although—as of this writing—SIMBAD does not).

The original Caldwell Catalog [Moore 1995] includes it as object 103 "NGC 2070" but calls it a bright nebula only. Therefore, it is not clear whether Caldwell 103 is intended to be only the nebula, or the nebula and cluster.

NGC 2088: The SL [Shapley and Lindsay 1963], RNGC, *NGC 2000.0*, and *DSFG1e* catalogs and the *Uranometria 2000.0* (first edition) atlas all give an incorrect position for this object. The KMHK catalog (no. 1227) gives a correct position (1950.0: 5^h 41^m 14.8^s –68° 29′ 14″) that is used here. S. Mencinsky [private communication, 1995] first noted the error in *Uranometria 2000.0* (on the cover of volume 2), and one of us [BA] confirmed that it had originated in the SL catalog, which then propagated to the RNGC and *NGC 2000.0*.

NGC 2094 = KMHK 1251 and KMHK 1260: The KMHK catalog incorrectly assigns the NGC 2094 identity to another object, KMHK 1260. In fact, KMHK 1251 is the real NGC 2094. John Herschel's position for this object (his h 2959), updated to 2000.0, is 05^h41^m 42.6^s –68°21′ 59″. There is nothing precisely at this position on the DSS, but following this is the cluster KMHK 1251, at 05^h42^m 06.9^s –68°21′ 42″. Therefore, KMHK 1260 (at 05^h42^m 13.7^s –68°55′ 02″) cannot be NGC 2094, and in fact, KMHK 1251 is NGC 2094.

NGC 2105: S. Mencinsky [private communication, 1995] has noted that some sources give a position for this object that is slightly off in declination. One of us [BA] found that Shapley and Lindsay (SL 687) gave coordinates that are too far north by about 30′; the RNGC used the same coordinates; and *NGC 2000.0* repeated the error. *Uranometria 2000.0* (first edition) and the *DSFG1e* also made the same error. The position (2000.0: 05^h 44^m 19.8^s–66° 55′ 02″) and diameter (48″) given here are measured from the DSS.

NGC 2134: S. Mencinsky [private communication, 1995] noted that *Uranometria 2000.0* (first editon) showed this as west of NGC 2133 instead of east of it. One of us [BA] found that Shapley and Lindsay (SL 760) gave correct coordinates of (1975.0) 05^h 52.4^m, –71° 07′. However, the RNGC, using the SL list as a reference, as an apparent typographical error, gave a 1975.0 RA of 05^h 50.4^m. This error propagated into *NGC 2000.0*, and apparently into *Uranometria 2000.0* and the *DSFG1e*. The position given here is updated from the 1950.0 one given by KMHK.

NGC 2158 = C0604+241: The RNGC incorrectly listed this as a globular cluster. The *Lund Catalogue* also incorrectly listed this as "globular?" in the alias list. As discussed in Archinal [1993, 56], this cluster has none of the properties of a globular cluster. It is not included in the globular cluster list of Djorgovski and Meylan [1993].

NGC 2168 = M 35 = C0605+243: Center difficult to determine due to very large cluster size (see Figure 4.65).

NGC 2175: This is the *nebula* around the cluster Collinder 84 (see page 118) and not the cluster itself.

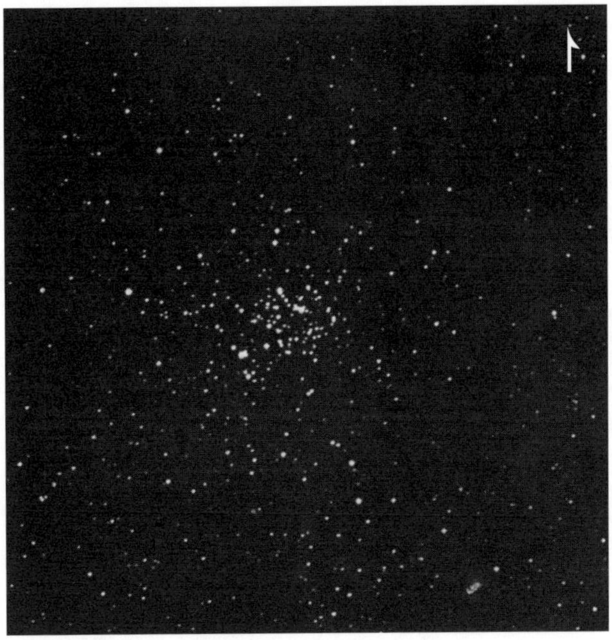

Fig. 4.65 *NGC 2168 = M 35, the large and famous cluster in Gemini. NGC 2158 is located in the lower right portion of this field, but its stars are too faint for it to appear in this approximately 2° field of view exposure. Photograph from Raab [1922, plate 7].*

NGC 2175.1 = C0607+206: Ideally the names "NGC 2175.1" and "NGC 2175s" for this cluster should be denigrated, since these names are not original to the NGC. Where possible, this cluster should probably just be referred to as C0607+206.

This cluster is incorrectly named NGC 2175 in the *Lund Catalogue* main data file and in the second part of the alias list ("NGC 2175s = C0607+206 NGC 2175").

NGC 2189 and NGC 2198: NGC 2189 is supposedly two clusters and NGC 2198 is supposedly a single cluster, both discovered by J. H. Safford with the Harvard 38-cm (15-inch) Merz and Mahler refractor, as reported by Bond [1863, 194].

NGC 2189: (Bond's "7a" and "7b") is listed as "Two Clusters, seen 1863 March 19 near two stars of the 10, 11th magnitude by J. H. Safford with the Great Refractor. In Harvard Zones." The positions of the stars are given as (1863.0) 06^h 04^m 44.9^s +01° 08′ 37″ and 06^h 05^m 47.2^s +01° 10′ 02″.

With such precise positions, these stars are identifiable as those in Table 4.1, Part A.

Both stars have two entries in the GSC (from different plates), but only one of each is shown here.

Unfortunately, between and around these stars there is no obvious cluster. The western star, GSC 00131-01117, does have a loose north-south group of eight stars following it. The eastern star, GSC 00131-01065, has 4 stars of

Table 4.1

Part A

GSC-id	2000.0 RA (h,m,s)	2000.0 Dec (°,′,″)	Position error (″)	Magnitude	Magnitude error	Plate type
0013101117	06 11 52.16	+01 06 58.9	0.4	12.26	0.47	00TV
0013101065	06 12 54.58	+01 08 06.0	0.3	12.19	0.47	00TV

Part B

GSC-id	2000.0 RA (h,m,s)	2000.0 Dec (°,′,″)	Position error (″)	Magnitude	Magnitude error	Plate type
0013101266	06 14 19.49	+00 58 16.4	0.4	9.85	0.47	00TV
0013100888	06 13 48.43	+00 58 05.4	0.4	10.67	0.47	00TV

equal brightness preceding it. However, in neither case are these what could be considered clusters.

NGC 2198: (Bond's "8") is listed as "A Cluster, seen 1863 March 19, by J. H. Safford, between two stars in the following position. With the Great Refractor. In Harvard Zones." The positions of the stars are given as (1830.0): for star of "10.11 mag." $06^h\,06^m\,27.8^s$ +01° 01′ 10″, and for the star of "9.10" magnitude $06^h\,07^m\,12.7^s$ +01° 00′ 27″.

These stars are identifiable in Table 4.1, Part B. The western star has two entries in the GSC (from different plates) but only one is shown here.

Unfortunately, once again, the DSS shows no obvious cluster between these two stars. The only thing between the stars is a slight condensation at $06^h\,14^m\,08^s$ +00° 58.0′ (2′ diameter, 11 stars). There is a grouping just south of GSC 00131-00888, at $06^h\,13^m\,49^s$ +00° 55.0′ (2′ diameter, 10 brighter and 10 background stars). There is also a triangular grouping of stars above the GSC 00131-01266 (actually double) star, at $06^h\,14^m\,18^s$ +01° 01.6′ (5′ diameter, 25 stars). However, none of these objects really stand out from the rich Milky Way background, and only the first condensation explicitly matches Safford's position.

Robert Erdmann, Jr. [private communication, 1996] relates an attempt at observing these objects (with a telescope of unknown aperture). At the position of NGC 2189, Erdmann reports there is nothing obvious. For NGC 2198, he does in fact say that: "This one is very obvious visually. [It's] a sparse, irregular cluster about 15′ in diameter, and indeed does lie between two stars, one about 10th mag and the other about 11th mag. It forms an irregularly shaped "ring" or "circlet" of about 12 to 13, 11th to 12th magnitude stars. Two 11th mag stars lie close together just slightly off center inside the "ring" of the cluster." Although, at first glance this would seem to indicate the object was located, it appears likely that the two 11th magnitude stars close together were the stars Safford designated. This description is possibly of a group of stars around Safford's stars rather than between them.

In any case, it seems clear that the existence of these objects is in doubt. Further visual observations may eventually help to determine what it was Safford saw. For now these objects are listed here as "not found?."

Fig. 4.66 *NGC 2218, the small group of stars (and likely asterism) at the center of this image. This identification is made probably for the first time since its discovery by E. J. Cooper in 1853, by comparison with Cooper's original position. 17′ field of view. Image courtesy the Palomar Observatory and Digitized Sky Survey created by the Space Telescope Science Institute, operated by AURA, Inc. for NASA. Reproduced with permission from AURA/STScI.*

NGC 2218: This object was discovered by E. J. Cooper on January 13, 1853. It was first reported in his *Markree Catalogue* Volume 3 [Cooper 1854, 53], at a given position of 06 15 50 +19 24.9 with the notation "Faint cluster." This information is essentially repeated by A. Auwers [1862, 226] who lists this as his object no. 22.

Just northwest of Cooper's position on the DSS is a small (1.2′ diameter) triangular shaped asterism of about 20 stars (to the limit of the DSS). This is assumed the correct object. The position, diameter, and number of stars given here were measured or estimated from the DSS image, shown here as Figure 4.66. It includes stars GSC

1336-00358 (GSC magnitude 12.0), 1336-01104 (13.1), and 1336-00698 (11.5).

NGC 2226: This is the "compressed core" portion of the cluster NGC 2225. The size of this "core," as measured on the DSS, is about 47″ in diameter.

NGC 2232 = C0624-047: As noted by S. Gottlieb [private communication, 1995], the position of NGC 2232 is too far to the west in most sources, including the RNGC, *Sky Catalogue 2000.0*, the *Lund Catalogue*, *NGC 2000.0*, *Uranometria 2000.0* (first edition), and the *DSFG1e*. When listed, its size appears to be too small in these sources, with the overall group of stars (measured from a DSS image) about 53′ in diameter. This cluster was discovered by William Herschel on October 16, 1783, and listed by him as his number 25, class 8 ("Coarsely scattered clusters of stars") object with description "The 10 Monoc. surrounded by many Bst." Although he gave the position as that of 10 Mon (V = 5.035, B2V), the overall group appears to be centered just west of there. The second brightest star of this group, HD 45321 (V = 6.141, B2.5V), is just northwest of this position.

NGC 2237 and NGC 2244 = NGC 2239 = C0629+049: NGC 2237 is the Rosette Nebula (see Figure 4.67). It has been given the name C0627+050, use of which should be avoided since the NGC 2237 designation applies to the nebulosity only. NGC 2244 is the Rosette Nebula cluster. Alister Ling [letter of September 2, 1992] has noted that NGC 2239 is the same cluster as NGC 2244. The separate entry for NGC 2239 should be removed from the *Lund Catalogue* (and the equivalence with NGC 2244 added to the alias list). *Sky Catalogue 2000.0* Vol. 2 is also incorrect having a separate entry for NGC 2239. Further details are given in [Archinal 1993, 58].

Some sources (SIMBAD currently and the original *Caldwell Catalog*) give a position for the Rosette Nebula that is too far east in RA by almost 2 time minutes. The position given here is that of HD 46150, V = 6.75, the brightest star near the center of the "hole" of the nebula.

The original *Caldwell Catalog* lists the nebula as its number 49 and the cluster as number 50. The nebula, as with many references, is incorrectly named "NGC 2237-9," when, as noted above, it is NGC 2237.

NGC 2239: See previous entry.

NGC 2243 = C0627-312: Kaluzny, *et al.*, [1996] as part of a search for W UMa variable stars, plot the star density vs. radius for this cluster [Kaluzny, *et al.*, 1996, 308]. The curve flattens out at 250″, implying a cluster diameter of 8.3′. However, stars beyond the 300″ radius continue to show a main-sequence (to 450″, or 15′). The 8.3′ value is used here for the cluster diameter since it more closely determines the diameter where the cluster would appear to merge into the stellar background. Note that this is a larger value than the 5′ of the *Lund Catalogue*. In any case, the Kaluzny, *et al.*, study revealed two W UMa and three detached eclipsing binary systems.

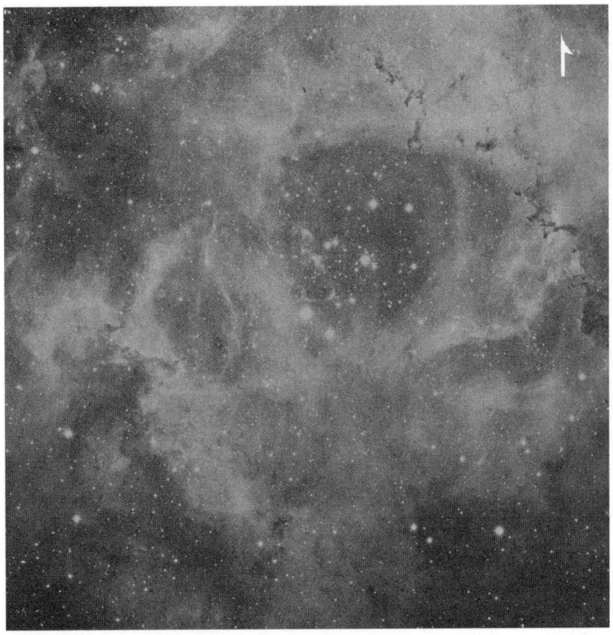

Fig. 4.67 *A portion of the famous Rosette Nebula (NGC 2237), showing at its core the Rosette Nebula star cluster NGC 2244 = NGC 2239. The star cluster and nebula is an easy naked-eye object from a dark site. 1° field of view DSS-S image. © ROE.*

NGC 2244: This is the cluster in the Rosette Nebula. See above under NGC 2237.

NGC 2249: S. Mencinsky [private communication, 1995] has noted that the real NGC 2249 is 5′ south of the RNGC position. One of us [BA] has determined that the position was originally wrong in the Shapley and Lindsay [1963] list (SL 893), and that this incorrect position propagated into the RNGC (with only a minor 0.1m change in the RA). *NGC 2000.0* repeats the error, using the RNGC as its source. *Uranometria 2000.0* (first edition) and the *DSFG1e* also make the same error. The position obtained from the DSS is (2000.0) $06^h\ 25^m\ 50.0^s\ -68°\ 55'\ 12''$. The diameter is 56″ for the main concentration and a maximum of 85″ including outliers.

NGC 2253: The identity of this object, William Herschel's VII.54, is discussed in Archinal [1993, 59–60]. It was proposed that this is a small group of stars observed in approximately the correct position for this object by A. Ling.

However, Ling has now pointed out [private communication, 1995] that this group of stars is probably not the correct object, and that NGC 2253 is likely the galaxy UGC 3511. This identification was apparently suggested by Su-

Fig. 4.68 *NGC 2262, an impressive, but previously "lost" cluster, positively identified using William and John Herschels' original positions. Apparently Collinder [1931] published a position that was quite far off, but which was repeated by most later 20th century references. 17′ field of view. Image courtesy the Palomar Observatory and Digitized Sky Survey created by the Space Telescope Science Institute, operated by AURA, Inc. for NASA. Reproduced with permission from AURA/STScI.*

san French, assuming that Herschel had made a 30′ error in the declination (this being about 30′ south of Herschel's discovery position). However, H. Corwin [private communication, 2002] has recently pointed out that it is unlikely that W. Herschel would have called this small faint galaxy a class VII star cluster.

Therefore, the true identity of NGC 2253 continues to be unclear, although it is listed in the catalog here as the group of stars originally noted by Ling.

NGC 2262: One of us [BA] has investigated the identity of this object after being contacted by Timo Karhula [private communication, 1998]. With a 44-cm telescope at 100x power, Karhula was unable to observe any cluster-like object at the position cited by *Sky Catalogue 2000.0*, Vol. 2 or *MegaStar* software. He did, however, notice a group of stars 18′ ESE that had the appearance of a real cluster on the DSS, see Figure 4.68.

The original discovery positions were checked in order to verify that this group was the correct object. NGC 2262 was first seen by William Herschel (his H.VII.37) and John Herschel (h 400). Once it was ascertained that WH's "77 Ori" is now known as HR 2334 in Monoceros, a re-reduction of his observations resulted in a position on the east side of this group—with only about a 1′ error. John Herschel's position, once updated to 2000.0, is dead-on (with 1″ accuracy) for the northern "comp part" of the cluster that he noticed. The NGC position also matches that of both of the Herschel's quite well.

The question arises as to why this position was incorrect in later references. It appears that Collinder listed the position incorrectly in 1931. Shapley [1930] and Trumpler [1930] did not list this cluster, but Collinder did, as his no. 109 at (1900.0) 06^h 33.2^m +01° 16′ (which updates to (2000.0) 06^h 38.4^m +01° 11′). He says in his notes that this cluster is not visible on the Franklin-Adams charts, so it is not clear where he got this (bad) position. Collinder's poor position must have propagated forward. As Karhula noted, *Sky Catalogue 2000.0* has a similar position. Lyngå's 1987 *Lund Catalogue* has nearly the same position, as does the *DSFG1e*. *NGC 2000.0* repeats the *Sky Catalogue 2000.0* position. SIMBAD also had the incorrect position, but has since been corrected.

This appears to be yet another case of a perfectly real and impressive cluster having been partly "lost" because someone got the position or identity wrong. SIMBAD only cites one reference for this object—not surprising since it would have been hard to find without the correct position.

The information in this catalog was obtained after an examination of the DSS image. The total diameter of 4′ and number of stars of approximately 180 includes the outer reaches of the cluster, although there is clearly a more concentrated inner portion only about 2′ in diameter with about 80 stars total. The Trumpler type of II2r was also estimated and matches fairly well the Ruprecht [1966] value of I2p. Lyngå estimated II1m. It is surprising that they did not notice the positional error.

NGC 2282 = IC 2172 = BFS 54: This is the nebulosity around Cl vdB 85, see page 118.

NGC 2287 = M 41 = C0644-206: This bright cluster in Canis Major is visible to the unaided eye under favourable conditions, 4° south of Sirius (see Figure 4.69). It is partially resolved in binoculars and makes a fine sight in a rich-field telescope. On the southwest edge of the cluster lies the V = 6.08 star 12 CMa (= HK CMa). The first major study of NGC 2287 was undertaken by Cox [1954] who obtained magnitudes and colors of 106 stars in the area using a photoelectric photometer on a 61-cm refractor. From these observations an angular diameter of 30′ was found together with a distance of 0.725 kpc. A more recent survey was undertaken by Feinstein, et al [1978], and their paper gave a useful summary of data from the more important papers in the intervening period, together with a photographic finding chart identifying some of the stars mentioned in the text. 12 CMa was thought to be a cluster member having a similar radial velocity to the mean of the confirmed member stars. If it is indeed a genuine cluster member, it does have some peculiarities. Among the observed stars, seven were reported as being possible red giants; in addition, a

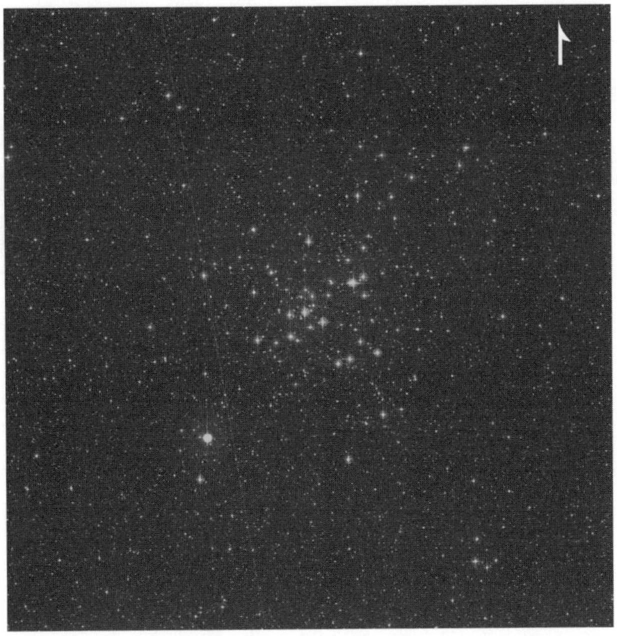

Fig. 4.69 *NGC 2287 = M 41, the beautiful naked-eye cluster, about 4° south of Sirius in Canis Major. Many references give a position for this cluster that is 1 time minute too far east. The dotted line is a satellite trail on the original 78′ field of view Sky View/DSS-S image © ROE.*

Fig. 4.70 *NGC 2323 = M 50, the 15′ diameter naked-eye cluster in Monoceros. 30′ field of view DSS-S image © ROE.*

yellow star (HD 49126) appeared to be slightly variable with an observed range V = 7.24–7.33. The distance of NGC 2287 is given as 0.63 kpc, almost identical to that of Collinder 121, 4°.6 away in angular separation. Since this would equate to only 60 pc at the estimated distance, there may be some physical connection.

Note also that the NGC and RNGC, under the 2287 designation, incorrectly called this M 14 (noted by Mallas and Kreimer [1978, 95]). Also many references (the NGC, RNGC, *NGC 2000.0* [Sinnott 1988], the *Lund Catalogue*) give a position for this cluster that is 1 minute of RA too high. The correct position is (2000.0) $06^h\ 46^m.1$, –20° 46′. See Archinal [1993, 60] for more information.

NGC 2314: This is a galaxy that has been incorrectly identified as a cluster in the past. The use of the name "C0703+753" should be avoided. The position, total V magnitude, UGC, and PGC aliases available here were obtained from the RC3. The position was checked via the DSS and found good to 1″.

NGC 2323 = M 50 = C0700-082: B. Skiff has suggested [private communication, 1998] that the center of this large cluster can best be defined as the position of the star BD –08° 1700 (see Figure 4.70). That position is used here.

NGC 2409 = Bochum 4 = C0728-168, and Bochum 5: Brian Skiff has noted [private communication, 1995] that NGC 2409 is Bochum 4. Therefore, NGC 2409 should be the preferred name and added to the *Lund Catalogue* alias list. Skiff also gives the position as that of the "dominating (but non-member) central star BD-16 1994 at" (2000.0) $07^h\ 31^m\ 37^s$, –17° 11.4′.

One of us [BA] has also determined from the DSS and the discovery reference [Moffat and Vogt 1975a] that Bochum 5 is definitely a separate cluster of stars. It is a larger group of bright stars to the northeast of NGC 2409—at (2000.0) $07^h\ 32.1^m$ –16° 57′. It appears to have approximately 50 stars that stand out from the background and includes some nebulosity, apparently part of vdB 97 = Sh2 302 = RCW 7. The Trumpler type from the *Lund Catalogue* should be changed to note the nebulosity. It is given as I2pn in this catalog.

NGC 2422 = NGC 2478 = M 47 = C0734-143: This cluster has two NGC designations, NGC 2422 and NGC 2478. The latter is from Messier's listing of the cluster at an incorrect position, and the former from William Herschel's rediscovery of the cluster. The total magnitude includes the approximate combined magnitude for ADS 6216 (HD 60997 and HD 60998), centrally located in the cluster (see Figure 4.71 on page 166).

From a strict historical perspective it can be argued that the name NGC 2478 should be preferred since Messier discovered it first. However, the 2422 designation is kept here as the primary one due to historical usage after Messier's error.

NGC 2428 and NGC 2430: A re-reduction shows that William Herschel's original observations of these objects on December 31, 1785 are essentially correct. They are his VIII.47 and VIII.46 respectively.

A 30′ DSS image shows a reasonable concentration of stars—possibly a real cluster—that is NGC 2428. This lies at (2000.0) $07^h\ 39^m\ 18^s$ –16° 31.0′, right on H's position (the RNGC and *NGC 2000.0* positions match this as well). The diameter is hard to estimate since the field is rich, but it is roughly 13′ including approximately 50 stars.

D. Riddle reports [private communication, 1996] an observation with his 46-cm (18-inch) telescope at 65x: "About 60 stars in two parallel streams running to the north-west. About 45 arc minutes across. The surrounding star fields are as rich, but this cluster stands out because its stars are brighter. This cluster compares well with Ruprecht 151 that lies just to the northeast. The streams of stars are aligned from the NW to SE." His size of 45′ is too large, even including a number of brighter stars around the periphery of the main cluster. Herschel says the stars are of "equal size," so he must not have intended those as included stars. If the cluster is extended along Riddle's star streams to the NW (past HD 61486, V = 8.7), it reaches 18–20′ in maximum extent.

NGC 2430 appears as a smaller group at the top of this same image at (2000.0) $07^h\ 39^m\ 30^s$ –16° 20.4′, diameter 7.5′, and including about 20 brighter stars. This does not quite match H's description of a "vL" type VIII cluster, but it is a reasonable concentration at the correct position. Herschel's "vL" actually better matches the whole 3/4 degree field, including his NGC 2428; but since he observed these objects *at the same time,* he must have had these two groups in mind. The *NGC 2000.0* position is reasonable, but the RNGC position is too far west. Included stars are HD 61612 V = 10.4) and HD 61553 (at V = 8.0, the latter is the brightest star of the group). Riddle describes this apparent asterism as "a coarse scatter of about 15 stars, ~20 arc minutes. A pretty field."

It should be noted that in Archinal [1993, 24 and 64] NGC 2428 is incorrectly listed as H.VIII. *48*. The [p. 64] description under "NGC 2428" is also of H.VIII.48 = NGC 2260, and *not* of NGC 2428.

Fig. 4.71 *NGC 2422 = M 47 = NGC 2478, the large (25′ diameter) naked-eye cluster in the (northern hemisphere) winter Milky Way of Puppis. 1° field of view DSS-S image © ROE.*

NGC 2451, PMG 1, and PMG 2: A large but relatively poor grouping, NGC 2451 is a pretty object in a small aperture, appearing as a spiral of stars centered on the orange-colored c Puppis (HD 63032), V = 3.61 (see Figure 4.72). It was first studied in depth by Feinstein [1966] and Williams [1966, 1967a], who both carried out photometry on stars in the region. The latter made measurements of 213 stars, concluding that the stars did form a cluster and derived a distance of 0.33 kpc and an age of 2.3 x 10^7 years. In a following paper Williams [1967b] also suggested that NGC 2451 and Collinder 140, and perhaps Cr 135 and Cr 173, are associated forming an old OB association. A more recent investigation was carried out by Levato and Malaroda [1975] who measured the spectral types of 23 stars in the central area of the group. The *lucida*, or brightest star, c Pup, was found to be of type K5 IIa; in addition, another K giant and two G8 giants were also suggested to be members of a cluster. A distance of 0.29 kpc

Fig. 4.72 *NGC 2451, a group of stars that has recently been determined via proper motion studies [Röser and Bastian, 1994] to not be physically associated. However, some of the stars in this field are associated as part of the Puppis Moving Groups 1 and 2. 120′ x 110′ field of view DSS-S image © ROE.*

was determined, but it was noted that the "cluster" required more radial velocity and proper motion studies.

Röser and Bastian [1994] have determined via proper motion studies that the group of stars known as NGC 2451 is not a true cluster, i.e., the stars are not physically associated in space. However, they do point out the likely existence of a true association here and the possible existence of a second association. They term the first association the "Puppis Moving Group" and provide no name for the second. In this catalog, these are listed as PMG 1 and PMG 2.

PMG 1 is a common proper motion group of at least 24 stars, situated in the sky in a 4 square degree area around NGC 2451. The brightest star is HD 61831 (V = 4.83), and a distance of 220 pc is estimated from the cluster CMD. PMG 2 is a possible common proper motion group of up to 16 stars at the same location in the sky. This group of stars shows a CMD that indicates a distance of 400 pc with the brightest star being about V = 6.3. (No size is indicated for this group.) The position of NGC 2451 (originating from the *Lund Catalogue*) is used for both of these objects. It is unlikely that these objects would stand out during a visual inspection of this area (or an image of it) without reference to Röser and Bastian's data.

Later work [Platais, *et al.*, 1998], via the use of Hipparcos data, has confirmed the existence of PMG 1 as a true cluster. However, the cluster has unfortunately had the name "NGC 2451B" associated with it, a clearly incorrect and spurious name since there is no mention of this group in the NGC itself.

B. Skiff has reported that NGC 2451 is too large to easily check its position using the SkyView utility and the DSS.

NGC 2568 = Pismis 1 = C0815-369: The *Lund Catalogue* notes these names as being equivalent in the alias list, but uses the Pismis name as the preferred name. Obviously the NGC name should have priority. This cluster should not be confused with the "Pismis" cluster, better known as Haffner 16 (see page 132).

NGC 2579 = C0819-360, and AH03 J0822.2-3624: The CDS February 20, 1995 version of the *Lund Catalogue* contains a slightly different position than the ADC version for NGC 2579. Neither is as precise as a DSS position (measured by one of us [BA]) of (2000.0) $08^h\ 20^m\ 53^s$ $-36°\ 12'.8$. NGC 2579 (see Figure 4.74) is mostly a quadruple star involved in nebulosity (which SIMBAD indicates is known as Gum 11), but in a rich Milky Way field. There is likely no physical cluster here at all, but if so, the Trumpler type should include nebulosity (should be changed to "IV 2 p n").

A further mystery though is that at the original ADC version position of (2000.0) $08^h\ 22.2^m\ -36°\ 24'$, there actually is a group of about 20 stars over a 12′ diameter. In the catalog here, this group is named (for the first time) AH03 J0822.2-3624 (see Figure 4.73). Did Lyngå or someone else see this on the POSS or otherwise observe it instead of the real NGC 2579? There are several stars listed in this area of the sky in SIMBAD with "NGC 2579" designa-

Fig. 4.73 *AH03 J0822.2-3624. This sparse group of stars lies at the Lund Catalogue (NASA/ADC version) position given for NGC 2579, but it is not NGC 2579. See Figure 4.74 for an image of the true NGC 2579. 17′ field of view DSS-S image © ROE.*

Fig. 4.74 *NGC 2579, a quadruple star involved in nebulosity (appearing as a nebulous pair of stars at the center of this image). DSS-S image © ROE. 17′ field of view SkyView/DSS-S image © ROE.*

Fig. 4.75 *NGC 2632 = M 44 = Praesepe or the Beehive cluster, the large easily naked-eye cluster in Cancer. Photograph from Bailey [1908, plate 1, figure 2], with a 90′ field of view.*

Fig. 4.76 *The large group NGC 2669 in Velor, containing the condensation of fainter stars (at center) Harvard 3. 30′ field of view DSS-S image © ROE.*

tions—indicating that someone likely was observing in the wrong area. New measurements may be needed both on this group and the real NGC 2579 in order to determine if either is a physical cluster. The brightest star of this group is HD 70742 (V = 9.5, B8/B9II). HD 70679 (V = 10.4, A0V), and HD 70697 (V = 11.1, A) are also in this group.

NGC 2632 = M 44 = Praesepe = The Beehive: Brian Skiff has noted [private communication, 1995] that the oft given position for this cluster "is that of 39 Cnc = HD 73665, which is at the edge of the main body of the cluster, about 20′ north of 'truth.'" He suggests a better position to be that of "the central red giant cluster member, HD 73710" located at (2000.0) $08^h\ 40^m\ 22^s$ +19° 40.2′. The latter position is given in this catalog. See Figure 4.75.

NGC 2645 = C0837-460: van den Bergh and Hagen [1975] (as vdB-Ha 40) and Brian Skiff [private communication, 1995] have independently noted that this is the same object as Pismis 6. Therefore, NGC 2645 should be the preferred name for this and added to the *Lund Catalogue* alias list. Skiff gives the position as that of the "nearly-central pair HD 73919/CoD-45 4352″ at (2000.0) $08^h\ 39^m\ 04^s$, –46° 13.6′. This matches John Herschel's position of (apparently) the same star (HD 73919) at (1830.0) $08^h\ 33^m\ 20.5^s$, NPD 135° 37′ 39″; or (2000.0) $08^h\ 39^m\ 00.7^s$, –46°13′ 26″.

NGC 2669 and Harvard 3: Harvard 3 = C0845-527 is a condensation of fainter stars within a larger cluster with brighter stars, NGC 2669 = C0843-527 (see Figure 4.76). However, the proper identification of these objects and several other objects cataloged in this area is sorted out here for the first time.

The identification of NGC 2669 is still not absolutely certain, but very likely. It was discovered by John Herschel on April 11, 1834, his object "h 3140." Herschel gave a position of (1830.0) $08^h\ 40^m$ ± NPD 143° 21′ ±, and a description "Cluster VIII class. A L, poor, loose cl of stars, 10....14m." [Herschel 1847, 89] At Herschel's position there is no obvious cluster. The DSS shows only a few scattered faint stars, which although fitting his described magnitude range, have no appearance of a cluster.

It was Robert Trumpler [1930, 175] who found the most likely candidate for Herschel's missing cluster, by noting "NGC 2669.—Declination of NGC corrected by +1°." Sure enough, one degree north of Herschel's position and slightly east is a cluster fitting Herschel's description.

Some question remains whether this really is the correct object. The brightest star (HD 75105) shines at magnitude V = 7.69, which seems low for the "10....14m" values given. It is well known that Herschel underestimated (in brightness) magnitudes in this range (in comparison to the modern magnitude scale) so the magnitude difference is not unreasonable. There is the question of the position though. Why did Herschel assign a ± sign to his right ascension and north polar distance? Was there some problem with his "sweep" as he searched for stars that evening in a long declination strip? This was his sweep no. 440, and it turns out there are almost no other objects observed in that sweep that we can check. However, he did discover h 3219 [Herschel, 1847, 93], which today is known as NGC 3105.

This catalog gives (measured from the DSS) a 2000.0 position of 10^h 00^m 39^s –54° 47.3′ for this cluster. Herschel measured a position (updated to 2000.0) of 10^h 00^m 40.3^s –54° 47′ 13″. The difference is only 12 arcseconds—without accounting for precession, nutation, proper motion, etc. Clearly, Herschel was having no trouble measuring positions that night. Apparently the ± he used merely meant that the cluster was very large, and he was giving a position for the approximate center. One must assume that he simply made a blunder in writing down the north polar distance off by 1°. However, he also measured the right ascension a little too far west. This can only be explained by some further error, or by the assumption he was giving an approximate value—accurate to only 1 or 2 minutes of time in right ascension.

In any case, we assume in this catalog that it is the obvious cluster—about one degree north of Herschel's (and the NGC's) position that should be referred to as NGC 2669.

Many other problems have arisen in the identification of this cluster. For one, the NGC lists the 10th century Arabic astronomer Al Sûfi as an observer—i.e., the discoverer—of this cluster. As the late Kenneth Glyn Jones [1975, 9] explained in his useful book, *The Search for the Nebulae*, the identification of h 3140 with Al Sûfi's 8th object was proposed by H. Schjellerup in 1874, in his French translation of Al Sûfi's work. However, Glyn Jones points out that G. Bigourdan later proposed that it is far more likely that the object Al Sûfi observed was the much larger cluster IC 2391 about 1° to the west.

In the same year (1930) that Trumpler identified the likely NGC 2669, H. Shapley, in his famous *Monograph* on Star Clusters, listed a new object at nearly the same position known as Harvard 3. Yet Shapley gives a size of only 7′ and says the fifth brightest star was 10.4. This does not fit well with the large group that Trumpler found with a diameter of 14′. It also does not fit well with the number of stars in that area brighter than magnitude 10. Had Shapley found a different cluster? An examination of a DSS image of this area does show a large cluster with mixed bright and faint stars. However, a closer look shows that the center of the cluster has the bulk of the fainter stars. In fact, it must have been this condensation in the larger cluster to which he referred. Shapley's position does not match the true position of this condensation very well, but this is true of many of his positions (e.g. for Harvard 5). In addition, an examination of the Franklin-Adams chart no. 33—which shows this area of the sky—reveals that the coordinate graticule overlay poorly matches the sky coordinates. Thus, if Shapley used the F-A chart (as he likely did), a poor position was almost guaranteed.

The following year in 1931, P. Collinder published his dissertation on star clusters. He included both star clusters in this immediate vicinity. NGC 2669 was listed as his number 199, and Harvard 3 as number 202. The Cr 202 information is similar to Shapley's concerning Harvard 3, with Collinder giving only a slightly larger size (10′) but an identical position. And the Cr 199 information is indeed similar to Trumpler's, with sizes of 15′ (estimated by Lundmark, Collinder's dissertation adviser) and 12′ (estimated by Collinder). However, Collinder apparently did not notice that Harvard 3 was essentially part of NGC 2669—presumably he (and Lundmark) looked for these clusters on the F-A charts at different times. He too gives poor positions—for both objects.

Many years later, the Harvard 3 cluster was discovered yet again, this time in 1975 by van den Bergh and Hagen as their object no. 52. Once again, the association with the probable (larger) NGC 2669 was missed.

The *Lund Catalogue* addressed the problem designations here by just assigning them all to one cluster, i.e., making NGC 2669, Harvard 3, Cr 199, and Cr 202 all the same object (also called C0843-527 and OCl 768). VdB-Ha 52 (or C0845-527) is listed as an entirely separate object, with no indication that this is Harvard 3 in the middle of NGC 2669. The given positions are also poor. The *DSFG1e* gives an entry only for NGC 2669, but with a poor position.

After checking out all of these identification problems, we are left with two "clusters," one inside of the other. The overall large cluster should be known as NGC 2669, with the included smaller cluster of fainter stars, Harvard 3. This catalog includes these objects in that fashion, with positions, diameters, and numbers of stars estimated from the DSS. The brightest star in NGC 2669 is HD 75105 (V = 7.69, B8III/IV).

NGC 2682 = M 67 = C0837+120: This cluster was discovered prior to 1779 by Johann Gottfried Köhler, as reported by J. E. Bode in the 1780 publication of the *Astronomisches Jahrbuch* for 1782 [Glyn Jones, 1975, 50-52]. This preceded the independent discovery of this object by Messier on April 6, 1780. This rich open star cluster lies only 1.8° west of the V = 4.2 star α Cancri (see Figure 4.77 on page 170). It is visible to the unaided eye from a good site and was seen in that fashion by one of us [BA] at the 1994 Texas Star Party. NGC 2682 is unusual in several respects, not the least of which is that it is so far from the Galactic plane. This would suggest that, like the Hyades, it is very close, or, alternatively, it is very ancient, having remained intact for many circuits around the Galaxy and gradually having been perturbed into an orbit which takes it above the normal range for open clusters. In this case it is the latter interpretation which is correct. From a visual inspection one might intuitively guess this because of it being so condensed and rich with faint stars. If the nearby explanation was correct, the cluster would be larger

Fig. 4.77 *NGC 2682 = M 67, the old and rich open cluster in Cancer, a naked-eye object from a dark sky. 1° field of view. Image courtesy the Palomar Observatory and Digitized Sky Survey created by the Space Telescope Science Institute, operated by AURA, Inc. for NASA. Reproduced with permission from AURA/STScI.*

Fig. 4.78 *NGC 2818, an open cluster and planetary nebula in Pyxis. Note that the NGC 2818 designation applies to* both *objects, and not one or the other. Many references incorrectly call the planetary nebula "NGC 2818A." 17′ field of view SkyView/DSS-S image © ROE.*

and the stars more separated and individually brighter. However, the evidence for its great age is from its photometry and spectrometry. Important studies of the colors and magnitudes of stars in NGC 2682 were undertaken by Johnson and Sandage [1955], and Eggen and Sandage [1964], observing stars down to 16th magnitude. The spectral types of the stars were found to range from B9 to K4, and when plotted on to an H-R diagram, it is clear that most of the brighter stars have evolved away from the Main Sequence and form a pattern which bears a remarkable similarity to a weakly populated globular cluster. This is reinforced by the presence of a population of "blue stragglers"; stars which lie to the blue side of the Main Sequence turn-off point and, which, had they been normal stars, one would have expected to have evolved towards the red giant phase. The most comprehensive photometric study of NGC 2682 to date is that of Gilliland, *et al.*, [1991] who have reported on extensive CCD photometry of the core region of the cluster and provide UBVR measures of 257 stars. More accurate Cousins BVRI photometric data for a much smaller number of stars (29) is provided by Chevalier and Ilovaisky [1991]. As far as practical photometry techniques are concerned, NGC 2682 has been found useful as a CCD standard-star field because it contains a large number of moderately bright, well-separated stars of color indices ranging from B – V = –0.1 to 1.4, all within a few square arc minutes. The old open clusters of the Galaxy are useful tracers of the structure, formation and evolution of the disk, and in recent years some observers have undertaken spectroscopic investigations in order to improve the basic data. As a result of this, the age of NGC 2682 has been refined to around 5.0 Gyr, a reduction on some previous estimates, but still making it among the half dozen or so oldest known open clusters in the Galaxy.

NGC 2818 = C0914-364: The first observation of this object was made by James Dunlop [1828] from Paramatta, in New South Wales, Australia, and was cataloged by him as Δ564. He noted the cluster first with a smaller nebulosity involved (see Figure 4.78). John Herschel also observed this field, listing it as h 3154 and describing it as a planetary nebula in the field of an open star cluster. In the NGC description it appears that the 2818 designation is applied specifically to the planetary nebula. However, to complicate matters, its presence in the cluster is mentioned, but the cluster is not given any separate designation. Arguably, from the historical records, the designation NGC 2818 could be said to apply to the cluster/planetary nebula combination, but this may cause confusion. In an attempt to resolve the matter, Sulentic and Tifft [1973] split the two objects in the *RNGC*, calling the open cluster NGC 2818 and the planetary nebula NGC 2818A. However, there are no historical grounds for this, and we feel that this designation should be avoided. A more satisfactory solution might be to identify the planetary nebula as NGC 2818, and identifying the cluster by one of its alternative designations, Melotte 96 or Collinder 206.

Fig. 4.79 *NGC 2982 = Ruprecht 80, an obvious group of 15-20 stars in Vela. 24′ field of view SkyView/DSS-S image © ROE.*

Fig. 4.80 *NGC 3247 = Westerlund 2, a small (1.1′ diameter) but nebulous cluster of approximately 25 stars, at the center of the image here. See Figure 4.81 for a histogram equalization stretch of this same*

Of course, the presence of a planetary nebula within an open cluster might just be a projection effect, as it is in the more well-known case of NGC 2438 and the cluster NGC 2437 (= M 46). Evidence of a genuine physical association in the case of NGC 2818/2818A, though, was first provided by Tifft, *et al.*, [1972] who noted that the radial velocity of the nebula was similar to that of two stars in the cluster. Further observational evidence of the association was also presented by Dufour [1984] based on an analysis of its physical properties and chemical composition. This occurrence is very important in the study of planetary nebulae, which are notoriously difficult to investigate because of the problems of measuring their distance. In this instance the distance, size and progenitor mass can be determined to an unusual degree of accuracy. The cluster itself is not otherwise particularly exceptional, being an intermediate-age Population I grouping at a distance of some 3.5kpc.

Brian Skiff [private communication 1995] gives a position for the cluster of approximately (2000.0) 09^h 16^m 10^s –36° 37.1′, a value which is used here. He also gives the position of the planetary nebula as (2000.0) 09^h 16^m 01.48^s –36° 37′ 36.5″ and notes it is GSC 7164-3813.

NGC 2982 = Ruprecht 80 = C0940 - 438: The DSS shows (see Figure 4.79) an obvious group of 15–20 stars at Ruprecht's position, and this group matches well the description by Ruprecht (Ru 80) and John Herschel (h 3184 = NGC 2982). Although Herschel's coordinates (both in his Cape Observations and the GC/NGC) are off, there are no other candidates for his object in this area. His description also matches well, especially once one realizes (as suggested by Steve Gottlieb [private communication, 1996]) a "preceding * 10′m" in his description is one of "two of 10′m" he also describes. "10′m" here is assumed to mean 10th magnitude, although the meaning of the single quote is uncertain. However, it seems clear that NGC 2982 and Ru 80 must be the same.

NGC 3105: On the DSS, this cluster has an oval shape and is very similar in appearance to one of Isserstedt's [Isserstedt and Schmidt-Kaler, 1968] "stellar rings."

NGC 3218 = NGC 3183: Archinal [1993, 67] describes how NGC 3218 is a duplicate identity for the galaxy NGC 3183.

NGC 3231: This is identifiable on the DSS as a possible star cluster centered at (2000.0) 10^h 27^m 29^s, +66° 47.9′ and with a rough diameter of 9.5′ and 19 stars. This is a very good match for J. Herschel's (h 704) position (2000.0) 10^h 26.8^m +66° 48′, and description ("A cluster of 20 stars more or less, 10, 11, and 12 m, scattered over a space of 10′ diam. A star 7 m s."). The "star 7 m s" is HD 90318, V = 7.9. B. Skiff [private communication, 1995] had previously identified this object as the "diamond-shaped asterism of seven stars" on the west side of the possible cluster cited here.

NGC 3247 = Westerlund 2 = C1022-575, and Collinder 220: NGC 3247 and Westerlund 2 are the same nebulous star cluster, see Figures 4.80 and 4.81. John Herschel was unable to determine a good position for this object when he discovered it (even though he observed it

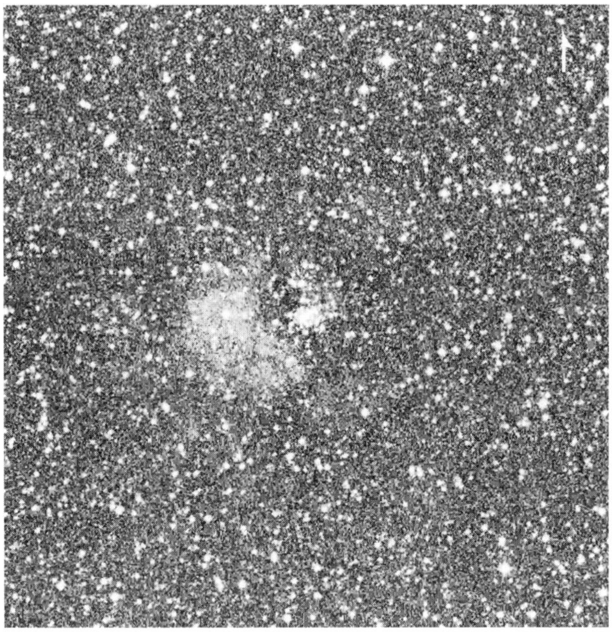

Fig. 4.81 *NGC 3247 = Westerlund 2. This is a histogram equalization stretch of the 17′ field of view SkyView/DSS-S image shown in Figure 4.80. © ROE.*

Fig. 4.82 *NGC 3446, a likely cluster of about 26 stars in a diameter of 6.5′. The ringed galaxy ESO 264-G047 is at center left. 17′ field of view SkyView/DSS-S image © ROE.*

three times), and his poor position propagated into the NGC and later catalogs. However, he did see a cluster and nebula here, so the preferred name is NGC 3247. A DSS image shows that the cluster consists of about 25 stars and is 1.1′ in diameter, centered at $10^h\ 24^m\ 01^s$ –57° 45.5′. The nebula, however, is about 4.5′ in size and centered at $10^h\ 24^m\ 11^s$ –57° 45.7′.

Unfortunately, due to the poor original position, Collinder mistakenly thought he had found NGC 3247 when he apparently discovered a new object, his Cr 220. The DSS shows this to be a scattered group of some 50 stars, about 10′ in diameter, centered on $10^h\ 25^m\ 52^s$ –57° 55.6′. NGC 3247 was listed in this position in many later catalogs. This is probably why Westerlund [1960] thought he had found a new cluster (Westerlund 2) when he came across the real NGC 3247.

The cluster identified in the *Lund Catalogue* as NGC 3247 should be named (only) Collinder 220. It is unclear if the other data given for this cluster should apply to the real NGC 3247 or to Collinder 220. The *Lund Catalogue* distance reference for NGC 3247 is to a "private communication" ("Buscombe, W.:1978") that cannot be easily checked. The ESO catalog correctly identifies ESO 127-SC18, equivalent to "OCl-807" (the real NGC 3247). However, it incorrectly identifies the Cr 220 cluster ESO 127-SC19 as "N 3247 = OCl-809." The *DSFG1e* lists only NGC 3247 and apparently identifies it correctly, although not with as good a position as given.

Alternate names for the cluster NGC 3247 are h 3250, GC 2106, OCl 807, We 2, vdB-Ha 95, C1022-575, and ESO 127-SC18. The use of the names OCl 809 and C1024-576 should probably be avoided since they were assigned to NGC 3247, but at the position of Cr 220. The nebula NGC 3247 is also known as Gum 29, RCW 49, Bran 300B, GRS 284.30 –00.30, and GRS 284.31–00.33. The only alternate name for Cr 220 is ESO 127-SC19.

Brian Skiff (in his 1995 list of cluster positions) should be acknowledged as the first source to indicate the confusion over the NGC 3247 name, and Harris and Harris [2000] first clearly stated the likely equivalence of NGC 3247 and We 2 that resulted in further checking.

NGC 3446: This object appears on the DSS as a possible real cluster at (2000.0) $10^h\ 52^m\ 17^s$ –45° 09.6′, see Figure 4.82. It contains about 26 stars in a diameter of 6.5′. There is a good match with J. Herschel's (h 3301) two positions and descriptions, including his diameter of 7′. Brian Skiff originally noted [private communication, 1995] the visibility of this group on the DSS, but gives a slightly different position and diameter (including additional stars to the west). He notes the presence of a "nice faint (R)SB0/a galaxy at the E edge of the group," which S. Gottlieb [private communication, 1995] has identified as ESO 264-G047 at (2000.0) $10^h\ 52^m\ 37.7^s$; –45° 09′ 44.7″ with position angle 65° and a size of 1.3′ X 1.0′.

NGC 3503 = Pismis 17 = C1059-595: NGC 3503 should be the preferred name for what is indicated to be Pismis 17 in the *Lund Catalogue* (the NGC 3503 name is not even present in the alias list). One of us [BA] has checked John Herschel's and Pismis's original descriptions against a DSS image of this area. The *DSFG1e* (chart 427) incorrectly lists this object under both names. The duplicate Pismis 17 entry should be deleted. (Actually only the machine readable version and the printed *DSFG1e* index list it this way—the chart 427 printed table only lists NGC 3503 and does indicate it "was Pi 17.")

Also note that Pismis's original estimate of the diameter as 0.6′ (given in some *Lund Catalogue* and other references) appears to be too small. A size of 1.5′ has been estimated from the DSS and used here. The involved nebula (also known as NGC 3503) is about 1.0′ by 1.5′ in size.

NGC 3519 = Ruprecht 93 = C1102-611: Brian Skiff has pointed out [private communication, 1995] and one of us [BA] confirmed that NGC 3519 is the same cluster as Ruprecht 93. J. Herschel's original (h 3314) position and description match well that of Ruprecht [Alter, *et al.*, 1966]. This area has also been observed by J. Kay [private communication, 1996] with a 20-cm (8-inch) Schmidt-Cassegrain telescope. She further confirmed the position and description and noted that there is only one cluster. The Skiff position is used here, (2000.0) $11^h\ 04^m\ 03^s$ –61° 22.1′. It is that of the primary star GSC 8958-2086, of a 7″ double star. Ruprecht's diameter of 4′ and listing of 28 stars seems essentially correct.

The *Lund Catalogue* does not list the NGC 3519 identity. This name should be added to the alias list, and by discovery priority, it should be included there and in the other catalog files as the primary name.

NGC 3572 = Collinder 239 = C1108-599: The identity of this object has sometimes been confused since Collinder [1931, B12] unfortunately labeled it "NGC 3572b." This is as opposed to Collinder 240 (see page 120) his "NGC 3572a," inside of which this cluster is contained. The position and diameter given here were obtained via the DSS.

NGC 3676: In Archinal [1993, 69], following a suggestion by B. Skiff, it is assumed that this object is a group of stars. At the NGC position, there is a small asterism of 5 stars. However, S. Gottlieb [private communication, 1995] has pointed out that 30′ south of this position, at (2000.0) $11^h\ 25^m\ 37.5^s$ –11° 08′ 23″ is the galaxy MCG –02-29-029. This galaxy matches the original discovery description by Muller (no. 436 on the list by O. Stone from Leander McCormick Observatory) including "2 st 10 nf, sf." The McCormick NGC observations are well known for their poor positions (see for example, the NGC, page 10). It appears reasonable to assume that Muller made a 30′ error in reading the declination. In addition, accounting for only precession, his right ascension was only 3^s too far west. Clearly this galaxy is the correct object (and not the group of stars).

Fig. 4.83 NGC 4184 = Ruprecht 102, a sparse possible cluster, or perhaps just an "absorption hole" in the Milky Way in Crux. The "tear" at the left edge is a defect in this 17′ field of view SkyView/DSS-S image. © ROE.

NGC 4184 = Ruprecht 102 = C1210-623: One of us [BA] has found that there is no cluster at the *Lund Catalogue* position given for Ru 102, but nearby at J. Herschel's position for h 3384 (NGC 4184) is a cluster fitting the *Lund Catalogue* description. Therefore, the preferred name of Ru 102 should be changed to NGC 4184, and the position given as (2000.0) $12^h\ 13^m\ 39^s$, –62° 43′ 26″ (measured from the DSS). See Figure 4.83.

NGC 4409 = NGC 4420: Archinal [1993, 69–70] describes in detail how NGC 4409 is a duplicate identity for the galaxy NGC 4420. The position given here is that of NGC 4420 from NED, where a total B magnitude (from the RC3) of 12.92 is listed. The size (also from the RC3) is 2′ by 1′.

NGC 4426 = NGC 4427: As pointed out by Harold Corwin, J. L. E. Dreyer long ago (in the NGC notes [p. 220]) stated that these are the same object. The name NGC 4426 has priority, since it is the d'Arrest discovery (NGC 4427 is a Bigourdan discovery). In the Second IC [p. 372] it is pointed out that this is just two stars. The position and size given here were measured by one of us [BA] from the DSS. The brighter (SE) star is GSC 01991-00329, GSC magnitude 16.2. The separation of the stars was measured as 14."

NGC 4439 = C1225-598: The second part of the *Lund Catalogue* alias list has the wrong (alternate) OCl number

Fig. 4.84 *NGC 4755, John Herschel's fabulous "Jewel Box" cluster in Crux. 24′ field of view DSS-S image © ROE.*

for this cluster. It is "OCl 884.1." (E.g. it currently reads: "OCL 84.1 = C1225-598 NGC 4439").

NGC 4755 = C1250-600: One of the most striking and spectacular open clusters visible in the southern sky, NGC 4755 lies near the V = 1.20 variable star β Crucis and near the edge of the great dark nebula, the Coal Sack, see Figure 4.84. It was discovered by Lacaille but is commonly known as "Herschel's Jewel Box" after Sir John Herschel noted [1847, 17] that the color of its stars "give it the effect of a superb piece of jewelry" and is dominated by the bright, blue B5Ia supergiant star κ Crucis, which has an absolute magnitude of $M_v = -7.0$ (V = 5.90). As an object of some prominence, NGC 4755 has been studied by a number of investigators, UBV measurements first being made by Arp and van Sant [1958]. In this instance, photoelectric photometry was carried out on 17 stars and photographic photometry on another 202. The first significant spectral observations were made by Feast [1963], who measured MK spectral types and radial velocities of 35 stars. In the course of this survey a number of supergiant stars were detected. Subsequently, UBV photometry of 60 stars was presented by Perry, *et al.*, [1976], who also measured 37 of them in the *uvby*β system. A major UBV photometric survey was performed by Dachs and Kaiser [1984] who presented photoelectric magnitudes and colors for 86 stars and photographic magnitudes and colors for an additional 553 stars in and around NGC 4755. Analysis of the measurements resulted in the identification of 203 probable cluster members brighter than magnitude 16.0. The cluster stars are generally of spectral type B, but there are a number of red stars in the field as well; however, most of these are non-members. A distance of 2.3 kpc was derived and an age for the cluster of between 8–11.5 million years. A more recent study was conducted by Sagar and Cannon [1995], who carried out UBVRI CCD photometry of 813 stars reaching down to V ~20 mag. Visual fitting of the ZAMS to the cluster sequence gives a cluster distance of 2.1±0.2 kpc. The reddening across the cluster appears to be variable with a mean value of E(B−V) = 0.41 mag. and a range of about 0.05 mag. Also, the authors found that the dispersion in the evolutionary ages of the cluster members suggested that star formation in the parent molecular cloud of the cluster could have continued for at least 6–7 million years. The data indicates that massive stars formed about 4 million years before the bulk of the low mass stars.

NGC 5120 = Ruprecht 166 = C1322-631: Lauberts [1982] listed this cluster as ESO 96-SC11 and noted the equivalency of NGC 5120 and Ruprecht 166. One of us [BA] confirmed it by comparing J. Herschel's description (his h 3496) and position with Ruprecht's [Alter, *et al.*, 1966, 5], and this area on the DSS. The position given here is from Lauberts ((1950.0) $13^h\ 22^m\ 18^s$, −63° 11.9′), while the other data originates from the *Lund Catalogue* (for Ru 166).

The *Lund Catalogue* does not list the NGC 5120 identity. This name should be added to the alias list, and by discovery priority, it should be included there and in the other catalog files as the primary name.

NGC 5284: J. Herschel discovered this object [1847, 106, h 3532], describing it as "Cl class VIII. L; v rich; loosely sc; st 7.8....16; it is an outlier of the milky way [sic], but very rich and much insulated." A careful re-examination of that observation shows that Herschel's reference star was HD 119744 (V = 9.3). The "object" is a roughly 20′ diameter patch of Milky Way following that star. There are several patches of dark nebulosity in this area, which are probably what Herschel refers to when he says "much insulated." This object is identified here (for the first time since its discovery) as the Milky Way patch, centered on the star HD 119837 (V = 10.6).

Lauberts [1982] listed this as "ESO 133-? 04." However, an examination of the ESO entry shows that this must have been nothing more than a "placeholder" entry for NGC 5284. The "?" in the name, a "OC ?" comment, and a 1 arcminute position indicate that there was no recognition of the Milky Way patch as the correct object. The ESO entry is included as an alias name here.

NGC 5460 = C1404-480: NGC 5460 is a large and moderately rich cluster to the east, and slightly south of ζ Centauri (V = 2.60). In 1931, Collinder [1931] reported that it contained 45–50 stars spread over a field some 50

Fig. 4.85 *NGC 6067, a rich cluster with approximately 100 stars in a 12′ diameter, and located in Norma. 30′ field of view DSS-S image © ROE.*

Fig. 4.86 *NGC 6087, the "S Normae cluster" an irregularly shaped 15′ diameter grouping around the variable star S Normae (nominally V=6.54). 30′ field of view DSS-S image © ROE.*

arcmin in diameter. In 1971, Clariá [1971] performed UBV photoelectric photometry on 64 stars down to magnitude 13 in and around the cluster and Hβ photometry on 16 of these. Analysis of the data showed that at least 37 of the observed stars were members and that the cluster was aged somewhere between the Pleiades and the α Persei cluster (about 40 million years). A distance of 0.78 kpc was derived. The most comprehensive photometric survey of NGC 5460, by Clariá, *et al.*, [1993], provided UBV observations of 155 stars brighter than mag. 14.0; 65 of these are probable members of the cluster. A number of red stars found in the sample examined are not believed to be members. In this instance a distance of 0.74kpc was found but a considerably greater age of 1.1 Gyr.

NGC 5822 = Lodén 2104 = C1501-541: Brian Skiff noted, while examining a draft copy of the second edition of *Uranometria 2000.0*, that NGC 5822 appears to be the same group as Lodén 2104 (whose existence was derived here and, therefore, in the draft *Uranometria* from an entry in SIMBAD). Indeed this becomes obvious when Lodén's discovery paper [1979b] is referred to, where he notes that this group consists of "candidate" stars for membership in the cluster NGC 5822. So in this catalog, Lodén 2104 is simply given as an alias name for NGC 5822.

NGC 6067 = C1609-540 and NGC 6087 = C1614-577: In the rich southern Milky Way fields of Norma, not far from the direction of the Galactic center, lies the small, rich open cluster of NGC 6067, see Figure 4.85. It has a membership of about 100 stars in a field only 12′ in diameter. The importance of this cluster lies in its possible association with two Cepheid variables, QZ Nor (= HD 144972, 3.7864-days) which lies 18 arcmin from the cluster center, and V340 Nor (= CPD –53°7400A, p = 11.287 days) which lies 2 arcmin from the cluster center. The former was recognized as a Cepheid perhaps belonging to NGC 6067 by Eggen [1980, 1983] who found a common distance of about 1.32 kpc. However, he suggested that the latter, despite its greater proximity, was actually a member of the background Nor OB1 association. The richness of the field and the superposition of the cluster against the association makes membership and distance determinations difficult. A further investigation was carried out by Coulson and Caldwell [1985] who published UBVRI photometry and radial velocity data. They concluded that both Cepheids were likely to be cluster members with a common distance of 1.74 kpc. Another Cepheid, GU Nor, lies at a distance of about 1° from the cluster center and is, therefore, not likely to be associated.

The original *Caldwell Catalog* [Moore, 1995] mistakenly lists its object 89 as "NGC 6067," when by the position, magnitude, and alternate name "S Nor Cluster," this object is in fact NGC 6087 (see Figure 4.86). NGC 6067 is about 4 degrees north-northwest of NGC 6087 (and S Normae)

NGC 6087: See previous entry.

NGC 6216 (C1645-446) and NGC 6222 (C1646-446): As noted in [Archinal 1993, 72–73] these objects were discovered by John Herschel as h 3648 and h 3650, respectively. Herschel's observations of these objects, although not made at the same time, clearly indicate that separate 4′ and 20′ diameter objects (respectively) were observed. The *Lund Catalogue* alias list is, therefore, incorrect in listing these objects as equivalent. The 4′ diameter object it describes is clearly NGC 6216 (incorrectly called NGC 6222 in the main catalog files). Collinder also incorrectly assumes these objects are identical [Collinder 1931, B37] and wrongly associates Cr 314 with NGC 6222, since Collinder and Lundmark give sizes of around 4′ for Cr 314.

A search should still be made for the 20′ diameter NGC 6222. Unfortunately the DSS shows nothing resembling Herschel's description at his position (2000.0: 16^h 50^m 46.5^s –44° 43′ 33″). The designations OCl 989, Melotte 152, and Raab 114 require checking to see which object they apply to, although it seems likely they refer to NGC 6216 (the only obvious (4′ diameter) object in this area).

While reviewing a draft of this book, M. Morel, S. French, and P. Teutsch [private communications, 2002; e-mail from Morel to amastro list, 2002—see Appendix E] independently all proposed that NGC 6222 might be a possible concentration of stars, southeast of Herschel's position. The proposed area covers a diameter of 50′ (Morel) or 20′ (French and Teutsch) centered on 16h 52^m 50^s –44° 29′ (Morel), 16^h 51^m 36 s –44° 43.2′ (French), or 16^h 51.6^m –44° 24′ (Teutsch). Morel notes that this concentration is not visible on the DSS, but is visible by plotting stars in the area, and on chart 355 of Vehrenberg's *Falkau Atlas*. Star counts in the –44° zone of the *Cordoba Durchmusterung* also showed an increase in this area.

Unfortunately, the identification of stars in these areas with Herschel's object is still problematic. As Tom DeMary [e-mail to amastro list, 2002—see Appendix E] and French note, there are three fairly bright stars (TYC 7880-4155-1, V = 9.36; TYC 7880-2242-1, V = 9.59; and TYC 7880-2148-1, V = 9.75) in this area that Herschel should have seen. The fact that he did not mention such a prominent triangle of stars is suspicious. As with several other objects discovered by the Herschels, the identity of this object will probably have to await a thorough check of the original manuscript observations, and even then may still not be certain.

As a final aside about NGC 6222, the *Lund Catalogue* alias list indicates that NGC 6222 has been canceled from the catalog; its entry should not have appeared in the main file of that catalog in any case.

NGC 6231 = C1650-417: Situated just to the north of the naked-eye double star ζ Sco. is NGC 6231 (visible without optical aid as a small hazy spot). Even with just a small RFT, this cluster can be resolved into a number of bright, intensely blue-white stars and is quite spectacular. Additionally, it is one of the most interesting clusters in the southern sky and has been thoroughly studied by professional astronomers. An early study by Morgan, *et al.*, [1953] showed the presence of 70 OB stars in a region just 1° x 2°, in the neighborhood of NGC 6231. The cluster itself is at the southern end of the aggregate and the nebula IC 4628 at the northern end. (The field of stars lying in between is cataloged as Cr 316, and a more strongly concentrated sub-group involving IC 4628 is cataloged as Tr 24) On the basis of the cluster distance being 1.4 kpc, Morgan, *et al.*, estimated the dimensions of the aggregate, now known as the Sco OB1 association, as being 25 x 50 pc. UBV observations of 43 possible members of the association were presented by Bok, *et al.*, [1966] who obtained a distance of 1.8 kpc and individual absolute magnitudes for the stars between –1.2 and –7.3. More UBV photometry and spectral classifications were obtained by Schild, *et al.*, [1969] who showed that, in addition to the substantial population of luminous and massive OB stars, there were also two Wolf-Rayet stars (HD 151932-WN7 and HD 152270-WC7); two other stars, HD 151804 and HD 152408 were found to be supergiants with P Cygni lines. In this study, an age of just 5 million years and a distance of 2.0 kpc were derived. More comprehensive photometry and spectroscopy of the Sco OB1/Tr 24 region was carried out by Heske and Wendker [1984, 1985] which supported the physical association of the groups and also pointed out the existence of a substantial population of pre-main sequence stars (about 40% of which showed photometric variability). However, they arrived at a distance estimate of 2.3 kpc, and from this concluded that NGC 6231 was probably a foreground object. This contradicted almost all previous work including the contemporary study of van Genderen, *et al.*, [1984], who had concluded that NGC 6231 was the core of the Sco OB1 association, and the distance was 1.6 kpc. A comprehensive analysis of the Sco OB1 region was undertaken by Perry, *et al.*, [1991], making extensive use of previously published data (a comprehensive listing of observational data for stars in the region is given in their Table 3, which includes variable stars and suspected variables). The evidence examined clearly suggests that NGC 6231 is the nucleus of the Sco OB1 association at a distance of about 2.0 kpc but throws some doubt on the reality of the Tr 24 grouping. It may be a chance superposition of early type stars along the line of sight. Balona and Laney [1995] obtained CCD *uvby*β photometry of stars in the NGC 6231 cluster and a distance close to that obtained in 1984 by van Genderen, *et al.*, By comparing the cluster sequence with theoretical models, they derive an age of 5 Myr.

NGC 6250 = C1654-457: The CDS February 20, 1995 version of the *Lund Catalogue* contains a slightly different position than the ADC version. Neither is as precise as a DSS position (measured by one of us [BA]) of (2000.0) 16^h 57^m 55^s, –45° 56.1′.

NGC 6318 = vdB-Ha 218 = C1712-393: Both S. Gottlieb [private communication, 1995] and J. Kay [private communication, 1996] have independently noted that the NGC and vdB-Ha identities are for the same object. The separate *Lund Catalogue* entries should be combined. The position and diameter here are from an estimate by one of us [BA] from the DSS. The magnitudes are from the *Lund Catalogue*, for NGC 6318 (reference 50, "Bochum-Strasbourg magnetic tape catalog of open clusters 1977"). The associated IRAS source name here is from the SIMBAD entry for vdB-Ha 218.

NGC 6374 = NGC 6383: J. Kay noted [July 24, 1996] that although there is an obvious cluster that fits the description of NGC 6383, there is no cluster visible at the (e.g. *DSFG1e*) position for NGC 6374. This was also noticed much earlier by Antalovà [1972, 133]. Examining the original observations of these objects (h 3687 and h 3689 respectively) shows that the descriptions are very similar, including a "bright" star in the cluster. In John Herschel's description of NGC 6374 he specifically notes the star is "B = 6125." This identifies the star as Brisbane 6125, which one of us [BA] has identified as HD 159176. Since this is the primary star of NGC 6383, it becomes clear that Herschel's position for NGC 6374 was incorrect and that these two NGC objects are the same object.

This implies that almost all modern catalogs (the *Lund Catalogue*, the *DSFG1e*) are incorrect in maintaining a separate listing for NGC 6374 as a cluster. The *Lund Catalogue* at least has "canceled" this cluster, but its alias list should now also be changed to show that the two NGC designations are identical. The *DSFG1e* indicates that NGC 6374 is "Probably not a cluster." That entry should be removed entirely. Collinder [1931], the RNGC, and *NGC 2000.0* apparently give incorrect identities. The catalog here uses the *Lund Catalogue* data for NGC 6383 and includes NGC 6374 as an alias for NGC 6383. The NGC 6383 name has discovery priority as J. Herschel made his observation of it first (h 3689, in sweep 478, August 3, 1834).

NGC 6444 = Ru 132 = C1746-348: The diameter (3′) and number of stars (8) estimated for this cluster by Lyngå in the *Lund Catalogue* are clearly too small. The *DSFG1e* repeats the small number of stars. A DSS image of this area shows that this is a large scattered cluster, and John Herschel used those very terms to describe his h 3706 [Herschel 1847, 116]. The size and number of stars estimated from the DSS is 12′ and 50 stars. The 12′ estimate agrees with an alternate estimate in the *Lund Catalogue* and with the *DSFG1e*.

The *Lund Catalogue* alias list gives the equivalence with Ruprecht 132 twice. One of these lines should be removed.

Fig. 4.87 *NGC 6480, a Milky Way star cloud, on the right side of this figure with the dark nebula, LDN 1788 on the left side. This is a histogram equalization stretch of a 45′ field of view DSS-S image. Compare with the discovery drawing in Figure 4.88. © ROE.*

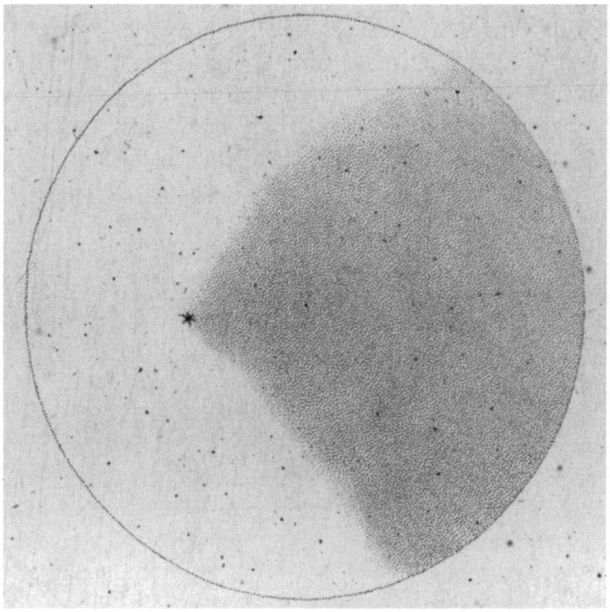

Fig. 4.88 *The discovery drawing of NGC 6480 by John Herschel (his "h 3713½") reproduced from [Herschel, 1847, plate V, figure 2]. Note that this is a negative image, and that many of the "stars" or black dots on this image are printing defects in the original and not really stars (e.g. note the stars* outside *the drawn circle).*

NGC 6480: This is a Milky Way starcloud, with a wide-open triangular shape on one side, first observed by

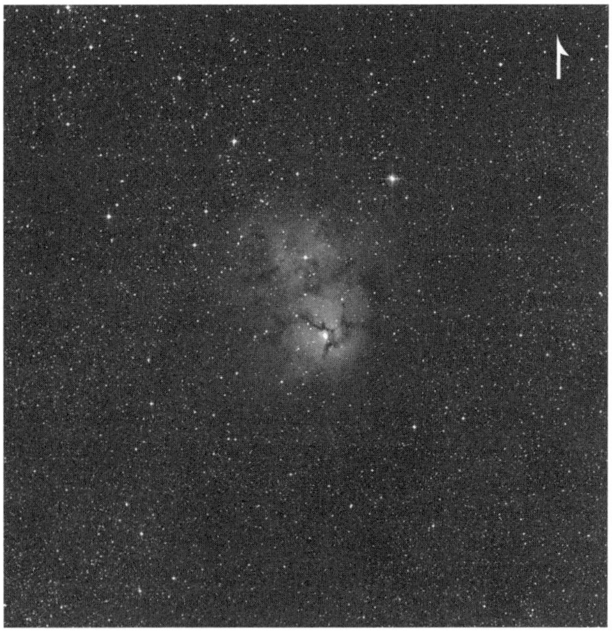

Fig. 4.89 *NGC 6514 = M 20 and the surrounding star field. 1° field of view DSS-S image © ROE.*

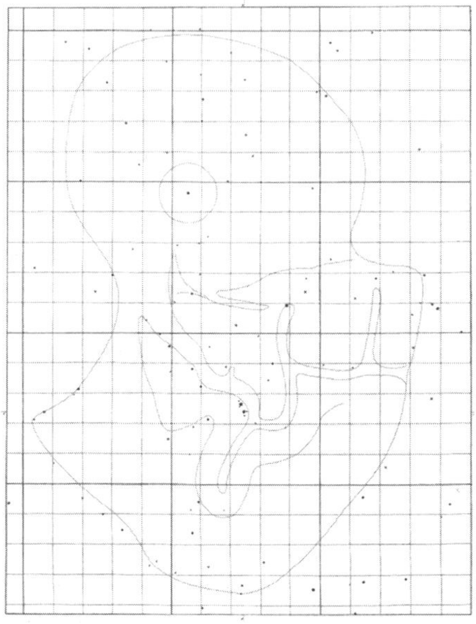

Fig. 4.90 *NGC 6514 = M 20, in a drawing by M. Trouvelot (at 103x) from 1874 showing the cluster stars and a rough outline of the nebulosity. The smallest squares are 65.1″ on a side, with a field of view of approximately 17′ by 22′. From the* Harvard Annals *8 (1876), plate 10.*

John Herschel in the summer of 1837, see Figures 4.87 and 4.88. Herschel listed this object in his "Cape Observations" [1847, 116] with the description: "An extraordinary B nebulous portion of the milky way [sic], on a black ground v L; an angle taken where there is a * 12 m. [See fig. 2, Pl. V., copied from a diagram made at the time, which represents this remarkable and instructive object as marked by a well defined contour.] [previous brackets are Herschel's]." The figure, shown here as Figure 4.88, (later found to have south up and east at the right) shows a star at right center of the field at the apex of a angle in the edge of a Milky Way starcloud situated toward the left. Yet, even with a position, this extended description, and a figure there apparently were no further observations of this until modern times. The first-known observation since Herschel's was when one of us [BA] simply took a look at Herschel's position while observing with several other individuals at the Texas Star Party in May, 1994. [O'Meara 1994, 97]. This took place after presenting an evening lecture on the subject of the nonexistent star clusters.

John Herschel's designation of this object carries an unusual history. His original description of this object carried no designation but followed the object h 3713. However, later in the same publication [p. 132] he called this h 3713½. In the GC this object is no. 4342, but here he gives his "h" designation as "h 3713′." Dreyer, in the NGC, erroneously listed this as "h 3713" (while also correctly listing NGC 6483 as h 3713). Archinal [1993, 77] made a typographical error and erroneously listed this as "h 3613½."

As to the starcloud itself, a DSS image shows this to be a wide "V" shaped front of stars with an apex pointing east including the star GSC 7378-01423 (GSC magnitude ~12—Herschel had estimated 12) at the apex. The dark cloud on the eastern side (into which the "V" extends) is apparently LDN 1788. The position of GSC 7378-01423 (2000.0: $17^h\ 54^m\ 34.7^s$ –30° 26′ 29″) is used in this catalog for the starcloud. The north-south extent of the "V" opening is about 17′ which is used for the diameter.

NGC 6506: There is a typographical error related to this object in [Archinal 1993, 77]. John Herschel's description of this cluster [1847, 116, h 3717] should read "A very loose but very rich cluster, which fills many fields. Stars small."

NGC 6514 = M 20 = C1759-230: The Trifid Nebula and star cluster, see Figures 4.89 through 4.92. The NGC and M designations apply to both the star cluster and nebulae. Messier only notes the cluster under his description of M 20, but adds under his description of M 21 that both objects were involved in nebulosity. The famous double star at the center of the Trifid shape is HD 164492 and is actually located on the western side of the star cluster. HD 164514 is on the north side. The size comes from an estimate of H. S. Hogg (via the *Lund Catalogue*) and the Trumpler type comes from the *DSFG1e*.

This cluster is very close to the cluster Bochum 14 = C1758-237. The *Lund Catalogue* lists Bochum 14 separately in its main catalog, "print" catalog, and alias list, and indeed Bochum 14 is a real separate cluster between M 20 and M 8. However, the *Lund Catalogue* incorrectly lists Bochum 14 in the alias list as being the same object as NGC 6514.

Fig. 4.91 *NGC 6514 = M 20, the celebrated Trifid Nebula and Star Cluster. Although now known mostly as a famous emission (bottom) and reflection (top) nebula, Messier's apparent main interest was the involved star cluster, the most obvious feature in his small telescope. The nebula is only briefly mentioned under his description of M 21. This photograph is by Keeler [1908, plate 55] and is reproduced here with north up and east to the left (in the original publication, south is up). The field of view is approximately 23' x 24'. Compare with Figure 4.89, 4.90, and 4.92.*

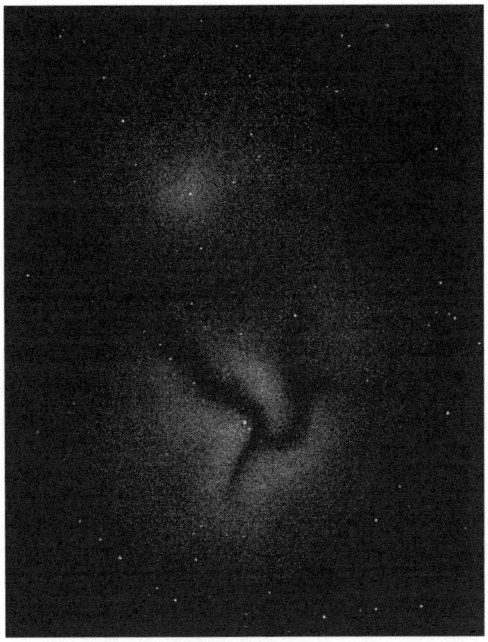

Fig. 4.92 *NGC 6514 = M 20, in another drawing attempting to illustrate the nebula and cluster, based on (and to the same scale as) Figure 4.90. From the* Harvard Annals *8 (1876), part 2, chapter 1, plate 32.*

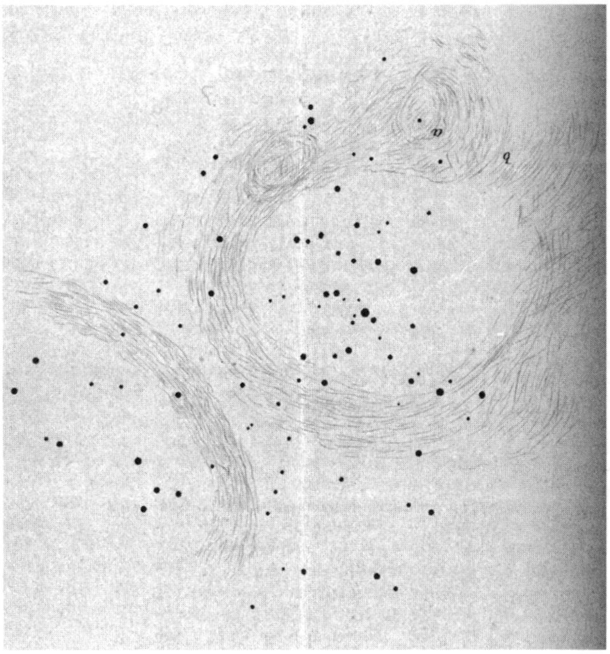

Fig. 4.93 *NGC 6523 = M 8, the Lagoon Nebula and Star Cluster, as drawn by E. E. Barnard [1889]. The field of view is about 55' by 58'.*

NGC 6523 = NGC 6530 = NGC 6533 = M 8 = C1801-243: This is the star cluster in the "Lagoon Nebula," and clearly by Messier's published descriptions, the nebula and cluster comprise M 8, later named NGC 6523. See Figures 4.93 through 4.95. John Herschel, in his Cape Observations and the GC, Dreyer in the NGC, and all later authors (to date) unfortunately indicate a separate designation (h 3725 = GC 4366 = NGC 6530) for the cluster. In the catalog here, following Messier's description, the GC and NGC (and all later references) are considered incorrect, and these designations are considered the same. However, the position and other data apply only to the star cluster and not to the associated nebulosity (the "Lagoon Nebula").

Regarding the "NGC 6533" identification, this is William Herschel's V.13. H. Corwin has shown [private communication, 1996] that this is in fact a re-observation of the M 8 nebulosity and cluster.

As to earlier observations than Messier's, Glyn Jones [1975, 21] suggests, for some reason, that Flamsteed was the discoverer of the cluster (c. 1680). However, Glyn Jones quoted Flamsteed's description of this object, his no. 2446, as at the position of 7 Sgr, a "Nebula preceding Sagittarius' bow." Although this seems to describe the nebulosity, and not the cluster, it is possible that Flamsteed did see the cluster in his small telescope and just considered it part of the nebula. In any case, Le Gentil apparently was the first to describe both the cluster and the nebula in 1747

Fig. 4.94 *NGC 6523 = M 8, the Lagoon Nebula and Star Cluster. Compare with Figures 4.93 and 4.95. 30′ field of view DSS-S image © ROE.*

Fig. 4.95 *NGC 6523 = M 8, the Lagoon Nebula and Star Cluster. This photograph is from Keeler [1908, plate 56]. Approximately 53′ x 44′ field.*

[Glyn Jones 1975, 41, 43]. Lacaille also described the nebula (but not the cluster) in 1755, as his class III, no. 13 object [Glyn Jones 1975, 47–48].

NGC 6554: This is John Herschel's [1833, 460] h 1995, which he observed at (1830.0) $17^h\ 59^m\ 5.3^s$, NPD 108° 26′ 52″. He described it as "A v coarse and scattered but p rich cluster of L and S stars. Has several double stars in it."

The DSS reveals a very loose scattering of bright stars in this area including a number of doubles. It is difficult to decide upon a center and size, but a rough position of (2000.0) $18^h\ 08^m\ 55^s$ –18° 22.8′ and diameter of 20′ is adopted here.

J. Kay [private communication, 1995] reported her observations of this object with a 20 cm (8-inch) *f*/10 Schmidt-Cassegrain telescope. At low power (66x, 46′) "there is a scattering of stars which hardly appear to make up a cluster grouping. What is remarkable, is the number of double stars, all similar in brightness and [nearly] equal in [separation]. In the field, lies a brilliant 8th magnitude deep [orange] star. North of here [$18^h\ 09.1^m$ –18° 26′] lies the first double, the most northern pair found in [Sh 2-38]. This gives the whole grouping a diameter of 18′ with a center at $18^h\ 08^m\ 40^s$, –18° 20′." At high power (140x, 28′) "There are 35 stars in this loose grouping which are 11–12th magnitude. In a sweep east and west of here, the star numbers decrease greatly, the fields almost barren. While this grouping of stars and double stars hardly rates as a cluster, these stars are more concentrated than those in the immediate fields." She concluded, "No real clustering of stars seen, but the view of those attractive double stars is worth noting and searching for."

Pothier reported [private communication, 1996] his (edited) description, viewing with a video image-intensified 70-cm (27.5-inch) Cassegrain at *f*/3.4: "12 stars of V mag 12 with 10 others of mag 13–14, very sparse cluster without condensation; a double star (mag 12 and 12.5) stands in the middle; other doubles are seen on the northern and western sides. Estimated size of 15′."

Both of these observations confirm the object's identity as essentially a large sparse group of stars containing many doubles.

NGC 6595 = NGC 6590: This is *not* Collinder 371, see page 122, but is a bright nebula included in it.

NGC 6603 = C1815-184: NGC 6603 is an extremely rich open cluster embedded in the M 24 star cloud, only 12° away from the direction of the Galactic center, see Figure 4.96. Many references, including the *Lund Catalogue* alias list, incorrectly indicate that this is the same object as IC 4715 = M 24. M 24 (see page 140) is the large Milky Way star cloud that contains NGC 6603 but not the same object as NGC 6603. In addition, the "n" in the *Lund Catalogue* Trumpler type is incorrect, as no nebulosity is visible in this cluster on DSS images.

The appearance of the "star cloud" is due to the presence of a "window" in the gas and dust clouds in that direction. This enables observers to see to a greater distance towards the center of the Galaxy and, therefore, through a greater depth of stars. NGC 6603 has been studied by Bica, *et al.*, [1993], whose primary interest was in globular clus-

Fig. 4.96 *NGC 6603, a rich open cluster within the Small Sagittarius Star Cloud, IC 4715 = M 24 (not to be confused with M 24, as many references do). 17′ field of view SkyView/DSS-S image © ROE.*

Fig. 4.97 *NGC 6649, a heavily reddened open cluster in Scutum. The small curved line at upper left is a defect in this 17′ field of view SkyView/DSS-S image itself. © ROE.*

ters in the central parts of the Galaxy, but whose attention was attracted to this object by its very richness. They even suggest that NGC 6603 might be one of the very rare galactic counterparts of young clusters in the Magellanic Clouds with globular cluster characteristics (the so-called "blue globulars"). In this investigation, Bica, *et al.*, used CCD cameras to prepare B, V color-magnitude diagrams of the cluster in order to derive reddening, distance and age estimates. The field around the cluster was also studied in order to determine whether there is any physical association with the star cloud. The observations show that the main sequence is comparatively blue and that the cluster is quite young (about 200 million years is derived). However, the cluster also includes a small population of 11 red giants, one of which is exceptionally red, with (B – V) ~ 2.38. A distance estimate of 3.6 kpc was derived. The surrounding field appears to contain age components in the range 200–600 million years and seems to be at an approximate distance of 4.2 kpc. The uncertainty ranges in the figures for the cluster and the field suggest that there is a genuine physical relationship.

NGC 6647: There is a typographical error concerning this object in Archinal [1993]. In the main catalog (p. 28), this is incorrectly listed as Struve 7. Struve 7 (or Σ 7) is actually NGC 6648. NGC 6647 was discovered by William Herschel as his H.VIII.14 and observed by John Herschel as his h 2014.

NGC 6649 = C1830-104: NGC 6649 is a heavily reddened open cluster close to the Galactic equator in the small constellation of Scutum, see Figure 4.97. This object is important because it contains a Cepheid variable, V367 Scuti. It was discovered by Roslund and Pretorius [1963] and established to be a cluster member by the research of Thé and Roslund [1963] and Tammann [1969] who obtained more extensive observations of the star and cluster. An important study of V367 Sct and NGC 6649 was carried out by Madore and van den Bergh [1975] in which the color excesses of individual stars were determined to establish that the visual absorption in front of the cluster amounts to more than 4 mag. Photographic photometry was performed on 416 stars and photoelectric photometry on 68 of them. A color-magnitude diagram was produced on the basis of the latter. This showed a well-developed main sequence with a small number of more evolved stars. Stars 49 and 117 are red giants, and the latter is variable. V367 Sct (star 64), the Cepheid, has a period of 5.2551 days and magnitude range of about V = 11.3–11.9. The brightest star in the cluster, star 42, is a binary (ADS 11441) with components of V = 9.74 and V = 11.4, separation 4″.

NGC 6683 = C1839-063: Alister Ling has noted that the *Lund Catalogue* position for this cluster is slightly off (4–5′ too far south) [Archinal 1993, 79–80]. The position is the GSC position of the central star GSC 05125-01649. The brightest star is GSC 05125-02853, as checked on the DSS [by BA]. The GSC magnitude (11.42 ± 0.32) checks with the *Lund Catalogue* value (11.41) used here. Likewise, the

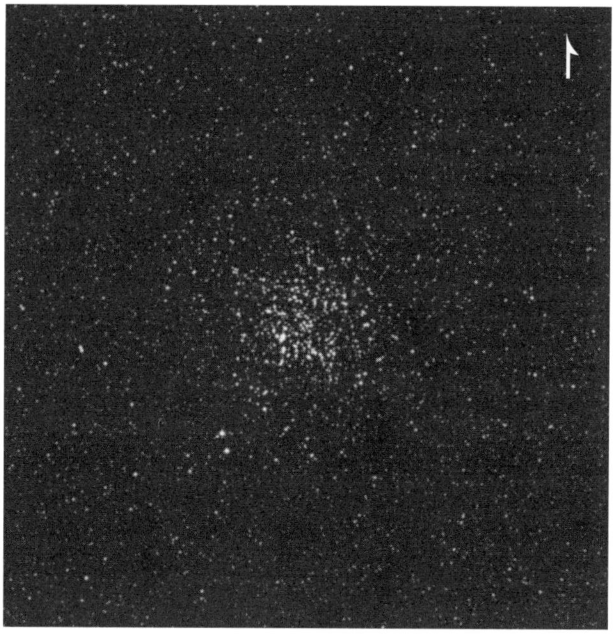

Fig. 4.98 *NGC 6705 = M 11, the rich and beautiful "Wild Duck" cluster, so named by W. H. Smyth due it's "V"-shaped appearance in small telescopes. 24′ field of view DSS-S image © ROE.*

measured diameter (3.5′ to 4′) is close enough to the Lund value of 3′.

NGC 6684: This galaxy is incorrectly listed in some older references (see [Ruprecht, *et al.*, 1981]) as a Galactic globular cluster. Names such as "GCl 102" and "C1846-652" that have been used for this should be denigrated and their use avoided in the future.

NGC 6698: The NGC actually contains a typographical error for the NGC number itself. This is listed as "NGC 6678" on page 183 of the NGC (between NGC 6697 and NGC 6699). Dreyer repeats this error by incorrectly labeling William Herschel's VI.15 as "NGC 6678" [Dreyer 1912, 1, 291]. One of us [BA] also made a typographical error related to this object in [Archinal 1993, 90]. William Herschel's reference star for this object (NGC 6698 = H.VI.15) was σ Sge (not ρ).

NGC 6705 = M 11 = C1848-063: This spectacular cluster in Scutum was discovered by Gottfried Kirch on September 1, 1681, see Figure 4.98. With his small telescope, he was unable to resolve it, and described it thus: "Its shape was unlike that of the comet which I found in the telescope … on the morning of November 4th, 1680, and therefore, I was at first uncertain whether the phenomenon was a comet or a nebulous star. When, for successive days, its form and position remained unchanged, it was easy to decide that it was not a comet but most certainly a nebulous star." It was subsequently recorded by Charles Messier on May 30, 1764; with a better telescope he was able to describe it as a "Cluster of a large number of little stars … not seen without a good instrument; with an ordinary glass … it resembles a comet …; in the cluster there is a star of 8th magnitude." It is often known as the "Wild Duck" cluster following a 19th century observation by English amateur astronomer Admiral W.H. Smyth, who compared the V-shape of the main body of the cluster stars to "a flight of wild ducks." In the past, some references have considered this object a globular cluster—it is clearly an open cluster. Therefore, the "Globular?" line should be removed from the *Lund Catalogue* alias list. In 1956, Johnson, *et al.*, [1956] obtained photoelectric and photographic photometry of around 400 stars brighter than V = 15, and found 25 yellow giant stars among them. An age determination of about 500 million years was derived. Later, McNamara and Sanders [1977] looked at the cluster membership on the basis of proper motions and suggested that there were probably about 870 members down to magnitude 16.5 and found that the cluster possessed an extensive halo of low mass stars. The presence of the halo around the cluster was confirmed by extended, improved photometry performed by Solomon and McNamara [1980], and Mathieu [1984]; the latter also concluded that the total mass of the cluster must be around 5000 times that of the Sun.

A deep CCD investigation by Brocato, et al [1993], covering 5780 stars down to V = ~22 in two selected fields near the center of NGC 6705 shows that the cluster's main sequence is well populated down to at least V = 20.5, and perhaps even down to the observational limit. Analysis of the observations indicates a cluster age of about 150 million years, somewhat less than many earlier estimates, and a distance of about 1.7 kpc.

NGC 6724, Poole J1855.0+1047, Poole J1855.8+1046, and Poole J1857.0+1027: NGC 6724 is an object that has long resisted identification, see Figure 4.99. However, after a number of searches of this area by various individuals, at least one identity has been found with some likelihood, and two other asterisms or possible clusters have been located.

To review, NGC 6724 is John Herschel's h 2024 [Herschel 1833, 462], with his 1830.0 position $18^h\ 49^m\pm$ NPD 79° 51′ 30″. This updates to (2000.0) $18^h\ 57^m\pm$ +10° 21′ 31″. The description reads only "A cluster discovered with the 7-feet equatorial, Sept 5, 1828." There is no sweep number.

An examination of this specific position on the DSS shows a slight "knot" of stars (at 2000.0, $18^h\ 56^m\ 53^s$ +10° 21′ 44″) which very closely matches Herschel's measured position. However, this is so small and so undifferentiated from the background that it is unlikely to be the object in question.

Unfortunately, there are no other groups of stars visible here on the DSS that particularly stand out—although there

Table 4.2
Identification of NGC 6724

Name	Type	2000.0		Size	No. Stars	Comments
		RA	DEC			
NGC 6724	cl?	18 56 45	+10 26 47	3	10	Identity not certain.
Poole J1855.0+1047	cl?	18 55 02.7	+10 47 21	6	40	Center is HD 230024. Ling's "AstA near NGC 6724."
Poole J1855.8+1046	ast?	18 55 53	+10 46 17	3.5	15	Ling's "AstB near NGC 6724."
Poole J1857.0+1027	MW	18 57 04	+10 27	~20	—	Either includes NGC 6724, or may be NGC 6724. Diameter from Lederman.

Fig. 4.99 *NGC 6724. As explained in the text, the small group of 10 or so stars at the center of this figure may be NGC 6724 and is indicated as such in the catalog here—but the identity is not entirely certain. 17′ field of view SkyView/DSS-N image.*

are many non-descript groups and apparently an overall Milky Way star cloud.

In particular, while examining DSS images of this area, Russell Lederman [private communication, 1996] suggested: "The thing I did notice was that the 20′ x 20′ area centered at 18^h 55.8^m +10° 21′ (1975) is surrounded by a zone of dark nebula separating the similar appearing center from the areas beyond the dark ring. Although hard to see at first, it does appear as a 20′ x 20′ cloud that is brighter than the areas outside the encircling dark ring, and its irregular shape brings to mind the number '8' where the lower circle in the '8' is half the diameter of the northern circle." A 1° DSS image in this area shows the features Lederman indicated.

With these conflicting suggestions of what appears in this area on the DSS, perhaps the only way to resolve (or partially resolve) the identity of this object is to rely on visual observations. The following observations, by Archinal, Poole, Pothier, Ling, and Gottlieb are relevant. They are listed in chronological order.

Archinal : As reported in the *Monograph* [80–81], One of us [BA] observed this area with a 15 cm (6-inch) *f*/10 reflector (in 1990) and 31.1-cm (12.5-inch) *f*/5.4 reflector (in 1991). The detailed observations previously presented will not be repeated here. However, a rough "parallelogram of stars" was observed and seemed to stand out. The DSS shows this to be a group at (2000.0) 18^h 56^m 45^s +10° 26′ 47″ and about 3′ in size. Although the observations indicated a possible unresolved background of stars, the DSS image does not support this. This appears to be just a group of 10 or so stars, generally brighter than the rich background Milky Way in this area. Eight of these stars are in the GSC.

Poole: Randall M. Poole [1993] reported his (undated) observation of this area with a 20-cm *f*/6 reflector observing in suburban skies with a limiting magnitude of 4.5. He lists this object at (2000.0) 18^h 57.0^m +10° 22′. His description reads: "40′ diameter collection of thirty stars 10th magnitude and fainter in elliptical ring shape elongated southwest to northeast. Two concentrations of faint stars on the northern perimeter. 68x." This sounds like it generally is the larger star cloud (later) noted by Lederman, but the "concentrations" noted are significant.

Pothier: Yann Pothier listed [private communication, 1996] his observation of this area in August, 1993, using a 71-cm Cassegrain reduced to *f*/3.4 and an image intensifier coupled to a video camera. This combination resulted in a maximum field of 30′. He reports (with some minor editing): "NGC 6724: about 30 very faint stars of magnitude 14 and fainter are condensed in a rather ill-defined (although dense) cluster; it is hard to decide where the borders are but we decided its diameter could probably be close to 6′. Some magnitude 12 stars are found nearby. Our description matches [Archinal's] well but both are not corresponding well to Poole's who tells us about a 40′ elongated cluster of magnitude 10 stars."

Ling: Alister Ling has reported [private communication, 1995 and 1996] observations of three possible groups of stars or clusters in this area made in 1995. He notes "I took a couple of looks at this area visually last summer, and was not able to come to any definite conclusion. As you will see from my notes, I found two other candidates which were much better, but being almost 30′ away, are probably not right. The candidates look so nice they may even be real."

Because of their importance, they are reproduced here in their entirety. There has been some editing, including spelling out of abbreviations. Comments in brackets are by Ling.

> "AstA near NGC 6724" Diameter: 5′. 18^h 55.1^m +10° 47.5′ (2000.0). 46-cm (18-inch) *f*/4.3 NEWT Mt. Kobau, BC. 1995/08/26; Lim.mag: 6.2; Seeing: 5″. At 287 power, it stands out reasonably, a dumbbell shape with 2 areas, NW and SE, more vacant than the other two. NE side has more stars granulating. Surprised nothing is plotted here. Discovered this trying to hop to PK 43+3.1. [Digital Sky Survey shows a nice bright group on top of a Milky Way starfield.]
>
> "AstB near NGC 6724" Diam: 3′. 18^h 55.9^m +10° 46.5′ (2000.0). 18-inch *f*/4.3 NEWT Mt. Kobau, BC. 1995/08/26; Lim.mag: 6.2; Seeing: 5″. Does not stand out as well as "A," but it grabs one's attention at 71 power as a collection of faint stars 15–20 in number. Could be an absorption hole in the Great Rift where stars can shine through. Surprised nothing is plotted here. Discovered this trying to hop to PK 43+3.1. [Digital Sky Survey shows a fairly rich cluster that stands out moderately well.]
>
> "OC NGC 6724" RNGC class 7; Diam: 2–3′. 18^h 56.7^m +10° 26.5′ (2000.0).
>
> 18-inch *f*/4.3 NEWT Mt. Kobau, BC. 1995/08/26; Lim.mag: 6.2; Seeing: 5″. Not well defined. Sweeping at 287x: the only object that is worthy of mention is a circular asterism of 7 or 8 stars (6 brighter). Group appears to be surrounded by a darker annulus, darkest and broadest on the west side, thinner on the east. About 10′. Not remarkable at 71 power except for its circular appearance.
>
> 12.5-inch *f*/5.6 NEWT Blackfoot, AB. 1995/09/23; Lim.mag: 6.4; Seeing: 3″. At 65 power, the only thing that's really eye-catching is a circlet, actually a double circlet. The west one is a bit of a box, but the east is more of a circlet, about 2–3′ across and a better eyecatcher at 255 power. More stars closer to the smaller east one. h 2024: "A cluster discovered with the 7-feet equatorial, Sept 5, 1828." Position is 4′ north of Herschel's, and description is only a fair match with that in the Archinal *Monograph*. It does not mention the nicer groups about 30′ NW. [Position is the center of the east circlet and size measured on *MegaStar*. The image from SkyView shows a very rich Milky Way. Nothing stands out except the A and B objects 30′ to the NW. Not worth printing on a 9-pin printer.]

Comparing these observations to the DSS shows that Ling's "OC NGC 6724" (or his preceding "circlet") to be the same object as described by Archinal. The "parallelogram of stars" is indeed better described as a "circular asterism," although even Ling indicated this preceding circlet of two is a "bit of a box." Ling's 6 to 8 stars could just as easily be claimed as the few (10) observed by Archinal. The positions also match exactly given the uncertainties of both. Ling's following circlet was not noticed in Archinal's visual observations, and is not obvious on the DSS image. However, there are several stars within a few arcminutes following the main object that could be considered part of it or perhaps another circlet. Two of these stars are GSC stars. The observation by Pothier appears to be of this same group although with a few more outlying stars.

Gottlieb: After seeing these observations and an earlier version of these comments, Steve Gottlieb [private communication, 1996] also provided his observations of this area. He observed this field in July, 1995 with his 44.5-cm (17.5-inch) and recorded the 3′ group seen by Archinal and Ling. His notes read: "at 100x (20 mm Nagler) appears as a small indistinctive group in a rich milky way [sic] field. Stands out better at 220x (9 mm Nagler) which increases the number of stars to 15 in a 2.5′ x 2.0′ region (slightly elongated E-W). There are five brighter mag 12–13 stars and 10 faint stars in the group which appears most likely to be an asterism." Considering the suggestion this might be a larger object, he adds, "Apparently the surrounding 'rich milky way field' was not detached from the surrounding field (at least at 100x) to make it stand out as a noteworthy object, so I think the smaller asterism is a better object. The few extra stars I picked up (beyond the 10 or so mentioned by [Archinal]) were only seen at higher power, so were probably in the mag 15+ range."

But the question remains—what did Herschel actually observe? There is no indication of the field of view or magnification since this was seen with his "7-feet equatorial." This object was not observed in one of his "sweeps;" therefore, we can not compare it with other observations of that sweep. However, his "7-feet" was probably a long focal length 20-cm (8-inch) with a speculum metal mirror. Of the telescopes and images considered here, Archinal's 15-cm (6-inch) *f*/10 reflector would seem to best approximate the view (although Poole's is similar). His observations indicate this group was almost "too easy" to see, showing up as soon as it came into the field. His second observation through a 31-cm (12.5-inch) was clearly not as obvious, and the views that Gottlieb and Ling described through their 44.5-cm (17.5-inch) and 46-cm (18-inch) respectively were also not of anything obvious. The view through Pothier's 71-cm (24-inch) sounds similar. The DSS image is covered with fainter Milky Way background stars. It appears the differences (based on aperture) in the modern observations support the identification of the smaller group of stars as the object Herschel had in mind. However, given Poole's observation and the appearance of this area on the DSS, the larger area in general cannot be ruled out, particularly if Herschel was using very low power or had a particularly dark night, etc. It appears unlikely that Herschel had in mind the two other groups that Ling noted, if only because there clearly is something much closer to Herschel's position.

So we are left with the conclusion that either the small 3′ group, or the much larger star cloud that contains it is, the object that Herschel had in mind. For now, in the catalog here, NGC 6724 is listed as the small group—but we will probably never know its identity for certain.

Setting the question of NGC 6724 aside for the moment, what can be determined about Ling's other two groups? For the first object ("AstA near NGC 6724," at 2000.0: 18^h 55.1^m +10° 47.5′), the DSS does show a nice grouping of stars just northwest of HD 175539 (V = 8.8). According to SkyView, this group includes HD 230024 as its brightest star (although the SkyView positions appear a little off for both stars, e.g. about 1′ too far southwest). An improved position for this star and the group (since the star is well centered) measured from the DSS is 18^h 55^m 02.7^s +10° 47′ 21″. About 40 stars stand out from the background in a diameter of about 6′. This object is a much better looking star cluster than a large number of other nondescript cataloged objects. Therefore, it could be a real physical cluster. SIMBAD lists no objects within the boundaries of this group.

For Ling's second object ("AstB near NGC 6724," at 2000.0: 18^h 55.9^m +10° 46.5′), a ¼° square DSS image shows a very rich Milky Way field, with a scattering of about seven 9–12th magnitude stars. At the given position there is a concentration of stars. However, similar concentrations or groups appear elsewhere in the field as well. So the group here (as Ling notes) does not stand out as well as the "A" object. A bright star, SAO 104258 (V = 8.8), just precedes the group, while HD 230121 (V = 9.1) closely follows it. The DSS shows an improved position of 18^h 55^m 53^s +10° 46′ 17″ and a diameter of 3.5′. About 15 stars stand out from a very rich background including 4 GSC stars. Two brighter GSC stars lie detached from the group on its north and northeast edge. Again, SIMBAD lists no objects within this group.

R. Poole's observation clearly indicated "Two concentrations of faint stars on the northern perimeter." Comparing his position and overall size for the star cloud shows that he had seen Ling's "asterisms." Although this is not a detailed description, it is good enough for discovery priority. In this catalog the two asterisms and the star cloud are indicated by a "Poole" coordinate name (i.e., Poole J1855.0+1047, Poole J1855.8+1046, and Poole J1857.0+1027).

Table 4.1 on 183 summarizes the situation (positions were all estimated from the DSS by Archinal).

NGC 6743: This is John Herschel's [1833, 462] h 2028, which he lists at (1830.0) 18^h 54^m 47.7^s, NPD 60° 58′ 3″. His description is: "A p L, poor cl of stars forming irreg groups or patches, 11.12 m; diam = 8′." Updated to 2000.0, this position is: 19^h 01^m 27.5^s +29° 16′ 15″.

The DSS immediately shows an apparent cluster at this location, centered on the bright star HD 176970 = SAO 86712 (V = 8.2), at (SIMBAD, 2000.0) 19^h 01^m 26.65^s +29° 17′ 14.3″. A diameter of 8′ (matching Herschel's) includes a 4′ central portion, as well as some outer bright stars (including the second and third brightest of the group to the northwest). There are several clumps of 2, 3, and more stars that account for Herschel's "irreg groups or patches." About 35 stars stand out from the background.

A. Ling reported [private communication, 1995] an observation of this object as well. However, it turns out that he had discovered an apparent asterism 2° to the south at (2000.0) 19^h 01^m 29^s +27° 18.0′. With a diameter of 5′, this includes about 12 stars, the brightest one 8.1 mag. This has been added to the catalog as Ling 1.

NGC 6774 = Ruprecht 147 = C1913-163: Brian Skiff noted, while examining a draft copy of the second edition of *Uranometria 2000.0*, that NGC 6774 and Ruprecht 147 are likely the same cluster. NGC 6774 is John Herschel's h 2034 = GC 4481, observed by him twice with coordinates (from his first observation) of (2000.0) 19^h 16^m 41.3^s −16° 16' 05". His two descriptions of it read, "A fine, L, loosely scattered cl of large with some small stars. Fills 2 or 3 fields", and "A very large straggling space full of loose stars, 8, 9, and 10 m." Ruprecht 147 was first listed in Alter, *et al.*, [1961, pp. 2–3], at position (2000.0) 19^h 16.6^m −16° 16' with a size of 22' x 48' and 66 stars from magnitude 9 and fainter.

An examination of a 1.5° field of the DSS shows a 45′ sized "V"-shaped group of bright stars which seems to match both Herschel's and Ruprecht's positions and descriptions. So clearly these are the same object, a sparse possible open cluster. The center is estimated from the DSS to be at the position of HD 180228, or approximately (2000.0) 19^h 16.3^m −16° 19.5′, and the 45′ value is used for the diameter. This group appears to contain approximately 40–100 stars, with 40 used for the number of stars in the catalog. The Trumpler type (IV2p) and the magnitude of the brightest star (9.0) are from the *Lund Catalogue* which notably gives the same Trumpler type and brightest star magnitude for NGC 6774 and Ruprecht 147. The *Lund Catalogue* should have the NGC 6774 and Ruprecht 147 entries combined into one.

NGC 6819 = C1939+400: The *Lund Catalogue* incorrectly lists this as "globular?" in the alias list. It is not included in the globular cluster list of Djorgovski and Meylan [1993]. See Figure 4.100.

NGC 6827 = Berkeley 48 = C1946+210: The *Lund Catalogue* notes the equivalency of NGC 6827 with Be 48 in the alias list, but incorrectly does not give NGC 6827 as the primary name there or in the main catalog files. It gives a position that is about 2′ too far south and a size for the

Fig. 4.100 *NGC 6819, a very rich 5′ diameter cluster in Cygnus, mistaken in some early references as a Galactic globular cluster. 17′ field of view. Image courtesy the Palomar Observatory and Digitized Sky Survey created by the Space Telescope Science Institute, operated by AURA, Inc. for NASA. Reproduced with permission from AURA/STScI.*

Fig. 4.101 *NGC 6846, a tiny (0.8′ diameter) cluster with few modern observations since many references gave a position for it 2° too far south. The planetary nebula K 4-41 (arrowed) lies about 2′ northeast of the cluster center. 17′ field of view. Image courtesy the Palomar Observatory and Digitized Sky Survey created by the Space Telescope Science Institute, operated by AURA, Inc. for NASA. Reproduced with permission from AURA/STScI.*

cluster of 4′ (referencing Setteducati and Weaver [1960]) rather than the 2′ diameter that the DSS shows. The position given here is measured from the DSS and is for the central "clump" of stars. The given measured diameter here (2′) is clearly better than the *Lund Catalogue* value (4′).

NGC 6846 = C1954+302: There appear to be few modern observations of this cluster, primarily because almost all modern references give a position that is 2 degrees too far south. Although the NGC itself gives a correct position, this positional error apparently originated with Collinder [1931] (this being Collinder 410). Even Collinder notes [ibid, page B42] that he could not find this object on the Franklin-Adams charts. He does mention that Pease [1917] had photographed it, but a check of Pease's paper contained no reference to this object (Collinder may have misread NGC 6826 for NGC 6846). The incorrect position by Collinder was apparently repeated in nearly all references that followed, including the RNGC; Ruprecht, *et al.*, [1981]; the *Lund Catalogue*; *NGC 2000.0*; *Uranometria 2000.0* (first edition); the *Lund Catalogue*; and the *DSFG1e*. Ruprecht [1966] also gives a wrong Trumpler classification, probably based on looking at the wrong field.

The positional error was first noticed by S. Gottlieb [private communication, 1994] who checked Stéphan's [1873; 1874] original discovery position. Among modern references only SIMBAD was found to have the correct position—and this may have originated from Gottlieb's note. The position ($19^h\ 56^m\ 28.1^s$ +32° 20′ 55″) and diameter (50″) given here were measured [by BA] from the DSS. The center and brightest GSC object in the cluster is GSC 2673-02510. The GSC indicates this to be a nonstellar object at magnitude 12.8 ± 0.4, although the DSS shows this as an apparent clump of stars. The approximate number of stars (40) and Trumpler type (II2m) were estimated from the DSS image, see Figure 4.101.

Gottlieb noted that about 2′ to the northeast is the planetary nebula K 4-41. This is at $19^h\ 56^m\ 34.0^s$ +32° 22′ 12″, and is also known as PK 68+1°1 = IRAS 19546+3214 = PN G 068.7+01.9. See Acker, *et al.*, [1992], for an image [part 1, page 179] of the planetary and cluster, and data [part 2, page 280] on the planetary. It is the southern of three stars near that location. Gottlieb noted that it was not visible in his 33-cm (13-inch) telescope, but was "barely visible" using an [O-III] filter and a 44.2-cm (17.5-inch) telescope.

NGC 6873: This is *not* the group of stars around θ Sge as suggested by Archinal [1993, 88] and Skiff [1990, 46]. As John Herschel indicated [1833, 466, h 2068] and as mentioned in the NGC itself, NGC 6873 is the group around the double star Σ 2631, see Figure 4.102. As first suggested by Steve Gottlieb [private communication, 1995], Herschel apparently gave a right ascension that is 1^m too far east. When the RA is corrected, the match is better than 10″—

Fig. 4.102 *NGC 6873, the barely detectable 14′ long east-west chain of stars at the center of the image here, and as John Herschel, the discoverer noted, "hardly to be called a cluster." 30′ field of view. Image courtesy the Palomar Observatory and Digitized Sky Survey created by the Space Telescope Science Institute, operated by AURA, Inc. for NASA. Reproduced with permission from AURA/STScI.*

Fig. 4.103 *NGC 6885 and Collinder 416. NGC 6885 is the large group of stars in the image, centered on the bright star 20 Vul. The concentration of stars just northwest (to the upper right) of 20 Vul, but still in NGC 6885, is the group Collinder 416. 19 Vul is the bright star at the top of the field. There is a small flattened circlet of about 9 stars just south of 19 Vul (here arbitrarily cataloged as AH03 J2011.9+2644), and this is at William Herschel's position for his H.VIII.22 = NGC 6882. However, as described in the text, NGC 6882 is probably the same object as NGC 6885. 45′ field of view. Image courtesy the Palomar Observatory and Digitized Sky Survey created by the Space Telescope Science Institute, operated by AURA, Inc. for NASA. Reproduced with permission from AURA/STScI.*

quite good for Herschel's positions. Visual observations by Gottlieb and one of us [BA] essentially confirm his descriptions and this identification. The size given here (14′) is essentially just the length of a string of stars observed by Gottlieb (as measured on the DSS) which is probably Herschel's "Coarse straggling group of stars 10...13m hardly to be called a cluster." Agreeing with this description and the visual observations of Archinal and Gottlieb, the object is listed with type "ast?" here, i.e., it is likely an asterism. The position, "diameter" (length in this case), and number of stars have been measured from the DSS. The magnitudes for the components of Struve 2631 are from SIMBAD. A typographical error in Archinal [1993, 88] should be noted. For τ Sge, read θ Sge.

NGC 6874 = Basel 6 = C2005+382: By rough position and lack of anything obvious at the precise *Lund Catalogue* Basel 6 position, it appears that the NGC 6874 and Basel 6 identities are equivalent. If so, the *Lund Catalogue* (which lists Basel 6) should note the equivalency with NGC 6874 and use this as the preferred name in all its files.

The DSS does show a cluster just preceding the position (the RNGC coordinates) as described by both William (H.VIII.86) and John (h 2069) Herschel. Updating their positions to 2000.0 shows excellent agreement, even at the 1s level for John Herschel's measurements of his "10m" star, the brightest star of the cluster. However, the Basel 6 identity could still use more rigorous checking since this cluster is about 1^m west and 7′ south of the Lund position (20^h 06.8^m +38° 21′) for Basel 6. See [Archinal 1993, 88–89] for more information.

NGC 6882: This is probably NGC 6885, given next.

NGC 6885 = C2009+263 (also =? NGC 6882), Collinder 416 = C2009+264, and AH03 J2011.9+2644: The identifications for NGC 6885 and NGC 6882 are not entirely clear. William Herschel discovered these on successive nights (September 9 and 10, 1783) as his objects H.VIII.20 and H.VIII.22. His descriptions for these objects are nearly identical, and he places them only 15′ apart (north and south of each other) in the sky. However, there is only one large group of scattered stars here that vaguely matches his description of either object; a group around 20 Vulpeculae—here group "A." Further confusion is caused by a slightly smaller scattering of fainter stars on the northwest side of 20 Vul—here group "B," the most part of which is included within the larger group A.

So just what is what here? Herschel's position for NGC 6885 = H.VIII.20 is preceding 20 Vul. He describes it as "A Cl. of co. sc. st. not rich.," i.e., "a cluster of course scattered stars, not rich." This, along with its designation as an eighth class object by Herschel, indicates that it is probably "A," the large group around 20 Vul. However, it cannot be ruled out that Herschel meant the group "B," NW of 20 Vul, particularly since he did not explicitly mention that 20 Vul was a member of the cluster. In any case, John Herschel observed the larger group around and including 20 Vul (as his h 2071) and firmly indicated that he believed that this was H.VIII.20. Since this assumption seems reasonable, and following the historical precedent he established, we will assume the same here.

Herschel's position for NGC 6882 = H.VIII.22 lies about 15′ north of here, and he describes it as "A Cl. of co. sc. st." At Herschel's position on the DSS, see Figure 4.103, there is a small flattened circlet of 9 stars, including HD 192043 (V = 7.60, SIMBAD). It is possible that this is the object he had in mind, and this apparent asterism is included in the catalog here with the (arbitrary) name "AH03 J2011.9+2644." Interestingly, this has the appearance of one of Isserstedt's "stellar rings." However, the overall size of this group of approximately 4′ is just a little too small to easily match Herschel's description and class VIII designation. Herschel also does not mention such a ring of stars. H. Corwin [private communication, 1998] points out that it is just as likely that Herschel made a 15′ mistake, and that H.VIII.22 is the same object as H.VIII.20 = NGC 6885 (group "A"). Corwin notes that several of Herschel's observations that night had positional errors (although this one of 15′ would be the largest). Although it seems unusual that Herschel would catalog the same object twice, Corwin points out that this was not unheard of. He cites NGC 4208 = NGC 4212 as a case where he cataloged an object twice, and doing so only about 5 minutes apart. Therefore, until further information can some day be gleaned from Herschel's original observations (in the possession of the Royal Astronomical Society), the assumption is made here that NGC 6882 is the same object as NGC 6885 (group "A").

What about later researchers? Trumpler [1930] seems the first to have realized that there were two groupings here, the larger one around 20 Vul ("A"), and the smaller one NW of it ("B"). He writes [ibid, 175]: "In the region around 20 *Vulpeculae* two clusterings seem to be superposed: A loose clustering of 20–30 mostly faint stars, about 8′ in diameter, with center at $20^h\ 7^m\ 28^s$ +26° 15.0′ (1900) was identified with NGC 6882. The course group of a few bright stars clustered around 20 Vulpec, with a diameter of about 22′ was identified with NGC 6885. In each of the two clusters a physical relationship of the stars is indicated by the magnitude spectral class diagram, but the two clusters are evidently at different distances." He gives (1900) 20^h 07.8^m, +26° 11′ as the position of NGC 6885. Unfortunately, this does not correspond to our assumption that NGC 6885 and NGC 6882 are both the larger group. In fact, if our assumptions are correct, this means that Trumpler *discovered* the smaller group "B." However, he did not name it, and therefore, it was Collinder who assigned a name to this group for this first time (his number 416). That name is used here.

However, it should be noted that Collinder made mistakes here, too. He gave positions that matched Trumpler's identities, with Collinder 416 being at the position of (Trumpler's) smaller group, and Collinder 417 at the position of the larger group (NGC 6885). Unfortunately, he assigns the larger size and brighter total magnitude to the smaller and fainter group. He further indicated that 20 Vul is in *both* groups and assigned two different Boss star catalog numbers to it (in his Cr 416 vs. Cr 417 write-up).

Problems continued until more recent times. The *Lund Catalogue* indicates Cr 416 (group "B") is part of NGC 6885 (group "A"), in disagreement with Trumpler who found they were at different distances. The *DSFG1e* incorrectly lists group "B" as NGC 6882. The original *Caldwell Catalog* object 37, although listed as "NGC 6885," according to the given magnitude and diameter, is almost certainly Collinder 416.

In the catalog here the large group "A" around 20 Vul is assumed to be NGC 6885 = Cr 417, probably equivalent to NGC 6882. The smaller group or cluster "B" to the northwest of 20 Vul, discovered by Trumpler, is Cr 416. The position of Cr 416 has been measured from the DSS and Trumpler's size of 8′ for it is confirmed (and used here), although the cluster is actually elongated NE to SW. Modern studies should still be done to confirm Trumpler's assertion that these are two independent (or even physically bound) groups of stars.

The star 20 Vul is assumed to be the brightest star in the NGC 6885 group (also known as the "20 Vulpeculae Cluster"), so its V magnitude (5.91 from SIMBAD) is used as that of the brightest star. However, that star was apparently not used by Skiff in his determination of the total magnitude of the cluster (probably because it is so much brighter than the other stars of the cluster [private communication from Skiff, 1996]), given as 8.1.

NGC 6904: This is John Herschel's h 2074, placed by him [Herschel 1833, 466] at (1830.0) $20^h\ 14^m\ 29.7^s$, NPD 64° 47′ 10″. This was described as "A small straggling cluster of stars 10.11 m. One of the 9 m, whose place is taken." S. Gottlieb [private communication, 1995] and Y. Pothier [private communication, 1996] have now reported observations of this apparent asterism of stars.

The DSS reveals that Herschel's star, "One of the 9 m," is HD 340139 = SAO 88571, at V = 8.4 (updating only for precession, Herschel's position is accurate to better than 1″). The "cluster," an apparent asterism, is contained in a 3′ diameter, and includes about 15 stars. The central position is on a star at $20^h\ 21^m\ 48.3^s$ +25° 44′ 22." This is a rich field with a number of comparable stars farther out, including about 8–10 up to 7′ to the north. However, Herschel's "small" implies he had the 3′ group in mind.

Gottlieb's description: "N6904 appears to be a random scattering of brighter stars mainly noticeable because it includes mag 8 SAO 88571. The brighter stars form a rectangle with side of 3′–4′ and a string of brighter stars off the NW vertex extends another 4′ to the N. There are roughly two dozen stars mag 9.5–13 in the group besides the mag 8 star. Richest around mag 9.5 SAO 88575 [= HD 340140] at the SE corner of the rectangle."

Pothier's (edited) description, viewing with a video image-intensified 61-cm (24-inch) Cassegrain at *f*/3.4: "North-South elongated cluster, about 12′ x 6′; 1 star of mag 11, 2 of mag 12, 2 of mag 13, 10 of mag 14 and 10 of mag 15; major stars are forming a Great Bear mini-constellation; sparse and not well detached from the background." Pothier's "Great Bear" shape is visible in the DSS image, with the handle and bowl of the "Big Dipper" being the stars on the north side, and the main 3′ group being the right side of the bowl.

NGC 6991 and h 2091: Although the case of NGC 6991 is discussed in [Archinal 1993, 90], one of us [BA] has since resolved the correct identities. This determination is based on W. Herschel's original observation (H.VIII.76) and an examination of the area via SkyView/DSS. Herschel's "st. 6 m." is clearly the V = 5.67 star HD 199478 (the vdB 137 star), which is on the east side of this large (25′ diameter) group of stars. There are about 35 brighter stars in the group that stand out from the rich Milky Way background. The central position is (2000.0) $20^h\ 54.9^m$ +47° 25′. Some of the nebulosity involved is IC 5076, which appears to be associated with HD 199478. The estimated Trumpler type is III2mn. As S. Gottlieb has noted [private communication, 1996] the information previously given in the *Lund Catalogue* and the corrected position in [Archinal 1993] (2000.0, $20^h\ 54.5^m$ +47° 17′) apply instead to J. Herschel's object here, h 2091. (In addition, the diameter listed in the *Lund Catalogue* print file is 5′, while the diameter given in the main data file is 6.0′ (both citing reference 320)). The object listed as NGC 6991 in the *DSFG1e* (chart 85) is h 2091, and its name and position should be changed to that just mentioned. The size, number of stars, and description are correct. A new entry should be added to the *DSFG1e* for the real NGC 6991 itself. In *Uranometria 2000.0* (first edition), the symbol for NGC 6991 is too small and should be moved to the other (west) side of HD 199478. h 2091 should be plotted at the correct position inside the NGC 6991 symbol. No "C" names have as of yet been assigned these objects.

NGC 6994 = M 73 = C2056-128: This object is the well-known group of 4 stars, specifically GSC 05778-00802, –00492, –00509, and –00594, see Figure 4.104. Brian Skiff [private communication, 1998 and a message to the amastro list, e-mail of December 26, 2001] has recently looked into the likelihood of whether these stars are physically associated. Two of the stars are in the *ACT* catalog and thus have relatively good proper motions now determined, while the other two are in the *GSC 1.2* and the *AC2000* catalogs, and thus can have reasonable proper motions determined. Brian notes that over the 76 year span of the data:

Fig. 4.104 *NGC 6994 = M 73, the well-known group of 4 stars cataloged by Messier. B. Skiff has shown that the component stars are physically unrelated and this is, therefore, just an asterism. 17′ field of view SkyView/DSS-S image © ROE.*

> All the stars are moving southeast, but how much of this is due to reflex solar motion I have no idea. At the level of precision available, the two stars with motions from the ACT are not related. For the other two stars, the errors are such that they differ only at the one-sigma level, so the results are equivocal.

Regarding the colors of these stars, Brian notes:

> the Tycho photometry for –0802 gives V = 10.31 and B – V = 1.03, with errors of +/– 0.06 and 0.10, respectively; for –0509 the values are V = 11.10 and B – V = 0.66, with errors of 0.13 and 0.18. These suggest that –0802 is a K0 giant and that –0509 is a G dwarf. That they have similar brightness, of course, implies that they must be at greatly different distances, since the absolute magnitudes would be roughly +1 and +5.

He finally concludes:

> All this argues (if not utterly conclusively) for pretty much what we've assumed all along, which is that the stars are unrelated in space.

This conclusion is fully supported by a recent study in which high-resolution spectra were obtained of the 6 brightest stars in the area of NGC 6994. Odenkirchen and Soubiran [2002] have determined from these spectra and Tycho-2 catalog proper motions that these stars definitely do not form a physical system.

Collinder appears to have misidentified M 73 in his 1931 monograph on star clusters. As NGC 6994, this object is listed under his number 426, as having "200?" stars and possibly being a globular cluster. P. Teutsch [private communication, 2002] has pointed out that Collinder probably confused M 73 with the globular cluster NGC 6981 = M 72, about 5.5^m of right ascension to the west. So although Collinder's position matches that of M 73, his descriptive information appears to be for M 72.

NGC 6996 and NGC 6997 (C2054+444): Many modern references (the RNGC, the *Lund Catalogue*, *Sky Catalogue 2000.0* Vol. 2) reverse the identities of these two objects. NGC 6997 (H.VIII.58) is an obvious cluster superimposed on the eastern portion of the famous "North American Nebula," NGC 7000, see Figure 4.105. NGC 6996 (h 2094) is an asterism, or (as John Herschel says) "a clustering portion of the Milky Way" about 1° north of NGC 6997. Observations and correct identities of these objects are discussed at length in [Archinal 1993, 90–92] and the *Caldwell Objects* [O'Meara 2002]. *Uranometria 2000.0* (first edition) and the *DSFG1e* (chart 85) incorrectly label and list as NGC 6996 what is certainly NGC 6997.

In addition, the diameter given in the *Lund Catalogue* print file for "NGC 6996" is 7′, while the diameter given in the main data file is 8.0′ (both cite reference 320). The 8.0′ value has been used here since it matches the visual appearance [as observed by BA].

NGC 7023: This is a reflection nebula with the star cluster Collinder 427 involved on its west side. Almost all modern catalogs to date, except here and in the *Caldwell Objects* [O'Meara 2002], incorrectly list the cluster as NGC 7023. See the entry for Collinder 427 on page 125 for more information.

NGC 7134: This object was discovered by C. H. F. Peters [1881], who lists it at (1860.0) 21^h 41^m 20^s, –13° 37.7′. He comments: "Very small, but not very faint; nearly south of a star 11^m. In the position of G. C. 6010 (Marth 454): 21 40 1, –13 53, I have no nebula drawn upon my chart."

One of us [BA], D. Riddle [private communication, 1995], and S. Gottlieb [private communication, 1996] have now observed this object, and its existence has been verified on the DSS. Updating Peters' position to 2000.0 shows that this is a group of 4 GSC stars just south of an 12th magnitude GSC star. The 4 stars are GSC 05796-01213, 05796-01241, 05796-01172, and 05796-01247. Peters' "star 11^m" is GSC 05796-01217. The DSS shows it quite well as an arc of 4 equally-bright, equally-spaced stars, convex to the 12th magnitude star above it. At low magnification this group would probably look nebulous. The total GSC magnitude of the group is 13.4, the brightest star is at 14.2, and the maximum size is 29″. This identity confirms B. Skiff's earlier identification of this object reported in Archinal [1993, 96].

As an aside, the latter part of Peters' description apparently indicates that Peters did not see GC 6010 = NGC 7131 (galaxy at (SIMBAD, 2000.0) 21^h 47.6^m –13° 11′, also identified as MCG –02-55-002 = PGC 67359 from SkyView).

NGC 7394: Dana Patchick and Susan French [private communication, 2002] have noted that the positions given for this cluster at one place in Archinal [1993, p. 98] are incorrect due to typographical errors. The positions there should read 22^h 50.6^m +52° 10′ for 2000.0 and 22^h 49.5^m +52° 02′ for 1975.0.

NGC 7423 = Berkeley 57 = C2253+568, and h 2191: It has previously been pointed out [Archinal 1993, 98–100] by Dreyer [1912] that NGC 7423 and h 2191 are not the same object. The identity of NGC 7423 is clear, although there appear to be no modern observations of h 2191, apparently a large Milky Way patch around NGC 7423.

Alister Ling [letter of December 18, 1988 (see also Archinal 1993, 98–100) has pointed out that NGC 7423 and Be 57 are equivalent identities. Therefore, the *Lund Catalogue* (which lists Be 57) should note the equivalency with NGC 7423 and use that as the preferred name in all its files.

NGC 7510 = C2309+603: Lying just in Cepheus, against the border with Cassiopeia, can be found the open cluster NGC 7510, see Figure 4.106. This area of the sky is rich in clusters and nebulae which have been the subject of several investigations, notably by Lozinskaya, *et al.*, [1986]. They found that NGC 7510, Bas 3 and the Cas OB2 association constitute a single grouping, involved with a number of nebulous features (the most prominent of which is Sh 2-157). This object is a large, irregular ring, whose structure may have arisen from the interaction of the intense stellar wind from HD 219460 against a surrounding HII region (HD 219460 is a Wolf-Rayet star belonging to the cluster Mrk 50 = Bas 3). NGC 7510 itself is surrounded by a dust shell, associated with CO emission, some 3° x 2° in size; this is also a stellar wind blown feature. Fenkart and Schröder [1985] have carried out photographic photometry of 314 stars in the region of NGC 7510 but found only 50 to be likely members, the earliest spectral type among these being O6. A distance of 3.14 kpc was derived. CCD photometry of NGC 7510 has been obtained by Sagar and Griffiths [1991], covering 592 stars reaching down to V = 21. The color-magnitude diagram produced from this data shows a broad but well-defined main sequence with little

Fig. 4.105 *In our opinion this is one of the finest astrophotographs ever taken. The North American Nebula (originally named by Max Wolf, the "America" nebula) or NGC 7000 is shown in all its splendor. Just barely visible (at right center, at the position of "West Virginia") is the condensed cluster NGC 6997. NGC 6996 is probably the small patch of Milky Way just below the dark ("Hudson's Bay" nebula B 352 at the top of the image. NGC 6996 has an even smaller dark nebula B 353 to the east (left). The open cluster Collinder 428 is on the left side of the nebula (on the "California coast"). IC 5070, the Pelican Nebula is at the right of this image. Other Barnard dark nebulae shown here (all of these were apparently discovered on this image) are B 358 as a small oval area at the lower left, and B 355, a tiny "V" shaped patch of dark nebula (with the "V" pointing west) south of the bright hook of "Mexico." Photo by E. E. Barnard [1927, plate 46, taken September 4, 1905], with an approximately 3.7° field of view.*

evidence that stars are starting to evolve towards the red giant phase. As a result, an upper limit of 10 million years has been assigned as the age of the cluster. A distance of 3.16 kpc was arrived at and is in good agreement with other estimates.

NGC 7708: This apparent asterism is discussed in detail in Archinal [1993, 100–102]. S. Gottlieb [private communications, 1996] has provided an additional observation essentially confirming the earlier information. However, he noted that although the figure 31 published there is a good representation, it has been inverted (south is up and east is to the right in that drawing). This has been confirmed against the DSS. The brightest star of this group (centered in the figure, but actually on the northwest side of the group) is HD 221774 (V = 7.3). This is almost certainly the star used by Herschel for the group's position. Essentially, the rest of the (40–50) stars in the group are GSC stars. An improved position and size have been measured from the DSS and used here. The values are (2000.0) 23^h 36^m 30^s +72° 51.0′, and 30′.

There is also a minor error in Archinal [1993, 101]. For "23x, 172′," read "41x, 95′."

Table 4.3
Stars of NGC 7833

GSC-id	2000.0		Position error (″)	Magnitude	Magnitude error
	RA (h,m,s)	Dec (°,′,″)			
0173502056	00 06 33.67	+27 38 10.0	0.3	14.60	0.40
0173501814	00 06 30.39	+27 38 24.9	0.3	14.16	0.40
0173501920	00 06 32.46	+27 39 23.8	0.3	14.41	0.40

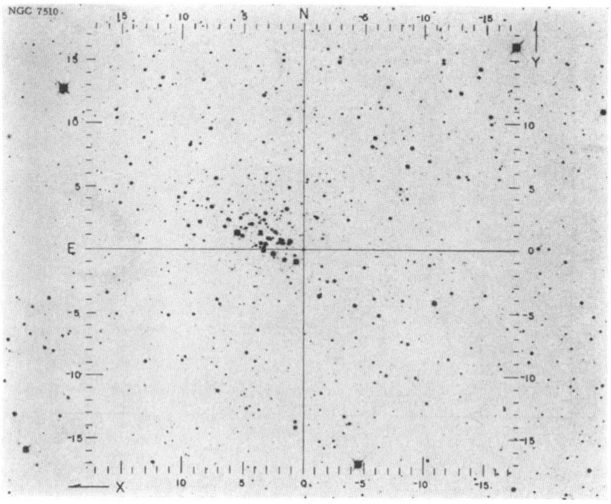

Fig. 4.106 *NGC 7510, a rich 7′ diameter cluster in Cepheus. Photograph from Hoag, et al., [1961, p. 484]. The area within the gridded border is about 17′ on a side.*

Fig. 4.107 *NGC 7790, a cluster forming a pair with NGC 7788 (not shown here). These clusters are about 2° to the north-northwest of β Cas. 17′ field of view. Image courtesy the Palomar Observatory and Digitized Sky Survey created by the Space Telescope Science Institute, operated by AURA, Inc. for NASA. Reproduced with permission from AURA/STScI.*

NGC 7790 = C2355+609: To the north of, and slightly preceding the V = 2.27v star β Cas, lies a pair of small clusters, NGC 7788 and NGC 7790, see Figure 4.107. The latter is of particular interest including three Cepheid variables; CF Cas and CE Cas a/b, the latter two of which form a binary pair. The first significant investigation of NGC 7790 and its Cepheids was that of Sandage [1958] who made UBV photoelectric measurements of 33 stars and performed photographic photometry on 100 more. A color-magnitude diagram was drawn up showing a well-populated main sequence, with a small number of evolved stars. Many red stars were found at V < 14, but these were noted as being merely field stars and not physically connected with the cluster. A distance of 3.63 kpc was derived. Photoelectric photometry was carried out on CF Cas to derive a period of 4.87513 days, but the proximity of the components of the CE Cas pair made it impossible to study these Cepheids in much detail (however, since then the period of CE Cas a has been determined as 4.4462 days, and the period of CE Cas b as 5.1275 days). During this investigation, a new eclipsing binary (QX Cas) was also found in the cluster. More detailed UBV photometry was carried out on the cluster by Pedreros, *et al.*, [1984], who carried out photoelectric and photographic photometry on 405 stars. In the process he discovered a slight error in the earlier photometry of Sandage—his color values were slightly too blue. An analysis of the new photometric data suggested that 94 stars were probable members of the cluster, and further examination of the stellar density in fields around it gave about 150 as the likely overall membership. A distance determination of 2.89 kpc was made, consistent with other recent estimates.

NGC 7833: This is Bigourdan's no. 101, first listed in Bigourdan [1887]. Its given position was (for 1860.0) $23^h 59^m 21^s$ NPD 63° 08′ with description: "Petit amas de 2′,5 de diam., formé d`étoiles très faibles parmi lesquelles on soupçonne un peu de nébulosité." ("Little group of 2.5′ diameter, made up of faint stars among which one suspects a little nebulosity.") The same position appears in the NGC, although the description was abbreviated to "Cl, vS, vF, 2′.5, nebs?"

This position updates to (2000.0) $00^h\ 06^m\ 32.6^s$, +27° 38.8′. At precisely that location on the DSS, shown here as Figure 4.108, is a group of 4 stars and an apparent faint galaxy (and two very faint outlying stars) that Bigourdan must

Fig. 4.108 *NGC 7833, a small group of 3 or 4 stars and a faint galaxy, only recently identified (and observed) since its discovery by Bigourdan in the 1880's. In this image the group appears as a trapezoid of 4 stars at the center of the image, with the upper left star barely detectable as being "nebulous" and, therefore, the galaxy. (There are also curved line defects on the DSS image on the right.) 17′ field of view. Image courtesy the Palomar Observatory and Digitized Sky Survey created by the Space Telescope Science Institute, operated by AURA, Inc. for NASA. Reproduced with permission from AURA/STScI.*

have seen. This group is precisely 2.5′ in diameter, so there is no question that he saw this group.

The northern of these stars is GSC 01735-01920, while the southern two stars are GSC 01735-02056 and 01735-01814 with data as it appears in Table 4.3. These stars have multiple GSC entries (for various plates), but only one entry per star is given here.

In this catalog, Bigourdan's position and diameter are used, and a brightest star magnitude of 14.1 (from GSC 01735-01814). There is a bright equal double star, position angle at about 5°, just southwest of this group. This is GSC 01735-01837, a "nonstellar" GSC object at magnitude 9.9.

A number of recent visual observations of this object have been reported. One of us [BA] made apparently the first modern observation of this area with the Warren Rupp Observatory (near Mansfield, OH) 79-cm (31-inch) *f*/7 reflector on October 3, 1994. Under very poor transparency (thin cirrus clouds), the double star (GSC 01735-01837) was quickly noticed. The telescope was centered (using the NGC coordinates) on what was thought to be just a fainter double star, but was Bigourdan's object. Sky conditions prevented the resolution of this group into more stars, and the identification was not really felt confirmed; but it was noted that this spot certainly looked "fishy."

S. Gottlieb [private communication, 1995] reports an observation with his 44.5-cm (17.5-inch) reflector: "this asterism consists of four faint stars mag 14.5–15 within a 1.3′ diameter although three of the stars form a very small triangle with the fourth star 1′ N. The faintest of the four stars is the northern star in the small triangle. Located 2′ NE of a close well-matched double star and in the same low field with NGC 1 and 2 which are just 10′ ENE." Gottlieb's asterism of four faint stars is clearly the object. The double star is GSC 01735-01837.

A. Ling [private communication, 1996], reported his observation of August 15 from Mt. Kobau (BC, Canada) using his 46-cm *f*/4.3 Newtonian reflector. Ling notes: "I have a candidate: start at the really bright star significantly p, and head east through a N/S double, about the same distance farther on is an arc of 4 stars which the followingmost is the brightest which looks like a double. Hard to tell with the seeing. Immediately f that and a little N is a group of 3 or 4 faint stars of which the southern one is nebulous also the Sf of the end double is somewhat nebulous at times." This description clearly indicates that the "brightest which looks like a double" is GSC 01735-01837, and it is Bigourdan's object that is being observed. Further it even appears that the nebulosity of the faint involved galaxy was visible.

In any case, the visual observations confirm the appearance of this group of stars and faint galaxy as nebulous, probably as Bigourdan also observed it.

OGLE-CL SMC0144 = OGLE-CL SMC0236: Pietrzyński, *et al.*, [1998] listed this cluster twice in their compilation of SMC clusters, once as the cluster OGLE-CL SMC0144, and a second time as the cluster candidate OGLE-CL SMC0236. The coordinates and images they present for these two entries show they are one and the same object.

OGLE-CL SMC0166: This possible cluster in the SMC is listed by Pietrzyński, *et al.*, [1998, 186] at the exact same position as their cluster candidate OGLE-CL SMC0165. This problem was also noted by Bica and Dutra [2000], who obtained the correct coordinates from Pietrzyński. The Bica and Dutra position is therefore used in the catalog here.

OGLE-CL SMC0175: This is Brück 31, see page 116.

OGLE-CL SMC0212: See [H86] 134 on page 131.

OGLE-CL SMC0213: This is [H86] 134, see page 131.

OGLE-CL SMC0236: This is OGLE-CL SMC0144, see page 193.

o² Cygni group: This apparent asterism is one of Webb's [1962, 112] "fine fields", see Figure 4.109. Alister Ling [private communication, 1995] reported that this is a group of stars including o² (Flamsteed 32) Cygni. He indicated that there is nothing of note other than that this is a

Fig. 4.109 *o^2 Cygni group, a likely asterism of stars, and one of Webb's [1962, p. 112] "fine fields." 45' field of view. Image courtesy the Palomar Observatory and Digitized Sky Survey created by the Space Telescope Science Institute, operated by AURA, Inc. for NASA. Reproduced with permission from AURA/STScI.*

Fig. 4.110 *Pismis 11, including the star HD 80077 (the brightest star here just above center), perhaps the intrinsically brightest known B type star in the Milky Way Galaxy. 17' field of view SkyView/DSS-S image © ROE.*

sparkling sight in a large aperture telescope (46-cm *f*/4.3 in this case). However, the DSS reveals that o^2 is involved in nebulosity, with a strong streak of it trending east-west just north of the star. The position, number of stars (7), and size (19′) given here are estimated from the DSS image.

P Cygni cluster: This possible cluster lies around (mostly on the north and west side of) the shell star P Cygni. It was discovered by W. Feibelman [1995] during an attempt to photograph the shell using the 30-inch refractor at Allegheny Observatory on 1960 July 20/21. The cluster was later independently discovered by Turner [1985a] via star counts in the field and photometry of stars near P Cygni. The position and size (3.7′) given here are estimated from a DSS image, where the enhancement of stars around P Cygni is just detectable. Turner estimated a size for this group of 4–5′. The number of stars is estimated from Feibelman's discovery photograph which is shown on the cover of the February, 1995 issue of the J. Roy. Ast. Soc. Canada. Turner noted that P Cygni and the cluster lie in the middle of the 8′ by 11′ NNW-SSE trending Isserstedt stellar ring number 274, with which the cluster should not be confused.

Phoenix dwarf galaxy: This was discovered by Schuster and West [1976] and suggested by them to be either a possible distant globular cluster or dwarf galaxy. It was shown to be a dwarf galaxy by Canterna and Flower [1977]. SIMBAD (from an unknown source) also lists this with the somewhat misleading name of the "Schuster-West cluster." It lies 4' NNE of a moderately bright (but apparently non HD or BD) star, at $01^h50^m\ 58.8^s\ -44°29'\ 56''$.

Pismis 1 = NGC 2568: see page 167.

Pismis 5 = C0835-394: The *DSFG1e* (charts 363, 397) position appears to be off (in comparison with the *Lund Catalogue*). Skiff [private communication, 1995] gives a position of (2000.0) $08^h\ 37^m\ 39^s\ -39°\ 34.8'$ based on an examination of the DSS.

Pismis 11 (C0915-495) = vdB-Ha 60 (C0914-498): Pismis 11 [Pismis 1959] is an apparently undistinguished cluster in the southern constellation of Vela, see Figure 4.110. It is of Trumpler class III 3 p and consists of less than a dozen stars in a field 2′ in diameter. The brightest obvious member is the B0III star LS 1267 (V = 11.07), situated near the center of the cluster; most of the rest of the stars are of mag. 12–14. The faintness of the cluster is primarily the result of its considerable distance of 3.2 kpc. The interest of this cluster results from a 1977 study by Moffatt and Fitzgerald [1977] into the parameters of very luminous supergiant stars. They drew attention to the likelihood that the star HD 80077, at a distance of 2′, is associated with the cluster. The similar degree of reddening points to this, but the conclusion is also supported by the spectroscopic, photometric and linear polarization measurements made by subsequent observers, particularly Knoechel and Moffatt [1982] and Steemers and van Genderen [1986]. These investigations show that HD 80077, which has been classified as being of spectral type B2Ia⁺e, is the brightest known B type supergiant in the Galaxy with a luminosity of $M_v = -9.5$ ($M_{bol} = -11.5$:). Some slight variability in the measurements suggest that HD 80077 may be a binary, although a more probable explanation is that it is a supergiant pulsator. A number of B-type supergiants are microvariables and exhibit quasi-periodic light variations of about 0.07 magnitude. In view of the remarkable super-superluminous characteristics of the star, Steemers and van Genderen have been prompted to classify HD 80077 as a "hypergiant."

By coordinates and size, vdB-Ha 60 is clearly the same as Pi 11. The *Lund Catalogue* indicates this, but under separate entries in its alias list. It still incorrectly gives these objects as separate entries (the vdB-Ha 60 entry should be removed completely and just left as an alias to Pi 11). The C0914-498 designation is preferable considering the true position of the cluster. The position of Pi 11 was corrected in the February 20, 1995 CDS version of the *Lund Catalogue*, but the vdB-Ha 60 position has been used here.

Pismis 17 = NGC 3503: see page 172.

Pismis 18 = IC 4291: see page 138.

Pismis 22 = C1609–517: Pismis's original position for this cluster appears to have been about 0.7^m too far west. As B. Skiff pointed out [private communication, 1999], Westerlund independently discovered this cluster in 1969. Westerlund simply called this the "Anon Cluster," but here it has been given the alias name "Westerlund 3" for the first time (Westerlund having previously discovered or rediscovered two other clusters, We 1 and NGC 3247 = We 2.). Van den Bergh and Hagen [1975] also list this cluster as their vdB-Ha 187 at the same incorrect position used by Pismis. The position and diameter used here were measured from the DSS with the cluster assumed to be centered on Westerlund's star no. 1 (V = 11.71).

Pismis 24 and 'unknown' about G 353.1+0.6: Pismis 24 is also known as vdB-Ha 227 = C1722-343. An image from the DSS (shown here as Figure 4.111) and a search for nearby objects in SIMBAD reveal Pismis 24 to be a cluster with a number of interesting associations. A nebula on the DSS, just to the north of the cluster, is the possible supernova remnant NGC 6357. (If this is an SNR, it is one of a very few SNR that is visible with small telescopes). The nebula has a host of other identifications, including h 3682, W 22 (which includes W 22B), CTB 40, RCW 131, Sh 2-11, SNR 353.2+00.7 (alternatively SNR 353.2+00.9), G 353.2+0.9, GRS 353.21 +00.91, NRL 12, [PT56] 36, [L89b] 353.186+00.887, GRS 353.19 +00.91, GAL 353.21+00.91, and [CH87] 353.206+0.905.

Fig. 4.111 *Pismis 24, a rather poor cluster in Scorpius but of interest due to its possible association to the suspected supernova remnant NGC 6357 (faintly visible on this image as a small patch above center). The bright spot just left of center appears to be a defect on DSS itself. 17′ field of view SkyView/DSS-S image © ROE.*

The Pismis 24 cluster also contains a pair of 11th magnitude stars, oriented roughly east-west. This is the double noted by John Herschel during his discovery of h 3682 = NGC 6357. The west star of the pair is HD 319718, at V = 10.43, the brightest star of the cluster. The eastern star is itself a closer double.

The DSS shows a 20″ sized object of unknown type just to the east of Pismis 24. This is cataloged as a nonstellar object, GSC 07383-00677. Its appearance is that of an inverted comma. This is probably some foreign material that was on the digitized plate, as it does not appear on the POSS-I print.

About 11′ to the southeast of Pismis 24 lies an unnamed group of stars involved in the faint nebulosity G 353.1+0.6. From the DSS, the position is (2000.0) $17^h\ 25^m\ 32^s\ -34°\ 24.3′$ and the diameter is 2.6′, and includes about ten stars. According to an investigation by Neckel [1984], measurements of six of these stars indicate at least four appear to be associated—and may also be a cluster. Neckel [1984, 61] gives a distance of 1.74 kpc for these four O and B stars. Lortet, *et al.*, [1984] also identify this group, but give a designation of G 353.1+0.7 for the nebulosity.

Finally, it should be noted that the original discovery position of Pismis 24 from Pismis [1959, 37] is quite poor. It is listed there as (1950.0) $17^h\ 22.0^m\ -34°\ 18′$ with a 4.0 diameter, 10 stars, and a note that it is involved in nebulosity. This position is actually very close to that of the unnamed group just described, and it would be easy to assume

Fig. 4.112 *Poole J1855.0+1047, an obvious asterism or even possible cluster, near (and a suggested identity) for NGC 6724. 17′ field of view. Image courtesy the Palomar Observatory and Digitized Sky Survey created by the Space Telescope Science Institute, operated by AURA, Inc. for NASA. Reproduced with permission from AURA/STScI.*

that unnamed group is what Pismis had found. However, the indication of nebulosity suggests that Pismis had probably noted the other cluster with a poor position and size. Pismis 24 was listed by van den Bergh and Hagen [1975, 15] as their no. 227, giving a much better position of (1950.0) $17^h\ 21.5^m$ –34° 08′), a 1.5′ size, and a description as a "vP" (very poor) cluster. They also note "Pismis 24?" with the interrogatory due to the poor Pismis position.

The positions and diameters given in this catalog have been measured from a DSS image.

Platais cluster: See "Anon. Platais" on page 112.

PMG 1 and PMG 2: See NGC 2451 on page 166.

PMH79 1: The "PMH79 1" name is given here for the first time, originating from the discovery publication (author initials and date): Pismis, *et al.*, 1979. This is a possible cluster involved with the large H-II region, Sharpless 2-140 (Sh 2-140). It includes 5 BD stars including HD 211880 = +62°2061 as the brightest star (V = 7.75, B0.5V). The number of stars (21, actually the number of stars with photometry), magnitude of the brightest star, and possible distance (900 pc) are from the Pismis, *et al.*, paper. The position and diameter (including all of the 21 stars) were measured, and the Trumpler type estimated, by one of us [BA] from a DSS image.

Poole J1855.0+1047, Poole J1855.8+1046, and Poole J1857.0+1027: A possible cluster, probable asterism, and a Milky Way star cloud, see Figure 4.112. Near NGC 6724, see page 182.

PWM78 3 = C2306+606: The "PWM78 3" name is given here for the first time originating from the discovery publication (author initials and date) Pfleiderer, *et al.*, 1978. Besides "C2306+606," this object has no other given name in the *Lund Catalogue* (other than Lund number 976).

Quintuplet Cluster: This is RAFGL 2004, see with "Central Cluster" on page 117.

Reiland 1 = Bergeron 1: This possible cluster was first reported in Walter Scott Houston's "Deep-Sky Wonders" column [Houston, 1988] as "Reiland's Nebulous Cluster," (see Figure 4.114). The shorter name "Reiland 1" has been adopted here. Tom Reiland of Glenshaw, Pennsylvania, was observing IC 1470 with a 20-cm *f*/5.3 Newtonian "when he happened upon a smaller and fainter object about 12′ south and slightly west of it. At first, he thought it might be a comet, but increasing the power from 54x to 130x revealed half a dozen stars spread across 30″ with a hint of nebulosity." Houston goes on to say that although this object appears on the POSS, Reiland was unable to find it in any catalog. Houston was able to find the nebulosity listed in the BFS catalog (which Houston described but did not name). He also reports his observation of it with a 25-cm *f*/6 reflector, where he immediately saw it once he observed it with a UHC nebula filter.

In draft versions of this book, this group of stars was called Bergeron 1 due to the independent discovery of this object by Joe Bergeron [private communication, 1997]. P. Teutsch, while reviewing such a draft, noted the identity with Reiland's object. The "Bergeron 1" name is maintained here as an alias name for this object.

As usual with small groups of stars like this, it is uncertain whether this is a cluster. However, the association of the group with the nebula BFS 15 = WB89 239 = IRAS 23026+5948 argues strongly that the stars are physically associated. The nebula and possible cluster appear about 10′ south of IC 1470 in Cepheus. An examination of the DSS shows 4 or 5 brighter stars over an area of 1′, with about as many fainter stars involved in a nebula about 25″ in size. The position is (2000.0): $23^h\ 04^m\ 45.3^s$ +60° 04′ 40″.

Reticulum = Sérsic cluster: This object, when initially discovered by Sérsic [1974], was thought to be a dwarf galaxy and a likely member of the Local Group. Later studies showed it to be a globular cluster, and it has often been included in lists of Galactic globular clusters. However, recently it was shown by Walker [1992] to be a member of the Large Magellanic Cloud, essentially at the same distance as the main body of the LMC.

Fig. 4.113 *Ruprecht 90, another "lost" Ruprecht cluster (due to a poor position by Ruprecht) recently identified by T. Karhula. 17′ field of view SkyView/DSS-S image © ROE.*

Fig. 4.114 *Reiland 1. A possible cluster of stars in the nebulosity BFS 15, about 10′ south of IC 1470 in Cepheus, first reported by Tom Reiland [Houston, 1988]. 17′ field of view. Image courtesy the Palomar Observatory and Digitized Sky Survey created by the Space Telescope Science Institute, operated by AURA, Inc. for NASA. Reproduced with permission from AURA/STScI.*

ρ Ophiuchi cluster: This is more properly known as "Grasdalen 1," see page 131.

Ruprecht 80 = NGC 2982: see page 171.

Ruprecht 90 = C1029–579: T. Karhula has provided the position ($10^h31.0^m$ –58°27′) of a group of stars that on the DSS (see Figure 4.113) appears to match Ruprecht's description. This is a north-south scattering of some 50 stars about 6′ by 10′ in size. Ruprecht described [Alter, *et al.*, 1961] a group that was 4′ by 9′ with 47 stars. Therefore, this has been accepted as the correct identification of Ru 90 here. The position is also incorrect in the *Lund Catalogue* and the *DSFG1e*.

Ruprecht 91 = C1045–572: The original listing of this cluster by Ruprecht [Alter, *et al.*, 1961, 3] gives a position that is of the star HD 93662 (V = 6.35, variable?, M1II). It also gives a diameter of 1.7′ and the number of stars as 56. There is nothing in this area of the sky with that many stars in such as small area. If one assumes the diameter is 17 arcminutes rather than 1.7, this matches the rich field of stars fairly well. Clearly the diameter is wrong in the original discovery listing. A DSS image shows an 18′ or so diameter grouping of about 50 fairly bright stars, trending somewhat NW to SE.

For the first time since its discovery 40 years ago, this cluster has now been properly identified. Of course this begs the question, how many other of the difficult to locate Ruprecht clusters also are listed with the wrong diameter?

Ruprecht 93 = NGC 3519: see page 173.

Ruprecht 98 = C1155–642: T. Karhula has provided the position ($11^h58.8^m$ –64°34′) of a group of stars that on the DSS (shown here as Figure 4.115) appears to match Ruprecht's description. This is what appears to be a real cluster about 7′ x 10′ in size (elongated north-south or perhaps slightly north-northeast to south-southwest), and containing about 20 brighter stars. Ruprecht described [Alter, *et al.*, 1961] a group that was 7′ by 10′ with 18 stars. Therefore, this has been accepted as the correct identification of Ru 98 here. Again, the position is incorrect in the *Lund Catalogue* and the *DSFG1e*.

Ruprecht 122 = vdB-Ha 202 = C1651-408: The *Lund Catalogue* incorrectly lists this cluster as vdB-Ha 202. The Ruprecht discovery year dates to 1961, while the vdB-Ha discovery year is 1975; therefore, the Ruprecht name clearly has priority. The name should be changed from vdB-Ha 202 to Ru 122 in all the *Lund Catalogue* files, and in the alias file vdB-Ha 202 shown as an alias name for Ru 122.

Ruprecht 147 = NGC 6774: see page 185.

Ruprecht 158 = C0850-373: The position here was obtained from a DSS image (see Figure 4.116). This object appears as a tiny (probable) asterism of 7 stars. Other data are from Ruprecht *et al.*, [1981]. The *Lund Catalogue* alias

Fig. 4.115 *Ruprecht 98, yet one more "lost" Ruprecht cluster recently identified by T. Karhula. 30′ field of view SkyView/DSS-S image © ROE.*

Fig. 4.116 *Ruprecht 158, a tiny (probable) asterism of 7 stars. 17′ field of view SkyView/DSS-S image © ROE.*

list has the sign missing from the IAU name for this cluster. It is given (correctly) in the main catalog as "C0850-373."

Ruprecht 166 = NGC 5120: see page 174.

Schuster 1 = C1002-556: We were unable to locate this cluster on the DSS; we thought it might not exist. However, B. Alessi [private communication, 1998] found that it does

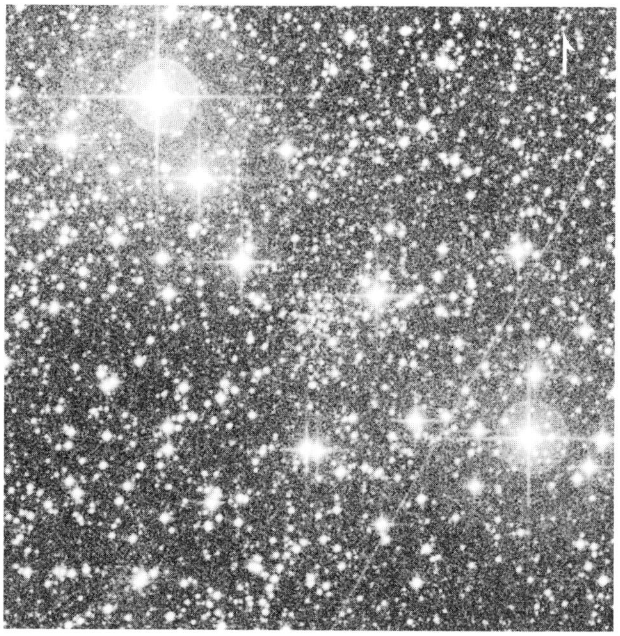

Fig. 4.117 *Schuster 1, a very faint rich cluster and possible Galactic globular cluster candidate. The cluster is not visible on the digitized sky survey, but it does appear in this 17′ field of view DSS-II (south) image. The line running diagonally across the right side is an image artifact. © ROE.*

appear as a small cluster of very faint stars on the DSS-II (see Figure 4.117). The position (2000.0, 10 ^{h} 04^{m} 39.0 ^{s} –55° 51′ 29″), diameter, number of stars, and Trumpler type were all estimated from the DSS-II image. This cluster appears "open" in the DSS-II image, but its stars are faint enough that the possibility exists that it is a faint extended Galactic globular cluster. Data for a color-magnitude diagram should probably be obtained in order to verify the cluster type.

The *Lund Catalogue* gives three slightly different positions for this object, i.e., in 1950.0 coordinates in the "print" file and in 1950.0 and 2000.0 coordinates in the main data file. These are all close, but should be corrected to correspond to the value given above. It is apparently coincidental that the cluster lies in the midst of the stars of the Lodén 1 cluster.

SGR A*: See the "Central Cluster" on page 117.

Shk 1 or Shakhbazian 1: This is a galaxy cluster of 17 galaxies discovered by Shakhbazian [1957]. It has occasionally been mistaken for a Galactic globular cluster using such names as C1052+407 and EQ 1052+407. Hesser and Shawl [1985] incorrectly list this as a globular cluster.

Skiff J0058.4+6828: This likely star cluster was discovered by Brian Skiff [e-mail to the amastro mailing list, September 24, 1999] while doing galaxy classifications on POSS-II images. On the DSS it appears as a fairly convincing 7′ diameter cluster of 30 stars with a Trumpler type of II2r. The brightest star is TYC 4296 1455 1 = GSC 04296-01455 on the west side of the cluster at V = 10.16. The cluster also contains IRAS 00551+6812, which Skiff identifies as an apparent red star near the center of the cluster, GSC 4296-0534 = USNO A2.0 1575-00590078 (B = 14.6, B – R = 3.6).

Skiff J0507.2+3050: This is a possible cluster that was noted by Brian Skiff while checking identities for a weak Galactic nebula with which it appears to be associated [private communications, 1998]. It appears as a 5′ to 6′ diameter group of similarly bright stars, particularly on a copy of the POSS-II J film of the area. The center star, GSC 02389-00693, is brighter than the others so would not likely be a member (if the cluster is real in the first place).

Skiff and SIMBAD give many identities for the nebula, including: PN G173.7-05.8, IRAS 05039+3045, UGCA 100, DG 50, LBN 173.80-05.83, LBN 809, PK 173-05 1, PN ARO 175, and PN K 2-1. Despite the indications of many of these names, the nebula is not a planetary nebula or external galaxy.

Skiff J0614.8+1252: This possible cluster was listed in Luginbuhl and Skiff [1990, 180 and 335] (under the name "A0612+12") and additional information was reported by Brian Skiff [private communication, 1998]. Skiff first observed it in the mid-1970s with a 25-cm telescope, noting it as a nebulous patch 10′ east of NGC 2194. In another observation with his 15-cm telescope he described it as [with abbreviations spelled out] "conspicuous at 80 power; about half a dozen stars resolved at 140 power." This was from Anderson Mesa, near Flagstaff, Arizona, on November 16, 1988. He reported two observations with a 30-cm telescope. The first is "10′ east [of NGC 2194], is group of fifteen magnitude 13.5 stars in a 3′ by 2′ area elongated north-south." The second is "10′ east [of NGC 2194], is 2.5′ by 1.25′ cluster of 20 stars with a brighter central star and bright star on the south end of [the] north-south cluster. Stars evenly distributed, most stars magnitude 12.5." His message notes that this cluster is one of two that "look like reasonable groupings on the DSS" (the other is Skiff J0619.3+1832) and "might even be real."

The DSS (see Figure 4.118 on page 199) does show a respectable concentration of stars that has the appearance of a real compact cluster. A bright star just to the north is HD 253905. This catalog uses Skiff's position, his estimate of 20 stars, and an estimated diameter and Trumpler type from the DSS of 5.0′ and II2m, respectively.

Skiff J0619.3+1832: This possible cluster was also reported by Brian Skiff [private communication, 1998]. He first observed it from Anderson Mesa, near Flagstaff, Arizona, on November 16, 1988 with his 15-cm telescope. His observation reads [abbreviations spelled out]: "Conspicuous group consisting of three clumps of stars in 20′ area, 50 stars total. A wide pair lies in a dark area in middle of clumps." He described the appearance of this on the POSS as: "including BD+18 1170, magnitude 9, G0; groups northwest/southwest of main body are not conspicuous here. Magnitude 12 pair near center of main group. Pair west: 23″; position angle 145°." He further called this a "sparse group" when examined on the DSS with an 0.25° field.

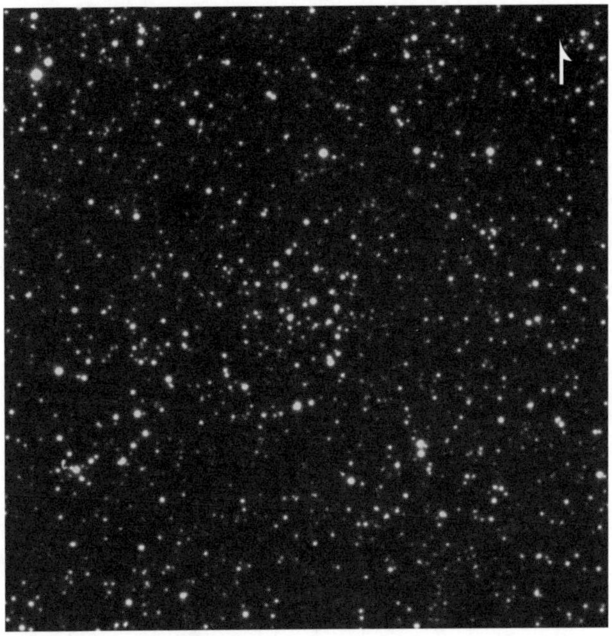

Fig. 4.118 *Skiff J0614.8+1252, a likely cluster discovered visually in the mid-1970's by B. Skiff. 17′ field of view. Image courtesy the Palomar Observatory and Digitized Sky Survey created by the Space Telescope Science Institute, operated by AURA, Inc. for NASA. Reproduced with permission from AURA/STScI.*

SIMBAD indicates that the involved bright star BD+18 1170 is also known as HD 254979 and gives a slightly conflicting V magnitude and spectral type of 8.9 and F7IV. A search by position in SIMBAD and an examination of this area on the DSS via SkyView (see Figure 4.119) shows that the main group includes the stars HD 254980, HD 255066, and HD 254875. The "clump" to the northeast contains HD 255102, HD 255065, HD 255144, and HD 255101. The infrared source IRAS 06162+1837 is on the northwest side of the main group. Just south of the main group of stars is the galaxy CAP 0616+18 = IRAS 06165+1826 = Weinberger 171 = ZOAG 192.96+01.52 at the unusually low Galactic latitude of +1.5°.

Skiff J1942.3+3839: This possible open cluster is named and reported on here for the first time, see Figure 4.120. Brian Skiff discovered it visually on June 16, 1988, while observing with his 15-cm refractor from Kitt Peak Observatory [private communication, 1997]. It was

Fig. 4.119 *Skiff J0619.3+1832, a likely cluster discovered visually with a 15-cm telescope in 1988 by B. Skiff. 45′ field of view. Image courtesy the Palomar Observatory and Digitized Sky Survey created by the Space Telescope Science Institute, operated by AURA, Inc. for NASA. Reproduced with permission from AURA/STScI.*

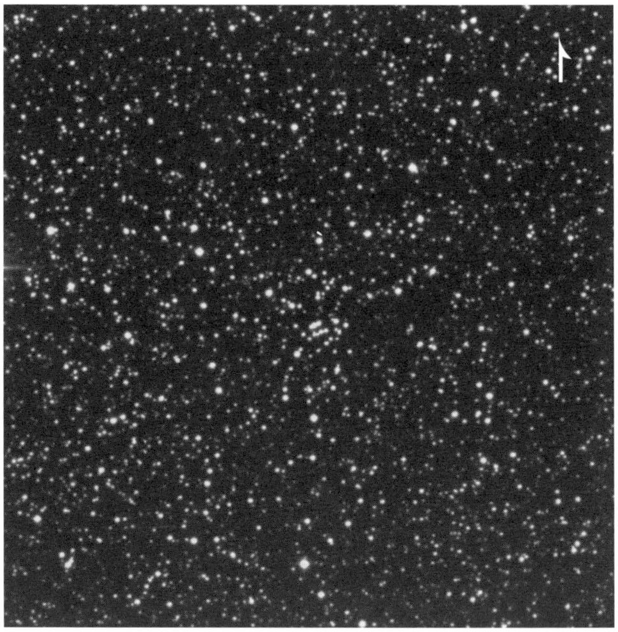

Fig. 4.120 *Skiff J1942.3+3839, another likely cluster discovered visually with a 15-cm telescope in 1988 by B. Skiff. 17′ field of view. Image courtesy the Palomar Observatory and Digitized Sky Survey created by the Space Telescope Science Institute, operated by AURA, Inc. for NASA. Reproduced with permission from AURA/STScI.*

noticed while starhopping to nearby NGC 6819. His observation reads:

> ...found immediately W of a mag. 7 star, conspicuous at 50x. 80x/140x: about 10' W of mag. 7 star. Cluster outliers to 10' diameter, possibly including many field stars. Concentrated, somewhat nebulous (i.e., unresolved) core about 3' across with a dozen stars over background, but generally irresolved. 10' area includes about 50 stars mag. 11 and fainter.

Skiff reported a position from the DSS of (2000.0) 19^h 42^m 24^s +38° 39.0′ and a diameter of about 3′ for the main body of the cluster. He noted that HD 186506 (V = 6.4, "K0 in the HD catalog, but the UBV colors indicate about a K2III") is a bright star just to the east of the cluster.

Philipp Teutsch independently discovered this group (his Teutsch J1942.4+3839) during his examination of a POSS print of this area in 1989.

Skiff J2330.2+6015: This is listed here for the first time, see Figure 4.121 on page 201. This possible open cluster was noted by Brian Skiff [private communication, 1997] while checking the position of the variable star V582 Cas. Skiff describes it as "a few brighter stars aligned N-S over a circular group of much fainter stars." The DSS shows that V582 Cas = GSC 04280-01858, which lies on the north side of the cluster (at 2000.0: 23^h 30^m 11.3^s +60° 16′ 46″), appears to be the brightest star of the cluster. However, Skiff points out that since this is an "old" SRa or Mira variable, it "is presumably not a member of the putative cluster, but in the foreground." The Rosino, *et al.*, [1976] discovery paper for the star indicates a magnitude range from 14.8–16.2 in B and a period of 300 days, spectral type M 5. The GSC (quasi V) magnitude for the star is 12.2 ± 0.25. One of us [BA] has estimated the size (2.8′), number of stars (40) and Trumpler type (II2m) from a DSS image.

SL 87: See NGC 1737, *et al.*, on page 153.

SL 178: See NGC 1783 on page 155.

SL 232: See NGC 1833, *et al.*, on page 155.

SL 415: See NGC 1925 and SL 415, on page 157.

SL 601: This is an LMC cluster in the association NGC 2042, see page 160.

SSWZ94 4: This is one of six "Berkeley" type star clusters noted by Saurer, *et al.* [1994], and shown here as Figure 4.122. One of us [BA] noticed that this object, in their image (their figure 6d) and on the DSS and DSS II, has some of the characteristics of a remote Galactic globular cluster. However, this object has since been proven by Frinchaboy and Phelps [2002] to be a rich, old and distant open cluster. They derive a distance of 6.19 ±0.57 kpc, and an age of 1.53 ±0.28 billion years. They have also confirmed that 4 of the other 6 SSWZ94 objects are old open clusters, with only the existence of cluster 5 (their cluster E) as a physical group unconfirmed. Their data further sug-

Fig. 4.121 *Skiff J2330.2+6015, a likely cluster discovered by B. Skiff, while checking the position of V582 Cas, the (circled) brightest star (but a likely non-member) on the north side of the group. 17′ field of view. Image courtesy the Palomar Observatory and Digitized Sky Survey created by the Space Telescope Science Institute, operated by AURA, Inc. for NASA. Reproduced with permission from AURA/STScI.*

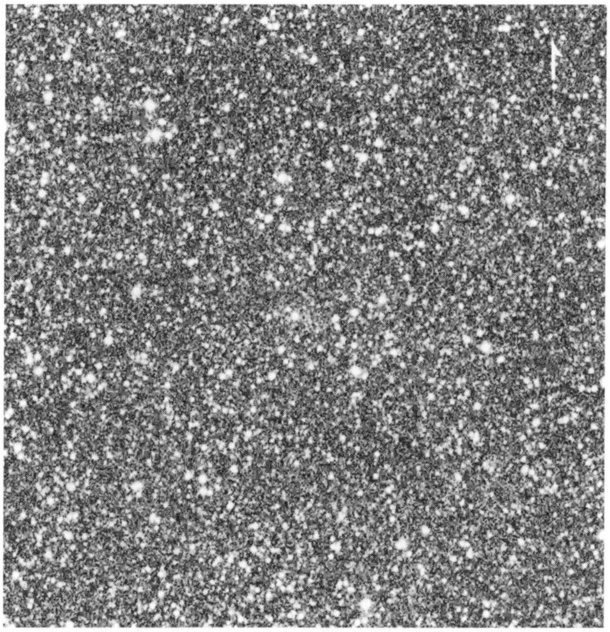

Fig. 4.122 *SSWZ94 4, only faintly visible at the center of this histogram equalization stretch image. This cluster has quite recently been shown by Frinchaboy and Phelps [2002] to be a rich, old, and distant open cluster. 17′ field of view SkyView/DSS-S image (C) ROE.*

gest that SSWZ94 1 is the most distant known Milky Way open cluster, at 11.97 ±1.10 kpc.

Note that the position in the catalog here has been measured from the DSS-II as both the original Saurer, *et al.* and Frinchaboy and Phelps positions are not on the cluster.

Stephenson 2: This is a very reddened Galactic cluster, discovered by Stephenson [1990]. It was discovered on the basis of the density of reddened stars on a 5.2° square plate. With 84 such stars on the plate and a mean surface density of 3.1 per square degree, the area of this cluster contained 10 such stars. This is a density of 6000 per square degree, in an area 1.5′ by 4′. Just a few extremely faint stars are visible at this location on the DSS and the red sensitive POSS chart shows no concentration of stars. The brightest stars (number 1 and 3) are at I magnitude 13.1 and V magnitude 19.7 (the later value used here for that of the brightest star). Stephenson estimated an approximate distance of 33 kpc.

The existence of this cluster was confirmed by Nakaya, *et al.*, [2001], who obtained deep images in visible (V and R) and infrared (I, J, H, and K) colors using the University of Hawaii 2.2-meter telescope at Mauna Kea Observatory. Their data revealed about 25 early type stars at a reddening level (11.2 magnitudes in V) that matched the red supergiant stars noted by Stephenson. They also found 5 more slightly fainter supergiants. They estimate an angular size of the cluster of about 3.5′ by 4.5′, a distance of 1.5 kpc (which appears much more reasonable than the earlier estimate by Stephenson), and an age of about 730 Myr. These values and their estimate of the position of the cluster are used here.

Stock 1 = C1933+251: This group of stars was first reported by Stock [1956] to be a possible cluster of A type stars. Due to a lack of any detailed studies of these stars over the years since then, the true existence of such a cluster has been in doubt. However, Osborn, *et al.* [2002] recently published a study showing that many of the stars in this group do indeed form a true physical cluster. They obtained *BVRI* photometry of approximately 160 stars and available proper motion information on 12 stars in this area. Their study showed that 17 stars were definite members and 2 more were likely members. Of these, only 1 is not a B or A type star, thus verifying Stock's original result. These cluster members all reside within a diameter of approximately 52′, centered on the 7.10 visual magnitude star HD 184928. That diameter is used in the catalog here, although the overall apparent group of stars extends out to a diameter of perhaps 80′. The total magnitude, within a 50' diameter, is V = 5.2, with HD 184590 contributing about 20% of the total light.

Stock 6 = NGC 886: see page 93.

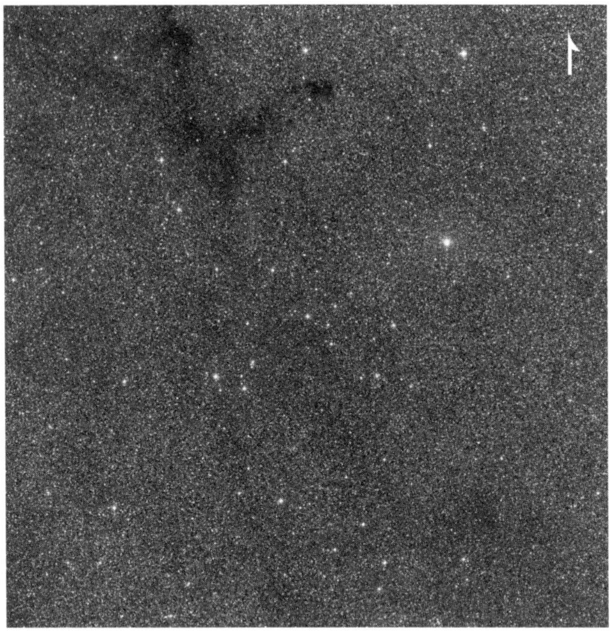

Fig. 4.123 *Stock 1, a large group of A type stars theorized by J. Stock to be a cluster. Osborn,* et al. *[2002] have shown that there is a 52′ diameter group of at least 17 stars centered here that are related. The visual appearance though is of a scattered group of stars with a diameter of as large as 80′. 120′ field of view. Image courtesy the Palomar Observatory and Digitized Sky Survey created by the Space Telescope Science Institute, operated by AURA, Inc. for NASA. Reproduced with permission from AURA/STScI.*

Fig. 4.124 *Stock 11, identified here as a likely asterism of four HD stars with spectral types (as indicated by Stock) near A0. 24′ field of view. Image courtesy the Palomar Observatory and Digitized Sky Survey created by the Space Telescope Science Institute, operated by AURA, Inc. for NASA. Reproduced with permission from AURA/STScI.*

Stock 8 = C0524+343: This cluster is involved with the nebulosity IC 417.

Stock 11 = C2330+552: As with many of the Stock clusters, this object was first listed in the Alter, *et al.*, [1958, 1167] compilation by private communication from Stock, see Figure 4.124. Stock indicated the stars of this cluster were all of type A0. At his position, there are three bright 8–9th magnitude HD stars, but only one (HD 221326, the closest) is type A0. Instead, in this catalog, his supposed cluster is identified as a group about ½° farther to the northwest containing four HD stars all of type near A0. These stars (and their spectral type from SIMBAD) are HD 236149 (A0), HD 236150 (B8V), HD 240318 (A2), and HD 240321 (A0). However, this group still does not have the appearance of a cluster and is listed here with type "ast?" since it probably is only an asterism. The *DSFG1e* suggests that this is "probably not a cluster." A modern check of the spectral types, colors, and proper motions of stars in this area would be useful in order to confirm or refute the existence of a real cluster. The position should be corrected in the *Lund Catalogue* and the *DSFG1e*.

As an interesting side note, this is the only object in the *Lund Catalogue* where the reference for the angular diameter is not "320" (Lyngå's examination). However, the given diameter of 10′ matches that from Stock, so is assumed to be correct.

Stock 15 = C1204–592: There is nothing at Stock's original position (updated to 2000.0: $12^h09.5^m$ –59°46′) for St 15. However, T. Karhula has provided the position ($12^h10.5^m$ –59°29′) of a group of stars which on the DSS appears to match Stock's description (which appears in Alter, *et al.*, 1958]). This appears to be a possible cluster, agreeing in size (12′), numbers of stars (30) and magnitude (10–11 magnitude stars). Therefore, this has been accepted as the correct identification of St 15 in this catalog. This is only 19′ from Stock's position, which is not unreasonable for a 12′ diameter cluster. The position is incorrect in the *Lund Catalogue* and the *DSFG1e*. In fact, the *Lund Catalogue* 2000.0 position ($12^h06.9^m$ –59°28′) appears as if it may be the 1950.0 position based on Stock's coordinates. Therefore, it is possible that the position has just been given for the wrong epoch in that catalog (and possibly earlier catalogs).

Stock 18 = C2359+643: The *Lund Catalogue* gives an RA for this that is greater than 24 hours.

Stock 23 = C0312+598: This cluster was popularized by Walter S. Houston [1978] after being brought to his attention by John Pazmino. See Figure 4.125 on page 203. The center and brightest star is HD 20040 (V = 7.6). The position and diameter here were measured from the DSS.

Fig. 4.125 *Stock 23, on the Camelopardalis/Cassiopeia border. 1° field of view. Image courtesy the Palomar Observatory and Digitized Sky Survey created by the Space Telescope Science Institute, operated by AURA, Inc. for NASA. Reproduced with permission from AURA/STScI.*

The star magnitudes and the spectral type are from SIMBAD.

SU Cygni group and Mandushev 1: The SU Cygni group is a possible (but currently unlikely) star cluster around the Cepheid variable (period 3.8^d) SU Cygni. Apparently the first published reference to this possible cluster was in an unsigned article in the JRASC [1994b]. There it is stated: "The possible existence of a cluster surrounding the Cepheid was first proposed by Nancy Evans based upon her impressions of the field of the Cepheid as seen through the eyepiece of the DDO 1.8-m telescope in the 1970s." This was actually a follow-up article to the possible discovery of a planetary nebula in the same field [JRASC 1994a].

Obviously, the discovery of an open cluster containing a classical cepheid variable star would be an important discovery since the relationship could be used to help define the Cepheid period-luminosity relation and, therefore, the scale of the universe. There are currently only a few known cases of Cepheids associated with a star cluster.

At first, a detailed follow-up study by Turner, *et al.*, [1997] showed via photometric evidence that a cluster is unlikely. About two dozen B and A type stars randomly distributed in the field do lie at a common distance (1086±60 pc), but these are probably part of the Vul OB4 association.

Further, visual observations of this area reveal no trace of any cluster. A. Ling reports [private communication, 1995] that nothing like a cluster was seen here using a 45.7-cm (18-inch) *f*/4.3 Newtonian reflector at 71 or 287 power. This observation was from Mt. Kobau, BC, on August 25, 1995. One of us [BA] was unable to see any trace of a cluster while observing with R. Bunge's 51-cm (20-inch) *f*/6.4 Newtonian at 163 and 390 power with and without a nebula filter. (The planetary nebula was not visible.) The cluster was not seen while observing with a 15-cm (6-inch) *f*/10 Newtonian at 145 power. These observations were made from Pocomoke River State Park, MD, on October 4, 1997.

However, Turner, *et al.* [1998] have investigated this area further. Their goal was to check whether a group of stars noted earlier in this area by G. Mandushev was a true physical group. They found it was not. This group is included in the catalog here as the asterism "Mandushev 1" as identified from the figures of the Turner, *et al.* paper. The coordinates given in the paper (and later by Dias, *et al.* [2002]) are quite a ways off and a corrected position is included here.

Turner, *et al.* did find that at least 14 stars in this area do have the appearance of the "scattered remains of the parent cluster for SU Cyg". Still, the authors note that the term "possible cluster" seems appropriate for this group, and that if it is a physical cluster it is so advanced toward total dissolution it "is now no longer recognizable as a distinct clump in the sky". So it still seems unclear whether a cluster definitely exists here or not; and even if so, whether SU Cygni is a member.

Terz N 5 = C1708-271: This is also known as Terzan-Ju 5, and originally thought to be a Galactic globular cluster [Terzan and Ju 1980]. However, Djorgovski and Meylan [1993, 333] determined it as either an asterism or nebulosity with stars superimposed.

Terz N 15, Terz N 16, and Terz N 17: Terz N 15 (or Terzan-Ju 15) was originally thought to be the nucleus of a Galactic globular cluster [Terzan and Ju 1980]. Terz N 16 (or Terzan-Ju 16 or TBJ 2) and Terz N 17 (or Terzan-Ju 17 or TBJ 1) have been thought to be Galactic globular clusters by later references. However, they have been confirmed to be galaxies [Djorgovski, *et al.*, 1990; Djorgovski and Meylan 1993, 333]. They do have "C" style names assigned but use of which should be avoided since they are now known not to be star clusters.

Terz N 23: Also known as Terzan-Ju 23, this was originally thought to be a globular cluster. Djorgovski and Meylan [1993, 333] reported that it was either a distant globular cluster or a galaxy with stars superimposed. However, Bica, *et al.*, [1995] have determined that this object is a small emission nebula having the spectral characteristics of a planetary nebula, and it is listed as such here.

Terz N 33, Terz N 34, and Terz N 35: Terz N 33 and Terz N 34 (sometimes called "Terzan-Ju" rather than "Terz

Fig. 4.126 θ *Sagittae group, an asterism of bright stars just to the east of NGC 6873. 45′ field of viewe. Image courtesy the Palomar Observatory and Digitized Sky Survey created by the Space Telescope Science Institute, operated by AURA, Inc. for NASA. Reproduced with permission from AURA/STScI.*

Fig. 4.127 *Trumpler 1, a small concentrated cluster close to NGC 581 = M 103 in Cassiopeia. 17′ field of view. Image courtesy the Palomar Observatory and Digitized Sky Survey created by the Space Telescope Science Institute, operated by AURA, Inc. for NASA. Reproduced with permission from AURA/STScI.*

N" as in SIMBAD) were originally thought to be Galactic globular clusters. Terz N 35 was originally thought to be a globular cluster or planetary nebula [Terzan and Ju 1980]. However, they have all been confirmed to be galaxies [Djorgovski, *et al.*, 1990; Djorgovski and Meylan 1993, 333]. They do have "C" style names assigned but use of which should be avoided since they are now known not to be star clusters.

Teutsch J0544.3+2848: Teutsch described this as a possible asterism, a "scattered group with fainter background stars, little condensed." He also noted: "Near NE-edge of SNR Simeis 147. A wisp of the SNR curves around the eastern side of the field, some nebulosity seems to surround the star-group, leaving an apparent central clearing. Located nearly at galactic anticenter."

Teutsch J0625.6+1336: Teutsch lists this as a possible cluster and describes it as "Either coarse group rich in faint stars or faint cluster with superimposed curved line of brighter stars in NW-part." Regarding the location, he adds that this is nearly at the Gemini and Orion border but still in Gemini, 6' W of the bright star HD 257145 (V = 8.20).

Teutsch J0631.9+1151: Teutsch added here regarding the position that this possible cluster is located 5.5' NE of the bright star HD 46075 (V = 6.65, B6III) and 3' from the Monoceros and Gemini border.

θ Sagittae group: This is likely an asterism of bright stars around and including θ Sge noted by Brian Skiff [1990, 46], see Figure 4.126. Skiff had thought that this group was NGC 6873, but that was later determined to be a possible asterism just to the west of this position (see NGC 6873 on page 186). The position, diameter, and number of stars given here are from an examination of the DSS. The brightest V magnitude (6.5, SIMBAD) is for the primary of θ Sge. The name "Sagitta cluster" (or "Theta Sge") is used here for the first time.

Trapezium cluster = NGC 1976: see page 159.

Trumpler 1 = C0132+610: This small, concentrated open cluster can be found a short distance from the more conspicuous NGC 581 (= M 103) in Cassiopeia, see Figure 4.127. It is a young system and lies at the outer edge of the Perseus spiral arm. In a 1974 study Steppe [1974] measured 116 stars in the field and found that there were 37 cluster members, and that the diameter of the system was 7′.4; a distance of 2.98 kpc was derived, greater than previous estimates, which ranged from 2.15 to 2.74 kpc. This paper also included a photographic chart of the cluster. Photoelectric photometry was carried out on the cluster by Joshi and Sagar [1977] who observed 43 stars and arrived at a distance value of 3.3 kpc, an apparent integrated magnitude of 8.61 and an interstellar reddening factor (A_v) of 1.66 mag. A well-defined cluster main sequence was found from their CMD, but with no giant branch. An estimate for the age of the cluster is given in both papers as being about 10 million years.

Fig. 4.128 *The spectacular Eta Carinae nebula, including the cluster Trumpler 16. The cluster itself is mostly covered by nebulosity in this image but lies mainly in the region around the central and southern part of the nebula. The southern portion of the cluster is also known as Collinder 234, as noted in the text. From a photograph by Bailey [1908, plate 4.]. Note that the appearance of the nebula in this image is significantly different than more recent images such as from the DSS. The field of view here is approximately 3° by 4°.*

Trumpler 10 = C0846-423 = Lac II-6: B. Skiff noted [private communication, 1998] that Trumpler 10 is Lacaille's class 2, number 6 object (Lacaille star no. 3528). This identification of Lac II-6 has not been made by previous researchers of the work of Lacaille [Gingerich 1960; Glyn Jones 1975; Evans 1992].

Trumpler 16 = C1043-594 = Eta Carinae cluster: See Figure 4.128 on page 205. The *Lund Catalogue* alias list indicates identities for this of Collinder 233 and Collinder 234. A check of Collinder's description (actually the identification is by Lundmark only, Collinder 1931, B12) shows that Cr 234 is just the southern part of the main η Carinae cluster. Therefore, the identity of Cr 234 with Cr 233 should be removed from the *Lund Catalogue* alias list, and a separate entry added for Cr 234 noting it is part of Tr 16 = Cr 233. The OCl 829 designation should apply to Tr 16 and OCl 830 should apply to Cr 234. A new "C" designation should be added for Cr 234 (the 2000.0 position is 10h 45m 12.9s –59° 44′ 47"). An examination of Cr 234 via SkyView/DSS reveals that the center and brightest star

Fig. 4.129 *Trumpler 32 and the "stellar ring", Isserstedt 690 (circled). The latter is just detectable as an arc of 10 or so stars E (to the lower left of) the cluster. 24' field of view DSS-S image © ROE.*

is HD 93343, and that this group has a concentric arc of 10 stars from the NW to E side. The *DSFG1e* (chart 427) does correctly list Tr 16 and Cr 234 separately, although it remains to be checked whether the data for these entries are correct.

Trumpler 30 = C1753–353: This is a supposed star cluster discovered by E. E. Barnard and shown on his [1927] Atlas plate 24. The DSS shows this as a 20' diameter condensation in a rich Milky Way background. The *Lund Catalogue* diameter (8.0') and Collinder's and Lundmark's sizes (15 x 12, 12 x 8) [Collinder 1931] are clearly too small. The brightest star is HD 163251, at (SIMBAD) V = 7.71 with spectral type B7II/III. However, this is brighter than the Lundmark and *Lund Catalogue* total magnitude of (photographic) 8.8, so it is not clear whether it should be considered a cluster member.

Trumpler 32 = C1814-133 and Isserstedt 690: The *Lund Catalogue* position for Tr 32 is substantially (26 time seconds) too far west (see Figure 4.129). The correct position is that of GSC 5689-00194, at (GSC) $18^h\ 17^m\ 10.35^s$ –13° 20′ 39.9″. Kharchenko and Schilbach [1995] in their recent study of this area gave a position that was substantially off. The *Lund Catalogue* diameter of 6.0 appears to be too small. The DSS shows this to have a rough diameter of at least 12′, with outliers even beyond that. E.g., Kharchenko and Schilbach [ibid.] gave a distance of 1720 pc and a corona semiradius of 2.4 pc, corresponding to a cluster corona diameter of 9.6′. They claimed a maximum diameter of 12.9 pc, which implies a maximum diameter of fully 52′ on the sky.

One of Isserstedt's "stellar rings," Iss 690, appears as a flattened ring of stars on the southeast side of Tr 32. The DSS shows it at $18^h\ 17^m\ 25^s$ –13° 22.8′ about 2.5′ high by 4′ long (Isserstedt gave 4.42′). SkyView shows that only one of the "ring" stars is a GSC star (GSC 5689-00256 on the northeast corner).

These stars may be outliers of Tr 32. Therefore, it is worthwhile to compare the (independent) distance estimates of Tr 32 and Iss 690 to see if they are similar. Assuming Isserstedt's figure of 7.1 pc for the absolute size of the minor axis diameter of any stellar ring [Isserstedt 1970, abstract], and 2.5′ for this ring gives a "Isserstedt" distance of 9800 pc. This does not match Kharchenko and Schilbach's estimate of 1720 pc nor even earlier estimates they cite (Trumpler 1870 pc; Shapley, 5500 pc; Barkhatova, 760 pc). Such a result does not bode well for the Isserstedt theory that the minor axis diameters of rings have an absolute size. However, it is difficult to tell (from their figure 10) whether the "ring" stars are true members of the cluster or not. If they are not, then the ring and cluster are not connected and nothing can be determined about the Isserstedt theory.

Trumpler 37: This is more correctly known as IC 1396, see page 134.

UKS 2 = vdB-Ha 66: see page 207.

"unknown" cluster about G 353.1+0.6: See Pismis 24 on page 195.

Upgren 1 = C1232+365: The galaxy fields of Canes Venatici are an unlikely place to find an open cluster; yet, near the star 6 CVn is the Upgren 1 group, see Figure 4.130. This was first identified by Upgren and Rubin [1965] during an objective-prism study of the distribution of stars in the region of the North Galactic Pole. They noticed a fairly compact group of 7 bright (V = 7.3–9.9) F-type stars within a field of 15′ diameter. Photometric and spectrographic measurements suggested that they formed a physically associated group lying at a distance of about 0.14 kpc, with a mean radial velocity of –30 km/s. The small number of stars involved made it difficult to make a good estimate of the age. It was suggested that this would be similar to the age of M 67 (NGC 2682), one of the oldest clusters known. Only a few studies were made of Upgren 1 after its discovery increasing its membership to 10 stars, but otherwise the original assessment of its status remained valid until Gatewood, *et al.*, [1988] found that the grouping was probably a chance alignment of two dynamically different sets of stars. More recently, Stefanik *et al.*, [1997] showed that one of the sets formed by five stars includes a long-period binary and an unusual triple system.

Fig. 4.130 *Upgren 1, a likely asterism in Canes Venatici. (There is a curved line defect on the DSS image on the bottom left of the group.) 45′ field of view. Image courtesy the Palomar Observatory and Digitized Sky Survey created by the Space Telescope Science Institute, operated by AURA, Inc. for NASA. Reproduced with permission from AURA/STScI.*

Ursa Major Moving Cluster: This is Collinder 285, see page 122.

vdB = GS-SET: This object—not to be confused with "vdB 0" or "Cl vdB 1"—is apparently a double star. B. Herbit found it in a search for globular clusters of M 31. This was only after a careful examination (a 100-hour search) of a Palomar 122-cm (48-inch) Schmidt plate, taken by S. van den Bergh [1972] of a region NE of M 31. Only 12 compact nonstellar objects were found on the plate and all but one turned out to be nuclei of elliptical galaxies. The remaining object was thought to be a distant globular cluster of M 31. The Hale 5-meter telescope was used to determine that for this object V = 15.99, B – V = 0.82, and U – B = 0.25 (colors consistent with a globular cluster). This was reported by Sargent, *et al.*, [1977], although a name was not assigned to the object.

Bònoli, *et al.*, [1988] reported a low radial velocity for this object, called by them "vdb," as determined with spectra taken with the Kitt Peak 4-meter telescope. Careful analysis of a CCD image taken with the Loiano 152-cm telescope showed that this object was a double star with total V = 16.17 (close to the Hale telescope value), and component V magnitudes of 16.84 and 17.03.

Huchra, *et al.* [1991] listed this object in a table of "Confirmed Stars, etc." in their study of M 31 globular clusters. However, they also assigned the very cryptic name "GS-SET." A close study of a footnote to their table reveals that this is an acronym for "*G*lobular cluster *s*uspect from *S*argent, *et al.*, 1977."

This object must now be kept track of in order to keep it from being confused with real M 31 globular clusters, and other van den Bergh discoveries.

vdB clusters: See also entries beginning with Cl vdB, starting on page page 118.

vdB-Ha 60 = Pismis 11: see page 194.

vdB-Ha 66 = UKS 2 = ESO 166-SC11 = C0923-545: Many references (e.g. the *DSFG1e*, the Astronomical Almanac) list this as a globular cluster. However, Djorgovski and Meylan [1993, 333] note that this "is probably *not* a globular cluster, but rather an open cluster." They give the UKS, ESO and coordinate name for this object. W. Harris's 1996 list of globular clusters also does not include this object.

It is B. Skiff [private communication, 1995] who apparently first noted that this is also vdB-Ha 66. By discovery priority this should be the cluster's name. From an examination of a DSS image he also says that this "is almost certainly not a globular, but a fairly rich" open cluster.

The *Lund Catalogue* at least correctly includes this object as an open cluster. However, the alias names should be added (UKS 2 and ESO 166-SC11), and Skiff's coordinates (2000.0: $09^h\ 25^m\ 16^s\ -54°\ 43.1'$) and size of 1.5′ should be used. Those values are used in the catalog here.

vdB-Ha 133 = Harvard 5: see page 132.

vdB-Ha 155 = C1354-593: J. Kay noted [private communication, 1996] that she was unable to locate this cluster, while observing the area with an 20-cm (8-inch) Schmidt-Cassegrain telescope. She initially thought that this object might be NGC 5381, but that was not possible since vdB-Ha 156 was listed by van den Bergh and Hagen as NGC 5381. There is nothing approximating a cluster at the vdB-Ha 155 position on the DSS—although the diffraction pattern of Hadar (β Cen) strongly interferes in this area of the sky. There is also essentially no information in the *Lund Catalogue* beyond the discovery position and diameter (11′), so this object was probably not located by Lyngå. SIMBAD has no entries for this object, and there appear to be no amateur observations published of it. It would appear this "cluster" does not exist. However, further observations should be made, and other photographs of this area should be examined to confirm this. Photographs at different epochs may show the cluster better since Hadar has such a substantial proper motion. The object is listed here with its discovery position and size and type "nf?" for "not yet found."

Information on this object is listed in the discovery paper [van den Bergh and Hagen 1975, 14] as follows: position of (1950.0) $13^h\ 54^m$: –59° 20′, diameter 11′, moderate richness, "certainly real," noted to be clearly visible on a blue Curtis Schmidt IIaO plate, but no information is given about the visibility on a red plate. Perhaps the discovery plate could be located and checked in order to ascertain the identity of this object.

vdB-Ha 202: This is Ruprecht 122, see page 197.

Westerlund 1 = C1644–457: This is a faint (V>14.5 stars) heavily reddened cluster. It was located on the DSS-II red image, with assistance from S. French [private communication, 2002] by comparison with Westerlund [1961, plate 1] discovery photographs. Westerlund [1968] later explains how this cluster was independently discovered as an infrared source. On the DSS-II, the core of the cluster is 53″ in size, while the overall size is about 3′ (as used in the catalog here), agreeing with Westerlund's [1968] estimate of 3′ by 2′ in size. Since this cluster is so reddened, it is difficult to see on the DSS and the DSS-II blue images. The non-member star HD 151018 (V = 8.73, O+...) is on the northeast side.

Westerlund 2: This is NGC 3247, see page 171.

Westerlund 3: This is Pismis 22, see page 195.

Chapter 5
The Discovery of Globular Clusters

Every recognized globular cluster except one bears a number from the New General Catalogue *of Dreyer, an indication that in spite of great distance and the faintness of the individual stars, all of these objects were known prior to 1880.*

—Harlow Shapley, *Star Clusters* [1930]

By comparison with the great Messier 13, the rich Omega Centauri, or the luminous 47 Tucanae, some of these recent objects look pathetic.

—Helen Sawyer Hogg (1905–1993) in Hogg [1958]

5.1 Early Discoveries of Globular Clusters

While many open clusters are apparent to the unaided eye and have been known to observers of the night sky since before written records were kept, the history of globular clusters is very much shorter. Theoretically, under reasonably clear, dark skies, there are several globular clusters that fall within the range of normal human eyesight and which could have been detected as small, nebulous spots. No doubt early observers did pick these out, but nothing has come down to us in writing. No one will ever know who really first saw M 13, M 22, ω Centauri or 47 Tuc.

The first recorded discovery of an object now classified as a globular cluster was that of M 22 (NGC 6656) which lies among the starfields of Sagittarius. Steven Hynes has seen this with the unaided eye from a dark site in Sri Lanka without much difficulty. The credit for the discovery is usually attributed to John Abraham Ihle, a German astronomer about whom almost nothing is known. The reported date of the discovery is August 26, 1665, although in a 1682 paper, Gottfried Kirch says: "... afterwards, however, we established that it had been reported a little earlier by John Hevelius." We are not aware of the existence of any supporting evidence for this claim.

Although it was cataloged as a star by Ptolemy, Edmond Halley discovered that ω Centauri is a globular cluster. Halley was the son of a wealthy and influential London merchant and had a talent for mathematics; even as an undergraduate at Queen's College, Oxford, he developed an improved method for determining the elements of planetary orbits. Halley is best known for his prediction that the comet of 1682, which now bears his name, would again return in 1758. He can also be credited with producing the first star catalog of any significance for the southern sky. In 1676, at the age of just 20 and on his own initiative, he used his family's influence with the East India Company to obtain free passage to the island of St. Helena (latitude 16° S.) in the South Atlantic Ocean. Over a period of almost two years he made an accurate catalog of the positions of some 341 stars, which was published in 1679 as the *Catalogus Stellarum Australium*. It was during the course of this work in 1677, that he found the non-stellar nature of ω Cen. Obviously, with the limited equipment at his disposal he could make no further comment on its nature but to record its brightness and position.

Halley is also credited with the discovery of M 13 (NGC 6205), perhaps the finest northern hemisphere globular cluster, which he found in 1714. He says:

> This is but a little Patch, but it shews itself to the naked Eye, when the sky is serene and the Moon absent.

In between these discoveries by Halley, the German astronomer Gottfried Kirch found the globular cluster M 5 (NGC 5904) on May 5, 1702. This object, though fairly bright, lies in a fairly obscure part of Serpens and is, therefore, a surprising early discovery.

By the time of the discovery of M 13, it was becoming increasingly obvious to astronomers that nebulae of all sorts were probably a fairly common phenomenon. In a *Philosophical Transactions* paper, Edmond Halley [1715] wrote:

> There are undoubtedly more of these which have not yet come to our Knowledge, and some perhaps bigger, but though all these Spots are in Appearance but little, and most of them but of few Minutes in Diameter; yet since they are among the Fixt Stars, that is, since they have no Annual parallex, they cannot fail to occupy Spaces immensely great, and perhaps not less than our whole Solar System. In all these so vast Spaces it should seem that there is a perpetual uninterrupted Day, which may furnish Matter of Speculation, as well to the curious Naturalist as to the Astronomer.

As a result of the increasing interest more thorough searches were undertaken so that by the end of the eighteenth century almost half of the presently known number of globular clusters had been discovered, mostly by Lacaille, Messier, Méchain and William Herschel.

5.2 The Observations and Theories of William Herschel

The importance of William Herschel's work in the history of astronomy is difficult to overstate. Although he had learned some fundamentals of astronomy from his father as part of his general education, he did not take a serious interest in astronomy until the age of 35. This in itself is remarkable but even more so when one considers that within ten years he had become the leading telescope-maker of his time and the discoverer of Uranus, the first major planet of the Solar System to be found in recorded history. Of greater relevance to the subject of this book is the fact that within fifteen years he discovered over 2300 new nebulae and clusters, most of them during the seven-year period 1781–1788.

With this database of observational material to work with, Herschel devised a classification and naming scheme, dividing the objects into eight categories as described in Chapter 1. Interestingly, there is no separate item here for globular clusters, although category VI is "very compressed, rich clusters of stars." Some of Herschel's discoveries of globular clusters ended up here, but others, those not resolved into stars, were usually listed under category I or II ("bright nebulae" and "faint nebulae").

Although not given a separate classification in the Herschel scheme, he certainly recognized that they were different from the ordinary "irregular" clusters. He obviously gave considerable thought to their nature and expressed his conclusions in several papers. In his second catalog of nebulae and clusters [Herschel, W. 1788], he argued that globular clusters were separate sidereal systems, and that the stars being crowded together showed that they were "nearly of an equal magnitude," with just a small variation in brightness range "in some such proportion as one full-grown plant of a certain species may exceed another full-grown plant of the same species." He also showed that the apparently globular form was actually real and that, as appears to be the case in visual observation, the clusters are increasingly condensed towards the center. As evidence in support of this he pointed out that many have a bright central "nucleus" and argued that this would not be the case if the component stars were equally scattered through the sphere. As to the origin of the spherical figure, he suggested it was due to "the action of central powers," probably "the known central force of gravity," and not to "any random scattering of stars," pointing out that the proof of this lay in the condensation of stars towards the center. Of course, there are a number of rich open clusters which have a "quasi-globular" form, and some globulars which have a loose, slightly irregular form. Herschel was not able to discriminate between them but thought that in these there was evidence of "a tendence towards sphericity by the swell of the dimensions the nearer we draw towards the most luminous place, denoting as it were a course, or tide of stars setting towards a center."

One particularly interesting conclusion Herschel reached was that the action of the "central force" would produce effects "proportional to the time of its action," and therefore, the globular clusters must be much older than those of a more irregular form. He clearly imagined that over a period of time, the "irregular clusters" would also be drawn under gravity into a globular form and suggested that this might form the basis of scheme to estimate the relative ages of clusters.

In a more detailed paper on the classification of nebulae, Herschel [1814] considered the subdivision of the various types of nebulae and clusters. Obviously, the "irregular" and "globular" varieties were the two main groupings, but among the "clusters of a peculiar description" he mentioned M 4 and M 30. He considered that the true globular clusters were "undoubtedly the most interesting objects in the heavens" and estimated that, for example, M 72 (NGC 6981) might contain several hundreds of stars. Pointing out that a number of globular clusters, such as M 9 (NGC 6333), M 14 (NGC 6402), M 62 (NGC 6266) and M 75 (NGC 6864) seemed to be miniatures of the normal globular clusters, with fainter and more closely packed stars, he supposed that they were more distant objects.

5.3 Of Scale and Structure in the Galaxy

Herschel had no true idea of the distance, size, stellar content and distribution of globular clusters and, to all intents and purposes, little more of any great significance was learned about them until the early years of the twentieth century.

At this time, Böhlin [1909] wrote a paper called "On the Galactic System, with Regard to its Structure, Origin and Relations in Space," in which he had speculated that the Galaxy originated as an enormous planetary nebula. He envisioned that this rotating sphere of gas had condensed into different sorts of structures, the spiral nebulae being "products of the broken parts of the shell, while the Milky Way … is derived from its equatorial belt." In addition to this, he did correctly propose that the system of globular clusters was symmetrically situated about the center of the Galaxy, and that the Solar System must be at considerable distance from it because of the peculiar distribution of the globular clusters.

Bohlin's theory was generally overlooked, probably largely because of its obscure place of publication, but his view on the origin of the Galaxy would not have earned the rest of his paper much credibility. However, to be taken more seriously was the astronomer P. J. Melotte [1915], who produced a short paper on "The Distribution of Star Clusters" based on an examination of the Franklin-Adams photographic star charts. He cataloged 245 objects and divided them into four classes; Class I, with 83 objects, covered the globular clusters. In the conclusion to his paper he noted:

> Taking the clusters as a whole it is found that the majority are distributed over a zone ± 30° of the galactic plane, and that comparatively few, nearly all belonging to Class I, fall outside these limits. Further, there is a marked tendency for the globular clusters to crowd together towards a point about longitude 325°, whilst opposite this point the clusters appear spread out over a somewhat wider range in the latitude and include some of the most extended.

Nevertheless, the landmark of the time was the series of papers started by Harlow Shapley [1915] (Figure 1.5 on page 7). Shapley conducted an extensive investigation into the distribution of open and globular clusters and also looked at the magnitudes and colors of individual stars in the clusters using the recently built 1.52-m (60-inch) reflector at Mount Wilson (erected 1908). The object of the exercise was described as follows:

> First, it is hoped that considerable advance can be made in our understanding of the internal arrangement and physical characteristics of these objects. Secondly, and probably of more importance, it is hoped that through the acquisition of a clearer appreciation of stellar clusters, particularly of globular systems, some contribution can be made to the knowledge of our own galactic system. For it is quite obvious that a globular cluster, whether considered as entirely extraneous to our galactic domain or not, is in itself a stellar system on a great scale—a stellar unit which without doubt must be comparable to our own galactic system in many ways, though possibly differing from it fundamentally in others.

At this stage, it is important to know that Shapley had a good grounding in photometry through Frederick Seares at the University of Missouri, and that he achieved his doctorate based on a dissertation on the properties of eclipsing binaries. With his interest in variable stars, he would certainly have been well aware of the work of Henrietta Swan Leavitt. Under the direction of Solon I. Bailey at Harvard in 1906, Miss Leavitt used plates of the Magellanic Clouds taken at the Arequipa station to produce a list of 808 variables in the Large Magellanic Cloud and 969 in the Small Magellanic Cloud. Remarkably, these discoveries had been made manually using just a magnifying eyepiece and an unbelievable amount of patience and perseverance. (S. O'Meara [private communication, 2002] points out the magnifier was probably a *flyspeck magnifier*, which has different sized dots on it, which can be used to compare star brightnesses.) Furthermore, in 1908 she had shown that the Cepheids in the SMC exhibit a very neat relationship between their median apparent magnitudes and the periods of their light variations—the brighter the magnitude, the longer the period. This is now called the period-luminosity relationship.

In 1914, while on his way to take up his post at Mount Wilson, Shapley spent a few days at Harvard and engaged in several conversations with Bailey. Both had an interest in variable stars, and Bailey suggested that Shapley should take advantage of the power of the Mount Wilson reflector to make measures of the variable stars in globular clusters. Shapley discovered and studied a great many RR Lyrae and Cepheid variables in the clusters and calibrated Leavitt's period-apparent magnitude relationship in terms of absolute magnitude showing that Cepheids and RR Lyrae variables could be used as "standard candles" in the determination of galactic distances. By this means, Shapley made reasonably accurate estimates of the distances of 25 globular clusters and used this information, together with the distribution of the systems, to identify the direction of the center of the Galaxy and place the Sun at a distance of about 50,000 light-years from it [Shapley 1918a, 1918b]. This figure was startlingly high; and although most astronomers accepted the likelihood of the *relative* distances of the globular clusters being correct, many could not accept the *absolute* distances that Shapley had derived. The "island universe" theory of the spiral nebulae was beginning to gain credibility, but if Shapley's figure for the size of the Galaxy was correct, the theory was in serious trouble. Shapley himself spoke against the "island universe" theory, preferring to think of the spiral nebulae as objects within the Galaxy or gas clouds just beyond it.

A consistent opponent of Shapley's ideas on the scale of the Galaxy was Heber D. Curtis of Lick Observatory. On 1920 April 26, the two men were brought together at the Smithsonian Institution's National Museum of Natural History to put forward their theories; this meeting was subsequently dubbed "The Great Debate." However, in his 1969 reminiscences, Shapley [1969] says:

> ... I don't think the word "debate" was used at the time. Actually, it was a sort of symposium, a paper by Curtis and a paper by me, and a rebuttal apiece. ... Anyway, it was a pleasant meeting, and our subject matter was the scale of the Universe. That was what I was prepared to talk about and did talk about, and I think I won the "debate" from the standpoint of the assigned subject matter. I was right and Curtis was wrong on the main point—the scale, the size. It is a big Universe, and he viewed it as a small one. From the beginning, Curtis picked on another matter: Are the spiral galaxies inside our system or outside? He said that they are outside our system. I said "I don't know what they are, but according to certain evidences they are not outside." But this was not the assigned subject. Curtis, having set up this straw man, won on that.

Fig. 5.1 *Heber D. Curtis (1872-1942). This photograph originally appeared in the Publications of the Astronomical Society of the Pacific (McMath, 1942, PASP, 54, 69). Copyright 1942, Astronomical Society of the Pacific; reproduced with permission of the Editors.*

Fig. 5.2 *Palomar 1, one of the first Galactic globular clusters to be discovered on the (then new) Palomar Sky Survey. This cluster has recently been determined to be the youngest such cluster, or perhaps instead the oldest known open cluster. 17′ field of view. Image courtesy the Palomar Observatory and Digitized Sky Survey created by the Space Telescope Science Institute, operated by AURA, Inc. for NASA. Reproduced with permission from AURA/STScI.*

In truth both were right and wrong on different parts of their arguments. Shapley is probably one of the few great astronomers to be wrong by actually having *over*estimated size in the Universe! The size of the Galaxy is now believed to be little more than half that proposed by Shapley (because he was completely unaware of interstellar reddening). Nevertheless, his general view of large scale structure in the Universe was correct, contrary to the rather conservative standpoint adopted by Curtis. On the other hand, Curtis was correct to believe that the spiral nebulae are galaxies in their own right of a generally similar size to our own Galaxy. Thus, the modern view of the Universe is a combination of the ideas put forward by both Shapley and Curtis.

5.4 Modern Discoveries of Globular Clusters

An examination of a modern listing of globular clusters associated with our own Galaxy will show that the vast majority have NGC designations, indicating discovery in the nineteenth century or before. Globular clusters are comparatively large and bright objects, visible over significant astronomical distances. Larger amateur astronomical telescopes can detect globular clusters associated with the Andromeda Galaxy and M 33. The visibility of galactic systems is enhanced by the fact that they are halo objects and often found above the galactic plane. It is, therefore, not that surprising that so many were visually found so long ago. Of course, because of our particular vantage point, in a spiral arm some considerable distance from the hub of the Galaxy, it is likely that many globular clusters will be hidden behind the gas clouds and star fields in the foreground. In addition, there is a population of fairly low density, low surface brightness objects, which would be even more prone to being obscured, and in some cases, may even be confused with rich galactic clusters. As a result, it might be expected that most of the globular clusters in modern catalogs which do not have NGC designations are likely to be less grand examples of the species and probably also at low galactic latitude, and this proves to be the case.

Following the publication of the NGC in 1888, the next significant batch of globular cluster discoveries was not reported until 1955, when George Abell [1955] published a preliminary list of 73 planetary nebulae and 13 globular clusters (see e.g., Figure 5.2) found on the newly published *National Geographic—Palomar Observatory Sky Survey* (POSS), which is now available over the Internet as the Digitized Sky Survey. This was carried out using a 1.2-meter (48-inch) Schmidt telescope and covered the entire northern sky down to Declination –33°. A total of 935 pairs of plates make up the POSS; one set is blue sensitive, using Kodak 103a-O plates, and the other is red sensitive, using Kodak 103a-E plates plus a red Plexiglass filter. Each plate covers a field of 6° x 6° at a scale of 1 mm = 67″, and the limiting magnitude is 21 in the blue and 20 in the red.

Table 5.1
The globular cluster systems listed by George Abell on the Palomar Observatory Sky Survey plates.

Name	2000.0 R.A	2000.0 Dec	Con	Diam	Br*	Notes
Pal 1	03 33.4	+79 35	Cep	2.8′	16.3	Possibly an old open cluster
Pal 2	04 46.1	+31 23	Aur	2.2′	18.8	Highly obscured
Pal 3	10 05.5	+00 04	Sex	1.6′	18.0	
Pal 4	11 29.3	+28 58	UMa	1.3′	18.0	
Pal 5	15 16.1	–00 07	Ser	3.2′	15.5	Very loose structure
Pal 6	17 43.7	–26 13	Oph	0.6′	20.0	Highly obscured
Pal 7	18 10.7	–07 12	Ser	8.0′	15.7	= IC 1276. Highly obscured
Pal 8	18 41.5	–19 49	Sgr	2.6′	15.4	
Pal 9	18 55.1	–22 42	Sgr	2.7′	14.0?	=NGC 6717.
Pal 10	19 18.0	+18 34	Sge	4.0′	18?	Highly obscured
Pal 11	19 45.2	–08 00	Aql	5.0′	17.0	
Pal 12	21 46.5	–21 05	Cap	2.9′	14.6	
Pal 13	23 06.7	+12 46	Peg	0.7′	17.0	

In the mid-1950s this represented a tremendous improvement on the photographic star charts previously available, and as a result, many new objects of all kinds have been found. Indeed, from time to time, the POSS plates still reveal secrets. Although they are also included in the main catalog of globular clusters, the 13 systems listed by Abell are shown in Table 5.1.

The characteristics of the Palomar globular cluster systems are typical of the more recent discoveries: small, faint and usually highly obscured. Small size and faintness may be either intrinsic or due to distance, or a combination of both. Other than the globular clusters with the "Pal #" designation (to which two more have been added since the original list by Abell), the largest list of post-NGC objects is that of Terzan [1966, 1967, 1968, 1971], who has found about a dozen systems in the direction of the Galactic center; Terzan 1, for example, is only 2°.7 from the direction of the Galactic center and is heavily obscured by dust.

It is now believed that the bulk of the globular cluster system (GCS) of our own Galaxy has been discovered which has made it possible to draw some general conclusions. It appears that the galactic GCS has two main components. The *disk* subsystem is rather flattened and the clusters within it have typical rotational velocities of 170 km/s, and are comparatively metal-rich. To describe metal (in this case elements heavier than Hydrogen and Helium) content the term *metallicity* is used. This is usually written as a logarithmic difference between the relative abundance of iron in the atmosphere of a star and the relative abundance of iron in the atmosphere of a reference star. This difference is written in the form:

$$\left[\frac{Fe}{H}\right] = \log\left(\frac{Fe}{H}\right)_{\rm star} - \log\left(\frac{Fe}{H}\right)_{\rm ref}$$

On this logarithmic scale, metal rich clusters have a metallicity [Fe/H] > –0.8. The *halo* subsystem rotates more slowly and consists of comparatively metal-poor clusters, [Fe/H] < –0.8; it is sometimes subdivided into an inner halo within 7 kpc of the Galactic Center and an outer halo population [Zinn 1985; Armandroff 1989].

Using Hubble Space Telescope images, Larsen & Brodie [2000] have conducted a study of the globular cluster populations in the nearby S0 galaxy NGC 1023 which lies at a distance of about 9 Mpc. Here they find evidence for at least three distinct cluster populations. Two of these populations have luminosity functions and sizes which are consistent with those in other galaxies; however, the third population is fainter and much more extended. With effective radii perhaps 5 or 6 times greater than the other two, it is suggested that they might have a different formation history.

5.5 Globular Clusters in Other Galaxies

Globular clusters can be found around many other galaxies, and one of the first places one might look is the Magellanic Clouds, two of the nearest galaxies to our own. Indeed, because of the proximity of the Clouds, and the comparative brightness of globular clusters as stellar systems, a number of these clusters were actually included in the NGC: for example, NGC 121 is associated with the Small Magellanic Cloud (SMC); and NGC 1466, NGC 1786, NGC 1835, NGC 1978, NGC 2121, NGC 2210 and NGC 2257 are associated with the Large Magellanic Cloud (LMC). Most of the brighter are about magnitude V = 10–12, so can be detected as small hazy spots in small amateur instruments. Since the NGC, important lists of Magellanic Cloud globular clusters have been produced by Kron [1956], Lindsay [1958], Shapley and Lindsay [1963], and

Hodge and Sexton [1966]; and integrated UBV photometry of 61 SMC and 147 LMC globulars was given by van den Bergh [1981]. Observations of the LMC and SMC clusters show substantial differences between the systems and those attached to the Galaxy itself; the photoelectric measurements made by Gascoigne and Kron [1952] first showed that, in addition to the normal "red" globulars, there appeared to be a population of "blue" globulars. The most conspicuous, NGC 1866, was found by Sandage and Arp [1957] to have a color-magnitude diagram similar to the rich open cluster NGC 6705 (= M 11). Further research suggested [van den Bergh 1991] that the entire star cluster system of the Magellanic Clouds is not directly comparable with that of our own Galaxy, differing in several respects:

1. The Magellanic Clouds contain a class of populous open clusters that has no Galactic counterpart (this is particularly true in the case of the LMC).
2. Star clusters in the Magellanic Clouds have systematically larger radii than those in the Galaxy, typically three times larger.
3. Magellanic Cloud star clusters of all ages are generally individually more flattened than those in the Galaxy.

As far as the "blue globular clusters" are concerned, the term is now considered to be inappropriate. Not only are some of the "blue globulars" actually red, but there are several differences in the characteristics of these objects which would separate them from true globulars; primarily, their masses are an order of magnitude lower, and secondly, they are somewhat younger with ages of about 10 Gyr compared with 12–16 Gyr for true globulars.

Further afield, studies have been made of the globular cluster systems of other Local Group galaxies. As one might expect, these have concentrated on the Andromeda Galaxy (M 31 = NGC 224, see e.g., Figure 5.3), and one of the most important catalogs resulting from this work is that of Crampton, *et al.*, [1985] which lists identification, positional and magnitude data for 509 M 31 globular clusters (or suspected globular clusters). A list of objects previously misclassified as M 31 globulars is also given. A statistical study of the globular clusters listed by Crampton, *et al.* shows that despite being considerably more numerous, the colors, sizes and spatial distribution of the M 31 systems are similar to that of the Galaxy. There is the same decrease in luminosity and increase in size of the objects with increasing distance from the center of the Galaxy; this can be explained by the increasing likelihood that extended clusters near to the bulge will be tidally disrupted. Battistini, *et al.*, [1987] list 353 globular cluster candidates for M 31 (somewhat less than Crampton, *et al.*). Improved photometry for 75 globular clusters, and cluster candidates, has been obtained by Reed, *et al.*, [1992], who note that the colors and morphologies of some objects suggest that they are

Fig. 5.3 *[ME53] II, also known as Mayall II or less usefully, "G1", the brightest globular cluster in the Andromeda galaxy = M 31, and the intrinsically brightest globular cluster in the Local Group of galaxies. Its apparent magnitude is 13.7, within reach of modest amateur telescopes. HST image derived from visible and near-infrared images taken in July, 1994. The size of this field is about 20″ and north is 10° clockwise from the top. Michael Rich, Kenneth Mighell, and James D. Neill (Columbia University), Wendy Freedman (Carnegie Observatories), and NASA.*

faint, background galaxies; so the actual number of globular clusters in M 31 is still unclear. In addition to the problem of classifying the faint, nebulous spots around the galaxy, there is also the problem of actually finding such objects when they are projected against the bulge of the galaxy. This, of course, affects estimates of the total numbers. To relieve this situation, Aurière, *et al.*, [1992] have made a study of a 7′.7 x 7′.7 field, centered on the nucleus of M 31 based on R passband CCD imagery and a special analysis procedure. As a result of this, 35 reliable globular candidates were found, 23 of which were already known, plus another 4 possibles. The objects identified in this survey have generally small cores and are fainter than those in the more outlying regions, as is the case with our Galaxy. The authors suggest, in agreement with the conclusions of Crampton, *et al.*, that the probable cause of this is tidal disruption; but also add, that as a consequence, these globular clusters could have released hard binaries into the bulge of M 31 (explaining the high incidence of observed X-ray binaries and optical novae).

Other globular clusters and globular cluster candidates have been found in other Local Group galaxies, but particular note should be made of the Fornax dwarf galaxy. This has a relatively bright integrated magnitude of V = 8.4, but its light is spread over an area some 20′ x 14′ in size. As a result, its surface brightness is extremely low, and it is very difficult to detect by visual observation. Therefore, it was missed by the observers whose work was compiled into the NGC. However, associated with the galaxy are several globular clusters, the brightest of which was discovered by John Herschel who was totally unaware of the background galaxy. Its existence did not come to light until 1938, a century later. This cluster was subsequently cataloged as NGC 1049 (see Figure 5.4 on page 215); it is 0.8′ in diameter and V = 12.6.

Beyond the Local Group, many galaxies have been shown to have associated systems of globular clusters; for example, the bright, nearby spiral galaxy NGC 3031 (M 81). At 3.2 Mpc, this system would seem to be an excellent candidate for a globular cluster search program, but, until recently results were limited. Puche [1986] and Brodie and Huchra [1991] managed to identify only 8 objects between them. The problem is that the brightest globular clusters at this distance are of V = 18 and appear stellar to ground-based instrumentation. However, an extensive photometric, astrometric and image structure study of the M 81 field by Perelmuter and Racine [1995] indicated the existence of a substantial globular cluster system containing over 200 objects. Perelmuter, *et al.*, [1995] obtained spectra of 82 bright globular cluster candidates, and confirm the classification of 25 of these, (only 3 of which were previously known). There are 11 objects brighter than V = 19, and the brightest of all is [PBH95] 90103 (V = 18.01).

In the nearby Sculptor group of galaxies, a small number of globular clusters have been positively identified. Liller & Alcaino [1983a, 1983b] conducted a visual search for possible globular clusters in the fields of NGC 55 and NGC 253 and listed 114 diffuse objects as candidates. However, spectroscopic analysis of these candidates by Beasley & Sharples [2000] confirmed only 14 in NGC 253 and 1 in NGC 55. The brightest of these objects is of mag(B) 17.6, and the rest lie in the range mag(B) 19-20.

NGC 4594 (the Sombrero Galaxy) has one of the most extensive globular cluster systems known to be associated with a spiral galaxy. Forbes, et. al [1997] used the CTIO Schmidt telescope to obtain B and I imaging of a field 31′ x 31′ centered on NGC 4594 and found over 400 globular clusters, deriving magnitudes, B–I colours and metallicities.

However, the massive elliptical galaxies that dominate some galaxy clusters, such as NGC 4472 (M 49) and NGC 4486 (M 87), may have several thousand globular clusters around them. The case of M 87, the dominant galaxy of the Virgo Cluster, is particularly remarkable. There are at least 6000 globular cluster candidates plus, presumably, an even greater number whose presence has not been detected because of their small size and faintness at that distance. Some estimates put the total number of globular clusters for M 87 at 30,000 [Racine 1980].

Fig. 5.4 *NGC 1049, the brightest globular cluster in the Fornax Dwarf galaxy. 17′ field of view SkyView/DSS-S image © ROE.*

The use of the Hubble Space Telescope has greatly aided the study of globular clusters in more distant galaxies. For example, the *HST* has been used to obtain data on the galaxy NGC 5846 (Forbes, *et al.*, [1996b]), which is the dominant elliptical in a small, compact group which lies some 13 Mpc beyond the Virgo cluster. In this instance, over 1200 globular clusters were detected. The observers determined the globular cluster luminosity function and a distance modulus of (m-M) = 32.32 ± 0.23.

There has been some attempt to link the size of the globular cluster system of an individual galaxy with the characteristics of the host galaxy itself; a parameter called "specific frequency" has been derived as a quantitative measure from the formula:

$$S = N \cdot 10^{0.4(M_v + 15)} \qquad \textbf{(5.1)}$$

where N is the total number of globular clusters and M_v the absolute visual magnitude of the host galaxy. The calculation of S is very sensitive to the absolute magnitude of a galaxy, so there may well be errors. Nevertheless, an interesting trend can be seen. Massive galaxies in rich clusters tend to have fairly high S values of about 12 to 18; elliptical galaxies in the Virgo cluster have an S value of about 6 and those in the sparse Fornax cluster have an S value of about 3. The interpretation of these results is not entirely clear, but suggests that interactions between galaxies might be a relevant factor in the formation of some globular cluster systems. Certainly, the environment of the host galaxy is important in some way.

Observations by the *HST* of NGC 1275, the central object of the Perseus galaxy cluster (Abell 426), have shown that there is a concentration of luminous, blue unresolved objects surrounding it [Holtzman, *et al.*, 1992], suggested to be young globular clusters. Analysis of the photometry of these objects, the brightest of which is V = 19.2, by Richer, et al [1993] confirms the identification and leads to the conclusion that they have formed continuously over at least the past few hundred million years (probably from the massive cooling flow which is known to exist around NGC 1275). The masses of the clusters, estimated from their luminosity and an assumption that the mass-to-light ratio will be the same as in the young globulars in the LMC, works out to be around one million solar masses.

A remarkable discovery of recent years is that the globular cluster M 54 (= NGC 6715), together with the globular clusters Arp 2, Terzan 7 and Terzan 8, are associated with the heavily obscured Sagittarius Dwarf Spheroidal galaxy, the nearest to the Milky Way. Indeed, there is reason to believe that M 54 may be the nucleus of this galaxy; more detailed notes are given in the extended notes in Chapter 7.

Finally, even in the most remote objects in the Universe, there may be evidence for the formation of globular clusters. In two papers, Peng and Weisheit [1991a, 1991b] have argued that the highly-ionized metal absorption lines found in the spectra of some quasars could originate in proto-globular clusters.

Chapter 6
The Astrophysics of Globular Clusters

The man who says we have learned all there is to know is merely a fool, as is any man who thinks he knows all the answers about any one phase of the universe.

—Louis Bromfield (1896-1956), *Out of the Earth*

The perfect sphere—the form once commonly held to be an essential attribute of celestial bodies—is, according to observation and competent theory, a thorough illusion. There is exceedingly small chance of null rotation, and rotation is the end of sphericity. Oblateness, prolateness, and ellipsoidicity characterize planets, stars, nebulae, and galaxies. We now find that even the globular clusters belie their name. In a universe of moving particles the conception of the perfect figure vanishes with the growth of precision in measurement and attentiveness to detail.

—Harlow Shapley, *Star Clusters* [1930]

Well, "globular cluster" is a good Herschel term, but it tells nothing about the color-magnitude diagram.

—Walter Baade (1893–1960) [1963]

6.1 The Age and Origin of Globular Clusters

Globular clusters are found as a feature of the halo of most galaxies, in particular, the more massive spirals and ellipticals. They are also found in connection with a number of small, low mass dwarf galaxies, such as the Fornax system. The great majority of globular clusters appear to be extremely ancient. There are several things that point to this conclusion. First, the metallicity (the generally low abundance of elements heavier than helium) suggests they formed during an epoch when the chemical evolution of the Universe had not progressed very far and the proportion of the heavier elements in circulation was much smaller. Typically, the ratio of hydrogen: helium: heavier elements is about 75:23:2, with the 2% heavier elements figure being pretty well an upper limit and the amount of iron present between 0.1 and 0.03 the solar value. Second, if the color-magnitude diagrams of globular clusters are compared with stellar evolution models, it is found that many stars have turned off the main sequence; this is what would be expected of a system in a highly evolved state. A normal star spends most of its life on the main sequence, the actual time being primarily dependent on its mass; e.g. a star like the Sun will spend about 10 Gyr on the main sequence, while a star of, say, 9 times that mass will spend only 20 million years there. Thus, if one could find out the mass of the most massive star which is still remaining on the main sequence in a globular cluster, it would be possible to determine a minimum age for the cluster. Of course, there are uncertainties in establishing which stars are just about to leave the main sequence and also in the theoretical models for the main sequence evolution of stars of varying masses. Nevertheless, the calculations have led to globular cluster age estimates varying from 11.5 Gyr to 18 Gyr, although recent findings on the age of the Universe suggest that the high-end ages must be excessive. However, since globular clusters are usually resident in the halo of galaxies, the age determination may well be roughly applicable to the halo as a whole.

Because typical globular clusters are so old, maybe even pre-dating their host galaxies, and the cosmic environment is so different now from what it was in eons past, it is not likely that much direct observational evidence of their normal origin will be available. As a result, it is not even possible to be sure that the present population of globular clusters is typical of those which initially formed or whether they just represent a selection whose characteristics let them survive [Fall and Rees 1977]. Therefore, the subject of the origin of globular clusters is primarily one for theoreticians and somewhat speculative. However, in view of the similar range of ages to those of the galaxies, it would not be unreasonable to suppose that globular clusters came about in some way during the early stages of galaxy formation, (a theory first discussed in any adequately convincing way by Eggen, *et al.*, [1962]). Perhaps as the gas forming a protogalaxy began to collapse, subcondensations formed. These would stand a better chance of survival around the periphery of the system where they would be less prone to disruption by shockwaves within the collapsing material. Alternatively, it is possible that the collapse of the proto-globular cluster could have been triggered by shockwaves in the protogalaxy. It is plausible that these broke up into many more protostellar condensations as they collapsed, and if the system was sufficiently dense and massive, the stars which subsequently formed stayed together under the influence of their mutual gravitational attraction in a dynamically stable globular form (incidentally, the term "globular" is a fairly exact adjective, the mean ratio of the major and minor axes is 0.93 [White and Shawl 1987], which is pretty close to being exactly round). Another scenario for the formation of globular clusters involves their condensation from cooling flows in the material of the forming protogalaxy; there is some evidence for the validity of this theory in the apparent discovery of this process in action around the galaxy NGC 1275 [Richer 1993]. Luminous blue objects, suggested to be young clusters, have been found surrounding the nucleus; it is believed that they formed from cooling flow gas clouds which are confined by weak magnetic fields. Collisions between clouds in the central regions of the galaxy then cause some of them to become unstable to collapse and form globular clusters. Yet another possibility is that globular clusters originated as small dwarf galaxy-like subsystems of the primary galaxy which were gradually merged into its halo. Support for this viewpoint can be found in the mass and number of stars in globular clusters, which are comparable to some present Local Group dwarf galaxies; the clouds from which they formed must have been incredibly massive and could well have been subject to disruption if they had merely been fragments of a larger protogalactic cloud. Formation as semi-independent systems would also account for the apparent age differences between the globular clusters and their host galaxies.

Finally, although the emphasis in this section has been on the great age of typical globular clusters, it needs to be stated that there are exceptions. First, it has been noted that in some galaxies (such as the Magellanic Clouds), there is a population of apparently young, rich, globular-like cluster, which at one time were commonly (though inappropriately) called "blue globulars." The status of these objects is not entirely clear and is discussed in Section 5.5 on page 213. Within our own Galaxy, it has been suggested by Knödlseder [2000], based on a study of the morphology and stellar content of the Cygnus OB2 association using 2MASS infrared observations, that the classification is untenable. The mass, density and size of the group are said to resemble more closely the characteristics of young globular clusters like those found in the LMC. Second, also within our Galaxy, there is a subset of globular clusters including Arp 2, Palomar 12, Ruprecht 106, Terzan 7, and IC 4499 [Buonanno 1994] where, although having typical CMDs, the main sequence turn-off luminosities suggest that they are significantly younger (by perhaps 3-5 Gyr) than the mainstream globular cluster system. These may have been captured from one of the satellite galaxies or formed during a close interaction between the Galaxy and one of the satellite systems; they all lie at least 16 kpc from the Galactic center and several lie close to the recently discovered Sagittarius dwarf spheroidal galaxy [Ibata 1994] and may well be members. There is reason to believe that the massive globular cluster NGC 6715 (= M 54) may well even be the nucleus of the Sagittarius dwarf.

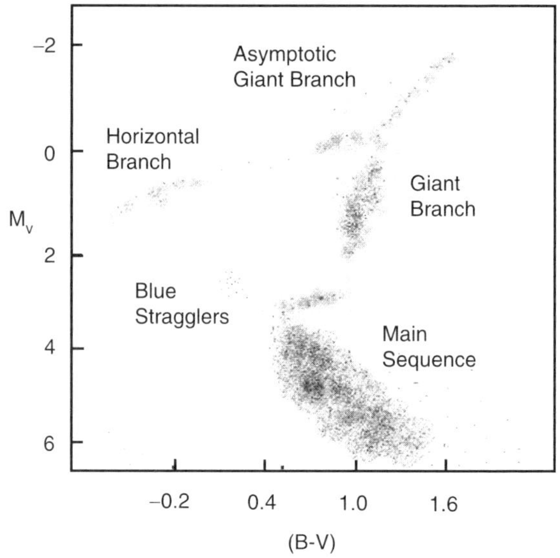

Fig. 6.1 *A generalized H-R diagram of a globular cluster, identifying the major features. The vertical axis is absolute V magnitude (M_V), while the horizontal axis is the color index (B magnitude minus V magnitude).*

6.2 The Evolution of Globular Clusters

By whatever mechanism they form, the subsequent evolution of globular clusters is somewhat easier to model since many of the mechanisms are also evident in open clusters, and the physical laws are, in principle, fairly well understood. First, the residual gas from which the cluster stars formed, which might well be of a quite substantial mass, is removed from the cluster by stellar winds and radiation pressure. In addition, a cluster passing through the plane of a spiral galaxy will lose interstellar material tidally and by ram pressure. This will reduce the mass of the cluster and its ability to hold itself together. With the gravitational grip reduced, the cluster will expand in size and the stars on the periphery will find themselves less strongly bound and escape; only minimal gravitational perturbations will be needed in order for other stars to escape from the system and into the halo of the parent galaxy. Each star lost reduces the mass of the cluster still more, adding to the effect; and, in the meantime, the most massive stars are evolving and losing still more mass through the formation of initially, intense stellar winds and eventually, planetary nebulae. As a result, mass loss by this means is the dominant feature of globular cluster evolution for several billion years, and it is quite probable that a substantial number of clusters do not survive the process and are totally disrupted.

The disruption of many globular clusters through mass loss does not continue at such a significant rate indefinitely. After perhaps 10 Gyr or so, when most stars of greater than solar mass have already evolved, stellar dynamical effects become more important. Gravitational interactions between individual stars in orbit around the nucleus of the cluster tend to result in a "relaxation" of the stellar velocity distribution. A gravitational encounter between two stars will result in a transfer of energy between them, the exact degree of this effect being largely dependent on their respective masses. If the ratio of the masses is quite high, the lighter one of them may acquire sufficient additional kinetic energy that its velocity will be increased to a value in excess of the escape velocity of the cluster. In consequence, a slow "evaporation" of the cluster occurs. Of course, for every star that gains energy, there is another that loses; the more massive star, having lost velocity through the transfer of kinetic energy, will move into an orbit which takes it closer to the center. Over time this process causes the central region of the cluster to contract and become more densely packed with massive stars. This increases the rate of evaporation of stars from the outer edge of the cluster and the likelihood of "two-body" gravitational encounters in the nucleus. It should be noted that not every star which gains velocity during gravitational encounters will actually escape the cluster; many will merely be placed into a more eccentric orbit about the nucleus of the cluster.

Therefore, it is clear that, in theory, the contraction of the cluster nucleus should result in "gravothermal collapse" and becoming infinitely dense in a finite amount of time. However, there are other considerations. Increasing core density results in an increasing likelihood that binary stars will be formed and, in a manner analogous to the process by which the gravitational collapse of a protostar is halted when the nuclear reactions in the core increase to a level which balances the pressures, the formation of tight binaries can generate enough energy to balance out the energy loss from two-body encounters. The basic principles of this mechanism were first demonstrated by Hénon [1961]. Computer simulations since then have shown the viability of this theory; core collapse is eventually brought to a halt when the center of the cluster contains only a few tens of stars and interactions between the stars begin to produce hard binaries. As a state of evolution beyond this, it is perfectly possible that some of the less massive of these binaries will be ejected by gravitational interaction with the more massive ones, reversing the process yet again, causing oscillations in the core density!

Needless to say, the individual circumstances of each globular cluster will be different. In some, such as M 15, observations do indicate a state of core collapse. Others evidently do have a number of binaries at the center and still others, in lieu of this, may be centrally dominated by massive black-holes perhaps dating back to the origin of the cluster itself. Here, core collapse would be halted by the black hole swallowing up stars which came too close.

Discussion of a globular cluster's evolution would not be complete without taking into account its individual environment. A globular cluster cannot be considered in isolation, since it lives within the gravitational field of its parent galaxy. Clearly, the size, shape and mass of the galaxy and the size, mass, density and proximity of the globular cluster are related. For example, it is found that the clusters which are closest to the nucleus are generally the smallest, because of the tidal effect of the galactic bulge, although this is only an approximate rule for the obvious reason that the critical parameter is really its minimum galactocentric distance. Most globular clusters are in elliptical orbits about their parent galaxy, and it is highly improbable that at the time of observation all the globular clusters will be at the closest point in their orbit. In spiral systems, it is likely that the orbits of some globular clusters will actually pass through the disk, at which time there will be a number of significant influences on them, not only the interactions of individual stars or groups of stars, but also the tidal effect of nearby giant molecular clouds. The effect on a globular cluster of disk passage has been studied by Chernoff and Shapiro [1988] who find that disk heating dominates and can greatly affect the evolution of clusters, particularly those within 5 kpc of the galactic center. Core collapse is a probable outcome in this case, and some clusters will be completely disrupted.

6.3 Stellar Populations in Globular Clusters

Since globular clusters are extremely ancient groupings of stars, with little, if any, available gas content from which new ones might be formed, it follows that effectively all of the stars must be in a fairly advanced state of evolution. In addition, because they are so old, their ratio of heavy elements is comparatively low. It might be expected, therefore, that there will be intrinsic differences between these stars and those we see nearby in the solar environment.

In the early years of the twentieth century, Shapley showed that the brightest stars in globular clusters were red, while the faintest were blue, contrary to astronomers' experience of stars in our immediate neighborhood. Later, Baade [1944] produced his classic paper in which he reported that he had succeeded in resolving individual stars in the Andromeda Galaxy (M 31 (NGC 224)) and its satellite galaxies. From the color-magnitude diagram he was able to produce, he divided the stars into two types: Population I -stars like those in the solar neighborhood and in open clusters of which the brightest representatives are blue and get redder as they get fainter; and Population II -comprising those stars making up elliptical galaxies and the halo component of disk galaxies including globular clusters. Here, the brightest stars in the class are not so bright as in Population I and are red and become bluer as they get fainter.

From the schematic diagram of a typical globular cluster CMD (**Figure 6.1 on page 218**) it can be seen that one of the most conspicuous features is the red giant branch, containing bright stars which have evolved away from the main sequence. This explains why Shapley found that the brightest stars of the globular clusters tend to have a reddish color. (Of course, the main sequence stars still make up the bulk of the mass of the cluster even though their contribution to the cluster's light output is not as significant.) As one might expect, among the stars of the red giant branch and the asymptotic giant branch (AGB) are a number of red variables, mostly semi-regular and irregular types. In relatively metal rich clusters are found a small number of Mira long-period variables which are believed to be luminous AGB stars and precursors of planetary nebulae.

Trailing from the top of the red giant branch down towards the blue end of the CMD but still several magnitudes brighter than the main sequence stars are the stars of the horizontal branch. These contribute about 15% of the visible wavelength light of a typical globular cluster and include the RR Lyrae variables which account for about 90% of variable stars in a globular cluster. They are radially pulsating giant stars of spectral types A to F with periods in the range 0.2–1.2 days and an amplitude of 0.2 – 2.0 mag. at visible wavelengths. Because they are so commonly found in globulars, they are also known as cluster-type variables. There are several sub-groups of RR Lyrae variables, the main ones being those stars which pulsate in the fundamental mode (RRab) and those which pulsate in the first overtone (RRc). Interestingly, there is a small but significant group of globular clusters which has few, if any, RR Lyrae variables, and these are normally characterized either by greater than average metallicity and a very red horizontal branch or intermediate metallicity and a very blue horizontal branch. From the viewpoint of the visual observer, the horizontal branch is important as it determines, at least to some extent, whether or not a cluster will be resolved.

It should be noted that the CMD of a group of Population I stars, like those in the solar neighborhood, is characterized by a paucity of stars of intermediate color between the brightest blue and the brightest red stars (it has very little in the way of a horizontal branch). This is called the Hertzsprung Gap. An obvious consequence of this difference is that the presence of RR Lyrae variables is a good indicator of the existence of the presence of Population II stars.

The globular cluster CMD also shows a small number of stars which look as if they ought to be part of the main sequence but are above the turnoff point where the main sequence stars begin to evolve towards the red giant branch. These stars are brighter and bluer than the main sequence stars and are called *blue stragglers*. They were first noticed by Sandage in the globular cluster M 3 (NGC 5272) and have since been found in most other globular clusters as well as in open clusters and field halo stars. Their nature remained a mystery for some time; however, high-resolution observations of the core area of the globular cluster NGC 104 (47 Tucanae) using the *Hubble Space Telescope* [Paresce, *et al.*, 1991] have shown a particularly high density of blue stragglers which supports one particular theory—they are massive objects of a binary nature or origin, formed by stellar collisions and coalescence which have drifted into the core and accumulated there.

The advanced state of evolution of stars in globular clusters has also given rise to another exotic form, *millisecond pulsars*. These objects exist in the field population of galaxies generally but not in the numbers or concentration found in globular clusters. For example, following their discovery, a dedicated search for millisecond pulsars in NGC 104 by Manchester, *et al.*, [1991] found 10 such objects with pulse periods ranging from 5.756780 ms to as fast as 1.7858 ms.

One would normally explain a high-speed pulsar as being recently formed; the theory is reasonably well understood. Pulsars are rapidly rotating neutron stars which emit beams of relativistic particles from their magnetic poles. When the rotation axis of the neutron star is at a different angle to the magnetic axis, the beam sweeps out a cone in space. As it does so, the beam will sometimes point in the direction of the Earth and be detected as a regular pulse of radio emission (the period between pulses being a direct measure of the rotation rate of the neutron star). As time passes, the pulse rate gradually slows, typically by about 1 part in 10^{15} each rotation, as the neutron star converts rotational energy into radiation. If this is the case, one might expect that any pulsars detected in globular clusters would have a comparatively long pulse period, certainly not in the millisecond range. A clue to the solution of this problem can be found from the observation that virtually all the known millisecond pulsars are members of low-mass binary systems with orbital periods between 10 and 100 days. It is proposed that millisecond pulsars originate from low-mass X-ray binaries involving an old neutron star and a rapidly evolving companion in an advanced state of evolution. As the companion expands to fill its Roche lobe, matter spills over onto the neutron star increasing its mass and angular momentum. As a result, the neutron star spin rate is increased eventually into the millisecond range. Once this possibility is appreciated, the core of globular clusters becomes an obvious place to search for millisecond pulsars; not only are they of a sufficient age to fit in with the timescale required for the evolution of normal binaries but, in cases where the core is massive and dense, there is also a high probability that accreting binary systems will form by the tidal capture of solitary neutron stars.

6.4 The Structure of Globular Clusters

The evolution of globular clusters and the nature of their stellar populations has already been briefly described, and from this one might correctly imagine that their structure is a direct consequence of these factors and that they are not just globes of randomly mixed stars orbiting in neat circles around a nucleus. The high density of massive blue stragglers in the core of NGC 104 has already been mentioned; these did not just drift into the center by accident. Their movements were governed by well understood physical laws. A globular cluster is an ancient, self-gravitating star system whose members of different masses are continually interacting individually and collectively. As a result, mass segregation occurs with heavier objects (including neutron stars and white dwarfs) and binaries gradually drifting into the core where the density is perhaps 10,000 stars per cubic parsec. A certain amount of stratification will occur with a high density of massive stars in the center and objects of increasingly lower mass and lower stellar density further out. As a consequence of gravitational interactions with stars of greater mass, the outer regions of a globular cluster will tend to be populated with fairly low mass, high velocity stars in eccentric orbits. Of course, the lower density of stars in the outer regions of globular clusters makes them easier to investigate, and early attempts to gauge the nature of the stellar population of globular clusters by studying the stellar population in the outer regions were misleading.

Concerning the structure of a globular cluster, consideration needs to be given to the gaseous component; however, this turns out to be remarkably small. When a cluster is young, it would be expected to be more-or-less stripped of its remnant gas and dust by the stellar winds from hot, young stars. Over a long period it should be replaced by material ejected from the outer layers of evolved stars. Between leaving the main sequence and becoming a white dwarf, a typical star loses about 0.2 $M_\odot$ of material, some of which may go to form a planetary nebula. Of course, every few hundred million years or so, the orbit of a globular cluster will take it through the galactic plane, and during this time much accumulated material will be swept out by gas ram pressure due to the interstellar medium in the disk. Nevertheless, the time between galactic plane transits is sufficiently long for perhaps 100 – 1000 $M_\odot$ of new material to build up, but, for the most part, this is just not seen. Observational searches show that in many clusters there is less than 1 $M_\odot$ of gas and dust, orders of magnitude less than theoretical predictions [Tayler and Wood 1975]. It is true that some globular clusters do appear to contain small dark patches which cannot be explained merely as random light variations in the otherwise uniform density of stars; a historical review of the observations is given by Roberts [1988]. Multicolor polarization and CCD observations of specific globular clusters [Forte and Mendez 1988, 1989], show that the phenomenon is to be found fairly frequently and that the dark patches are small clouds of dust (and presumably molecules) whose origin is probably related to the process of mass ejection during the red giant phase of a star's evolution. However, it is by no means clear that these objects could also contain the missing intracluster gas; indeed, at the moment, it seems highly unlikely. There are several possible explanations which might resolve the problem. In the case of the lower mass clusters, the stellar wind velocity alone from the old stars might well be enough to ensure a steady outflow of gas from the cluster. In the case of the more massive clusters, it has already been noted that the more massive, energetic stars accumulate in the core, and it could be that the stellar wind from these will drive out a lot of the intracluster gas. In particular, the presence of a number of millisecond pulsars would be an ideal source of energy to drive out intracluster gas [Spergel 1991]. Radio observations of the planetary nebula Pease 1 (= PK 065–27°1) in the globular cluster M 15 show that it is asymmetric with a tail pointing away from the pulsars in the cluster center. This may be direct evidence of the process in action.

6.5 Directions of Globular Cluster Research

Globular clusters are undoubtedly remarkable objects. They are discrete systems of ancient stars and generally a similar chemical composition. They are ideal subjects in which to study the evolution of old stars, internal cluster dynamics, binary formation and stellar mergers, together with more exotic phenomena such as pulsars, x-ray sources and blue stragglers. The oldest clusters can also be used to set a lower limit on the age of the Universe itself.

In recent years, increasingly sophisticated data recording and analysis systems have been developed, such as advanced CCD photometric systems, adaptive optics and multi-object spectroscopes using fibre optics. These, together with the *HST* and other space telescopes now sending back data, and large (8-meter or greater) ground-based telescopes, provide the opportunity to give even more exact attention to these problems and even reach into the very core of the nearer globular clusters at the sub-parsec level.

The use of large ground-based telescopes, or those in space, could enable turn-off apparent magnitude and color to be derived with greater accuracy and for a larger number of stars. Such equipment could also be put to use in the more accurate determination of chemical abundances, which are vital for comprehensive theoretical models to be produced. In this context, there are several important areas that need investigation. For example, stellar evolution theory predicts the dredge up of CNO processed material in globular cluster stars at the base of the RGB (red giant branch) and possibly also in the later stages of AGB (asymptotic giant branch) evolution with a well-defined correlation between C and N abundances and stellar luminosity. These predictions are pretty well fulfilled in the case of metal-poor field stars and in a small number of globular clusters, but the situation is more complex than this in the bulk of globular clusters. It may well be that in the very dense stellar environment of a globular cluster stellar surface abundances are modified, but this needs to be clarified.

One of the greatest persistent problems in astrophysical research is that of distance measurement, and globular clusters are no exception. Accurate determination of the absolute magnitude of the turn-off point is dependent on this. There are several methods by which globular cluster distances could be derived, the traditional means being by the use of RR Lyrae variables. The measurement of the RGB tip is also used, although this requires detailed observation of all bright stars in sometimes dense and populous clusters to reduce the impact of statistical fluctuations.

However, other methods are now available. For example, by using local subdwarfs with known metallicity and accurate parallax determinations as measured by the *Hipparcos* astrometric satellite, a match with globular cluster main sequence stars of the same metallicity can be made. From this, accurate absolute magnitudes and distances can be derived. Also, if any of the millisecond pulsars found in some of the globular clusters are sufficiently radio bright, their position could be measured via very-long baseline interferometry over a period of time and their parallax measured directly.

The *HST* can be used to study globular clusters in the nearby Local Group spiral NGC 224 (M 31) down to the level of the horizontal branch. All these globular clusters can be considered as being at essentially the same distance, and, by comparing the horizontal branch apparent magnitude and cluster metallicity figures with those in the Galactic globular cluster system, another check on the distance scale is provided.

The nature of extragalactic globular cluster systems may possibly be used to investigate galaxy formation itself, particularly in relation to elliptical galaxies. These galaxies could be produced in a single burst of star formation early on in the evolution of the Universe due to the collapse of a massive cloud of gas, or they could develop continuously through a series of galaxy mergers, an idea first proposed by Toomre and Toomre [1972]. Many investigations, by means of numerical simulations and observational studies have shown that this scenario is not only likely, but also very probable. Ashman and Zepf [1992] have shown that the greater specific frequency of globular clusters in elliptical galaxies compared to spirals could be a product of galaxy mergers. Their model predicts that elliptical galaxies produced from mergers will have different populations of globular clusters. Metal-poor cluster populations should be associated with progenitor spirals, and more metal-rich populations should form during the merger. It should be possible to discriminate between this 'bimodal' distribution for ellipticals arising through mergers and the 'unimodal' population which would be the product of collapse models. On the basis of this, several studies of individual galaxies have supported the merger model. An alternative model [Forbes, *et al.*, 1996a] suggests that, while tidal stripping from nearby galaxies might contribute to the globular cluster population in the outer regions of some cD galaxies, most clusters actually formed in situ. The bimodal distribution is suggested to have arisen as a result of star formation occurring in two distinct phases from gas of different metallicity. In this scenario, the metal-poor globular clusters formed at an early stage of the evolution of the galaxy, during the collapse of the protogalactic cloud; whereas the metal-rich clusters formed later, out of more enriched gas.

Within the individual local globular clusters, the mass, luminosity, metallicity and age of stars is known with greater accuracy than for field stars. They can, therefore, be used to verify various aspects of stellar evolution theory. Having a substantial population of stars of similar age and metallicity together in one place makes it easier to see what happens; for example, when the primary differentiating parameter is mass. As in any problem, the more variables that can be eliminated, the easier the matter can be resolved. Also, in the case of a globular cluster, any anomalies or exceptions to established rules are more apparent enabling more detailed investigation to be carried out. The presence of millisecond pulsars and blue stragglers has been mentioned earlier; concentrations of these objects in globular clusters make it easier to study such exotic phenomena.

Another question requiring further attention is that of the "missing mass," the apparent discrepancy between the mass which should be present in a system comprising evolved stars and the amount of intracluster matter observed to exist. While some explanations have been offered for the shortfall, as discussed earlier, the details are far from being fully understood. High spatial resolution observations from an 8-meter class ground-based telescope could be used to differentiate between small areas of diffuse emission from dust and point sources of emission. These could be brown dwarfs or carbon stars, and might enable a more definitive explanation to be given.

Investigations to determine the Hubble constant, and therefore, the age of the Universe based on galaxy redshifts, are at the forefront of modern astrophysics. Because of the significance of this parameter, it is necessary to have verification by as many different means as possible. The age of globular clusters is clearly important in this respect; these systems are believed to be very ancient and, therefore, are one consideration which may impose a constraint on cosmological models. Clearly, it would be difficult to construct a Universe which was younger than the globular clusters. The earliest possible time for the formation of globular clusters is likely to have been around 10^7 years after the Big Bang, when the temperature of the "primordial soup" had fallen to about 300 K, but something like 10^8 years afterwards is perhaps more probable, when the earliest galaxies began to form. Unfortunately, the potential sources of error in determining globular cluster ages are quite significant and include distance, chemical composition, reddening, photometry errors and uncertainty in stellar structure models and determining the main-sequence turn-off point. A review of globular cluster ages by Chaboyer [1995] has suggested that, after taking into account all possible random and systematic errors, an uncertainty of 5 Gyr is associated with any age determination using the traditional main-sequence turn-off (MSTO) method. By this means, the age of a globular cluster can be determined through looking at the main sequence turn-off point on the CMD and linking the observable magnitude and colors of stars to the corresponding absolute values of luminosity and temperature in theoretical models for systems with the same chemical composition. The problem is largely that in fitting isochrones the position of the MSTO is not a point on the CMD but an extended region. Jimenez and Padoan [1996] have suggested an alternative method which is claimed to have an accuracy level ten times greater; this is based on establishing accurate stellar evolutionary tracks and on photometry for globular clusters complete down to the main sequence, counting the numbers of stars in the red giant branch. Applying this method to the globular cluster NGC 4590 (M 68) gives an age of 16.4±0.2 Gyr where $(m - M)_v = 15.3$.

However, analysis of results from several lines of observation using the Hubble Space Telescope over the past few years as part of the Key Project on the Extragalactic Distance Scale suggest that the age of the Universe is rather less than this. Integrating HST data with Hipparcos parallaxes and other observations (for example, the recalibration of the supernova standard candle) Freedman, *et al.* [2001] find a value for the Hubble Constant of:

$$H_0 = 72 \pm 8 \text{ km/s/Mpc}$$

which means an age for the Universe of:

$$13 \pm 2 \text{ billion years}$$

Improved accuracy of globular cluster dating, to set a lower bound on the age of the Universe, will, therefore, no doubt continue to be a primary goal of research.

Chapter 7
Catalog of Galactic Globular Clusters

A full [sic] knowledge of the distribution of stars in time and space is, of course, an unattainable dream. If we had, indeed, a clear picture of the ages, arrangement, and masses of the stars in even a single globular cluster, we should begin to know what is going on in this universe; but we are denied complete information.

—Harlow Shapley, *Star Clusters* [1930]

7.1 Introduction

This chapter provides general information on all Galactic globular clusters. Currently 150 such objects are known to exist in the Milky Way. Of these, 107 were listed in the *New General Catalogue* [Dreyer, 1888] or *Index Catalogue* [Dreyer, 1895, 1908]. Thus, a substantial number of these clusters were known to exist by the end of the 19th century (although not all of these were known at that time to definitely be of "globular" type). All of these should be detectable in moderate-aperture amateur telescopes.

Those clusters with other than NGC and IC designations are discoveries made during the 20th century. The majority of these were found during the last half of that period. This was when the Palomar Sky Survey (POSS, [National Geographic Society, 1955]) and other deep photographic sky surveys became available, and a number of such clusters were discovered (and continue to be discovered) on images from these surveys. During the last two decades of the 20th century globular clusters began to be discovered in other wavelengths (e.g., Liller 1 in the X-ray; UKS 1, 2MASS-GC01, 2MASS-GC02 in the infrared). Several obscure objects discovered earlier were also revealed by observations with large instruments to be globular clusters. This includes NGC 6540, NGC 6749, and IC 1257. Also included are objects that have been discovered fairly recently, but were originally thought to be open clusters, such as ESO 280-SC06, ESO 452-SC11, ESO 456-SC38, and vdB-Ha 176. All of these objects are discussed below in detail.

Many of the recently discovered objects are unusually small, highly obscured and, therefore, difficult targets. Amateurs will find these to be difficult visual targets. Often, one may have to be content in seeing only the few brightest stars of a cluster and very little to nothing of the rest of it. Some clusters (e.g., Liller 1) are likely invisible to amateur observers, except perhaps from the right latitude, under ideal conditions, and with a large telescope. However, almost all of these objects are suitable targets for deep CCD imaging by amateurs. For example, Tracy Knauss and the late Mike Morton produced a number of fine images of the some of the faintest of these clusters, using a 46-cm (18-inch) telescope from less than ideal conditions near Houston, Texas. A selection of their images is reproduced in Section 7.3 beginning on page 252.

Professional astronomers will find many of these globular clusters to be difficult targets to locate and to observe. In the past many of these objects had catalog positions that were arcminutes in error, and even more recent compilations still give positions in error by many arcseconds. The positions we provide here are precise to the arcsecond level relative to the *Guide Star Catalogue*-based reference system of the Digitized Sky Survey. The *GSC* is known to have up to 2 or 3 arcsecond errors in absolute accuracy relative to the International Celestial Reference Frame (ICRF, [Ma, *et al.,* 1998]). So for small clusters, or at least clusters with well-defined centers, the positions here should be accurate to that few arcsecond level. For large clusters, or those that have diffuse central regions, the accuracy probably degrades to the several arcsecond level due to the difficulty of manually picking the cluster center. We hope that these precise positions will finally put an end to the difficulties that professionals (and amateurs) have experienced in the past in locating and identifying these objects. The images shown in Section 7.2 beginning on page 232 and Section 7.3 beginning on page 252 should also assist greatly in locating some of the fainter objects.

Professionals have also found that even when an object is located, it may be quite difficult to obtain useful data. As you will see in the Extended Notes below, some of these objects (e.g., Palomar 1) are still not conclusively distinguished as either a Galactic globular cluster or an old open cluster. This can happen for several reasons. The individual cluster stars may be too faint to obtain their magnitudes and colors at a sufficient level of accuracy. Observations of stars, both in the horizontal branch and the much fainter main sequence of the cluster color magnitude diagram (see Figure 6.1 on page 218), must be observed with high accuracy in order to determine a definitive age—hence, the identification as a globular cluster. The stars of a cluster—particularly those where "core collapse" has occurred—may also appear too close to resolve from each other. Finally, infrared sensors are just now reaching a desired level where photometry of the individual stars in the infrared is now possible. Many of these problems are eliminated if a sufficiently large or high resolution telescope is used, such as the Hubble Space Telescope or one of the Keck telescopes. However, observing time on these instruments is a precious commodity. Requests for time to only determine the color-magnitude information of a globular cluster have often been refused. Such observations will probably have to wait until they are part of another more comprehensive observing proposal.

In the remainder of this chapter, we present (in Section 7.2) Extended Notes on the Galactic globular clusters. This includes general information on the identification and the astrophysics of such clusters. Globular clusters that have been misidentified as something else in the past are noted, as are common past catalog errors. For the most recently discovered objects, the evidence is presented confirming that these are indeed likely to be globular clusters.

Some information is presented that will be useful for amateurs, particularly magnitudes and general appearance. Information is given on the 4 planetary nebulae known to exist in globular clusters. For the 3 fainter planetaries, we provide descriptions based on some of the only known visual observations, made by one of us [BA].

Following this, we present in Section 7.3 an image gallery of faint Galactic globular clusters. As noted above, these are CCD images taken by Tracy Knauss and the late Mike Morton. We feel it is particularly valuable to present these since they are little photographed clusters, and should prove useful to amateurs and professionals alike for identification purposes.

Finally, beginning on page 227, we present the main catalog of Galactic globular clusters. These data are extracts of the data for the general catalog of Galactic objects included in Table 4.1 beginning on page 49. However, it is reproduced here in more compact form for convenience. The collection of the data here was done as part of the creation of the overall set of catalog data, as described in Appendix B beginning on page 279. The catalog fields here are as described in Section 4.2 beginning on page 42.

One column is shown in this extract that is not present in Table 4.1. This is the "HB Vm", which is the V magnitude of the horizontal branch of the globular cluster. This is not only of astrophysical interest, but of interest to observers as well. This is the magnitude at which large numbers of stars start to become visible (i.e., the magnitude where the horizontal branch stars become visible) and, therefore, is an indication of the magnitude where the cluster will become "resolved out". If an observer or photographic or CCD camera can reach to this magnitude, the cluster should start to appear resolved.

Table 7.1: Catalog of Galactic Globular Clusters

Name	Type	2000.0 R.A.	Dec.	Con	Dia. (′)	Tot. Vm	HB Vm	Bt* Vm	V Sur	Dist. (pc)	S #	2U #	Ref	Comments and Alias Names
NGC 104	gcl	00 24 05.2	−72 04 51	Tuc	50.0	4.0	14.1	11.7	12.5	4600	24	204	55	See notes. Moore: 47 Tucanae. Aliases: 47 Tuc; Mel 1; EQ 0021−723; 1E 0021.8−7221; 2E 0021.8−7221; 2E 82; 1ES 0021−72.3; Ksi Tuc; Caldw 106; C0021−723
NGC 288	gcl	00 52 45.5	−26 34 51	Scl	13.0	8.1	15.3	12.6	13.7	8400	18	158	99	See notes. Archinal: Position measured from DSS. Aliases: Mel 3; EQ 0050−268; C0050−268
NGC 362	gcl	01 03 14.3	−70 50 54	Tuc	14.0	6.8	15.4	12.7	12.5	8600	24	204	55	Aliases: Mel 4; EQ 0100−711; Caldw 104; C0100−711
NGC 1261	gcl	03 12 15.3	−55 13 01	Hor	6.8	8.3	16.8	13.5	12.5	16000	24	202	55	Aliases: Mel 19; EQ 0310−554; Caldw 87; C0310−554
Palomar 1	gcl	03 33 20.8	+79 34 57	Cep	2.8	13.6	16.76	16.3	15.8	13700	1	7	99	See notes. Youngest Galactic globular cluster or oldest open cluster. Faint, not obvious on DSS or DSS-II. Archinal: Position measured from DSS. Aliases: (5) VII Zw 7; EQ 0325+794; C0325+794
AM 1	gcl	03 55 02.7	−49 36 52	Hor	0.5	15.8	20.9	18.2	14.3	125900	18	190	6	Aliases: E 1; ESO 201-10; E; C0354−498
Eridanus	gcl	04 24 44.5	−21 11 13	Eri		14.7	20.4	17.6		80300	19	156	55	Aliases: (5) UGCA 91; ESO 551-01; EQ 0422.6−2118; EQ 0423−21; C0422−213
Palomar 2	gcl	04 46 05.9	+31 22 51	Aur	2.2	13.0	21.7	18.8	14.7	26000	5	59	55	See notes. Has been listed incorrectly as a galaxy, with designations MCG +05-12-001 = PGC 15963. [Lederman and Gottlieb, 1996] Aliases: (5) MCG +05-12-001; (5) PGC 15963; EQ 0443+313; C0443+313
NGC 1851	gcl	05 14 06.3	−40 02 50	Col	12.0	7.1	16.1	13.2	12.5	12200	19	173	6	Aliases: Caldw 73; C0512−400
NGC 1904	gcl	05 24 10.6	−24 31 27	Lep	9.6	7.7	16.2	13.1	12.6	13000	19	155	55	M 79. Aliases: M 79; Mel 34; EQ 0522−245; 1E 0522.1−2433; C0522−245
NGC 2298	gcl	06 48 59.2	−36 00 19	Pup	5.0	9.3	16.2	13.4	12.8	10100	19	172	6	Aliases: EQ 0647−359; C0647−359
NGC 2419	gcl	07 38 08.5	+38 52 55	Lyn	4.6	10.3	20.2	17.3	13.6	83500	5	57	6	Aliases: EQ 0734+390; Caldw 25; C0734+390
Pyxis	gcl	09 07 57.8	−37 13 17	Pyx?	4.0	12.9 0	18.7	15.2	15.9	40000	20	170	54	See notes. Pyxis globular cluster. Discovered in 1995. May belong to LMC or SMC. See Weinberg [1995], and Irwin, Demers, and Kunkel [1995]. Alias: [W95] 3
NGC 2808	gcl	09 12 02.6	−64 51 47	Car	14.0	6.2	16.2	13.5	11.9	9200	25	210	6	Aliases: EQ 0911−646; C0911−646
E 3	gcl	09 20 59.3	−77 16 57	Cha		11.4	15.8	17.0		7300	25	218	6	Alias: C0921−770
Palomar 3	gcl	10 05 31.4	+00 04 17	Sex	1.6	13.9	20.5	18.0	14.9	90800	13	113	55	Has been listed incorrectly as a galaxy, with designations UGC 5439 = MCG +00-26-017 = CGCG 08-35. [Lederman and Gottlieb, 1996] Aliases: (5) Sex C; (5) UGC 5439; (5) MCG +00-26-017; (5) CGCG 08−35; EQ 1003+003; C1003+003
NGC 3201	gcl	10 17 36.8	−46 24 40	Vel	20.0	6.9	14.8	11.7	13.4	5000	20	186	55	See notes. Aliases: Mel 99; EQ 1015−461; Caldw 79; C1015−461
Palomar 4	gcl	11 29 16.8	+28 58 25	UMa	1.3	14.2	20.8	18.0	14.8	97900	6	72	6	Aliases: UMa glb; EQ 1126+292; C1126+292
NGC 4147	gcl	12 10 06.2	+18 32 31	Com	4.4	10.4	16.9	14.5	13.6	18800	13	72	6	Aliases: GCRV 7290; EQ 1207+188; CSI+18-12076; C1207+188
NGC 4372	gcl	12 25 45.4	−72 39 33	Mus	5.0	7.2	15.6	12.2	10.7	5200	25	209	55	Aliases: Mel 112; EQ 1223−724; Caldw 108; C1223−724
Ruprecht 106	gcl	12 38 40.2	−51 09 01	Cen	2.0	10.9	17.8	14.8	12.4	19800	25	184	6	See notes. Skiff: Nice globular cluster!. Aliases: OCl 887; Lund 623; (5) C1235−509; C1236−508
NGC 4590	gcl	12 39 28.0	−26 44 34	Hya	11.0	7.3	15.6	12.6	12.5	9300	21	150	55	M 68. Aliases: M 68; Mel 113; EQ 1236−264; C1236−264
NGC 4833	gcl	12 59 35.0	−70 52 29	Mus	14.0	8.4	15.6	12.4	14.1	5800	25	209	55	See notes. Aliases: Mel 115; EQ 1256−706; Caldw 105; C1256−706
NGC 5024	gcl	13 12 55.3	+18 10 09	Com	13.0	7.7	16.9	13.8	13.3	18500	14	71	55	M 53. Aliases: M 53; Mel 117; C1310+184
NGC 5053	gcl	13 16 27.0	+17 41 53	Com	10.0	9.0	16.7	13.8	14.0	16100	14	71	6	See notes. Aliases: Cr 267; OCl 970; EQ 1313+179; C1313+179
NGC 5139	gcl	13 26 45.9	−47 28 37	Cen	55.0	3.9	14.5	11.5	12.6	4900	21	184	9	See notes. The great ω Centauri globular cluster. Aliases: Omega Cen; Mel 118; Caldw 80; C1323−472
NGC 5272	gcl	13 42 11.2	+28 22 32	CVn	18.0	6.3	15.6	12.7	12.6	10100	7	71	55	M 3. Aliases: M 3; Mel 119; EQ 1339+286; 1E 1339.8+2837; C1339+286
NGC 5286	gcl	13 46 26.5	−51 22 24	Cen	11.0	7.4	16.5	13.5	12.6	9300	25	183	55	Aliases: Mel 121; EQ 1343−511; Caldw 84; C1343−511
AM 4	gcl	13 56 21	−27 09.7	Hya	3.0	15.9	21.6	20.5	18.3	30300	21	149	55	See notes. Position from Skiff. Archinal: Diameter approximate, estimated from DSS image. Aliases: AM 1353−265; C1353−269

Table 7.1: Catalog of Galactic Globular Clusters

Name	Type	2000.0 R.A.	Dec.	Con	Dia. (′)	Tot. Vm	HB Vm	Bt* Vm	V Sur	Dist. (pc)	S #	2U #	Ref	Comments and Alias Names
NGC 5466	gcl	14 05 27.3	+28 32 04	Boo	9.0	9.2	16.6	13.8	14.0	15800	7	70	55	Aliases: Mel 124; C1403+287
NGC 5634	gcl	14 29 37.3	−05 58 35	Vir	5.5	9.5	17.8		13.2	25000	14	129	55	Aliases: Mel 126; EQ 1427−057; C1427−057
NGC 5694	gcl	14 39 36.5	−26 32 18	Hya	4.3	10.2	18.5	15.5	13.4	32800	21	148	6	Aliases: EQ 1436−263; Caldw 66; C1436−263
IC 4499	gcl	15 00 18.5	−82 12 49	Aps	8.0	10.1	17.7	14.6	14.6	19100	25	216	55	Aliases: Mel 129; EQ 1452−820; C1452−820
NGC 5824	gcl	15 03 58.5	−33 04 04	Lup	7.4	9.1	18.5	15.5	13.4	32400	21	166	6	Aliases: EQ 1500−328; 1E 1500.7−3251; C1500−328
Palomar 5	gcl	15 16 05.3	−00 07 14	Ser	8.0	11.8	17.4	15.5	16.3	23000	14	108	99	See notes. Archinal: Faint. Not obvious on DSS or DSS II, but visible as a 8.0′ faint cluster between two bright stars. Aliases: (5) UGC 9792; (5) MCG +00-39-016; (5) CGCG 21−61; (5) Ser Dwarf; EQ 1513+000; C1513+000
NGC 5897	gcl	15 17 24.5	−21 00 37	Lib	11.0	8.4	16.3	13.3	13.6	12600	21	148	55	Aliases: Mel 132; C1514−208
NGC 5904	gcl	15 18 33.8	+02 04 58	Ser	23.0	5.7	15.0	12.2	12.5	7600	14	108	55	M 5. Aliases: M 5; Mel 133; EQ 1516+022; C1516+022
NGC 5927	gcl	15 28 00.5	−50 40 22	Lup	6.0	8.0	16.6	14.5	11.9	8000	25	182	55	Aliases: vdB-Ha 173; Mel 134; EQ 1524−505; C1524−505
NGC 5946	gcl	15 35 28.5	−50 39 34	Nor	3.0	8.4	17.2		10.8	10500	25	182	55	Aliases: vdB-Ha 175; Mel 135; EQ 1531−504; C1531−504
vdB-Ha 176	gcl	15 39 07.3	−50 03 02	Nor	3.0	14.0	19.0	16.3	16.4	13400	25	182	55	See notes. Recently shown to very likely be a Galactic globular cluster by Ortolani, *et al.* [1995]. Aliases: ESO 224-SC8; ESO 224-8; C1535−499
NGC 5986	gcl	15 46 03.5	−37 47 10	Lup	9.6	7.6	16.5	13.2	12.5	10300	21	165	55	Aliases: Mel 136; EQ 1542−376; C1542−376
Palomar 14	gcl	16 11 00.3	+14 57 49	Her?	2.5	14.7	20.0	17.6	16.7	72400	15	88	99	See notes. Center is GSC 00957-00359. Aliases: AvdB gcl; Arp 1; EQ 1608+150; AvdB; C1608+150
Lynga 7	gcl	16 11 03.0	−55 18 52	Nor	2.2		17.25	16.3		7200	26	196	55	See notes. Recently shown to be a likely Galactic globular cluster by Tavarez and Friel [1995]. Aliases: Lund 689; OCl 949; vdB-Ha 184; C1607−551
NGC 6093	gcl	16 17 02.5	−22 58 30	Sco	10.0	7.3	16.2	12.5	12.3	8400	22	147	55	M 80. Aliases: M 80; Mel 142; EQ 1614−228; C1614−228
NGC 6121	gcl	16 23 35.5	−26 31 31	Sco	36.0	5.4	13.4	10.8	13.2	2000	22	147	55	M 4. See notes. Aliases: M 4; Mel 144; EQ 1620−264; C1620−264
NGC 6101	gcl	16 25 48.6	−72 12 06	Aps	5.0	9.2	16.6	13.5	12.7	14900	26	207	55	Aliases: Mel 143; EQ 1620−720; Caldw 107; C1620−720
NGC 6144	gcl	16 27 14.1	−26 01 29	Sco	7.4	9.0	16.5	13.4	13.3	9900	22	147	55	Aliases: Mel 147; EQ 1624−259; C1624−259
NGC 6139	gcl	16 27 40.4	−38 50 56	Sco	8.2	9.1	17.9	15.0	13.7	9100	22	165	6	Aliases: EQ 1624−387; C1624−387
Terzan 3	gcl	16 28 40.1	−35 21 13	Sco		12.0	17.3	15.0		25200	22	165	6	Alias: EQ 1625−352
NGC 6171	gcl	16 32 31.9	−13 03 13	Oph	13.0	7.8	15.6	13.0	13.4	6400	15	127	55	M 107. Aliases: M 107; Mel 148; EQ 1629−129; C1629−129
ESO 452-SC11	gcl	16 39 25	−28 23.9	Sco	1.2	12.0	16.6	15.3	12.4	10300	22	147	99	See notes. Aliases: ESO 452-11; C1636−283
NGC 6205	gcl	16 41 41.5	+36 27 37	Her	20.0	5.8	15.0	11.9	12.3	7200	8	50	55	M 13. See notes. Aliases: M 13; Mel 150; EQ 1639+365; C1639+365
NGC 6229	gcl	16 46 58.9	+47 31 40	Her	4.5	9.4	18.0	15.5	12.7	31600	8	35	6	Aliases: EQ 1645+476; C1645+476
NGC 6218	gcl	16 47 14.5	−01 56 52	Oph	16.0	6.1	14.7	12.0	12.1	5600	15	107	55	M 12. Aliases: M 12; Mel 151; EQ 1644−018; C1644−018
NGC 6235	gcl	16 53 25.4	−22 10 38	Oph	5.0	8.9	16.7	14.0	12.4	9600	22	146	55	Aliases: Mel 154; EQ 1650−220; C1650−220
NGC 6254	gcl	16 57 08.9	−04 05 58	Oph	20.0	6.6	15.1	12.0	13.1	4300	15	107	55	M 10. Aliases: M 10; Mel 157; C1654−040
NGC 6256	gcl	16 59 32.6	−37 07 17	Sco	4.1	11.3	18.2	15.3	14.4	10200	22	164	6	See notes. Aliases: vdB-Ha 208; Lund 1104; EQ 1656−370; C1656−370
Palomar 15	gcl	16 59 50.9	−00 32 28	Oph		14.2	19.9	17.1		41100	15	107	55	See notes. Has been wrongly listed as galaxy UGC 10642 = MCG +00-43-006 = CGCG 25-16 = PGC 59400 = Kara 781. [Lederman and Gottlieb, 1996] Aliases: Zwicky 1; (5) UGC 10642; (5) MCG +00-43-006; (5) CGCG 25−16; (5) PGC 59400; (5) Kara 781; EQ 1657−004; C1657−004
NGC 6266	gcl	17 01 12.6	−30 06 44	Oph?	15.0	6.4	16.3	13.2	12.3	5500	22	164	55	M 62. Aliases: vdB-Ha 210; M 62; Mel 159; EQ 1658−300; C1658−300
NGC 6273	gcl	17 02 37.7	−26 16 05	Oph	17.0	6.8	17.0	14.0?	13.0	10800	22	146	55	M 19. Aliases: M 19; Mel 160; EQ 1659−262; C1659−262
NGC 6284	gcl	17 04 28.8	−24 45 53	Oph	6.2	8.9	16.6		12.9	11800	22	146	55	Aliases: Mel 162; C1701−246
NGC 6287	gcl	17 05 09.4	−22 42 29	Oph	4.8	9.3	17.1	14.5	12.7	6800	22	146	55	Aliases: Mel 163; EQ 1702−226; C1702−226

Table 7.1: Catalog of Galactic Globular Clusters

Name	Type	2000.0 R.A.	Dec.	Con	Dia. (′)	Tot. Vm	HB Vm	Bt* Vm	V Sur	Dist. (pc)	S #	2U #	Ref	Comments and Alias Names
NGC 6293	gcl	17 10 10.4	−26 34 54	Oph	8.2	8.3	16.5	14.3	12.9	8500	22	146	55	Aliases: vdB-Ha 215; Mel 164; EQ 1707−265; C1707−265
NGC 6304	gcl	17 14 32.5	−29 27 44	Oph	8.0	8.3	16.2	14.5	12.8	6000	22	146	55	Aliases: vdB-Ha 216; Mel 165; EQ 1711−294; C1711−294
NGC 6316	gcl	17 16 37.4	−28 08 24	Oph	5.4	8.1	17.8	15.0	11.8	12800	22	146	6	Aliases: vdB-Ha 219; EQ 1713−280; C1713−280
NGC 6341	gcl	17 17 07.3	+43 08 11	Her	14.0	6.5	15.2	12.1	12.2	7500	8	34	55	M 92. Aliases: M 92; Mel 168; EQ 1715+432; C1715+432
NGC 6325	gcl	17 17 59.2	−23 45 57	Oph	4.1	10.2	17.3	14.7?	13.3	6000	22	146	6	Aliases: EQ 1714−237; C1714−237
NGC 6333	gcl	17 19 11.8	−18 30 59	Oph	12.0	7.8	16.2	13.5	13.2	7500	15	146	55	M 9. Aliases: M 9; Mel 167; EQ 1716−184; C1716−184
NGC 6342	gcl	17 21 10.2	−19 35 14	Oph	4.4	9.5	16.9	15.0	12.7	12000	15	146	6	Aliases: EQ 1718−195; C1718−195
NGC 6356	gcl	17 23 35.0	−17 48 47	Oph	10.0	8.2	17.7	15.1	13.2	16700	15	146	55	Aliases: Mel 171; EQ 1720−177; C1720−177
NGC 6355	gcl	17 23 58.6	−26 21 13	Oph	4.2	8.6	17.2		11.7	7000	22	146	6	See notes. Aliases: Cr 330; OCl 1036; EQ 1720−263; C1720−263
NGC 6352	gcl	17 25 29.2	−48 25 22	Ara	9.0	7.8	15.2	13.4	12.6	6100	22	181	6	See notes. Aliases: Cr 328; Mel 170; OCl 993; vdB-Ha 226; EQ 1721−484; Caldw 81; C1721−484
IC 1257	gcl	17 27 08	−07 05.6	Oph	1.7	13.1	19.8	17.5	14.3	24000	15	126	99	See notes. This has been shown to be a distant globular cluster. = GSC 5079-0033. Aliases: OCl 51; Lund 751; (5) Ced 144; C1724−070
Terzan 2	gcl	17 27 33.4	−30 48 08	Sco	0.6	14.3	19.8		13.2	2100	22	164	6	See notes. Aliases: HP 3; vdB-Ha 228; Lund 1113; C1724−307
NGC 6366	gcl	17 27 44.3	−05 04 36	Oph	13.0	9.5	15.7	13.6	15.1	4000	15	106	55	Aliases: Mel 173; EQ 1725−050; C1725−050
Terzan 4	gcl	17 30 38.9	−31 35 44	Sco		16.0	21.6?			16900	22	164	6	Aliases: HP 4; EQ 1727−315; C1727−315
Haute Provence 1	gcl	17 31 05.2	−29 58 54	Oph	1.2	12.5	18.6	16.0	12.9	9100	22	164	6	Aliases: vdB-Ha 229; Dufay 1; EQ 1727−299; C1727−299
NGC 6362	gcl	17 31 54.8	−67 02 53	Ara	15.0	8.1	15.3	12.7	14.0	7700	26	207	55	Aliases: Mel 172; EQ 1726−670; C1726−670
Liller 1	gcl	17 33 24.5	−33 23 20	Sco	0.3	15.8	24.4	20.5	13.2	10200	22	164	6	See notes. Aliases: Liller I; (4) IRAS 17302−3327; (4) IRAS 17298−3329; EQ 1730−333; C1730−333
NGC 6380	gcl	17 34 28.0	−39 04 09	Sco	3.6	11.5	19.5	17.0	14.3	4000	22	164	55	Aliases: Ton 1; Pi 25; vdB-Ha 233; C1731−390
Terzan 1	gcl	17 35 47.0	−30 28 46	Sco		15.9	21.4	18.5		5900	22	164	99	Aliases: vdB-Ha 235; ESO 455-23; HP 2; C1732−304
Tonantzintla 2	gcl	17 36 10.5	−38 33 12	Sco		12.2	18.2			8200	22	164	6	Aliases: Pi 26; vdB-Ha 236; C1732−385; EQ 1733−390; C1733−390
NGC 6388	gcl	17 36 17.0	−44 44 06	Sco	10.4	6.8	17.2	14.8	11.9	11000	22	181	55	Aliases: vdB-Ha 234; Mel 174; EQ 1732−447; C1732−447
NGC 6402	gcl	17 37 36.1	−03 14 45	Oph	11.0	7.6	17.2	14.0	12.8	10100	15	106	55	M 14. Aliases: M 14; Mel 175; EQ 1735−032; C1735−032
NGC 6401	gcl	17 38 36.9	−23 54 32	Oph	4.8	7.4	18.0	15.5	10.8	6300	22	146	6	Aliases: EQ 1735−238; C1735−238
NGC 6397	gcl	17 40 41.3	−53 40 25	Ara	31.0	5.3	12.9	10.0	12.8	2200	26	195	55	Aliases: Mel 176; EQ 1736−536; Caldw 86; C1736−536
Palomar 6	gcl	17 43 42.2	−26 13 21	Oph?	1.2	11.6	19.1		12.0	5900	22	146	99	Aliases: ESO 520-21; EQ 1740−262; GCl 75; (2) JaFu 1; C1740−262
NGC 6426	gcl	17 44 54.7	+03 10 13	Oph	4.2	10.9	18.1	15.2	14.0	17500	15	106	6	See notes. Aliases: Cr 346; OCl 81; EQ 1742+031; C1742+031
Djorgovski 1	gcl	17 47 28.3	−33 03 56	Sco	0.8	13.6	20.80		13.1	8800	22	164	6	
Terzan 5	gcl	17 48 04.9	−24 46 47	Sgr	2.4	13.9	22.5	20.5	15.8	14600	22	146	55	See notes. Archinal: Position measured from DSS. Aliases: Terzan 11; C1745−247
NGC 6440	gcl	17 48 52.6	−20 21 34	Sgr	4.4	9.3	18.7	16.7	12.5	7000	22	146	6	Alias: C1746−203
NGC 6441	gcl	17 50 12.9	−37 03 04	Sco	9.6	7.2	17.5	15.4	12.1	10700	22	164	99	Aliases: vdB-Ha 248; Mel 180; (2) JaFu 2; C1746−370
Terzan 6	gcl	17 50 46.4	−31 16 31	Sco	1.4	13.9	22.3	20.5	14.6	1500	22	164	6	See notes. Aliases: HP 5; vdB-Ha 249; Lund 1117; C1747−312
NGC 6453	gcl	17 50 51.8	−34 35 55	Sco	7.6	10.2	17.5	14.3	14.6	10100	22	164	6	Aliases: vdB-Ha 251; EQ 1748−346; C1748−346
UKS 1	gcl	17 54 27.2	−24 08 43	Sgr	2.0	17.3	25.5	22?	18.8	7400	22	146	55	See notes. Visible mostly in the infrared. Aliases: EQ 1751−241; UKS 1751-24.1; C1751−241
PWM78 2	gcl?	17 58 39.4	−05 04 21	Oph	2.0						15	106	8	See notes. Very reddened possible cluster. Difficult to make out on DSS. 40" diameter probable plate defect at 17 58 52.1 −05 09 48. Alias: C1755−050
NGC 6496	gcl	17 59 02.0	−44 15 54	Sco?	5.6	8.6	16.5	14.3	12.3	5700	22	181	55	Aliases: Mel 185; EQ 1755−442; C1755−442
Terzan 9	gcl	18 01 38.8	−26 50 23	Sgr	0.2	16.0	20.3	17.2	12.5	13800	22	145	6	Aliases: EQ 1758−268; C1758−268

Table 7.1: Catalog of Galactic Globular Clusters

Name	Type	2000.0 R.A.	2000.0 Dec.	Con	Dia. (′)	Tot. Vm	HB Vm	Bt* Vm	V Sur	Dist. (pc)	S #	2U #	Ref	Comments and Alias Names
ESO 456-SC38	gcl	18 01 49.1	–27 49 33	Sgr	9.9	9.90	17.6	15.5	14.9	5500	22	145	55	See notes. Near NGC 6520 and Barnard 86. Aliases: Djorg 2; EQ 1758–278; E456-SC38
NGC 6517	gcl	18 01 50.6	–08 57 32	Oph	4.0	10.1	18.0	16.0?	13.1	6100	15	126	6	Aliases: EQ 1759–089; C1759–089
Terzan 10	gcl	18 02 58	–26 04.0	Sgr	1.5	14.90	21.9	19.7	15.8	4800	22	145	55	See notes. Alias: EQ 1800–260
NGC 6522	gcl	18 03 35.0	–30 02 02	Sgr	9.4	9.9	16.9	14.1	14.8	7200	22	163	55	See notes. Position measured from DSS. Aliases: vdB-Ha 256; EQ 1800–300; C1800–300
NGC 6535	gcl	18 03 50.7	–00 17 49	Ser	3.4	9.3	15.8	12.8	12.0	6900	15	106	55	Aliases: Mel 189; EQ 1801–003; C1801–003
NGC 6528	gcl	18 04 49.6	–30 03 21	Sgr	5.0	9.6	17.1	15.5	13.1	6600	22	163	6	Aliases: vdB-Ha 257; EQ 1801–300; C1801–300
NGC 6539	gcl	18 04 49.8	–07 35 09	Ser?	7.9	8.9	18.3	15.9	13.4	4000	15	126	55	Aliases: Mel 190; EQ 1802–075; C1802–075
NGC 6540	gcl	18 06 08.6	–27 45 55	Sgr	1.5	14.6	15.30		15.5	3400	22	145	6	See notes. Aliases: Cr 364; OCl 11; Lund 808; Djorg 3; C1803–278
NGC 6544	gcl	18 07 20.6	–24 59 51	Sgr	9.2	7.5	14.9	12.8	12.3	2500	22	145	6	See notes. Aliases: Cr 366; Mel 192; OCl 17; EQ 1804–250; C1804–250
NGC 6541	gcl	18 08 02.2	–43 42 20	CrA	15.0	6.3	15.3	12.1	12.2	6600	22	181	55	Aliases: Mel 191; EQ 1804–437; 1E 1804.4–4343; Caldw 78; C1804–437
2MASS-GC 1	gcl?	18 08 21.8	–19 49 47	Sgr	3.3						15	145	99	See notes. Discovered in infrared, but visible on DSS-II image.
2MASS-GC 2	gcl?	18 08 36.5	–20 46 44	Sgr	1.9						22	145	99	See notes. Discovered in infrared, only a few faint stars visible on DSS-II image.
ESO 280-SC06	gcl	18 09 07	–46 25.3	Ara?	1.4		17.4	14.0		21900	22	181	99	See notes. The Galaxy's most recently recognized globular cluster. See Ortolani, *et al.* [2000].
NGC 6553	gcl	18 09 17.3	–25 54 28	Sgr	9.2	8.3	16.9	15.3	13.1	3500	22	145	99	Archinal: Position measured from DSS. Aliases: Mel 193; EQ 1806–259; C1806–259
NGC 6558	gcl	18 10 17.6	–31 45 47	Sgr		8.6	16.7			8800	22	163	99	See notes. Archinal: Position measured from DSS. Aliases: Cr 368; Mel 194; OCl 3; vdB-Ha 259; EQ 1807–317; C1806–317
IC 1276	gcl	18 10 44.2	–07 12 27	Ser	8.0	10.3	17.7	15.7	14.8	8900	15	126	55	Also widely known as Palomar 7. Aliases: Pal 7; EQ 1808–072; C1808–072
Terzan 11	gcl	18 12 15.8	–22 44 31	Sgr		16.4	20.5	18.5?			22	145	6	See notes. Aliases: Terzan 12; EQ 1809–227
NGC 6569	gcl	18 13 38.9	–31 49 35	Sgr	6.4	8.4	17.5	14.9	12.4	8700	22	163	55	Aliases: vdB-Ha 260; Mel 195; EQ 1810–318; C1810–318
NGC 6584	gcl	18 18 37.7	–52 12 54	Tel	6.6	7.9	16.5	13.5	12.0	9600	26	195	55	Aliases: Mel 196; EQ 1814–522; C1814–522
NGC 6624	gcl	18 23 40.5	–30 21 40	Sgr	8.8	7.6	16.1	14.0	12.3	8100	22	163	55	Aliases: vdB-Ha 262; Mel 199; KOHX 13; C1820–303
NGC 6626	gcl	18 24 32.9	–24 52 12	Sgr	13.8	6.9	15.7	12.0	12.6	5900	22	145	55	M 28. Aliases: Mel 200; M 28; C1821–249
NGC 6638	gcl	18 30 56.2	–25 29 47	Sgr	7.3	9.2	16.5	14.2	13.5	8500	22	145	6	Aliases: EQ 1827–255; C1827–255
NGC 6637	gcl	18 31 23.2	–32 20 53	Sgr	9.8	7.7	15.9	13.7	12.7	10100	22	163	55	M 69. See notes. Aliases: M 69; NGC 6634; Mel 202; EQ 1828–323; C1828–323
NGC 6642	gcl	18 31 54.3	–23 28 35	Sgr	5.8	8.9	16.3		12.7	8000	22	145	6	See notes. Aliases: Cr 381; Mel 203; OCl 29; EQ 1828–235; C1828–235
NGC 6652	gcl	18 35 45.7	–32 59 25	Sgr	6.0	8.5	16.0	13.3	12.4	14300	22	163	55	Aliases: Mel 207; EQ 1832–330; C1832–330
NGC 6656	gcl	18 36 24.2	–23 54 12	Sgr	32.0	5.2	14.2	10.7	12.7	3000	22	145	55	M 22. See notes. Aliases: Mel 208; M 22; EQ 1833–239; 1E 1833.3–2357; C1833–239
Palomar 8	gcl	18 41 29.9	–19 49 33	Sgr	5.2	10.9	17.3	15.4	14.5	28500	15	145	6	Aliases: EQ 1838–198; C1838–198
NGC 6681	gcl	18 43 12.7	–32 17 31	Sgr	8.0	7.8	15.6	13.0	12.3	9200	22	163	55	M 70. Aliases: M 70; Mel 211; EQ 1840–323; C1840–323
NGC 6712	gcl	18 53 04.3	–08 42 22	Sct	9.8	8.1	16.3	13.3	13.1	6800	16	125	6	See notes. Aliases: Mel 215; OCl 72; OCl 72.0; C1850–087
NGC 6715	gcl	18 55 03.3	–30 28 42	Sgr	12.0	7.7	18.2	15.2	13.1	21200	22	163	55	See notes. M 54. This may be the nucleus of the Sagittarius Dwarf Galaxy as well as a Galactic globular cluster. Aliases: M 54; Mel 216; EQ 1851–305; C1851–305
NGC 6717	gcl	18 55 06.2	–22 42 03	Sgr	5.4	8.4	15.6	14.0	12.1	7300	22	145	6	See notes. This is also widely known as Palomar 9. It contains IC 4802, a clump of stars NE of the nucleus. Aliases: Cr 395; Pal 9; OCl 37; (2) IC 4802; EQ 1852–227; C1852–227
NGC 6723	gcl	18 59 33.2	–36 37 54	Sgr	13.0	6.8	15.5	12.8	12.4	8700	22	163	55	Aliases: Mel 217; EQ 1856–367; C1856–367
NGC 6749	gcl	19 05 15.3	+01 54 03	Aql	4.0	12.4	19.7	16.5	15.4	7300	16	105	55	See notes. Aliases: Be 42; OCl 91; Lund 876; (5) C1902+017; EQ 1902+017; C1902+018
NGC 6752	gcl	19 10 51.8	–59 58 55	Pav	29.0	5.3	13.8	10.5	12.6	4200	26	194	55	Aliases: Mel 218; EQ 1906–600; Caldw 93; C1906–600
NGC 6760	gcl	19 11 12.1	+01 01 50	Aql	9.6	9.0	17.5	15.6	13.9	6100	16	105	6	See notes. Aliases: Mel 219; OCl 92; C1909+009
NGC 6779	gcl	19 16 35.5	+30 11 05	Lyr	8.8	8.4	16.3	13.2	13.1	9800	8	49	55	M 56. Aliases: Mel 220; M 56; EQ 1914+300; C1914+300

Table 7.1: Catalog of Galactic Globular Clusters

Name	Type	2000.0 R.A.	Dec.	Con	Dia. (′)	Tot. Vm	HB Vm	Bt* Vm	V Sur	Dist. (pc)	S #	2U #	Ref	Comments and Alias Names
Terzan 7	gcl	19 17 43.7	−34 39 27	Sgr		12.0	17.9	15.0		21900	22	163	55	May also be a member of the Sagittarius Dwarf Galaxy as well as a Galactic globular cluster. Alias: EQ 1914−347
Palomar 10	gcl	19 18 02.1	+18 34 18	Sge	4.0	13.2	19.4	18 ?	16.2	10600	16	67	6	Alias: EQ 1916+184
Arp 2	gcl	19 28 44.1	−30 21 14	Sgr	2.3	13.0	18.2	15.5	14.8	28300	22	162	55	May also be a member of the Sagittarius Dwarf Galaxy as well as a Galactic globular cluster. Aliases: EQ 1925−304; C1925−304
NGC 6809	gcl	19 39 59.4	−30 57 44	Sgr	19.0	6.3	14.4	11.2	12.7	4800	22	162	55	M 55. Aliases: M 55; Mel 221; EQ 1936−310; C1936−310
Terzan 8	gcl	19 41 45.0	−34 00 01	Sgr		12.4	18.0	15.0		22800	22	162	55	May also be a member of the Sagittarius Dwarf Galaxy as well as a Galactic globular cluster. Aliases: EQ 1938−341; C1938−341
Palomar 11	gcl	19 45 14.4	−08 00 26	Aql	10.0	9.8?	17.4	15.5	14.8	13300	16	125	6	Aliases: EQ 1942−081; C1942−081
NGC 6838	gcl	19 53 46.1	+18 46 42	Sge		8.4	14.5	12.1		3900	16	66	6	M 71. See notes. Aliases: Cr 409; M 71; Mel 226; OCl 117; GCRV 12241; EQ 1951+186; CSI+18-19515; C1951+186
NGC 6864	gcl	20 06 04.8	−21 55 17	Sgr	6.8	8.6	17.5	14.6	12.8	18500	23	144	55	M 75. Aliases: M 75; Mel 228; EQ 2003−220; C2003−220
NGC 6934	gcl	20 34 11.6	+07 24 15	Del	7.1	8.9	17.1	13.8	13.2	14900	16	84	55	Aliases: Mel 230; EQ 2031+072; Caldw 47; C2031+072
NGC 6981	gcl	20 53 27.9	−12 32 13	Aqr	6.6	9.2	16.9	14.2	13.3	18100	16	124	55	M 72. Aliases: M 72; Mel 233; EQ 2050−127; C2050−127
NGC 7006	gcl	21 01 29.5	+16 11 15	Del	3.6	10.6	18.8	15.6	13.4	39100	16	83	6	Moore: Very distant. Aliases: GCRV 13202; EQ 2059+160; CSI+16-20591; Caldw 42; C2059+160
NGC 7078	gcl	21 29 58.3	+12 10 01	Peg	18.0	6.3	15.9	12.6	12.6	10500	16	83	55	See notes. M 15. Contains planetary nebula Pease 1 = K 648. For chart, see Skiff [1992]. Aliases: M 15; (2) Pease 1; Mel 234; C2127+119
NGC 7089	gcl	21 33 27.0	−00 49 12	Aqr	16.0	6.6	16.1	13.1	12.6	11900	17	103	99	M 2. Archinal: Position measured from DSS. Aliases: M 2; Mel 235; EQ 2130−010; C2130−010
NGC 7099	gcl	21 40 22.0	−23 10 45	Cap	12.0	6.9	15.1	12.1	12.3	7400	23	143	55	M 30. Aliases: M 30; Mel 237; EQ 2137−234; C2137−234
Palomar 12	gcl	21 46 38.8	−21 15 03	Cap	2.9	11.7	17.1	14.6	14.0	19300	23	143	55	Has been listed incorrectly as a galaxy, e.g. MCG −04-51-013 = RC2 A2143−21 = Cap Dwarf. [Lederman and Gottlieb, 1996] Aliases: Cap gcl; (5) MCG −04-51-013; (5) RC2 A2143−21; (5) Cap Dwarf; EQ 2143−214; C2143−214
Palomar 13	gcl	23 06 44.4	+12 46 19	Peg	0.7	13.8	17.7	17.0	13.0	24400	17	82	55	This globular cluster also has been listed incorrectly as a galaxy, with designation CGCG 430-61. [Lederman and Gottlieb, 1996] Aliases: Peg gcl; (5) CGCG 430−61; EQ 2304+124; C2304+124
NGC 7492	gcl	23 08 26.7	−15 36 41	Aqr	4.2	11.2	17.6	15.5	14.3	25100	17	122	6	See notes. Aliases: Mel 242; OCl 111; EQ 2305−159; C2305−159

7.2 Extended Notes on Galactic Globular Clusters

This section includes extended notes on various objects in the catalog of Galactic globular clusters. These notes clarify identifications that in the past were uncertain, clarify nomenclature that in the past has been confused, and note errata regarding catalogs. Objects are presented in alphabetical and numerical order by preferred cluster name and number. In some cases where an object is commonly known under more than one name or under an incorrect name, a reference is given to the main entry. Brief comments are usually given alone in the main catalog.

Note that all objects listed are currently thought to be or are thought very likely to be Galactic globular clusters. Information on objects previously thought to be such clusters, but later confirmed to be something else, is listed earlier in the extended notes section of Chapter 4. This includes objects such as AM 2, Bica 1, Dejc 1, ESO 93-SC8, Grindlay 1, Hogg 9, IC 1311, IC 4802, Kodaira 1, NGC 609, NGC 2158, NGC 6684, NGC 6705 = M 11, NGC 6819, Reticulum, Shk 1, Terz N 5, Terz N 15, Terz N 16, Terz N 17, Terz N 23, Terz N 33, Terz N 34, Terz N 35, and vdB-Ha 66 = UKS 2. Objects listed here, but not yet confirmed as globular clusters, include 2MASS-GC01, 2MASS-GC02, and PWM 78 2. Also note that it may be possible that Alessi J12130-6242 and Schuster 1—described in Chapter 4—are globular clusters.

Acronyms and abbreviations used here are given along with the catalog in Chapter 4.

Particular acknowledgment is made of the tables of globular cluster information provided by S.G. Djorgovski and Brian Skiff. This material was previously described in detail in Chapter 4. Some additional material for this catalog was also obtained from data published by W. Harris [1996] and data to have been published by W. Harris and H. Harris [2000].

2MASS-GC 1 and 2MASS-GC 2: These are two possible globular clusters discovered by Hurt, *et al.*, (see Appendix E) during the course of the infrared Two Micron All Sky Survey (2MASS). They were both found "during spot-checks of the data during 2MASS quality assurance reviews," while the second cluster was "noted as a probable globular by 2MASS telescope operator Joselino Vasquez in his log." These objects lie at a very low Galactic latitude (< 0.7°), separated by just over 1°. The first cluster has an estimated visual magnitude extinction of 21.5 ± 1.0 magnitudes, a K magnitude diameter of 3.3′ ± 0.2′, and integrated core magnitude in K of 7.2 ± 0.4. The same statistics for the second object are 18.0 ± 1.0 magnitudes of extinction, a diameter of 1.9′ ± 0.2′, and a core K magnitude of 5.5 ± 0.2.

The discoverers claim there is no trace of the clusters on Digitized Sky Survey images. However, as one of us has

Fig. 7.1 *Arp-Madore 4 (AM 4), a very faint 3′ diameter Galactic globular cluster, shown here in a contrast enchanced stretch of a 17′ field of view SkyView/DSS-S image. © ROE.*

noted [e-mail from BA to the amastro list, June 20, 2000], there are stars on the DSS at the positions of both clusters. These may be foreground stars, but some may be the brighter stars of the clusters. Several seem to match stars on the infrared images in the paper. On the DSS-II red image, the cluster 2MASS-GC01 actually does show up as a rich group of scattered stars. For 2MASS-GC02, there is no obvious cluster on the DSS-II red image, however. If anything, there is a lack of stars at the given position, showing there must be a substantial dark cloud in front of the cluster. It is surprising that GC01 is definitely visible on the DSS-II, given the extinction estimate, and that the extinction for GC01 is supposed to be greater than that of GC02. In large enough telescopes, it would seem likely that the brightest stars of these clusters should be detectable in visible wavelengths, and the GC01 cluster should be resolvable as a real cluster. The visibility of the GC01 object may be an indication that a systematic search of DSS-II images (to say nothing of 2MASS images) would reveal some further such objects.

AM 4 = C1353-269 = AM 1353-265: See Figure 7.1. The position given here (2000.0, $13^h\ 56^m\ 21^s$ –27° 09.7′) was taken from Skiff's listing of globular cluster data. The positions from Djorgovski and Meylan [1993] and Harris [1996] appear to be too far west by about 7′.

Berkeley 42 = NGC 6749: see page 245.

Djorgovski 3 = NGC 6540: see page 241.

ESO 280-SC06: This object is the most recent (and

150th) one to be determined a Galactic globular cluster. It was originally discovered as part of the ESO/Uppsala Survey of the ESO(B) Atlas [Lauberts, 1982] and listed as a 1.5′ diameter open cluster under the ESO 280-SC06 name. Ortolani, *et al.*, [2000] in a systematic inspection of southern cluster images noted that on the DSS II this object appeared to have a dense core, suggesting it might be a globular cluster. They confirmed this supposition after obtaining high-resolution images and color-magnitude data of the cluster stars with the 1.5-meter Danish telescope at ESO (La Silla). Their data show that this appears to be a poorly populated, metal-poor globular cluster with a compact core. The brightest star appears to be about V = 14.0, the magnitude of the horizontal branch is V_{HB} = 17.4 ±0.2, and the reddening is E(B – V) = 0.07. An inspection of their published image shows a diameter of roughly 1.4′ (their model diameter is 1.23′). They derive a distance of 21.9 ±2.0 kpc from us and 14.5 kpc from the Galactic center, placing this cluster in the halo on the opposite side of the Galaxy. The cluster is located in the southern constellation of Ara, and B. Skiff's estimate of its position (2000.0: 18^h 09^m 07^s –46° 25.3') is used in this catalog.

ESO 452-SC11 = C1636-283: This object has recently been shown to be a probable Galactic globular cluster by Minniti, *et al.*, [1995] (where it is either called ESO 45 or ESO 45-SC11). The K magnitude of the brightest star is given as about 8.5 [ibid, page 1693]. It is not included in the list of Djorgovski and Meylan [1993], but is included in the companion list of Peterson [1993]. This cluster appears as a 70″ diameter (used here) condensation of 15–20 faint stars on the DSS.

B. Wilson reports that it has been observed visually at various times by Andrew Murrell, Jose Sancho and herself [private communication, 1996], and Steve Mencinsky, and that CCD images of it have been obtained with the 46-cm (18-inch) *f*/5 reflector of the George Observatory, see Figure 7.22 on page 253.

ESO 456-SC38 = Djorgovski 2: This is one of three Galactic globular clusters found by Djorgovski [1987]. However, as Djorgovski later noted [Djorgovski and Meylan 1993, 332] it had been previously cataloged by Lauberts [1982] who had classified it as an open cluster. Ortolani, *et al.*, [1997] provide further confirmation that this is a globular cluster via a color-magnitude diagram from V and I CCD photometry. They measure a horizontal branch V magnitude of approximately 17.6 and estimate a distance of 5.5±0.8 kpc.

For those wishing to observe it, S. Mencinsky [private communication, 1995] has noted that the cluster appears on a photograph (of Barnard 86 and NGC 6520) in *Burnham's Celestial Handbook* [1978], p. 1643, 25.5 mm from the right and 30.2 mm from the top side on the upper photo.

Fig. 7.2 *IC 1257, although discovered in 1890 by Spitaler, has only recently been shown [Harris, et al., 1997] to be a galactic globular cluster in Serpens. 17′ field of view DSS-S image © ROE.*

IC 1257 = C1724-070: This object has recently been confirmed as a distant Galactic globular cluster [Harris, et al 1997], see Figure 7.2. Czernic Crute (Los Angeles, CA) had queried Brian Skiff as to whether this object might be a globular cluster [private communication, 1996]. This set into motion a chain of events which led to B. Madore taking CCD images of the cluster with the Hale 5-meter telescope. R. Phelps and William Harris then confirmed the object's type from a color magnitude diagram made from that data. Harris reported that a preliminary reduction of the data indicated: the color-magnitude diagram shows that it is unquestionably a globular cluster, which is moderately heavily reddened; it has the telltale marks of a metal-poor halo cluster which are (a) a blue horizontal-branch population and (b) a steep red-giant branch. Field contamination is bad but not critical.

A literature search revealed that very little is known about this object. There appeared to be no direct professional observations of it other than its discovery in 1890 by Spitaler. It is listed as an open cluster by Shapley [1930, 232], Hogg [1959a, 201], Ruprecht [1966, 36], and the *Lund Catalogue*. It also appears as an open cluster on the *Atlas of the Heavens* [Becvar, 1962]. Neither Trumpler [1930], Collinder [1931], nor Becvar [1964] listed it. Surprisingly, it is listed (Ced 144) as a reflection nebula by Cederblad [1946] (it certainly does not have the appearance of one on the DSS). However, other than its position, size, number of stars, and Trumpler type, little information is provided by any of these references.

Amateur observations of this object are somewhat more revealing. Burnham [1978, p. 1231] lists this as having a diameter of 1′ with description "vS, F, vC; possibly a distant globular cluster." The *Webb Society Deep-Sky Observer's Handbook*, Vol. 3 [Barker 1980, 148] lists this object giving the position and noting "Classification uncertain. No data available." Meketa [1984, 18], however, gives a significant observation (perhaps relying on Burnham's listing?):

> Exactly 2° south of NGC 6366 lies IC 1257, an unusual object that may or may not be a globular cluster. If it is a globular it must be extremely remote to account for its apparent small size and underluminosity. In my 18-inch it shows only under excellent conditions and then as a threshold object about 1″ [ed. note: author may have mistyped arcseconds for arcminutes] in diameter. There is no trace of resolution or detail and even the size and shape are indistinct. Observers with large telescopes and dark skies may have better luck with this elusive cluster.

Kepple and Sanner [1987, 22] listed this object giving its position and a size of 1.0′. Kepple gives an observation:

> IC 1257 Globular Cluster (?): 12½-inch–16 mm: Very small, a faint compact haze of light, not resolved.

Czernic Crute reported on his own observations and an earlier observation by Chris Schur in an article *The Spectacular Globular Clusters of Ophiuchus*, which appeared in August, 1996 (see Appendix E).

One of us [BA] observed this object. It was seen the night of August 16–17, 1996 from the summit of Reddish Knob, a mountaintop on the Virginia/West Virginia state line, in Greg Dillon's 46-cm (18-inch) reflector. It appeared as an approximately 14th magnitude 2′ diameter glow with some hint of glow or resolved stars beyond this to perhaps a diameter of 5′. It was at times, with extreme difficulty, visible in a 15-cm (6-inch) *f*/10 reflector. Barbara Wilson, observing with four others, reported [private communication, 1996] observing IC 1257 on the same night, using Larry Mitchell's 91-cm (36-inch) reflector.

S. George Djorgovski planned to make observations with the Hale 5-meter (200-inch) to definitely determine the object type [private communication, 1996], but this proved unnecessary after Madore's successful observations with the same telescope.

The morphology of this object (on the DSS and from the visual observations) indicated that it was likely a globular cluster. However, the possibility that this is a faint, very distant and compressed open cluster, or perhaps a galaxy, was not ruled out until the color-magnitude diagram was obtained.

The position given here (2000.0: 17^h 27^m 08.5^s, –07° 05′ 35) is the GSC 5079-0033 position (which matches Spitaler's quite well). The total V magnitude (13.1), V magnitude of the brightest star (17.12), the V magnitude of the horizontal branch (19.8), the diameter (100″), and the distance (24 ± 2 kpc) are all from Harris, *et al.*, [1997]. The diameter is that for which the color-magnitude diagram of the cluster begins to appear the same as that of the background stars. It matches reasonably well the diameter (2′) observed visually by Archinal. However, large-aperture photometry in blue light shows continued growth out to a diameter of 5.2′.

Note that the *Lund Catalogue* alias list is missing the Lund number (751), although this is in the print file of the catalog. It is correctly listed in the alias file as OCl 51. This object should be removed from the *Lund Catalogue*, since it is now proven to be a globular cluster.

IRAS 1833-2357 = GJJC 1: Planetery nebula in NGC 6656 = M 22, see page 243.

Liller 1 = C1730-333: Most globular clusters in our Galaxy have been discovered by visual or photographic means, but Liller 1 is unusual in having been discovered as a result of its X-ray emission. Following the discovery by Lewin [1976; Lewin and Joss 1981] of the multiple-burst X-ray source MXB 1730-335, astronomer William Liller [1977] took a series of moderately deep plates of the area using the CTIO 4-meter reflector. On the red and infrared plates, a compact (16″ x 13″) globular cluster of stars was detected within 1′ of the position of the X-ray burst source. It was not seen on blue or yellow plates showing it to be heavily reddened. However, lying close to the direction of the center of the Galaxy (l = 354.81°, b = –0.16°), this was to be expected. The cluster was very faint and was estimated by Liller to be of m_r = +21. About a dozen individual stars were resolved. From this and the size of the cluster, the object was estimated to be at a distance of about 10 kpc. It remains among the faintest known globular clusters in the Galaxy. Using the ESO 3.5-m (140-inch), *f*/2.2 NTT (New Technology Telescope), Ortolani, *et al.*, [1994] have found that the cluster is so heavily obscured that its brightest giants are just at the detection limit in V. Therefore, any serious study needs to be carried out at longer wavelengths. In doing so, they found that the giant branch of the cluster was clearly detected, and the CMD reached the horizontal branch at I = 19.9. The giant branch indicates a very metal-rich cluster. The authors made a comparative study of the CMD of the cluster and some 20,000 stars in a field surrounding it ~10′ x 8′. From the similarities detected it was concluded that Liller 1 is located at the distance of the bulge bulk stellar population close to the Galactic center.

Lyng 7 = C1607-551: Although this cluster was thought to be an old open cluster, it was recently demonstrated to be a Galactic globular cluster [Tavarez and Friel 1995]. An improved position is given here from Harris's

Fig. 7.3 *NGC 104, or 47 Tucanae, the second brightest globular cluster in the sky. 60′ field of view DSS-S image © ROE.*

[1996] list. As with IC 1257 this object should be removed from the Lund open cluster catalog.

M 54 = NGC 6715: see page 244.

M 71 = NGC 6838: see page 246.

NGC 104 = 47 Tucanae = C0021-723: This spectacular globular cluster, the second brightest after ω Centauri, lies deep in the southern sky close to the Small Magellanic Cloud, see Figure 7.3. It was first reported telescopically as a cluster by the French astronomer Lacaille in his *Mémoires* of 1755 following his expedition to the Cape of Good Hope during 1751–1753. It was described merely as "like the nucleus of a fairly bright comet." Its brightness makes it an obvious target for investigation but, like many other important southern objects, the paucity of large telescopes in the southern hemisphere until the last few decades held up a detailed survey.

However, as long ago as 1956, Gascoigne and Burr [1956] observed that there was a change in color with radius in the globular, the inner parts of the cluster being significantly redder than the outer parts. This finding was established by UBV measurements obtained by Chun [1976], who confirmed the earlier observations of Lloyd-Evans [1974]. This showed the effect produced by an excess of the brightest giants per unit luminosity in the inner parts of the cluster. Interestingly, during his expedition to the Cape in 1834–1838, John Herschel reported that this globular included "an interior mass of rose-tinted stars." compared with white ones in the outer regions. Whether this is an accurate visual report of the measured phenomenon or purely subjective is difficult to say.

CCD photometry in B and V for 8800 stars in the field of NGC 104 was obtained by Hesser, *et al.*, [1987]. The data consisted of the results of two long exposure frame pairs made using the CTIO 4-meter telescope extending from the horizontal branch turnoff down to V ~ 24 and two other short exposure fields nearer to the cluster center. From these a CMD and luminosity function were constructed for the cluster covering an 11-magnitude range of luminosity. Among the findings from this survey, a metallicity model was derived which produced an excellent match to the shape of the entire CMD from the lower main sequence up to and including the horizontal branch. The age of the cluster was estimated at 13.5±2 Gyr, similar to that of the more metal-poor nearby globular clusters. No evidence of any binaries was detected.

Surprisingly, NGC 104 has only one known RR Lyrae variable (V9; V ~ 13.1–14.1, P –0.736852^{d}.), which has been studied by Carney, *et al.*, [1993]. The other two candidates, V12 (HV 814) and UX Tuc (HV 809), have been eliminated.

High-resolution observations of the massive and dense core of NGC 104 with the Faint Object Camera of the *Hubble Space Telescope* have revealed a high density of "blue stragglers" [Paresce, *et al.*, 1991]. These may represent part of the "missing" population of binaries; and their presence in the core but not in the peripheral regions would be due to their considerable mass.

HST observations have been used to identify in this cluster a new class of variable stars [Edmonds and Gilliland, 1996]; these are K giants which lie along a narrow band in the CMD which joins the faint end of the AGB and the RGB. The K giant variables (KGV's) have periods of between 2–4 days and V amplitudes in the range 5–15 millimagnitudes. The variations are consistent with low-overtone radial pulsation or non-radial pulsation, and the group may include the nearby K giant Arcturus (α Boo).

In addition to being one of the brightest globular clusters, NGC 104 is one of the nearest; its estimated distance of 4.1 kpc [Meylan 1988] makes it only half the distance of most other galactic globular clusters. This proximity, together with the mass and density of the core, makes it a suitable object to check for low luminosity phenomena (such as millisecond pulsars). These are believed to be old neutron stars which have been "recycled" in low-mass X-ray binary systems or formed by the accretion-induced collapse of white dwarfs in binaries. Manchester, *et al.*, [1991] have discovered 11 of these remarkable objects in 47 Tuc (by far the largest number in any individual globular cluster system).

NGC 288 = C0050-268: This globular cluster is situated in the constellation of Sculptor, less than a degree from the

Fig. 7.4 *NGC 288, a globular cluster in Sculptor, near the south Galactic pole. 30′ field of view DSS-S image © ROE.*

Fig. 7.5 *NGC 3201, a globular cluster in Vela, with an unusually large number of RR Lyrae stars. 45′ field of view DSS-S image © ROE.*

South Galactic Pole; it is, therefore, easily studied, free from any obscuring gas and dust in the galactic plane (see Figure 7.4). Nevertheless, it was poorly studied until recent decades probably due to its moderately southern declination. By 1980 it was one of only 13 globular clusters for which main-sequence photometry had been published. A preliminary color-magnitude diagram (CMD) was published by Cannon [1974] (based on photoelectric photometry of 47 stars), and a more detailed CMD (using 280 stars) was produced by Alcaino [1975b]. These were useful in showing NGC 288 to be unusual in having exclusively blue horizontal-branch (HB) stars (typical of metal-poor clusters) but a giant branch of moderate steepness normally considered to be a more typical feature of globular clusters with a higher metallicity. There is a gap near the base of the sub-giant branch (yet to be explained). This was identified by Alcaino and Liller [1980] in a more detailed study. Photographic photometry of 911 stars was carried out, extending the photoelectric limit to V ~ 20.6. It was established that the position of the main-sequence turn-off lies at V = 18.8, and, for the cluster as a whole, a distance modulus of 14.70 was derived. The authors determined an age of 14.5±2.5 Gyr.

NGC 3201 = C1015-461: This globular cluster lies in the southern constellation of Vela. It is a large, bright, open system and has an unusually large number of RR Lyrae variables, see Figure 7.5. In her 1973 compilation Helen Sawyer Hogg [1973] listed 88 variables, of which 83 are of the RR Lyrae type. The first photometric investigation of NGC 3201 was carried out by Menzies [1967] and some of the UBV results were later summarized by Alcaino [1974]. Menzies produced a CMD based on 315 stars down to V = 15.6 and found that the giant branch was not very well defined. However, there was a well defined horizontal branch, evenly populated across the RR Lyrae gap with 27 definite and 5 possible RR Lyrae variables in the observed region. The cluster was further observed, down to a similar magnitude level, by Alcaino [1976] who, from BV photographic photometry of 313 star down to V = 16.3, derived a true distance modulus of $(m - M)_0 = 13.68$. On this basis the distance from the Sun to NGC 3201 is 5.4 kpc, and its angular diameter is 14 pc. The Galactic latitude of b = +8°.64 gives a distance of 0.8 kpc above the Galactic plane.

NGC 3201 appears to be a typical halo cluster, but White and Kraft [1972] found an unusually high heliocentric radial velocity of +493 km s^{-1}. Even removing the effect of the Sun's motion through space only reduces this to +240 km s^{-1}. While the cluster probably does not have enough space velocity to escape the Galactic system, it will certainly be in a retrograde orbit.

The first study to reach down to the turn-off point was that of Alcaino and Liller [1981] who looked at 1452 stars to V = 19.4. The turn-off point was found to be at V = 18.0 ± 0.1 and B–V = 0.61 ± 0.03, and an age of 11±2 Gyr was derived. Some support for this determination was subsequently derived by an independent method; Cacciari [1984a, 1984b] made a study of RR Lyrae variables in NGC 3201, finding their mean magnitude to be V(RR) = 14.76±0.08 and deriving an age of 12±3 Gyr.

Fig. 7.6 *NGC 4833, a metal-poor globular cluster in Musca. 30′ field of view DSS-S image © ROE.*

Fig. 7.7 *NGC 5139, or ω Centauri, the largest and brightest globular cluster in the sky, and likely the nucleus of a galaxy captured by the Milky Way in the distant past. Photograph by Pickering and Fleming [1897, plate 6]. The field of view appears to be approximately 40′ high.*

A BVRI CCD photometric investigation of 488 stars in NGC 3201 by Alcaino, *et al.*, [1989] enabled four different CMDs to be constructed (V *vs* B–V, V *vs* V–R, V *vs* V–I and V *vs* B–I). In each case, the main sequence turn-off points fell close to V = 18.2 ± 0.1. The magnitude difference between the turn-off and the horizontal branch was derived at 3.44 ± 0.12, in remarkably good agreement with the mean value of 3.44 ± 0.18 for 36 clusters observed by Peterson [1986]. In addition, from the mean of all the diagrams, a cluster age of 16 ± 3 Gyr was determined. More recent UBVI CCD photometry of NGC 3201 was conducted by Brewer, *et al.*, [1993], looking at two specific fields, one being centered on the core of the cluster and the second at a distance of 7 core radii. UBV photometry in the core field reached just below the main sequence turn-off and revealed 31 blue straggler candidates. A value of $(m–M)_V$ = 14.2 was found for the distance modulus.

NGC 4833 = C1256-706: NGC 4833 is a comparatively poorly studied globular cluster in a dense field only 8° South of the Galactic plane in the small southern constellation of Musca, see Figure 7.6. Alcaino [1971] published photographic photometry of 261 stars down to V = 16.3, and Menzies [1972] published photographic photometry of about 800 stars with a photoelectric sequence of 26 stars down to V = 16.7. The work of Menzies suggested a cluster of low metallicity confirmed by more recent investigations of Geisler, *et al.*, [1992]. Demers and Wehlau [1977] obtained BV photometry of variable stars in the cluster and expanded the number of known RR Lyrae periods to 15. BV photographic photometry of 868 stars by Samus, *et al.* [1995a] reached the cluster's main sequence turn-off point at V = 19.2. This indicates a fairly normal system, though with a hint of a deficiency in the stellar population of the sub-giant branch, as may be found in other metal-poor globular clusters.

NGC 5053 = C1313+179: Although this is not included in the main data or print file of the *Lund Catalogue*, the alias list incorrectly lists this as "globular?" It actually is a globular cluster according to the list of Djorgovski and Meylan [1993].

NGC 5139 = ω Centauri = C1323-472: ω Centauri is undoubtedly the brightest and most spectacular globular cluster in the night sky, but at Declination –47° is hidden from observers living in Europe and most of North America. See Figure 7.7. From a good site, it is clearly visible with the unaided eye as a hazy "star" of about 4th magnitude, and some resolution is possible with even small telescopes. Since it is visible without optical aid, no-one can be sure who first observed it; but the first recorded sighting was that of Edmond Halley from the island of St. Helena in the South Atlantic in 1677. During his trip to South Africa in 1833–34, Sir John Herschel reported of this object:

> The noble globular cluster Omega Centauri is beyond all comparison the richest and largest object of its kind in the heavens. The stars are literally innumerable, and as their total light affects the eye hardly more than a star of 4th magnitude, the minuteness of each star may be imagined …

With moderate aperture telescopes, a conspicuous feature of ω Cen is its elliptical shape rather than circular like most other globular clusters (interpreted as an effect of rotation). The size, brightness and ease of resolution suggests that this globular cluster must be one of the nearest. Together with its fairly low obscuration (E(B–V) = 0.15 [Peterson 1993]), this makes it an obvious target for astronomical investigation.

The first investigations of ω Cen were concerned with its stellar content. In 1893, a physical count of stars visible on a plate obtained with the 33-cm refractor at Arequipa, Peru, resulted in almost 6400 distinct star images being detected. Among these, searches were made for variables, resulting in the publication of a catalog by Bailey [1902]. Since the variable stars in ω Cen included both cluster variables and longer period Cepheids, Shapley [1918b] used this data in his work on the distances of globular clusters. Other historically important catalogs of variable stars in ω Cen. have been produced by Martin [1939] and include the important series of compilation catalogs produced by Helen Sawyer-Hogg [1973].

A comprehensive study of ω Cen, involving photographic photometry and proper motion determinations of several thousand stars, was conducted by the Royal Greenwich Observatory [1966], and the CMD subsequently published was discussed by Dickens and Woolley [1967]. The primary finding of this was that the giant branch of the cluster was abnormally wide. This was confirmed by photographic UBV magnitudes obtained by Geyer [1967] from a smaller sample of stars; it was also suggested that the bluer giants lie on an asymptotic branch which is clearly separated. The unusual width of the ω Cen. giant branch was found in photoelectric UBV data obtained by Cannon and Stobie [1973], and it is believed that the cause of this is a wide range of surface chemical composition among the evolved stars of the cluster.

The large apparent size of ω Cen is not just a visual effect. It is genuinely a huge and massive object with an absolute magnitude of $M_v = -10.40$ [Gunn and Griffin 1979], comparable to some Local Group dwarf spheroidal galaxies [Zinn 1980]. However, the main difference is that these tend to be considerably larger and much less compressed. In a study of the dynamical masses of globular clusters, Mandushev, *et al.*, [1991] found a lower limit of 2.4×10^6 $M_\odot$ for this cluster. At a meeting of the American Astronomical Society on June 2, 1994, Georges Meylan, of the European Southern Observatory, reported radial velocity measurements of 469 cluster members [*Sky & Telescope* 1994; Meylan, *et al.*, 1994]. The indication from these is that the cluster may have a mass of 5.1×10^6 $M_\odot$; on this basis, it is arguable whether ω Cen should be considered a globular cluster or really ought to have some greater status, such as a dwarf spheroidal galaxy! Indeed, Bassino and Muzzio [1995] point out that, since M 54 has recently been found to be the probable nucleus of the Sagittarius Dwarf Galaxy, it is possible that ω Centauri may have originated in the same way, as the nucleus of a dwarf galaxy captured by our own.

Fig. 7.8 *NGC 6121 = M 4, the large, bright globular cluster just west of Antares (out of the field on the left). The globular cluster NGC 6144 is at upper left. The bright star at the top right edge is σ Sco (V = 2.912 variable, B1III), surrounded by the nebula Sh 2-9. The diameter of M 4 has been measured at 36′ at the 25 magnitudes per square arcsecond background level, but its appearance here in this 2° field is closer to that of the much smaller 15′ diameter measured at the 22 magnitudes per square arcsecond level. 2° field of view DSS-S image © ROE.*

NGC 6121 = M 4 = C1620-264: NGC 6121 is a large bright globular cluster found by De Chesaux in 1746, Lacaille in 1751, and rediscovered by Messier on 1764 May 8, see Figure 7.8. It is located just over 1° west of the bright star Antares in Scorpius. From a good location and with a clear sky, it can be seen without optical aid. For the visual observer with a small-to-medium sized telescope, its most conspicuous feature is a central "bar" of brightish stars, oriented more-or-less North-South. This was first recorded by Herschel in 1783.

From the astrophysical perspective, NGC 6121 is one of the nearest globular clusters and is of importance because of being one of the largest and most open systems of its type in the Galaxy. However, although it is a visually impressive object, it is less conspicuous than it might be, suffering almost 1.5 magnitudes of extinction as its light has to pass through the Sco-Oph dark cloud complex.

A number of photometric studies of the cluster have been carried out. The earliest of any significance was

Greenstein [1939], who looked at the colors and magnitudes of 660 stars brighter than m(pg) 15.6 within 13′.5 of the cluster center and produced a CMD down to the horizontal branch. More comprehensive studies down to about the same level have been published by, among others, Alcaino [1975a] and Lloyd-Evans [1977]. BVRI photographic photometry of 1421 stars in NGC 6121, reaching down to about 3 magnitudes below the turn-off was presented by Alcaino and Liller [1984]. This study included a comprehensive summary of the results of all previous photometric and spectroscopic studies of the cluster.

From BVI CCD photometry, Alcaino, *et al.*, [1988] inferred an age of 17±1.5 Gyr based on the main-sequence turn-off, while Buonanno, *et al.*, [1989] derived a comparable 16.2 Gyr, using a relationship between cluster age and the magnitude difference between the turn-off and the horizontal branch. This age of roughly 16 Gyr has been supported by investigations using other methods; for example, Caputo [1987] using RR Lyrae variables.

Deep CCD photometry from V ~ 12 of the red giant branch to V ~ 25 on the main sequence has been obtained by Kanatas, *et al.*, [1995]. This reaches much fainter than any previous photometric study and has resulted in a CMD covering a rich sample of stars brighter than V = 19. By comparing nearby metal-poor subdwarfs with the cluster main sequence, an apparent distance modulus has been derived of $(m{-}M)_V = 12.84 \pm 0.19$, consistent with previous studies, as is the age of around 16 Gyr.

The proximity of NGC 6121 has made it a suitable candidate in which to study a comparable population of white dwarf stars. Using the Wide Field Planetary Camera 2 (WFPC2) on the *Hubble Space Telescope*, Richer, *et al.*, [1995], discovered the first extensive sequence of cooling white dwarfs seen in a globular cluster. The CMD location of the sequence and the cumulative luminosity function have been used to show the basic correctness and completeness of current theoretical models.

NGC 6205 = M 13 = C1639+365: Most of the brighter Galactic globular clusters are southern hemisphere objects. M 13 is the most important and brightest of those fewer northern hemisphere systems. See Figures 7.9, 7.10, and 8.4 (on page 263). It is a naked-eye object in clear, dark skies; but the first known observation was made by Edmond Halley in 1714, who commented merely that it "… is but a little Patch, but it shews itself to the naked Eye when the sky is serene and the Moon absent." It was observed by Charles Messier on 1764 June 1 and described as "Nebula without stars …; it is round and bright, the center brighter than the edges. It is between two stars of the 8th magnitude." Using the best telescopes of his time, William Herschel resolved it into a great many stars, and estimated that it contained perhaps 14,000. In the second half of the nineteenth century, observations by John Herschel and, especially, Lord Rosse, showed something more irregular than the standard depiction of the cluster. It contained curved lines of stars emanating from a brighter center, which itself showed three dark radiating streaks. The curved lines of stars show up on some photographs and are much an aperture-dependent feature of the cluster (see, for example, the photographs of the cluster on p. 981, 983 and 985 of *Burnham's Celestial Handbook* [Burnham 1978]). The existence of the dark streaks across the center, however, has proven a matter of more long-standing controversy, but it does appear that there is some degree of obscuration or the appearance of a slight reduction in the star-density. Other globular clusters appear to exhibit such features; for example, M 3, M 62, M 30 and M 15 [Hogg 1959; Roberts 1960]. Mathematical simulations and other theoretical studies [Kanagy and Wyatt 1978] would seem to rule out the chance arrangement of stars as an explanation for the observed phenomena, leaving dust concentrations as the probable answer. This has been confirmed by polarization and photometry by Forte and Mendez [1989].

Fig. 7.9 *NGC 6205 = M 13, the great globular cluster in Hercules. The galaxy NGC 6207 is in the upper left corner. 45′ field of view. Image courtesy the Palomar Observatory and Digitized Sky Survey created by the Space Telescope Science Institute, operated by AURA, Inc. for NASA. Reproduced with permission from AURA/STScI.*

Because of its brightness and convenient northern location, M 13 has been the subject of many studies. A detailed proper motion study of the cluster was carried out by Cudworth and Monet [1979] and a comprehensive dynamical investigation by Lupton, *et al.*, [1987]. From this and other data, Leonard, *et al.*, [1992] have looked at the mass and stellar content of the cluster. They found that the proper motions were a much better guide than radial velocities in

Fig. 7.10 *NGC 6205 = M 13, in a drawing (with an unknown telescope) from the* Harvard Annals *8 (1876), plate 25. The field of view appears to be about 40′ high. Compare with the drawing by G. Bakos shown in* ***Figure 8.4****.*

determining the mass of the system and that the kinematic evidence favored a slightly smaller distance value of 6.5 kpc. On this basis, the mass is around 500,000–600,000 $M_{\odot}$. It is suggested that about half the cluster mass is in the form of low mass stars, possibly brown dwarfs. Guarnieri, *et al.*, [1993] have measured 3532 stars in the cluster by means of B and V CCD photometry and obtained a color-magnitude diagram down to the Main Sequence. In addition to the obvious goal of producing a more complete and homogeneous CMD, this work was also carried out as a step in a program involving the spectroscopy of blue stars. Surprisingly the only complete CMD for M 13 was that published by Sandage in 1970, and this was based largely on photographic magnitudes with only a small number of photometric measures. Most other studies, such as that of Penny and Griffiths [1991] which produced V and R CCD measures of 400 stars, have tended to look mostly at the brighter stars of the cluster.

NGC 6256 = vdB-Ha 208 = C1656-370: This is a globular cluster and should be removed from the *Lund Catalogue*. See Djorgovski and Meylan [1993] and *Astronomical Almanac* [USNO and RGO 1999] lists of globular clusters. (Note that the *Lund Catalogue* alias list does note "Globular?" It includes this under two different entries for C1656-370 which should have been combined.)

It is also important to note that this object is not equivalent to Terzan 12 or any other Terzan object. See Terzan 11 (page 251) for further information.

NGC 6352, NGC 6355, and NGC 6426: (NGC 6352 = C1721-484, NGC 6355 = C1720-263, and NGC 6426 = C1742+031) Although these are not included in the main data or print file of the *Lund Catalogue*, the alias list incorrectly lists these objects as "globular?" They actually *are* globular clusters according to the list of Djorgovski and Meylan [1993].

NGC 6441 = C1746–370 and JaFu 2: Before 1989, only one planetary nebula was known to exist within a globular cluster. That was Pease 1 in M 15 = NGC 7078 (see page 247). However, Gillett, *et al.*, [1989] reported the discovery of a planetary nebula in M 22 = NGC 6656 (see page 243) thus doubling the number of such objects known. In 1997, the number was doubled once again to four such objects with the discovery by Jacoby, *et al.*, [1997] of planetary nebulae likely associated with *both* Palomar 6 and NGC 6441.

JaFu 1 is discussed under Palomar 6 on page 248. JaFu 2 in NGC 6441 is located at (2000.0) $17^h\ 50^m\ 10.8^s$ $-37°\ 03'\ 25.6''$, 37″ SW of the center of NGC 6441. The JaFu name originates from the names of two of the authors, Jacoby and Fuller. A finder chart is available in Figure 1 of the Jacoby, *et al.*, paper. The planetary nebula's diameter is 4.9″, and the estimated distance is 9.1 kpc. The close proximity to NGC 6441 makes a strong argument that it is associated with the globular cluster itself. Jacoby, *et al.*, show that the likelihood of such an association by chance is only 0.001. In addition, the reddening and metalicity of the planetary is essentially identical to that of the cluster as opposed to that of the general Galactic bulge background (and foreground) stars. However, they caution that only a proper motion study can unequivocally establish that the two are associated.

The only known visual observation of the JaFu planetary nebulae was by one of us [BA] and Larry Mitchell on May 20, 2001 at the Texas Star Party. At 7:38 UT, using Mitchell's 91-cm reflector and a 10 mm eyepiece (411x), the JaFu 2 planetary was visible as an "elongated spot." It was at the tip of an elongated isosceles triangle of "stars," as shown on the Jacoby, *et al.*, finder chart. Although seeing was poor due to low elevation (about 15°), the planetary was definitely seen. It could be held in view with averted vision about 80–90% of the time. A UHC nebula filter did not improve the view since it made the apparent nebula too faint to be seen. Certainly this observation was made with a very large (by amateur standards) telescope from a good observing site (near Fort Davis, Texas, with very good transparency). However, it demonstrated that such observations are possible with such an amateur instrument whose size is no longer uncommon. It will be interesting to see how much smaller aperture telescopes will show the JaFu nebulae. As of this writing (early 2003) no other visual observations of the JaFu nebulae are known to have been reported.

NGC 6522 = C1800-300: The position here (2000.0, $18^h\ 03^m\ 35.0^s$ $-30°\ 02'\ 02''$) is measured from the DSS. The positions from Djorgovski and Meylan [1993] and Harris [1996] appear to be off by several arcseconds.

Fig. 7.11 *NGC 6540 = Djorgovski 3. Although discovered by William Herschel in 1784, this object was not suspected to be a galactic globular cluster until independently discovered by G. Djorgovski in 1987. B. Skiff identified these as the same object in 1994, and Bica, et al., [1994] made yet another independent discovery of it and confirmed that it was a globular cluster. 17′ field of view DSS-S image © ROE.*

NGC 6540 = Djorgovski 3 = C1803-278: NGC 6540 is a small nebulous object in Sagittarius embedded in a rich field only 4°.7 from the direction of the Galactic center, see Figure 7.11. It was discovered by William Herschel [1786] in 1784 and listed as H II 198 (the designation indicating that it was the 198th object in his second category of deep-sky objects, "Faint nebulae"). He was fairly vague in his description, but noted that it was pretty faint, small, and irregularly elongated. He said that it was "easily resolvable," but the fact that he included it as a "faint nebula" rather than as category VI, VII or VIII, which are different classifications of star cluster, suggests that he was unable to resolve it into stars. The comment probably indicated that it was easily separated out from the background. John Herschel [1864] suggested that it might be a cluster and listed it in his *General Catalogue of Nebulae* as object number 4371. Included as 6540 in the *New General Catalogue* [Dreyer 1888], the description was brought forward directly from the GC.

From that point on little observational work seems to have been done on this object. It was listed by Collinder [1931] as Cr 364, who limited his description to a note that the center is "undissolved" and that it is elliptical, about 0.8′ x 0.5′ in P.A. 95°. He expressed some surprise that William Herschel observed it visually, as it "lies at the limit of our present instrumental resources."

Modern references are fairly hard to come by. It is listed in the standard open cluster reference, the 1987 *Lund Catalogue of Open Cluster Data* [Lyngå 1987], where it is cataloged as C1803-278, OCl 11 and Lund 808; it is listed as being of Trumpler type I 1 p n:b, with a membership of 10 stars, angular diameter 1.5′ and total V magnitude 14.6. In the *Atlas Coeli Catalogue* [Becvar,1964], one-time mainstay of amateur astronomers' reference sources, it is also listed as a mag. 14.5 open cluster of 20 stars, Shapley class g (very rich and concentrated). There is no "New Description" listed for it in the *RNGC* [Sulentic and Tifft 1973], and *NGC 2000.0* [Sinnott 1988] lists it as an open cluster with the old NGC description and a magnitude of m(p) 15.0. It is not mentioned in *Exploring the Southern Sky* [Laustsen 1987] or *Astronomical Objects for Southern Telescopes* [Hartung 1984]. In *Webb Society Deep-Sky Observer's Handbook* Volume 7, *The Southern Sky* [Hynes 1987], it is briefly described by Victor Hirsch using a 15.2-cm reflector as a "very faint cluster, visible as just a diffuse spot." Perhaps the best, modern visual description is to be found in the *Observing Handbook and Catalogue of Deep-Sky Objects* by Luginbuhl and Skiff [1990]. Luginbuhl says: "In 25 cm this cluster is just visible as a tiny, faint patch involved with a partially resolved 1′ string of stars that bends S at its W end. With 30 cm the cluster seems quite elongated at low power due to this string. At 225x the string is resolved into seven or eight faint stars in an arc concave to the N, running through the center of the cluster and out the E and W ends. The cluster is a 30″ spot centered on the arc and is without resolution."

Classification problems often arise when faint objects are not observed adequately, and the case of NGC 6540 is no exception. The object appears to have been classified as an open cluster on the basis of comparatively little evidence; on the face of it, John Herschel's suggestion that it might be an object of this type was more-or-less passed down from one catalog to another without being questioned. Although, with the benefit of hindsight, the continual references to it being a small, rich object involved in nebulosity might have given some cause to question the classification.

The first indication of a problem came with its inclusion in a list of probable globular clusters by Djorgovski [1987] as Djorgovski 3. However, a cross-check of identifications does not appear to have been carried out at this time. This object was also included in a subsequent catalog by Djorgovski and Meylan [1993], and some association was made with NGC 6540; it is stated: "Djorg 3 is a very compact cluster seen in the field of NGC 6540, a much brighter and more extended foreground open cluster." Certainly, the object does lie within a group of brighter stars, but there is nothing in the historical evidence to suggest that this motley collection of stars was ever thought to be the object listed in the NGC as object 6540!

As Brian Skiff first noted [private communication, 1994] NGC 6540 and Djorgovski 3 are the same object. He confirmed this with Djorgovski and Harold Corwin. (Confirmation has also been made with Djorgovski directly [private communication, 1995]).

Therefore, this entry should be removed from the main *Lund Catalogue* since it is a globular cluster and indicated as such in the alias list. The *DSFG1e* (chart 339, 377) entry should be listed as a globular cluster rather than an open cluster, and the Trumpler type and number of stars removed from the entry.

Confirmation that NGC 6540 is actually a globular cluster was finally supplied by Bica, *et al.*, [1994] who suspected that the very compact star cluster that they had seen on Sky Survey Schmidt plates might actually be a globular cluster. Cross-checking identifications showed that the object was not only the open cluster NGC 6540 but also the globular cluster Djorgovski 3! To confirm the nature of the object, Bica, *et al.*, obtained deep CCD images with the ESO 3.55-m NTT and Danish 1.54-m telescopes, as well as CCD integrated spectra in the range 370–1000 nm using the 1.52-m telescope. They estimate a horizontal branch V magnitude of 15.9, a reddening of E(B – V) = 0.6 magnitudes and a distance of 3.5 kpc ± 0.4 pc. Structurally, they show the cluster has a compact nucleus of about 20″ diameter. The cluster is elongated in a north-south direction in its outer parts, while the inner parts are progressively twisted towards the east and west. The authors conclude that the cluster has characteristics in common with post core collapse clusters.

NGC 6544 and NGC 6558: Although these are not included in the main data or print file of the *Lund Catalogue*, the alias list incorrectly lists them as "globular?" They actually *are* globular clusters according to the list of Djorgovski and Meylan [1993].

NGC 6637 = NGC 6634 = M 69 = C1828-323: NGC 6637 is a small globular cluster discovered by Lacaille in 1752 as his object class I, number 11. See Figure 7.12. Messier reobserved it and noted in his original description that this was a Lacaille discovery. Yet for some unknown reason, John Herschel listed it under two different entries in the GC. The Messier observation is given under GC 4411, while the Lacaille discovery is under GC 5076. The latter is in a supplement on the last page (p. 137) of the GC; perhaps this was a hurried addition. The error propagated into the NGC where the Lacaille discovery is listed as NGC 6634 and the Messier observation as NGC 6637. This error was noted as early as 1960 by O. Gingerich [1960] with the notation "[Lacaille I] 11, listed in the NGC erroneously as 6634." Actually from a historical perspective, the NGC 6634 name should have priority over NGC 6637, but realistically if an NGC designation is used for M 69, it will probably be the latter one.

Fig. 7.12 *NGC 6637 = M 69, a low-metalicity globular cluster in Sagittarius near NGC 6681 = M 70, and NGC 6652. 17′ field of view DSS-S image © ROE.*

The cluster itself lies some 2°.5 N.E. of ε Sgr and within 3° lie the other globular clusters NGC 6681 (M 70) and NGC 6652. It was identified as having a slightly unusual late spectral type of G5 by Kinman [1959] and Kron and Mayall [1960]. A CMD for the cluster was obtained by Hartwick and Sandage [1968]; looking at 467 stars, they found that the stubbiness of the horizontal branch and the magnitude rise of the giant sequence was similar to 47 Tuc, which also has a fairly late spectral type of G3. A true distance modulus was determined of $(m - M)_0$ = 15.2±0.5, corresponding to a distance of 11 kpc—Kinman had earlier derived 7.5 kpc—and height from the Galactic plane of 2.1 kpc. On this basis the diameter of the cluster would be 22 pc and its absolute magnitude M_V = –8.1. However, Hartwick and Sandage made it clear that the magnitude calibrations were tentative, being based, in the absence of a photoelectric sequence, on photographic transfer plates from NGC 6356 (for which photoelectric photometry did exist). Photoelectric BV photometry for NGC 6637 was later obtained by Harris [1977] and used to recalibrate the Hartwick and Sandage CMD. The need for substantial systematic corrections was found, and the giant branch of the cluster was seen to be bluer and markedly steeper than thought before. As a result of this revision, a true distance modulus $(m - M)_0$ = 15.0 was derived, placing NGC 6637 at a distance from the Sun of 10 kpc and 2 kpc below the Galactic plane.

In a more recent work, Richtler, *et al.*, [1994] and Richtler [1995] reported CCD photometry of the cluster which showed that NGC 6637 is quite an old globular cluster. The metallicity indicated by the CMD morphology was lower than that indicated by integral aperture photometry, casting doubt on its classification as a disk object. Also, the position in the Galactic bulge indicated that its orbit may have been strongly tilted against the Galactic plane. Similar metallicity and (B–V) values have been obtained by Ferraro, *et al.*, [1994] adding weight to these conclusions.

NGC 6642: Although this is not included in the main data or print file of the *Lund Catalogue*, the alias list incorrectly lists this as "globular?" It actually is a globular cluster according to the list of Djorgovski and Meylan [1993].

NGC 6656 = M 22 = C1833-239, and IRAS 1833-2357 = GJJC 1: This very bright globular cluster is visible to the unaided eye from a good location and was the first of its type to be discovered, see Figure 7.13 on page 243. It is usually credited to Abraham Ihle who apparently found it in 1665 while observing Saturn. Charles Messier saw it on 1764 June 5, describing it merely as: "this nebula is round, contains no stars ..." In fact, it does not appear to have been resolved into stars until observed by William Herschel some years later. In more modern times, Bailey found 16 variable stars, mostly of the RR Lyrae type; and a star count by Duncan in 1918 from a plate obtained with the 1.5-m. Mount Wilson reflector showed at least 75,000 star images. Possibly the first modern study of real significance was that of Arp and Melbourne [1959] who obtained photovisual and photographic magnitudes of over 400 stars in the cluster. They produced a CMD of the system from the observations and noted that in many ways M 22 was similar to M 13. A distance of 3.3 kpc was derived. Recent photometric studies have been carried out by Alcaino [1977], Alcaino and Liller [1983], and Cudworth [1986]. These reach fainter magnitudes. From this point of view, the object is not as easy to study as its brightness might suggest, because it lies in a rich part of the Milky Way. Results tend to be contaminated by field stars, and, being close to the galactic plane, it is substantially reddened. Nevertheless, the CMD results obtained suggest that M 22 is not untypical of most globular clusters. An unusual "gap" found in the red giant branch by Alcaino was closed by the more detailed work of Cudworth, but there does appear to be a gap in the sub-giant branch at V = 15.0. An interesting finding from Cudworth's paper concerns the space velocity of the cluster. It has been known for some time that M 22 has a fairly substantial outward velocity; however, it has a surprisingly small velocity component in the direction of Galactic rotation. The indications are that its orbit takes it on a course which plunges through the Galactic plane, most recently about 3.6-million years ago.

Fig. 7.13 *NGC 6656 = M 22, the brightest globular cluster visible from mid-northern latitudes, easily seen in Sagittarius with the unaided eye on a dark night. 45′ field of view DSS-S image © ROE.*

The comparatively blue horizontal branch of the cluster, together with its steep red-giant branch, implies that M 22 is a low metal-abundance object similar to M 13; however, the picture is confused by substantial star-to-star differences (see the work of Cohen [1981], Peterson [1980] and Pilachowski, *et al.*, [1982]). A new photographic CMD for M 22 has been obtained by Samus, *et al.*, [1995b] based on BV photometry of 3373 stars. It reaches the main sequence turn-off point at V ~ 17.7, but the sample includes numerous field stars. A systematic difference in color compared to the photometry obtained by Cudworth was revealed, which the authors suggest is due to insufficient account of color equation in the previous study. It was found that the structure of the CMD is typical of globular clusters of intermediate metallicity and similar to that found by Cudworth and Alcaino and Liller (except that the V = 15.0 "gap," does not stand out so obviously). A comprehensive list of variables and suspected variables in and around M 22 has recently been published by Kravtsov, *et al.*, [1994].

One of the most interesting discoveries about M 22 in recent years relates to the association by Gillett, *et al.*, [1989] of the unusual source IRAS 18333-2357 with a planetary nebula within the cluster. This planetary is now also known as GJJC-1 (= PK 010–08°1). It was found to be an extended emission-line nebulosity about 10″ x 7″ in size. The ionized gas is extremely oxygen and neon rich (relative to the hydrogen) compared with typical planetary nebula. Gillett, *et al.*, also report that (using the NASA

ITRF 3-meter telescope on Mauna Kea) "Visual inspection of this field under good seeing conditions clearly shows that the bulk of the optical emission emanates from two stars ... separated by about 1″ in north-south direction. ... spectroscopic observations of this region revealed a third source, an extended emission line region closely aligned with the stellar pair." Their spectroscopic and photometric investigations seem to indicate that the extended region is the planetary nebula itself. The blue southern star (V ~ 14.3) is probably the source of ionizing photons for the nebulosity (i.e., the central star), and probably a member of M 22. The northern star (V ~ 14.7) appears to be an unrelated background field star.

The planetary was further studied by Cudworth [1990], who made proper motion studies confirming it as a cluster member. Checking historical photographic plates suggested that the object may have brightened by about 0.2 mag since 1900, but no evidence for variation was found on shorter timescales.

Robert Bunge and one of us [BA] made what may be the first visual detection of this planetary nebula on August 3, 1997. Observing with the Rupp Observatory (Mansfield, Ohio) 79-cm *f*/7 reflector, the pair of stars described by Gillett, *et al.*, was visible as a slightly out-of-round object at 343x and 780x. It was found by locating the variable star "V8," as indicated on Plate I of Evans [1975], and then using the Gillett, *et al.*, figure 1a chart, which shows the V8 star and the (stellar appearing) pair of stars. A UHC nebula filter resulted in this pair becoming invisible. However, with no filter, moving one's eye on and off the merged pair showed an obvious "blinking" effect which did not occur for nearby stars of the same brightness. This essentially confirmed that the central part of the planetary nebula—or at least its unusual ionizing star—was indeed observed. It is odd that Gillett, *et al.*, do not report a similar blinking effect visually, but perhaps the brightness of the two stars overpowered this effect in the 3 meter telescope.

It is interesting to note that not long after our observation, this planetary was described as an "Ultimate Observing Challenge" by Jakiel [1997; 1998], who notes "If any object is impossible to see, this small planetary nebula comes close." He reports that many observers, using apertures up to 25-inches, have unsuccessfully tried to see this object. In our experience this was not a particularly difficult object to observe, taking only about 10 minutes to find and verify. It appears that one simply requires a fairly large telescope (by amateur standards), high magnification, reasonable seeing conditions, and good finder charts. However, perhaps Jakiel is correct if he is referring to the overall (10″ x 7″) planetary as being a challenge to observe, since that is quite a bit larger than the nearly stellar area of nebulosity seen by us.

Fig. 7.14 *NGC 6715 = M 54, the likely nucleus of the Sagittarius Dwarf galaxy and a captured Galactic globular cluster. The 25 magnitudes per square arcsecond diameter of M 54 is 12′, fully half the size of this 24′ square image. However, at the 22 magnitudes per square arcsecond level it is only 4.1′ in size, similar in its appearance on the image here. DSS-S image © ROE.*

NGC 6712 = C1850-087: Although this is not included in the main data or print file of the *Lund Catalogue*, the alias list incorrectly lists this object as "globular?" It actually is a globular cluster, according to the lists of Djorgovski and Meylan [1993] and Astronomical Almanac [USNO and RGO 1999].

NGC 6715 = M 54 = C1851-305: M 54 is a bright globular cluster which can be found about 1°.5 southwest of ζ Sagittarii, see Figure 7.14. It was discovered by Messier on 1778 July 24 and described as being a very faint nebula with a brilliant center but containing no stars. It is a bright, dense cluster but difficult to resolve in small instruments, which suggests that it is a massive object lying at some distance.

A review of globular cluster data by Harris and Racine [1979] gives an apparent distance modulus $(m - M)_V$ = 17.11, distance R = 13.0 kpc and an absolute magnitude M_V = –9.41; the same study giving 47 Tuc a comparable absolute magnitude M_V = –9.43. Clearly, there are brighter, more massive systems, but M 54 is at the top end of the range. Additional evidence that this globular cluster is a significant object in the Galactic globular cluster system was provided by Illingworth [1975] who obtained a mass of $1.03 \pm 0.23\ M_\odot \times 10^6$.

In a more recent compilation of globular cluster data, Peterson [1993] gives an increased distance to M 54 of 21.2

kpc. Then, R. Ibata, G. Gilmore, and M. Irwin [1994] announced their amazing discovery of the Sagittarius Dwarf Spheroidal galaxy, the closest galaxy to our own. The center of the new Sagittarius dwarf galaxy lies at approximately R.A. $18^h 52^m$, Dec. –30° 30′ (2000), almost identical with the position of M 54. They speculated that four globular clusters in its vicinity, M 54, Arp 2, Terzan 7 and Terzan 8, may be associated with that dwarf galaxy. They pointed out that M 54 lies at the center of the densest clump of stars in the Sagittarius dwarf galaxy. Sarajedini and Layden [1995] and Bassino and Muzzio [1995] further suggested that there is a very good possibility M 54 is actually the nucleus of the Sagittarius dwarf! It has actually been suggested previously [Zinnecker, *et al.*, 1988; Freeman 1990] that if nucleated dwarf galaxies are cannibalized by giant ones, their nuclei might survive as globular clusters. Supporting evidence includes the fact that the stars of M 54 and the dwarf galaxy are at the same distance to within measurement error. The revised distance indicates that the luminosity of M 54 is comparable with that of ω Centauri (NGC 5139), the previously intrinsically brightest known Galactic globular cluster.

Therefore, one could argue that M 54 is not a globular cluster at all but a galaxy nucleus and should be removed from catalogs of Galactic globular clusters (such as the one here). However, the Sagittarius dwarf is currently undergoing capture by the Milky Way galaxy. Therefore, one could also argue that even if M 54 was at one point not a part of our Galaxy, it is now and can be considered a Galactic globular cluster. In this catalog it is still included as such, while acknowledging its dual nature.

NGC 6717 = Palomar 9 = C1852-227 and IC 4802: See Figure 7.15. Although this is not included in the main data or print file of the *Lund Catalogue*, the alias list incorrectly lists this object as "globular?" It actually is a globular cluster according to the lists of Djorgovski and Meylan [1993] and *Astronomical Almanac* [USNO and RGO 1999].

After a suggestion by Brian Skiff that this object may be equal to IC 4802, Harold Corwin [private communication, 1995] showed that IC 4802 is a clump of stars just northeast of the nucleus of NGC 6717. Corwin writes:

> Finally, IC 4802 = Big 434 which Brian has said is = NGC 6717, was found by Bigourdan and observed on two nights. His position for IC 4802 was referred to NGC 6717 (found by WH [William Herschel] and observed twice by JH [John Herschel], once from England, once from South Africa), so the two objects cannot be identical if we are to believe Bigourdan's observations. However, looking at POSS1, the IIIaJ and IIIaF southern survey films, and SkyView, IC 4802 turns out to be clump of stars northeast of the nucleus of NGC 6717. So, it bears the same relationship to NGC 6717 as NGC 3189 does to NGC 3190, or NGC 5906 to NGC 5907: it's a part of the larger object.

Fig. 7.15 *NGC 6717 = Palomar 9, in close proximity to 35 Sgr, and therefore, difficult to observe. The tiny "clump" of stars on its northeast (upper left) side is known as IC 4802. 17′ field of view contrast enhanced DSS-S image © ROE.*

> The proximity to 35 Sgr probably provided some field glare that contributed to the "nebulosity" that the Herschels and Bigourdan saw.

NGC 6749 = Berkeley 42 = C1902+018: There is a lengthy discussion of this object in [Archinal 1993, 81–83]. There it is noted that Alister Ling first determined (and it was confirmed) that NGC 6749 and Be 42 are the same object, see Figure 7.16 on page 246. It was reported by Brian Skiff that most older references place this object about 7′ south and 0.1^m west of the correct position. He pointed out that this object was almost certainly a globular cluster, although a reliable color-magnitude diagram was still needed (in 1993).

In any case, both Djorgovski and Meylan [1993] and the *Astronomical Almanac* [USNO and RGO 1999] list it as a globular cluster. In addition Rosino, *et al.*, [1997] recently published a definitive study on this object showing it to be a globular cluster. They consider it a metal-poor globular cluster passing through the Galactic disk. They give a distance of 7.3 ± 0.9 kpc, a reddening of E(B – V) of 1.4 magnitudes, V magnitude for the brightest stars of 16.5 with color V–I of 3.0. The horizontal branch magnitude is V = 19.7.

Since the *Lund Catalogue* only contains Galactic open clusters, the entries for Be 42 should be removed. Also while the *Lund Catalogue* uses the name C1902+018—which is used here—the Almanac and Peterson [1993, 344] list this as C1902+017.

Fig. 7.16 *NGC 6749 = Berkeley 42, shown using a contrast enhanced stretch of a 17′ field of view DSS-S image. © ROE.*

Fig. 7.17 *NGC 6838 = M 71, a Galactic globular cluster in Sagitta, until the 1950's thought to possibly be only a particularly rich open cluster. 17′ field of view. Image courtesy the Palomar Observatory and Digitized Sky Survey created by the Space Telescope Science Institute, operated by AURA, Inc. for NASA. Reproduced with permission from AURA/STScI.*

NGC 6760 = C1909+009: Although this is not included in the main data or print file of the *Lund Catalogue*, the alias list incorrectly lists this as "globular?" It actually *is* a globular cluster according to the lists of Djorgovski and Meylan [1993] and the *Astronomical Almanac* [USNO and RGO 1999].

NGC 6838 = M 71 = C1951+186: M 71 is a curious object embedded in a rich starfield in Sagitta. Visually, it appears to have a more irregular shape than most other globulars, see Figure 7.17. It was discovered by Méchain on 1780 June 28 and independently found by Messier on October 4 of the same year, who described it as being faint and containing no stars. It was possibly also seen earlier by de Chéseaux, prior to 1747 [Glyn Jones, 1975].

Although this is clearly a globular cluster according to all modern catalogs of globular clusters (e.g. Djorgovski and Meylan [1993]), many references describe the question of whether it is open or globular as uncertain. For example, although this is not included in the main data or print file of the *Lund Catalogue*, the alias list incorrectly lists it as "globular?"

This cluster was identified by Morgan [1956; 1959] as being in a small group of high metallicity globulars, but further studies were hampered by the dense starfield in which the cluster lies. In particular, crowding made it extremely difficult to obtain photoelectric standards of sufficient faintness. As a result, the first significant study of M 71 was probably that of Arp and Hartwick [1971], who obtained UBV photoelectric observations of 48 stars in the field of the cluster. The data was used to generate a CMD with a short, red horizontal branch and gently sloping giant branch. Reddening for the cluster was derived of E(B – V) = 0.31 ± 0.02 and a distance modulus $(m - M)_0$ = 13.07±0.21, together with a comparatively young age of 7.6 Gyr. They noted a relatively strong extension of the main sequence beyond the turn-off point.

Deep CCD photometry of the central area of M 71 was obtained by Richer and Fahlman [1988] in a search for white dwarfs in the cluster. A faint blue stellar sequence was found but somewhat fainter than if the stars had similar properties to field DA white dwarfs. The colors and magnitudes are better matched by DB stars or systems slightly more massive than typical disk white dwarfs. (DA white dwarfs are characterized by spectra showing only Balmer lines of hydrogen; DB stars have spectra with helium lines only. The former exist across a temperature range of T_{eff} 6,000–90,000 K, while the latter lie in a more restricted temperature range of T_{eff} 12,000–30,000 K). An unexpected result was the discovery of a very blue sequence of stars running roughly parallel to the main sequence. These are too luminous to be single white dwarfs and their characteristics are suggestive of them being either foreground white dwarfs or cluster cataclysmic variables (CVs). Most CVs are "dwarf novae" and are interacting binary systems comprising a cool main sequence star. This fills its Roche lobe and loses matter to an accretion disk surrounding a white dwarf companion, resulting in occasional explosive outbursts. Over 50 blue stragglers were identified, about 1% of all stars measured, and, excluding these, the binary frequency in the cluster center is low. The data indicated a reddening, E(B − V) = 0.28 and, from a fit of local subdwarfs to the main sequence [Fahlman, *et al.*, 1985] of M 71, an apparent distance modulus of $(m - M)_V = 13.70$ was derived. Taken together with a horizontal branch apparent magnitude of V = 14.42, as determined by Cudworth [1985], this places the horizontal branch at $M_V = 0.72$, much like 47 Tuc which is of similar metallicity. The paper by Cudworth is also useful as it gives photographic photometry and membership probabilities for stars in M 71 that are brighter than V = 16.85.

Hodder, *et al.*,[1992] have constructed a CMD of M 71 using deep CCD photometry. Comparing this with theoretical isochrones gives an age of 14–16 Gyr. In this study, 989 stars in a selected field of the cluster were also examined for variability, but changes in light amplitude were detected in just four.

NGC 7078 = M 15 = C2127+119: This showpiece globular cluster of the northern sky lies in the constellation of Pegasus and was discovered by Jean-Dominique Maraldi on 1746 September 7 while following De Chesaux's comet. He described it merely as "a fairly bright nebulous star which is composed of many stars." See Figure 7.18. Messier did not observe the object until 1764 June 3 and was unable to resolve it. He did remark on the brilliant center which is the hallmark of this object when observed with small to medium-sized amateur instruments. The brilliance of the core of M 15 is not illusory; the central excess brightness was measured by Newell and O'Neill [1978].

The first reasonably deep photoelectric photometry was a UBV sequence obtained by Sandage [1970] as part of a study of its color magnitude diagram. Important photographic photometry was obtained by Sandage and Katem [1977]. More recent deep CCD photometry was carried out by Fahlman, *et al.*, [1985] and comparisons made with the earlier work. It was found that there was a systematic error in the results of Sandage and Sandage and Katem in the sense that fainter stars (V > 19.7) were measured to be too bright in V. As a result, the main sequence of the cluster had been misplaced on the CMD.

Fahlman, *et al.*, studied the luminosity function of the cluster down to V = 22.8 and, by fitting observations of nearby subdwarfs to the cluster main sequence, obtained a distance modulus of $(m - M)_V = 15.53 \pm 0.21$, greater than previously found, and from stellar evolution theory, derived an age of 16±3 Gyr.

The core of M 15 has been the subject of many papers in recent years, as it is a classic candidate for a globular cluster with a collapsed core. Taking the surface brightness and star distribution measurements of Newell, *et al.*, [1976], Illingworth and King [1977] found that the only way to reconcile the observed luminosity and velocity dispersion of the cluster was to put a lot of the mass—indeed, almost 50% of it—into white dwarfs. They found that there ought to be neutron stars as well and, because of their high mass, these should congregate at the center and provide sufficient additional mass to explain the profile.

Fig. 7.18 *NGC 7078 = M 15, one of the most heavily studied star clusters, as well as a showpiece of the northern sky. M 15 is the prototypical collapsed core globular cluster. The planetary nebula Küstner 648 = Pease 1 appears as a small oval in the upper left. This is the first planetary nebula ever detected in a globular cluster. It was cataloged as a star by Küstner in 1921. Via spectra taken with the Mt. Wilson 100-inch telescope, it was determined to be a planetary nebula by F. G. Pease in 1928. It has been shown to be visible with modest amateur telescopes, as long as a good finder chart or image (such as this) is available and a nebula filter is used to "blink" the field of view. It was the first discovered of the four known planetary nebulae in globular clusters. WFPC2 HST image, with unknown field of view, but probably less than 2.5′. The Hubble Heritage Team (STScI/AURA) and NASA.*

U-band images of the core of M 15 obtained with the *HST* Planetary Camera were used by Lauer, et al [1991] to resolve stars down to the main sequence turn-off (m_U = 19.4) in the cluster center. Yanny, *et al.*, [1993] have used the same instrument to obtain comparative V and I data, and Ferraro and Paresce [1993] have used the *HST* Faint Object Camera to show the existence of at least 9 candidate blue straggler stars in the central 22″ x 22″.

M 15 is of interest being the first globular cluster in which a planetary nebula was discovered. This is PK 65–

27.1 (Pease 1) and was found by Pease [1928]. It is about 1.0″ in diameter and of magnitude m_v = 14.95 and lies at $21^h 29^m 59.4^s$ +12° 10′ 26″ (2000.0) [Adams, *et al.*, 1980]. Observational information and a photographic finder chart is given in an article by Skiff [1992].

NGC 7492 = C2305-159: Although this is not included in the main data or print file of the *Lund Catalogue*, the alias list incorrectly lists this as "globular?" It actually is a globular cluster, according to the list of Djorgovski and Meylan [1993].

ω Centauri = NGC 5139: see page 237.

Palomar 1 = C0325+794: See Figure 5.2 on page 212. Rosenberg, *et al.*, [1998a, 1998b] present the first high quality color-magnitude and spectral data on this cluster. They indicate that this is the youngest known Galactic globular cluster but leave open the possibility that it is one of the oldest known open clusters, with an estimated age of 6.3–8 Gyr years. In this catalog it is listed as a globular cluster, but the evidence is clearly weak. *No* RR Lyrae stars or horizontal branch stars were found. The cluster is estimated to have a total mass of about 1300 (± 600) solar masses, and less than 500 stars were actually measured down to two magnitudes below the main-sequence turnoff point. Therefore, this object is missing most of the characteristics of a globular cluster—except that it is quite old for an open cluster, and is about 3.5 kpc above the Galactic plane—far more than any previously known open cluster.

As to its overall appearance, this globular cluster is faint enough that it is not obvious on either the DSS or DSS-II but can be seen by using a histogram equalization display of image from these surveys. Since a diameter for this cluster appears to be unavailable, it was measured at 2.5′ from the DSS, and that value appears in the catalog here.

It is interesting to note that this globular cluster has at least once been listed incorrectly as a galaxy with designation VII Zw 7 [Lederman and Gottlieb 1996].

Palomar 2 = C0443+313: This object is the subject of a recent study by Harris, *et al.*, [1997]. The results of that study include the first reliable and deep color-magnitude diagram (down to a V magnitude of approximately 24), which shows conclusively that this object is a Galactic globular cluster. The brightest V magnitude of the cluster stars is approximately 18.8, although they will appear fainter visually since the cluster is very reddened. The horizontal branch is at approximately V = 21.7. A distance modulus of 17.1±0.3 places the cluster at 26±4 kpc from the Sun or about 34 kpc from the Galactic center. Based on its structural parameters and radial velocity, Harris, *et al.*, speculate that this cluster is now moving toward its closest approach to the Galactic center while on a highly elliptical orbit.

Palomar 5 = C1513+000: On both the DSS and the DSS-II, this appears as a very faint cluster, visible only with a histogram equalization display of the DSS images. It has an 8.0′ diameter and lies between two moderately bright stars. The position given by Djorgovski and Meylan [1993] and Harris [1996] is about 0.5′ too far north, and a corrected position measured from the DSS is given here. The diameter of 3.2′ given by Skiff (out to the 25 magnitude per square arcsecond isophote) appears to be too small by at least a factor of two, so the 8.0′ estimate is given as the diameter in this catalog.

Lederman and Gottlieb [1996] have pointed out that this cluster has been listed several times as a galaxy (UGC 9792, MCG +00-39-016, CGCG 21-61, and the Serpens Dwarf Galaxy).

Palomar 6 = C1740–262 and JaFu 1: JaFu 1 is a planetary nebula that is likely associated with the Galactic globular cluster Palomar 6, similar to the case of JaFu 2 and NGC 6441 (described above). The JaFu 1 and 2 discoveries were reported by Jacoby, *et al.*, 1997. JaFu 1 is located at (2000.0) $17^h 43^m 57.4^s$ –26° 11′ 52″, 230″ to the WNW of the cluster center. A finder chart is available in Figure 1 of the Jacoby, *et al.*, paper. The planetary nebula's diameter is 8″ and distance 5.9 kpc.

The association of JaFu 1 with Palomar 6 is less certain than that of JaFu 2 with NGC 6441, if only because of the relatively large angular distance (the 230″ noted above) between the cluster and the planetary. However, Jacoby, *et al.*, point out that this is still well within the tidal radius (of 490″) of Palomar 6 and make several arguments for membership of the planetary nebula to the cluster. Some examples are: a) the radial velocities are similar, b) the reddening is similar—although there is significant disagreement between published values of this for Palomar 6, and c) the estimated mass for the nebula is similar to what would be expected at the derived distance. In summary they estimate that there is only a 0.5% chance that the two objects are unrelated. As with JaFu 2, it will be necessary to obtain proper motion data in order to establish a certain connection between the two.

As described under NGC 6441 on page 240, both of the JaFu planetary nebulae were observed by one of us [BA] and Larry Mitchell using Mitchell's 91 cm *f*/4.5 reflector. JaFu 1 was observed first at 7:07 UT on the night of May 20, 2001, at the Texas Star Party and was certainly the more difficult of the two nebulae to observe. Once Palomar 6 was found (which was not all that easy), the Jacoby, *et al.*, finder chart was used to quickly locate the area of the planetary nebula. It was bracketed by two "obvious" (15th magnitude?) stars shown close to the nebula on the (blown up) portion of the finder chart. Using various eyepieces in the 16 to 8 mm focal length range (i.e., at 257x to 514x) the nebula was visible between 20–30% of the time with diffi-

Fig. 7.19 *Palomar 15, the last of the "Palomar" globular clusters, but unlike the others discovered by F. Zwicky [1959]. The cluster is sparse enough and the stars faint enough that it is only faintly visible in the middle of this 17′ field of view SkyView/DSS-S image. © ROE.*

cult averted vision. The roughly estimated total visual magnitude was about 17.5 to 18. Stars on the finder chart as faint as the one just NW of the star bracketing the planetary on the W were visible (probably to magnitude 18 or so). However, seeing was quite variable; the view would have improved under better seeing conditions. An O-III filter made most stars in the area (except the two bracketing ones) invisible. A UHC filter did not substantially change the appearance of the nebula, although the stars became slightly fainter.

Even though this was a fairly definite observation of the planetary nebula, it was certainly a difficult observation and does not bode well for seeing it in smaller apertures. However, it might be observable with smaller telescopes given better seeing conditions than what we were experiencing. As described under NGC 6441 on page 240, these are still the only known visible observations of this nebula.

Palomar 9 = NGC 6717: see page 245.

Palomar 14 = C1608+150: Most references (Djorgovski and Meylan [1993]; Harris [1996]; SIMBAD) give a position that is slightly off (by under 1′), usually to the southeast or east of the correct position. An examination of the DSS shows that the center of the cluster is GSC 00957–00359. The GSC position (2000.0: $16^h\ 11^m\ 00.33^s$ +14° 57′ 49.5″) has been adopted here.

Palomar 15 = C1657-004: See Figure 7.19. Despite its name, Palomar 15 was not one of the globular clusters listed by Abell [1955] and to which the "Pal #" designation is normally given. It was first reported by Zwicky [1959] who claimed that it contained about 400 stars and was included as an "anonymous" cluster in the list of Palomar-type clusters produced by Kinman and Rosino [1961]. The Palomar designation for this object seems to have been first applied by Kukarkin [1974], in 1974.

The first significant study of Pal 15 was published by Harris and van den Bergh [1984] who noted that the previously quoted position was incorrect. From star counts and color magnitude diagrams, and assumptions about the reddening, Pal 15 was found to be an outer-halo object with $R_{gc} \sim 60$ kpc. It was found to have a completely blue horizontal branch unlike all the other outer-halo clusters except NGC 2419. The normal CMD morphology of a globular cluster has a completely red horizontal branch with giant branches that are of intermediate color and slope. In addition, Pal 15 was observed to have the largest core radius and lowest central concentration of any known globular cluster. These unusual characteristics have prompted other investigations, such as that of Seitzer and Carney [1990], who obtained CCD BV photometry of the cluster. They found that the application of improved corrections for reddening considerably reduced the galactocentric distance of Pal 15 to $R_{gc} \sim 30$ kpc, (although this is still a substantial distance, and the dereddened integrated absolute visual magnitude was $M_v = -5.1$). A consequence of the reduced distance estimate is a reduction in the size of the core radius, but this still remains fairly high in comparison with other systems.

Extended CCD photometry of 644 stars down to $V \sim 24$ by Harris [1991] was sufficient to reach the main sequence turnoff. Comparing the results with other moderately metal-poor globular clusters suggested that it has a basically normal CMD morphology for its type (blue horizontal branch and moderately steep giant and subgiant branches, and a possible age of 14 Gyr). The remarkably high reddening earlier found by Seitzer and Carney was confirmed and an analysis of the additional data produced a galactocentric distance of about $R_{gc} \sim 36$ kpc. An interesting result of this work was that Palomar 15 appears to contain a significant number of "blue stragglers;" at least six 22nd magnitude objects of this type were found in a rough sequence forming a luminous upward extension of the main sequence. None of the studies have resulted in the discovery of any RR Lyrae variables. It is speculated that Palomar 15 may be one of the last outlying survivors of an original population of sparse, low-luminosity globular clusters that formed in the inner halo.

Most references (Djorgovski and Meylan [1993]; Harris [1996]; SIMBAD) give a position for this that is too far east by several arcminutes. An examination of the DSS

Fig. 7.20 *PWM78 2 is visible as a concentrated group of stars in this histogram equalization stretch image. This object seems to have the appearance of a Galactic globular cluster, but no study has been made of the stars' colors in order to verify whether it is such a cluster or only a reddened distant open cluster. 17′ field of view SkyView/DSS-S image © ROE.*

shows that the center of the cluster is at (2000.0) $16^h\ 59^m\ 50.9^s$ –00° 32′ 28″, and that position has been adopted here.

PWM78 2 = C1755-050: This is the second object of 4 possible, very reddened star clusters listed by Pfleiderer, et al [1978]. (The "PWM 78" designation is used here for the first time.) One of us [BA] determined from a DSS image that it is possible that this is a previously unknown Galactic *globular* cluster. This object barely shows up on the DSS as a rise in the background. It is best shown in a histogram equalization display, such as Figure 7.20. It is located at (2000.0) $17^h\ 58^m\ 39^s.4$ –05° 04′ 21″ and has a diameter of about 2.0′. The appearance is not definitely that of globular cluster, but it does appear that follow up observations to obtain a color-magnitude diagram of the cluster would be worthwhile. At the very least, this is probably a significant (reddened and very distant) galactic cluster.

The DSS shows another unusual object nearby at $17^h\ 58^m\ 52^s.1$ –05° 09′ 48″ with a diameter of 40″. However, this is apparently a plate defect as there is nothing present here in the USNO A1.0 catalog.

SIMBAD and NED include nothing of real interest in the area, except IRAS 17557–0509, which has a position reasonably close to the cluster. However, Skiff suggested that this source is probably just a red star. The fairly bright star HD 163976, V = 7.41, is just to the east of the cluster. He reported an observation with the Lowell Observatory 107-cm (42-inch) reflector:

> A ten-minute unfiltered exposure with the 42-inch + 2k SITe chip shows only a weak gathering of stars for PWM78 2, but a fair amount of unresolved haziness. There's clearly a cluster here, but this image doesn't really say anything definitive to me. I think it's worth looking into some more...

There appear to be no references to this object in the literature besides a brief mention of it in the discovery paper and the assignment of a "C" name by Lyng [1983].

Pyxis: This distant globular cluster was first identified in 1995 by Weinberger as a possible globular cluster. Irwin, Demers, and Kunkel [1995] confirmed its identity. At a distance of some 40,000 parsecs, this cluster may be a detached cluster of one of the Magellanic clouds. The horizontal branch magnitude is (R) 18.7. The cluster appears to be about 4′ in diameter on UK Schmidt Telescope plates and has a core radius of 1.3′. Weinberger [1995] reproduces an image (his figure 1c) from a SERC J plate. An R-band CCD image of the cluster is reproduced on plate L3 in the Irwin, *et al.*, paper.

Ruprecht 106 = C1236-508: This is a globular cluster and should be removed from the *Lund Catalogue*. See e.g. Djorgovski and Meylan [1993] and *Astronomical Almanac* [USNO and RGO 1999] lists of globular clusters. Note that the *Lund Catalogue* alias list does note "Globular?" Also while the *Lund Catalogue* uses the name C1236-508—which is used here—the Almanac lists this as C1235-509.

Terzan 2 = vdB-Ha 228 = C1724-307: This is a globular cluster and so (as vdB-Ha 228) should be removed from the *Lund Catalogue*. See Djorgovski and Meylan [1993], and *Astronomical Almanac* [USNO and RGO 1999] lists of globular clusters. See Figure 7.24 on page 253.

Terzan 5 = C1745-247: See Figure 7.27 on page 253. This cluster was briefly also known as "Terzan 11," but should no longer be referred to by that name since it was reassigned by Terzan to another cluster. See Terzan 11 below.

In addition, the position given in some references [e.g. Djorgovski and Meylan 1993; Harris 1996] is too far south by a few arcminutes. An improved position, measured from the DSS, is given here.

Terzan 6 = vdB-Ha 249 = C1747-312: This is a globular cluster and (as vdB-Ha 249) should be removed from the *Lund Catalogue*. See Djorgovski and Meylan [1993], and *Astronomical Almanac* [USNO and RGO 1999] lists of globular clusters. See Figure 7.28 on page 253.

Terzan 10: See Figure 7.32 on page 253. Liu, *et al.*, [1994] have demonstrated via infrared photometry that this is a globular cluster. Ortolani, *et al.*, [1997] provide further confirmation of this via a color-magnitude diagram from V and I CCD photometry. They measure a horizontal branch V magnitude of approximately 21.9 and estimate a distance of 4.8 ±1.0 kpc. This cluster is not visible on the DSS.

Terzan 11 = C1809-227: This object was originally known as Terzan 12, see Figure 7.33 on page 253. The literature has become extremely confused over its proper identity. Terzan objects numbers 9 to 12 were reported in Terzan [1971a]. Unfortunately it was soon discovered that the original Terzan 11 was a rediscovery of Terzan 5. Even more unfortunately, rather than drop the usage of the 11 name, Terzan himself suggested that the original Terzan 12 be renamed to Terzan 11. This was done in a very short and cryptic note in Terzan [1971b]. The situation was described in detail by Ivan King [1972]. King noted Terzan 5 and a nearby star comprise the infrared source IRC-20385.

Further complicating this situation is the incorrect listing by many authors [Madore 1980; Hesser and Shawl 1985; Hirshfeld and Sinnott 1985; Peterson 1993; Pryor and Meylan 1993] of Terzan 12 as the same object as NGC 6256. There is no connection whatsoever between NGC 6256 (= vdB-Ha 208) and any of the Terzan objects. This incorrect identity can be traced back to Kukarkin [1974] where it apparently was used for the first time.

It is clear that a number of publications since the early 1970s have mixed up the Terzan 5, 11, and 12, and NGC 6256 names. It is likely that this will continue to happen. Much confusion in actually determining which data belongs to which object would be alleviated if authors would simply follow IAU recommendations and include *both* the name(s) *and* coordinates of any object to which they refer.

UKS 1 = C1751-241: This object was first reported on by M. Malkan, et al [1980]. They note: UKS 1751-241 is completely invisible on the Palomar O (blue) and E (red) Survey prints. It was discovered by Longmore and Hawarden [private communication] on IV-N infrared plates taken with the 48 inch (1.2 m) UK Schmidt telescope; on these plates it appears as a small round, hazy patch, no brighter than I (0.83 micrometers) ~16 mag. One of us [BA] confirmed that this object is not visible on the DSS or IRAS surveys. Several authors have since only listed this object with no new data or even suggested that it may not exist.

However, the existence of this object and its type as a Galactic globular cluster was confirmed by Minniti, *et al.*, [1995]. They present a K band image [ibid, 1689], which shows a cluster approximately 2′ in diameter. The brightest stars appear to be about K magnitude 9.5 [ibid, 1692]. CCD images of the cluster (shown here as Figure 7.34 on page 253) have been obtained by M. Morton, T. Knauss, and B. Wilson using the 46-cm (18-inch), *f*/5 reflector of the George Observatory [B. Wilson, private communication, October, 1996; Wilson, 1998, 8–10]. It has been observed visually by David Tosteson using a 63.5-cm (25-inch), *f*/5 telescope from the 1998 Texas Star Party held at the Prude Ranch near Ft. Davis, Texas [O'Meara 1998b, 88–89]. Ortolani, *et al.*, [1997] provide further confirmation that this is a globular cluster via a color-magnitude diagram from I and Gunn z (instrumental magnitude) CCD photometry. They measure an I magnitude for the brightest giant stars of 10.0. Given various assumptions regarding the reddening and metallicity of this cluster, they estimate a distance of 7.4 ±1.2 kpc.

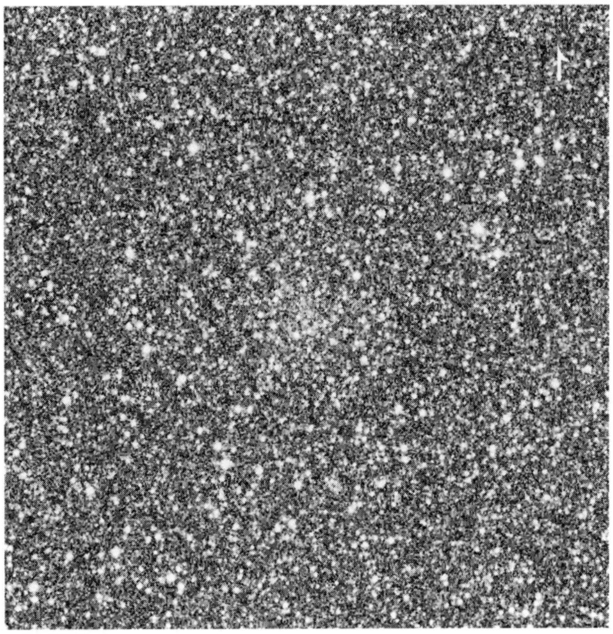

Fig. 7.21 *VdB-Ha 176, a faint grouping of stars shown only recently (in 1995) to likely be a Galactic globular cluster. It is shown here in a histogram equalization stretch of this 17′ field of view DSS-S image. © ROE.*

vdB-Ha 176 = C1535-499: Ortolani, *et al.*, [1995] have recently shown this to very likely be a galactic globular cluster, or at least, a borderline object between a globular cluster and a disk cluster. See Figure 7.21. It has a definite red horizontal branch and an extended red giant branch. They estimate a true distance modulus of 15.63 magnitudes, and a distance from the Sun of 13.4 kpc. It is located slightly above the galactic plane at a distance from the galactic center similar to that of the Sun, but on the other side of the Galaxy.

The position and total V magnitude given here are from Harris's [1996] list, the size is from the *Lund Catalogue*, while the brightest V magnitude, magnitude of the horizontal branch, and distance are from the Ortolani, *et al.*, study.

As with several other objects, since this has now been shown to be a Galactic globular cluster, it should be removed from the *Lund Catalogue*.

vdB-Ha 208: This is NGC 6256, see page 240.

vdB-Ha 228: This is Terzan 2, see page 250.

vdB-Ha 249: This is Terzan 6, see page 250.

7.3 A Gallery of Faint Galactic Globular Clusters

Below are a number of CCD images of faint Galactic globular clusters taken by Tracy Knauss and the late Mike Morton. They are included here in order to assist amateur and professional astronomers alike in locating and identifying these clusters, as few published images of any of these objects exist. Many of them are not easily visible on the Digitized Sky Survey, and some (e.g. ESO 452–SC11) are essentially invisible on the survey—even with a histogram equalization scaling of survey images.

All of these images were made with a Cookbook 245 plus CCD camera. They were obtained using the 18-inch, *f* /4.5 fork-mounted Newtonian telescope in the East Dome of the Houston Museum Of Natural Science's George Observatory, at Brazos Bend State Park south of Houston, Texas (see Appendix E). A total of 4 images of each cluster were obtained, and these were appropriately processed with dark and flat fields in order to create the final images. The field size of the ESO 452-SC11 image is approximately 6′ by 11′. The field size of the other images is 8′ by 10′. Note that these images are compressed somewhat in the vertical direction. North is up and west is to the right unless otherwise noted (i.e., for the Terzan 5 and Terzan 6 images).

These images are reproduced here with the kind permission of Tracy Knauss and are dedicated to the memory of Mike Morton.

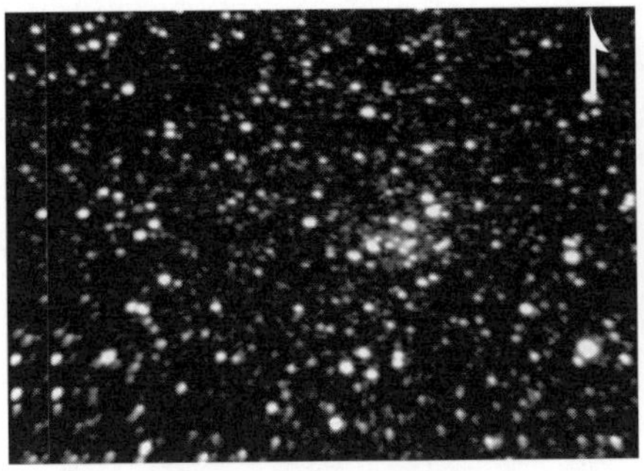

Fig. 7.22 *ESO 452-SC11.*

Fig. 7.23 *Terzan 1.*

Fig. 7.24 *Terzan 2.*

Fig. 7.25 *Terzan 3.*

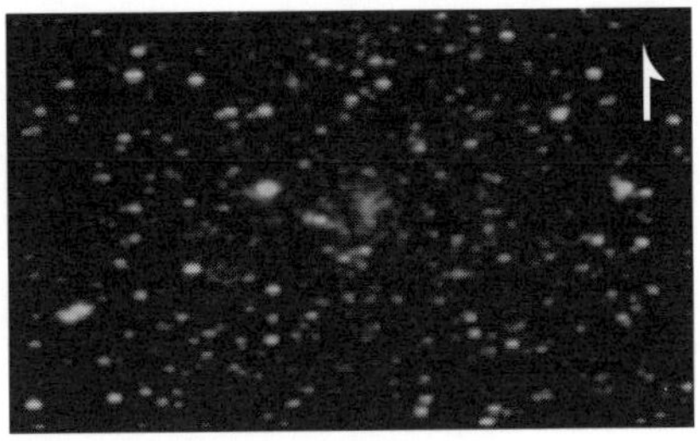

Fig. 7.26 *Terzan 4.*

Fig. 7.27 *Terzan 5 (with south-southeast up).*

Fig. 7.28 *Terzan 6 (with north-northwest up).*

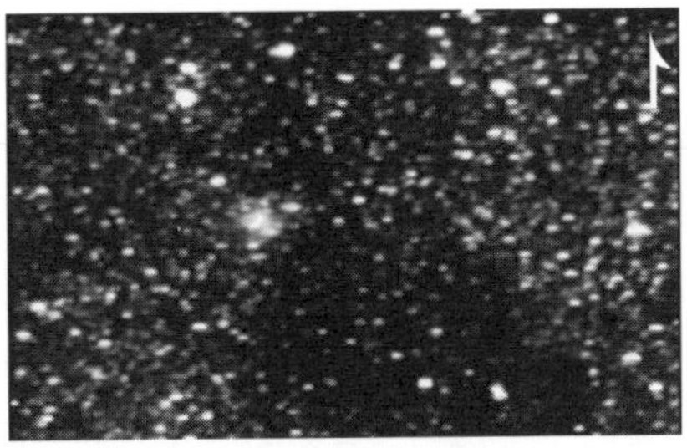

Fig. 7.29 *Terzan 9.*

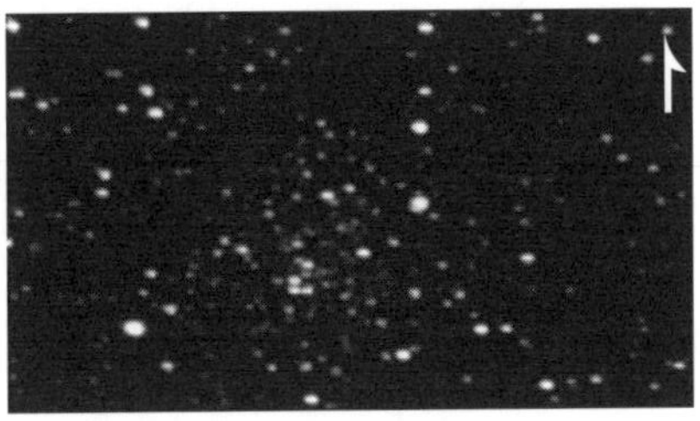

Fig. 7.30 *Terzan 8.*

Fig. 7.31 *Terzan 7.*

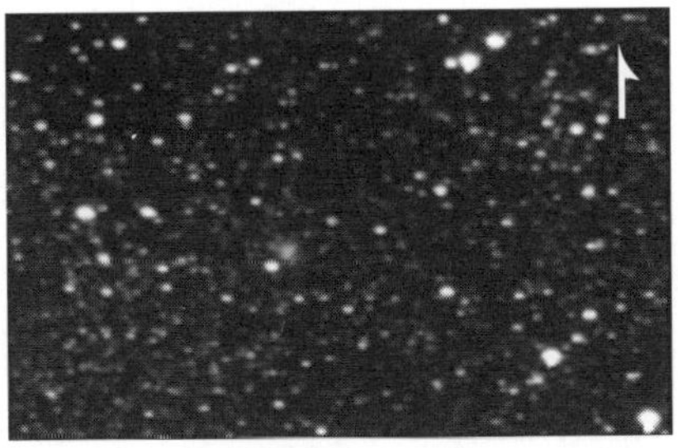

Fig. 7.32 *Terzan 10.*

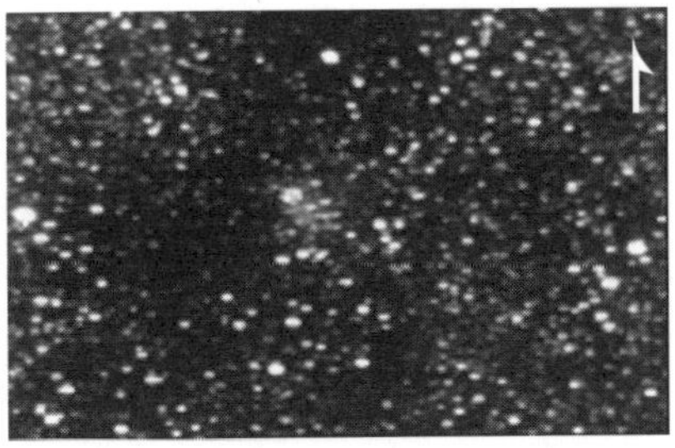

Fig. 7.33 *Terzan 11.*

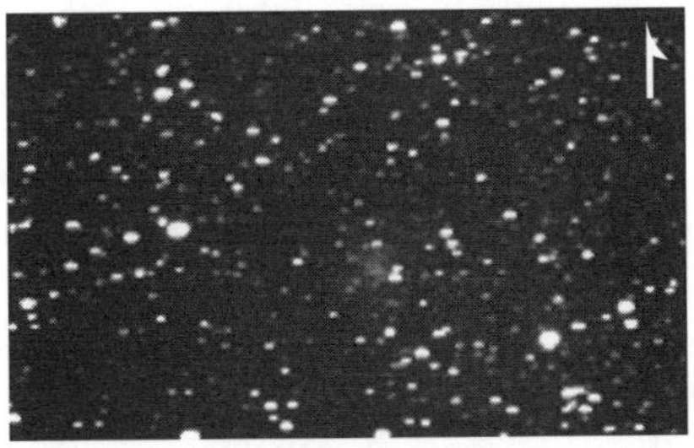

Fig. 7.34 *UKS 1.*

Chapter 8
Observing Open and Globular Star Clusters

Darkness brings out stars. When it is dark, look for the stars.

—William M. Rausch (1890-1975).[1]

8.1 Observing Open Clusters: Introduction

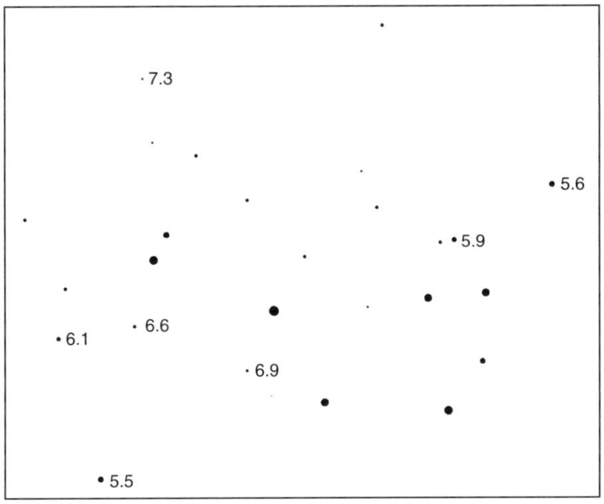

Fig. 8.1 *The Pleiades = M 45, showing a selection of stars down to V magnitude 7.5 over an approximately 1.6° wide field.*

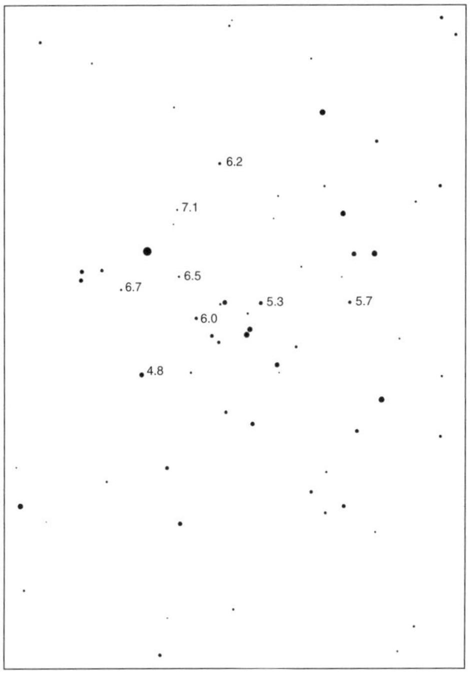

Fig. 8.2 *The Hyades, showing a selection of stars down to V magnitude 7.5, over this approximately 9° high field.*

From the observational point of view, one of the great things about open star clusters is that interesting observations can be made with equipment of any size, or even none at all. For the naked eye, resolved clusters can make a good test of visual acuity. The Pleiades are a case in point, and in Chapter 1 reference was made to the number of stars which had been counted in this group even before the invention of the telescope. There are ten stars which are brighter than visual magnitude 6 and should, therefore, present few problems to observers with reasonably good eyesight and a dark, clear site. However, the compactness of the group makes resolving the cluster a little more problematical. Nevertheless, for the sake of interest, a chart of the brighter Pleiades stars, together with relevant magnitude data, is given at Figure 8.1, to enable the observer to conduct personal experiments. Because of the greater separation of the stars, the Hyades (which are in convenient proximity to the Pleiades) are probably a better grouping on which to test individual sensitivity in detecting faint light. For comparison, a chart of the brighter Hyades stars, together with relevant magnitude data, is given at Figure 8.2. In conducting these comparative observational experiments, it is important to note the difference in altitude of the two groups, although it is quite a straightforward matter to work out when, during a particular night, they will be at the same altitude. To obtain the most favorable result, it will be necessary to work out at what altitude the Hyades culminates and observe it then, having previously observed the Pleiades when they passed through that same altitude.

A number of other open star clusters and asterisms can be resolved without the help of optical aid; in the northern skies, for example, there is the α Per group, Melotte 111 (the Coma star cluster), Collinder 399 (Brocchi's Cluster)

1. W. Rausch was the grandfather of BA.

and to a lesser extent, M 44 (Praesepe). In the southern skies, some stars can be seen in IC 2391 (the o Vel cluster) and IC 2602 (the θ Carinae cluster), and we suspect that keen eyes might also pick out a few stars in M 7, which contains five stars brighter than visual magnitude 6.0. For example, Jeff Medkeff reports [private communication, 2002] being able to see 4 of the stars from Sierra Vista, Arizona. M 6, M 8, and M 34 are on the fringe of naked-eye resolvability.

From a clear, dark site where the Milky Way is prominent, it is a rewarding exercise to lie back in a deck-chair, with a red light and a small scale star atlas, such as *Norton's 2000.0*, *Cambridge Star Atlas 2000.0*, or *Bright Star Atlas 2000.0*, and slowly scan through the galactic plane trying to match up the enhancements in the Milky Way background with known star clusters. Some are quite prominent, such as NGC 869 and 884 (the Perseus Double Cluster), Collinder 399, NGC 6231 and NGC 6475 (M 7). However, many more are just small and subtle brightness enhancements.

With the aid of even a small pair of binoculars, the number of clusters which can be detected and resolved increases dramatically. Here it is simply not good enough to sit back and hand-hold the equipment. Even small, lightweight binoculars need to be tripod-mounted to be adequately effective. One of us [SH] likes to use 10x50 binoculars which are a nice compromise between cost, portability, ease-of-use and resolution. They are particularly good for taking on vacation and have been used on a number of occasions to extend viewing further down into the southern sky. In conjunction with this sort of equipment, a more detailed star atlas, such as Tirion's *Sky Atlas 2000.0*, or the venerable *Atlas Coeli*, is advisable. If one is restricted solely to this sort of equipment, a detailed plotting of binocular clusters would be an interesting and educational project. One amateur astronomer who has undertaken this, as part of a much more detailed all-sky survey of binocular features in the Milky Way, is Colin Henshaw using 12x40 binoculars, from sites in the U.K., Zimbabwe, and Botswana.

Many larger clusters (larger than 30′ in diameter) benefit from observation with small telescopes—the greater field of view making the clusters stand out better against the background. For many years one of us [SH] has successfully used a 10.5-cm (4.25-inch) RFT (rich-field telescope) for the observation of such clusters. This type of instrument is fairly compact and can normally be below as hand-luggage on aircraft, thus enabling it to be used on vacation breaks to lower latitude destinations for the observation of objects which would normally be below the horizon. His usual observing site in the U.K. is at latitude 53°N. However, he finds that one of the great pleasures of observational astronomy has been to use the RFT from the more equable climates, and more favorable geographical locations of the Mediterranean region (latitude 35°N–40°N), the Canary Islands (latitude 28°N), and as far south as Sri Lanka (latitude 7°N). As a result his observational experience has been expanded deep into Puppis and Vela, and also the Scorpius and Centaurus regions which are otherwise inaccessible.

With larger amateur telescopes the possibilities are greater still, and there is no 'optimum aperture' for observations. Every size of telescope is capable of undertaking some sort of project of interest, and some of these will be discussed in the following sections.

The visual observation of open clusters is to be recommended as a pursuit for observers living in a light-polluted environment. Other types of deep-sky object are extended and can be severely affected by encroaching light. However, because open clusters are made up of discrete point sources, the main disruptive effect in this respect is sky glow, which drowns the faintest stars, and any extended nebulosity that might be involved with the cluster.

8.2 Sketching an Open Cluster

Open star clusters are not only among the most beautiful of celestial sights, but they are particularly challenging to render with pencil and paper and require totally different skills than those needed to draw nebulous objects. While the problem with nebulae is training the eye to pick out faint detail and catch the nuances of subtle shadings, open clusters really require an eye for geometry and the ability to gauge relative stellar magnitudes.

Before starting to sketch a cluster, it is well worth just letting the object sit in the field of view for a while so that you can get a sense of its form and structure. Then let it drift a little to establish the orientation of the field, and look to see if there are any features of the cluster's structure which run parallel or at right-angles to the direction of drift.

When you eventually decide to start your sketch, start with a fairly low power eyepiece or one in which the entire cluster will comfortably fit. Look for the brighter stars in the cluster and plot those first as a sort of skeleton around which to build the final picture. Then, having established the reference frame, mark the orientation and scale on it and start to build in the fainter stars. Look especially for patterns; triangles, squares and right-angles are particularly useful. Having marked in a particular star, check its relative position against the stars which you put in as the skeleton. In the case of larger clusters particularly, it is also worthwhile to stop from time to time and compare the telescopic view with what you have on paper. You may well find that if you have been concentrating on one part of the cluster, the scale of the drawing has started to diverge from that on the other side! An example of how a cluster sketch is built up from geometric patterns is given in Figure 8.3. This

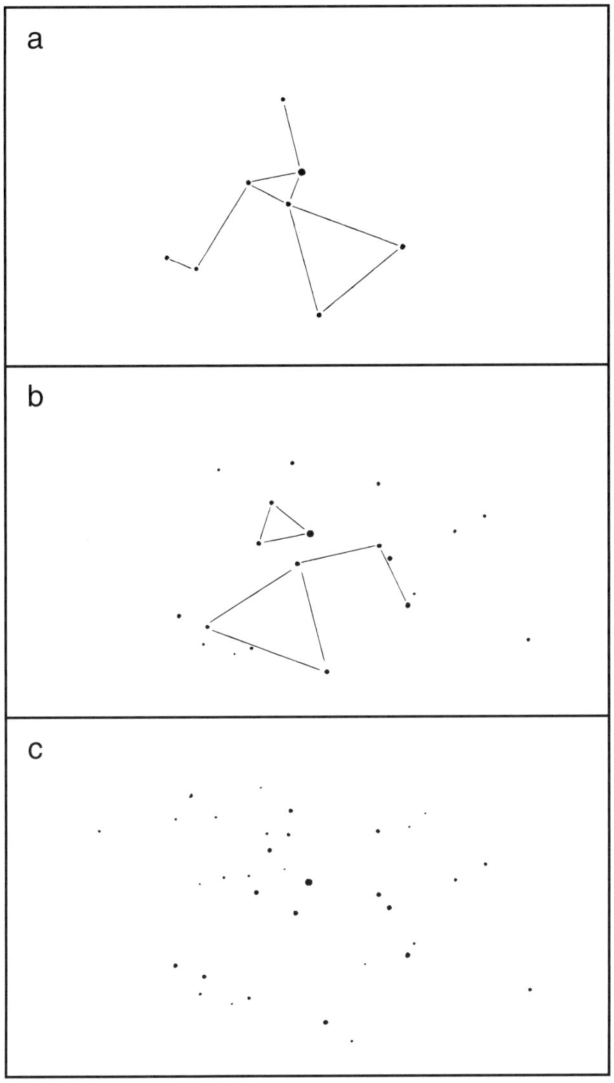

Fig. 8.3 *Diagram showing the construction of a sketch of NGC 2451 from geometric patterns of stars. South is up and east is to the right.*

shows how Steven Hynes constructed a low power sketch of NGC 2451.

Having completed a low power sketch, use an eyepiece of higher magnification to look for fainter stars. It is important to be systematic to avoid missing any. Again, look for patterns; a successful search method is to identify a particular triangle of brighter stars and check the area within that before looking for another well-defined area and repeating the process. While you have the higher magnification eyepiece in place, you should also be sure to examine the stars you plotted earlier to check for color and faint companions.

Obviously, this process could be repeated several times as the complexity of the individual cluster warrants, but always remember to make regular 'overview' observations using a slightly lower power eyepiece to check that your estimate of the scale and relative stellar brightnesses is not going astray.

Finally, having completed the sketch, use a nebular filter in the original low power eyepiece to check for the presence of faint nebulosity and place this on the sketch as well. In this range of accessories, a narrow-band filter, such as an Hβ filter or perhaps an [O III] filter, is likely to give the best results, but, whichever is used, make sure to specify the type in your notes.

A pencil with an eraser on the end is recommended when making sketches at the telescope; making corrections and deletions is easier. However, for a more permanent record, use a black-ink pen. Not only does it look better in your record book, but if you send the sketches off for publication, they look a lot better. The screening process used when printing illustrations in a book or magazine renders pencil stars a most unpleasant grey color.

Of course, the process described above for sketching an open cluster can be used as guidance for an accompanying descriptive report. Start by recording the location of the cluster relative to any other important celestial features, particularly bright stars. Then, with a low-power eyepiece in place, note the overall impression of the cluster. Is the cluster round or elongated? Record the Position Angle (P.A.) of any extension. Is there a large or small range of brightness within the stars? Make an estimate of the magnitude range and the magnitude of the brightest star. How are the stars distributed? Are the brighter stars scattered fairly evenly among the fainter stars, or concentrated either to the center or to one side of the cluster? Are there any other obvious morphological features? For example, do stars form regular geometric shapes, or are there chains of stars? In the latter case, say where they originate, perhaps relative to the center or some other specific feature of the cluster, and describe their structure (i.e., length, number and magnitude of stars, direction of any curvature).

Having done this, add to the description any features which become apparent at higher magnifications. For example, does the cluster contain any faint patches of nebulosity or perhaps unresolved stars? Does the overall star density seem to change with increasing power? Obviously, if any double stars are found, make an estimate of the positive angle and separation of the pair; or even better, measure it! Estimate the relative brightness of the stars. Look out for any colored stars and remember to identify double and colored stars on your sketch.

8.3 Observational Projects for Open Clusters

8.3.1 Double Stars The observation of double stars remains one of the primary areas of observational astronomy where the amateur can still make a significant scientific contribution. Firstly, their measurement over a period of time helps to differentiate between genuine, gravitationally bound binaries and those which are merely optical pairs. Having achieved this, the analysis of the orbital motion of a binary provides valuable data on stellar masses; indeed, it is the only direct way of obtaining this information. Furthermore, anomalies in the orbit of a pair may reveal the presence of unseen companions, adding to the base of statistical data on the frequency of multiple systems.

Despite the undoubted value of double star observation, it remains a minority interest across the entire astronomical community, both amateur and professional. There are a number of reasons for this. From the amateur point of view the comparative scarcity of suitable equipment is a consideration. For both amateurs and professionals, the work is not only painstaking but also requires commitment over a long period of time and cannot produce quick results. Only a very few visual binaries have an orbital period shorter than the human lifespan.

Open clusters are extremely good sites for finding double and multiple stars, and many of the systems listed in the *Washington Visual Double Star Catalogue* 1996.0 (*WDS*) [1996; see Appendix E for web address] are to be found in and around clusters. The *WDS* is the modern standard catalog of double and multiple systems listing 78,100 such objects. However, this only gives the basic, essential data about the systems and does not list any associations with clusters. A useful, if lengthy, project for an amateur astronomer would be to go through the *WDS* and our catalog of cluster data and cross-reference the two.

For the purposes of making a sketch of an open cluster, it is possible to make reasonably satisfactory visual estimates of double star observational parameters (accurate to about 5° in P.A., 2″ in Separation, and 0.2 mag for the brightness of each component). However, in order to make scientifically valuable observations, it is necessary to use a micrometer or CCD camera. It is not within the scope of this publication to describe the use of either of these or the reduction of observations. However, there are a small number of extremely useful books which cover the subject of micrometer measurements. Those by Argyle [1986] and Couteau [1981] can be particularly recommended, and the former even includes information on the construction of a simple diffraction-grating micrometer, which can be built at home with simple materials and at little cost. The subject of CCD imaging is well covered by various texts listed here in the bibliography (page 477).

8.3.2 Variable Stars In addition to double stars, open clusters can also be found to contain variable stars. In many instances, these may be merely line-of-sight associations; the *General Catalogue of Variable Stars (GCVS)* [1985-87] records over 30,000 known variables in the Galaxy, and it would not be surprising to find some apparently within the boundaries of open clusters. In fact, there are about 1,500 variables in or near to identified open clusters and another useful project that amateurs could undertake is to create and maintain a cross-referenced database of the GCVS and our catalog.

Table 8.1
A list of brighter variable stars in the field of the Pleiades star cluster (maxima >13.0). Data taken from GCVS.

Name	2000.0		Mag. Range	Type
	R.A.	Dec.		
LO Tau	03 42.7	+23 59.4	11.6 – 18.6	UV Cet
LZ Tau	03 43.6	+24 13.9	12.2 – 15.9	UV Cet
V624 Tau	03 43.7	+24 22.5	8.23 – 8.25	δ Sct
MS Tau	03 43.9	+24 25.6	12.8 – 17.2	UV Cet
V739 Tau	03 43.9	+23 57.4	12.8 – 20.0	UV Cet
MX Tau	03 44.4	+24 04.1	12.6 – 16.1	UV Cet
V744 Tau	03 44.9	+24 46.4	12.5 – 20.0	UV Cet
OU Tau	03 45.5	+24 18.2	12.6 – 14.6	UV Cet + BY Dra
PP Tau	03 46.5	+24 07.2	12.4 – 15.7	UV Cet
PY Tau	03 46.9	+24 27.5	12.1 – 19.2	UV Cet
V534 Tau	03 47.1	+24 49.2	8.26 – 8.30	δ Sct
FL Tau	03 47.2	+23 42.6	12.6 – 13.5	UV Cet
V647 Tau	03 47.3	+24 08.4	8.25 – 8.30	δ Sct
V650 Tau	03 47.4	+23 40.7	7.76 – 7.79	δ Sct
V703 Tau	03 47.5	+24 41.1	12.2 – 14.9	UV Cet
QX Tau	03 47.6	+23 58.3	12.4 – 15.7	UV Cet + BY Dra
V342 Tau	03 48.2	+23 58.2	12.7 – 19.5	UV Cet
V344 Tau	03 48.3	+24 55.0	12.7 – 19.8	UV Cet
V346 Tau	03 48.3	+23 58.4	12.9 – 17.9	UV Cet
V660 Tau	03 48.5	+23 18.0	12.4 – 14.5	UV Cet + BY Dra
SY Tau	03 48.8	+23 31.5	10.7 – 11.7	Lb
BU Tau	03 49.2	+24 08.2	4.77 – 5.50	γ Cas
V664 Tau	03 49.3	+24 46.6	12.6 – 14.7	UV Cet
II Tau	03 49.7	+24 19.1	12.4 – 16.9	UV Cet
V384 Tau	03 51.6	+23 11.0	12.0 – 16.5	UV Cet
V679 Tau	03 52.0	+24 39.8	12.6 – 14.2	UV Cet

Many of these variables are genuine cluster members and include a wide range of types (for a detailed account of modern variable star classifications, see John Isles' *Variable Stars* [1990]). In the very young clusters, particularly those which are still involved with their nebulosity, are to be found a good selection of "nebular variables" and flare stars. The Pleiades is the cluster with the richest collection of variable stars with over 500 apparently associated with it, many being faint flare stars (dwarf M-type stars, prototype UV Ceti). It also includes the binocular variable BU Tau (= Pleione), which is of the γ Cas type ("shell stars"). These are fairly massive, rapidly rotating stars of spectral type Be, and the light variations are caused by an outflow or "shell" of matter ejected from the equatorial region, causing a short-lived fade in the brightness of the star. A list of some of the brighter variable stars in the Pleiades is given in Table 8.1. Other shell stars in open clusters include V373 Car in NGC 2516, V3508 Sgr in IC 4725 (M 25) and V1322 Cyg, which may be a member of NGC 6913 (M 29).

Table 8.2
List of selected Cepheid variables in galactic open clusters and associations.

Cluster	Cepheid	P(days)	Mag. Range	Notes
NGC 129	DL Cas	8.000669	8.63 – 9.26	
Cas R2	SU Cas	1.949319	5.70 – 6.18	
C0634+031	CV Mon	5.378898	9.90 – 10.7	Cl vdB 1
Vel OB5	SW Vel	23.4744	7.44 – 8.96	
Ruprecht 79	CS Vel	5.90		
Lyng 6TWN	r 1 0 7	8 6		
NGC 6067	QZ Nor	3.7864		(1)
	V340 Nor	11.285		(1)
NGC 6087	S Nor	9.75411	6.12 – 6.7	
C1814-191a	WZ Sgr	21.849708	7.45 – 8.53	
IC 4725	U Sgr	6.744925	6.34 – 7.08	
NGC 6649	V367 Sct	5.2551		
NGC 6664	EV Sct	3.09		
Trumpler 35	RU Sct	19.69767	8.87 – 10.02	(1)
Collinder 394	BB Sgr	6.63699	6.69 – 7.29	(1)
NGC 6834	SV Vul	45.035	6.73 – 7.76	
NGC 7790	CE Cas a	4.4462		(2)
	CE Cas b	5.1275		(2)
	CF Cas	4.87513		

Notes
(1) Cluster membership still open to question.
(2) CE Cas a and CE Cas b form a binary pair.

In the older clusters, or at least those with massive stars that have evolved rapidly, there is another range of variables; the irregular and semi-regular red giants and supergiants, such as those in NGC 869 and 884, the Perseus Double Cluster. These include S Per, T Per, RS Per, SU Per, YZ Per, AD Per, BU Per, FZ Per, KK Per, PP Per, PR Per, and V439 Per (although it should be noted that the physical association of some of these is only suspected rather than confirmed). The detection of a reddish or orange color in a star within a cluster may well indicate that it is a known or suspected variable and in these cases, it is well worth checking out in a star catalog.

Of the more evolved sorts of variable star which have been found to be associated with open clusters, perhaps the most interesting are the Cepheid variables (a list of Cepheids in open clusters and associations is given in Table 8-2 and additional information about some of these is given by Hynes [1987]). These stars are extremely important in astrophysical terms, being one of the primary "standard candles" in the determination of the cosmic distance scale. The reason for this is that they exhibit a simple, well-defined relationship between their mean absolute magnitudes and their periods. Once the apparent magnitude, m, is known and the absolute magnitude, M, has been found, the distance can be derived from the equations discussed in Section 1.7 on page 8.

In addition, Cepheid variables are sufficiently luminous as to be observable in other galaxies up to several Mpc distant, and work with the *Hubble Space Telescope* has extended this out to the distance of the Virgo Cluster. To refine the accuracy of the Cepheid distance scale, it will still be necessary to use nearby Cepheids as calibration points.

Cepheid variables can also provide valuable information about stellar interiors through pulsation theory. This has shown that a Cepheid's period is determined largely by its mass and radius; thus, if the radius can be determined observationally, it is possible to infer the mass. The radius can be calculated from the luminosity and effective temperature; the mass determined from this is called the "pulsational mass."

The presence of Cepheids in open star clusters or associations makes some of their observational parameters, such as luminosity, easier to determine and refine. A detailed account of the need for such investigations and the methods by which they are carried out is given by Schmidt [1984].

Obviously, it is important to be sure of the reality of the cluster membership, and normally this can be determined by three tests:

1. Proximity—clearly, there is a greater likelihood of a Cepheid being a genuine cluster member if it is at the center of the cluster rather than on the outskirts.
2. Radial Velocity—stars sharing a common R.V. normally are associated. However, for less well-studied clusters there may not be enough accurately known radial velocities for this to be a reliable factor in determining membership.
3. Reddening—although the degree of reddening can vary over a cluster diameter, a common degree of reddening can be taken as being indicative of association.

Most stars are known to exist in pairs or multiple systems, and the observation of visually resolvable pairs was discussed in Section 8.3.1 on page 257. However, a good many systems of this type cannot be resolved and, by accident of geometry, undergo mutual eclipses, causing apparent variability. The largest number of these are the Algol-type (EA) eclipsing binaries, named after Algol (β Persei). They are characterized by normal steady brightness with sometimes rapid, deep fades in brightness at well-defined intervals. There may also be a smaller secondary fade midway between the primary fades. In some cases, the stars orbit so closely to each other that each is deformed in shape by the other, and the change in the shape of the profile presented causes variations in brightness to be observed, sometimes in addition to eclipse phenomena (this is the situation in the case of the β Lyrae [EB] variables).

These eclipsing binaries are a particularly common variety of variable star and occur frequently in open clusters. In the Trapezium cluster at the heart of the Orion Nebula, two of the four brightest stars are eclipsing binaries (star A = V1016 Ori, and star B = BM Ori). These are simple Algolid (EA) systems where the variation is due solely to the eclipses; however, one cluster where some of the more exotic types can be found is the ancient, high-latitude cluster NGC 188. Here, there are at least six W UMa contact binaries, one evolved longer period binary and an FK Com star (one that is the descendant of a contact binary, formed by coalescence of the progenitor's components) [Kaluzny and Shara 1987]. Unfortunately, none of these stars is brighter than mag(B) 14.0.

8.3.3 Nebulae As a result of the comparative youth of star cluster systems, many will still have some associated nebulosity. This may be either emission (HII) nebulosity or reflection nebulosity, or in some cases, a bit of both. From the visual point of view, emission nebulae tend to be the brighter, but the main observational characteristic is normally only apparent photographically, when emission nebulae are clearly reddish in color and reflection nebulae are blue. There is no real difference in the composition of these two types of nebulae, but the cause of the red color in emission nebulae is the ionization of the hydrogen gas by the UV radiation from the hot cluster stars which produces particularly strong emission lines of Hα in the red part of the spectrum. In reflection nebulae, the radiation from the stars is not sufficiently intense (due either to the lower surface temperature or greater distance) to ionize the gaseous material and is, instead, scattered by it. Perhaps the best example of an emission nebula surrounding a cluster is the Orion Nebula which surrounds the Trapezium, but observers will find bright nebulae of this type involved, for example, with the clusters NGC 2244, NGC 2264, NGC 6514 (M 20), NGC 6523 (M 8) and NGC 6611 (M 16). Bright reflection nebulae are less common, and the best known example is that enveloping the Pleiades cluster.

A significant problem in the observation of nebulae associated with star clusters is that the brightness of the stars tends to swamp the fainter light of the nebulae. The effect of this can be greatly reduced by the use of nebular filters, such as broad band and narrow band Hβ filters. The former is a general purpose filter having a bandpass which encompasses the [O III] lines at 500.7 nm and 495.9 nm, and the Hβ line at 486.1 nm. This cuts out not only a great deal of light pollution emission but also a significant amount of the stellar continuum, greatly enhancing the contrast of diffuse and planetary nebulae. The Orion "Ultrablock" filter is such a filter, as are certain ones from DayStar, Parks and Celestron. A Hβ filter is a rather more specialized item, with a narrow bandpass centered on the 486.1 nm Hβ line. Because this line is a prominent feature in the spectra of diffuse nebulae, and because so much of the rest of the visible spectrum is rejected, the Hβ filter can be useful in the observation of faint diffuse nebulae.

In connection with sketching an open cluster, observers might well find it worthwhile to check clusters for nebulosity using an Hβ filter after having completed a drawing. If the nebulosity is bright enough to be visible without a filter in the first place, the use of a broad band filter might bring out more detail.

8.3.4 Cluster Verification Quite often, when sweeping around the sky, observers might come across small groupings of stars which they suspect to be clusters. Of course, we know the chances are pretty high that the apparent association is a projection effect of unrelated stars at different distances. Such a group is only an optical/geometric effect in our line of sight, by definition, an asterism. Wouldn't it be nice to be able to check whether a group of stars is physically associated or not? One should check the catalog here to see if the object has been listed as a cluster by previous observers. However, the data here are only as good as their source material and, in any event, may not give any indication either way as to whether a particular grouping is a physical cluster.

With the on-line publication of the *Hipparcos* and *Tycho* databases it is now possible to make checks on the likely association of individual stars. Data transfer rates and storage space requirements would make it impractical to download the entire database, but selections can be downloaded, and using the *VizieR* viewing facility of the Centre de Données astronomiques de Strasbourg (CDS) and requesting data from the Hipparcos (I/239) and Tycho-2 (I/259) catalog, inputting stellar designation or positional data will produce parallax, proper motion, magnitude, B – V and spectral type data. Brian Skiff [1998a] has used this method to show that Collinder 399 (Brocchi's Cluster) is, in fact, an asterism.

As an extension to this, another worthwhile project is to do some work on some of the objects whose type is not definitely known, i.e., where it is not clear whether the object is an asterism or a true star cluster. The various star catalogs discussed in Section 2.7 on page 24 can be used to check the proper motions and colors of possible cluster stars at least to some level. For example, the proper motions can be plotted (along with their uncertainties) to see if the motions of possible cluster stars are similar, at least as long as those motions are not zero, given the uncertainties. Similarly, color-magnitude diagrams can be plotted for possible cluster stars. The uncertainties of the magnitudes must be considered as sometimes they will be too large to allow the data to be used. However, if a clear main sequence can be seen—different from that of surrounding Milky Way stars—it will argue strongly that the group being considered is a physical star cluster. Finally, the *Hip-*

parcos catalog, described in Section 2.7, can also be used to check the parallaxes (distances) of nearby possible cluster stars. Stars with similar distances and proper motions (taking the uncertainties of such data fully into account) are very likely physically with each other.

Brian Skiff pointed out that it would be quite worthwhile to determine for each open cluster the definitive reference. He writes [private communication, 1997]:

> It would be great if each object that's been studied in any useful way could have one (or possibly two) papers cited that might be termed 'definitive' in the sense of providing visual observers the best source for photometry, finder chart, etc. For most objects (which is only about 450 of them), just citing the one-and-only photometric study might work well enough.

This would be a good project for the interested reader. Such a compilation would be useful for Galactic globular clusters, but to some extent this already exists due to Skiff's earlier work. The *DSFG1e* includes references (originating with Skiff) for fundamental information on most of the Galactic globular clusters, and Skiff still maintains such a list [Skiff 1995a; see Appendix E for web address].

Mention has previously been made of Isserstedt's Stellar Rings [*Sky & Telescope* 1967; Isserstedt and Schmidt-Kaler 1968; Isserstedt 1970; Isserstedt and Schmidt-Kaler 1973]. Indeed, one of us [BA] found such an object northeast of NGC 6795. Amateurs could now investigate whether a number of these rings are true physical associations of stars by checking their parallaxes and/or proper motions, and their colors, via the use of Hipparcos/Tycho or similar data.

8.4 Observing Globular Clusters: Introduction

Although some of the larger and brighter globular clusters can be picked up by the naked eye or as small, bright, hazy spots in average sized binoculars, more can be seen in small aperture rich-field telescopes where brightness gradients and sometimes even a certain amount of fringe resolution, or "granularity" can be detected. Nevertheless, the observation of globular clusters is more the realm of the medium-to-large aperture telescope.

Using a 20-cm telescope, for example, the amateur astronomer should be able to identify and resolve a substantial number of Galactic globular clusters, particularly those from the Messier catalog. In the northern hemisphere, the best target is M 13 (NGC 6205)—see Figures 7.9, 7.10 on page 240, and 8.4 on page 263—which lies one-third of the way along the imaginary line joining η and ζ Herculis. This showpiece object is one of the nearer globulars and can be seen by the naked-eye. But even in a comparatively small telescope, it is little short of spectacular. Not too far away, but less often observed, is M 92 (NGC 6341); this is only a little less bright than M 13 and can be clearly resolved around the edges with a 20-cm (8-inch) instrument with some resolution across the central area. In the constellation of Canes Venatici, near its border with Boötes and Coma Berenices, observers with smaller telescopes should search out M 3 (NGC 5272), and slightly further south, the globular cluster M 53 (NGC 5024) near α Com. These should also show a significant amount of resolution. Just qualifying as a northern globular is M 5 (NGC 5904) in Serpens; this is a large, well-resolved and splendid object in smaller telescopes. In the southern hemisphere, particularly in Sagittarius and Scorpius towards the center of the Galaxy, are many fine globular clusters. Perhaps the best example for small and medium aperture telescopes in this region is M 22 (NGC 6656); this is undoubtedly visible without optical aid from a good site and reveals an incredible amount of detail, with "fingers" of stars stretching outwards from the center and little clumps and groups of resolved and partially resolved stars scattered all over the place. Another intriguing object is M 4 (NGC 6121) near Antares in Scorpius; although one of the nearer globular clusters, this object is substantially obscured and not as well resolved as one might expect. However, it is distinguished by a distinct band (or, two parallel bands) of stars across the center. In addition to these objects, the two finest globular clusters in the sky are resident at southerly declinations, 47 Tucanae (NGC 104) and ω Centauri (NGC 5139). Both are at least partially resolved in a small RFT (rich field telescope) and are spectacular objects in telescopes of fairly modest aperture.

None of these objects requires exceptionally large aperture telescopes to enjoy, and all have their own special features. Most globular clusters tend to take high magnification well, and one should not be reluctant to make use of short focal length, high magnification oculars. As always with deep sky observation, it pays to use the best quality optics one can afford, and this means not only the mirrors or lenses in the telescope itself but also the eyepieces. A telescope is only as good as the weakest link in its optical train, and the value of even the most expensive instrument is wasted if used in conjunction with a poor eyepiece. In the observation of globular clusters, this may mean the difference between mere "granularity" and full resolution. Pretoria, Orthoscopic, Plössl, Erfle and Nagler eyepieces are recommended as suitable choices.When not in use they should be kept in dust-proof containers away from any dampness and cleaned only with the greatest of care.

Other than the use of good quality eyepieces, the visual study of globular clusters need not be very expensive, in that no special equipment, such as nebular filters, is required (although some observers in light-polluted areas might benefit from the use of an LPR—light pollution reduction—type of filter).

Most globular clusters can be easily found using a star atlas such as *Sky Atlas 2000.0* by Wil Tirion. This shows stars down to about mag. 8, and it should be possible to "star-hop" to a good proportion of the known population of Galactic globular clusters. However, for some of the fainter objects, a more detailed star atlas, such as *Uranometria 2000.0*, would be better. This superb sky atlas plots most of the known globular clusters. However, there is a group of small, faint, obscured globular clusters which require even better charts to locate, and they represent a challenge even to users of large aperture instruments. These are systems typified by the Palomar objects which have been discovered over the past few decades usually on deep Schmidt plates. The observation of these objects will be discussed later.

8.5 Describing and Sketching Globular Cluster Fields

However a particular globular cluster is found, and whatever aperture is used in its observation, most amateur astronomers will want to record their find by describing and sketching it. As always, the first thing to do is to gauge its appearance against the surrounding starfield and establish the cardinal points. Because the stars of a globular cluster are generally so much fainter than the field stars, and the overall structure of a cluster so much more delicate, the most satisfactory method of reproducing such an object on paper is to treat it like a nebula. Use a pencil, but employ an ink pen to plot the field stars. This contrast emphasizes the comparative faintness of the globular cluster stars. Of course, for those globular clusters which are not resolved, the treatment of the object as a nebula and the use of pencil is even more appropriate.

As with a sketch of any astronomical object, a globular cluster drawing should show the orientation and scale of the field and details of the telescope, eyepiece and any other accessories used. It is useful to compile detailed, written notes to supplement field drawings as comparisons are easier to make with other observations later. During the compilation of a sketch and notes, observers might prefer to adopt a check-list of points to look out for, such as the following:

1. How large is the object? A specific estimate in terms of arcmin is preferable to vague terms such as "very small" or "large." To do this successfully, observers need to be familiar with the field diameters of their eyepieces. This can be done by viewing starfields and comparing them with an accurate atlas or by timing a star's drift across the field. Some globular clusters show an almost stratified structure; the sizes of the different "shells" can be estimated.
2. Does the cluster show any structure? First, look critically at the shape; is it round?

   We tend to make assumptions about the shape of globular clusters from the standard book illustrations we see, and the round shape is perhaps the first. True, most are round, or nearly so, but some are noticeably elliptical. This may be intrinsic, as in the case of ω Centauri, but in other cases it may be due to different factors, such as the presence of obscuring dust (in the case of M 4), or perhaps just the uneven distribution of stars. A globular cluster which appears perfectly round on a photograph may well appear elliptical, or even irregular, visually due to the presence of clumps of stars at a particular magnitude, which are "swamped" by fainter stars on the photograph. The appearance of a globular cluster is critically aperture-dependent. Within the overall shape, is there any evidence for "shells" of structure? For example, a globular cluster may have a bright central region or "core," and perhaps even a star-like nucleus. Around the central region an unresolved fainter area may be found with a shell of faint stars resolved at the periphery. Make notes about such structure, including the size of the shells. In unresolved clusters, is the surface brightness even, or does it vary? What is the brightness gradient? Is there any sign of "granularity"?
3. How well is the cluster resolved? Can stars be resolved across the entire face of the cluster, or just in outer shells, or just at the periphery, or not at all? If the cluster is not resolved, is there any evidence of mottling or granularity which might be indicative of borderline resolution? If stars are resolved, can you estimate the magnitude of the brightest stars? How are the stars distributed; are they spread fairly uniformly across the face of the cluster, or are they gathered together in little clumps, or are they formed into streams or arcs?
4. Can any unusual structural features be seen? Two globular clusters, NGC 7078 (M 15) and NGC 6656 (M 22), are known to contain planetary nebulae, and these may be detectable using fairly large aperture amateur telescopes and nebular filters. They would not be seen during a casual observation and would require a deliberate search and high-resolution finder charts. Some globular clusters appear to contain darker patches; can any evidence of these be found?

Using very large amateur telescopes, some observers have reported being able to "see through" some of the larger, closer, less compact globular clusters with little black spots being visible between the stars, even near the center. In what clusters can this phenomenon be detected, and with what aperture?

8.6 Observational Projects for Globular Clusters

Several projects are suggested from the above list of glob-

Fig. 8.4 *NGC 6205 = M 13, the great Hercules globular cluster, in a drawing courtesy of Gaspar Bakos, at 229x,, using a 44.4 cm reflector telescope, showing approximately a 35′ field. Note the pattern of "dark lanes," which appear obvious (and are often reported as having a "propeller shape") visually in telescopes of large (of order 0.5 m or larger) aperture. The galaxy IC 4716 is also visible as a tiny oval, just below the parallelogram of 4 faint stars at the upper left.*

ular features to check. First, think about the size of globular clusters. If you have sets of globular cluster data to compare, one feature which may become apparent is the variation in listed diameters.This does not mean that the compilers of the catalogs were necessarily negligent, simply that the criteria used were different in each case. Certainly, none can be relied upon as more than just a guide for the visual observer. It would be a worthwhile exercise to do a visual survey of globular clusters to gauge the visual diameter using a variety of different instruments and compare the results with published data.

In view of the comparative uniformity of globular cluster structure in many cases, another project for visual and photographic observers would be seeking out irregularities. The visibility of many of these is often dependent on minor variations in observing parameters; such as a change in atmospheric seeing and transparency, or the use of a filter, or a greater or lower power eyepiece to change the contrast level, or the apparent layout of the visible field. A case in point is the "Propeller" in M 13 in Hercules. Recorded as a distinct feature by Lord Rosse, its reality was subject to debate for many years before being photographed. In small telescopes, it is often difficult to see because of low contrast (and possibly because observers expect to find it in the exact center, whereas it is located off-center), but in many photographs, particularly from larger telescopes, the density of stars "drowns" it. Is there any visible evidence of the "dark patches" known to exist in some clusters, or can these be detected photographically?

Useful estimates can be made of the magnitude of the brightest stars in the cluster. These will be red giants at the tip of the red giant branch. Estimates of the magnitude where resolution ends could indicate the horizontal branch magnitude.

As a project for the reader (amateur or professional) it would be useful to take the Trager, *et al.*, [1995a; 1995b] globular cluster magnitude profiles and integrate them out to the 22nd or 25th magnitude per square arcsecond level. Assuming the data were well-calibrated, this would give total magnitudes for globular clusters that should be more reliable than previous measurements.

A related project would be to compare visual estimates of globular cluster total magnitudes and diameters to cataloged values. The diameters given here are those out to an isophotal magnitude of 25 magnitudes per arcseconds (or at the recommendation of Brian Skiff based on visual checks and checks on the digitized sky survey, double that out to 22 magnitudes if data is not available at 25 magnitudes). The magnitudes could be compared to those given here (from van den Bergh, *et al.*, [1991] via B. Skiff) or to magnitudes determined as described above. The visual estimates could be the individual's own estimates or those derived from amateur descriptions of these objects. In particular it is noted that Stephen O'Meara, in his book on the Messier objects [O'Meara 1998a], made consistent visual estimates of the magnitudes of the Messier globular clusters. These might be quite useful for comparison purposes.

8.7 Astrophotography of Open and Globular Clusters

Deep-sky astrophotography is a subject which requires a book all to itself, and, indeed, the subject has been adequately covered elsewhere (see Bibliography). Therefore, it is not proposed to discuss this aspect in too much detail. However, it is worth commenting that in many respects, because of their brightness and size, taking photographs of open clusters is probably easier than any other type of deep-sky object. The first astrophotography both authors ever attempted was to record images of the Hyades and Pleiades clusters using an undriven camera with a 135mm telephoto lens [SH] and 50mm lens [BA]. With short duration exposures and ISO 200 or 400 film, little star-trailing is noticeable, and the image recorded will show about as many stars as you could see using a good pair of 10 x 50 binoculars. Obviously, using a driven camera-mount, or a camera mounted "piggy-back" on a telescope, significantly longer exposures are permitted. A 5-minute exposure using ISO 200 film, with a 135mm telephoto lens having a diameter of about 50mm, should yield stars as faint as magnitude 11.5 over a field about 15° x 10°. With even a small aperture driven telescope, quite respectable impressions of star clusters can be produced. If you have the facility to do piggyback astrophotography, one point to bear in mind is that it would probably be worthwhile to stop down the aperture and increase the exposure time. This will improve the quality of most pictures by reducing the effect of the distortions in a fast lens at full aperture.

In astrophotography with larger telescopes, there is scope for greater quality and quantity in the results which can be achieved. However, there are a few important points to bear in mind. First, considerable attention should be paid to precise focussing. The greater the amount of a star's light concentrated in the smallest area, the clearer the image. Also the limiting magnitude reached will be fainter, and the number of faint stars drowned by brighter companions will be less. The focus point can change during the course of an exposure due to temperature changes, although the effect should be minimal in the case of short exposures. The introduction of filters will make a difference. It will not be possible to obtain fine star images if the telescope optics are not precisely aligned; therefore, regular checks of the collimation are called for. Needless to say, reflectors, particularly Newtonians, are the most prone to problems in this respect.

Although star clusters generally, and open clusters in particular, will tend to require shorter exposures than gaseous nebulae, guiding is an important consideration. If the image does not remain stationary on the film, the image will be blurred. Unfortunately, the causes of guiding errors are several and include the polar axis alignment accuracy, periodic errors in the gear train, telescope flexure and power fluctuations. Changes in air mass density and wind levels can be a source of problems. A common technique for monitoring the guiding accuracy is the use of a separate guide telescope attached to the main instrument, through which the astronomer checks the progress of the exposure by keeping a star centered on crosshairs. This system can be flawed, however, by differences in the flexure of the two instruments through temperature changes and changes in respective position and support over a period of time. A more satisfactory technique is "off-axis" guiding, in which a "sample" of the main image is directed to a separate eyepiece where it can be monitored.

8.8 CCD Imaging

Like astronomical photography, CCD astronomy is a fairly specialized topic. Covering this rapidly growing field is beyond the scope of our text here. Interested observers are advised to explore the increasing number of books available on the subject, such as those listed here in the bibliography. A simple Web search will also reveal a wealth of examples of amateur CCD imaging, often including details and discussions of observing techniques.

However, it should be noted that once one has become proficient in the use of a CCD camera, there are many valuable applications that could be attempted. The study of star clusters is certainly among these. It can easily be seen from the catalog data given here in Chapter 4 and the Appendices—or other catalogs or research papers—that there remain many gaps and uncertainties in the basic data on star clusters. This includes such simple things as the magnitude of the brightest star of each cluster and the total integrated magnitude of the cluster. The observer would need to become familiar with one of the main photometric systems, such as the Johnson-Cousins UBVRI, or the narrower band Strömgren uvbyβ system. Proper filters to place observations into one of these systems will also be required. But once the proper set up and procedures are achieved, some substantial accomplishments may be within reach.

For many objects, even relatively bright ones, basic data on the individual stars is so lacking it is not yet certain whether they form a physical group or not. Good B and V magnitude measurements of such stars, given sufficient signal to noise, might help to establish whether a true cluster exists or not. Over a period or years, or in comparison to existing catalog data (such as those discussed in Section 2.7) it might also be possible to measure the proper motions of prospective cluster member stars in order to determine their membership one way or the other.

It should also be fairly easy to monitor variable stars in open clusters and perhaps to even discover some. An advanced amateur could be the first to publish good light-curves for such stars.

Similarly, an amateur could measure double and multiple star systems within known or possible clusters, and submit this information to professionals for use in determining orbits of such systems. The final results of such a project may be years to decades in the making, but it is possible that only through the collection of such data by amateurs will many of these systems ever have reliable orbits determined.

In the case of globular clusters, there is still considerable uncertainty in both the magnitudes and sizes. A uniform catalog of sizes and total magnitudes down to the point where the cluster fades to a V magnitude of 25 per square arcsecond (the standard usually adopted for galaxies) would be most useful. An amateur could also experiment in determining in a systematic way the center of light of these clusters and thereby measure their coordinates even more precisely then we have given here (in a manor similar to work by J. Medkeff; see Appendix E).

As with open clusters, there is also an opportunity to monitor and even detect cluster variables. One could also search out unusual morphological features such as star patterns, dark lanes, and patches of possible nebulosity.

The field of CCD astronomy at present seems unlimited in its potential, both for professionals and amateurs alike. We hope that amateurs can become involved in this work and contribute to the overall knowledge of star clusters and for that matter astronomy in general.

However, whether you observe visually, photographically, or with CCDs, and whether you collect data for research purposes or observe for relaxation and enjoyment, we simply hope you do observe—and see for yourself these wonders of the heavens—the star clusters.

Appendix A
Nomenclature, Acronyms, and Abbreviations

Following is a list of nomenclature, acronyms, and abbreviations used for the catalog entries and notes given here along with their explanations. The list is presented in alphabetical (uppercase of the same letter preceding lowercase, numbers preceding letters, and brackets ignored) order by preferred cluster name and number.

For a given catalog name that contains a list of objects (or even one supposedly new object), information given includes:

- A description of what type and sometimes how many objects the catalog contains. If not obvious (derived from the author or authors' names) an explanation of the catalog name is also included.
- A reference is given in the form of the author's name(s) and publication year in brackets. These references are listed in the back of the book.
- The numbering system is given ("Numbered from 1 to 10").
- Sometimes further comments are provided (if there is some additional information in the Extended Notes). In addition, preferred names for specific objects are sometimes given (using an equal sign). This is usually because a name is *not* the discovery name, but was thought to be so at the time the catalog was published.

For additional information on astronomical nomenclature, see the *Dictionary of Nomenclature of Celestial Objects* maintained by the IAU on the world wide web. Some of the material here has been obtained from that source, but much has been independently developed.

The names given here are sometimes ones that are in more common use than a name recommended by the IAU. For example, "Cl" has been dropped from in front of many names ("Cl Collinder" becomes "Collinder" or just "Cr"), and brackets have been dropped from around some names in order to shorten them.

Also note that just because a catalog name is given here, that does not mean that the objects cited are incorporated into the catalog here (since many of these catalogs are not specifically of star clusters). So far as can be determined, this is the case for objects that are, or have been suspected to be, Galactic star clusters. However, the catalog given here is not complete beyond the Milky Way, and does not include other objects whose type has never been in question (planetary nebulae, infrared sources, radio sources, galaxies). To determine if any of these catalogs have been completely incorporated, one can check the list of object alias names listed in Appendix C.

1E: X-ray sources. [Vaiana, *et al.*, 1981]. "Numbered" using truncated B1950.0 positions.

1ES: X-ray sources. [Elvis, *et al.*, 1992]. "Numbered" using truncated B1950.0 positions.

2E: X-ray sources, from the second version of the Einstein Observatory catalog. [Harris, *et al.*, 1994]. "Numbered" using truncated B1950.0 positions or a number from 1 to 4809.

2MASS: Two possible Galactic globular clusters discovered in the infrared Two Micron All Sky Survey (2MASS). [Hurt, *et al.*, See Appendix A for web address]. "Numbered" GC01 and GC02.

Abell or ACO: Northern clusters of galaxies. Originally by Abell [1958]. Revised by Abell, Corwin, and Olowin [1989]. Numbered 1 to 4076, and "S" 1 to 1174 ("S" for supplementary).

Abt: A single Galactic open cluster. [Abt, *et al.*, 1980]. Numbered 1. Mrk 6 = Abt 1.

ACH: 15 globular clusters in M 31. [Aurière, *et al.*, 1992]. Numbered 1 to 15.

ADS: "Aitken Double Star" general catalog of double and multiple stars. A few of the "multiple stars" are possible clusters or have clusters around them (see ADS 6366 cluster and ADS 13292 on pages 111 and 112). [Aitken 1932]. Numbered 1 to 17180.

AGB: Acronym for "asymptotic giant branch," a feature of globular cluster color-magnitude diagrams.

AH03: Ten possible clusters or asterisms that were otherwise unnamed before now. Three are possible Galactic open clusters (AH03 J0748.6–2656, AH03 J0822.2–3624, and AH03 J1725.5–3424), which, although previously discovered, have been recognized here as clusters for the first time. AH03 J2011.9+2644 is a probable asterism that could possibly be NGC 6882 (see the Extended Notes for NGC 6885 on page 187). Six of these objects, AH03 J0521.3–6954, AH03 J0524.4–6958, AH03 J0535.7–6912, AH03 J0535.9–6910, AH03 J0536.1–6912, and AH03 J0537.3–6919 are apparently previously undiscovered clusters in the LMC. The designation indicates the current authors' initials and the year of publication of this book.

AL: Five small southern star clusters. [Andrews and Lindsay 1967]. Numbered 1 to 5.

Alessi Jhhmmm±ddmm or Alessi: 41 asterisms or open clusters. 24 were reported by Brazilian amateur astronomer Bruno Alessi, to B. Archinal [private communications, 1997, 1998]. 3 of these and 17 additional objects are listed in Dias, *et al.* [2002]. 24 numbered using truncated J2000.0 positions, and 3 of these and the 17 others numbered from 1 to 20. LeDrew 1 = Alessi 1; LeDrew 2 = Alessi 12; LeDrew 4 = Alessi 2; LeDrew 5 = Alessi 19; Alessi J20046–1030 = Alessi 10; Alessi J07354–1505 = Alessi 17; Alessi J07372–2623 = Alessi 18; French 1 = Alessi J21075+1619.

Al Sûfi's cluster: Single asterism, named after its first discoverer, the ancient Persian astronomer, Al Sûfi (903-986 AD) (see Collinder 399 in Extended Notes). Usually not numbered. Cr 399 = Al Sûfi's cluster.

Alter: The single Galactic cluster King 14. Original reference unknown—this name from *Lund Catalogue* alias list. Numbered 1.

AM: Four clusters, numbered 1 to 4. Nos. 1 and 4 are Galactic globular clusters. No. 3 is a cluster in the SMC. For AM 1 to 3, see Madore and Arp [1979], for AM 4 see Madore and Arp [1982]. Also names AM 0430-392, AM 4 = AM 1353-265, AM 3 = AM 2346-731 were listed as part of a survey for southern peculiar galaxies and associations. See [Arp and Madore 1987].

And: Four suspected dwarf galaxy companions of M 31 [van den Bergh 1972]. Numbered I to IV.

Anon. Platais: Single cluster including V1726 Cygni. See Platais [1979] and Extended Notes on page 112.

Ant or Antalová or Av: Four Galactic open clusters. "Ant 4" name used here for first time, rather than Antalová's misleading name "NGC 6374" (quotes are significant). See Antalová [1972]. Numbered 1 to 4.

AO84 or [AO84]: Nine groups of nearby (GJ or *Gliese Catalogue*) stars found from their space motions to be possible moving clusters. Agekyan and Orlov [1984]. Numbered I to IX.

Apr or Apriamasvili: The Apriamasvili name is also variously transliterated Apriamashvili or Apriamaswili. A single Galactic open cluster in Scutum. Later also known as Basel 1. See Apriamasvili [1964]. Numbered 1.

Arches Cluster: A single massive infrared cluster near the Galactic center, so named apparently due to "arched filaments" previously detected in the area in the radio (20 cm). First identified as a cluster in Nagata, *et al.*, [1995]. Not numbered. [NHS93] 17 = Arches Cluster

Archinal: A single possible Galactic open cluster, reported here for the first time. See Extended Notes on page 113. Numbered 1.

Arcturus group: A likely asterism of scattered stars around Arcturus, first noted by Mattison and Burritt [1856a and 1856b]. Not numbered.

Arp: Two Galactic globular clusters. For Palomar 14 = Arp 1, see Arp and van den Bergh [1960]. Reference for Arp 2 is unknown. Numbered 1 and 2.

Auner: A single Galactic open cluster found in a ghost image of Sirius on the POSS. [Auner, *et al.*, 1980]. Numbered 1.

AvdB: Arp and van den Bergh Galactic globular cluster. This is Palomar 14. [Arp and van den Bergh 1960]. Numbered 1.

Av-H or Aveni-Hunter or Av-Hunter: A single possible cluster around BM And. See Aveni and Hunter [1969]. Numbered 1.

[B90]: Radio sources in M 31. [Braun 1990]. Numbered 1 to 534.

BA: "Baade and Arp" nebula in M 31. [Baade and Arp 1964]. "BA 1-," numbered 1 to 688; "BA 2-," numbered 1 to 68; "BA 3-," numbered 1 to 30; and "BA 4-," numbered 1 to 40.

Barkhatova or Bar: Two open clusters. [Barkhatova 1958a, b]. Numbered 1 and 2.

Basel or Bas: "Basel Astr. Institute." open clusters. For Basel 1 to 6 see Becker and Fenkart [1971]. For Basel 11b, see Grubissich [1973]. For Basel 17, see Steppe [1977]. For Basel 20, see Topaktas, *et al.*, [1982]. References for the other Basel objects are unknown. Numbered 1 to 20, with 11A and 11B. Apr 1 = Bas 1.

bd or BD: "Bonner Durchmusterung" star catalog. [Schonfeld 1886; Argelander and Küstner 1903]. Numbered with format "± DD NNNNNA," where "± DD" indicates 1855.0 declination zone, and "NNNNNA" is a star number with possible suffix.

Bergeron: A single possible Galactic open cluster, independently discovered by Joe Bergeron in 1997. See Extended Notes on page 196 for Reiland 1. Numbered 1. Reiland 1 = Bergeron 1.

Berkeley or Be: "University of California at *Berkeley*" possible Galactic open clusters. [Setteducati, A. F., and H. F. Weaver 1960]. Numbered 1 to 104. St 24 = Be 3; NGC 1798 = Be 16; Bi 12 = Be 26; Bi 11 = Be 27; Bi 10 = Be 28; Bi 9 = Be 30; Bi 7 = Be 32; Bi 8 = Be 32; Ru 7 = Be 33; Bi 13 = Be 34; Ru 34 = Be 38; Ru 37 = Be 40; Ru 42 = Be 41; NGC 6749 = Be 42; NGC 6791 = Be 46; NGC 6827 = Be 48; IC 1310 = Be 50; NGC 7423 = Be 57; and Ru 4 = Be 74.

BFS: HII regions and CO radial velocities. [Blitz, *et al.*, 1982]. Numbered 1 to 65.

BH: See [HB90] on page **272** and vdB-Ha on page **277**.

BHB2000: 435 globular clusters in NGC 205 = M 31, and 199 miscellaneous objects previously thought to have been globular clusters in NGC 205. Numbered similar to HBK below, but here with a very complicated system where: a) "nnn-mmm" implies Bol nnn and SKHB mmm; b) "nnnD-mmm" implies Bol Dnnn and SKHB mmm; c) "nnn-ammm" implies Bol nnn, and if Dnnn: [CCS85] nnn, if Hnnn or Bnnn: [V62] nnn; and d) nnnD-ammm implies Bol Dnnn and if Dnnn: [CCS85] nnn, if Hnnn or Bnnn: [V62] nnn. Also DAO implies [CCS85], BA implies BA 3-, NB implies Nbol, VB implies [V62], and VH implies (both) [H32] and [V32]. The origin of names "EX8" and "GS-1" are unknown.

Biurakan or Bi: Also transliterated as Byurakan or Bjurakan. Named after Biurakan Observatory, outside Yerevan in Armenia. 13 Galactic star clusters. The original reference for numbers 1 to 6 is Iskudarian [1959]. The original reference for numbers 7 to 11 is Iskudarian [1960]. The original reference for number 12 and 13 is unknown. Numbered 1 to 13. Mrk 50 = Bi 3; Mrk 6 = Bi 4; Mrk 38 = Bi 5.

Bica: One object, a likely supernova remnant [Bica 1994; Bica, *et al.*, 1995]. Numbered 1.

Blanco or Bl: One Galactic open cluster. [Blanco 1949]. Numbered 1.

Bochum or Bo: 15 Galactic open clusters. For Bochum 1 to 6, see Moffat and Vogt [1975a]. For Bochum 8 to 13, see Moffat and Vogt [1975b]. For Bochum 13 and 14, see Moffat and Vogt [1975c]. For Bochum 15, see FitzGerald, *et al.*, [1976]. Numbered 1 to 15. NGC 2409 = Bochum 4; vdB-Ha 90 = Bochum 8.

Bok: One Galactic open cluster. Philip, *et al.*, [1977]. Numbered 1. NGC 1901 = Bok 1.

Bol and Bol D: Globular clusters in M 31. Named after *Bol*ogna, Italy. For Bol 1 to 288 and Bol D1 to Bol D132, see Battistini, *et al.*, [1980]. For Bol 289 to 513 and Bol D133 to D350, see Battistini, *et al.*, [1987]. Numbered 1 to 513, and D1 to D350. Nos. 334 and 359 are missing. Bol D327 = Bol D325; ACH 1 = Bol D53

BRAN: Nebulae of unknown nature. [Brand, *et al.*, 1986]. Numbered 1 to 400, with some letter suffixes.

BRHT: Binary star cluster candidates in the Large Magellanic Cloud [Bhatia, *et al.*, 1991]. Numbered 1a, 1b, … 64b.

Brocchi's or Brocchi's cluster: Single asterism, named after its independent discoverer, D. F. Brocchi (see Collinder 399 in Extended Notes on page 123). Usually not numbered. Cr 399 = Brocchi.

Brück Clusters in the SMC [Brück 1976]. Numbered 1 to 168.

[BS95]: Newly discovered clusters in the SMC. [Bica and Schmitt 1995]. Numbered 1 to 284.

[BW88]: see "Cl [BW88]" on page 270.

C.95 or [CSS95]: Galactic open clusters in Gemini OB molecular cloud complex, discovered (and probably visible only) in the infrared. [Carpenter, *et al.*, 1995]. Numbered 1a, 1b, 2, 3, 4a, 4b.

Chhmm_ddd: "IAU style" general name for Galactic cluster. "Numbered" using truncated B1950.0 positions.

C84: X-ray sources around M 31. [Crampton, *et al.*, 1984]. Numbered 1 to 116.

Caldwell or Caldw: 109 nonstellar objects, supposedly the "best" beyond the Messier objects. The name originates from the legal surname ("*Caldwell*-Moore") of Patrick Moore [Moore and Pepin 1995]. Numbered 1 to 109.

Canali: Single (likely) asterism near M 104 [Canali 1997]. Numbered 1.

[CCS85] or CCS85: Possible globular clusters in M 31. [Crampton, *et al.*, 1985]. Numbered 1 to 109.

CD: Cordoba Durchmusterung star catalog. [Thome 1892, 1894, 1900, 1914; Perrine 1932]. Numbered with format "±DD NNNNNA", where "±DD" indicates 1875.0 declination zone, and "NNNNNA" is a star number with possible suffix.

CDS: Centre de Données astronomiques de Strasbourg (Strasbourg Stellar Data Center, see Appendix E for address).

Cederblad or Ced: Reflection nebulae, although Ced 144 = IC 1257 is a globular cluster. [Cederblad 1946]. Numbered 1 to 215, some with suffixes "a" to "o."

Central cluster: This is the name often given (e.g., by Figer, *et al.*, [1999]) to the dense infrared cluster of stars in the central parsec of the Galaxy, i.e., the Galactic Center. Not numbered.

CGCG: 31,350 galaxies and galaxy clusters on the

POSS. [Zwicky, *et al.*, 1960a; Zwicky and Herzog 1960b, c; Zwicky, *et al.*, 1960e; Zwicky and Kowal 1960f]. Numbered in format FFF-NNN ("FFF" is POSS field number, and "NNN" is object number) or using truncated B1950.0 positions.

Cl [BW88]: One cluster, discovered in the radio, in NGC 1579. [Becker and White 1988]. Numbered 1.

Cl Skiff: See entry under "Skiff" on page 276.

Cl vdB or vdB: "vdB" is a double star that was an M31 globular cluster candidate. See "GS-SET" on page 271, or "vdB" under the Extended Notes on page 118. "vdB 0" or "Cl vdB 0" is the brightest globular cluster in M 31 [van den Bergh 1969]. "vdB 1" or "Cl vdB 1" is a Galactic open cluster [van den Bergh 1957]. Other "Cl vdB" objects are galactic open clusters associated with nebulae "vdB" [van den Bergh 1966]. In the latter case, clusters are named Cl vdB 80, 83, 85, 92, 130, 150, 152.

CMD: Acronym for "Color-Magnitude Diagram."

CNO: Acronym for "Carbon, Nitrogen, and Oxygen," material in globular star clusters.

Collinder or Cr: 471 Galactic open clusters—most previously cataloged. See Collinder [1931]. Numbered 1 to 471.

CPD: Cape Photographic Durchmusterung star catalog. [Gill and Kapteyn 1896, 1897, 1900; Gill 1903]. Numbered with format "±DD NNNNNA", where "±DD" indicates 1875.0 declination zone, and "NNNNNA" is a star number with possible suffix.

CSI: Stars in the SIMBAD database. [Jung, *et al.*, 1973]. Numbered based on (BD) declination zone and truncated B1950.0 positions.

[CS95]: See "C.95" on page 269.

CTB: Galactic radio sources. Name originates from *C*al*t*ech observations, list *B*. [Wilson and Bolton 1960]. Numbered 1 to 110.

[CV98]: Five possible clusters near M 67 [Chupina and Vereshchagin, 1998], with the name assigned here using both authors' initials and the publication year. The name "Chupina" (acknowledging only one of the authors) has been given to these clusters in Dias, *et al.* [2002]. Numbered 1 to 5.

Czernik or Cz: Supposed Galactic star clusters. See Alter, *et al.*, [1966, 1, 6]; Czernik [1966]. Numbered 1 to 45. Cz 33, 34, 35, and 36 are dwarf galaxies or galaxy clusters.

Δ or Dunlop: Nonstellar objects [Dunlop 1828]. Numbered 1 to 629.

Danks: Two Galactic open clusters. Discovered by Danks, *et al.*, [1983], and called there C1310-624 and C1309-624; named by Lundström and Stenholm [1984]. Numbered 1 and 2.

[DB00]: 58 possible infrared star clusters near the Galactic nucleus, discovered by Dutra and Bica [2000]. Numbered 1 to 58.

[DB01]: 42 possible infrared star clusters discovered by Dutra and Bica [2001]. Numbered 1 to 42.

DDO: *D*avid *D*unlap *O*bservatory dwarf galaxies. van den Bergh [1959]. Numbered 1 to 222.

Dejc: A possible globular cluster, later shown to be a galaxy. [Dejc 1963]. Numbered 1.

Djorg: Galactic globular clusters, see Djorgovski [1987]. Numbered 1 to 3. ESO 456-SC38 = Djorg 2, and NGC 6540 = Djorg 3.

Do or Dolidze: 47 possible Galactic open clusters. For Do 1 to 11, see Dolidze [1961a]. For Do 12 to 46 (numbered there 1 to 35) see Dolidze [1961b, 20–21]. Original reference for Do 47 unknown. Numbered 1 to 47. Be 87 = Do 7.

DoDz: 11 possible Galactic open clusters. [Dolidze and Dzimselejsvili 1966]. Numbered 1 to 11.

DSFG1e: *Deep Sky Field Guide* (First Edition) [Cragin, *et al.*, 1993].

DSFG2e: *Deep Sky Field Guide*, (Second Edition) [Cragin and Bonanno, 2001].

DSS: Digitized Sky Survey [AURA 1995]. DSS-N are images from the Palomar Observatory Sky Survey [National Geographic Society 1955], while DSS-S are images taken with the U. K. Schmidt telescope.

Dufay: A single Galactic globular cluster. See "HP" on page 272. Numbered 1. HP 1 = Dufay 1.

Dunlop or Δ: See Δ .

E: Three distant Galactic clusters discovered on ESO (B) plates. [Lauberts 1976] Numbered 1 to 3. "E" is also sometimes used as an abbreviation for "ESO" (see ESO).

[EC95]: One infrared cluster involved in Sh 2-269. This designation used here for the first time. [Eiroa and Casali 1995]. Numbered 1.

EQ: Objects of unknown type included in SIMBAD. These designations are meant to be used in SIMBAD only—their use should otherwise be avoided. Numbered using truncated B1950.0 coordinates.

Eridanus: Single Galactic globular cluster (named after constellation). [Cesarsky, *et al.*, 1977]. Usually no number.

ESO: Objects on *ESO* (B) survey. [Lauberts 1982]. Numbered using FFF-ttNNN format, where "FFF" is the ESO field number, "tt" is an indication of object type (e.g. "SC" for star cluster, "G" for galaxy), and NNN is a sequence number.

[Espin]: Nonstellar objects, usually now listed by their IC number, e.g. IC 1299, 1304-1307, 1310, 1311, 1314, 1363, 1369, 1378, 1400, 1402, 1434, and 1442. [Espin 1894]. Numbered 1 to 15.

Fei: A single possible Galactic open cluster. [Feinstein 1964]. Numbered 1.

FJJ NGC 147 and FJJ NGC 185: Planetary nebulae—and some globular clusters—in Local Group galaxies. [Ford, *et al.*, 1977]. Numbered FJJ NGC 147 "I" to "IV" and FJJ NGC 185 "I" to "VIII."

Fleming: Nebulae discovered by W. Fleming [Pickering 1901] and listed in Harvard College Observatory [1908]. These are actually the "HN" or "Harvard Numbers" in the latter publication, but were assigned to the Fleming name by Dreyer in the Second IC. IC numbers usually take precedence to these names. Numbered from 56 to 67, and 69 to 108.

Fornax: Fornax dwarf galaxy.

[FM80] 1: A possible open cluster discovered by FitzGerald and Moffat [1980], along with Waterloo 7. This name is assigned here for the first time. The name "Waterloo 8" has been assigned to this object by Dias, *et al.* [2002] but it appears obvious that FitzGerald and Moffat did not wish to use that name or they would have done so in the original paper. Numbered 1.

Fr or Frolov: A single Galactic open cluster. [Frolov 1977]. Numbered 1.

French: One object, also known as the "Toadstool" [French 1997]. Numbered 1. See "French 1" in Extended Notes on page 131.

Frolov: See "Fr" above.

Frost: Nebulae found by R. H. Frost. [Harvard College Observatory 1908]. Numbered 786 to 1238.

GAL: Objects identified by Galactic coordinate, as given in various papers and by SIMBAD. Usually given in a format such as GAL lll.lll±bb.bb, where lll.lll and ±bb.bb are the Galactic longitude and latitude of the object, respectively.

Gam Vel cluster or Gamma Velorum cluster : Galactic cluster around the Wolf-Rayet star γ^2 Velorum [Brandt, *et al.*, 1971]. This name is as suggested in Brandt, *et al.* The name "Brandt 1" (acknowledging only one of the paper's authors) has been given to these clusters in Dias, *et al.* [2002]. Not numbered.

GC: Nonstellar objects. For GC 1 to 5079, see [Herschel 1864]. For GC 5080 to 6251 see [Dreyer 1879]. Numbered 1 to 6251. Later incorporated into the NGC.

GCl: Galactic (supposed) globular cluster. [Alter, *et al.*, 1958; Alter, *et al.*, 1970; Ruprecht, *et al.*, 1981]. Numbered 1 to 125, with some ".1" suffixes. Dejc 1 = GCl 4 and NGC 6684 = GCl 102 are galaxies.

GCRV: "*G*eneral *c*atalogue of stellar *r*adial *v*elocities." [Wilson 1953]. Numbered 1 to 15106.

Gingrich: A single Galactic open cluster which, along with the involved nebula, is commonly known as IC 348 [Gingrich 1922]. Usually not numbered. IC 348 = Gingrich.

GJ: Stars from the Gliese "Catalog of Nearby Stars" [1969] and a supplement by Gleise and H. Jahreiss [1979] (hence, GJ). Originally numbered from 1.0 to 965.0 (with 1529 stars total).

GJJC: A single planetary nebula in NGC 6656 = M 22. [Gillett, et al. 1989]. Numbered 1. IRAS 18333–2357 = GJJC 1.

GLC: Galactic (supposed) globular cluster. Numbered using truncated B1950.0 coordinates.

GM 1-: Cometary nebulae. At least one, GM 1-24, has an embedded infrared cluster (IRAS 17136-3617). [Gyulbudaghian and Maghakian 1977a, b]. Numbered 1 to 79.

Gr or Grasdalen: A single infrared Galactic open cluster, associated with the ρ Ophiuchi dark cloud. [Grasdalen, *et al.*, 1973]. Numbered 1.

Graff 1 or Graff cluster: A single Galactic open cluster [Graff 1922]. Numbered 1. IC 4756 = Graff 1.

Graham: A single Galactic open cluster (including CPD –62°1822, –62°1823, and –62°1824). [Graham 1970, 712, 716]. Numbered 1.

Grasdalen: See "Gr".

Grindlay or Gri: Grindlay 1 is a supposed Galactic globular cluster that apparently does not exist. [Grindlay and Hertz 1981]. Numbered 1.

GRS: "*G*alactic *r*adio *s*ource," a designation created by SIMBAD. Numbered by Galactic longitude and latitude.

GS-SET: A double star, once a suspected dwarf companion of M 31, and also once a suspected globular cluster in M 31. Also known as "vdb" having been first photographed by van den Bergh [1972] although the discovery was by B. Herbst [Sargent, *et al.*, 1977, 948]. The "GS-SET" name apparently originates from (of all things!) an abbreviation for "*g*lobular cluster *s*uspect from *S*argent, *et al.*, 1977." (See Huchra, *et al.*, [1991, Table 2]). Not numbered. In SIMBAD under "NAME GS-SET."

GSC: "*G*uide *S*tar *C*atalog." [Lasker, *et al.*, 1990]. Numbered FFFFF-NNNNN, where "FFFFF" is an internal field number, and "NNNNN" is a running number.

GUM: Southern HII regions and planetary nebulae. [Gum 1955]. Numbered 1 to 97.

H or H. Nonstellar object discovered by William Herschel. See Dreyer [1912] for a reprinting of Herschel's lists. Numbered with leading object type, from "I" to "VII." Do not confuse "H" with "Ha" for "Harvard" (see below).

h: Nonstellar objects discovered by John Herschel. [Herschel 1833, 1847]. Numbered 1 to 4015. Further objects using a ½ or a prime are listed in Herschel [1833 and 1847], but only numbered in the GC [Herschel 1864] and the NGC [Dreyer 1888]. Further objects whose numbers are given in square brackets are in the SMC and in parentheses are in the LMC, from lists in Herschel [1847, 151-164]. These are numbered from 1 to 226 in the SMC and from 1 to 919 in the LMC.

[H32]: Globular clusters in M 31. [Hubble 1932]. Numbered 1 to 140.

[H60b]: Globular clusters in the LMC. Note that few of these objects (only [H60b] 11 according to Suntzeff, *et al.* [1992]) are true old red globular clusters. [Hodge 1960]. Numbered 1 to 14, with 12 and 13 missing from the original paper.

H81 B-: Open clusters in M 31. [Hodge 1981]. Numbered 1 to 413.

[H85]: Associations in the SMC [Hodge 1985]. Numbered 1 to 70.

[H86]: Star clusters in the SMC [Hodge 1986]. Numbered 1 to 213.

H88: Clusters in LMC. [Hodge 1988]. Numbered 1 to 390.

Ha or Harvard: 21 Galactic star clusters. [Shapley 1930]. Numbered 1 to 21. Ha 3, 5, 6, 8, 9, 10, 13, 16, 20, and 21 were new. Do not confuse "Ha" with "H" for William Herschel—see above.

Haf or Haffner: Galactic star clusters. [Haffner 1957]. Numbered 1 to 17, 18a, 18b, 18c, 19 to 22 and (1) to (5); later (1), (3), (4), (5) became 23 to 26.

Harvard: See "Ha".

[HB90]: One cluster, the southeastern component of NGC 242. This designation, derived from the author's initials and the publication year, is preferred over the "BH" designation used in the original paper, which is not explained and could be confused with other uses of "BH" in astronomical nomenclature (see "vdB-Ha"). [Hatzidimitriou and Bhatia 1990]. Numbered one.

HBK: Globular clusters in M 31 [Huchra, *et al.*, 1991]. 150 objects numbered according to their Bol and SKHB designations (e.g. HBK 291-9 is also Bol 291 = SKHB 9).

[HC69]: Galactic radio sources. [Holden and Caswell 1969]. Numbered 1 to 45.

HD and HDE: "*H*enry *D*raper" star catalog and *E*xtension. For HD, see Cannon and Pickering [1918–1924]. For HDE, see Cannon [1925] and Cannon and Mayall [1949]. Numbered 1–225300 (for HD) and 225301–359083 (for HDE).

HEAO: X-ray sources. [Marshall, *et al.*, 1979]. Numbered using truncated B1950.0 coordinates.

Hen N or Henize N: Nebulae in the LMC with the name originating from author and "*n*ebulae." Given in SIMBAD as "LHA 120-N," which originates from "Lamont-Hussey alpha, field 120: LMC Nebula." [Henize 1956, Table 2]. Numbered 1 to 121.

Herbig-Haro or HH: Herbig-Haro objects. See Herbig [1974] for numbers 1 to 43.

HJD93 or [HJD93]: Clusters in NGC 4314. [Benedict, *et al.*, 1993]. Numbered 1 to 14.

HM: A single Galactic open cluster. [Havlen and Moffat 1977]. Numbered 1.

HN: "Harvard Numbers", assigned to nebula discovered at the Harvard College Observatory and reported in Harvard College Observatory [1908]. When these numbers are used here, the actual discoverer's name has been used rather than "HN". See "Fleming". Numbered 1 to 108.

Ho or Hogg: Southern Galactic open clusters. [Hogg 1965]. Supposedly new objects numbered from 1 to 23, while all objects numbered from 1 to 133. The use of these latter numbers should be denigrated.

Hodge: Use of this name should be avoided, since P. Hodge has participated in the creation of many catalogs of star clusters and associations in the Magellanic Clouds and Andromeda galaxy. See and use instead the designations such as [H60b], [H81] B–, [H85], [H86], [H88], [HS66], [HW], and [LH].

HP: "Obs. de *H*aute *P*rovence." Original reference for HP 1 is unknown, but IAU nomenclature page suggests the authors are J. Dufay, E. Berthier, and Morignat. It is also suggested there that Terzan 1 = HP 2; Terzan 2 = HP 3; Terzan 4 = HP 4; and Terzan 6 = HP 5. Therefore, see Terzan [1967; 1968]. Numbered 1 to 5.

[HR91]: A single infrared cluster involved in the bipolar HII region Sh 2-106. This designation used here for the first time. [Hodapp and Rayner 1991]. Numbered 1.

HRD or H-R diagram: Acronym for "Hertsprung-Russell diagram."

[HS66]: Star clusters in the LMC. [Hodge and Sexton 1966]. Numbered 1 to 455.

HW: Clusters in the SMC. [Hodge and Wright 1974]. Numbered 1 to 86.

[I92a]: Nonstellar objects in M 33. [Ivanov 1992]. Numbered 1 to 185.

IC: Nonstellar objects. [Dreyer 1895 and 1908]. See also Sinnott [1988]. Numbered 1 to 5386.

II Zw, III Zw, and VII Zw: Compact galaxies, lists II, III, and VII. [Zwicky and Zwicky 1971].

IRAS: Point infrared source (from the *I*nfra *r*ed *A*stronomical *S*atellite). [Joint IRAS Science Working Group 1988]. Numbered using truncated B1950.0 coordinates.

Iskudarian or Isk: One supposed cluster of white dwarf stars in Lyra. [Iskudarian and Saakian 1961]. Also see entry in Extended Notes on page 141. Numbered 1.

Iss or Isserstedt: "Stellar rings" of stars, which Isserstedt and others have hypothesized may have similar absolute sizes and may serve as distance indicators in the Galaxy. For Iss 1 to Iss 1002 see Isserstedt [Isserstedt and Schmidt-Kaler 1968]. For Iss 1003 to 1067, see Isserstedt [1970]. Numbered 1 to 1067.

JaFu: Two planetary nebulae associated with Galactic globular clusters. The JaFu name originates from the first two characters of the names of two of the authors (Jacoby and Fullton) [Jacoby, *et al.*, 1997]. Numbered 1 and 2.

Johansson: A single likely open cluster in Norma [Johansson, 1980]. Name assigned in Dias, *et al.* [2002]. Numbered 1.

Kara: Isolated galaxies. [Karachentseva 1973]. Numbered 1 to 1051. Palomar 15 = Kara 781.

[KCW94]: Ultracompact HII regions observed by radio. [Kurtz, *et al.*, 1994]. Numbered using Galactic coordinates.

Kemble: Two probable asterisms. Kemble 1 is usually known as "Kemble's Cascade." [Houston 1980 and 1985]. Kemble 2 is usually known as "Mini Cassiopeia" [Kemble 1995]. Also see listings for both in the Extended Notes on pages 141. Numbered 1 and 2.

King: For King 1 to 21, see King [1949]. King notes that Rebecca B. Jones discovered clusters 2, 3, and 5, and Carl K. Seyfert found cluster 6. For King 22, see King [1961]. For King 23 to 27, see King [1966]. Numbered 1 to 27. NGC 609 = King 3; Be 18 = King 22; Cz 28 = King 23; Cz 32 = King 24; and Cz 40 = King 27.

KMHK or KMH90: Clusters in the LMC. [Kontizas, *et al.*, 1990]. Numbered 1 to 1762.

Kodaira or Kod: A single reddened star once thought to be a Galactic globular cluster. [Kodaira, *et al.*, 1995]. Numbered 1.

KOHX: Globular cluster X-ray sources. Origin of acronym is unknown. [Bratolyubova-Tsulukidze, *et al.*, 1976]. Numbered 1 to ?.

Kron: Clusters in the SMC. [Kron 1956]. Numbered 1 to 69.

Küstner: A catalog of stars in the Galactic globular cluster NGC 7078 = M 15. Noteworthy since Küstner 648 (or "K 648") was later determined to be a planetary nebulae (= Pease 1). [Küstner 1921]. Numbered 1 to 1137.

L61: Emission line objects in the SMC (including several nebulous star clusters) [Lindsay 1961]. Numbered 1 to 593.

Lacaille or Lac: Nonstellar objects noted by Nicolas Louis de Lacaille (1713–1762). See Gingerich [1960]; Glynn Jones [1975]; Evans [1992] for modern discussions of these objects. Trumpler 10 = Lac II-6 and IC 2395 = Lac III-3 have been identified here (by B. Skiff) for the first time.

[LAL96]: Two clusters in NGC 1333. Name used here for the first time. [Lada, *et al.*, 1996]. Numbered 1 and 2.

Latyshev or La: Two groups of nearby (GJ or *Gliese Catalog*) stars, found from their space motions to be possible moving clusters. See Latyshev [1972; 1977]. Numbered 1 and 2.

LBN: *L*ynds *b*right *n*ebulae. [Lynds 1965]. Numbered 1 to 1125, or numbered with Galactic coordinates.

[LDEG91]: Four infrared clusters in, respectively, NGC 2023, NGC 2024, NGC 2068 (= M 78) and NGC 2071. Named here for the first time. [Lada, *et al.*, 1991]. Numbered 1 to 4.

LDN: Lynds dark nebulae. [Lynds 1962]. Numbered 1 to 1802, with some letter suffixes.

Lederman: One apparent asterism. See Extended Notes on page 143. Numbered 1.

LeDrew: Several possible clusters discovered by G. LeDrew [private communication, LeDrew, 2001]. Numbered 1 to 8 (in decreasing order of likelihood as a true cluster).

Leo: Names of dwarf galaxies in the constellation Leo, Leo I, and Leo II = Leo B.

Levy-Wallach or Levy-W. Four apparent asterisms. Levy-Wallach J2204.3+4508 is a stellar ring [Levy, 2001, p. 116], while Levy-Wallach J1948.2+3743, Levy-Wallach J2108.8+0620 and Levy-Wallach J2340.6+5618 are star streams. See entries under these names in the Extended Notes starting on page 143. Numbered using truncated J2000.0 coordinates.

LH: 122 associations in the LMC. [Lucke and Hodge 1970]. Numbered 1 to 122. Note that although called "associations" by Lucke and Hodge, most of these are

LMC clusters, and many are NGC objects.

LHA 115-N: Nebulae in the SMC. This is the same as "Henize N," but in the SMC only. [Henize 1956, Table 4]. Numbered 1 to 90.

LHA 120-N: This is the same as "Henize N".

Liller: A single Galactic globular cluster. [Liller 1977]. Numbered 1.

Lindsay or Lind: Open clusters in the SMC. [Lindsay 1958]. Numbered 1 to 116 (Lindsay's table III) and 1 to 14 (Lindsay's table II of "possible clusters"). The latter 14 identifications are not included in the catalog here.

Ling: A single asterism or possible cluster, discovered by Alister Ling [private communication, 1995]. See NGC 6743 on page 185. Numbered 1.

LkHA or LkHα: Emission line stars. For no. 101 (the only one cited here) and a partial explanation of the abbreviation, see [Herbig 1956]. Numbered 1 to 359, and 425, 427, 428 and 513.

Lodén or Lo: 50 Galactic clusters or groups of stars among various fields. See Lodén [1973; 1977, 1979a, b, 1980, 1981] and Johansson [1981] (the latter reference is for Lo 2326. Reference for Lo 1296 is unknown. Numbered (not sequentially) from 1 to 2313.

Loiano: A single faint Galactic cluster in Vulpecula, named after the Loiano Observing Station of the Bologna Astronomical Observatory, discovered by Bernabei and Polcaro [2001]. Numbered 1.

Lund Catalogue: Galactic open clusters. [Lyngå 1987]. Numbered 1 to 1212.

LW: Clusters in the outer LMC. [Lyngå and Westerlund 1963]. Numbered 1 to 483.

Lyngå: Galactic open clusters. For Lyngå 1 to 14, see [Lyngå 1964]. The reference for Lyngå 15 is unknown. Numbered 1 to 15.

M or Messier: Nonstellar objects. [Messier 1784]. See also Mallas and Kreimer [1978], Glynn Jones [1991], Pennington [1998], and O'Meara [1998a]. Numbered 1 to 110.

Mackie: A single likely asterism found by G. Mackie on 2000 August 3-4 at the Mt. Kobau Star Party and reported by A. Whitman [Whitman and Mackie, 2000; Mackie, 2001; see Appendix A for web address]. Numbered 1.

Maffei: Infrared sources, later found to be galaxies. [Maffei 1968]. Numbered 1 and 2.

Mandushev 1: An asterism near SU Cygni, as described in Turner, *et al.* [1998]. Name first given in Dias, *et al.* [2002]. Numbered 1.

Mayall: See "[Me 53]".

Markarian or Mrk: See Mrk.

Markov: A single likely asterism, discovered by Paul Markov of Toronto, Canada, on 2001 July 4–5 [Markov, 2001; also see Appendix A for web information]. Numbered 1.

Mayer: Galactic open clusters. Original reference unknown—appears in the *Lund Catalogue*. Numbered 1 to 3.

MC or [MBB72]: Radio sources in the LMC. [McGee, *et al.*, 1972]. Numbered 1 to 102.

MC: Same as [MBB72] above. Name originates from "*M*agellanic *C*loud."

MCG: Morphological Catalog of Galaxies. [Vorontsov-Vel'yaminov and Krasnogorskaia 1962; Vorontsov-Vel'yaminov and Arkhipova 1963, 1964, 1968, 1974.] "Numbered" with format ±F1-F2-NNNN, where "F1" is the declination band and "F2" is the field number of a POSS field, and "NNNN" is the object number in that field.

[MD78]: Clusters in M 33 (except no. 53 is a background galaxy). [Melnick and D'Odorico 1978]. Numbered 1 to 58.

[ME53]: Four nebulous objects in M 31 [Mayall and Eggen 1953]. Numbered I to IV.

Melotte or Mel: Galactic star clusters, visible on the Franklin-Adams Chart Plates. [Melotte 1915a]. Numbered 1 to 245.

Messier: See "M" above.

MGM: Infrared sources near the Galactic center. [Moneti, *et al.*, 1992 and 1994]. Numbered 1 to 7 [Moneti, *et al.*, 1992] and 8 [Moneti, *et al.*, 1994] and sometimes with sub-components. RAFGL 2004 = MGM 5.

Min 2- or Minkowski 2-: Emission nebulae [Minkowski 1947]. Numbered from 57 to 74.

MKN: Markarian galaxy catalogs. See Markarian and Lipovetskij [1971] for MKN 369 = Dejc 1, the only MKN entry in the catalog here. Numbered 303 to 401 (in this reference). Also see "Mrk".

MLA: Emission objects in M 31. [Meyssonnier, *et al.*, 1993]. Numbered 1 to 1515. At least two globular clusters.

Moffat: A single Galactic open cluster. [Moffat 1976]. Numbered 1.

MOL: The *Master Optical List* of nonstellar objects of Dixon and Sonneborn [1980]. This list includes 182855 entries, many of which are different names for the same object. The entries (fortunately) are not numbered separately.

Mrk or Markarian: 50 Galactic O-type star clusters. [Markarian 1951]. Only Mrk 6, 18, 38, and 50 were new discoveries. Numbered 1 to 50. Also see "MKN".

Muzzio: A single Galactic open cluster. Original reference unknown—appears in the *Lund Catalogue*. Numbered 1.

NBol: *N*ew *Bol*ogna catalog of possible globular clusters in M 31. [Battistini, *et al.*, 1993]. Numbered 1 to 108.

[NHS93]: Bright infrared sources within 1° of the Galactic center. [Nagata, *et al.*, 1993]. Numbered from 1 to 50.

NGC: Nonstellar objects. See Dreyer [1888]. See also Sulentic and Tifft [1973]; Sinnott [1988]; Archinal [1993]. Numbered 1 to 7840.

NRL: "Naval Research Laboratory" radio sources. [Haddock *et al.*, 1954]. Numbered 1 to 24.

NPD: North Polar Distance. In degrees, this is the same as 90° minus declination.

OCl: Galactic (supposed) "Open cluster." [Alter, *et al.*, 1958; Alter, *et al.*, 1970; Ruprecht, *et al.*, 1981]. Numbered 1 to 1303, with some ".1" suffixes.

OCISM: "*O*pen *C*lusters and *I*nter*s*tellar *M*atter," i.e., open clusters associated with nebulae. [Leisawitz 1988]. Numbered 1 to 128.

OGLE-CL: Clusters and candidate clusters in the SMC. [Pietrzyński, *et al.*, 1998]. Numbered from 0001 to 0238, with prefix "SMC", e.g. OGLE-CL SMC0001. Note (see entries below): Brück 31 = OGLE-CL SMC0019 = OGLE-CL SMC0175 and OGLE-CL SMC0144 = OGLE-CL SMC0236.

OHSC: Clusters in the outer LMC. [Olszewski, *et al.*, 1988]. Numbered 1 to 37.

P.95 or [PBH95]: Globular clusters in M 81. [Perelmuter, *et al.*, 1995]. Numbered 1 to 82.

Palomar or Pal: Supposed galactic globular clusters (some were later shown to be open clusters). For Palomar 1 to 13, see Abell [1955]. For Palomar 14 see Arp and van den Bergh [1960]. For Palomar 15 see Zwicky [1959]. Numbered 1 to 15.

[PAV78]: HII regions in M 31. [Pellet, *et al.*, 1978]. Numbered 1 to 981.

Pazmino: A single Galactic open cluster, so named by Houston [1978]. Stock 23 = Pazmino's cluster. Not usually numbered. See further information in Extended Notes on page 202.

[PBH95]: See "P.95".

Pease: A single planetary nebula within the Galactic globular cluster NGC 7078 = M 15. [Pease 1928]. Numbered 1. Küstner 648 = Pease 1.

[PFJ93]: X-ray objects in M 31. [Primini, *et al.*, 1993]. Numbered 1 to 86.

PGC: "Principal Galaxies Catalog." [Paturel, *et al.*, 1989]. Numbered 1 to 73197.

Phoenix: Phoenix dwarf galaxy, discovered by Schuster and West [1976] as a possible globular cluster or galaxy, and identified as a galaxy by Canterna and Flower [1977]. Not numbered.

[PKL98]: Several newly found nearby Galactic star clusters and associations, identified via Hipparcos proper motion data by Platais, Kozhurina-Platais, and van Leeuwen [1998], from which names and date the acronym has been assigned. Numbered from 1 to 20 corresponding to Table 1 of the paper. PMG 1 = [PKL98] 10.

Pismis or Pi: Southern Galactic star clusters. For Pismis (unnumbered), see Pismis [1957]. For Pismis 1 to 26, see Pismis [1959]. Pismis (unnumbered) is Haffner 16, see in the Extended Notes on page 132. Pismis 1 to 24 are open clusters. Alter, *et al.*, [1970] also assigned the Pismis [1959] globular clusters (Ton 1 and Ton 2) the names Pismis 25 = Ton 1, and Pismis 26 = Ton 2. NGC 2568 = Pi 1, NGC 2645 = Pi 6, NGC 2659 = Pi 9, NGC 3503 = Pi 17, IC 4291 = Pi 18, NGC 6380 = Ton 1 = Pi 25.

Platais: See "Anon. Platais".

PMG: *P*uppis *m*oving *g*roup. [Röser and Bastian 1994]. Numbered 1 and 2.

PMH79: A single Galactic open cluster. [Pismis, *et al.*, 1979]. Numbered 1. Named here for the first time. See additional details in the Extended Notes on page 196.

Poole: Three objects, including a likely cluster, a possible asterism, and a Milky Way patch, in the vicinity of NGC 6724. Named here for the first time. See Extended Notes for NGC 6724 on page 182. [Poole 1993]. Numbered with truncated J2000.0 coordinates.

POSS: Palomar Observatory Sky Survey [National Geographic Society 1955].

[PRT94]: A single infrared cluster involved with NGC 3576. This designation is used here for the first time. [Persi, *et al.*, 1994]. Numbered 1.

PTB93 or [PTB93]: Possible Galactic open clusters. [Pasztor, *et al.*, 1994]. Numbered 1 to 10.

PWM78: Four possible, very reddened, Galactic star clusters. [Pfleiderer, *et al.*, 1978] Numbered 1 to 4. The "PWM78" name is used here for the first time. "PWM78 3" is also listed as C2306+606 (with no alternate name) in the *Lund Catalogue*.

Pyxis: Pyxis Galactic globular cluster. See Weinberger [1995]. Usually not numbered.

Quintuplet Cluster: A single massive infrared cluster near the Galactic center, so named due to its five obvious components. First identified as a multiple source and likely massive star cluster in Nagata, *et al.*, [1990]. Not numbered. RAFGL 2004 = Quintuplet cluster.

Raab: Galactic open clusters (all previously known). [Raab 1922]. Numbered 1 to 152.

RAFGL: *Revised Air Force Geophysical Laboratory* catalog of infrared sources. [Price and Walker 1983]. Numbered 1 to 7247 in runs, with some letter suffixes.

RC2: *Second Reference Catalogue* of galaxies. [de Vaucouleurs, *et al.*, 1976]. Numbered with "A" prefix followed by truncated B1950.0 coordinates.

RC3: *Third Reference Catalogue* of galaxies. [de Vaucouleurs, *et al.*, 1991]. Numbered with "A" prefix followed by truncated B1950.0 coordinates.

RCW: Hα emission regions. [Rodgers, *et al.*, 1960]. Numbered 1 to 182.

Reiland 1: A single possible Galactic open cluster reported as discovered by Tom Reiland according to Houston [1988b], and called by Houston there "Reiland's Nebulous Cluster." See Extended Notes on page 196. Numbered 1.

Reticulum: A single globular cluster within the LMC in the constellation Reticulum. See "Reticulum" in the Extended Notes on page 196. Usually not numbered.

RFT: Rich-field telescope.

Ro or Roslund: Galactic open clusters. [Roslund 1960]. Numbered 1 to 7.

Ruprecht or Ru: Galactic star clusters. For Ru 1 to 147, see [Alter, *et al.*, 1961, 2–3]. For Ru 148 to 175, see [Alter, *et al.*, 1966, 1, 5–6]. Ru 176 is first listed in the catalog of Ruprecht, *et al.*, 1981, with the source being a 1973 private communication from Ruprecht. Numbered Ru 1 to 176. NGC 2982 = Ru 80; NGC 3519 = Ru 93; NGC 4184 = Ru 102; NGC 5381 = Ru 109; NGC 6444 = Ru 132; NGC 5120 = Ru 166.

[S73]: Possible globular clusters in M 31. [Sharov 1973]. Numbered 1 to 25.

Schuster or Sch: Single Galactic open cluster. Original reference unknown. Numbered 1. See Extended Notes on page **198**.

Schuster-West or Sch.-West: Phoenix dwarf galaxy. See "Phoenix" on page 275 and in the Extended Notes on page 194. Not numbered.

Ser Dwarf: The globular cluster Palomar 5, mistaken to be a dwarf galaxy in the constellation Serpens. Not numbered.

Sersic or Sérsic: Single LMC globular cluster, usually known as "Recticulum." [Sérsic 1974]. See Extended Notes on page 196 under "Recticulum."

Sex C: The globular cluster Palomar 3, mistaken to be a dwarf galaxy in the constellation Sextans. Not numbered.

SGC: *Southern Galaxy Catalogue* [Corwin, *et al.*, 1985]. "Numbered" using B1950.0 coordinates.

Sh 1-: Sharpless's first list of supposed HII regions. Superseded by Sh 2-designations [Sharpless 1953]. Numbered 1 to 142.

Sh 2-or Sh2: Sharpless's second list of supposed HII regions. This catalog is often misleadingly represented only by an "S." [Sharpless 1959]. Numbered 1 to 313.

Sher: A single star cluster near η Carinae. [Sher 1964]. Numbered 1.

Shk: A galaxy cluster. [Shakhbazian 1957]. Numbered 1. Has been mistaken for a Galactic globular cluster—see Extended Notes on page 198.

Shorlin: Two possible open clusters around Wolf-Rayet stars in Carina [Turner, 1999]. Numbered 1 and 2.

SIMBAD: Astronomical object database, from acronym for "Set Identifications, Measurements, and Bibliography for Astronomical Data." See Appendix E for web address.

SKHB: Globular Clusters in M 31. [Sargent, *et al.*, 1977]. Numbered 1 to 355.

Skiff or Cl Skiff: Seven possible Galactic open clusters discovered or at least first clearly pointed out by Brian Skiff. "Cl" may be used as a prefix so as to avoid confusion with possible planetary nebulae discovered by Skiff. For Skiff J0458.2+4301, see Skiff [1995b]. For Skiff J0614.8+1252, see Luginbuhl and Skiff [1990]. Objects Skiff J0058.4+6828, Skiff J0507.2+3050, Skiff 0619.3+1832, Skiff J1942.3+3839, and Skiff J2330.2+6015 are reported here in print for the first time. See page 198 and following. Numbered using truncated J2000.0 coordinates.

SkyView: See Appendix A starting on page 455 for internet address.

SL or [SL63]: Clusters in the LMC. [Shapley and Lindsay 1963]. Numbered 1 to 898.

SPD: South Polar Distance. In degrees, this is the same as 90° plus declination.

SSWZ94: Six possible Galactic clusters of "Berkeley" type. This name first used here, derived from authors' names and publication year. See Saurer, *et al.*, [1994]. Numbered 1 to 6.

Steine: One likely asterism or possible cluster, discovered visually in a 25-cm telescope on October 14, 2001 and reported by M. Steine of Oslo, Norway [private communication, 2001]. Numbered 1.

Stephenson or Ste: Two Galactic open clusters. For Ste 1, see Stephenson [1959]. For Ste 2, see Stephenson

[1990]. Numbered 1 and 2. Ste 1 was discovered by Gordon Grant.

STF or Σ: Double and multiple stars. [Struve 1827].

Stock or St: Loose Galactic open clusters. For Stock 1 and 2, see Stock [1956]. Other Stock objects were first listed (by private communication from Stock) in Alter, *et al.* [1958] and (for Stock 24) Alter, *et al.* [1970]. Numbered 1 to 24.

Terz N or Terzan-Ju: Nonstellar objects near the Galactic center. For Terz N 1 to 24, see Terzan and Ju [1980]. For Terz N 25 to 41, see Terzan [1985]. Numbered 1 to 41.

Terzan: Possible Galactic globular clusters. For Terzan 1, see Terzan [1966]; for Terzan 2, see Terzan [1967]; for Terzan 3 to 8, see Terzan [1968]. For Terzan 9 to 12, see Terzan [1971a 1971b] and King [1972]. Numbered 1 to 12, but the use of "12" should be denigrated. See explanation under Terzan 11 in Extended Notes in Chapter 7. Terzan 5 = (original) Terzan 11; Terzan 11 = (original) Terzan 12.

Teutsch: 32 possible Galactic open clusters, found by P. Teutsch [private communication, 2001] on the DSS or DSS II. Numbered using truncated J2000.0 coordinates. Skiff J1942.4+3839 = Teutsch J1942.4+3839; ADS 13292 = Teutsch J2002.3+3518.

TF: X-ray sources in M 31. [Trinchieri and Fabbiano 1991]. Numbered 1 to 108.

Toadstool: A possible Galactic cluster, named for its appearance. [French 1997]. Not numbered. French 1 = Toadstool.

Tombaugh or Tom: Five Galactic star clusters. For Tom 1 and 2, see Tombaugh [1938]. For Tom 3 to 5, see Tombaugh [1941]. Numbered 1 to 5. IC 166 = Tom 3.

Ton: Two Galactic globular clusters. [Pismis 1959]. Numbered 1 and 2. Later also named Pismis 25 and Pismis 26, by Alter, *et al.*, [1970]. NGC 6380 = Ton 1.

Trumpler or Tr: Galactic open clusters. [Trumpler 1930]. Numbered 1 to 37. IC 2157 = Tr 4; NGC 2479 = Tr 8; IC 1311 = Tr 36; IC 1396 = Tr 37.

Turner: Ten open clusters, possible open clusters, or asterisms, found by D. G. Turner and others. The names for these clusters were first published in Dias, *et al.* [2002]. Numbered 1 to 9 and 11. C1947+272 = Turner 1; WZ Sgr cl = Turner 2; C1814–191b = Turner 3; C1814–190 = Turner 4; GT Car cl = Turner 6; and SU Cyg cl = Turner 9.

TXS: Texas survey of radio sources. [Douglas, *et al.*, 1996]. "Numbered" using truncated B1950.0 coordinates.

UGC and UGCA: Uppsala Observatory, *General Catalog of Galaxies*. [Nilson 1973]. Numbered 1 to 12921. UGCA objects are in Nilson [1974], numbered 1 to 440.

UKS: Two Galactic globular clusters discovered with "United Kingdom Schmidt." [Malkan, *et al.*, 1980]. Numbered 1 and 2. vdB-Ha 66 = UKS 2. See entries for UKS 2 and vdB-Ha 66 in the Extended Notes in Chapter 4 (vdB-Ha 66) and Chapter 7 (UKS 1) for more information.

UMa cl: Named after the constellation Ursa Major, this is Collinder 285, the Ursa Major moving cluster. This should not be confused with the Ursa Major *galaxy* cluster, or the Ursa Major globular cluster, Palomar 4. Not numbered.

UMa glb: The globular cluster Palomar 4 in the constellation Ursa Major. This should not be confused with the Ursa Major moving cluster, Collinder 285. Not numbered.

Up or Upgren: A possible open cluster, later found to be an asterism. [Upgren and Rubin 1965]. Numbered 1.

UBVRI: Photometric system including magnitudes in ultraviolet, blue, visible, red, and infrared light.

ubvyβ: Photometric system including magnitudes in ultraviolet, blue, yellow, and Hydrogen β light.

[V62]: Globular clusters in M 31. [V62] B- objects are from an included list by Baade. [Vetesnik 1962]. Numbered 1 to 140 (the same objects as [H32] above) and 195 to 327 (identified by others).

[V64]: Associations in M 31. [van den Bergh 1964]. Numbered 1 to 188.

vdB: See "Cl vdB" on page 270.

vdB-Ha: Possible open clusters in the southern Milky Way. Sometimes confusingly abbreviated "BH". [van den Bergh and Hagen 1975]. Numbered 1 to 262. Note that many objects listed as newly discovered had previously been found. See individual entries in the Extended Notes starting on page 207 and in Chapter 7.

VII Zw: See "II Zw" on page 273.

W: Radio sources. [Westerhout 1958]. Numbered to 1 to 82.

[W95]: Nonstellar objects. [Weinberger 1995]. Numbered 1 to 8.

Wa: Seven "mini-clusters" (or asterisms?) usually involved in nebulosity. See Moffat, *et al.*, [1979]; FitzGerald and Moffat [1980]. Numbered 1, 2, 3, 6, and 7. Discovery reference for 6 (and 4 and 5 if they exist) unknown.

WB89: IRAS sources. [Wouterloot and Brand 1989]. Numbered 1 to 1302.

WDS: "Washington Double Star Catalog" [Worley and

Douglass 1996]. Objects listed by 2000.0 right ascension and declination.

We or Westerlund: Three Galactic open clusters. Note that Westerlund 1 was discovered after Westerlund 2. For We 1, see Westerlund [1961]. For We 2, see Westerlund [1960]. For We 3—used here for the first time—see Westerlund [1969] (where this cluster is called "Anon cluster.") Numbered 1 to 3.

WFPC2: Acronym for the Hubble Space Telescope's "Wide Field and Planetary Camera 2."

WG71: Clusters in the SMC. [Westerlund and Glaspey 1971]. Numbered 1 to 18.

WHI: 35 dwarf galaxy candidates, one of which (WHI B0200-03) is an open cluster. [Whiting, *et al.,* 2002]. The cluster has also been given the name "Whiting 1" in Dias, *et al.,* [2002]. Numbered using truncated B1950.0 coordinates.

Wilk's cluster: Independent discovery of Mel 71 [Schüller 1931]. Not numbered. Mel 71 = Wilk's cluster.

[WR]: Wolf-Rayet stars, from van der Hucht, *et al.*, [1981]. Numbered from 1 to 158, with some lettered numbers (e.g., 38a, 38b).

[WSB85]: Possible globular clusters in M 31. [Wirth, *et al.*, 1985]. Numbered 1 to 148.

WSTB 36W and WSTB 37W: Radio sources in M 31. [Bystedt, *et al.*, 1984; Walterbos, *et al.*, 1985]. Numbered 1 to 403 and 1 to 269 respectively.

WR: Wolf-Rayet stars, from van der Hucht, *et al.,* [1981]. Numbered from 1 to 158, with some lettered numbers (e.g. 38a, 38b).

Z: See CGCG on page 269.

ZAMS: Zero age main sequence.

Zwicky: One Galactic globular cluster, later known as Palomar 15. [Zwicky 1959]. Palomar 15 = Zwicky 1.

Appendix B
Catalog Sources, and Methods

It was our original intention to compile the information for the catalog primarily from only a few major sources. This was our plan under the assumption that the data of interest would be well determined. We now know how naive that assumption was. In a surprisingly large number of cases data were found to be conflicting or in error, and a wide range of disparate sources were checked for additional information.

Nevertheless, a few major sources provide the bulk of the data that is presented here. For data on open clusters and suspected clusters of our Galaxy, the main source was the *Lund Catalogue* of Göstå Lyngå [1987]. This was supplemented with additional data on open clusters, asterisms, and the bright Magellanic Cloud clusters from the first edition of the *Deep Sky Field Guide* by Cragin, *et al.*, [1993]. An important source of updated information on clusters, particularly a number of poorly identified NGC clusters, was the 1993 compilation by one of us [BA], *The "Non-existent" Star Clusters of the RNGC*. Another very important source has been a compilation by Brian Skiff (September 1995) of newly measured star cluster positions obtained for a large number of open clusters and asterisms. To provide some completeness on objects of possible interest and to include additional extragalactic clusters, information was also extracted from the SIMBAD database (as of February 1996) for all objects considered to be star clusters.

Three major sources were used for information on Galactic globular clusters. The primary list of such objects and their coordinates was obtained from the compilation by Djorgovski and Meylan [1993]. Total magnitudes and some additional information were obtained from a compilation by Brian Skiff (in August, 2001). Some additional information and further alternate names were obtained from Peterson [1993].

Beyond these major sources, a wide range of references and supporting material were consulted. As mentioned above, this was primarily in order to resolve discrepancies between the major sources of data and to eliminate other errors. However, substantial new work and results are also included in this publication for the first time.

In this regard, the reader should keep in mind the differences between primary and secondary sources of data. Primary sources are those for which the data is original, e.g., the authors of those sources have derived the data from observation, direct measurements at the telescope, photographic plates, photometry, or the Digitized Sky Survey (DSS [AURA 1995]). One obvious type of primary reference is the paper or publication announcing the discovery of a cluster or clusters. Secondary sources are those that have already compiled the data from earlier primary (and even other secondary) sources. In point of fact, most sources used here actually have some combination of newly derived and compilation data, and therefore, are partially both primary and secondary. However, primary data has obviously been given priority in the catalog over secondary data. In addition, a large number of discovery publications were examined in order to confirm the identity of many objects.

The material in the following sections continues the discussion of these various sources of data. The major sources highlighted above are each treated separately. Each is listed along with basic information about that catalog and source, with an indication of what data were used for this catalog. A final section also discusses the various other sources used.

We hope it will be apparent that by considering and comparing several (mostly) independent major sources of data, and then consulting a large number of other sources, that we have come up with an excellent catalog of star clusters, asterisms, and misidentified star clusters. Certainly we know that errors remain, and they are our responsibility. However, we believe this to be the best and most complete catalog of star clusters ever made and the best that can reasonably be made at this point in time.

B.1 The *Lund Catalogue*

The *Lund Catalogue* is Gösta Lyngå's 1987 compilation, *Catalogue of Open Cluster Data*, Fifth Edition. This is a computer readable catalog of Galactic open cluster data from Lyngå. This catalog consists of 5 files including an introduction; the primary catalog, a print or edit file version of much of the primary data, a list of references, a list of cluster names and aliases, and a list of Galactic coordinates.

Although it was eventually found that this catalog contains a number of errors, it still proved invaluable in providing a basic listing of Galactic clusters, alternate names for these clusters, and fundamental data regarding them. The alternate (or alias) names form the bulk of the list of alias names generated in the production of this catalog. Other basic data, used for many of the clusters, include the position, diameter, total magnitude, Trumpler type, magnitude of the brightest star, and distance.

Lyngå used a very large number of sources (527 references) for the information he presents; therefore, his work should be considered primarily a compilation catalog or a secondary source. However, since he conducted an examination of most of the clusters on the first Palomar Observatory Sky Survey (POSS) or similar photographic material, much of the information regarding positions, diameters, and Trumpler types is original to his work. In addition, the total visual (V) magnitude data that Lyngå provides are also unique to his catalog. Skiff derived these magnitudes via examination of the "best" references for each cluster and the summing of the magnitudes of the individual stars of the clusters. A recent study [Battinelli, *et al.*, 1994] has shown that this total V magnitude information is one of the best such compilations.

B.2 The Deep Sky Field Guide, First Edition

The Deep Sky Field Guide (DSFG1e) [Cragin, *et al.*, 1993] is a compilation catalog listing information on all the objects plotted in the *Uranometria 2000.0* (first edition) atlas [Tirion, *et al.*, 1987a, b]. A file containing the open cluster information of this catalog was kindly provided by the authors and publisher of the *DSFG1e* [private communication with P. Remaklus]. Objects in this list include all Milky Way clusters, asterisms, and Magellanic clusters included in the *DSFG1e*. Data included are object names, the 2000.0 right ascension and declination (usually only to 0.1^m and 1′), the total magnitude, the size of the object (in arcminutes), the number of stars, the magnitude of the brightest star, the (first edition) *Uranometria 2000.0 (U2K1e)* chart number, and various comments.

There were a number of advantages and disadvantages in using data from this work. The primary advantage is that the *DSFG1e* is fairly complete in the inclusion of groups or asterisms of stars (whereas, by definition, the *Lund Catalogue*—supposedly—had none). It was important to obtain information on these objects in particular so that the assembled catalog would be relatively complete in terms of observable groups and asterisms of stars as well as of true star clusters. A secondary advantage is that the sources used for the first edition of the *DSFG* are relatively independent of the sources used for the *Lund Catalogue*. The *Lund Catalogue* appears to be primarily based on new data collected by Lyngå and others, references to modern professional work and the relatively modern compilation by Ruprecht, *et al.*, [1981]. The *DSFG1e* data and objects on the other hand—at least for open clusters and asterisms—appear to have originated primarily from a series of earlier compilations and star atlases. This probably includes recent compilations such as in *Sky Catalogue 2000.0*, volume 2 [Hirshfeld and Sinnott 1985], and the *Atlas of the Heavens* Catalogue [Becvar 1964], which in turn seem to have as their primary sources the basic 1930–31 references on star clusters by Shapley [1930], Trumpler [1930], and Collinder [1931]. This also probably assures that objects shown on most popular twentieth century star atlases, such as *SkyAtlas 2000.0* [Tirion 1981], the *Atlas of the Heavens* [Becvar 1962], and *Norton's Star Atlas* [Norton 1973], are included. Finally, the *DSFG1e* data also includes a number of improvements regarding the identification of objects, due to recent work by amateurs and professionals in general and to the work spent in creating *Uranometria 2000.0* and the *DSFG1e* specifically.

There are some (minor) disadvantages of the *DSFG1e* that should be mentioned. For one, the use of older references can be problematic as some of these may be out of date, and/or had copying errors. For another, the *DSFG1e* did not include objects that were not already in the first edition of, and also adopted the object names as used in, *Uranometria 2000.0*. However, by using the *Lund Catalogue* as a reference and by checking individual discrepancies between the two, these problems are practically eliminated.

The actual procedure involved in merging the data of these two catalogs was to first create a preliminary database using the *Lund Catalogue* data. Next, the *DSFG1e* data was merged with the Lund data. Object by object, a check for a match was done based on the object names and positions. If a match was found, data from the *DSFG1e* was only used where not already available from the *Lund Catalogue* (e.g., when a magnitude might be missing or if the *DSFG1e* had useful comments). The differences between the *Lund Catalogue* and *DSFG1e* values (if any) were also obtained for later examination. If no match was found, the *DSFG1e* data was added as a new object in the database. Finally, as problems in either original dataset were uncovered, further changes were made to the database.

B.3 The "Non-Existent" Star Clusters of the RNGC

Another important source of information for the database was *Monograph* Number 1 of the Webb Society, *The "Non-Existent" Star Clusters of the RNGC*, written by one of us [BA] in 1993. This work was primarily an attempt to establish identifications for a number of NGC objects likely to be, or at some point indicated to be, star clusters, groups of stars, or resolvable objects. These NGC objects were generally listed as type 7 or "nonexistent" in the RNGC [Sulentic and Tifft 1973]—hence the name of the *Monograph*. Some known star clusters with identification problems or large positional errors (e.g., M 41) were also included in this work, bringing the total number of objects considered to 229. Where available, information was included on object type, position, size, number of stars, total magnitude, and magnitude of the brightest star.

As with the merging of the other sources, this material was merged with the now combined *Lund/DSFG1e* database. However, matches were made primarily by the NGC names, and the *Monograph* data had priority over the earlier data. In other words, information in the *Monograph*, which has been carefully researched, was always used in preference to any other data. Comments regarding some of the more difficult object identification problems were also added to the Extended Notes section below.

It should be noted that the work here should not be considered a general update of the *Monograph*. In the following Extended Notes, known errors in the *Monograph* have been indicated (uncertain identifications that have been resolved have been commented on, and notes on several additional NGC objects have been added). However, not all the objects mentioned in the *Monograph* have additional data here, including a number that have now been observed by various people.

B.4 Information from Brian Skiff on Galactic Clusters and Asterisms

Early in 1995 one of us [BA] and Brian Skiff began investigating whether better positions could be obtained for clusters in some systematic way. Skiff had looked into whether some dense star catalog (such as the GSC) could be used to mathematically search the area of a known cluster in order to find the center of it. Likewise, Archinal used lists of stars in star clusters (obtained via SIMBAD) to do a similar investigation. The result was surprising. It was always easier to simply look at an image of a cluster and estimate the center by eye than it was to attempt "calculating" it in some way.

During much of the rest of 1995, Skiff proceeded to do just that for a large number of star clusters. Using a preliminary version of the catalog given here, he used the NASA/GSFC SkyView utility, available on the World Wide Web, to display images of the clusters from the digitized sky survey. The end result [private communication, 1995] was a list of clusters, including greatly improved positions, as well as diameters and other comments for some selected objects. The original list included 811 objects, including practically all Galactic open clusters and asterisms from 00^h to $13^h\ 45^m$ of (2000.0) right ascension. Skiff has continued to make minor corrections and additions to his list. The version used for the final catalog here is that of September 7, 1998. The current version is available from the Lowell Observatory public FTP site.

This information was in turn merged into the now growing database, this time with the coordinates (when available) given priority. Comments by Skiff (edited for readability) were added to the comment field of the database. Diameters, available for only a subset of objects, were not used generally. However, they were considered in cases where there were discrepancies between other sources.

B.5 SIMBAD

SIMBAD is a general database of astronomical objects, maintained by the Centre de Données astronomiques de Strasbourg (CDS) in Strasbourg, France. Information on star clusters was obtained from this database for a number of reasons. For one, it was hoped that the SIMBAD database would be relatively complete in terms of clusters included, both Milky Way and extragalactic. For another, it was hoped the references that SIMBAD keeps track of for each object (indeed as one of its primary functions) would be useful in obtaining new data on various objects. The references would also help in resolving discrepancies in data sources on other objects. Finally, it was hoped that the data would be relatively accurate, having likely been obtained from recent astronomical references.

In fact, the SIMBAD database did prove remarkably useful in terms of the number of objects included. Although regarding Milky Way open cluster and asterisms, very few new objects (not already in the *Lund Catalogue* and *DSFG1e*) were uncovered; the size of the database increased substantially due to the number of extragalactic objects included, primarily from the LMC, SMC, and the Andromeda Galaxy (M 31). Further SIMBAD does list a large number of references for many of these objects—although it unfortunately lists very few (or in some cases none) for little known objects or probable asterisms. The latter situation exists simply because these objects and asterisms have not been studied recently and no new information exists.

Although in the long run those advantages outweighed the problems encountered, there were a number of difficulties with the SIMBAD data that required a great deal of time to resolve. Primary among these was the duplication of a large number of objects. Many objects had multiple entries under different names. Eventually these problems were eliminated by the comparison of the objects' coordinates and other information, including discovery publications and the *Lund Catalogue* alias list, (which indicated the equivalence of many of the listed names). Other problems were also found and dealt with including occasional typographical errors in coordinates and names, incorrect designations, objects with no references or coordinates, incorrect object types, etc. Over a thousand entries were at one point identified as being for *stars* in clusters rather than for *star clusters*. In any case, all problems were reported to SIMBAD personnel. This assured that if later searches by others were made in the SIMBAD database, that these problems would generally not be encountered. Of course, some problems could not be resolved for objects with either multiple types or multiple names referenced to different types. Generally these items have been noted in the catalog comments or extended notes.

In practice, the SIMBAD data was obtained and used as follows. First, a batch submission was made to SIMBAD requesting information on all "C" named objects. Such a set of objects should supposedly include all the Galactic clusters and asterisms, most of which have such names assigned. A second batch submission was also done for all objects with type "star cluster." Although there would be many objects duplicated from the first search, the second search would also return objects without "C" names and many extragalactic clusters for which "C" names are not usually assigned. These two searches were made in February 1996.

The search for "C" names returned 1344 such objects. The search for all star clusters returned 3250. The information returned consisted of one or more names for each object, the 1950.0 coordinates (in most cases), the total V magnitude (in many cases), and a list of references. Two more merges were then done with the current database. As before, matches were located either by name or position. If a match occurred, the earlier data were retained. Discrepancies, if any, were printed out. If additional names were found in SIMBAD or only SIMBAD had a total V magnitude, those data were added to the database. If no match was found, the object was added as a new entry. Checks were then made to see if any objects in the database had similar coordinates or whether multiple matches were found with the previous data. These cases were examined individually, usually revealing problems with the SIMBAD data (i.e., duplicate entries for the same object). Changes were then made to fix these problems during or after the SIMBAD data processing, and problems with the SIMBAD data were reported to the CDS. This process was done repeatedly until no further such problems were found.

A large number of extragalactic objects without coordinates were also dropped from the catalog at this point. These objects were often extremely faint possible clusters (e.g. recently discovered by the *HST*) for which little data beyond a name and an image exist. It was felt that listing these objects here would be of little value. A number of "C" objects were also eliminated that had no information beyond their name. Most of these were eventually determined to be galaxies (e.g. "CGCG" not "C" objects) or even clusters of galaxies. These sorts of problems were also reported to the CDS. In all, data from about 700 SIMBAD entries were eliminated, while data from about 1000 new entries were retained.

B.6 Information from Djorgovski and Meylan [1993] on Galactic Globular Clusters

The primary source for the identification of Galactic globular clusters and for their positions was a compilation listing by Djorgovski and Meylan [1993]. This appeared in the appendix of the 1993 ASP Conference Series (volume 50) publication "Structure and Dynamics of Globular Clusters," which they edited. Their list contained the names and some alias names, B1950.0 and J2000.0 positions, Galactic longitude and latitude positions, and position references for 143 objects thought to be Galactic globular clusters at that time. The positions were given to a precision of 0.1 seconds of right ascension and 1 arcsecond of declination. Although many of the positions were compiled from earlier works, a number of the positions provided were new measurements (e.g., from the preliminary Digitized Sky Survey) provided there for the first time. They estimated that the errors for most of the objects should be 2 to 3 arcseconds in either coordinate. An electronic copy of this information was provided by Djorgovski [private communication, 1995].

Djorgovski and Meylan also provided ample notes regarding a number of objects that have been considered as Galactic globular clusters in the past but have now been rejected for one reason or another. Most of these objects are mentioned briefly in the extended notes given below, and all are included (under their correct object type) in the catalog here.

As with the open cluster and other data discussed above, the data here were merged directly into the growing database. Here the data (coordinates) were given priority over earlier entries.

It should be noted that a few objects in the Djorgovski and Meylan list have now been found *not* to be Galactic globular clusters. Conversely, a few additional such clusters have been identified (e.g. ESO 452-SC11, IC 1257). Corrections in this regard have been applied to the database (e.g. the final catalog here) and notes have been provided in the extended notes and in Chapter 7. In a few cases (e.g. ESO 452-SC11, NGC 6522) improvements have been made to the given coordinates.

B.7 Information from Brian Skiff on Galactic Globular Clusters

For several years now Brian Skiff has been maintaining his own table of globular cluster information. This work is described in Skiff [1995a]. His table summarizes important parameters of Galactic globular clusters and some extragalactic globular clusters (e.g., in Fornax). Included are 2000.0 positions, diameters, total V magnitudes, V magnitude and B–V magnitude of the brightest stars, and V magnitude of the horizontal branch. Although this is entirely a compilation catalog relying on earlier references (cited in a separate file by Skiff), much of this data has not been assembled elsewhere. In particular Skiff's diameters have been obtained from digitized light intensity profiles by Trager, *et al.*, [1995a, b]. The diameters are those where the intensity falls to 25 magnitudes per square arcsecond (or in cases when data is unavailable to the 25th magnitude level, where the intensity falls to the 22nd magnitude level). This information is unique in that almost all other sources for globular cluster diameters are based on varying sources and/or models for the internal structure of the clusters. Skiff's are the only values based entirely on measuring the diameter out to a consistent limiting background magnitude. The total V magnitudes are from an earlier compilation by S. van den Bergh, *et al.*, [1991]. These V magnitudes are based on the total light of the clusters out to what was estimated to be half of their total diameter. (For consistency it would be useful to compute the total magnitudes from profiles, but that has not been done here.) His summary of information on the magnitudes and colors of the brightest stars of the clusters (obtained from the tip of color-magnitude diagrams) is also unavailable elsewhere.

The version of this data used here is that of August 4, 2001. As with the other sources of data above, this information was merged into the database for this catalog. The values for magnitudes and diameters have been used in preference to all other sources.

B.8 Information from Peterson [1993] on Galactic Globular Clusters

Charles J. Peterson [1993] (in the appendix to Djorgovski and Meylan's Conference Series publication described above) provides basic data on the photometric properties of Galactic globular clusters. This information has been used as an additional source of alias names (including IAU style coordinate names), total V magnitude, V magnitude of the horizontal branch, and distance. These are essentially compilation data, derived from earlier publications cited by Peterson, including a number of original publications (with primary data) by Peterson and others. An electronic copy of Peterson's table was provided by Djorgovski [private communication, 1995].

This data was read and merged into the database used to generate this cluster catalog. Most of the IAU style names for Galactic globular clusters in the current catalog originate from this source. Likewise, almost all of the distances for such objects originate here. However, only a few of the magnitude values have been used in cases where the Skiff list (discussed just above) did not have any data.

Peterson's list includes ESO 452-SC11, which Djorgovski and Meylan did not include in their list. In fact, Minniti, *et al.*, did not confirm this object as a Galactic globular cluster until 1995. See the Extended Notes in Chapter 7 for additional information on this cluster.

B.9 Information from Kontizas, *et al.*, [1990] on LMC Clusters

The primary source for fainter and smaller clusters in the Large Magellanic Cloud is the LMC cluster catalog of Kontizas, *et al.*, [1990], designated here with the abbreviations KMHK or KMH90. This catalog contains identifications, coordinates, diameters, and a "compact" or "loose" designation for 1762 clusters. These objects are in a 25 degree by 25 degree area centered on the LMC, but *not* including the very crowded 3.5 square degree area around the main bar of the LMC.

As with the other primary sources listed above, the data were compared with our (growing) primary catalog. Matches found via the cluster names and alias names were used to add any missing alias or diameter information. Clusters with no matches were simply added to the primary catalog. The designation of a cluster as "compact" or "loose" was added to the comment field.

Later checks for duplicate objects and incorrect identities did reveal a number of problem objects (approximately 25). The identities were sorted out and appropriate changes made to the catalog, including removing duplicate objects, correcting identifications and alias names, and adding comments to the catalog or the Extended Notes.

The inclusion of this catalog into the growing primary catalog database was done to complement data on brighter and more significant LMC objects, obtained from the *DSFG1e* and SIMBAD.

The end result is a catalog that is by no means complete for all LMC star clusters, but still includes the vast majority of LMC clusters, as well as the brightest and most significant.

B.10 Information from Pietrzyński, *et al.*, [1998] on SMC Clusters

As part of the "Optical Gravitational Lensing Experiment", to look for gravitational lensing of Magellanic Cloud stars by Galactic stars, Pietrzyński, *et al.*, [1998] created a catalog of Small Magellanic Cloud star clusters. This catalog was incorporated into the primary catalog here in order to improve the basic data on SMC clusters.

Their catalog consists of data on 238 clusters or possible clusters, of which 72 were thought to be new. The authors provided information, such as coordinates, radii, approximate number of stars, alias names, finding charts, and color magnitude diagrams. They separate their data into clusters and "cluster candidates".

Once again, this information was compared with our existing primary database matching objects by name, having their data replaced or additional data added as appropriate, and simply adding objects that did not match. The designation used for objects in this catalog is "OGLE-CL SMC" (the "SMC" used in order to differentiate objects from a similar planned catalog of LMC clusters). Note that in this case the coordinates of the OGLE catalog were adopted in preference to those of other sources, since checks of coordinates of several objects on the DSS showed that the OGLE values were quite good. Also, as opposed to the LMC, where such information is currently hard to come by, the OGLE catalog provides information on the number of stars and photometry for many individual stars. This information was read and for each cluster the total magnitude obtained by summing the individual magnitudes, and the magnitude of the brightest star also determined. The resulting values and number of stars were added to the primary catalog. Finally, approximately 10 errors noted in the catalog were corrected, with notations about such problems added to the comments or Extended Notes. One example of such problems is that two clusters were listed twice in the OGLE compilation (i.e., OGLE-CL SMC0019 = OGLE-CL SMC0175 and OGLE-CL SMC0144 = OGLE-CL SMC0236, see the Extended Notes for more information).

As with the LMC, it is likely that some SMC clusters are missing from the OGLE compilation and, therefore, from the final catalog here. However, the incorporation of this data (with the existing data from the *DSFG1e* and SIMBAD), results in a catalog of clusters that is largely complete for the SMC (more so than for the LMC), with statistics on numbers of stars and magnitudes that is perhaps more complete than even for our own Galaxy.

B.11 Information from Other Sources

As described in the Extended Notes, alternate sources were consulted for a number of objects. These sources were used to obtain additional basic information on clusters, to verify information or the identity of clusters, or in several cases even identify the cluster for the first time since its discovery. References to these sources are indicated by citations at the appropriate point in the text, with the full text of the references listed in the References (starting on page 459).

A number of sources were repeatedly consulted for information on many specific and new clusters. Although often cited individually, mention of these sources bears repeating here.

- The Digitized Sky Survey (DSS) proved invaluable in identifying clusters. The diameters, numbers of stars, positions, and even basic identifications were measured or confirmed using DSS images. In most cases these images were obtained through the very useful SkyView utility, operated at the GSFC. As described above, Brian Skiff has provided much useful information on these objects using this utility and the DSS. A number of additional clusters and problems were also investigated by one of us [BA] in order to compile the catalog and notes given here. In particular, objects with uncertain identifications and all Messier objects not checked by Skiff were examined in this way.

  The procedure used by one of us [BA] was to obtain a DSS image (in .GIF and .FITS format) of the area of the sky expected to contain a cluster. These images were often overlaid with the identification of stars and other objects from the various catalogs available via SkyView (e.g. the HD, GSC, and "optical identifications" catalogs). The SAOimage software was then used to examine these images, and using the "world coordinate system" information contained in the images, positions for clusters and specific stars were measured.
- The SIMBAD database was often consulted to obtain better basic information on stars associated with such clusters. In this way the brightest and/or most centrally located stars ("center stars") of clusters were identified and further basic information obtained. In particular, such information as additional names, positions, V magnitudes, and spectral types was often obtained from SIMBAD for these stars.
- The NASA Extragalactic Database (NED) was consulted in several cases where a supposed star cluster was found to be a galaxy or even a cluster of galaxies. It was also used to obtain information on some galaxies that appear in the same line of sight as a star cluster.
- The table of Galactic Globular clusters in the "Astronomical Almanac" was often consulted regarding basic information on such objects, in particular alternate names.
- Likewise, the paper on and tables of information on Galactic Globular clusters by William Harris [1996] was also consulted for more current information on clusters. In particular the identification of objects here as clusters or not is in general agreement with Harris' lists.
- The famous catalog by P. J. Melotte [1915a] was consulted to confirm the identities of the objects there. The Melotte numbers obtained from the *Lund Catalogue* were checked against this list and appropriate corrections made (as noted for individual objects in the Extended Notes). Melotte number identities for Galactic Globular clusters (i.e., not in the *Lund Catalogue*) were added so that all Melotte numbered objects are present here.
- Likewise, the famous catalog by Per Collinder [1931] was consulted to confirm various identities. The Col-

linder numbers obtained from the *Lund Catalogue* were checked against this list and appropriate corrections made (as noted for individual objects in the Extended Notes). A few objects not in modern catalogs have been added so that all Collinder numbered objects are present here.

- A copy of the Franklin-Adams [RAS 1936] photographic star charts was examined in the case of several clusters listed by Melotte, Collinder, and others where the identities or positions were uncertain. Several clusters were identified for the first time since their discovery through the use of this material, in particular by comparison to the DSS.
- The catalog of southern clusters by Sidney van den Bergh and Gretchen L. Hagen [1975] was examined carefully and all such vdB-Ha identities have been included here. A number of objects are identified here for the first time as previously discovered NGC and other named objects. In addition, the uncertain cross identifications included by them have all been checked.
- R. Lederman and S. Gottlieb [1996] have recently listed a number of star clusters that were incorrectly identified as galaxies in various catalogs. These identities have been incorporated in the list of alias names here and appropriate comments added. The use of such names should in general be denigrated, meaning they are included here only so that further confusion about possible galaxies in the areas of these clusters can be avoided.
- Similarly, the identifications of a number of missing Czernik "Galactic globular clusters" have been confirmed. These objects, although listed by Czernik (as Cz 33, 34, 35, and 36) [Alter *et al.*, 1966, 1, 6], do not appear in later compilations on star clusters. They have been reclassified as dwarf galaxies and even galaxy clusters.
- A cross correlation has been performed against the original *Caldwell Catalog* of Sir Patrick Moore [Moore and Pepin 1995]. This is a catalog of 109 "neglected" interesting deep-sky objects beyond those listed by Messier. The primary reason for considering this catalog here was to make sure that the Caldwell numbers were available in the list of alias names. However, during the comparison process a number of errors were noted in the original *Caldwell Catalog*, and a few cases of errors in the catalog here were found. These *Caldwell Catalog* errors have since been corrected [O'Meara, 2002; O'Meara, private communication, 2002]. All of these cases are noted in the Extended Notes and errors were removed from the catalog here.
- A great deal of miscellaneous information on star clusters has been provided by the amateur astronomer Bruno Alessi of Sao Paulo, Brazil, and has been incorporated into this catalog. Included is Alessi's discovery of a number of asterisms or possible star clusters, mostly found by searching for clumps of GSC stars or by searching DSS images. Further, Alessi provided information on several recently discovered clusters (that were not listed in the 1996 SIMBAD search), and on about 100 clusters listed only in the ESO catalog by Lauberts [1982].
- Information on a few newly discovered clusters (over the last 10 years or so) has been added by consulting the original discovery references for these clusters. They were mostly infrared or radio clusters noted to be missing from earlier draft versions of the catalog here after reviewing a list of star clusters by Hugh Harris and William Harris [2000]. Although many of these objects have stars that are only visible in the infrared, they have been included due to their importance. Several of these are clusters associated with otherwise well-known NGC and even Messier nebulae. These clusters include—with the nebula name first and the cluster name in parenthesis—NGC 1333 (two clusters, [LAL96] 1 and 2), NGC 2023 ([LDEG91] 1), NGC 2024 (the "Flame Nebula," with cluster [LDEG91] 2), NGC 2068 (Messier 78, with cluster [LDEG91] 3), NGC 2071 ([LDEG91] 4), and NGC 3576 ([PRT94] 1). There are also new such clusters around GM 1-24 (IRAS 17136-3617), IRAS 18274+0112, LkHα 101 (Cl [BW88] 1), Sh 2-106 ([HR91] 1), and Sh 2-269 ([EC95] 1). Note that for most of these objects, the names of the involved *nebulae*, and that of the *clusters*, are different since the original discovery of the nebulae included no mention of any clusters. Unfortunately most of these star clusters are missing from SIMBAD, apparently because references to them have been assigned to the named nebulae—so they were not found in the 1996 SIMBAD search used in the catalog here (see the section about SIMBAD on page 281).
- Entries have been added for the nine moving clusters hypothesized by Agekyan and Orlov [1984]. They surmised the existence of these groups by looking for nearby stars that have the same space velocity, as indicated by W. Gliese's [1969] *Catalogue of Nearby Stars*. To determine information for the entries, the positions and V magnitudes of the individual stars were collected and used appropriately. The positions and diameters are only rough approximations, with the positions having been computed from the average of the direction cosines of the individual stars. These are probably only significant to tens of degrees. The "diameters" were computed from the maximum arc distance between two involved stars (generally ranging around 170°). The brightest V magnitude is the magnitude of the brightest star. The total magnitude is com-

puted from the magnitudes of all the member stars. Note that [AO84] VII probably represents the local stars of the Ursa Major Moving cluster (Collinder 285). Also note that [AO84] I includes the Sun and the solar system—we all may be part of a star cluster!

- Following the convention of Suntzeff, *et al.*, [1992] and Dutra, *et al.*, [1999], only these 15 objects are classified as old globular clusters in the LMC: NGC 1466, NGC 1754, NGC 1786, NGC 1835, NGC 1841, NGC 1898, NGC 1916, NGC 1928, NGC 1939, NGC 2005, NGC 2019, NGC 2210, NGC 2257, [H60b] 11, and Reticulum. All other clusters in the LMC are cataloged here as open clusters, although many are of the intermediate young "blue globular" type.
- A check of this catalog has also been made against the listing by Welch [1991] of 203 SMC clusters. Welch's catalog provides the first precise set of coordinates for many of these clusters and also summarizes the names and alias names for them. This information serves as an additional check on SMC cluster positions and names, which (as explained above) is mostly now derived from the "OGLE-CL SMC" catalog of Pietrzyński, *et al.*, [1998]

  For those who may refer to Welch's list, it is important to note that the IC designations in the list are missing their leading "1". That is, in the "NGC/IC" column in the paper, for 611, 612, 624, 626, 655, and 662, read 1611, 1612, 1624, 1626, 1655, and 1662 respectively.
- Barmby, *et al.* [2000] recently completed a catalog of globular clusters in NGC 205 = M 31. Included are 435 globular clusters and 199 miscellaneous objects previously thought to be such globular clusters. Names similar to those of HBK were used as were (inexplicably) a number of new names derived in a very complicated way as partially explained in the nomenclature listing in Appendix A under [BHB2000]. In the catalog here, these objects are listed by their original discovery names, with the [BHB2000] names listed as aliases. When available, the positions, total V magnitudes, and object types have been used in the catalog here, in preference to earlier values, mostly obtained via SIMBAD. They do not give coordinates for the objects previously thought to be globular clusters. We did not include such objects in the case where our catalog did not already have an entry (and coordinates) for them.
- Platais, Kozhurina-Platais, and van Leeuwen [1998] have recently identified 19 new (and verified one already known) nearby Galactic star clusters and associations, based on Hipparcos proper motion data. The 10 new clusters (but not the 9 associations) have been added to the catalog, using the acronym [PKL98]. The positions, diameters, number of stars, and distances used are from their compilation. The diameters were computed from their given radii. The number of stars in this case may be quite small (as small as 3). This is actually the number of Hipparcos stars in the group (which are listed in their paper) rather than a total possible number including fainter stars (for which no estimate is given). As to object type, their "possible open cluster" objects are assigned type "cl?", and their "very likely open cluster" objects are assigned type "cl", in the catalog. The one previously known object they list is their object no. 10, for which they give a spurious name of "NGC 2451B." The original and correct name for this cluster is the Puppis Moving Group (or PMG 1 in the catalog) as given by the discoverers, Röser and Bastian [1994].
- Two recent lists of infrared clusters discovered by Dutra and Bica [2000, 2001] using 2MASS data have also been included. The first list is of 58 clusters or possible clusters discovered near the Galactic center. The second list is of 42 possible Galactic clusters found at various locations. Although they indicate that some of the objects on the first list can be detected in optical wavelengths (presumably on the DSS), it is unlikely that all of these objects can be detected or at least seen well at such wavelengths. Except for cases where their existence as true clusters is fairly certain, they have been included in the catalog here as "possible clusters" (e.g. with type "cl?"). It is apparent from the comments by Dutra and Bica that there is a wide range of uncertainty as to whether most of these objects are real physical clusters.
- A list of 32 possible clusters or asterisms communicated to us by Philipp Teutsch (of Mils, Austria) [private communication, 2001] has also been incorporated into the catalog. These are groups of stars found by Teutsch during examination of POSS prints in 1989 (heretofore unpublished). These objects are sparse enough or similar enough in density to that of the background field that most do not have the unambiguous appearance of a definite open cluster. However, many of them could very well be open clusters, and none can be rejected as possible open clusters based on their appearance alone. Like so many sparse groups of stars, any definitive knowledge of whether these objects are real clusters will have to wait until decent color, proper motion, and/or radial velocity information becomes available for the component stars. For now they have been included here as candidate clusters, and because they should be observable objects in at least large amateur telescopes. As to the data available so far for these objects, the positions, diameters, Trumpler types, and numbers of stars are all measurements and estimates from Teutsch, based on the POSS and DSS/DSS II appearance. The magnitudes of the brightest stars are approximate values obtained from the USNO SA2.0

star catalog.

- Late in the process of completing this book, Dias, *et al.* [2002] published their "New catalogue of optically visible open clusters and candidates." One of the authors of that work, B. Alessi, has also supplied [private communication, 2002] us with a slightly updated version of their catalog. In order not to delay publication of this book any further we have not done a completely rigorous comparison of their data with ours. However, some comparison work was done, mostly in order to verify that there were no gross errors in our catalog due to incorrect positions or diameters. Some differences in position and diameter were certainly found, but these cases were mostly those of large and/or diffuse clusters or possible asterisms whose positions and diameters are ambiguous or a few cases where there was a genuine disagreement and no obvious error on our part.

  A check was also done on the completeness of our work, to see if any objects had been missed from our catalog. This process did lead to a number of objects being added to our catalog. Objects we had missed included a few objects discovered over the last few decades and not well reported (e.g. with no references in SIMBAD or other catalogs that we used). This included for example ESO 103-**14, ESO 217-SC08, ESO 260-SC06, ESO 260-SC07, ESO 332-SC08, [FM80] 1 ("Waterloo 8" in Dias, *et al.* [2002]), Johansson 1, and Lóden 2326. Other objects we had missed were all fairly new discoveries (e.g., from over the last 5 years) also not well reported or reported via private communication to Dias, *et al.* These objects included Alessi 3 to 6, 8, 9, 11, 14 to 16, and 20; [CV98] 1 to 5 ("Chupina" 1 to 5 in Dias, *et al.*; Gamma Velorum cluster ("Brandt 1" in Dias, *et al.*), Mandushev 1; Shorlin 1 and 2; Turner 5, 7, 8, and 11; and WHI B0200-03 ("Whiting 1" in Dias, *et al.*). A number of alias names were also added (e.g. other Alessi and Turner names).

  Readers should also be aware that the Dias, *et al.* catalog includes some types of data which we have not compiled in our catalog here. This includes useful information such as the cluster B-V magnitude, estimated age, average proper motion, radial velocity, and metallicity.

Finally, we would like to acknowledge that no source of data can be considered rigorously complete, and our catalog here is no exception. We have tried to compile a complete list of all known clusters and asterisms, and objects that have ever been suspected as such, for the Milky Way, at least through the year 2001. This catalog should also be complete in regard to globular clusters and suspected globular clusters in the Andromeda Galaxy and the Fornax Dwarf Galaxy. We have also included the vast majority of the obvious or brighter clusters (or at least studied clusters) of the Large and Small Magellanic clouds.

However, scientific papers on star clusters continue to be published on a weekly (if not almost daily) basis. Catalog compilations related to star clusters in some way continue to be published on a regular basis as well. To find the most current information the reader is encouraged to browse current papers at any large library or on-line via the Astrophysics Data System (see Appendix E for Web address), where most recently published papers on astronomy—or at least their abstracts—are available. The *Catalogues* section of the CDS Web site also is regularly updated information on and the contents of new astronomical catalogs as well.

B.12 Editing, Checking, and Formatting of the Final Database

It should perhaps be more clearly stated that after each new dataset was brought in to the existing database, the database was edited to eliminate the known errors from each of the new datasets. These errors were found by various means, but primarily by checking a printout comparing the values from the current database with those from the new dataset. Obvious discrepancies (e.g., name, coordinates, magnitudes, etc.) were then tracked down and resolved where possible. This was referenced to the original discovery data and to the Digitized Sky Survey. Also, the final database was examined for duplicate listings of the same object. This occurs in a (disconcerting) number of cases for all of the input catalogs. The many cases where problems were found (other than in SIMBAD) are described in the Extended Notes. A list of the changes needed due to the errors or duplications in the various datasets were prepared, and this was used to "automatically" edit the main database after each dataset was brought in. This same method was used to add data obtained from the various alternate sources.

Aside from numerous corrections that were found to be necessary and applied during the incorporation of data from the various sources, a final check was also made of all the catalog objects by examining *all* of them on the digitized sky survey. For each object the following steps were then taken.

- A simple check was made to see if an obvious cluster existed at the catalog position. If a single obvious cluster was found, well centered at the catalog position, no further change was made.
- In cases where a single obvious cluster was found close to the catalog position (a few arcminutes), a new position was measured from the DSS and used.
- In cases where multiple clusters were found in a field (e.g. Magellanic Clouds), and no single cluster was at the specified coordinates, checks of the original

sources were made. For several NGC objects this included checking the original discovery observations (and drawings) by John Herschel. In these cases appropriate comments or Extended Notes were added.

- If the cluster was extremely faint and difficult or impossible to verify on the DSS (as for many Magellanic Cloud clusters) a notation was added to the comment field to this effect. Defects in the DSS images were also noted.
- Although no general search for such was conducted, five otherwise apparently uncataloged clusters in the LMC were noted and added (with names "AH03 ...") as additional entries.
- In the case of Galactic objects that were not immediately found, significant steps were undertaken to try to identify them. Where known, the original discovery references were examined (a number of Collinder clusters were properly identified in this way, probably for the first time since their listing by Collinder). Several NGC objects, previously considered nonexistent were found in this way. Searches for such objects were also made on DSS images with much larger sizes (up to 4° at times), on DSS images with different "stretching" of the display, and on DSS II images (in areas of the sky where the DSS II is complete). Searches were also made—and a few dozen objects found—by examining plots of stars. Some of this was done by looking at plots of USNO A2.0 stars using a special version of the HyperSky software. A copy of this program was provided by its author, Brian Cuthbertson, and due particularly to the capability of displaying portions of the sky with different magnitude cutoffs (something not possible with DSS images), several objects were identifiable. For some clusters with bright stars, similar plots with the *MegaStar* software (created by Emil Bonanno) were also helpful. As a last resort, a few objects (e.g., Cr 428 on the "west coast" of the North American nebula, NGC 7000) were confirmed by the visual observation by one of us [BA] using various telescopes. In the end, all but about 100 Galactic objects were identifiable. The remaining unidentifiable objects were designated with an "Id?" notation in the comment field. These are mostly "nonexistent" NGC objects whose identities have not been thoroughly checked, or relatively obscure Collinder, Ruprecht, and other clusters on which information is incomplete or missing.
- Of course, as the final step, it was necessary to present this data in some usable form. Software was written to read the main database, perform some useful calculations and output several items. Computed quantities include the constellation, the surface brightness, the *Sky Atlas 2000.0* chart numbers, and the second edition *Uranometria 2000.0* chart numbers. The output files included:
  - The final formatted catalog of star clusters and asterisms. This catalog, sorted by J2000.0 right ascension, is presented in Table 4.1 and Appendix C.
  - A final formatted catalog of true or suspected Galactic Globular clusters. This catalog, sorted by J2000.0 right ascension, is presented in Chapter 7.
  - A list of all known alias names of the objects given. This list was output in a name per line format and is presented in Appendix D, Table D.3. The list is sorted by the alias (including preferred) names.

Together with the Extended Notes given in Chapters 4 and 7, this information comprises the most complete catalog of star clusters and asterisms ever created.

Appendix C
Catalogs of Extragalactic Objects

This Appendix includes the catalogs of extragalactic star clusters, asterisms and other objects previously misidentified as clusters, in lists separated by parent galaxy and listed in order of 2000.0 right ascension in each of those lists. A wide selection of clusters from galaxies in the Local Group has been included, including a substantial number of clusters in the Large Magellanic Cloud and the Small Magellanic Cloud. All globular clusters and objects ever suspected to be globular clusters in M 31 and the Fornax Dwarf are included. Objects in the Sagittarius Dwarf Spheroidal galaxy are included as clusters within the Milky Way (which they now are or eventually will be) in the catalog data of Table 4.1 on page 162.

Chapter 4 (page 41) should be consulted for additional information about the catalog format and the objects included. The complete description of the creation of this catalog is given in Appendix B. Appendix A lists the origin of the various object names, i.e., the discovery references of the objects included here. The references themselves are listed in the back of this book. Section 4.4 includes Extended Notes for some of the extragalactic objects listed in this Appendix. These notes provide general (e.g. astrophysical) information on the most interesting clusters and identity information for objects improperly identified (by name or object type) in the past.

A list of all known alias names for objects in these tables is given later in alphabetical order in Appendix C (page 373). Therefore, given an object's name only, one should first look it up there, obtain the parent galaxy (and therefore the table in which an object is listed), the object's preferred name, and the 2000.0 right ascension, and then look it up under the appropriate galaxy section where the objects are listed in 2000.0 right ascension order.

Section 4.2 (page 42) describes the various columns of the catalog in detail. An abbreviated version of that description follows below in the section for each galaxy.

C.1 Column Headings for Clusters in the LMC Table

Name: Primary name of the object. See Appendix D, table D.3 for list of objects by names and alias names.

Type: Up to 4 character object type (as described in detail in Section 4.2).

2000.0 RA and DEC: 2000.0 right ascension and declination.

Con: 3 letter abbreviation for constellation, and a "*" flag if the object is near a constellation boundary.

Diam: Approximate object diameter in arcminutes.

Tot Vm: Total V magnitude of object.

2U #: *Uranometria 2000.0 Deep Sky Atlas* chart number on which the object is best placed.

Ref: Indication of source (reference) for original data or of changes made in the catalog here. See Section 4.2 for details.

Comments and Aliases: Common alternate names, miscellaneous comments, and list of alias names for the object. If "See notes." appears, see Section 4.4 for extended (astrophysical and/or identification) notes on the object. See Section 4.2 for explanation of numbers (2 through 5) that appear with some alias names.

C.2 Column Headings for Clusters in the SMC Table

Name: Primary name of the object. See Appendix D, table D.3 for list of objects by names and alias names.

Type: Up to 4 character object type (as described in detail in Section 4.2).

2000.0 RA and DEC: 2000.0 right ascension and declination.

Con: 3 letter abbreviation for constellation, and a "*" flag if the object is near a constellation boundary.

Diam: Approximate object diameter in arcminutes.

Tot Vm: Total V magnitude of object.

 # str: Approximate number of stars in object.

Bt* Vm: V magnitude of brightest (likely member) star.

V Sur: Average surface brightness of object, V magnitudes per square arcminute.

2U #: *Uranometria 2000.0 Deep Sky Atlas* chart number on which the object is best placed.

Ref: Indication of source (reference) for original data or of changes made in the catalog here. See Section 4.2 for details.

Comments and Aliases: Common alternate names, miscellaneous comments, and list of alias names for the object. If "See notes." appears, see Section 4.4 for extended (astrophysical and/or identification) notes on the object. See Section 4.2 for explanation of numbers (2 through 5) that appear with some alias names.

C.3 Column Headings for Clusters in M 31 Table

Name: Primary name of the object. See Appendix D, table D.3 for list of objects by names and alias names.

Type: Up to 4 character object type (as described in detail in Section 4.2).

2000.0 RA and DEC: 2000.0 right ascension and declination.

Tot Vm: Total V magnitude of object.

2U #: *Uranometria 2000.0 Deep Sky Atlas* chart number on which the object is best placed.

Ref: Indication of source (reference) for original data or of changes made in the catalog here. See Section 4.2 for details.

Aliases: Alias names, if any.

C.4 Column Headings for Clusters in the Fornax Dwarf Galaxy Table

Name: Primary name of the object. See Appendix D, Table D.3 for list of objects by names and alias names.

Type: Up to 4 character object type (as described in detail in Section 4.2).

2000.0 RA and DEC: 2000.0 right ascension and declination.

Diam: Approximate object diameter in arcminutes.

Tot Vm: Total V magnitude of object.

Bt* Vm: V magnitude of brightest (likely member) star.

V Sur: Average surface brightness of object, V magnitudes per square arcminute.

2U #: *Uranometria 2000.0 Deep Sky Atlas* chart number on which the object is best placed.

Ref: Indication of source (reference) for original data or of changes made in the catalog here. See Section 4.2 for details.

Comments and Aliases: Common alternate names, miscellaneous comments, and list of alias names for the object. If "See notes." appears, see Section 4.4 for extended (astrophysical and/or identification) notes on the object. See section 4.2 for explanation of numbers (2 through 5) that appear with some alias names.

Table C.1: Tables of LMC Objects

Name	Type	2000.0 R.A.	2000.0 Dec.	Con	Diam (′)	Tot. Vm	U#	Ref	Comments and Aliases
Lindsay 116	cl	01 55 34.7	−77 39 15	Hyi			214	99	Piatti, et al. 2001 have determined this is an LMC cluster projected in front of (and much closer than) the SMC.
NGC 1466	gcl	03 44 32.4	−71 40 16	Hyi	1.9		212	99	KMHK: Compact cluster. Aliases: LW 1; ESO 54-16; SL 1; KMHK 1
SL 2	cl	04 24 09.8	−72 34 17	Hyi	0.7		212	99	KMHK: Incorrect on Hodge-Wright Atlas (1967). Alias: KMHK 2
KMHK 3	cl	04 29 35.1	−68 21 23	Hyi	0.4		212	11	KMHK: Loose cluster.
NGC 1629	cl	04 29 36.3	−71 50 17	Hyi	1.0		212	11	DSFG: Extremely faint.; KMHK: Loose cluster. Alias: KMHK 4
[HS66] 8	cl	04 30 38.1	−66 57 20	Ret	0.3		212	11	KMHK: Loose cluster. Alias: KMHK 5
SL 4	cl	04 32 38.6	−72 20 28	Hyi	1.5		212	11	KMHK: Loose cluster. Alias: KMHK 7
KMHK 6	cl	04 32 48.2	−71 27 34	Hyi	0.8		212	11	KMHK: Loose cluster.
LW 5	cl	04 33 52.1	−70 38 31	Hyi?	0.3		212	11	KMHK: Incorrect on Hodge-Wright Atlas (1967). Alias: KMHK 8
KMHK 9	cl	04 34 55.0	−68 14 49	Dor?	0.6		212	11	KMHK: Loose cluster.
[HS66] 13	cl	04 35 27.8	−67 42 40	Dor	0.9		212	11	KMHK: Loose cluster. Alias: KMHK 11
LW 7	cl	04 35 36.6	−69 21 47	Dor	0.6		212	11	KMHK: Incorrect on Hodge-Wright Atlas (1967). Alias: KMHK 12
SL 5	cl	04 35 38.6	−73 43 57	Men	0.8		219	11	KMHK: Loose cluster. Alias: KMHK 14
LW 9	cl	04 35 58.9	−71 40 10	Men	0.4		212	99	KMHK: Loose cluster. Alias: KMHK 13
NGC 1641	cl?	04 36 06	−65 46.9	Dor	5.0		212	99	Archinal: Do not confuse with background galaxy SL 6 = ESO 84-G25! Aliases: h 2656; (4) SL 6
KMHK 10	cl	04 36 09.9	−58 51 33	Ret	0.4		202	11	KMHK: Loose cluster.
Reticulum	gcl	04 36 11.3	−58 51 48	Ret	5.9		202	55	See notes. Recently shown to be a globular cluster in the LMC [Walker, 1992]. Aliases: GLC 0435-59; ESO 118-31; Sersic cl; EQ 0435–59; Sersic 40-3
KMHK 15	cl	04 36 19.8	−70 10 23	Men	0.4		212	11	KMHK: Loose cluster.
KMHK 16	cl	04 36 37.1	−72 32 20	Men	0.7		212	11	KMHK: Loose cluster.
KMHK 19	cl	04 37 06.4	−72 01 12	Men	0.4		212	11	KMHK: Loose cluster.
KMHK 17	cl	04 37 11.4	−69 13 12	Dor	0.4		212	11	KMHK: Loose cluster.
NGC 1651	cl	04 37 31.8	−70 35 07	Men	2.5		212	11	KMHK: Compact cluster. Alias: KMHK 20
NGC 1644	cl	04 37 39.4	−66 11 58	Dor	1.6		212	11	KMHK: Compact cluster. Alias: KMHK 18
SL 8	cl	04 37 49.9	−69 01 46	Dor	1.0		212	11	KMHK: Loose cluster. Alias: KMHK 21
NGC 1649	cl	04 38 06.9	−68 46 41	Dor	0.4	11.2	212	56	See notes. GSC 09154-01699.; KMHK: Compact cluster. Aliases: ESO 55-SC31; KMHK 22
NGC 1652	cl	04 38 22.6	−68 40 21	Dor	1.0	9.3	212	56	See notes. GSC 09154-01135.; KMHK: Compact cluster. Aliases: ESO 55-SC32; KMHK 23
LW 15	cl	04 38 26.3	−74 27 50	Men	0.7		219	11	KMHK: Loose cluster. Alias: KMHK 25
SL 11	cl	04 39 05.8	−71 00 03	Men	1.3		212	11	KMHK: Loose cluster. Alias: KMHK 24
SL 13	cl	04 39 42.9	−74 00 59	Men	0.4		219	11	KMHK: Loose cluster. Aliases: LW 17; KMHK 31
KMHK 30	cl	04 39 43.7	−74 01 05	Men	0.6		219	99	KMHK: Loose cluster.
LW 20	cl	04 39 58.6	−71 37 07	Men	0.7		212	11	KMHK: Compact cluster. Alias: KMHK 27
SL 12	cl	04 39 59.3	−69 01 44	Dor	0.7		212	11	KMHK: Incorrect on Hodge-Wright Atlas (1967). Alias: KMHK 26
LW 22	cl	04 40 20.4	−72 36 43	Men	0.3		212	11	KMHK: Incorrect on Hodge-Wright Atlas (1967). Alias: KMHK 33
SL 14	cl	04 40 28.8	−69 38 58	Dor	0.7		212	11	KMHK: Compact cluster. Alias: KMHK 28
SL 15	cl	04 40 43.4	−68 21 21	Dor	0.9		212	99	KMHK: Loose cluster. Alias: KMHK 29
KMHK 32	cl	04 41 00.6	−68 18 04	Dor	0.4		212	11	KMHK: Loose cluster.
LW 24	cl	04 41 07.8	−70 47 10	Men	0.6		212	11	KMHK: Loose cluster. Alias: KMHK 35
KMHK 36	cl	04 41 25.4	−70 29 41	Men	0.3		212	11	KMHK: Loose cluster.

Table C.1: Tables of LMC Objects

Name	Type	2000.0 R.A.	2000.0 Dec.	Con	Diam (′)	Tot. Vm	U#	Ref	Comments and Aliases
LW 27	cl	04 41 33.6	−72 23 21	Men	0.9		212	11	KMHK: Incorrect on Hodge-Wright Atlas (1967). Alias: KMHK 39
LW 25	cl	04 41 46.4	−68 10 19	Dor	0.7		212	11	KMHK: Loose cluster. Alias: KMHK 37
KMHK 34	cl	04 41 50.7	−64 32 51	Dor	0.4		212	11	KMHK: Compact cluster.
KMHK 38	cl	04 41 54.3	−70 11 14	Men	0.4		212	11	KMHK: Loose cluster.
LW 28	cl	04 42 11.0	−69 21 51	Dor	0.6		212	11	KMHK: Loose cluster. Alias: KMHK 40
NGC 1673	cl	04 42 39.2	−69 49 09	Men?	0.7		212	11	DSFG: Very faint; brighter star on N border.; KMHK: Loose cluster. Alias: KMHK 43
LW 30	cl	04 42 51.2	−68 04 28	Dor	0.9		212	11	KMHK: Loose cluster. Alias: KMHK 42
[HS66] 23	cl	04 42 54.1	−70 07 26	Men	0.9		212	11	KMHK: Loose cluster. Alias: KMHK 45
SL 16	cl	04 42 59.1	−64 57 04	Dor	0.6		212	99	M. Morel has pointed out that KMHK does not identify this correctly as SL 16.
SL 19	cl	04 43 03.6	−69 49 24	Men?	0.7		212	11	KMHK: Incorrect on Hodge-Wright Atlas (1967). Alias: KMHK 47
KMHK 46	cl	04 43 14.5	−68 02 13	Dor	0.3		212	11	KMHK: Loose cluster.
KMHK 48	cl	04 43 14.5	−70 08 58	Men	0.7		212	11	KMHK: Loose cluster.
KMHK 58	cl	04 43 14.8	−73 48 44	Men	0.4		219	11	KMHK: Loose cluster.
KMHK 44	cl	04 43 26.7	−64 53 06	Dor	0.3		212	99	M. Morel has pointed out that this is not SL 16 as KMHK speculate. SL 16 is instead KMHK 41.
KMHK 51	cl	04 43 31.7	−70 24 30	Men	0.6		212	11	KMHK: Loose cluster.
SL 22	cl	04 43 37.2	−69 21 52	Dor	0.8		212	11	KMHK: Incorrect on Hodge-Wright Atlas (1967). Alias: KMHK 49
SL 23	cl	04 43 38.0	−69 42 44	Dor?	0.4		212	99	KMHK: Loose cluster. Aliases: LW 36; [HS66] 24; BRHT 23a; KMHK 50
BRHT 23b	**	04 43 41.8	−69 43 11	Dor?	0.3		212	99	Likely not a cluster as KMHK indicate, but just a pair of stars. BRHT is incorrect in calling this [HS66] 24. Alias: KMHK 52
KMHK 56	cl	04 43 44.9	−70 33 06	Men	0.7		212	11	KMHK: Loose cluster.
SL 24	cl	04 43 50.3	−69 52 19	Men	0.9		212	99	KMHK: Incorrect on Hodge-Wright Atlas (1967). Aliases: LW 38; KMHK 55
NGC 1676	cl	04 43 52.6	−68 49 34	Dor	0.8		212	99	DSFG: Extremely faint; very few stars.; KMHK: Loose cluster. Alias: KMHK 53
KMHK 57	cl	04 43 53.8	−70 27 24	Men	0.6		212	11	KMHK: Loose cluster.
LW 39	cl	04 43 59.4	−68 46 44	Dor	0.6		212	11	KMHK: Loose cluster. Alias: KMHK 54
LW 41	cl	04 44 11.5	−68 44 58	Dor	0.4		212	11	KMHK: Loose cluster. Alias: KMHK 59
KMHK 61	cl	04 44 14.6	−71 22 04	Men	0.6		212	11	KMHK: Loose cluster.
BRHT 59b	cl	04 44 17	−71 22.7	Men			212	5	
LW 43	cl	04 44 17.0	−71 22 20	Men	0.6		212	99	KMHK: Loose cluster. Aliases: BRHT 59a; KMHK 62
LW 45	cl	04 44 29.4	−73 34 30	Men	0.8		219	11	KMHK: Incorrect on Hodge-Wright Atlas (1967). Alias: KMHK 68
LW 44	cl	04 44 37.4	−68 14 15	Dor	0.3		212	11	KMHK: Loose cluster. Alias: KMHK 60
SL 28	cl	04 44 40.8	−74 15 37	Men	1.8		219	11	KMHK: Loose cluster. Aliases: ESO 32-19; LW 47; KMHK 71
KMHK 66	cl	04 44 46.6	−71 00 10	Men	0.3		212	11	KMHK: Loose cluster.
LW 46	cl	04 44 46.7	−69 38 30	Dor	0.3		212	11	KMHK: Loose cluster. Alias: KMHK 63
SL 27	cl	04 45 04.7	−68 47 43	Dor	0.3		212	11	KMHK: Loose cluster. Alias: KMHK 64
KMHK 67	cl	04 45 08.6	−69 48 09	Men?	0.4		212	99	KMHK: Loose cluster. Archinal: DSS overlap region.
SL 29	cl	04 45 12.6	−75 07 00	Men	0.8		219	11	KMHK: Loose cluster. Aliases: LW 50; KMHK 81
SL 26	cl	04 45 17.4	−67 17 36	Dor	0.9		212	99	KMHK: Loose cluster. Archinal: On DSS overlap boundary. Alias: KMHK 65
NGC 1841	gcl	04 45 24.2	−83 59 53	Men			219	99	Aliases: ESO 4-15; C0444+840
SL 31	cl	04 45 40.6	−70 59 24	Men	0.3		212	99	KMHK: Loose cluster. Archinal: On DSS overlap boundary. Morel has pointed out this is SL 31. Aliases: KMHK 75; LW 53
SL 34	cl	04 45 46.7	−73 26 53	Men	1.1		212	11	KMHK: Incorrect on Hodge-Wright Atlas (1967). Alias: KMHK 86
LW 55	cl	04 45 47.3	−73 26 53	Men			212	99	
KMHK 69	cl	04 45 50.0	−67 29 45	Dor	0.9		212	11	KMHK: Loose cluster.

Table C.1: Tables of LMC Objects

Name	Type	2000.0 R.A.	2000.0 Dec.	Con	Diam (′)	Tot. Vm	U#	Ref	Comments and Aliases
KMHK 70	cl	04 45 50.3	–67 29 52	Dor	1.0		212	99	KMHK: Loose cluster. Archinal: On DSS overlap boundary.
SL 33	cl	04 45 53.5	–72 21 05	Men	0.7		212	99	The original SL position is 10′ too far south. Aliases: KMHK 83; LW 56
KMHK 74	cl	04 45 58.4	–69 03 13	Dor	0.8		212	99	KMHK: Loose cluster. Archinal: On DSS overlap boundary.
SL 30	cl	04 46 02.7	–68 28 59	Dor	0.8		212	99	KMHK: Loose cluster. Archinal: DSS overlap region, difficult to see. Alias: KMHK 73
[HS66] 26	cl	04 46 04.6	–69 32 39	Dor	1.2		212	99	KMHK: Loose cluster. Archinal: DSS overlap region, difficult to see. Alias: KMHK 77
KMHK 72	cl	04 46 05.2	–66 54 41	Dor	0.4		212	99	KMHK: Loose cluster. Archinal: On DSS overlap boundary.
SL 36	cl	04 46 08.5	–74 53 20	Men	0.6		219	11	KMHK: Loose cluster. Aliases: LW 60; KMHK 97
KMHK 78	cl	04 46 11.8	–69 39 02	Dor	1.0		212	99	KMHK: Loose cluster. Archinal: DSS overlap region, difficult to see.
LW 62	cl	04 46 18.9	–74 09 35	Men	0.3		219	11	KMHK: Loose cluster. Alias: KMHK 96
LW 57	cl	04 46 22.4	–66 41 32	Dor	1.1		212	99	KMHK: Loose cluster. Archinal: DSS overlap boundary and not visible. Alias: KMHK 76
KMHK 79	cl	04 46 24.7	–68 18 12	Dor	0.3		212	11	KMHK: Loose cluster.
KMHK 91	cl	04 46 28.1	–72 33 59	Men	0.7		212	99	KMHK suggest that this may be SL 33, but SL 33 is more likely KMHK 83.
KMHK 85	cl	04 46 33.5	–69 02 40	Dor	0.9		212	11	KMHK: Loose cluster.
KMHK 82	cl	04 46 36.7	–67 45 38	Dor	0.4		212	11	KMHK: Loose cluster.
SL 35	cl	04 46 40.7	–67 41 08	Dor	0.6		212	11	KMHK: Loose cluster. Alias: KMHK 84
SL 37	cl	04 46 45.8	–72 23 42	Men	1.7		212	11	KMHK: Loose cluster. Alias: KMHK 98
KMHK 87	cl	04 46 46.8	–69 44 36	Dor?	0.6		212	11	KMHK: Loose cluster.
KMHK 88	cl	04 46 50.8	–69 43 21	Dor?	0.6		212	99	KMHK: Loose cluster. Archinal: Not visible on (short exposure) DSS image.
KMHK 80	cl	04 46 55.7	–64 50 24	Dor	0.6		212	99	KMHK: Loose cluster. Archinal: Faintly visible on (short exposure) DSS image.
LW 63	cl	04 47 15.6	–67 05 25	Dor	0.6		212	11	KMHK: Loose cluster. Alias: KMHK 89
KMHK 90	cl	04 47 16.2	–67 05 19	Dor	0.4		212	11	KMHK: Loose cluster.
KMHK 94	cl	04 47 18.3	–68 22 09	Dor	0.7		212	11	KMHK: Loose cluster.
KMHK 93	cl	04 47 24.1	–66 36 05	Dor	0.9		212	11	KMHK: Loose cluster.
KMHK 95	cl	04 47 26.4	–67 39 35	Dor	0.3		212	99	KMHK: Loose cluster. Archinal: Something faintly visible on (short exposure) DSS image.
KMHK 107	cl	04 47 27.1	–73 26 53	Men	0.6		212	11	KMHK: Loose cluster.
[HS66] 27	cl	04 47 27.8	–69 26 36	Dor	0.3		212	11	KMHK: Compact cluster. Alias: KMHK 99
KMHK 106	cl	04 47 29.1	–73 21 36	Men	0.9		212	99	KMHK: Loose cluster.
SL 41	cl	04 47 30.9	–72 35 16	Men	1.3		212	11	KMHK: Loose cluster. Alias: KMHK 105
KMHK 92	cl	04 47 34.1	–64 38 45	Dor	0.4		212	11	KMHK: Compact cluster.
NGC 1693	cl	04 47 39.9	–69 20 35	Dor	0.7		212	11	DSFG: Faint.; KMHK: Compact cluster. Alias: KMHK 100
KMHK 103	cl	04 47 41.0	–70 57 44	Men	0.4		212	11	KMHK: Loose cluster.
NGC 1695	cl	04 47 44.8	–69 22 28	Dor	1.5		212	11	DSFG: Relatively faint; brighter than nearby NGC 1693.; KMHK: Compact cluster. Alias: KMHK 101
[HS66] 28	cl	04 48 04.2	–68 47 30	Dor	0.7		212	11	KMHK: Loose cluster. Alias: KMHK 104
SL 42	cl	04 48 08.2	–66 46 08	Dor	0.6		212	11	KMHK: Compact cluster. Alias: KMHK 102
[HS66] 30	cl	04 48 27.4	–69 22 05	Dor	0.7		212	11	KMHK: Compact cluster. Alias: KMHK 109
NGC 1696	cl	04 48 29.8	–68 14 33	Dor	0.9		212	11	KMHK: Loose cluster. Alias: KMHK 108
NGC 1697	cl	04 48 37.0	–68 33 38	Dor	2.6		212	11	KMHK: Compact cluster. Alias: KMHK 110
[HS66] 32	cl	04 48 41.1	–69 13 51	Dor	0.7		212	11	KMHK: Loose cluster. Alias: KMHK 111
[HS66] 31	cl	04 48 56.2	–68 54 10	Dor	0.6		212	11	KMHK: Loose cluster. Alias: KMHK 113

Table C.1: Tables of LMC Objects

Name	Type	2000.0 R.A.	2000.0 Dec.	Con	Diam (′)	Tot. Vm	U#	Ref	Comments and Aliases
KMHK 123	cl	04 49 00.0	−72 38 23	Men	0.3		212	11	KMHK: Loose cluster.
KMHK 120	cl	04 49 03.2	−71 39 45	Men	0.4		212	99	KMHK: Loose cluster. Archinal: Faint, stellar looking on DSS.
SL 47	cl	04 49 03.3	−70 11 24	Men	0.4		212	11	KMHK: Incorrect on Hodge-Wright Atlas (1967). Alias: KMHK 117
NGC 1698	cl	04 49 04.0	−69 06 54	Dor	1.6		212	11	KMHK: Compact cluster. Alias: KMHK 115
LW 66	cl	04 49 04.2	−73 50 23	Men	0.7		219	11	KMHK: Compact cluster. Alias: KMHK 129
KMHK 112	cl	04 49 08.0	−67 20 31	Dor	0.6		212	99	KMHK: Loose cluster. Archinal: Something faintly visible on (short exposure) DSS image.
KMHK 114	cl	04 49 10.2	−68 00 27	Dor	0.7		212	11	KMHK: Loose cluster.
KMHK 121	cl	04 49 10.9	−71 11 46	Men	0.4		212	11	KMHK: Loose cluster.
KMHK 128	cl	04 49 13.9	−73 03 27	Men	0.3		212	11	KMHK: Loose cluster.
[HS66] 33	cl	04 49 16.5	−69 52 30	Men	0.8		212	11	KMHK: Loose cluster. Alias: KMHK 119
LW 65	cl	04 49 20.0	−73 11 15	Men	0.3		212	99	KMHK: Incorrect on Hodge-Wright Atlas (1967). Archinal: Very faint on DSS image. Alias: KMHK 132
KMHK 118	cl	04 49 20.3	−69 07 39	Dor	0.8		212	11	KMHK: Compact cluster.
KMHK 116	cl	04 49 20.5	−68 11 37	Dor	0.3		212	11	KMHK: Loose cluster.
NGC 1702	cl	04 49 25.9	−69 51 11	Men?	1.0		212	11	KMHK: Compact cluster. Alias: KMHK 122
SL 48	cl	04 49 27.5	−72 46 54	Men	0.7		212	11	KMHK: Loose cluster. Alias: KMHK 133
[HS66] 36	cl	04 49 33.6	−70 02 56	Men	0.4		212	11	KMHK: Compact cluster. Alias: KMHK 126
[HS66] 35	cl	04 49 33.7	−69 43 40	Dor?	0.4		212	11	KMHK: Compact cluster. Alias: KMHK 124
LW 69	cl	04 49 39.0	−72 14 54	Men	0.7		212	11	KMHK: Loose cluster. Alias: KMHK 137
KMHK 127	cl	04 49 39.6	−69 56 33	Men	0.6		212	11	KMHK: Loose cluster.
KMHK 125	cl	04 49 52.0	−67 41 15	Dor	0.3		212	99	KMHK: Compact cluster. Archinal: Stellar looking on DSS.
SL 53	cl	04 49 53.2	−75 37 40	Men	0.8		219	11	KMHK: Loose cluster. Aliases: LW 73; KMHK 160
NGC 1704	cl	04 49 55.5	−69 45 16	Dor?	1.7	11.5	212	11	KMHK: Compact cluster. Alias: KMHK 130
KMHK 134	cl	04 50 06.2	−69 25 44	Dor	0.9		212	11	KMHK: Loose cluster.
KMHK 135	cl	04 50 06.5	−69 25 41	Dor	0.7		212	11	KMHK: Loose cluster.
SL 52	cl	04 50 07.0	−71 38 58	Men	0.3		212	99	KMHK: Loose cluster. Archinal: Something faintly visible on (short exposure) DSS image. Alias: KMHK 141
SL 49	cl	04 50 10.4	−68 59 55	Dor	1.0		212	11	KMHK: Compact cluster. Alias: KMHK 136
LW 75	cl	04 50 14.0	−73 38 45	Men	1.0		219	99	Western part of SL 59. Aliases: KMHK 152; BRHT 24a; (3) SL 59
SL 51	cl	04 50 19.7	−67 05 19	Dor	0.3		212	11	KMHK: Loose cluster. Alias: KMHK 131
SL 59	2cl	04 50 20.2	−73 38 50	Men	1.7		219	99	Includes LW 75 = KMHK 152 = BRHT 24a on W and LW 76 = KMHK 157 = BRHT 24b on E. BRHT identification of SL 59 is incorrect. Aliases: (2) LW 75; (2) LW 76
KMHK 151	cl	04 50 21.3	−72 49 40	Men	0.6		212	11	KMHK: Loose cluster.
LW 76	cl	04 50 24.8	−73 38 58	Men	1.0		219	99	Eastern part of SL 59.; KMHK: Loose cluster. Aliases: KMHK 157; BRHT 24b; (3) SL 59
[HS66] 37	cl	04 50 28.2	−68 42 41	Dor	0.9		212	11	KMHK: Compact cluster. Alias: KMHK 139
SL 56	cl	04 50 32.1	−70 04 33	Men	0.8		212	11	KMHK: Compact cluster. Alias: KMHK 142
KMHK 143	cl	04 50 32.7	−70 09 57	Men	0.6		212	99	KMHK: Loose cluster. Archinal: Something faintly visible on (short exposure) DSS image.
KMHK 140	cl	04 50 36.0	−67 51 33	Dor	1.0		212	99	KMHK: Loose cluster. Archinal: Something faintly visible on (short exposure) DSS image.
NGC 1711	cl	04 50 37.4	−69 59 06	Men	2.4	10.1	212	11	KMHK: Compact cluster. Aliases: SL 55; KMHK 145
KMHK 138	cl	04 50 42.8	−66 13 50	Dor	0.4		212	99	KMHK: Compact cluster. Archinal: Stellar looking on DSS.
KMHK 144	cl	04 50 43.6	−69 05 19	Dor	0.4		212	11	KMHK: Loose cluster.

Table C.1: Tables of LMC Objects

Name	Type	2000.0 R.A.	2000.0 Dec.	Con	Diam (′)	Tot. Vm	U#	Ref	Comments and Aliases
SL 61	cl	04 50 44.9	−75 32 02	Men	2.4		219	11	KMHK: Loose cluster. Alias: KMHK 178
SL 54	cl	04 50 48.7	−72 34 37	Men	1.1		212	99	Identified as SL 54 (poor position) by M. Morel [Priv. Comm., 2002]. Aliases: KMHK 162; LW 78
KMHK 147	cl	04 50 53.7	−69 25 16	Dor	1.6		212	11	KMHK: Loose cluster.
NGC 1712	cl	04 50 57.1	−69 24 15	Dor	2.5		212	99	KMHK: Incorrect on Hodge-Wright Atlas (1967). Aliases: LH 1; KMHK 155; h 2685
SL 58	cl	04 50 59.9	−69 38 13	Dor	1.0		212	11	KMHK: Compact cluster. Alias: KMHK 153
KMHK 156	cl	04 51 01.2	−70 01 25	Men	1.1		212	11	KMHK: Loose cluster.
[HS66] 39	cl	04 51 03.6	−69 14 55	Dor	1.1		212	11	KMHK: Compact cluster. Alias: KMHK 154
KMHK 150	cl	04 51 08.0	−68 14 40	Dor	0.4		212	11	KMHK: Compact cluster.
[HS66] 38	cl	04 51 11.4	−67 32 06	Dor	0.6		212	11	KMHK: Compact cluster. Alias: KMHK 148
[HS66] 40	cl	04 51 11.9	−69 58 17	Men	0.6		212	11	KMHK: Loose cluster. Alias: KMHK 159
SL 57	cl	04 51 13.2	−65 36 38	Dor	0.9		212	99	KMHK: Compact cluster. Archinal: There is an apparent defect on the DSS just to the north of here. Alias: KMHK 146
KMHK 149	cl	04 51 18.9	−66 47 20	Dor	1.2		212	99	KMHK: Loose cluster. Archinal: Something faintly visible on (short exposure) DSS image.
KMHK 161	cl	04 51 23.9	−69 06 58	Dor	1.0		212	11	KMHK: Loose cluster.
KMHK 164	cl	04 51 23.9	−69 35 04	Dor	0.4		212	11	KMHK: Compact cluster.
KMHK 163	cl	04 51 29.9	−68 50 31	Dor	1.3		212	99	KMHK: Loose cluster. Archinal: Something faintly visible on (short exposure) DSS image.
[HS66] 41	cl	04 51 31.1	−67 27 16	Dor	0.3		212	11	KMHK: Compact cluster. Alias: KMHK 158
KMHK 166	cl	04 51 33.1	−69 34 19	Dor	0.3		212	11	KMHK: Loose cluster.
[HS66] 44	cl	04 51 37.7	−70 42 19	Men	0.7		212	11	KMHK: Loose cluster. Alias: KMHK 169
KMHK 170	cl	04 51 39.7	−70 39 18	Men	1.0		212	99	KMHK: Loose cluster. Archinal: Something faintly visible on (short exposure) DSS image.
[HS66] 43	cl	04 51 40.6	−68 46 00	Dor	0.8		212	11	KMHK: Compact cluster. Alias: KMHK 167
KMHK 183	cl	04 51 42.5	−72 13 13	Men			212	99	Archinal: Nearly stellar on DSS. SL 73 identity unknown.
KMHK 179	cl	04 51 45.0	−71 20 10	Men	0.3		212	11	KMHK: Loose cluster.
KMHK 188	cl	04 51 47.0	−72 49 43	Men	0.2		212	11	KMHK: Compact cluster.
KMHK 172	cl	04 51 51.1	−69 38 37	Dor	0.7		212	11	KMHK: Loose cluster.
NGC 1722	cl	04 51 51.5	−69 23 55	Dor	1.0		212	56	See notes. Contains KMHK 173 group of stars with IC 2111 nebula on north, and KMHK 171 group on south. Aliases: (2) IC 2111; (2) KMHK 171; (2) KMHK 173
IC 2111	neb	04 51 53.0	−69 23 32	Dor	0.4		212	56	See notes. Position and diameter from DSS. Nebula around three stars, possibly an unresolved cluster, KMHK 173. In NGC 1722. Aliases: (3) NGC 1722; (4) KMHK 173
KMHK 173	cl?	04 51 53.0	−69 23 32	Dor	0.4		212	56	See notes. Three stars, possibly an unresolved cluster, involved in nebulosity IC 2111. In NGC 1722. KMHK: Compact cluster. Aliases: BRHT 1b; (3) NGC 1722; (4) IC 2111
KMHK 171	cl	04 51 53.0	−69 24 25	Dor			212	56	See notes. Southern part of cluster (or association) NGC 1722. Alias: (3) NGC 1722
SL 66	cl	04 51 56.0	−70 23 23	Men	1.1		212	11	KMHK: Compact cluster. Alias: KMHK 180
KMHK 176	cl	04 51 56.3	−69 33 43	Dor	0.7		212	11	KMHK: Loose cluster.
SL 74	cl	04 52 01.4	−74 50 41	Men	0.7		219	11	KMHK: Loose cluster. Alias: KMHK 210
SL 62	cl	04 52 03.2	−65 36 17	Dor	0.3		212	11	KMHK: Loose cluster. Alias: KMHK 165
NGC 1714	cl	04 52 06.6	−66 55 25	Dor	1.2		212	11	KMHK: Compact cluster. Aliases: SL 64; KMHK 168
SL 68	cl	04 52 06.7	−73 13 18	Men	1.7		212	99	KMHK: Loose cluster. Alias: KMHK 198
LW 83	cl	04 52 06.8	−73 04 15	Men	0.6		212	99	KMHK: Loose cluster. Alias: KMHK 197
[HS66] 48	cl	04 52 08.4	−68 27 03	Dor	0.3		212	11	KMHK: Loose cluster. Alias: KMHK 177

Table C.1: Tables of LMC Objects

Name	Type	2000.0 R.A.	2000.0 Dec.	Con	Diam (′)	Tot. Vm	U#	Ref	Comments and Aliases
NGC 1727	cl	04 52 12.3	−69 20 16	Dor	2.5		212	99	KMHK: Compact cluster. Alias: KMHK 182
[HS66] 46	cl	04 52 19.1	−66 08 54	Dor	0.3		212	11	KMHK: Loose cluster. Alias: KMHK 174
SL 80	cl	04 52 21.1	−74 53 22	Men	0.6		219	11	KMHK: Loose cluster. Aliases: LW 88; KMHK 220
KMHK 187	cl	04 52 23.7	−69 21 39	Dor	1.5		212	11	KMHK: Compact cluster.
NGC 1718	cl	04 52 25.6	−67 03 09	Dor	2.0	12.3	212	11	DSFG: Compact and moderately bright.; KMHK: Compact cluster. Alias: KMHK 181
SL 63	cl	04 52 25.7	−65 24 31	Dor	0.4		212	11	KMHK: Loose cluster. Alias: KMHK 175
KMHK 189	cl	04 52 29.3	−68 49 41	Dor	0.7		212	11	KMHK: Compact cluster.
KMHK 192	cl	04 52 29.5	−70 00 24	Men	0.7		212	99	KMHK: Loose cluster. Archinal: Something faintly visible on (short exposure) DSS image.
SL 72	ast	04 52 33.8	−72 19 52	Men	0.7		212	99	Identified as asterism of 4 stars by M. Morel [Priv. Comm., 2002]. Same as Hodge-Wright Atlas [1967] id.
OHSC 1	cl	04 52 42.4	−75 16 36	Men	0.9		219	11	KMHK: Loose cluster. Alias: KMHK 231
[HS66] 52	cl	04 52 43.0	−68 46 54	Dor	0.8		212	11	KMHK: Compact cluster. Alias: KMHK 193
LW 86	cl	04 52 44.8	−72 31 05	Men	0.6		212	11	KMHK: Loose cluster. Alias: KMHK 214
[HS66] 51	cl	04 52 44.9	−66 53 04	Dor	0.6		212	99	See notes. KMHK: Loose cluster. Aliases: KMHK 190; (3) NGC 1731
KMHK 184	cl	04 52 45.0	−65 41 04	Dor	0.8		212	99	KMHK: Loose cluster. Archinal: Very faint on DSS image.
[HS66] 50	cl	04 52 45.9	−66 29 32	Dor	0.6		212	11	KMHK: Loose cluster. Alias: KMHK 185
SL 84	cl	04 52 46.0	−75 04 27	Men	1.3		219	11	KMHK: Loose cluster. Alias: KMHK 232
KMHK 186	cl	04 52 46.1	−66 29 36	Dor	0.8		212	11	KMHK: Loose cluster.
SL 70	cl	04 52 50.0	−67 23 55	Dor	1.0		212	11	KMHK: Loose cluster. Alias: KMHK 191
SL 79	cl	04 52 53.3	−71 39 32	Men	1.0		212	11	KMHK: Compact cluster. Alias: KMHK 213
KMHK 202	cl	04 52 54.3	−69 15 15	Dor	1.0		212	99	KMHK: Loose cluster. Archinal: Only scattering of stars visible on DSS image.
LW 87	cl	04 52 54.6	−72 10 21	Men	0.7		212	11	KMHK: Loose cluster. Alias: KMHK 217
KMHK 203	cl	04 52 54.8	−69 46 42	Dor?	0.7		212	11	KMHK: Compact cluster.
SL 75	cl	04 52 54.9	−68 55 08	Dor	1.6		212	11	KMHK: Compact cluster. Alias: KMHK 199
SL 71	cl	04 52 55.3	−67 26 59	Dor	0.8		212	11	KMHK: Compact cluster. Alias: KMHK 194
KMHK 228	cl	04 52 56.7	−74 00 54	Men	0.6		219	11	KMHK: Loose cluster.
KMHK 205	cl	04 52 59.1	−69 22 04	Dor	0.7		212	11	KMHK: Compact cluster.
KMHK 204	cl	04 52 59.8	−69 15 36	Dor	1.5		212	99	KMHK: Loose cluster. Archinal: Only scattering of stars visible on DSS image. Maybe large group?
KMHK 207	cl	04 53 00.1	−69 37 26	Dor	0.9		212	11	KMHK: Compact cluster.
NGC 1736	cl	04 53 02.3	−68 03 15	Dor	1.8		212	11	KMHK: Compact cluster. Alias: KMHK 200
KMHK 195	cl	04 53 04.6	−66 13 36	Dor	0.4		212	11	KMHK: Loose cluster.
KMHK 196	cl	04 53 04.9	−66 13 32	Dor	0.4		212	11	KMHK: Loose cluster.
KMHK 208	cl	04 53 06.7	−69 02 36	Dor	0.6		212	11	KMHK: Compact cluster.
SL 76	cl	04 53 09.0	−68 12 41	Dor	1.3		212	11	KMHK: Compact cluster. Alias: KMHK 206
SL 81	cl	04 53 09.8	−67 17 47	Dor	1.1		212	11	KMHK: Loose cluster. Alias: KMHK 201
OHSC 2	cl	04 53 10.1	−74 40 54	Men	0.3		219	11	KMHK: Loose cluster. Alias: KMHK 238
NGC 1732	cl	04 53 11.5	−68 39 03	Dor	0.9	12.3	212	11	DSFG: Relatively faint.; KMHK: Compact cluster. Alias: KMHK 209
KMHK 219	cl	04 53 29.0	−68 57 13	Dor	0.9		212	11	KMHK: Loose cluster.
KMHK 211	ptcl	04 53 30.4	−66 55 28	Dor	0.8		212	99	See notes. KMHK identify this as a cluster, but it appears to be mostly a double star at the center (same position as) NGC 1731. Alias: (3) NGC 1731

Table C.1: Tables of LMC Objects

Name	Type	2000.0 R.A.	2000.0 Dec.	Con	Diam (′)	Tot. Vm	U#	Ref	Comments and Aliases
NGC 1731	cl	04 53 30.4	−66 55 28	Dor	8.0		212	99	See notes. KMHK 211 at center. Also contains KMHK 212 (KMHK id is wrong) and [HS66] 51. Aliases: h 2691; LH 4; (2) [HS66] 51; (2) KMHK 211; (2) KMHK 212; (4) Hen N 4
NGC 1734	cl	04 53 33.9	−68 46 03	Dor	1.3		212	11	DSFG: Very faint.; KMHK: Compact cluster. Alias: KMHK 221
KMHK 212	ptcl	04 53 35.3	−66 55 25	Dor	0.7		212	99	See notes. KMHK incorrectly identify this as NGC 1731. It is a small clump of stars on the E side of the larger NGC 1731. Alias: (3) NGC 1731
[HS66] 56	cl	04 53 37.4	−67 52 22	Dor	0.7		212	99	KMHK: Loose cluster. Alias: KMHK 218
KMHK 215	cl	04 53 44.4	−66 36 50	Dor	0.7		212	11	KMHK: Loose cluster.
KMHK 216	cl	04 53 44.6	−66 36 47	Dor	0.7		212	11	KMHK: Compact cluster.
KMHK 222	cl	04 53 49.2	−66 49 21	Dor	0.6		212	99	KMHK: Loose cluster.
KMHK 229	cl	04 53 51.5	−69 34 18	Dor	0.7		212	99	KMHK: Compact cluster.
Henize N 83B	neb	04 53 58.8	−69 10 19	Dor	0.8		212	99	Nebulosity associated with NGC 1737. Aliases: (3) Hen N 83; (4) NGC 1737
NGC 1737	cl?	04 53 58.8	−69 10 19	Dor	0.8		212	99	See notes. Nebulous cluster or group of stars. Aliases: h 2698; (2) LH 5; (4) Hen N 83B
KMHK 230	cl	04 54 00.6	−68 37 58	Dor	0.6		212	11	KMHK: Loose cluster.
KMHK 237	cl	04 54 01.0	−69 59 46	Men	0.6		212	11	KMHK: Compact cluster.
Henize N 83A	neb	04 54 03.4	−69 11 57	Dor	1.0		212	99	Nebulosity associated with NGC 1743. Aliases: (3) Hen N 83; (4) NGC 1743
NGC 1743	cl?	04 54 03.4	−69 11 57	Dor	0.3		212	56	See notes. Nebulous cluster or group of stars. Cluster also known as SL 87 = KMHK 235, and nebula also known as Hen N 83A.; KMHK: Compact cluster. Aliases: Dunlop 114; h 2699; SL 87; KMHK 235; (2) LH 5; (4) Hen N 83A; (5) HD 31947; (5) CD–69 252; (5) CPD–69 302
NGC 1733	cl	04 54 04.9	−66 40 56	Dor	1.2		212	11	DSFG: Very faint.; KMHK: Compact cluster. Alias: KMHK 224
KMHK 227	cl	04 54 05.7	−67 21 07	Dor	0.4		212	11	KMHK: Loose cluster.
KMHK 223	cl	04 54 08.0	−65 46 40	Dor	0.3		212	99	KMHK: Loose cluster. Archinal: Very faint.
KMHK 241	cl	04 54 09.4	−70 13 12	Men	1.0		212	11	KMHK: Loose cluster.
Henize N 83D	neb	04 54 10	−69 11.2	Dor	0.7		212	99	Nebulosity in the middle of the triangle of NGC 1737, NGC 1743, and NGC 1748. Alias: (3) Hen N 83
NGC 1751	cl	04 54 11.9	−69 48 30	Men?	1.7		212	11	KMHK: Compact cluster. Alias: KMHK 239
Henize N 83	neb	04 54.2	−69 11	Dor	6.0		212	99	Overall nebulosity in this area, associated with LH 5, et al. Aliases: (3) Hen N 83; (4) LH 5
LH 5	ass	04 54.2	−69 11	Dor	6.0		212	99	See notes. Includes NGC 1737, NGC 1743, NGC 1745, NGC 1748, and nebula Hen N 83 (including IC 2114). Aliases: (3) NGC 1737; (3) NGC 1743; (3) NGC 1745; (3) NGC 1748; (4) Hen N 83
[HS66] 58	cl	04 54 13.3	−66 14 56	Dor	0.4		212	11	KMHK: Loose cluster. Alias: KMHK 226
SL 88	cl	04 54 15.5	−71 13 46	Men	0.8		212	11	KMHK: Loose cluster. Alias: KMHK 249
KMHK 225	cl	04 54 16.3	−65 29 11	Dor	0.3		212	99	KMHK: Loose cluster. Archinal: DSS image shows only a very faint star here.
NGC 1754	gcl	04 54 18.4	−70 26 31	Men	1.6		212	99	KMHK: Compact cluster. Alias: KMHK 247
KMHK 242	cl	04 54 18.7	−69 18 39	Dor	0.7		212	11	KMHK: Compact cluster.
NGC 1735	cl	04 54 20.2	−67 06 04	Dor	1.6		212	11	KMHK: Compact cluster. Alias: KMHK 234
NGC 1745	cl	04 54 20.9	−69 09 35	Dor	0.4		212	99	See notes. Nebulous cluster or group of stars. Aliases: h 2702; (2) LH 5
LW 91	cl	04 54 22.8	−73 21 20	Men	0.7		212	99	KMHK: Loose cluster. Alias: KMHK 274
IC 2114	neb	04 54 24.7	−69 11 00	Dor	0.6		212	99	See notes. Nebulosity associated with NGC 1748. NOT a "stellar planetary" as IC indicates. Aliases: Fleming 86; Hen N 83C; (3) Hen N 83; (4) NGC 1748
NGC 1748	cl	04 54 24.7	−69 11 00	Dor	0.6		212	99	See notes. Nebulous cluster or group of stars. Aliases: h 2704; (2) LH 5; (4) IC 2114
KMHK 236	cl	04 54 25.6	−66 44 31	Dor	0.6		212	11	KMHK: Loose cluster.
KMHK 244	cl	04 54 26.2	−68 31 02	Dor	0.6		212	11	KMHK: Compact cluster.

Table C.1: Tables of LMC Objects

Name	Type	2000.0 R.A.	2000.0 Dec.	Con	Diam (′)	Tot. Vm	U#	Ref	Comments and Aliases
SL 92	cl	04 54 26.7	−68 14 53	Dor	0.7		212	11	KMHK: Compact cluster. Alias: KMHK 240
KMHK 245	cl	04 54 27.2	−68 27 40	Dor	0.7		212	11	KMHK: Compact cluster.
KMHK 233	cl	04 54 28.6	−65 49 14	Dor	0.6		212	11	KMHK: Compact cluster.
SL 90	cl	04 54 30.2	−69 55 11	Men	1.0		212	11	KMHK: Loose cluster. Alias: KMHK 250
[HS66] 59	cl	04 54 37.2	−70 12 53	Men	1.3		212	11	KMHK: Loose cluster. Alias: KMHK 253
KMHK 262	cl	04 54 37.6	−70 48 33	Men	0.4		212	11	KMHK: Loose cluster.
KMHK 259	cl	04 54 39.7	−70 29 21	Men	0.6		212	11	KMHK: Loose cluster.
KMHK 264	cl	04 54 41.9	−70 21 28	Men	1.0		212	99	KMHK: Compact cluster.
SL 95	cl	04 54 42.1	−71 15 30	Men	1.0		212	11	KMHK: Loose cluster. Alias: KMHK 269
KMHK 260	cl	04 54 42.7	−70 14 55	Men	1.3		212	11	KMHK: Loose cluster.
KMHK 251	cl	04 54 42.9	−69 03 35	Dor	0.7		212	11	KMHK: Compact cluster.
[HS66] 60	cl	04 54 44.1	−68 58 57	Dor	0.7		212	11	KMHK: Compact cluster. Aliases: BRHT 43a; KMHK 252
BRHT 43b	cl	04 54 46	−68 57.7	Dor			212	5	
SL 100	cl	04 54 45.8	−70 22 53	Men	0.7		212	11	KMHK: Compact cluster. Alias: KMHK 265
KMHK 258	cl	04 54 45.9	−69 49 26	Men?	0.7		212	99	KMHK: Loose cluster. Archinal: Not visible on DSS image.
NGC 1756	cl	04 54 49.9	−69 14 14	Dor	1.1	12.2	212	11	KMHK: Compact cluster. Aliases: SL 94; KMHK 257
KMHK 243	cl	04 54 52.0	−64 55 00	Dor	0.8		212	11	KMHK: Compact cluster.
SL 103	cl	04 54 53.7	−71 23 25	Men	0.9		212	99	KMHK: Loose cluster. Alias: KMHK 277
[HS66] 62	cl	04 54 54	−70 34.9	Men			212	99	Archinal: Not visible on DSS image. Alias: BRHT 44a
KMHK 246	cl	04 54 55.3	−65 36 22	Dor	0.3		212	99	KMHK: Loose cluster.
SL 102	cl	04 54 56.4	−70 36 12	Men	0.6		212	11	KMHK: Incorrect on Hodge-Wright Atlas (1967). Alias: KMHK 275
KMHK 248	cl	04 54 56.5	−66 23 16	Dor	0.7		212	99	KMHK: Loose cluster. Archinal: Not visible on DSS image.
NGC 1749	cl	04 54 56.5	−68 11 19	Dor	1.2		212	99	KMHK: Loose cluster. Alias: KMHK 254
KMHK 255	cl	04 54 57.5	−68 08 55	Dor	1.3		212	11	KMHK: Loose cluster.
[HS66] 63	cl	04 55 01.0	−70 54 12	Men	0.6		212	11	KMHK: Loose cluster. Alias: KMHK 278
SL 96	cl	04 55 01.9	−67 42 52	Dor	0.9		212	11	KMHK: Loose cluster. Alias: KMHK 256
KMHK 271	cl	04 55 03.6	−69 27 43	Dor	0.6		212	11	KMHK: Compact cluster.
KMHK 270	**?	04 55 05.7	−69 03 29	Dor	0.4		212	99	KMHK: Compact cluster. Archinal: Double star only?
SL 106	cl	04 55 06.4	−69 40 26	Dor	1.5		212	99	KMHK: Compact cluster. Alias: KMHK 276
BRHT 44b	cl	04 55 07	−70 35.5	Men			212	5	
KMHK 263	cl	04 55 07.4	−67 28 58	Dor	0.6		212	11	KMHK: Compact cluster.
KMHK 279	cl	04 55 08.0	−70 14 50	Men	0.7		212	11	KMHK: Loose cluster.
SL 101	cl	04 55 10.1	−67 03 13	Dor	0.9		212	11	KMHK: Compact cluster. Alias: KMHK 261
LH 6	cl	04 55 11.1	−67 10 09	Dor			212	99	
[HS66] 61	cl	04 55 11.3	−67 29 51	Dor	0.7		212	11	KMHK: Compact cluster. Alias: KMHK 266
[HS66] 64	cl	04 55 13.4	−70 11 29	Men	0.4		212	11	KMHK: Compact cluster. Alias: KMHK 281
NGC 1755	cl	04 55 14.7	−68 12 20	Dor	2.6	9.9	212	11	KMHK: Compact cluster. Aliases: SL 99; KMHK 272
SL 108	cl	04 55 15.0	−71 06 17	Men	0.7		212	11	KMHK: Compact cluster. Alias: KMHK 287
KMHK 267	cl	04 55 19.6	−66 48 21	Dor	0.8		212	99	KMHK: Compact cluster.

Table C.1: Tables of LMC Objects

Name	Type	2000.0 R.A.	2000.0 Dec.	Con	Diam (′)	Tot. Vm	U#	Ref	Comments and Aliases
[HS66] 66	cl	04 55 21.0	–69 56 31	Men	0.7		212	99	KMHK: Loose cluster. Archinal: Scattered stars here, no cluster obvious on DSS image. Alias: KMHK 284
KMHK 297	cl	04 55 23.1	–71 23 42	Men	0.6		212	11	KMHK: Loose cluster.
KMHK 268	cl	04 55 23.2	–66 26 38	Dor	1.0		212	11	KMHK: Loose cluster.
KMHK 288	cl	04 55 24.1	–70 19 07	Men	0.4		212	11	KMHK: Loose cluster.
SL 105	cl	04 55 24.5	–68 32 28	Dor	1.2		212	99	KMHK: Compact cluster. Alias: KMHK 280
KMHK 273	cl	04 55 24.7	–67 03 42	Dor	0.7		212	11	KMHK: Compact cluster.
[HS66] 67	cl	04 55 27.7	–70 53 34	Men	0.6		212	11	KMHK: Loose cluster. Alias: KMHK 296
KMHK 282	cl	04 55 28.2	–68 50 26	Dor	1.0		212	99	KMHK: Loose cluster.
[HS66] 65	cl	04 55 30.5	–68 53 01	Dor	0.7		212	11	KMHK: Loose cluster. Alias: KMHK 283
KMHK 299	cl	04 55 32.3	–71 03 54	Men	0.6		212	11	KMHK: Loose cluster.
KMHK 289	cl	04 55 32.4	–69 30 38	Dor	0.4		212	11	KMHK: Compact cluster.
SL 118	cl	04 55 32.5	–74 40 36	Men	0.6		219	11	KMHK: Loose cluster. Aliases: LW 94; KMHK 323
SL 109	cl	04 55 33.1	–69 29 45	Dor	1.0		212	11	KMHK: Loose cluster. Alias: KMHK 290
KMHK 292	cl	04 55 35.4	–69 26 54	Dor	1.0		212	11	KMHK: Compact cluster.
KMHK 285	cl	04 55 39.5	–67 49 19	Dor	0.7		212	11	KMHK: Compact cluster.
KMHK 300	cl	04 55 39.6	–70 32 48	Men	1.0		212	11	KMHK: Loose cluster.
KMHK 286	cl	04 55 41.6	–67 47 01	Dor	0.6		212	11	KMHK: Compact cluster.
SL 111	cl	04 55 42.3	–71 25 02	Men	1.0		212	11	KMHK: Loose cluster. Aliases: BRHT 25a; LH 7; KMHK 303
SL 110	cl	04 55 44.4	–69 09 24	Dor	0.9		212	99	KMHK: Compact cluster. Alias: KMHK 294
SL 107	cl	04 55 45.1	–68 16 53	Dor	0.6		212	11	KMHK: Compact cluster. Alias: KMHK 291
KMHK 293	cl	04 55 46.1	–68 33 03	Dor	0.3		212	11	KMHK: Compact cluster.
KMHK 298	cl	04 55 47.3	–69 22 18	Dor	1.7		212	11	KMHK: Loose cluster.
NGC 1777	cl	04 55 48.5	–74 17 00	Men	2.1		219	11	DSFG: Superposed on the E side are two stars (approximate magnitude = 11.5v).; KMHK: Compact cluster. Aliases: LW 96; ESO 33-1; SL 121; KMHK 328
SL 112	cl	04 55 52.6	–69 42 39	Dor	1.6		212	99	KMHK: Loose cluster. Alias: KMHK 301
KMHK 312	cl	04 55 55.4	–71 24 59	Men	0.7		212	99	KMHK: Compact cluster. Alias: BRHT 25b
KMHK 343	cl	04 55 55.9	–75 08 19	Men	0.4		219	11	KMHK: Loose cluster.
NGC 1766	cl	04 55 57.7	–70 13 35	Men	0.7	12.2	212	11	DSFG: Moderately bright.; KMHK: Compact cluster. Alias: KMHK 304
LW 95	cl	04 55 57.9	–75 08 26	Men	0.6		219	11	KMHK: Loose cluster. Alias: KMHK 344
KMHK 306	cl	04 56 06.3	–69 39 26	Dor	0.9		212	99	KMHK: Loose cluster.
[HS66] 68	cl	04 56 06.5	–66 20 28	Dor	1.0		212	99	KMHK: Loose cluster. Alias: KMHK 295
[HS66] 70	cl	04 56 07.3	–70 18 30	Men	0.6		212	11	KMHK: Loose cluster. Alias: KMHK 313
SL 114	cl	04 56 07.8	–69 14 51	Dor	0.8		212	11	KMHK: Compact cluster. Alias: KMHK 305
KMHK 317	cl	04 56 17.6	–70 25 16	Men	0.4		212	11	KMHK: Loose cluster.
KMHK 302	cl	04 56 21.5	–66 17 47	Dor	1.0		212	11	KMHK: Loose cluster.
SL 117	cl	04 56 22.4	–68 58 01	Dor	2.2		212	11	KMHK: Compact cluster. Alias: KMHK 314
SL 116	cl	04 56 24.8	–68 48 15	Dor	1.5		212	11	KMHK: Compact cluster. Alias: KMHK 315
KMHK 309	cl	04 56 25.5	–67 56 20	Dor	1.0		212	99	KMHK: Loose cluster. Alias: BRHT 60b
BRHT 60a	cl	04 56 27	–67 56.0	Dor			212	5	

Table C.1: Tables of LMC Objects

Name	Type	2000.0 R.A.	2000.0 Dec.	Con	Diam (′)	Tot. Vm	U#	Ref	Comments and Aliases
NGC 1764	cl	04 56 27.4	–67 41 46	Dor	1.0		212	11	KMHK: Compact cluster. Alias: KMHK 308
NGC 1767	cl	04 56 27.4	–69 24 10	Dor	1.6		212	11	Associated with LH 8.; KMHK: Compact cluster. Aliases: SL 120; KMHK 318
KMHK 310	cl	04 56 28.8	–67 37 23	Dor	1.0		212	11	KMHK: Loose cluster.
SL 124	cl	04 56 31.3	–69 58 58	Men	1.0		212	11	KMHK: Compact cluster. Alias: KMHK 324
SL 123	cl	04 56 33.3	–69 22 12	Dor	1.1		212	11	KMHK: Compact cluster. Alias: KMHK 320
NGC 1761	cl	04 56 34.4	–66 28 24	Dor	1.2		212	99	KMHK: Compact cluster. Aliases: KMHK 307; h 2710
KMHK 311	cl	04 56 35.1	–67 01 03	Dor	0.7		212	99	KMHK: Compact cluster.
KMHK 327	cl	04 56 35.7	–70 25 29	Men	0.4		212	99	KMHK: Compact cluster.
OHSC 3	cl	04 56 36.7	–75 14 28	Men	0.4		219	99	KMHK: Compact cluster. Alias: KMHK 362
SL 119	cl	04 56 37.4	–68 09 53	Dor	1.0		212	11	KMHK: Compact cluster. Alias: KMHK 316
KMHK 319	cl	04 56 39.1	–68 38 06	Dor	0.6		212	11	KMHK: Compact cluster.
KMHK 321	cl	04 56 40.2	–68 40 02	Dor	0.8		212	11	KMHK: Compact cluster.
SL 135	cl	04 56 43.8	–73 51 46	Men	0.8		219	11	KMHK: Loose cluster. Alias: KMHK 356
[HS66] 75	cl	04 56 49.8	–71 24 52	Men	0.6		212	11	KMHK: Compact cluster. Alias: KMHK 347
LW 98	cl	04 56 50.9	–72 27 32	Men	0.9		212	99	KMHK: Incorrect on Hodge-Wright Atlas (1967). Alias: KMHK 351
KMHK 335	cl	04 56 51.9	–70 06 03	Men	0.6		212	99	KMHK: Loose cluster. Archinal: Barely visible on DSS.
BRHT 45b	cl	04 56 52	–68 00.3	Dor			212	5	
NGC 1775	cl	04 56 53.6	–70 25 48	Men	0.7	12.6	212	11	KMHK: Compact cluster. Aliases: BRHT 2a; KMHK 338
NGC 1772	cl	04 56 53.9	–69 33 23	Dor	1.5		212	11	KMHK: Compact cluster. Alias: KMHK 334
[HS66] 72	cl	04 56 54.1	–68 00 10	Dor	0.8		212	11	KMHK: Loose cluster. Aliases: BRHT 45a; KMHK 326
KMHK 340	cl	04 56 56.6	–70 25 39	Men	0.6		212	99	KMHK: Compact cluster. Alias: BRHT 2b
NGC 1768	cl	04 57 02.7	–68 14 54	Dor	0.9		212	11	KMHK: Compact cluster. Alias: KMHK 331
KMHK 325	cl	04 57 04.9	–66 42 36	Dor	0.6		212	99	KMHK: Compact cluster. Archinal: Barely visible on DSS, in group of brighter stars.
[HS66] 73	cl	04 57 06.1	–67 24 50	Dor	0.7		212	11	KMHK: Compact cluster. Alias: KMHK 330
KMHK 333	cl	04 57 08.0	–67 49 49	Dor	0.9		212	11	KMHK: Compact cluster.
KMHK 329	cl	04 57 09.4	–66 41 48	Dor	0.8		212	11	KMHK: Compact cluster.
SL 137	cl	04 57 10.2	–72 43 28	Men	1.0		212	99	KMHK: Loose cluster. Alias: KMHK 361
[HS66] 74	cl	04 57 11.6	–68 44 06	Dor	0.7		212	11	KMHK: Compact cluster. Aliases: LH 11; KMHK 339
KMHK 332	cl	04 57 14.2	–66 53 06	Dor	0.6		212	11	KMHK: Compact cluster.
IC 2117	cl	04 57 14.5	–68 26 30	Dor	1.8		212	99	KMHK: Compact cluster. Archinal: Not a planetary nebula as the IC indicates. Aliases: KMHK 341; Fleming 89
NGC 1770	cl	04 57 16.8	–68 24 41	Dor	1.6		212	99	KMHK: Incorrect on Hodge-Wright Atlas (1967). Aliases: KMHK 345; h 2715
KMHK 355	cl	04 57 22.1	–70 28 59	Men	0.4		212	11	KMHK: Loose cluster.
SL 126	cl	04 57 22.7	–62 32 07	Dor	0.7		212	99	KMHK: Loose cluster. Archinal: Very faint on DSS. Alias: KMHK 322
LH 12	cl	04 57.4	–68 25	Dor			212	5	
SL 132	cl	04 57 26.9	–67 41 08	Dor	1.1		212	11	KMHK: Compact cluster. Alias: KMHK 348
SL 131	cl	04 57 27.5	–65 49 29	Dor	0.9		212	99	KMHK: Loose cluster. Alias: KMHK 336
KMHK 346	cl	04 57 30.2	–66 54 40	Dor	1.2		212	11	KMHK: Loose cluster.
SL 134	cl	04 57 30.4	–68 21 47	Dor	1.0		212	11	KMHK: Compact cluster. Alias: KMHK 349
SL 136	cl	04 57 30.4	–69 03 10	Dor	1.0		212	11	KMHK: Loose cluster. Alias: KMHK 352

Table C.1: Tables of LMC Objects

Name	Type	2000.0 R.A.	2000.0 Dec.	Con	Diam (′)	Tot. Vm	U#	Ref	Comments and Aliases
SL 133	cl	04 57 34.6	−65 16 05	Dor	1.0		212	11	KMHK: Compact cluster. Alias: KMHK 337
LW 100	cl	04 57 35.5	−65 39 54	Dor	0.4		212	11	KMHK: Compact cluster. Alias: KMHK 342
LH 13	cl	04 57 44.1	−66 27 40	Dor			212	99	Archinal: Involved in impressive nebulosity on DSS image.
NGC 1782	cl	04 57 51.5	−69 23 37	Dor	1.2		212	99	KMHK: Compact cluster. Alias: KMHK 363
NGC 1789	cl	04 57 51.5	−71 54 08	Men	1.5		212	11	KMHK: Compact cluster. Alias: KMHK 375
LW 102	cl	04 57 52.3	−65 28 29	Dor	0.3		212	11	KMHK: Loose cluster. Alias: KMHK 350
SL 138	cl	04 57 54.7	−66 43 40	Dor	0.9		212	99	KMHK: Loose cluster. Alias: KMHK 354
KMHK 359	cl	04 57 54.7	−68 34 43	Dor	1.0		212	11	KMHK: Loose cluster.
LW 103	cl	04 57 55.3	−65 48 56	Dor	0.8		212	11	KMHK: Loose cluster. Alias: KMHK 353
SL 139	cl	04 57 56.1	−68 11 58	Dor	0.8		212	11	KMHK: Compact cluster. Alias: KMHK 358
KMHK 368	cl	04 57 56.1	−70 19 56	Men	0.6		212	11	KMHK: Loose cluster.
NGC 1774	cl	04 58 06.2	−67 14 32	Dor	1.8	10.8	212	11	KMHK: Compact cluster. Aliases: SL 141; KMHK 360
LW 106	cl	04 58 06.5	−75 32 30	Men	0.7		219	11	KMHK: Loose cluster. Alias: KMHK 399
KMHK 372	cl	04 58 07.5	−69 48 16	Dor?	1.3		212	99	KMHK: Loose cluster. Archinal: Doesn't stand out from background well on DSS image.
KMHK 376	cl	04 58 08.3	−70 24 12	Men	0.7		212	11	KMHK: Compact cluster.
[HS66] 76	cl	04 58 09.9	−69 03 40	Dor	0.7		212	99	KMHK: Compact cluster. Alias: KMHK 370
KMHK 365	cl	04 58 10.8	−68 03 42	Dor	1.2		212	99	KMHK: Loose cluster. Archinal: Very faint on DSS image.
SL 142	cl	04 58 15.2	−65 23 29	Dor	0.7		212	11	KMHK: Compact cluster. Alias: KMHK 357
KMHK 367	cl	04 58 15.2	−67 46 06	Dor	0.7		212	11	KMHK: Compact cluster.
LW 107	cl	04 58 15.6	−74 42 12	Men	0.8		219	11	KMHK: Loose cluster. Alias: KMHK 396
KMHK 371	cl	04 58 16.0	−68 49 19	Dor	0.7		212	11	KMHK: Compact cluster.
SL 143	cl	04 58 17.0	−67 03 04	Dor	1.0		212	11	KMHK: Compact cluster. Alias: KMHK 364
SL 146	cl	04 58 17.8	−70 04 51	Men	1.0		212	11	KMHK: Loose cluster. Alias: KMHK 377
KMHK 366	cl	04 58 19.2	−66 58 43	Dor	0.6		212	11	KMHK: Compact cluster.
KMHK 369	cl	04 58 21.1	−67 28 46	Dor	0.8		212	11	KMHK: Loose cluster.
KMHK 378	cl	04 58 22.2	−69 48 11	Dor?	0.7		212	11	KMHK: Compact cluster.
[HS66] 77	cl	04 58 28.8	−67 22 34	Dor	0.6		212	11	KMHK: Loose cluster. Alias: KMHK 373
KMHK 379	cl	04 58 30.7	−69 09 55	Dor	0.6		212	11	KMHK: Loose cluster.
KMHK 382	cl	04 58 36.0	−69 48 56	Dor?	0.4		212	11	KMHK: Loose cluster.
NGC 1776	cl	04 58 39.2	−66 25 46	Dor	1.1		212	11	DSFG: Moderately bright.; KMHK: Compact cluster. Aliases: LH 14; KMHK 374
NGC 1785	ast?	04 58 45	−68 49.4	Dor	4.0		212	99	See notes. Has NE-SW line of 9 stars. Includes HD 268840 (V=12.6), HD 268845 (V=12.4), and HD 268856 (B=11.4). Aliases: h (147); GC 1002
KMHK 381	cl	04 58 46.1	−68 38 13	Dor	0.9		212	11	KMHK: Loose cluster.
LW 110	cl	04 58 46.3	−75 13 12	Men	0.4		219	11	KMHK: Loose cluster. Alias: KMHK 414
SL 151	cl	04 58 51.3	−69 57 29	Men	1.0		212	11	KMHK: Compact cluster. Alias: KMHK 388
SL 157	cl	04 58 53.6	−72 22 42	Men	1.1		212	99	KMHK: Loose cluster. Archinal: Right on border of DSS overlap region. Alias: KMHK 398
SL 150	cl	04 58 56.5	−69 13 04	Dor	0.8		212	11	KMHK: Compact cluster. Alias: KMHK 386
KMHK 395	cl	04 58 58.9	−71 19 25	Men	0.3		212	99	KMHK: Compact cluster. Archinal: Meteor or satellite trail on DSS image, just to W (going NNE to SSW).
SL 147	cl	04 58 59.5	−66 47 44	Dor	0.7		212	99	KMHK: Loose cluster. Alias: KMHK 380

Table C.1: Tables of LMC Objects

Name	Type	2000.0 R.A.	2000.0 Dec.	Con	Diam (′)	Tot. Vm	U#	Ref	Comments and Aliases
KMHK 389	cl	04 59 01.3	−69 02 33	Dor	0.4		212	11	KMHK: Loose cluster.
KMHK 417	cl	04 59 05.7	−74 47 38	Men	0.4		219	99	KMHK: Loose cluster.
NGC 1791	cl	04 59 06.0	−70 10 03	Men	1.3		212	11	KMHK: Loose cluster. Alias: KMHK 391
NGC 1786	gcl	04 59 07.8	−67 44 40	Dor	1.6		212	99	KMHK: Compact cluster. Alias: KMHK 385
NGC 1783	cl	04 59 08.7	−65 59 16	Dor	3.0		212	56	See notes. Inner diameter 82", 180" with outliers. Included in LMC association NGC 1787.; KMHK: Compact cluster. Aliases: KMHK 383; (3) NGC 1787; SL 148
SL 166	cl	04 59 12.5	−74 39 25	Men	0.9		219	11	KMHK: Loose cluster. Aliases: LW 111; KMHK 419
OHSC 4	cl	04 59 13.7	−75 07 59	Men	0.6		219	11	KMHK: Loose cluster. Alias: KMHK 426
SL 158	cl	04 59 14.0	−70 15 22	Men	1.5		212	11	KMHK: Compact cluster. Alias: KMHK 397
SL 154	cl	04 59 14.7	−67 54 31	Dor	0.8		212	11	KMHK: Compact cluster. Alias: KMHK 390
BRHT 61b	cl	04 59 19	−68 50.9	Dor			212	5	
KMHK 392	cl	04 59 18.8	−68 50 53	Dor	0.6		212	99	KMHK: Compact cluster. Archinal: Very faint on DSS.
SL 152	cl	04 59 19.7	−65 33 30	Dor	0.9		212	11	KMHK: Compact cluster. Alias: KMHK 384
SL 153	cl	04 59 20.6	−66 19 08	Dor	1.2		212	11	KMHK: Compact cluster. Alias: KMHK 387
BRHT 61a	cl	04 59 21	−68 50.6	Dor			212	5	
KMHK 393	cl	04 59 25.2	−68 22 05	Dor	0.8		212	11	KMHK: Compact cluster.
SL 164	cl	04 59 25.3	−71 33 24	Men	1.0		212	11	KMHK: Compact cluster. Alias: KMHK 409
SL 160	cl	04 59 26.6	−70 24 58	Men	0.9		212	11	KMHK: Compact cluster. Alias: KMHK 402
[HS66] 78	cl	04 59 35.2	−68 52 31	Dor	0.6		212	11	KMHK: Compact cluster. Alias: KMHK 400
SL 156	cl	04 59 37.8	−66 49 29	Dor	1.0		212	99	KMHK: Loose cluster. Archinal: Very faint on DSS. Alias: KMHK 394
NGC 1793	cl	04 59 38.3	−69 33 27	Dor	1.3	12.4	212	11	DSFG: Relatively faint.; KMHK: Compact cluster. Alias: KMHK 405
NGC 1795	cl	04 59 46.8	−69 48 03	Dor?	1.6		212	11	KMHK: Compact cluster. Alias: KMHK 411
KMHK 403	cl	04 59 48.3	−68 18 56	Dor	0.7		212	99	KMHK: Compact cluster. Archinal: Very faint on DSS.
[HS66] 80	cl	04 59 49.0	−68 57 32	Dor	0.6		212	11	KMHK: Compact cluster. Alias: KMHK 408
[HS66] 82	cl	04 59 52.4	−70 06 10	Men	1.6		212	11	KMHK: Loose cluster. Alias: KMHK 413
SL 162	cl	04 59 53.8	−67 55 25	Dor	0.8		212	11	KMHK: Compact cluster. Alias: KMHK 406
BRHT 62b	cl	04 59 57	−67 48.3	Dor			212	5	
KMHK 420	cl	04 59 57.7	−71 22 45	Men	0.9		212	11	KMHK: Loose cluster.
SL 161	cl	04 59 58.6	−66 11 19	Dor	1.0		212	11	KMHK: Loose cluster. Alias: KMHK 401
[HS66] 81	cl	04 59 59.1	−69 30 35	Dor	0.8		212	11	KMHK: Loose cluster. Alias: KMHK 415
NGC 1787	ass	05 00.0	−65 50	Dor	23.0	10.9	212	56	See notes. Large association in LMC, includes NGC 1783, SL 152, SL 178, [HS66] 84, and LW 100. Aliases: h 2731; LH 15; (2) NGC 1783; (2) SL 152; (2) SL 178; (2) [HS66] 84; (2) LW 100
KMHK 416	cl	05 00 01.9	−70 08 16	Men	0.8		212	99	KMHK: Loose cluster. Archinal: Very faint on DSS.
KMHK 412	cl	05 00 04.3	−67 48 00	Dor	1.2		212	11	KMHK: Loose cluster.
BRHT 62a	cl	05 00 06	−67 48.1	Dor			212	5	
KMHK 407	cl	05 00 07.0	−66 15 54	Dor	0.7		212	11	KMHK: Loose cluster.
LW 112	cl	05 00 10.0	−65 25 27	Dor	0.6		212	99	KMHK: Loose cluster. Archinal: Very faint on DSS. Alias: KMHK 404
KMHK 453	cl	05 00 13.1	−75 45 08	Men	0.4		219	11	KMHK: Loose cluster.
KMHK 447	cl	05 00 14.7	−74 45 08	Men	0.4		219	11	KMHK: Loose cluster.

Table C.1: Tables of LMC Objects

Name	Type	2000.0 R.A.	2000.0 Dec.	Con	Diam (′)	Tot. Vm	U#	Ref	Comments and Aliases
KMHK 431	cl	05 00 16.8	−71 35 31	Men	0.3		212	11	KMHK: Loose cluster.
KMHK 410	cl	05 00 19.0	−65 28 42	Dor	0.8		212	99	KMHK: Compact cluster.
SL 169	cl	05 00 22.9	−70 56 36	Men	0.8		212	11	KMHK: Loose cluster. Aliases: BRHT 26a; KMHK 430
[HS66] 83	cl	05 00 26.1	−68 46 24	Dor	0.9		212	11	KMHK: Loose cluster. Alias: KMHK 421
KMHK 423	cl	05 00 28.2	−68 38 28	Dor	0.6		212	11	KMHK: Compact cluster.
KMHK 424	cl	05 00 30.7	−68 27 22	Dor	0.8		212	11	KMHK: Compact cluster.
SL 171	cl	05 00 32.9	−70 56 51	Men	0.7		212	11	KMHK: Loose cluster. Aliases: BRHT 26b; KMHK 434
NGC 1801	cl	05 00 35.1	−69 36 46	Dor	2.2	12.2	212	99	DSFG: Moderately bright.; KMHK: Compact cluster. Alias: KMHK 429
SL 167	cl	05 00 41.2	−66 53 37	Dor	1.3		212	11	KMHK: Compact cluster. Alias: KMHK 422
SL 168	cl	05 00 44.2	−65 27 18	Dor	1.0		212	11	KMHK: Compact cluster. Alias: KMHK 418
SL 175	cl	05 00 49.5	−71 03 09	Men	1.3		212	11	KMHK: Loose cluster. Alias: KMHK 454
[HS66] 85	cl	05 00 50.7	−67 48 14	Dor	0.8		212	11	KMHK: Loose cluster. Alias: KMHK 428
[HS66] 84	cl	05 00 52.0	−65 49 49	Dor	0.6		212	11	KMHK: Loose cluster. Alias: KMHK 425
KMHK 433	cl	05 00 56.2	−67 44 44	Dor	0.7		212	11	KMHK: Compact cluster.
[HS66] 90	cl	05 00 57.4	−70 10 26	Men	0.6		212	11	KMHK: Compact cluster. Alias: KMHK 441
[HS66] 86	cl	05 01 01.7	−67 55 01	Dor	0.8		212	11	KMHK: Loose cluster. Alias: KMHK 435
KMHK 432	cl	05 01 02.4	−66 44 53	Dor	0.6		212	99	KMHK: Loose cluster. Archinal: Very faint on DSS.
[HS66] 88	cl	05 01 04.1	−68 04 57	Dor	0.8		212	11	KMHK: Loose cluster. Alias: KMHK 436
NGC 1804	cl	05 01 05.1	−69 05 03	Dor		11.9	212	99	Alias: h 2742
KMHK 442	cl	05 01 05.6	−69 35 40	Dor	0.6		212	99	
LW 115	cl	05 01 10.0	−64 15 17	Dor	0.9		212	99	KMHK: Loose cluster. Archinal: Very faint on DSS. Alias: KMHK 427
SL 174	cl	05 01 11.6	−67 49 06	Dor	1.5		212	11	KMHK: Compact cluster. Alias: KMHK 439
KMHK 438	cl	05 01 13.6	−67 32 19	Dor	0.7		212	11	KMHK: Loose cluster.
SL 173	cl	05 01 21.9	−67 17 39	Dor	1.3		212	11	KMHK: Compact cluster. Alias: KMHK 440
KMHK 437	cl	05 01 22.1	−65 55 19	Dor	0.7		212	11	KMHK: Loose cluster.
KMHK 465	cl	05 01 25.1	−73 08 37	Men	0.6		212	11	KMHK: Loose cluster.
KMHK 466	cl	05 01 28.5	−73 03 48	Men	1.3		212	11	KMHK: Loose cluster.
KMHK 443	cl	05 01 28.8	−67 20 59	Dor	0.7		212	11	KMHK: Loose cluster.
SL 176	cl	05 01 29.3	−68 42 42	Dor	1.0		212	99	KMHK: Compact cluster. Alias: KMHK 448
SL 183	cl	05 01 33.3	−71 37 51	Men	0.9		212	11	KMHK: Loose cluster. Alias: KMHK 460
[HS66] 91	cl	05 01 42.5	−66 23 31	Dor	1.0		212	11	KMHK: Loose cluster. Alias: KMHK 446
SL 178	cl	05 01 44.3	−65 49 23	Dor	0.2		212	8	See notes. Included in LMC association NGC 1787. Aliases: ESO 85-SC31; KMHK 445; (3) NGC 1787
KMHK 451	cl	05 01 45.1	−67 34 01	Dor	0.6		212	11	KMHK: Compact cluster.
SL 179	cl	05 01 45.2	−67 05 38	Dor	1.2		212	11	KMHK: Compact cluster. Alias: KMHK 449
SL 177	cl	05 01 47.1	−65 29 25	Dor	0.8		212	99	KMHK: Loose cluster. Archinal: Very faint on DSS. Alias: KMHK 444
KMHK 452	cl	05 01 48.9	−67 28 27	Dor	1.5		212	99	KMHK: Loose cluster. Archinal: Only faint scattered background stars here on DSS.
KMHK 461	cl	05 01 51.4	−69 55 09	Men	0.7		212	11	KMHK: Compact cluster.
OHSC 5	cl	05 01 53.7	−75 28 07	Men			219	5	
KMHK 450	cl	05 01 54.1	−66 15 20	Dor	0.7		212	11	KMHK: Compact cluster.

Table C.1: Tables of LMC Objects

Name	Type	2000.0 R.A.	2000.0 Dec.	Con	Diam (′)	Tot. Vm	U#	Ref	Comments and Aliases
KMHK 457	cl	05 01 54.1	−68 23 41	Dor	0.8		212	11	KMHK: Loose cluster.
KMHK 464	cl	05 01 54.6	−70 31 24	Men	0.3		212	11	KMHK: Compact cluster.
KMHK 455	cl	05 02 03.5	−66 22 39	Dor	0.9		212	11	KMHK: Loose cluster.
KMHK 456	cl	05 02 05.4	−66 45 19	Dor	0.7		212	99	KMHK: Loose cluster. Archinal: Very faint on DSS.
SL 187	cl	05 02 10.4	−72 07 26	Men	1.3		212	11	KMHK: Loose cluster. Alias: KMHK 470
NGC 1806	cl	05 02 11.3	−67 59 11	Dor	2.2		212	11	KMHK: Compact cluster. Aliases: SL 184; KMHK 462
KMHK 471	cl	05 02 13.0	−70 50 13	Men	0.3		212	11	KMHK: Compact cluster.
[HS66] 92	cl	05 02 18.4	−68 32 43	Dor	0.7		212	11	KMHK: Loose cluster. Alias: KMHK 467
KMHK 458	cl	05 02 19.1	−65 32 38	Dor	0.6		212	99	KMHK: Loose cluster. Archinal: Very faint on DSS.
NGC 1805	cl	05 02 21.2	−66 06 41	Dor	2.2	10.6	212	11	KMHK: Compact cluster. Alias: KMHK 459
NGC 1815	cl	05 02 26.9	−70 37 13	Men	1.2		212	11	DSFG: Relatively bright.; KMHK: Compact cluster. Alias: KMHK 469
SL 192	cl	05 02 27.6	−74 51 52	Men	1.0		219	11	KMHK: Loose cluster. Aliases: LW 121; KMHK 489
[HS66] 94	cl	05 02 29.1	−70 17 32	Men	0.9		212	11	KMHK: Compact cluster. Alias: KMHK 468
[HS66] 93	cl	05 02 30.2	−66 00 43	Dor	0.7		212	11	KMHK: Loose cluster. Alias: KMHK 463
NGC 1813	cl	05 02 40.8	−70 19 06	Men	0.8		212	11	KMHK: Loose cluster. Alias: KMHK 472
KMHK 479	cl	05 02 57.1	−70 12 08	Men	0.9		212	11	KMHK: Loose cluster.
LH 16	cl	05 03 05.5	−69 02 14	Dor			212	99	
[HS66] 99	cl	05 03 14.1	−70 05 29	Men	0.7		212	11	KMHK: Compact cluster. Alias: KMHK 483
[HS66] 96	cl	05 03 22.8	−65 52 46	Dor	1.0		212	11	KMHK: Loose cluster. Alias: KMHK 473
NGC 1810	cl	05 03 22.8	−66 22 57	Dor	1.2	11.9	212	11	DSFG: Moderately bright.; KMHK: Compact cluster. Alias: KMHK 475
NGC 1823	cl	05 03 23.8	−70 20 12	Men	0.9		212	11	KMHK: Compact cluster. Aliases: LH 18; KMHK 487
[HS66] 100	cl	05 03 25.8	−69 44 17	Dor	0.7		212	11	KMHK: Loose cluster. Alias: KMHK 485
SL 193	cl	05 03 27.7	−65 22 38	Dor	0.7		212	99	KMHK: Loose cluster. Archinal: Very faint on DSS. Alias: KMHK 474
[HS66] 101	cl	05 03 27.7	−66 14 59	Dor	1.1		212	11	KMHK: Incorrect on Hodge-Wright Atlas (1967). Alias: KMHK 477
[HS66] 98	cl	05 03 28.3	−66 12 25	Dor	0.9		212	11	KMHK: Loose cluster. Alias: KMHK 478
SL 195	cl	05 03 31.8	−65 26 12	Dor	0.6		212	11	KMHK: Loose cluster. Alias: KMHK 476
SL 197	cl	05 03 33.5	−67 37 30	Dor	1.0		212	11	KMHK: Compact cluster. Alias: KMHK 482
SL 196	cl	05 03 35.0	−65 49 23	Dor	0.7		212	11	KMHK: Loose cluster. Alias: KMHK 480
LW 124	cl	05 03 38.2	−65 34 03	Dor	0.8		212	11	KMHK: Compact cluster. Alias: KMHK 481
LH 17	cl	05 03.7	−69 05	Dor			212	5	
NGC 1814	cl	05 03 45.4	−67 18 08	Dor	1.0	9.0p	212	11	DSFG: Coarse group of relatively bright stars.; KMHK: Compact cluster. Aliases: LH 19; KMHK 484
SL 200	cl	05 03 45.7	−70 24 12	Men	1.5		212	99	KMHK: Compact cluster. Alias: KMHK 492
KMHK 493	cl	05 03 46.1	−70 21 15	Men	0.6		212	11	KMHK: Compact cluster.
KMHK 494	cl	05 03 50.4	−70 22 19	Men	0.4		212	11	KMHK: Compact cluster.
NGC 1816	cl	05 03 51.2	−67 15 38	Dor	1.0	9.0p	212	11	DSFG: Coarse group of relatively bright stars.; KMHK: Incorrect on Hodge-Wright Atlas (1967). Alias: KMHK 488
KMHK 516	cl	05 03 56.1	−73 56 12	Men	0.4		219	99	KMHK: Loose cluster.
[HS66] 103	cl	05 03 58.5	−66 03 28	Dor	0.7		212	11	KMHK: Loose cluster. Alias: KMHK 486
KMHK 490	cl	05 04 01.5	−66 26 48	Dor	0.3		212	11	KMHK: Compact cluster.
[HS66] 104	cl	05 04 02.6	−70 37 37	Men	0.6		212	11	See notes. Smaller than 15", stars brighter than V=17.; KMHK: Compact cluster. Alias: KMHK 499

Table C.1: Tables of LMC Objects

Name	Type	2000.0 R.A.	2000.0 Dec.	Con	Diam (′)	Tot. Vm	U#	Ref	Comments and Aliases
NGC 1820	cl	05 04.1	−67 16	Dor		9.0p	212	54	DSFG: Coarse group of relatively bright stars.
NGC 1825	cl	05 04.1	−68 55	Dor		12.0	212	54	
KMHK 508	cl	05 04 09.3	−71 04 39	Men	0.4		212	11	KMHK: Compact cluster.
NGC 1818	cl	05 04 12.9	−66 26 06	Dor	3.4	9.7	212	11	KMHK: Compact cluster. Aliases: SL 201; KMHK 491
LH 20	cl	05 04.2	−69 01	Dor			212	99	Archinal: This association doesn't stand out much on DSS image.
NGC 1828	cl	05 04 21.0	−69 23 19	Dor		12.5	212	99	DSFG: Relatively bright. Alias: h 2761
NGC 1833	cl	05 04 22.3	−70 43 52	Men	2.1		212	56	See notes. Archinal: Checked against J. Herschel's obs. and DSS. Elongated NE to SW, 125" by 55". Not completely resolved on DSS. Aliases: h 2765; KMHK 510; (3) LH 24; (3) NGC 1845; (4) Hen N 190
KMHK 495	cl	05 04 25.5	−66 10 52	Dor	0.9		212	11	KMHK: Loose cluster.
KMHK 498	cl	05 04 26.9	−67 48 51	Dor	0.8		212	11	KMHK: Compact cluster.
LH 21	cl	05 04 27.5	−67 48 51	Dor			212	99	
KMHK 506	cl	05 04 29.7	−68 20 59	Dor	0.8		212	11	KMHK: Loose cluster.
BRHT 3b	cl	05 04 30	−69 21.3	Dor			212	5	
KMHK 505	cl	05 04 32.6	−67 58 32	Dor	0.7		212	11	KMHK: Compact cluster.
OHSC 7	cl	05 04 34.1	−75 40 47	Men			219	5	
KMHK 496	cl	05 04 34.6	−65 53 12	Dor	0.6		212	11	KMHK: Loose cluster.
KMHK 514	cl	05 04 36.2	−70 10 01	Men	0.6		212	11	KMHK: Loose cluster.
SL 209	cl	05 04 37.7	−70 54 37	Men	1.3		212	11	KMHK: Compact cluster. Aliases: LH 23; KMHK 518
OHSC 6	cl	05 04 39.0	−75 03 14	Men	0.7		219	11	KMHK: Loose cluster. Alias: KMHK 532
NGC 1830	cl	05 04 39.5	−69 20 30	Dor		12.6	212	99	DSFG: Relatively bright. Aliases: BRHT 3a; SL 207; h 2762
LW 126	cl	05 04 41.4	−65 39 46	Dor	0.7		212	11	KMHK: Loose cluster. Alias: KMHK 497
KMHK 502	cl	05 04 42.0	−66 12 47	Dor	0.7		212	11	KMHK: Loose cluster.
SL 204	cl	05 04 42.6	−66 02 03	Dor	1.3		212	11	KMHK: Loose cluster. Alias: KMHK 500
LW 129	cl	05 04 42.9	−66 00 23	Dor	0.7		212	11	KMHK: Loose cluster. Alias: KMHK 501
[HS66] 105	cl	05 04 43.4	−66 19 58	Dor	0.6		212	99	KMHK: Incorrect on Hodge-Wright Atlas (1967). Archinal: Very faint on DSS. Alias: KMHK 503
SL 219	cl	05 04 43.4	−72 59 39	Men	1.6		212	11	KMHK: Loose cluster. Alias: KMHK 526
LH 22	cl	05 04.7	−67 34	Dor			212	99	Archinal: Not obvious on DSS image. Several faint background objects here which could be the cluster.
SL 205	cl	05 04 45.5	−66 22 01	Dor	1.1		212	11	KMHK: Compact cluster. Alias: KMHK 507
SL 213	cl	05 04 49.8	−71 23 47	Men	0.4		212	11	KMHK: Loose cluster. Alias: KMHK 525
LW 127	cl	05 04 52.7	−65 07 27	Dor	0.7		212	11	KMHK: Loose cluster. Alias: KMHK 504
[HS66] 106	cl	05 04 55.6	−66 10 39	Dor	0.7		212	11	KMHK: Loose cluster. Alias: KMHK 509
NGC 1837	cl	05 04 56	−70 43 18	Men	1.3		212	56	See notes. Archinal: Checked against J. Herschel's obs. and DSS. Appears as N-S string of stars, with 20" clump of stars at N end. Aliases: h 2769; KMHK 523; (3) LH 24; (3) NGC 1845
SL 216	cl	05 04 57.4	−70 01 08	Men	0.7		212	99	KMHK: Compact cluster. Alias: KMHK 521
NGC 1829	cl	05 04 58.5	−68 03 39	Dor	2.1		212	11	KMHK: Compact cluster. Alias: KMHK 515
SL 211	cl	05 05 02.7	−68 54 34	Dor	0.6		212	99	Identified by M. Morel [Priv. Comm. 2002]. 1.2′ SE of HD 33477 (V=8.0) (not "SW" as in HW66). SL position is incorrect.
KMHK 511	cl	05 05 03.4	−66 29 59	Dor	0.9		212	99	KMHK: Loose cluster. Archinal: Not obvious on DSS image.
NGC 1835	gcl	05 05 06.6	−69 24 14	Dor			212	99	Aliases: CD−69 274; CPD−69 330; HD 269016; GV 534; SL 215; [FD70] S34
NGC 1822	cl	05 05 08.1	−66 12 43	Dor	0.8		212	11	DSFG: Faint.; KMHK: Compact cluster. Alias: KMHK 513

Table C.1: Tables of LMC Objects

Name	Type	2000.0 R.A.	2000.0 Dec.	Con	Diam (′)	Tot. Vm	U#	Ref	Comments and Aliases
KMHK 517	cl	05 05 08.9	−67 17 50	Dor	0.3		212	11	KMHK: Compact cluster.
LH 24	pass	05 05 09	−70 40.2	Men	10.0		212	56	See notes. SW portion of NGC 1845 association. Contains NGC 1833 (and associated Hen N 190), NGC 1837, and [HS66] 104. Aliases: (2) NGC 1833; (2) NGC 1837; (2) [HS66] 104; (3) NGC 1845
NGC 1845	ass	05 05 12	−70 35.4	Men	20.0		212	56	See notes. Association in LMC, contains LH 24 (with [HS66] 104), NGC 1833 and NGC 1837, and LH 26 (with SL 232). This is NOT just LH 26. Aliases: h 2770; (2) LH 24; (2) LH 26; (2) NGC 1837; (2) NGC 1833; (2) SL 232; (2) [HS66] 104
LW 132	cl	05 05 14.5	−74 43 35	Men	0.6		219	11	KMHK: Loose cluster. Alias: KMHK 542
NGC 1840	cl	05 05 19.9	−71 45 50	Men	0.6		212	56	See notes. This is KMHK 529. NGC 1840 may also be KMHK 551 to SE.; KMHK: Loose cluster. Alias: KMHK 529
KMHK 520	cl	05 05 24.1	−66 29 44	Dor	0.4		212	99	KMHK: Loose cluster. Alias: BRHT 27b
SL 214	cl	05 05 24.2	−63 17 09	Dor	1.0		212	99	KMHK: Loose cluster. Archinal: Not obvious on DSS image. Alias: KMHK 512
KMHK 519	**?	05 05 24.8	−65 28 49	Dor	0.4		212	99	KMHK: Loose cluster. Archinal: Two stars only?
SL 222	cl	05 05 26.2	−66 29 34	Dor	0.4		212	11	KMHK: Loose cluster. Aliases: BRHT 27a; KMHK 522
NGC 1826	cl	05 05 33.7	−66 13 51	Dor	0.9		212	11	DSFG: Faint.; KMHK: Compact cluster. Alias: KMHK 524
NGC 1836	cl	05 05 35.6	−68 37 42	Dor		12.2	212	99	Aliases: BRHT 4a; SL 223; h 2766
BRHT 4b	cl	05 05 41	−68 38.3	Dor			212	5	
SL 224	cl	05 05 42.7	−70 19 31	Men	1.3		212	11	KMHK: Compact cluster. Alias: KMHK 534
[HS66] 108	cl	05 05 49.3	−66 21 48	Dor	0.6		212	99	KMHK: Loose cluster. Archinal: Very faint on DSS, among several brighter stars. Alias: KMHK 528
[HS66] 110	cl	05 05 51.0	−66 01 47	Dor	0.6		212	11	KMHK: Loose cluster. Alias: KMHK 527
[HS66] 115	cl	05 05 53.6	−70 22 22	Men	1.5		212	11	KMHK: Loose cluster. Alias: KMHK 537
[HS66] 113	cl	05 05 54.8	−68 14 16	Dor	0.7		212	11	KMHK: Compact cluster. Alias: KMHK 531
LH 26	pass	05 05 57	−70 31.8	Men	10.0		212	56	See notes. NE portion of NGC 1845 association. Contains SL 232. Aliases: (2) SL 232; (3) NGC 1845
[HS66] 114	cl	05 06 02.7	−68 01 35	Dor	1.0		212	11	KMHK: Compact cluster. Alias: KMHK 533
LW 137	cl	05 06 03.3	−75 25 13	Men	1.0		219	99	KMHK: Compact cluster. Alias: KMHK 558
SL 225	cl	05 06 08.3	−68 26 42	Dor	0.6		212	99	Alias: (3) NGC 1838
LH 25	cl	05 06 08.8	−68 06 26	Dor			212	99	
KMHK 540	cl	05 06 09.5	−70 00 52	Men	0.7		212	11	KMHK: Compact cluster.
KMHK 541	cl	05 06 12.0	−69 58 27	Men	0.7		212	11	KMHK: Loose cluster.
[HS66] 116	cl	05 06 12.5	−68 03 47	Dor	0.7		212	11	KMHK: Compact cluster. Alias: KMHK 536
NGC 1831	cl	05 06 16.2	−64 55 09	Dor	3.9	11.2	212	11	KMHK: Compact cluster. Aliases: LW 133; SL 227; KMHK 530
SL 232	cl	05 06 22.2	−70 28 43	Men	1.2		212	8	See notes. This is J. Herschel's first h 2770 object (NGC 1845 is the second). Aliases: h 2770a; KMHK 545; (3) NGC 1845
SL 236	cl	05 06 22.6	−72 30 19	Men	1.0		212	11	KMHK: Loose cluster. Alias: KMHK 552
SL 228	cl	05 06 27.2	−66 54 23	Dor	1.3		212	11	KMHK: Loose cluster. Aliases: BRHT 28a; KMHK 538
LW 134	cl	05 06 27.5	−65 11 08	Dor	0.6		212	99	KMHK: Loose cluster. Archinal: Very faint on DSS image. Alias: KMHK 535
SL 235	cl	05 06 29.3	−71 49 24	Men	0.3		212	99	KMHK: Compact cluster. Alias: KMHK 551
BRHT 28b	cl	05 06 32	−66 54.5	Dor			212	5	
SL 229	cl	05 06 32.4	−68 21 55	Dor		13.28	212	99	Alias: BRHT 29a
SL 230	cl	05 06 34	−68 21.8	Dor		11.34	212	5	
NGC 1838	cl	05 06 34	−68 25 43	Dor	10.0	12.9	212	99	J. Kay in 1998 noted NGC 1838 is not SL 225 but contains it. Aliases: h 2767; (2) SL 225
LW 135	cl	05 06 40.8	−65 37 26	Dor	0.9		212	11	KMHK: Loose cluster. Alias: KMHK 539
KMHK 544	cl	05 06 42.2	−67 50 32	Dor	0.7		212	11	KMHK: Compact cluster.

Table C.1: Tables of LMC Objects

Name	Type	2000.0 R.A.	2000.0 Dec.	Con	Diam (′)	Tot. Vm	U#	Ref	Comments and Aliases
KMHK 546	cl	05 06 47.5	−68 03 19	Dor	0.4		212	99	KMHK: Compact cluster. Archinal: Not obvious on DSS, although a fairly bright star just south of this position.
SL 248	cl	05 06 52.1	−75 40 55	Men	0.7		219	11	KMHK: Loose cluster. Alias: KMHK 578
LH 27	cl	05 06 58.0	−69 08 57	Dor			212	99	
KMHK 549	cl	05 06 58.9	−68 06 51	Dor	1.0		212	11	KMHK: Loose cluster.
[HS66] 120	cl	05 07 01.9	−70 36 47	Men	0.9		212	99	KMHK: Loose cluster. Alias: KMHK 555
SL 233	cl	05 07 04.1	−63 38 52	Dor	0.6		212	11	KMHK: Loose cluster. Alias: KMHK 543
LW 138	cl	05 07 05.0	−65 55 42	Dor	0.7		212	11	KMHK: Loose cluster. Alias: KMHK 547
NGC 1847	cl	05 07 08.1	−68 58 17	Dor		11.1	212	99	DSFG: Relatively bright. Alias: h 2775
SL 239	cl	05 07 09.9	−66 40 14	Dor	0.8		212	99	KMHK: Compact cluster. Alias: KMHK 550
KMHK 554	cl	05 07 11.1	−68 18 02	Dor	0.6		212	11	KMHK: Compact cluster.
NGC 1842	cl	05 07 18.4	−67 16 23	Dor	0.8		212	11	DSFG: Extremely faint.; KMHK: Compact cluster. Alias: KMHK 553
LW 140	cl	05 07 22.0	−72 48 26	Men	0.6		212	99	KMHK: Loose cluster. Alias: KMHK 569
SL 238	cl	05 07 22.6	−64 25 48	Dor	1.0		212	99	KMHK: Loose cluster. Archinal: Very faint on DSS. Alias: KMHK 548
SL 246	cl	05 07 24.9	−70 48 38	Men	0.7		212	11	KMHK: Loose cluster. Alias: KMHK 561
NGC 1844	cl	05 07 30.4	−67 19 25	Dor	1.3	12.1	212	11	DSFG: Relatively faint.; KMHK: Compact cluster. Alias: KMHK 556
NGC 1846	cl	05 07 33.9	−67 27 39	Dor	2.8		212	11	KMHK: Compact cluster. Aliases: SL 243; KMHK 557
SL 249	cl	05 07 34.8	−70 44 52	Men	1.0		212	11	KMHK: Compact cluster. Alias: KMHK 562
LW 141	cl	05 07 35.2	−74 38 07	Men	0.8		219	11	KMHK: Loose cluster. Alias: KMHK 585
KMHK 565	cl	05 07 36.7	−71 10 20	Men	1.0		212	99	KMHK: Loose cluster. Archinal: Not obvious on DSS; in field of many scattered stars.
SL 245	cl	05 07 46.1	−66 25 49	Dor	0.7		212	11	KMHK: Loose cluster. Alias: KMHK 559
[HS66] 121	cl	05 07 46.5	−67 51 42	Dor	0.7		212	11	KMHK: Compact cluster. Alias: KMHK 560
KMHK 567	cl	05 07 48.7	−70 02 39	Men	0.7		212	11	KMHK: Compact cluster.
BRHT 30b	cl	05 07 49	−70 02.6	Men			212	5	
SL 252	cl	05 07 50.5	−70 23 29	Men	0.9		212	11	KMHK: Loose cluster. Alias: KMHK 570
LH 29	cl	05 07.9	−70 01	Men			212	5	
KMHK 572	**?	05 07 55.4	−70 01 58	Men	0.8		212	99	KMHK: Loose cluster. Archinal: Two stars only?
SL 255	cl	05 07 56.7	−70 03 24	Men	0.8		212	99	KMHK: Compact cluster. Aliases: BRHT 30a; KMHK 573
SL 251	cl	05 07 59.9	−69 52 27	Men?	1.6		212	11	KMHK: Compact cluster. Alias: KMHK 574
SL 256	cl	05 08 10.3	−71 10 23	Men	0.9		212	99	KMHK: Compact cluster. Aliases: LH 28; NGC 1848; KMHK 580
LH 30	cl	05 08.2	−69 13	Dor			212	5	
[HS66] 124	cl	05 08 18.0	−66 07 28	Dor	0.4		212	11	KMHK: Loose cluster. Alias: KMHK 564
KMHK 581	cl	05 08 18.2	−70 34 29	Men	1.6		212	11	KMHK: Loose cluster.
SL 254	cl	05 08 22.1	−66 13 14	Dor	0.6		212	99	KMHK: Loose cluster. Alias: KMHK 568
SL 253	cl	05 08 22.8	−65 52 09	Dor	0.8		212	11	KMHK: Loose cluster. Alias: KMHK 566
[HS66] 125	cl	05 08 25.7	−64 52 20	Dor	0.4		212	99	KMHK: Compact cluster. Archinal: Very faint on DSS. Alias: KMHK 563
SL 263	cl	05 08 32.2	−66 45 24	Dor	0.9		212	99	KMHK: Loose cluster. Archinal: Not obvious on DSS. Alias: KMHK 575
KMHK 587	cl	05 08 32.5	−70 26 56	Men	1.0		212	11	KMHK: Loose cluster.
LW 147	cl	05 08 34.9	−74 43 42	Men	0.9		219	11	KMHK: Loose cluster. Alias: KMHK 604
SL 258	cl	05 08 35.5	−64 54 31	Dor	0.7		212	11	KMHK: Compact cluster. Alias: KMHK 571

Table C.1: Tables of LMC Objects

Name	Type	2000.0 R.A.	2000.0 Dec.	Con	Diam (′)	Tot. Vm	U#	Ref	Comments and Aliases
SL 257	cl	05 08 40.1	−65 53 39	Dor	0.7		212	11	KMHK: Compact cluster. Alias: KMHK 576
NGC 1850	cl	05 08 46.7	−68 45 42	Dor	3.4	9.0	212	99	Archinal: May physically contain one to three star clusters. Aliases: h 2780; SL 261; (2) BRHT 5a; (2) BRHT 5b; (4) IRAS 05090–6849
Hodge 88 159	cl	05 08 46.8	−68 13 15	Dor			212	99	Archinal: Very faint on DSS image.
KMHK 579	cl	05 08 50.1	−65 40 22	Dor	0.3		212	99	KMHK: Loose cluster. Archinal: Very faint on DSS image.
KMHK 583	cl	05 08 50.6	−67 43 48	Dor	1.1		212	11	KMHK: Loose cluster.
SL 259	cl	05 08 51.6	−64 06 14	Dor	0.7		212	11	KMHK: Loose cluster. Aliases: LW 145; KMHK 577
KMHK 586	cl	05 08 51.7	−67 58 49	Dor	0.6		212	11	KMHK: Compact cluster.
BRHT 5b	ptcl	05 08 55	−68 45.3	Dor			212	99	Archinal: Southern portion of NGC 1850.
SL 272	cl	05 09 01.6	−72 21 41	Men	0.8		212	11	KMHK: Compact cluster. Alias: KMHK 601
[HS66] 129	cl	05 09 03.7	−66 18 54	Dor	0.4		212	11	KMHK: Loose cluster. Alias: KMHK 584
SL 266	cl	05 09 06.1	−69 42 58	Dor	0.9		212	11	KMHK: Compact cluster. Alias: KMHK 592
SL 270	cl	05 09 09.6	−70 36 47	Men	1.0		212	99	KMHK: Loose cluster. Archinal: Partially covered by fiber/hair on DSS image. Alias: KMHK 596
[HS66] 130	cl	05 09 15.5	−67 41 59	Dor	0.6		212	11	KMHK: Loose cluster. Alias: KMHK 588
KMHK 600	cl	05 09 19.5	−70 27 26	Men	0.7		212	99	KMHK: Compact cluster. Archinal: Very faint stellar object on DSS image.
NGC 1854	ptcl	05 09 20.6	−68 50 51	Dor			212	99	Archinal: Central portion of NGC 1855. Aliases: h 2782; (3) NGC 1855
NGC 1855	cl	05 09 20.6	−68 50 51	Dor	3.0	10.4	212	99	Archinal: Includes NGC 1854 as its central portion. Aliases: h 2783; (2) NGC 1854
SL 262	cl	05 09 21.2	−62 22 46	Dor	1.2		201	11	KMHK: Compact cluster. Aliases: ESO 119-40; LW 146; KMHK 582
KMHK 603	cl	05 09 22.3	−71 11 12	Men	0.4		212	11	KMHK: Loose cluster.
NGC 1852	cl	05 09 24.1	−67 46 47	Dor	1.8	12.0	212	11	DSFG: Compact cluster. The faint emission nebula Henize 25 lies just off the SSW edge.; KMHK: Compact cluster. Alias: KMHK 594
[HS66] 132	cl	05 09 28.7	−65 55 14	Dor	0.8		212	11	KMHK: Loose cluster. Alias: KMHK 589
NGC 1856	cl	05 09 30.6	−69 07 42	Dor		10.1	212	99	Alias: SL 271
LW 149	cl	05 09 32.1	−65 47 07	Dor	0.8		212	11	KMHK: Loose cluster. Alias: KMHK 591
NGC 1849	cl	05 09 34.5	−66 19 00	Dor	1.3	12.8	212	11	DSFG: Bright; round.; KMHK: Compact cluster. Alias: KMHK 593
KMHK 610	cl	05 09 35.4	−71 16 29	Men	0.6		212	99	KMHK: Loose cluster.
SL 269	cl	05 09 35.6	−67 48 39	Dor	0.8		212	11	KMHK: Loose cluster. Alias: KMHK 598
KMHK 606	cl	05 09 37.2	−70 14 11	Men	2.5		212	99	KMHK: Loose cluster. Archinal: Faint, among several stars of similar brightness.
[HS66] 140	cl	05 09 40.5	−70 21 27	Men	0.7		212	99	KMHK: Compact cluster. Alias: KMHK 608
LW 148	cl	05 09 40.7	−64 10 20	Dor	0.4		212	99	KMHK: Loose cluster. Archinal: Very faint on DSS image. Alias: KMHK 590
[HS66] 137	cl	05 09 43.3	−65 18 19	Dor	1.2		212	11	KMHK: Incorrect on Hodge-Wright Atlas (1967). Alias: KMHK 595
BRHT 47b	cl	05 09 43	−68 48.1	Dor			212	5	
[HS66] 139	cl	05 09 45.3	−68 47 21	Dor			212	99	Archinal: This agrees with BRHT chart, identifying this as BRHT 47a. This is the cluster closest to the [HS66] position. Alias: BRHT 47a
KMHK 612	cl	05 09 47.8	−70 28 46	Men	0.6		212	11	KMHK: Compact cluster.
[HS66] 148	cl	05 09 48.5	−70 07 56	Men	0.8		212	99	KMHK: Loose cluster. Archinal: Very faint group of stars in field of scattered faint stars on DSS image. Alias: KMHK 611
LH 31	cl	05 09 56.3	−68 53 46	Dor			212	99	
[HS66] 144	cl	05 09 57	−68 35 24	Dor	0.2		212	54	Compact cluster. This is BRHT 46b, pair with [HS66] 138 = BRHT 46a. Alias: BRHT 46b
[HS66] 138	cl	05 09 57.3	−68 35 29	Dor			212	99	Alias: BRHT 46a

Table C.1: Tables of LMC Objects

Name	Type	2000.0 R.A.	2000.0 Dec.	Con	Diam (′)	Tot. Vm	U#	Ref	Comments and Aliases
[HS66] 135	cl	05 09 58.3	−65 25 25	Dor	1.1		212	99	KMHK: Loose cluster. Archinal: Very faint on DSS, just SW of fairly bright star. Alias: KMHK 599
KMHK 609	cl	05 10 02.4	−68 14 44	Dor	0.7		212	11	KMHK: Loose cluster.
KMHK 624	cl	05 10 02.6	−72 46 20	Men	0.3		212	11	KMHK: Loose cluster.
SL 273	cl	05 10 03.7	−63 38 18	Dor	0.4		212	11	KMHK: Compact cluster. Alias: KMHK 597
SL 282	cl	05 10 10.4	−70 22 37	Men	1.0		212	11	KMHK: Loose cluster. Alias: KMHK 619
SL 295	cl	05 10 10.7	−75 32 37	Men	0.9		219	11	KMHK: Loose cluster. Aliases: LW 153; KMHK 639
[HS66] 143	cl	05 10 12.0	−64 58 13	Dor	0.6		212	99	KMHK: Loose cluster. Archinal: Very faint on DSS, just to E of obvious star. Alias: KMHK 602
SL 275	cl	05 10 15.2	−64 55 16	Dor	1.1		212	11	KMHK: Loose cluster. Alias: KMHK 605
BRHT 31b	cl	05 10 16	−68 29.9	Dor			212	5	
SL 278	cl	05 10 16.3	−68 29 32	Dor		13.63	212	99	Alias: BRHT 31a
KMHK 607	cl	05 10 17.7	−65 15 55	Dor	0.7		212	11	KMHK: Compact cluster.
BRHT 48b	cl	05 10 20	−68 52.7	Dor			212	5	
NGC 1861	cl	05 10 21.1	−70 46 40	Men	1.2		212	11	DSFG: Relatively faint.; KMHK: Compact cluster. Alias: KMHK 621
[HS66] 153	cl	05 10 30	−68 52.3	Dor			212	5	Alias: BRHT 48a
SL 291	cl	05 10 30.3	−70 54 36	Men	1.0		212	99	KMHK: Compact cluster. Alias: KMHK 626
LW 155	cl	05 10 32.0	−75 39 43	Men	0.4		219	11	KMHK: Loose cluster. Alias: KMHK 647
SL 281	cl	05 10 33.4	−67 07 40	Dor	1.6		212	11	KMHK: Loose cluster. Aliases: LH 32; KMHK 616
[HS66] 149	cl	05 10 36.3	−65 50 01	Dor	0.9		212	11	KMHK: Loose cluster. Alias: KMHK 613
SL 290	cl	05 10 36.6	−70 29 16	Men	1.6		212	11	KMHK: Compact cluster. Alias: KMHK 628
KMHK 633	cl	05 10 37.4	−71 17 39	Men	0.4		212	11	KMHK: Compact cluster.
NGC 1860	cl	05 10 39.5	−68 45 12	Dor		11.0	212	99	DSFG: Faint.
KMHK 614	cl	05 10 40.3	−65 35 23	Dor	0.7		212	99	KMHK: Loose cluster.
SL 294	cl	05 10 40.4	−70 03 50	Men	1.0		212	11	KMHK: Compact cluster. Alias: KMHK 627
SL 285	cl	05 10 40.6	−70 22 26	Men	1.3		212	99	KMHK: Loose cluster. Archinal: Very faint on DSS image. Alias: KMHK 629
KMHK 617	cl	05 10 41.9	−66 15 06	Dor	0.7		212	99	KMHK: Compact cluster. Alias: BRHT 32b
SL 283	cl	05 10 44.7	−66 15 40	Dor	0.7		212	11	KMHK: Loose cluster. Aliases: BRHT 32a; KMHK 618
SL 287	cl	05 10 49.0	−64 31 29	Dor	0.8		212	99	KMHK: Loose cluster. Archinal: Very faint on DSS image. Alias: KMHK 615
KMHK 622	cl	05 10 53.4	−67 28 12	Dor	0.6		212	99	KMHK: Loose cluster. Archinal: Very faint on DSS image.
KMHK 620	cl	05 10 54.8	−64 59 45	Dor	0.8		212	99	KMHK: Loose cluster. Archinal: Almost invisible on DSS image.
[HS66] 154	cl	05 10 56.8	−67 37 38	Dor	0.7		212	99	KMHK: Loose cluster. Archinal: Very faint on DSS image. Alias: KMHK 625
[HS66] 157	cl	05 11 05.5	−68 13 01	Dor	1.0		212	11	KMHK: Loose cluster. Alias: KMHK 631
SL 292	cl	05 11 08.3	−65 40 03	Dor	1.0		212	11	KMHK: Compact cluster. Alias: KMHK 623
KMHK 651	cl	05 11 08.5	−74 32 42	Men	0.6		219	11	KMHK: Loose cluster.
SL 293	cl	05 11 09.0	−67 40 57	Dor	0.8		212	11	KMHK: Compact cluster. Alias: KMHK 630
KMHK 640	cl	05 11 10.0	−71 32 23	Men	0.4		212	11	KMHK: Compact cluster.
[HS66] 156	cl	05 11 10.8	−67 37 38	Dor	0.4		212	99	KMHK: Loose cluster. Alias: KMHK 632
LH 33	cl	05 11.2	−69 10	Dor			212	5	
KMHK 634	cl	05 11 27.6	−65 26 59	Dor	1.7		212	99	KMHK: Loose cluster. Archinal: Not obvious on DSS image, among several scattered stars.
SL 298	cl	05 11 31.8	−66 58 29	Dor	2.6		212	99	KMHK: Compact cluster. Alias: KMHK 636

Table C.1: Tables of LMC Objects

Name	Type	2000.0 R.A.	2000.0 Dec.	Con	Diam (′)	Tot. Vm	U#	Ref	Comments and Aliases
NGC 1859	cl	05 11 32.6	−65 14 55	Dor	2.0		212	11	DSFG: Relatively bright.; KMHK: Compact cluster. Alias: KMHK 635
KMHK 643	cl	05 11 35.6	−70 02 33	Men	0.4		212	99	KMHK: Loose cluster.
NGC 1863	cl	05 11 39.8	−68 43 38	Dor		11.0	212	99	DSFG: Relatively bright. Alias: h 2791
SL 300	cl	05 11 41.7	−67 33 55	Dor	0.8		212	11	KMHK: Loose cluster. Alias: KMHK 638
SL 302	cl	05 11 44.0	−70 03 56	Men	1.5		212	11	KMHK: Compact cluster. Alias: KMHK 646
LW 157	ast?	05 11 52.2	−64 59 27	Dor	0.9		212	99	KMHK: Incorrect on Hodge-Wright Atlas (1967). Archinal: Three to five stars only? Alias: KMHK 637
KMHK 645	cl	05 11 58.7	−67 58 18	Dor	0.6		212	11	KMHK: Loose cluster.
SL 301	cl	05 12 04.7	−66 06 53	Dor	0.7		212	11	KMHK: Loose cluster. Alias: KMHK 641
[HS66] 162	cl	05 12 06.2	−66 18 09	Dor	0.4		212	11	KMHK: Loose cluster. Alias: KMHK 642
C0512–684	cl	05 12 08.3	−68 25 51	Dor			212	99	Archinal: Histogram equalization display of DSS image - or DSS-II image - shows two very small and faint clusters here. Which one?
LW 160	cl	05 12 18.2	−72 52 03	Men	0.7		212	11	KMHK: Loose cluster. Alias: KMHK 659
SL 303	cl	05 12 20.4	−64 18 18	Dor	0.9		212	11	KMHK: Loose cluster. Alias: KMHK 644
SL 314	cl	05 12 21.1	−73 23 35	Men	2.1		212	11	KMHK: Loose cluster. Alias: KMHK 663
SL 312	cl	05 12 24.3	−71 40 44	Men	1.0		212	99	KMHK: Compact cluster. Alias: KMHK 658
LW 159	cl	05 12 24.9	−64 01 40	Dor			212	99	Archinal: Not obvious on DSS. Just NW of asterism of three bright stars. Alias: SL 305
NGC 1865	cl	05 12 25.4	−68 46 19	Dor		12.9	212	99	
[HS66] 164	cl	05 12 27.3	−65 46 56	Dor	0.7		212	11	KMHK: Compact cluster. Alias: KMHK 648
SL 308	cl	05 12 27.9	−68 17 45	Dor	1.2		212	11	KMHK: Compact cluster. Alias: KMHK 653
SL 310	cl	05 12 29.5	−67 17 29	Dor	1.0		212	11	KMHK: Compact cluster. Aliases: LH 34; KMHK 652
NGC 1862	cl	05 12 33.6	−66 09 19	Dor	0.3		212	11	KMHK: Loose cluster. Aliases: BRHT 6a; KMHK 650
KMHK 655	cl	05 12 33.7	−68 03 49	Dor	0.4		212	11	KMHK: Compact cluster.
[HS66] 168	cl	05 12 35.0	−65 38 05	Dor	0.8		212	99	KMHK: Loose cluster. Archinal: Very faint on DSS image. Alias: KMHK 649
BRHT 6b	ast?	05 12 35.2	−66 09 03	Dor			212	99	Archinal: 2-3 stars only? Using BRHT table 1 identity for BRHT 6b (figure has BRHT 6a = NGC 1862 and BRHT 6b reversed).
NGC 1864	cl	05 12 41.1	−67 37 25	Dor	0.9		212	11	KMHK: Compact cluster. Alias: KMHK 656
KMHK 662	cl	05 12 48.2	−70 36 50	Men	0.7		212	11	KMHK: Compact cluster.
NGC 1878	cl	05 12 49.7	−70 28 19	Men	1.1		212	99	DSFG: Relatively faint.; KMHK: Compact cluster. Archinal: DSS image has fiber/hair just to south. Alias: KMHK 661
[HS66] 173	cl	05 12 52.6	−65 22 04	Dor	0.6		212	11	KMHK: Compact cluster. Alias: KMHK 654
NGC 1870	cl	05 13 11.0	−69 07 02	Dor		11.3	212	99	DSFG: Moderately bright. Aliases: SL 317; h 2799
NGC 1874	neb	05 13 11	−69 22.6	Dor	1.0	12.81	212	54	See notes. This nebulous object is sometimes mistaken for a cluster. Aliases: (3) SL 320; BRHT 7; (2) BRHT 7a; (2) BRHT 7b
SL 315	cl	05 13 11.2	−65 44 34	Dor	1.0		212	11	KMHK: Incorrect on Hodge-Wright Atlas (1967). Alias: KMHK 657
NGC 1872	cl	05 13 11.5	−69 18 45	Dor		11.0	212	99	DSFG: Bright. Alias: SL 318
BRHT 7b	neb*	05 13 11.5	−69 22 35	Dor	0.9		212	54	Southern part of NGC 1874. Mistaken for a cluster, and for NGC 1880 by BRHT. Aliases: (3) NGC 1874; (3) SL 320
LH 35	cl	05 13.3	−69 22	Dor			212	5	
LW 164	cl	05 13 16.1	−73 11 12	Men	0.4		212	11	KMHK: Loose cluster. Alias: KMHK 675
KMHK 660	cl	05 13 26.1	−65 43 59	Dor	0.4		212	11	KMHK: Compact cluster.
NGC 1881	cl	05 13.6	−69 18	Dor			212	2	DSFG: In a large complex in the LMC.

Table C.1: Tables of LMC Objects

Name	Type	2000.0 R.A.	2000.0 Dec.	Con	Diam (′)	Tot. Vm	U#	Ref	Comments and Aliases
NGC 1866	cl	05 13 38.6	−65 27 51	Dor	4.5	9.7	212	11	DSFG: Only a few stars brighter than magnitude 15.8.; KMHK: Compact cluster. Aliases: LW 163; SL 319; KMHK 664
NGC 1880	neb	05 13 39.2	−69 22 59	Dor	0.7		212	99	See notes. This nebulous object is sometimes mistaken for a cluster. Aliases: (3) SL 320; h 2808
NGC 1867	cl	05 13 41.6	−66 17 36	Dor	1.3		212	99	KMHK: Compact cluster. Archinal: The DSS shows an unusual short "arc" of some sort, just NE. Is it a real LMC object or plate defect? Alias: KMHK 665
SL 322	cl	05 13 43.4	−66 31 17	Dor	0.8		212	11	KMHK: Compact cluster. Alias: KMHK 666
NGC 1890	cl	05 13 47.2	−72 04 42	Men	1.2		212	11	KMHK: Compact cluster. Alias: KMHK 678
[HS66] 178	cl	05 13 48.4	−66 37 12	Dor	0.6		212	11	KMHK: Loose cluster. Alias: KMHK 667
NGC 1871	cl	05 13 52.4	−67 27 09	Dor	2.0		212	56	See notes. LMC cluster, part of NGC 1869 association.; KMHK: Incorrect on Hodge-Wright Atlas (1967). Aliases: LH 38; KMHK 669; (3) NGC 1869
LH 37	cl	05 13 53.6	−67 22 37	Dor	2.0		212	56	See notes. LMC cluster, part of NGC 1869 association. This is NOT NGC 1869 itself. Aliases: KMHK 671; (3) NGC 1869
NGC 1869	ass	05 13 53.6	−67 22 37	Dor	14.0		212	56	See notes. Association in LMC, including NGC 1871, LH 37, and NGC 1873. This is at same position, but IS NOT LH 37 itself. Aliases: (2) NGC 1871; (2) LH 37; (2) NGC 1873
SL 334	cl	05 13 55.9	−72 11 51	Men	0.4		212	11	KMHK: Loose cluster. Alias: KMHK 683
LH 39	cl	05 13.9	−69 31	Dor		10.86	212	5	Alias: SL 328
KMHK 686	cl	05 13 58.0	−73 09 31	Men	0.3		212	11	KMHK: Loose cluster.
NGC 1873	cl	05 14 01.7	−67 19 54	Dor	3.5		212	56	See notes. LMC cluster, part of NGC 1869 association.; KMHK: Loose cluster. Aliases: LH 36; KMHK 670; (3) NGC 1869
[HS66] 184	cl	05 14 10.2	−70 41 03	Men	0.8		212	11	KMHK: Compact cluster. Alias: KMHK 681
SL 329	cl	05 14 11.8	−64 48 44	Dor	1.3		212	99	KMHK: Compact cluster. Alias: KMHK 668
KMHK 672	cl	05 14 13.8	−66 23 40	Dor	0.8		212	99	KMHK: Loose cluster. Archinal: Very faint on DSS image. Just N of fairly obvious star.
LW 165	cl	05 14 23.3	−65 00 17	Dor	1.5		212	11	KMHK: Loose cluster. Alias: KMHK 673
SL 336	cl	05 14 28.8	−71 13 15	Men	0.9		212	11	KMHK: Compact cluster. Alias: KMHK 688
SL 337	cl	05 14 30.0	−73 06 55	Men	1.0		212	11	KMHK: Compact cluster. Alias: KMHK 692
NGC 1868	cl	05 14 36.1	−63 57 17	Dor	3.9		212	11	KMHK: Compact cluster. Aliases: LW 169; ESO 85-56; SL 330; KMHK 674
KMHK 687	cl	05 14 38.3	−70 04 02	Men	0.7		212	11	KMHK: Loose cluster.
KMHK 680	cl	05 14 39.8	−67 11 53	Dor	1.3		212	11	KMHK: Loose cluster.
SL 333	cl	05 14 44.1	−65 20 07	Dor	1.3		212	11	KMHK: Loose cluster. Alias: KMHK 676
[HS66] 187	cl	05 14 45.8	−68 20 39	Dor	0.9		212	11	KMHK: Loose cluster. Alias: KMHK 685
LW 171	cl	05 14 46.3	−65 36 30	Dor	1.0		212	99	KMHK: Loose cluster. Archinal: Very faint on DSS image. Alias: KMHK 679
[HS66] 185	cl	05 14 47.4	−64 59 18	Dor	0.7		212	11	KMHK: Compact cluster. Alias: KMHK 677
[HS66] 186	cl	05 14 49.0	−66 11 01	Dor	1.0		212	11	KMHK: Loose cluster. Alias: KMHK 682
SL 335	cl	05 15 00.1	−65 59 27	Dor	0.7		212	11	KMHK: Compact cluster. Alias: KMHK 684
NGC 1885	cl	05 15 06.9	−68 58 43	Dor		12.0	212	99	DSFG: Moderately bright.
[HS66] 195	cl	05 15 06.9	−70 22 41	Men	1.7		212	99	KMHK: Loose cluster. Archinal: Very faint on DSS image, among scattered stars. Alias: KMHK 695
SL 339	cl	05 15 17.9	−68 17 26	Dor	1.2		212	99	KMHK: Loose cluster. Alias: KMHK 691
OHSC 8	cl	05 15 18.7	−74 56 08	Men	0.4		219	11	KMHK: Loose cluster. Alias: KMHK 708
[HS66] 193	cl	05 15 21.6	−68 26 08	Dor	0.6		212	11	KMHK: Loose cluster. Alias: KMHK 693
LW 174	cl	05 15 26.6	−64 42 05	Dor	1.1		212	11	KMHK: Loose cluster. Alias: KMHK 689
[HS66] 199	cl	05 15 30.9	−70 53 12	Men	0.4		212	11	KMHK: Loose cluster. Alias: KMHK 703
SL 342	cl	05 15 32.6	−70 20 09	Men	1.3		212	11	KMHK: Compact cluster. Alias: KMHK 701

Table C.1: Tables of LMC Objects

Name	Type	2000.0 R.A.	2000.0 Dec.	Con	Diam (′)	Tot. Vm	U#	Ref	Comments and Aliases
NGC 1882	cl	05 15 32.8	−66 07 44	Dor	1.2		212	11	DSFG: Relatively bright.; KMHK: Compact cluster. Alias: KMHK 690
KMHK 704	cl	05 15 34.9	−70 45 07	Men	0.7		212	11	KMHK: Compact cluster.
SL 341	cl	05 15 36	−69 28.4	Dor			212	99	Alias: BRHT 8b
[HS66] 194	cl	05 15 37.8	−66 41 41	Dor	0.4		212	11	KMHK: Compact cluster. Alias: KMHK 694
KMHK 698	cl	05 15 40.2	−67 50 42	Dor	0.7		212	99	KMHK: Loose cluster.
[HS66] 196	cl	05 15 42.4	−66 15 21	Dor	0.6		212	11	KMHK: Loose cluster. Alias: KMHK 696
KMHK 697	cl	05 15 48.7	−66 01 42	Dor	0.4		212	11	KMHK: Loose cluster.
NGC 1894	cl	05 15 51.4	−69 28 13	Dor		12.2	212	99	DSFG: Relatively bright. Aliases: BRHT 8a; SL 344
[H60b] 1	cl	05 16.0	−68 56	Dor		12.40	212	99	Archinal: Not obvious on DSS image. Aliases: BRHT 33b; SL 353
[HS66] 202	cl	05 16 03.8	−71 48 19	Men	0.8		212	11	KMHK: Loose cluster. Alias: KMHK 709
NGC 1887	cl	05 16 05.3	−66 19 12	Dor	1.1		212	11	DSFG: Relatively bright.; KMHK: Compact cluster. Alias: KMHK 700
KMHK 707	cl	05 16 12.4	−70 30 10	Men	1.0		212	11	KMHK: Compact cluster.
SL 345	cl	05 16 17.1	−63 12 12	Dor	1.0		212	11	KMHK: Loose cluster. Alias: KMHK 699
OHSC 9	cl	05 16 21.9	−76 12 26	Men	1.0		219	11	KMHK: Loose cluster. Alias: KMHK 733
SL 347	cl	05 16 25.7	−66 49 24	Dor	1.2		212	11	KMHK: Compact cluster. Alias: KMHK 706
SL 346	cl	05 16 28.4	−63 09 58	Dor	0.7		212	11	KMHK: Loose cluster. Alias: KMHK 702
SL 352	cl	05 16 40.7	−70 32 28	Men	1.3		212	11	KMHK: Compact cluster. Alias: KMHK 715
NGC 1898	gcl	05 16 42	−69 39.4	Dor		11.86	212	99	Alias: SL 350
KMHK 705	cl	05 16 42.7	−62 01 22	Dor	0.4		201	11	KMHK: Loose cluster.
KMHK 735	cl	05 16 53.6	−74 38 35	Men	0.4		219	11	KMHK: Loose cluster.
SL 349	cl	05 16 54.6	−68 52 33	Dor	1.1		212	99	Archinal: BRHT has identities wrong on their figure of these clusters (e.g. this is not SL 344). Alias: BRHT 33a
KMHK 719	cl	05 16 59.2	−70 12 13	Men	0.6		212	11	KMHK: Loose cluster.
KMHK 724	cl	05 17 00.1	−71 53 53	Men	0.9		212	11	KMHK: Loose cluster.
KMHK 711	cl	05 17 01.6	−67 32 25	Dor	0.8		212	99	KMHK: Compact cluster. Archinal: Apparent plate defect appears as short line just SE of this on DSS.
KMHK 710	cl	05 17 06.7	−66 34 57	Dor	0.3		212	11	KMHK: Loose cluster.
SL 353	cl	05 17 10	−68 53.1	Dor		13.27	212	99	Alias: BRHT 33b
[HS66] 206	cl	05 17 11.6	−66 30 02	Dor	0.4		212	11	KMHK: Loose cluster. Alias: KMHK 713
KMHK 714	cl	05 17 13.8	−66 19 49	Dor	0.6		212	11	KMHK: Loose cluster.
[HS66] 207	cl	05 17 17.5	−66 25 15	Dor	0.6		212	11	KMHK: Loose cluster. Alias: KMHK 716
[HS66] 210	cl	05 17 22.5	−70 35 13	Men	0.9		212	11	KMHK: Loose cluster. Alias: KMHK 725
NGC 1903	cl	05 17 22.8	−69 20 13	Dor		11.9	212	99	Aliases: BRHT 9a; SL 356; h 2825
KMHK 718	cl	05 17 23.7	−66 23 04	Dor	0.7		212	11	KMHK: Loose cluster.
SL 357	cl	05 17 26.5	−69 22 30	Dor			212	99	Archinal: BRHT is missing the SL 357 = BRHT 9b identification in their table but have it in their figure. Alias: SL 357
NGC 1916	gcl	05 17 26.7	−69 22 34	Dor		10.4	212	99	
KMHK 717	cl	05 17 29.5	−65 30 53	Dor	0.6		212	11	KMHK: Loose cluster.
SL 354	cl	05 17 30.9	−63 25 18	Dor	1.6		212	11	KMHK: Loose cluster. Aliases: ESO 85-63; LW 177; KMHK 712
[HS66] 208	cl	05 17 30.9	−67 01 37	Dor	0.9		212	11	KMHK: Compact cluster. Alias: KMHK 721
NGC 1897	cl	05 17 31.6	−67 26 58	Dor	1.0		212	11	DSFG: Very faint.; KMHK: Compact cluster. Alias: KMHK 722

Table C.1: Tables of LMC Objects

Name	Type	2000.0 R.A.	2000.0 Dec.	Con	Diam (′)	Tot. Vm	U#	Ref	Comments and Aliases
NGC 1914	cl	05 17 39.4	−71 15 19	Men	2.2		212	99	Center of NW-SE elongated nebulous cluster. J. Herschel gave position of brightest star in SE end. Aliases: LH 40; KMHK 732; h 2830
SL 364	cl	05 17 41.6	−71 03 55	Men	0.4		212	11	KMHK: Compact cluster. Alias: KMHK 736
KMHK 731	cl	05 17 44.9	−70 20 46	Men	1.0		212	11	KMHK: Loose cluster.
KMHK 740	cl	05 17 47.5	−71 09 23	Men	1.3		212	99	KMHK: Loose cluster. Archinal: Very faint on DSS image.
[HS66] 214	cl	05 17 49.4	−70 48 03	Men	0.3		212	11	KMHK: Compact cluster. Alias: KMHK 738
SL 359	cl	05 17 49.7	−68 28 22	Dor	1.3		212	11	KMHK: Loose cluster. Alias: KMHK 727
SL 374	cl	05 17 49.7	−73 26 42	Men	1.6		212	11	KMHK: Loose cluster. Alias: KMHK 752
KMHK 720	cl	05 17 50.8	−63 47 43	Dor	0.7		212	99	KMHK: Loose cluster. Archinal: Very faint on DSS image.
KMHK 723	cl	05 17 52.9	−66 04 25	Dor	0.7		212	11	KMHK: Compact cluster.
[H60b] 2	cl	05 17.9	−69 40	Dor		12.32	212	99	Alias: SL 363
[HS66] 212	cl	05 18 02.1	−66 09 13	Dor	0.6		212	11	KMHK: Compact cluster. Alias: KMHK 726
KMHK 747	cl	05 18 05.4	−71 16 09	Men	0.6		212	99	KMHK: Loose cluster. Archinal: Very faint on DSS image.
Hodge 88 266	cl	05 18 09.5	−69 16 56	Dor	0.7		212	99	Archinal: Identified on DSS image via comparison with Hodge [1988] figure 6.
BRHT 10b	cl	05 18 10	−69 32.4	Dor			212	5	
SL 360	cl	05 18 11.1	−69 13 06	Dor	0.8	9.54	212	52	Cluster in LMC, inside association NGC 1910. Alias: (3) NGC 1910
KMHK 737	cl	05 18 15.0	−67 29 47	Dor	0.6		212	99	KMHK: Loose cluster. Archinal: Very faint on DSS image.
Hodge 88 267	cl	05 18 15.2	−69 15 02	Dor	0.8		212	99	Archinal: Identified on DSS image via comparison with Hodge [1988] figure 6.
[HS66] 215	cl	05 18 18.0	−65 41 25	Dor	1.2		212	11	KMHK: Loose cluster. Alias: KMHK 728
KMHK 750	cl	05 18 18.2	−70 43 23	Men	0.6		212	99	KMHK: Loose cluster. Archinal: Very faint on DSS image.
NGC 1902	cl	05 18 18.3	−66 37 35	Dor	1.6		212	11	DSFG: Relatively bright.; KMHK: Compact cluster. Alias: KMHK 734
NGC 1913	cl	05 18 19.2	−69 32 15	Dor		11.1	212	99	Aliases: BRHT 10a; SL 373; h (356)
SL 366	cl	05 18 20.4	−65 55 16	Dor	1.0		212	11	KMHK: Loose cluster. Alias: KMHK 729
NGC 1905	cl	05 18 23.0	−67 16 42	Dor	1.0		212	11	KMHK: Compact cluster. Alias: KMHK 739
NGC 1910	ass	05 18 23.8	−69 13 45	Dor	8.5	11.2	212	54	See notes. Association in LMC, including cluster SL 360. Aliases: Dunlop 129; LH 41; (2) SL 360
KMHK 742	cl	05 18 30.7	−67 54 51	Dor	0.6		212	11	KMHK: Compact cluster.
KMHK 743	cl	05 18 31.9	−67 50 41	Dor	0.6		212	11	KMHK: Loose cluster.
SL 372	cl	05 18 36.5	−64 06 44	Dor	0.8		212	99	KMHK: Compact cluster. Archinal: The DSS image shows a possible previously unidentified tiny cluster just to NW, at 05 18 30.3 -64 06 11. Alias: KMHK 730
[HS66] 217	cl	05 18 40.1	−66 13 06	Dor	0.9		212	11	KMHK: Loose cluster. Alias: KMHK 741
SL 375	cl	05 18 43.2	−66 30 23	Dor	0.6		212	11	KMHK: Compact cluster. Alias: KMHK 744
KMHK 753	cl	05 18 46.3	−68 34 34	Dor	1.3		212	99	KMHK: Loose cluster. Archinal: Very faint on DSS image.
SL 380	cl	05 18 46.5	−71 52 13	Men	1.6		212	11	KMHK: Incorrect on Hodge-Wright Atlas (1967). Alias: KMHK 767
LW 182	cl	05 18 48.3	−66 05 01	Dor	1.3		212	11	KMHK: Loose cluster. Alias: KMHK 745
KMHK 764	cl	05 18 51.8	−70 36 12	Men	0.7		212	11	KMHK: Loose cluster.
KMHK 751	cl	05 18 53.6	−66 58 07	Dor	0.7		212	99	KMHK: Loose cluster. Archinal: Very faint on DSS image.
KMHK 755	cl	05 18 56.7	−68 07 31	Dor	0.7		212	11	KMHK: Loose cluster.
SL 378	cl	05 18 57.9	−68 12 42	Dor	1.6		212	11	KMHK: Loose cluster. Aliases: BRHT 34a; KMHK 756
BRHT 34b	cl	05 18 58	−68 13.0	Dor			212	5	

Table C.1: Tables of LMC Objects

Name	Type	2000.0 R.A.	2000.0 Dec.	Con	Diam (′)	Tot. Vm	U#	Ref	Comments and Aliases
SL 377	cl	05 19 00.6	−65 05 39	Dor	0.7		212	11	KMHK: Compact cluster. Alias: KMHK 748
KMHK 749	cl	05 19 02.7	−65 05 33	Dor	0.7		212	11	KMHK: Compact cluster.
KMHK 759	cl	05 19 06.0	−68 30 23	Dor	0.7		212	99	KMHK: Loose cluster. Archinal: Very faint on DSS image.
NGC 1900	cl	05 19 08.8	−63 01 25	Dor	1.7		212	99	KMHK: Compact cluster. Archinal: DSS image has some sort of streak (plate defect?) to S. Aliases: LW 184; ESO 85-68; SL 376; KMHK 746
KMHK 758	cl	05 19 11.9	−67 29 21	Dor	1.0		212	11	KMHK: Loose cluster.
KMHK 754	cl	05 19 12.6	−65 51 21	Dor	0.4		212	11	KMHK: Loose cluster.
[HS66] 224	cl	05 19 14.9	−67 05 58	Dor	0.8		212	11	KMHK: Loose cluster. Alias: KMHK 757
KMHK 760	cl	05 19 14.9	−67 31 11	Dor	0.9		212	99	KMHK: Loose cluster. Archinal: Very faint on DSS image, only visible with histogram equalization display.
LH 42	cl	05 19 17.5	−69 38 47	Dor			212	99	Alias: [HS66] 223
BRHT 49b	cl	05 19 18	−69 47.4	Dor			212	5	
[HS66] 239	cl	05 19 22	−69 47.4	Dor			212	5	Alias: BRHT 49a
[HS66] 225	cl	05 19 23.4	−67 13 34	Dor	0.6		212	11	KMHK: Loose cluster. Alias: KMHK 765
[HS66] 226	cl	05 19 23.4	−67 42 49	Dor	0.6		212	11	KMHK: Loose cluster. Alias: KMHK 766
NGC 1911	cl	05 19 25.2	−66 40 55	Dor	0.4		212	11	KMHK: Loose cluster. Alias: KMHK 763
SL 385	cl	05 19 25.4	−69 32 27	Dor		12.78	212	99	Archinal: This is also BRHT 35a (BRHT table 1 - 35a/35b identities are reversed and incorrect in BRHT figure 1). Alias: BRHT 35a
SL 382	cl	05 19 25.5	−66 30 02	Dor	0.7		212	11	KMHK: Compact cluster. Alias: KMHK 762
NGC 1915	cl	05 19 28.1	−66 44 21	Dor	0.4		212	11	KMHK: Compact cluster. Alias: KMHK 761
SL 387	cl	05 19 33	−69 32.6	Dor		13.07	212	99	Archinal: This is also BRHT 35b (BRHT table 1 - 35a/35b identities are reversed and incorrect in BRHT figure 1). Alias: BRHT 35b
SL 383	cl	05 19 33.2	−68 16 24	Dor	1.1		212	11	KMHK: Compact cluster. Alias: KMHK 775
SL 394	cl	05 19 34.8	−71 52 29	Men	1.8		212	11	KMHK: Loose cluster. Alias: KMHK 789
OHSC 11	cl	05 19 34.8	−75 06 11	Men	0.7		219	11	KMHK: Loose cluster. Alias: KMHK 803
SL 396	cl	05 19 36.3	−73 06 37	Men	1.0		212	11	KMHK: Compact cluster. Alias: KMHK 796
SL 389	cl	05 19 36.4	−71 12 32	Men	1.7		212	11	KMHK: Loose cluster. Alias: KMHK 783
SL 400	cl	05 19 38.7	−75 48 31	Men	1.0		219	11	KMHK: Loose cluster. Aliases: LW 188; KMHK 809
[HS66] 229	cl	05 19 42.7	−66 14 41	Dor	0.6		212	11	KMHK: Loose cluster. Alias: KMHK 769
KMHK 771	cl	05 19 42.8	−66 49 56	Dor	0.7		212	11	KMHK: Loose cluster.
SL 384	cl	05 19 44.5	−65 47 05	Dor	0.8		212	99	KMHK: Loose cluster. Archinal: Very faint on DSS image. Alias: KMHK 768
KMHK 774	cl	05 19 44.5	−66 48 32	Dor	0.4		212	11	KMHK: Loose cluster.
NGC 1922	cl	05 19 50.0	−69 30 01	Dor		11.5	212	99	Alias: h (374)
SL 386	cl	05 19 51.3	−65 23 17	Dor	0.7		212	11	KMHK: Compact cluster. Alias: KMHK 770
[HS66] 230	cl	05 19 53.5	−67 20 21	Dor	0.6		212	11	KMHK: Loose cluster. Alias: KMHK 776
[HS66] 231	cl	05 19 55.0	−68 20 53	Dor	1.6		212	11	KMHK: Loose cluster. Alias: KMHK 779
KMHK 772	cl	05 19 55.7	−65 00 26	Dor	1.0		212	99	KMHK: Loose cluster. Archinal: Very faint and small on DSS image.
SL 395	cl	05 19 59.0	−70 39 58	Men	0.7		212	11	KMHK: Compact cluster. Alias: KMHK 793
KMHK 795	cl	05 20 00.0	−71 05 56	Men	0.3		212	11	KMHK: Compact cluster.
[HS66] 235	cl	05 20 03.5	−68 28 44	Dor	0.7		212	11	KMHK: Loose cluster. Alias: KMHK 784

Table C.1: Tables of LMC Objects

Name	Type	2000.0 R.A.	2000.0 Dec.	Con	Diam (′)	Tot. Vm	U#	Ref	Comments and Aliases
SL 388	cl	05 20 05.5	−63 28 46	Dor	1.3		212	11	KMHK: Compact cluster. Aliases: ESO 85-72; LW 186; KMHK 773
KMHK 777	cl	05 20 05.6	−66 20 35	Dor	0.6		212	11	KMHK: Loose cluster.
[HS66] 233	cl	05 20 09.4	−66 24 54	Dor	0.4		212	11	KMHK: Loose cluster. Alias: KMHK 778
[HS66] 234	cl	05 20 09.7	−66 27 18	Dor	0.4		212	11	KMHK: Loose cluster. Alias: KMHK 780
[HS66] 236	cl	05 20 15.7	−66 23 45	Dor	0.6		212	99	KMHK: Loose cluster. Archinal: Very faint on DSS image. Alias: KMHK 781
KMHK 787	cl	05 20 16.3	−67 09 24	Dor	0.4		212	99	KMHK: Loose cluster. Archinal: Very faint on DSS image.
NGC 1919	cl	05 20 17.1	−66 52 53	Dor	1.7		212	11	KMHK: Incorrect on Hodge-Wright Atlas (1967). Alias: KMHK 786
SL 399	cl	05 20 20.4	−70 46 08	Men	0.8		212	11	KMHK: Compact cluster. Alias: KMHK 799
KMHK 794	cl	05 20 24.1	−68 25 01	Dor	0.7		212	11	KMHK: Loose cluster.
LW 191	cl	05 20 27.4	−72 05 30	Men	0.7		212	11	KMHK: Compact cluster. Alias: KMHK 807
KMHK 801	cl	05 20 27.7	−70 27 03	Men	0.9		212	11	KMHK: Loose cluster.
[HS66] 237	cl	05 20 30.7	−64 48 07	Dor	0.6		212	11	KMHK: Loose cluster. Alias: KMHK 785
SL 398	cl	05 20 31.8	−65 16 56	Dor	1.1		212	11	KMHK: Compact cluster. Alias: KMHK 788
NGC 1920	cl	05 20 32.1	−66 46 45	Dor	1.8		212	11	KMHK: Compact cluster. Alias: KMHK 792
KMHK 790	cl	05 20 34.3	−65 48 40	Dor	0.6		212	11	KMHK: Loose cluster.
NGC 1926	cl	05 20 35.2	−69 31 33	Dor		11.8	212	99	Alias: LH 46
[HS66] 232	cl	05 20 36.8	−70 57 55	Men	0.8		212	11	KMHK: Compact cluster. Alias: KMHK 805
OHSC 10	cl	05 20 38.2	−63 07 49	Dor	0.4		212	99	KMHK: Loose cluster. Archinal: Not obvious or very faint on DSS image. Alias: KMHK 782
KMHK 798	cl	05 20 41.2	−67 36 26	Dor	0.7		212	99	KMHK: Loose cluster. Archinal: Very faint on DSS image.
SL 401	cl	05 20 50.2	−64 00 09	Dor	0.8		212	11	KMHK: Loose cluster. Aliases: LW 190; KMHK 791
NGC 1928	gcl	05 20 57.2	−69 28 40	Dor		11.9	212	99	Dutra, et al. 1999 have determined this is a true "old" LMC globular cluster.
KMHK 804	cl	05 20 58.0	−68 37 33	Dor	0.9		212	11	KMHK: Loose cluster.
LW 193	cl	05 20 58.6	−74 42 52	Men	0.6		219	11	KMHK: Loose cluster. Alias: KMHK 826
[HS66] 240	cl	05 21 00.7	−64 29 56	Dor	1.0		212	99	KMHK: Loose cluster. Archinal: Not obvious or very faint on DSS image. Alias: KMHK 797
SL 406	cl	05 21 00.9	−70 52 24	Men	0.6		212	11	KMHK: Compact cluster. Alias: KMHK 814
KMHK 812	cl	05 21 01.3	−70 30 37	Men	0.7		212	11	KMHK: Loose cluster.
KMHK 802	cl	05 21 02.1	−67 28 42	Dor	1.0		212	99	KMHK: Loose cluster. Archinal: Very faint on DSS image.
KMHK 800	cl	05 21 02.5	−66 03 09	Dor	0.6		212	11	KMHK: Loose cluster.
KMHK 806	cl	05 21 04.6	−68 21 37	Dor	0.6		212	11	KMHK: Loose cluster.
LH 44	cl	05 21.2	−69 04	Dor			212	5	Alias: SL 408
SL 407	cl	05 21 15.5	−68 26 42	Dor	1.6		212	11	KMHK: Compact cluster. Alias: KMHK 810
KMHK 819	cl	05 21 20.9	−71 24 22	Men	0.6		212	11	KMHK: Compact cluster.
AH03 J0521.3-6954	cl	05 21 23.0	−69 54 36	Men?	0.4		212	99	Archinal: Faint. Previously undiscovered LMC cluster, to N of NGC 1938 and NGC 1939.
NGC 1939	gcl	05 21 24.3	−69 56 20	Men?		12.9	212	99	The fainter of two, with NGC 1938 50" to SE. Dutra, et al. 1999 have determined this is a true LMC globular cluster. Aliases: BRHT 11b; SL 414
NGC 1938	cl	05 21 27.1	−69 57 00	Men?		11.8	212	99	The brighter of two (according to GC and NGC), with NGC 1939 50" to NW. Aliases: BRHT 11a; SL 413
KMHK 824	cl	05 21 30.5	−71 43 03	Men	0.4		212	11	KMHK: Compact cluster.

Table C.1: Tables of LMC Objects

Name	Type	2000.0 R.A.	2000.0 Dec.	Con	Diam (′)	Tot. Vm	U#	Ref	Comments and Aliases
NGC 1925	ass	05 21 31	−65 48.9	Dor	11.0		212	99	See notes. Large association of scattered stars. This is NOT a nebula as claimed in the original DSFG. Aliases: h 2837; (2) SL 415
NGC 1923	cl	05 21 34.5	−65 29 13	Dor	0.9		212	99	KMHK: Loose cluster. Aliases: LH 43; KMHK 808
OHSC 12	cl	05 21 37.1	−72 36 39	Men	0.4		212	11	KMHK: Loose cluster. Alias: KMHK 830
SL 409	cl	05 21 37.9	−66 05 34	Dor	1.1		212	11	KMHK: Loose cluster. Alias: KMHK 811
KMHK 816	cl	05 21 38.9	−67 56 18	Dor	1.5		212	99	KMHK: Compact cluster. Archinal: Not obvious on DSS image - in a large association.
SL 411	cl	05 21 41.7	−67 40 46	Dor	1.0		212	11	KMHK: Compact cluster. Alias: KMHK 817
SL 410	cl	05 21 45.1	−65 13 56	Dor	1.7		212	11	KMHK: Compact cluster. Alias: KMHK 813
KMHK 829	cl	05 21 46.3	−71 51 06	Men	0.7		212	11	KMHK: Compact cluster.
IC 2126	neb	05 21 49.7	−67 57 07	Dor	0.5		212	99	Archinal: Identified here as second brightest nebula in large complex. (Not a planetary nebula as IC indicates). Aliases: LH 47; Fleming 90
NGC 1934	*	05 21 54.0	−67 54 52	Dor			212	99	DSFG: In a large complex in the LMC. Archinal: Confirmed as a star using J. Herschel description and drawing, in comparison to DSS image. Alias: h 2842
KMHK 822	cl	05 21 56.8	−67 56 10	Dor	1.7		212	99	KMHK: Loose cluster. Archinal: Relatively large (~2′ diameter) LMC cluster, with patches of nebulosity.
NGC 1944	cl	05 21 58.1	−72 29 39	Men	3.3		212	11	KMHK: Compact cluster. Alias: KMHK 836
SL 416	cl	05 21 58.2	−67 11 07	Dor	0.7		212	11	KMHK: Loose cluster. Alias: KMHK 818
KMHK 815	cl	05 21 59.4	−64 34 57	Dor	0.3		212	11	KMHK: Loose cluster.
SL 415	cl	05 22 01.9	−65 50 05	Dor			212	99	See notes. Identified by M. Morel [Priv. Comm., 2002] as GSC 8890-00068. Alias: (3) NGC 1925
KMHK 820	cl	05 22 03.1	−66 52 19	Dor	0.7		212	11	KMHK: Loose cluster.
KMHK 823	**?	05 22 03.9	−68 09 14	Dor	0.4		212	99	KMHK: Loose cluster. Archinal: Two stars only?
KMHK 835	cl	05 22 07.8	−71 10 30	Men	0.7		212	11	KMHK: Loose cluster.
NGC 1933	*?	05 22 17.2	−66 09 15	Dor		13.83	212	99	See notes. This is GSC 08890-00548, listed in the GSC as nonstellar and at GSC magnitude 13.83 ±0.40. Alias: (3) h 2841
SL 433	cl	05 22 19.2	−74 36 20	Men	1.3		219	99	KMHK: Loose cluster. Aliases: LW 197; KMHK 843
KMHK 838	cl	05 22 20.7	−71 14 19	Men	0.6		212	99	KMHK: Loose cluster. Archinal: Not obvious or very faint on DSS image.
NGC 1937	cl	05 22 23.0	−67 53 56	Dor	2.0		212	99	DSFG: In a large complex in the LMC. Aliases: h 2845; LH 48
SL 424	cl	05 22 23.4	−68 09 39	Dor	1.5		212	11	KMHK: Compact cluster. Alias: KMHK 831
[HS66] 255	cl	05 22 26	−69 44.7	Dor			212	5	Alias: BRHT 50a
NGC 1932	cl	05 22 27.4	−66 09 06	Dor	1.2	11.84	212	56	See notes. Position, diameter from DSS. Includes GSC 08890-01063 and GSC 08890-00192 (GSC magnitudes 9.65 ±0.38 and 10.66 ±0.39). Aliases: SL 420; KMHK 825; (3) h 2841; (5) HD 271203
SL 421	cl	05 22 29.4	−66 31 43	Dor	1.0		212	11	KMHK: Compact cluster. Alias: KMHK 827
KMHK 828	cl	05 22 31.2	−66 35 47	Dor	0.9		212	11	KMHK: Loose cluster.
[HS66] 254	cl	05 22 33.8	−67 35 51	Dor	0.3		212	11	KMHK: Loose cluster. Alias: KMHK 832
LW 195	cl	05 22 35.4	−61 52 47	Dor	0.9		201	11	KMHK: Loose cluster. Aliases: ESO 119-61; KMHK 821
[HS66] 256	cl	05 22 36	−69 44.8	Dor			212	5	Alias: BRHT 50b
SL 432	cl	05 22 37.8	−72 51 36	Men	0.7		212	11	KMHK: Loose cluster. Alias: KMHK 842
NGC 1940	cl	05 22 44.2	−67 11 10	Dor	0.1		212	11	DSFG: Relatively bright.; KMHK: Compact cluster. Alias: KMHK 834
SL 428	cl	05 22 52.1	−65 42 52	Dor	0.7		212	11	KMHK: Loose cluster. Alias: KMHK 833
LH 49	cl	05 22 55	−68 03.6	Dor			212	5	
KMHK 840	cl	05 22 54.8	−68 06 52	Dor	0.7		212	11	KMHK: Compact cluster.
[HS66] 262	cl	05 22 57.1	−71 58 38	Men	0.7		212	11	KMHK: Loose cluster. Alias: KMHK 844

Table C.1: Tables of LMC Objects

Name	Type	2000.0 R.A.	2000.0 Dec.	Con	Diam (′)	Tot. Vm	U#	Ref	Comments and Aliases
KMHK 846	cl	05 23 02.1	−71 45 26	Men	0.7		212	11	KMHK: Compact cluster.
IC 2134	cl	05 23 06.6	−75 26 49	Men	1.0		219	11	KMHK: Compact cluster. Aliases: LW 198; ESO 33-19; SL 437; KMHK 864
NGC 1941	cl	05 23 07.1	−66 22 41	Dor	0.9		212	11	KMHK: Loose cluster. Alias: KMHK 839
[HS66] 258	cl	05 23 10.6	−64 40 51	Dor	0.4		212	11	KMHK: Loose cluster. Alias: KMHK 837
[HS66] 264	cl	05 23 11.8	−70 46 40	Men	0.9		212	11	KMHK: Loose cluster. Alias: KMHK 845
[HS66] 260	cl	05 23 13.7	−67 36 49	Dor	0.7		212	11	KMHK: Loose cluster. Alias: KMHK 841
[HS66] 267	cl	05 23 19.8	−70 21 22	Men	1.7		212	11	KMHK: Loose cluster. Alias: KMHK 847
LW 201	cl	05 23 23.2	−74 39 26	Men	1.0		219	99	KMHK: Loose cluster. Alias: KMHK 865
OHSC 13	cl	05 23 25.7	−72 56 47	Men			212	5	
OHSC 14	cl	05 23 29.3	−74 35 14	Men	0.4		219	11	KMHK: Loose cluster. Alias: KMHK 868
SL 435	cl	05 23 30.5	−71 25 36	Men	1.2		212	11	In association LH 50.; KMHK: Compact cluster. Aliases: KMHK 853; (3) LH 50
LH 50	ass	05 23.7	−71 23	Men	8.0		212	54	Includes cluster [SL63] 435 and nebulae Hen N 199 and Hen N 200. Aliases: (2) SL 435; (2) Hen N 199; (2) Hen N 200
SL 441	cl	05 23 42.1	−71 02 12	Men	0.8		212	11	KMHK: Loose cluster. Alias: KMHK 855
[HS66] 270	cl	05 23 52.1	−71 34 45	Men	1.6		212	11	KMHK: Loose cluster. Aliases: BRHT 51a; KMHK 860
OHSC 15	cl	05 23 59.3	−72 54 38	Men	0.4		212	11	KMHK: Compact cluster. Alias: KMHK 870
[HS66] 274	cl	05 24 06.2	−71 34 20	Men	0.9		212	11	KMHK: Compact cluster. Aliases: BRHT 51b; KMHK 866
[HS66] 269	cl	05 24 07.0	−65 53 53	Dor	0.7		212	11	KMHK: Loose cluster. Alias: KMHK 849
LW 204	cl	05 24 07.2	−73 09 58	Men	0.3		212	11	KMHK: Loose cluster. Alias: KMHK 873
LW 199	cl	05 24 08.2	−65 08 13	Dor	0.6		212	99	KMHK: Loose cluster. Archinal: Nothing obvious on DSS image. Alias: KMHK 848
SL 438	cl	05 24 10.6	−66 46 34	Dor	0.9		212	11	KMHK: Loose cluster. Alias: KMHK 851
SL 440	cl	05 24 12.6	−65 34 28	Dor	0.7		212	11	KMHK: Loose cluster. Alias: KMHK 850
[HS66] 272	cl	05 24 12.6	−68 30 09	Dor	0.9		212	11	KMHK: Compact cluster. Alias: KMHK 857
SL 451	cl	05 24 13.4	−75 34 00	Men	0.8		219	11	KMHK: Compact cluster. Aliases: LW 206; KMHK 883
SL 455	cl	05 24 17.2	−76 12 36	Men	1.6		219	99	KMHK: Loose cluster. Aliases: LW 207; KMHK 891
KMHK 852	cl	05 24 17.7	−66 01 22	Dor	0.4		212	11	KMHK: Compact cluster.
OHSC 16	cl	05 24 20.8	−74 50 27	Men	0.3		219	11	KMHK: Loose cluster. Alias: KMHK 881
AH03 J0524.4-6958	cl	05 24 22.1	−69 57 57	Men?	0.7		212	99	Archinal: Faint. Previously undiscovered LMC cluster, to S of NGC 1950.
KMHK 858	cl	05 24 28.0	−67 43 43	Dor	0.6		212	11	KMHK: Compact cluster.
SL 444	cl	05 24 30.4	−67 40 42	Dor	1.2		212	11	KMHK: Loose cluster. Alias: KMHK 861
NGC 1950	cl	05 24 32.1	−69 54 07	Men?		13.2	212	99	Alias: h 2859
KMHK 863	cl	05 24 37.7	−67 52 31	Dor	0.4		212	99	KMHK: Compact cluster. Archinal: Very faint on DSS image.
KMHK 854	cl	05 24 40.2	−63 12 09	Dor	0.4		212	11	KMHK: Loose cluster.
NGC 1942	cl	05 24 42.7	−63 56 19	Dor	1.1		212	11	KMHK: Compact cluster. Aliases: LW 203; ESO 85-81; SL 445; KMHK 856
SL 446	cl	05 24 47.8	−67 43 35	Dor	0.8		212	99	KMHK: Compact cluster. Alias: KMHK 869
[HS66] 277	cl	05 24 48.5	−67 05 11	Dor	0.7		212	11	KMHK: Compact cluster. Alias: KMHK 867
KMHK 862	cl	05 24 52.4	−65 47 03	Dor	0.6		212	11	KMHK: Loose cluster.
SL 448	cl	05 24 59.4	−63 02 53	Dor	1.0		212	11	KMHK: Loose cluster. Alias: KMHK 859
KMHK 876	cl	05 25 03.9	−68 44 03	Dor	0.7		212	11	KMHK: Compact cluster.

Table C.1: Tables of LMC Objects

Name	Type	2000.0 R.A.	Dec.	Con	Diam (′)	Tot. Vm	U#	Ref	Comments and Aliases
NGC 1949	cl	05 25 05.3	−68 28 20	Dor	1.3		212	11	KMHK: Compact cluster. Alias: KMHK 875
LW 210	cl	05 25 07.0	−73 01 48	Men			212	5	
KMHK 872	cl	05 25 08.4	−66 59 54	Dor	0.9		212	99	KMHK: Loose cluster. Archinal: Very faint on DSS image.
KMHK 880	cl	05 25 09.8	−70 33 49	Men	0.3		212	11	KMHK: Loose cluster.
SL 452	cl	05 25 10.0	−66 38 55	Dor	0.9		212	11	KMHK: Loose cluster. Alias: KMHK 871
NGC 1946	cl	05 25 16.0	−66 23 34	Dor	1.0		212	99	KMHK: Compact cluster. Alias: KMHK 874
SL 461	cl	05 25 20.8	−71 48 12	Men	2.0		212	11	KMHK: Loose cluster. Alias: KMHK 887
[HS66] 284	cl	05 25 24.2	−71 52 19	Men	0.4		212	11	KMHK: Compact cluster. Alias: KMHK 890
SL 456	cl	05 25 25.3	−67 29 18	Dor	1.7		212	99	KMHK: Loose cluster. Archinal: Discovered by J. Herschel, along with his h 2863 = NGC 1955. Aliases: LH 51; KMHK 879
LW 211	cl	05 25 28.0	−73 34 14	Men	0.6		219	11	KMHK: Loose cluster. Alias: KMHK 901
NGC 1958	cl	05 25 30.3	−69 50 10	Dor?		13.0	212	99	DSFG: In a very rich star field.
KMHK 878	cl	05 25 35.7	−64 45 30	Dor	0.7		212	56	See notes. Very faint. This is NOT NGC 1947, as KMHK claim. NGC 1947 lies 1° farther north.
NGC 1959	cl	05 25 36.1	−69 55 31	Men?		12.2	212	99	Alias: h 2865
LW 209	cl	05 25 44.4	−63 01 16	Dor	0.3		212	11	KMHK: Loose cluster. Alias: KMHK 877
LH 52	cl	05 25.9	−66 17	Dor			212	5	
KMHK 897	cl	05 25 57.8	−70 27 34	Men	0.4		212	99	Either a faint, small cluster here at the KMHK position, or a brighter group slightly north at 05 25 57.9 -70 27 28.
[HS66] 287	cl	05 26 00.7	−67 09 16	Dor	0.7		212	11	KMHK: Loose cluster. Alias: KMHK 884
[HS66] 288	cl	05 26 01.3	−67 15 26	Dor	0.9		212	11	KMHK: Compact cluster. Alias: KMHK 885
LH 53	cl	05 26.1	−66 14	Dor			212	5	
NGC 1955	cl	05 26 04.2	−67 29 52	Dor	1.8	9.0p	212	11	DSFG: Extended E-W.; KMHK: Loose cluster. Aliases: LH 54; KMHK 888
NGC 1951	cl	05 26 06.4	−66 35 50	Dor	1.9	10.6	212	11	DSFG: Extended N-S.; KMHK: Compact cluster. Aliases: SL 464; KMHK 886
[HS66] 289	cl	05 26 07.7	−68 38 03	Dor	1.3		212	11	KMHK: Loose cluster. Alias: KMHK 895
LW 212	cl	05 26 08.4	−64 33 40	Dor	1.0		212	99	KMHK: Loose cluster. Archinal: Very faint on DSS image. Alias: KMHK 882
SL 474	cl	05 26 08.5	−71 48 37	Men	0.9		212	99	KMHK: Loose cluster. Alias: KMHK 909
LH 56	cl	05 26.2	−71 34	Men			212	5	
KMHK 893	ast?	05 26 11.7	−66 40 05	Dor	0.7		212	99	Archinal: This is NOT SL 465 as KMHK claim. It appears to be only a single star with a few fainter stars to the W.
KMHK 907	cl	05 26 12.8	−70 58 53	Men	0.7		212	11	KMHK: Loose cluster.
SL 465	cl	05 26 13.7	−66 34 07	Dor	0.8		212	99	KMHK: Compact cluster. Archinal: Sparse group just NE of NGC 1951 = SL 464. KMHK fail to identify this as SL 465 (their KMHK 892). Alias: KMHK 892
SL 471	cl	05 26 14.3	−67 37 13	Dor	0.9		212	11	KMHK: Loose cluster. Alias: KMHK 894
SL 472	cl	05 26 14.4	−70 22 52	Men	1.7		212	11	KMHK: Loose cluster. Alias: KMHK 906
KMHK 910	cl	05 26 16.0	−71 49 17	Men	0.7		212	11	KMHK: Loose cluster.
SL 463	cl	05 26 16.2	−66 03 09	Dor	0.7		212	11	KMHK: Compact cluster. Alias: KMHK 889
NGC 1962	cl	05 26 19.4	−68 50 15	Dor			212	99	DSFG: In a large complex in the LMC. Alias: h 2866
LH 55	ass	05 26.4	−67 38	Dor			212	54	Aliases: (2) SL 471; (2) [HS66] 299
[HS66] 294	cl	05 26 23.2	−68 42 28	Dor	1.0		212	99	KMHK: Loose cluster. Alias: KMHK 902
SL 477	cl	05 26 23.7	−71 41 51	Men	1.5		212	11	KMHK: Compact cluster. Alias: KMHK 911
KMHK 898	***?	05 26 23.9	−68 02 48	Dor	0.3		212	99	KMHK: Compact cluster. Archinal: Three stars only?
KMHK 899	cl	05 26 24.3	−68 17 58	Dor	0.3		212	99	KMHK: Loose cluster. Archinal: Very faint on DSS image.

Table C.1: Tables of LMC Objects

Name	Type	2000.0 R.A.	2000.0 Dec.	Con	Diam (′)	Tot. Vm	U#	Ref	Comments and Aliases
SL 470	cl	05 26 25.7	−66 23 16	Dor	1.3		212	11	KMHK: Compact cluster. Alias: KMHK 896
SL 473	cl	05 26 29.4	−68 22 27	Dor	1.0		212	11	KMHK: Loose cluster. Alias: KMHK 904
KMHK 900	cl	05 26 29.5	−67 41 58	Dor	0.6		212	11	KMHK: Compact cluster.
NGC 1965	neb	05 26 29.6	−68 48 36	Dor			212	52	See notes. The DSFG incorrectly lists this as a cluster. Alias: (3) SL 476
LH 57	cl	05 26 32	−69 17.6	Dor			212	5	
NGC 1969	cl	05 26 32.1	−69 50 31	Dor?	0.8	12.5	212	99	DSFG: In a very rich star field. Triple with NGC 1971/72. Aliases: h 2872; (3) LH 59
[HS66] 299	cl	05 26 38.2	−67 39 20	Dor	0.8		212	11	KMHK: Loose cluster. Alias: KMHK 905
[HS66] 301A	cl	05 26 39.4	−71 58 50	Men	1.0		212	11	KMHK: Compact cluster. Alias: KMHK 917
LH 59	cl	05 26 42	−69 50.6	Dor?	7.0		212	99	Archinal: This association probably does NOT contain [HS66] 307, as LH claim, since [HS66] 307 is 9.1′ away to SSE. Aliases: (2) NGC 1969; (2) NGC 1971; (2) NGC 1972
NGC 1967	cl	05 26 44.6	−69 06 05	Dor		10.8	212	99	DSFG: Relatively bright. Aliases: SL 478; h (456)
NGC 1971	cl	05 26 45.0	−69 51 06	Dor?	0.8	11.9	212	99	DSFG: Relatively bright; in a very rich star field. Triple with NGC 1969/27. Aliases: BRHT 12a; SL 481; h 2875; (3) LH 59
NGC 1970	neb	05 26 45.3	−68 49 50	Dor			212	99	See notes. The DSFG incorrectly lists this as a cluster. Aliases: (3) SL 476; h 2869
LW 214	cl	05 26 48.1	−65 47 33	Dor	0.6		212	11	KMHK: Loose cluster. Alias: KMHK 903
NGC 1972	cl	05 26 48.1	−69 50 17	Dor?	0.9	12.6	212	99	DSFG: Relatively faint and compact group; in a very rich star field. Triple with NGC 1969/71. Aliases: BRHT 12b; SL 480; h 2876; (3) LH 59
KMHK 914	cl	05 26 59.1	−68 27 09	Dor	0.9		212	11	KMHK: Compact cluster.
KMHK 908	cl	05 27 02.0	−65 26 53	Dor	1.0		212	99	KMHK: Loose cluster. Archinal: Very faint on DSS image.
SL 487	cl	05 27 08.2	−71 01 21	Men	1.0		212	11	KMHK: Loose cluster. Alias: KMHK 925
[HS66] 302	cl	05 27 09.7	−66 53 07	Dor	0.8		212	11	KMHK: Loose cluster. Alias: KMHK 913
KMHK 912	cl	05 27 14.7	−66 05 58	Dor	0.7		212	11	KMHK: Compact cluster.
[HS66] 304	cl	05 27 15.5	−71 10 17	Men	1.0		212	11	KMHK: Compact cluster. Alias: KMHK 927
NGC 1987	cl	05 27 16.4	−70 44 14	Men	1.7		212	11	KMHK: Compact cluster. Aliases: SL 486; KMHK 926
SL 482	cl	05 27 18.3	−66 22 07	Dor	0.8		212	11	KMHK: Compact cluster. Alias: KMHK 915
SL 490	cl	05 27 18.4	−73 40 41	Men	0.9		219	11	KMHK: Loose cluster. Aliases: LW 217; KMHK 939
[HS66] 303	cl	05 27 22.6	−66 47 15	Dor	0.8		212	11	KMHK: Loose cluster. Alias: KMHK 916
NGC 2000	cl	05 27 30.5	−71 52 50	Men	1.7	11.9	212	11	DSFG: Relatively bright.; KMHK: Compact cluster. Alias: KMHK 932
KMHK 920	cl	05 27 35.4	−66 32 37	Dor	0.9		212	11	KMHK: Loose cluster.
KMHK 934	cl	05 27 37.7	−71 25 09	Men	1.7		212	11	KMHK: Loose cluster.
NGC 1986	cl	05 27 37.9	−69 58 19	Men?		11.1	212	99	
[HS66] 307	cl	05 27 38.0	−69 58 21	Men?			212	99	This is probably NOT in the association LH 59, as LH claim, since it is 9.1′ SSE of LH 59.
NGC 1968	cl	05 27 39.7	−67 27 20	Dor	1.1	9.0p	212	11	DSFG: Extended E-W and involved in nebulosity which also carries the same designation.; KMHK: Loose cluster. Aliases: LH 60; KMHK 924
LW 215	cl	05 27 42.6	−65 17 52	Dor	0.7		212	11	KMHK: Loose cluster. Alias: KMHK 919
KMHK 922	cl	05 27 44.3	−66 00 45	Dor	0.8		212	99	KMHK: Compact cluster. Alias: BRHT 36b
LH 62	cl	05 27 46.4	−70 27 16	Men			212	99	
SL 484	cl	05 27 46.5	−64 38 56	Dor	0.9		212	11	KMHK: Loose cluster. Alias: KMHK 918
SL 485	cl	05 27 50.0	−66 01 20	Dor	0.7		212	11	KMHK: Loose cluster. Aliases: BRHT 36a; KMHK 923
SL 491	cl	05 27 50.5	−68 24 50	Dor	0.7		212	11	KMHK: Loose cluster. Alias: KMHK 928

Table C.1: Tables of LMC Objects

Name	Type	2000.0 R.A.	2000.0 Dec.	Con	Diam (′)	Tot. Vm	U#	Ref	Comments and Aliases
LH 61	cl	05 27 51	−68 59.7	Dor		7.99	212	5	
[HS66] 305	cl	05 27 54.0	−64 10 30	Dor	0.7		212	99	KMHK: Loose cluster. Alias: KMHK 921
NGC 1974	cl	05 28 00.6	−67 25 22	Dor	1.7	9.0p	212	99	See notes. KMHK: Compact cluster. Archinal: This is also NGC 1991, due to a positional error by J. Herschel. Aliases: LH 63; KMHK 929; Dunlop 213; h 2877; h 2884; NGC 1991
[HS66] 311	cl	05 28 01.0	−71 50 05	Men	1.5		212	11	KMHK: Loose cluster. Alias: KMHK 949
SL 495	cl	05 28 03.8	−68 48 42	Dor	0.7		212	11	KMHK: Compact cluster. Alias: KMHK 933
KMHK 930	cl	05 28 13.2	−67 07 21	Dor	0.7		212	11	KMHK: Loose cluster.
[HS66] 309	cl	05 28 17.4	−66 55 33	Dor	0.7		212	11	KMHK: Compact cluster. Alias: KMHK 931
[HS66] 315	cl	05 28 17.8	−71 33 11	Men	0.7		212	11	KMHK: Loose cluster. Alias: KMHK 950
KMHK 941	cl	05 28 19.0	−68 40 56	Dor	0.6		212	11	KMHK: Compact cluster.
KMHK 936	cl	05 28 20.0	−67 02 19	Dor	0.6		212	11	KMHK: Loose cluster.
NGC 1994	cl	05 28 23.3	−69 08 29	Dor		9.8	212	99	DSFG: Relatively bright. Aliases: SL 499; h 2887
SL 497	cl	05 28 23.9	−67 38 30	Dor	1.0		212	11	KMHK: Compact cluster. Alias: KMHK 940
[HS66] 313	cl	05 28 25.4	−68 12 21	Dor	0.6		212	11	KMHK: Compact cluster. Alias: KMHK 942
[HS66] 314	cl	05 28 26.5	−68 58 55	Dor			212	99	
KMHK 945	cl	05 28 27.8	−68 39 01	Dor	0.4		212	11	KMHK: Loose cluster.
SL 496	cl	05 28 32.6	−65 10 23	Dor	0.7		212	99	KMHK: Loose cluster. Alias: KMHK 935
SL 498	cl	05 28 35.1	−67 13 30	Dor	1.3		212	11	KMHK: Compact cluster. Alias: KMHK 943
[H60b] 14	cl	05 28 38.6	−73 37 50	Men	1.1		219	99	KMHK: Compact cluster. Aliases: SL 506; LW 220; KMHK 967
SL 500	cl	05 28 39.3	−64 51 07	Dor	1.2		212	11	KMHK: Compact cluster. Alias: KMHK 937
KMHK 938	cl	05 28 43.7	−64 40 46	Dor	0.6		212	11	KMHK: Loose cluster.
[HS66] 318	cl	05 28 44.2	−67 03 36	Dor	0.7		212	11	KMHK: Loose cluster. Alias: KMHK 948
NGC 1978	cl	05 28 44.6	−66 14 08	Dor	3.9		212	11	KMHK: Compact cluster. Aliases: SL 501; KMHK 944
[HS66] 319	cl	05 28 47	−68 59.0	Dor			212	5	Alias: BRHT 52a
SL 505	cl	05 28 49.7	−71 37 59	Men	1.6		212	11	KMHK: Loose cluster. Alias: KMHK 960
OHSC 19	cl	05 28 49.7	−72 31 01	Men	0.6		212	11	KMHK: Loose cluster. Alias: KMHK 964
BRHT 52b	cl	05 28 53	−68 59.3	Dor			212	5	
[HS66] 324	cl	05 28 56.0	−71 07 12	Men	0.7		212	11	KMHK: Loose cluster. Alias: KMHK 961
KMHK 953	cl	05 28 57.2	−68 47 30	Dor	1.0		212	11	KMHK: Compact cluster.
SL 503	cl	05 28 59.6	−68 25 08	Dor	1.3		212	11	KMHK: Compact cluster. Alias: KMHK 952
LH 64	cl	05 29.0	−68 47	Dor			212	5	
[HS66] 317	cl	05 29 01.9	−64 17 15	Dor	0.6		212	11	KMHK: Compact cluster. Alias: KMHK 947
OHSC 17	cl	05 29 04.3	−63 46 06	Dor	0.3		212	11	KMHK: Loose cluster. Alias: KMHK 946
NGC 2001	cl	05 29 08.2	−68 45 17	Dor	1.7		212	11	DFSG: Stellar association. Extended NNE-SSW about 3:1.; KMHK: Loose cluster. Alias: KMHK 955
KMHK 969	cl	05 29 10.1	−71 48 52	Men	0.7		212	99	KMHK: Compact cluster.
[H60b] 3	cl	05 29.2	−68 18	Dor			212	99	Archinal: Not obvious on DSS image.
SL 502	cl	05 29 11.5	−66 35 30	Dor	1.0		212	11	KMHK: Compact cluster. Alias: KMHK 951
[HS66] 322	cl	05 29 20.9	−66 30 27	Dor	0.6		212	11	KMHK: Loose cluster. Alias: KMHK 954
SL 510	cl	05 29 21.1	−70 34 47	Men	0.8		212	11	KMHK: Compact cluster. Alias: KMHK 968

Table C.1: Tables of LMC Objects

Name	Type	2000.0 R.A.	2000.0 Dec.	Con	Diam (′)	Tot. Vm	U#	Ref	Comments and Aliases
KMHK 958	cl	05 29 23.9	−67 37 41	Dor	0.6		212	11	KMHK: Loose cluster.
OHSC 18	cl	05 29 30.3	−63 04 56	Dor			212	99	Archinal: Very faint on DSS image.
[HS66] 325	cl	05 29 36.6	−67 07 43	Dor	0.4		212	11	KMHK: Compact cluster. Alias: KMHK 963
KMHK 979	cl	05 29 39.1	−70 59 02	Men	0.9		212	11	KMHK: Loose cluster.
[HS66] 326	cl	05 29 39.2	−66 45 43	Dor	1.0		212	11	KMHK: Loose cluster. Alias: KMHK 962
[HS66] 329	cl	05 29 46.3	−71 00 03	Men	0.8		212	11	KMHK: Loose cluster. Alias: KMHK 984
KMHK 956	cl	05 29 46.8	−63 38 52	Dor	0.9		212	99	KMHK: Compact cluster. Archinal: Faint. DSS overlap region.
SL 511	cl	05 29 49.0	−64 26 20	Dor	1.2		212	99	KMHK: Loose cluster. Archinal: Not obvious on DSS image. DSS overlap region. Alias: KMHK 959
SL 509	cl	05 29 49.1	−63 38 58	Dor	0.9		212	99	KMHK: Compact cluster. Archinal: Faint group. DSS overlap region. Alias: KMHK 957
SL 512	cl	05 29 54.3	−66 04 29	Dor	0.7		212	11	KMHK: Loose cluster. Alias: KMHK 966
KMHK 971	cl	05 29 55.2	−67 18 37	Dor	0.7		212	11	KMHK: Compact cluster.
[HS66] 330	cl	05 29 57.6	−72 03 18	Men	1.6		212	11	KMHK: Loose cluster. Alias: KMHK 996
SL 513	cl	05 29 58.4	−66 45 29	Dor	1.0		212	11	KMHK: Compact cluster. Alias: KMHK 970
KMHK 975	cl	05 29 59.4	−67 52 44	Dor	0.3		212	11	KMHK: Compact cluster.
SL 516	cl	05 30 00.1	−66 58 42	Dor	0.9		212	11	KMHK: Compact cluster. Alias: KMHK 972
LH 65	cl	05 30 04.1	−66 56 37	Dor			212	99	
KMHK 974	cl	05 30 04.3	−66 52 21	Dor	1.0		212	11	KMHK: Loose cluster.
KMHK 983	cl	05 30 05.7	−68 38 13	Dor	0.8		212	99	KMHK: Loose cluster.
KMHK 976	cl	05 30 06.7	−67 01 46	Dor	0.8		212	11	KMHK: Loose cluster.
LH 66	cl	05 30.1	−71 05	Men			212	5	
SL 515	cl	05 30 08.9	−63 25 40	Dor	1.8		212	99	KMHK: Loose cluster. Archinal: Right on DSS overlap boundary. Alias: KMHK 965
NGC 2005	gcl	05 30 10.3	−69 45 09	Dor	1.8	11.6	212	99	DSFG: Relatively bright and compact. Archinal: Position and diameter measured from DSS.
KMHK 977	cl	05 30 10.4	−66 56 16	Dor	1.6		212	11	KMHK: Loose cluster.
KMHK 980	cl	05 30 11.5	−67 40 31	Dor	0.4		212	11	KMHK: Compact cluster.
KMHK 999	cl	05 30 12.7	−71 33 19	Men	0.6		212	11	KMHK: Compact cluster.
KMHK 985	cl	05 30 16.3	−68 27 31	Dor	0.7		212	11	KMHK: Loose cluster.
KMHK 997	cl	05 30 20.0	−70 25 01	Men	0.7		212	11	KMHK: Loose cluster.
NGC 2002	cl	05 30 21.4	−66 53 02	Dor	2.0	10.1	212	11	DSFG: Relatively bright.; KMHK: Compact cluster. Alias: KMHK 982
SL 525	cl	05 30 23.4	−64 01 06	Dor	0.6		212	11	KMHK: Loose cluster. Aliases: LW 225; KMHK 973
SL 521	cl	05 30 26.1	−65 54 36	Dor	2.4		212	11	KMHK: Loose cluster. Alias: KMHK 981
LW 231	cl	05 30 27.8	−75 20 57	Men	0.7		219	11	KMHK: Loose cluster. Alias: KMHK 1031
KMHK 987	cl	05 30 33.1	−66 54 14	Dor	0.7		212	11	KMHK: Compact cluster.
NGC 2010	cl	05 30 34.6	−70 49 10	Men	2.2		212	11	DSFG: Irregular in shape.; KMHK: Compact cluster. Alias: KMHK 1001
KMHK 993	cl	05 30 34.7	−68 09 27	Dor	0.7		212	11	KMHK: Loose cluster.
NGC 1997	cl	05 30 34.9	−63 12 10	Dor	1.3		212	11	KMHK: Compact cluster. Alias: KMHK 978
KMHK 986	cl	05 30 35.6	−66 31 36	Dor	0.6		212	11	KMHK: Loose cluster.
SL 536	cl	05 30 35.6	−71 48 39	Men	1.3		212	11	KMHK: Loose cluster. Alias: KMHK 1006
SL 522	cl	05 30 37.0	−67 11 10	Dor	1.0		212	11	KMHK: Compact cluster. Alias: KMHK 988
NGC 2004	cl	05 30 40.9	−67 17 17	Dor	2.7	9.6	212	11	KMHK: Compact cluster. Aliases: SL 523; KMHK 991

Table C.1: Tables of LMC Objects

Name	Type	2000.0 R.A.	2000.0 Dec.	Con	Diam (′)	Tot. Vm	U#	Ref	Comments and Aliases
KMHK 989	cl	05 30 46.6	−65 58 13	Dor	0.6		212	11	KMHK: Loose cluster.
SL 527	cl	05 30 50.1	−66 25 00	Dor	1.8		212	11	KMHK: Loose cluster. Alias: KMHK 995
SL 524	cl	05 30 50.2	−66 20 03	Dor	1.2		212	11	KMHK: Compact cluster. Alias: KMHK 994
LW 228	cl	05 30 52.7	−65 35 08	Dor	0.8		212	99	KMHK: Loose cluster. Archinal: On edge of DSS overlap boundary. Alias: KMHK 990
NGC 2003	cl	05 30 54.3	−66 27 59	Dor	2.1	11.3	212	11	KMHK: Compact cluster. Alias: KMHK 998
SL 539	cl	05 30 56.4	−70 41 42	Men	1.7		212	11	KMHK: Compact cluster. Alias: KMHK 1008
NGC 2009	cl	05 30 59.6	−69 10 56	Dor		11.0	212	99	DSFG: Relatively bright. Alias: h 2897
LW 234	cl	05 30 59.8	−74 40 16	Men	0.7		219	11	KMHK: Loose cluster. Alias: KMHK 1042
SL 543	cl	05 31 01.1	−71 53 36	Men	0.9		212	11	KMHK: Compact cluster. Alias: KMHK 1016
[HS66] 334	cl	05 31 02.1	−71 35 45	Men	1.7		212	11	KMHK: Loose cluster. Alias: KMHK 1014
SL 546	cl	05 31 02.5	−72 36 38	Men	0.6		212	11	KMHK: Compact cluster. Aliases: LW 233; KMHK 1026
KMHK 1000	cl	05 31 05.0	−66 41 58	Dor	0.9		212	11	KMHK: Loose cluster.
SL 529	cl	05 31 06.8	−63 32 31	Dor	1.1		212	11	KMHK: Compact cluster. Alias: KMHK 992
SL 545	cl	05 31 08.1	−71 57 46	Men	1.0		212	99	KMHK: Compact cluster. Alias: KMHK 1022
KMHK 1002	cl	05 31 09.0	−67 28 58	Dor	0.6		212	11	KMHK: Compact cluster.
LH 67	cl	05 31 09	−69 17.7	Dor			212	5	Alias: [HS66] 333
NGC 2018	cl	05 31 11.6	−71 04 11	Men	2.8		212	11	KMHK: Compact cluster. Alias: KMHK 1018
SL 541	cl	05 31 18.1	−68 48 52	Dor	1.0		212	11	KMHK: Loose cluster. Aliases: LH 68; KMHK 1009
SL 538	cl	05 31 19.8	−66 57 28	Dor	1.1		212	11	KMHK: Compact cluster. Aliases: BRHT 13b; KMHK 1004
NGC 2006	cl	05 31 19.9	−66 58 22	Dor	1.0	11.5	212	11	DSFG: Relatively bright open cluster SL 538, similar in size and brightness, lies 1′ N.; KMHK: Compact cluster. Aliases: BRHT 13a; SL 537; KMHK 1005
OHSC 20	cl	05 31 20.1	−63 40 16	Dor			212	5	
LW 230	cl	05 31 23.2	−63 15 38	Dor			212	5	
SL 548	cl	05 31 25.1	−72 02 33	Men	0.4		212	11	KMHK: Loose cluster. Alias: KMHK 1035
NGC 2016	cl	05 31.5	−69 56	Men?			212	54	DSFG: Slightly extended E-W.
KMHK 1007	cl	05 31 31.8	−66 01 10	Dor	0.7		212	11	KMHK: Loose cluster.
SL 540	cl	05 31 33.9	−63 53 45	Dor	0.7		212	11	KMHK: Loose cluster. Aliases: LW 232; KMHK 1003
[HS66] 337	cl	05 31 40.1	−66 15 49	Dor	0.7		212	11	KMHK: Loose cluster. Alias: KMHK 1010
KMHK 1025	cl	05 31 42.2	−68 48 43	Dor	1.5		212	11	KMHK: Loose cluster.
SL 555	cl	05 31 43.0	−72 08 46	Men	1.9		212	11	KMHK: Compact cluster. Alias: KMHK 1046
SL 552	cl	05 31 43.5	−68 32 12	Dor	1.3		212	11	KMHK: Loose cluster. Aliases: LH 71; KMHK 1024
KMHK 1037	cl	05 31 44.1	−70 48 12	Men	0.6		212	11	KMHK: Compact cluster.
[HS66] 342	cl	05 31 45	−70 18.6	Men			212	5	Alias: BRHT 53b
[HS66] 338	cl	05 31 45.3	−67 11 09	Dor	1.0		212	11	KMHK: Loose cluster. Alias: KMHK 1015
KMHK 1023	cl	05 31 46.0	−68 14 08	Dor	0.7		212	11	KMHK: Loose cluster.
KMHK 1011	cl	05 31 47.9	−65 15 53	Dor	0.7		212	11	KMHK: Compact cluster.
NGC 2015	ass	05 31 48	−69 14.9	Dor	5.6		212	99	Archinal: Long fiber/hair running across DSS image to E. Aliases: LH 74; (2) SL 557; (2) BRHT 15b; h 2901
[HS66] 345	cl	05 31 50	−70 17.4	Men			212	5	Alias: BRHT 53a
KMHK 1019	cl	05 31 50.7	−66 59 49	Dor	0.9		212	11	KMHK: Compact cluster.

Table C.1: Tables of LMC Objects

Name	Type	2000.0 R.A.	2000.0 Dec.	Con	Diam (′)	Tot. Vm	U#	Ref	Comments and Aliases
KMHK 1012	cl	05 31 50.8	−65 26 44	Dor	0.8		212	11	KMHK: Compact cluster.
SL 551	cl	05 31 51.8	−67 59 27	Dor	0.8		212	11	KMHK: Compact cluster. Aliases: BRHT 38a; KMHK 1027
KMHK 1033	cl	05 31 54.5	−68 46 06	Dor	0.6		212	11	KMHK: Loose cluster.
SL 550	cl	05 31 55.1	−66 07 47	Dor	0.8		212	11	KMHK: Compact cluster. Aliases: BRHT 37a; KMHK 1017
LH 73	cl	05 31 55.6	−68 40 53	Dor			212	99	
NGC 2019	gcl	05 31 57	−70 09.6	Men			212	99	Alias: SL 554
KMHK 1029	cl	05 31 57.0	−67 52 43	Dor	0.6		212	11	KMHK: Loose cluster.
BRHT 38b	cl	05 31 59	−67 58.4	Dor			212	5	
KMHK 1032	cl	05 31 58.9	−67 58 14	Dor	0.6		212	11	KMHK: Compact cluster.
KMHK 1021	cl	05 31 59.6	−66 16 58	Dor	0.7		212	11	KMHK: Loose cluster.
[HS66] 341	cl	05 31 59.8	−67 22 00	Dor	0.4		212	11	KMHK: Compact cluster. Aliases: LH 70; KMHK 1028
KMHK 1020	cl	05 32 00.0	−66 07 55	Dor	0.7		212	99	KMHK: Loose cluster. Alias: BRHT 37b
KMHK 1038	cl	05 32 02.0	−69 01 42	Dor	0.7		212	11	KMHK: Compact cluster.
SL 549	cl	05 32 03.6	−64 14 32	Dor	1.3		212	11	KMHK: Compact cluster. Alias: KMHK 1013
SL 561	cl	05 32 04.9	−70 41 56	Men	1.3		212	11	KMHK: Loose cluster. Alias: KMHK 1048
SL 557	cl	05 32 06.8	−69 14 27	Dor	1.3		212	99	Archinal: This is NOT NGC 2015, as SL and BRHT indicate. Aliases: BRHT 15a; (3) NGC 2015
SL 562	cl	05 32 06.8	−71 15 08	Men	1.7		212	11	KMHK: Compact cluster. Alias: KMHK 1052
[HS66] 343	cl	05 32 07.0	−66 40 19	Dor	1.0		212	11	KMHK: Compact cluster. Alias: KMHK 1030
[HS66] 348	cl	05 32 15.5	−70 22 53	Men	0.9		212	11	KMHK: Compact cluster. Alias: KMHK 1051
KMHK 1053	cl	05 32 16.2	−70 45 13	Men	0.6		212	11	KMHK: Compact cluster.
BRHT 15b	cl	05 32 17.8	−69 15 00	Dor			212	99	Archinal: With SL 557 to NW. Unresolved on DSS. Alias: (3) NGC 2015
KMHK 1036	cl	05 32 18.1	−66 24 15	Dor	0.8		212	11	KMHK: Compact cluster.
KMHK 1047	cl	05 32 18.5	−68 52 29	Dor	1.3		212	11	KMHK: Compact cluster.
NGC 2011	cl	05 32 19.8	−67 31 16	Dor	1.0		212	11	KMHK: Incorrect on Hodge-Wright Atlas (1967). Aliases: LH 75; BRHT 14a; SL 559; KMHK 1039
KMHK 1040	cl	05 32 20.2	−67 31 39	Dor	0.9		212	11	KMHK: Compact cluster. Alias: BRHT 14b
NGC 2014	cl	05 32 21.7	−67 41 58	Dor	1.8		212	11	KMHK: Incorrect on Hodge-Wright Atlas (1967). Aliases: LH 76; Hen N 57; SL 560; [MBB72] 57; KMHK 1043
KMHK 1045	cl	05 32 23.7	−67 59 50	Dor	0.6		212	11	KMHK: Loose cluster.
[H60b] 4	cl	05 32 25.4	−64 44 11	Dor	0.2		212	99	KMHK: Compact cluster. Aliases: SL 556; LW 237; KMHK 1034; ESO 86-SC9; ESO 053212–6446.2
SL 553	cl	05 32 29.2	−66 27 59	Dor	1.0		212	11	KMHK: Incorrect on Hodge-Wright Atlas (1967). Aliases: LH 72; KMHK 1041
KMHK 1056	cl	05 32 30.0	−71 10 47	Men	0.6		212	11	KMHK: Compact cluster.
NGC 2025	cl	05 32 33.6	−71 43 05	Men	1.9	10.9	212	11	DSFG: Relatively bright.; KMHK: Compact cluster. Alias: KMHK 1057
KMHK 1050	cl	05 32 36.5	−67 31 45	Dor	0.6		212	11	KMHK: Loose cluster.
KMHK 1062	cl	05 32 37.4	−71 57 21	Men	0.4		212	11	KMHK: Compact cluster.
KMHK 1064	cl	05 32 39.8	−71 56 01	Men	0.6		212	11	KMHK: Compact cluster.
KMHK 1049	cl	05 32 40.4	−66 51 44	Dor	0.6		212	11	KMHK: Compact cluster.
LW 243	cl	05 32 41.0	−73 07 22	Men	0.3		212	11	KMHK: Compact cluster. Alias: KMHK 1072
SL 565	cl	05 32 48.9	−70 27 20	Men	1.7		212	11	KMHK: Loose cluster. Alias: KMHK 1058
SL 564	cl	05 32 49.6	−67 20 39	Dor	0.6		212	11	KMHK: Compact cluster. Alias: KMHK 1054
SL 566	cl	05 32 50.3	−70 47 07	Men	1.2		212	11	KMHK: Compact cluster. Alias: KMHK 1061

Table C.1: Tables of LMC Objects

Name	Type	2000.0 R.A.	2000.0 Dec.	Con	Diam (′)	Tot. Vm	U#	Ref	Comments and Aliases
OHSC 21	cl	05 32 50.9	−72 13 29	Men	0.6		212	11	KMHK: Compact cluster. Alias: KMHK 1070
LW 238	cl	05 32 54.0	−63 38 18	Dor	0.7		212	11	KMHK: Compact cluster. Alias: KMHK 1044
KMHK 1055	cl	05 33 01.5	−67 50 58	Dor	0.9		212	11	KMHK: Loose cluster.
KMHK 1071	cl	05 33 01.8	−71 24 31	Men	0.7		212	11	KMHK: Compact cluster.
SL 568	cl	05 33 03.4	−70 30 51	Men	2.1		212	11	KMHK: Compact cluster. Alias: KMHK 1068
KMHK 1060	cl	05 33 08.2	−68 45 31	Dor	1.5		212	11	KMHK: Compact cluster.
SL 572	cl	05 33 10.0	−71 01 29	Men	0.8		212	11	KMHK: Compact cluster. Alias: KMHK 1073
SL 576	cl	05 33 14.2	−74 22 09	Men	1.7		219	99	KMHK: Compact cluster. Aliases: LW 239; KMHK 1092
LH 77	cl	05 33 16	−66 59.1	Dor			212	5	
SL 567	cl	05 33 18.1	−67 31 20	Dor	2.1		212	11	KMHK: Incorrect on Hodge-Wright Atlas (1967). Aliases: LH 78; KMHK 1059
SL 569	cl	05 33 20.1	−68 09 08	Dor	1.3		212	11	KMHK: Compact cluster. Alias: KMHK 1065
IC 2140	cl	05 33 22.2	−75 22 35	Men	2.1		219	11	KMHK: Loose cluster. Alias: KMHK 1106
KMHK 1069	cl	05 33 26.8	−68 39 30	Dor	0.6		212	11	KMHK: Loose cluster.
NGC 2021	cl	05 33 30.3	−67 27 12	Dor	0.9		212	99	KMHK: Compact cluster. Aliases: LH 79; SL 570; KMHK 1067
KMHK 1063	cl	05 33 37.2	−65 22 02	Dor	0.7		212	11	KMHK: Loose cluster.
NGC 2031	cl	05 33 41.3	−70 59 11	Men	3.4	10.8	212	99	DSFG: Bright; irregular shape.; KMHK: Compact cluster. Alias: KMHK 1084
SL 573	cl	05 33 44.8	−64 56 03	Dor	1.5		212	11	KMHK: Compact cluster. Alias: KMHK 1066
[HS66] 355	cl	05 33 47.0	−71 17 09	Men	0.6		212	99	KMHK: Loose cluster. Alias: KMHK 1087
KMHK 1077	cl	05 33 47.5	−68 25 09	Dor	0.7		212	11	KMHK: Loose cluster.
NGC 2028	cl	05 33 48.7	−69 57 03	Men?		12.9	212	99	DSFG: Relatively faint; somewhat extended NE-SW; greatest concentration of stars in SW end. Pair with SL574. Aliases: LH 80; SL 575; h 2912
KMHK 1075	cl	05 33 53.2	−67 40 47	Dor	0.8		212	11	KMHK: Loose cluster.
KMHK 1074	cl	05 33 57.8	−67 00 28	Dor	0.7		212	11	KMHK: Compact cluster.
KMHK 1076	cl	05 34 00.1	−66 50 26	Dor	0.8		212	11	KMHK: Compact cluster.
SL 584	cl	05 34 00.6	−71 56 09	Men	1.0		212	11	KMHK: Compact cluster. Alias: KMHK 1100
[HS66] 354	cl	05 34 03.9	−66 49 40	Dor	0.6		212	11	KMHK: Compact cluster. Alias: KMHK 1078
KMHK 1102	cl	05 34 04.2	−71 50 32	Men	0.6		212	11	KMHK: Loose cluster.
KMHK 1082	cl	05 34 08.6	−67 31 44	Dor	0.6		212	11	KMHK: Loose cluster.
KMHK 1079	cl	05 34 09.0	−66 38 02	Dor	0.6		212	11	KMHK: Loose cluster.
SL 580	cl	05 34 11.1	−68 35 29	Dor	1.0		212	11	KMHK: Compact cluster. Alias: KMHK 1086
SL 579	cl	05 34 13.8	−67 51 24	Dor	1.0		212	11	KMHK: Compact cluster. Alias: KMHK 1085
SL 583	cl	05 34 15.7	−68 32 37	Dor	0.9		212	11	KMHK: Compact cluster. Alias: KMHK 1088
SL 578	cl	05 34 19.5	−65 17 22	Dor	0.9		212	99	KMHK: Incorrect on Hodge-Wright Atlas (1967). Alias: KMHK 1080
KMHK 1083	cl	05 34 20.1	−66 19 34	Dor	0.6		212	11	KMHK: Loose cluster.
LW 244	cl	05 34 23.2	−65 03 31	Dor	0.7		212	11	KMHK: Incorrect on Hodge-Wright Atlas (1967). Alias: KMHK 1081
BRHT 63b	cl	05 34 27	−67 26.7	Dor			212	5	
SL 582	cl	05 34 29.5	−67 07 30	Dor	0.7		212	11	KMHK: Incorrect on Hodge-Wright Atlas (1967). Alias: KMHK 1091
BRHT 63a	cl	05 34 30	−67 27.2	Dor			212	5	
NGC 2033	cl	05 34 29.8	−69 46 49	Dor		11.6	212	99	DSFG: SW part of a large stellar association including NGC 2037 and NGC 2048. Alias: h (579)

Table C.1: Tables of LMC Objects

Name	Type	2000.0 R.A.	2000.0 Dec.	Con	Diam (′)	Tot. Vm	U#	Ref	Comments and Aliases
BRHT 39b	cl	05 34 30	−68 50.5	Dor			212	5	
SL 585	cl	05 34 30.8	−68 50 24	Dor	1.6		212	11	KMHK: Compact cluster. Aliases: BRHT 39a; KMHK 1099
[HS66] 357	cl	05 34 30.9	−68 41 48	Dor	0.7		212	11	KMHK: Loose cluster. Alias: KMHK 1097
NGC 2036	cl	05 34 32.1	−70 03 56	Men		12.8	212	99	DSFG: Relatively faint.
[HS66] 360	cl	05 34 33.5	−71 05 10	Men	0.8		212	99	KMHK: Compact cluster. Alias: KMHK 1108
LH 81	cl	05 34.6	−69 44	Dor		7.43	212	5	
[HS66] 358	cl	05 34 35.2	−66 04 17	Dor	0.7		212	99	KMHK: Loose cluster. Archinal: In DSS overlap region. Alias: KMHK 1090
SL 588	cl	05 34 39.3	−68 18 21	Dor	1.0		212	11	KMHK: Loose cluster. Alias: KMHK 1101
NGC 2037	cl	05 34 40.1	−69 44 48	Dor		10.3	212	99	DSFG: In SW part of a large stellar association.
KMHK 1098	cl	05 34 41.3	−67 30 14	Dor	0.9		212	99	KMHK: Compact cluster.
KMHK 1093	cl	05 34 41.7	−66 38 37	Dor	0.8		212	11	KMHK: Loose cluster.
NGC 2038	cl	05 34 42.4	−70 33 40	Men	1.7	11.9	212	99	DSFG: Relatively bright.; KMHK: Compact cluster. Alias: KMHK 1110
SL 586	cl	05 34 43.8	−66 57 47	Dor	1.0		212	11	KMHK: Compact cluster. Alias: KMHK 1094
KMHK 1095	cl	05 34 47.8	−66 27 59	Dor	0.7		212	11	KMHK: Compact cluster.
OHSC 22	cl	05 34 50.8	−63 37 55	Dor	0.8		212	11	KMHK: Loose cluster. Alias: KMHK 1089
KMHK 1111	cl	05 34 54.3	−70 25 34	Men	0.6		212	11	KMHK: Compact cluster.
[HS66] 361	cl	05 34 56.5	−71 28 59	Men	0.8		212	11	KMHK: Compact cluster. Alias: KMHK 1116
LW 247	cl	05 34 59.1	−72 22 58	Men	0.6		212	11	KMHK: Compact cluster. Alias: KMHK 1121
LH 87	cl	05 35 01	−69 43.7	Dor			212	5	
NGC 2027	cl	05 35 00.9	−66 54 59	Dor	0.7	11.9	212	11	KMHK: Compact cluster. Aliases: LH 84; KMHK 1105
LW 245	cl	05 35 06.8	−65 18 33	Dor	0.7		212	11	KMHK: Loose cluster. Alias: KMHK 1104
LW 246	cl	05 35 07.2	−65 12 09	Dor	0.4		212	11	KMHK: Loose cluster. Alias: KMHK 1103
SL 593	cl	05 35 08.1	−70 19 36	Men	0.8		212	11	KMHK: Compact cluster. Alias: KMHK 1114
KMHK 1107	cl	05 35 10.9	−66 37 05	Dor	0.8		212	11	KMHK: Compact cluster.
KMHK 1112	cl	05 35 15.2	−68 52 13	Dor	0.8		212	11	KMHK: Loose cluster.
KMHK 1109	cl	05 35 23.1	−65 29 18	Dor	0.7		212	99	KMHK: Loose cluster.
SL 594	cl	05 35 25.1	−68 41 31	Dor	0.8		212	11	KMHK: Compact cluster. Alias: KMHK 1117
LH 82	cl	05 35 29	−67 35.0	Dor			212	99	
[HS66] 363	cl	05 35 29.1	−70 21 00	Men	0.9		212	11	KMHK: Loose cluster. Alias: KMHK 1124
LH 85	cl	05 35.6	−68 52	Dor			212	5	
KMHK 1118	cl	05 35 36.8	−68 28 01	Dor	1.3		212	99	KMHK: Loose cluster. Archinal: Not obvious on DSS image.
NGC 2046	cl	05 35 37.4	−70 14 30	Men	1.3	12.6	212	11	DSFG: Relatively faint.; KMHK: Compact cluster. Alias: KMHK 1125
KMHK 1122	cl	05 35 38.6	−68 51 40	Dor	1.7		212	11	KMHK: Loose cluster.
KMHK 1128	cl	05 35 40.2	−71 17 40	Men	0.9		212	11	KMHK: Loose cluster.
NGC 2030	cl	05 35 41.1	−66 02 04	Dor	1.3		212	11	KMHK: Compact cluster. Alias: KMHK 1113
KMHK 1115	cl	05 35 41.7	−66 32 36	Dor	0.6		212	11	KMHK: Loose cluster.
AH03 J0535.7-6912	cl	05 35 41.9	−69 11 53	Dor	0.2		212	99	Archinal: Just to the west of NGC 2044 trio of clusters.
SL 596	cl	05 35 42.2	−68 40 04	Dor	0.8		212	11	KMHK: Compact cluster. Alias: KMHK 1123

Table C.1: Tables of LMC Objects

Name	Type	2000.0 R.A.	2000.0 Dec.	Con	Diam (′)	Tot. Vm	U#	Ref	Comments and Aliases
SL 603	cl	05 35 43.7	−75 57 31	Men	0.9		219	11	KMHK: Loose cluster. Aliases: LW 249; KMHK 1151
LH 83	cl	05 35.8	−66 02	Dor			212	5	Alias: Hen N 61
KMHK 1120	cl	05 35 49.4	−67 03 37	Dor	0.8		212	11	KMHK: Loose cluster.
LH 86	cl	05 35 54	−67 28.1	Dor			212	99	
NGC 2047	cl	05 35 54.2	−70 11 30	Men		13.2	212	99	DSFG: Very faint. Alias: h 2925
AH03 J0535.9-6910	cl	05 35 55.6	−69 09 50	Dor	0.4		212	99	Archinal: Just to N of NGC 2044 trio of clusters.
SL 602	cl	05 35 59.6	−69 11 50	Dor	0.6		212	99	Archinal: On W end of NGC 2044 trio of clusters. This is NOT NGC 2044 as SL claim. Aliases: BRHT 17b; (3) NGC 2044
NGC 2040	cl	05 36 06.1	−67 33 58	Dor			212	99	Aliases: LH 88; Hen N 59B
AH03 J0536.1-6912	cl	05 36 06.4	−69 11 47	Dor	0.2		212	99	Archinal: Cluster at center of NGC 2044 trio of clusters. Alias: (3) NGC 2044
NGC 2044	3cl	05 36 06.4	−69 11 47	Dor	2.0		212	99	DSFG: Irregular in shape. Archinal: Group of three LMC clusters, including BRHT 17a and b on E and W ends. Aliases: h (608); (2) BRHT 17b; (2) AH03 J0536.1-6912; (2) BRHT 17a
NGC 2051	cl	05 36 07.5	−71 00 43	Men	1.7		212	11	KMHK: Compact cluster. Alias: KMHK 1135
LH 90	cl	05 36.1	−69 11	Dor			212	5	Alias: SL 602
SL 601	cl	05 36 09.5	−68 54 42	Dor	0.9		212	56	See notes. Part of NGC 2042 association.; KMHK: Compact cluster. Aliases: KMHK 1130; BRHT 16a
KMHK 1131	cl	05 36 09.6	−68 55 40	Dor			212	56	See notes. Nearly stellar object, at the center and part of NGC 2042 association. Aliases: BRHT 16b; (3) NGC 2042
NGC 2042	ass	05 36 09.6	−68 55 40	Dor	9.0		212	56	See notes. ''L'' shaped association centered on KMHK 1131. Includes SL 601 and KMHK 1131. Aliases: h 2922; LH 89; (2) SL 601; (2) KMHK 1131
BRHT 16b	cl	05 36 10.5	−68 54 38	Dor			212	99	Alias: KMHK 1131
LH 89	cl	05 36.2	−68 57	Dor			212	5	
BRHT 17a	cl	05 36 11.9	−69 11 42	Dor	0.3		212	99	Archinal: This is NOT NGC 2044 as BRHT claim, but just the E end of it. Alias: (3) NGC 2044
KMHK 1133	cl	05 36 19.8	−68 51 55	Dor	0.7		212	11	KMHK: Loose cluster.
SL 612	cl	05 36 21.5	−73 17 39	Men	0.8		212	11	KMHK: Loose cluster. Alias: KMHK 1148
[HS66] 365	cl	05 36 21.6	−70 36 31	Men	0.6		212	11	KMHK: Compact cluster. Alias: KMHK 1138
KMHK 1119	cl	05 36 21.8	−61 47 14	Dor	0.9		201	11	KMHK: Loose cluster.
LW 248	cl	05 36 24.5	−65 16 13	Dor	0.7		212	11	KMHK: Compact cluster. Alias: KMHK 1126
NGC 2041	cl	05 36 28.0	−66 59 29	Dor	0.7	10.4	212	11	KMHK: Compact cluster. Aliases: SL 605; KMHK 1132
SL 620	cl	05 36 28.4	−74 24 18	Men	2.5		219	11	KMHK: Compact cluster. Aliases: LW 255; KMHK 1155
SL 607	cl	05 36 31.7	−68 48 42	Dor	1.7		212	11	KMHK: Compact cluster. Alias: KMHK 1137
SL 606	cl	05 36 33.4	−68 33 54	Dor	0.9		212	11	KMHK: Compact cluster. Alias: KMHK 1136
NGC 2056	cl	05 36 34.6	−70 40 15	Men	1.7	12.3	212	99	DSFG: Relatively bright.; KMHK: Compact cluster. Alias: KMHK 1140
KMHK 1134	cl	05 36 36.5	−67 17 14	Dor	0.4		212	11	KMHK: Compact cluster.
LW 250	cl	05 36 38.2	−64 23 08	Dor	1.0		212	11	KMHK: Compact cluster. Alias: KMHK 1129
SL 609	cl	05 36 40.0	−69 22 49	Dor	1.1		212	99	Aliases: LH 93; (3) NGC 2050
LH 92	cl	05 36.7	−67 27	Dor			212	99	Alias: (3) NGC 2055
SL 610	cl	05 36 42	−69 29.8	Dor	1.1		212	99	Aliases: LH 94; (3) NGC 2055
SL 617	cl	05 36 42.6	−71 08 57	Men	1.7		212	11	KMHK: Compact cluster. Alias: KMHK 1144
LH 91	cl	05 36.7	−66 27	Dor			212	5	
SL 618	cl	05 36 44.4	−71 21 32	Men	0.7		212	99	KMHK: Compact cluster. Archinal: DSS overlap region. Alias: KMHK 1146

Table C.1: Tables of LMC Objects

Name	Type	2000.0 R.A.	2000.0 Dec.	Con	Diam (′)	Tot. Vm	U#	Ref	Comments and Aliases
SL 604	cl	05 36 46.2	−62 53 03	Dor	0.8		212	11	KMHK: Loose cluster. Aliases: LW 251; KMHK 1127
[HS66] 370	cl	05 36 46	−69 26.5	Dor	2.0		212	99	Aliases: LH 98; (3) LH 96
SL 619	cl	05 36 46.5	−72 15 39	Men	2.0		212	11	KMHK: Loose cluster. Alias: KMHK 1152
NGC 2050	cl	05 36 54	−69 22.4	Dor	8.0		212	99	See notes. Identified by M. Morel in 2002. Aliases: (2) SL 609; (2) LH 97; (3) NGC 2055
NGC 2058	cl	05 36 54.7	−70 09 47	Men		11.9	212	99	DSFG: Pair with NGC 2059.
NGC 2057	cl	05 36 55.1	−70 16 14	Men	1.8	12.2	212	99	DSFG: Relatively faint.; KMHK: Compact cluster. Archinal: DSS overlap region. Alias: KMHK 1145
SL 615	cl	05 36 56.1	−68 42 49	Dor	0.7		212	99	KMHK: Loose cluster. Archinal: Sparse group. Even SL state: "Few stars, somewhat doubtful." Alias: KMHK 1143
LH 96	ass	05 37.0	−69 24	Dor	17.0		212	99	Aliases: (2) LH 97; (2) [HS66] 370; (3) NGC 2050
NGC 2059	cl	05 37 00.8	−70 07 43	Men		12.9	212	99	DSFG: Pair with NGC 2058.
[HS66] 367	cl	05 37 03.8	−66 22 03	Dor	0.8		212	99	KMHK: Compact cluster. Archinal: DSS overlap region. Aliases: LH 95; KMHK 1139
[HS66] 366	cl	05 37 04.7	−67 52 11	Dor	0.8		212	11	KMHK: Loose cluster. Alias: KMHK 1142
NGC 2055	ass	05 37 08	−69 25.5	Dor	15.0		212	99	See notes. Identified by J. Kay and M. Morel. Aliases: (2) NGC 2050; (2) LH 92; (2) SL 610; (2) LH 96; (2) [HS66] 370
SL 625	cl	05 37 09.3	−73 04 23	Men	0.7		212	11	KMHK: Compact cluster. Alias: KMHK 1162
KMHK 1156	cl	05 37 12.1	−71 17 09	Men	0.9		212	99	KMHK: Loose cluster. Archinal: Faint. DSS overlap region.
[HS66] 368	cl	05 37 14.1	−66 27 01	Dor	0.7		212	11	KMHK: Compact cluster. Alias: KMHK 1141
KMHK 1157	cl	05 37 16.2	−71 13 29	Men	0.7		212	99	KMHK: Compact cluster. Archinal: Very faint or not obvious on DSS image. DSS overlap region.
SL 624	cl	05 37 19.2	−71 06 58	Men	1.3		212	99	KMHK: Compact cluster. Archinal: DSS overlap region. Alias: KMHK 1158
KMHK 1150	cl	05 37 19.8	−68 13 03	Dor	1.3		212	11	KMHK: Loose cluster.
AH03 J0537.3-6919	cl	05 37 22.8	−69 19 27	Dor			212	99	Possible cluster noted by M. Morel within LH 97 and therefore NGC 2050. Alias: (3) LH 97
KMHK 1147	cl	05 37 23.7	−67 20 51	Dor	0.4		212	11	KMHK: Compact cluster.
NGC 2065	cl	05 37 35.9	−70 14 07	Men	2.6	11.2	212	99	KMHK: Compact cluster. Archinal: On DSS overlap region boundary. Alias: KMHK 1160
LH 97	ass	05 37.6	−69 20	Dor	4.0		212	99	Aliases: (2) [HS66] 371; (2) BRHT 54b; (2) AH03 J0537.3-6919; (3) NGC 2055
NGC 2053	cl	05 37 40.5	−67 24 50	Dor	1.2		212	11	DSFG: Faint.; KMHK: Compact cluster. Alias: KMHK 1154
KMHK 1175	cl	05 37 41.0	−74 00 38	Men	0.7		219	11	KMHK: Loose cluster.
NGC 2066	cl	05 37 41.2	−70 09 58	Men		13.1	212	99	DSFG: Very faint. Archinal: DSS overlap region. Difficult to make out cluster. Alias: h 2939
KMHK 1149	cl	05 37 44.2	−64 38 41	Dor	0.6		212	11	KMHK: Loose cluster.
KMHK 1153	cl	05 37 44.2	−66 25 35	Dor	0.3		212	11	KMHK: Compact cluster.
[HS66] 371	cl	05 37 45	−69 20.1	Dor			212	99	Aliases: BRHT 54a; (3) LH 97
[HS66] 372	cl	05 37 46.4	−70 22 29	Men	0.6		212	99	KMHK: Compact cluster. Archinal: DSS overlap region. Alias: KMHK 1163
BRHT 54b	cl	05 37 47	−69 20.9	Dor	0.3		212	99	Alias: (3) LH 97
IC 2146	cl	05 37 47.4	−74 46 58	Men	2.6		219	11	KMHK: Loose cluster. Aliases: LW 258; ESO 33-26; SL 632; KMHK 1178
NGC 2060	ass	05 37 48	−69 10.3	Dor	2.0		212	99	Archinal: Large sparse group in nebulosity. Aliases: h (642); LH 99
KMHK 1159	cl	05 38 01.5	−67 15 37	Dor	0.6		212	11	KMHK: Loose cluster.
KMHK 1161	cl	05 38 11.9	−66 34 58	Dor	0.7		212	11	KMHK: Loose cluster.
[HS66] 375	cl	05 38 14.5	−71 05 46	Men	1.0		212	11	KMHK: Loose cluster. Alias: KMHK 1172
[HS66] 373	cl	05 38 16.8	−67 05 44	Dor	0.6		212	11	KMHK: Loose cluster. Alias: KMHK 1164
[HS66] 374	cl	05 38 17.6	−68 34 00	Dor	0.6		212	11	KMHK: Compact cluster. Alias: KMHK 1165
NGC 2075	cl	05 38 20.5	−70 41 09	Men	2.0		212	11	KMHK: Compact cluster. Alias: KMHK 1173

Table C.1: Tables of LMC Objects

Name	Type	2000.0 R.A.	2000.0 Dec.	Con	Diam (′)	Tot. Vm	U#	Ref	Comments and Aliases
SL 629	cl	05 38 21.5	−68 46 53	Dor	1.0		212	11	KMHK: Compact cluster. Alias: KMHK 1169
SL 634	cl	05 38 21.5	−72 42 19	Men	0.8		212	11	KMHK: Compact cluster. Alias: KMHK 1179
KMHK 1167	cl	05 38 23.0	−68 24 22	Dor	0.9		212	11	KMHK: Loose cluster.
NGC 2072	cl	05 38 23.6	−70 13 56	Men	1.3	13.2	212	99	DSFG: Faint and very compact group.; KMHK: Loose cluster. Alias: KMHK 1170
KMHK 1177	cl	05 38 26.6	−70 36 33	Men	0.7		212	99	KMHK: Compact cluster. Archinal: Possible previously unidentified small (10" diameter) cluster just to N at 05 38 28.1 -70 35 37.
SL 628	cl	05 38 30.1	−67 19 57	Dor	1.0		212	11	KMHK: Compact cluster. Alias: KMHK 1166
NGC 2070	cl	05 38 42.4	−69 06 03	Dor	5.0	8.3	212	99	See notes. 30 Doradus cluster and Tarantula Nebula. Several stars associated with very bright nebulosity. Aliases: 30 Dor cl; Tar neb cl; SL 633; LH 100; GRS 279.40_−31.70; Caldw 103
KMHK 1174	cl	05 38 43.8	−68 26 45	Dor	0.7		212	11	KMHK: Compact cluster.
KMHK 1181	cl	05 38 47.3	−70 42 51	Men	1.0		212	11	KMHK: Loose cluster.
[HS66] 376	cl	05 38 49.3	−70 28 27	Men	0.8		212	99	KMHK: Loose cluster. Alias: KMHK 1180
LW 260	cl	05 38 53.2	−64 17 31	Dor	0.6		212	99	KMHK: Loose cluster. Alias: KMHK 1168
[HS66] 379	cl	05 38 55.5	−71 17 42	Men	0.8		212	11	KMHK: Compact cluster. Alias: KMHK 1186
KMHK 1187	cl	05 38 57.7	−71 21 24	Men	0.7		212	99	KMHK: Compact cluster.
NGC 2074	cl	05 39 03	−69 29.7	Dor			212	5	Alias: LH 101
KMHK 1185	cl	05 39 03.1	−70 13 52	Men	1.0		212	11	KMHK: Loose cluster.
LW 263	cl	05 39 08.4	−74 51 14	Men	0.7		219	11	KMHK: Loose cluster. Alias: KMHK 1208
SL 635	cl	05 39 08.6	−65 24 50	Dor	0.7		212	11	KMHK: Loose cluster. Alias: KMHK 1176
KMHK 1191	cl	05 39 10.1	−70 46 27	Men	0.6		212	11	KMHK: Compact cluster.
LW 261	cl	05 39 11.0	−64 08 06	Dor	0.9		212	11	KMHK: Loose cluster. Alias: KMHK 1171
OHSC 23	cl	05 39 11.2	−62 35 08	Dor			212	5	
IC 2148	cl	05 39 12.1	−75 33 48	Men	1.1		219	11	KMHK: Compact cluster. Alias: KMHK 1216
[HS66] 378	cl	05 39 13.7	−68 30 02	Dor	0.7		212	11	KMHK: Loose cluster. Alias: KMHK 1183
[HS66] 377	cl	05 39 20.7	−67 03 02	Dor	0.6		212	11	KMHK: Compact cluster. Alias: KMHK 1182
KMHK 1193	cl	05 39 27.9	−70 29 49	Men	0.8		212	11	KMHK: Compact cluster.
KMHK 1196	cl	05 39 29.7	−70 51 49	Men	0.4		212	11	KMHK: Loose cluster.
KMHK 1188	cl	05 39 29.9	−68 19 22	Dor	0.9		212	11	KMHK: Loose cluster.
SL 645	cl	05 39 33.7	−72 59 23	Men	0.8		212	11	KMHK: Loose cluster. Alias: KMHK 1207
SL 647	cl	05 39 34.7	−75 12 27	Men	0.9		219	11	KMHK: Loose cluster. Aliases: LW 267; KMHK 1223
NGC 2077	cl	05 39 34.9	−69 39 19	Dor			212	99	Archinal: NGC 2080 to NE. Aliases: BRHT 18a; h 2947
KMHK 1197	cl	05 39 36.6	−70 40 32	Men	0.8		212	11	KMHK: Loose cluster.
SL 638	cl	05 39 37.1	−65 38 22	Dor	1.3		212	11	KMHK: Loose cluster. Alias: KMHK 1184
KMHK 1200	cl	05 39 39.3	−70 42 50	Men	1.0		212	11	KMHK: Loose cluster.
[HS66] 381	cl	05 39 43.7	−70 17 07	Men	0.7		212	11	KMHK: Compact cluster. Alias: KMHK 1199
NGC 2080	cl	05 39 44.6	−69 38 42	Dor			212	99	Archinal: NGC 2077 to SW. Aliases: BRHT 18b; Hen N 160A; [MBB72] 76; MC 76; h 2950
KMHK 1189	cl	05 39 49.3	−66 08 11	Dor	0.7		212	11	KMHK: Loose cluster.
KMHK 1190	cl	05 39 49.8	−66 06 44	Dor	0.6		212	11	KMHK: Loose cluster.
KMHK 1203	cl	05 39 51.8	−71 01 41	Men	0.6		212	11	KMHK: Compact cluster.

Table C.1: Tables of LMC Objects

Name	Type	2000.0 R.A.	2000.0 Dec.	Con	Diam (′)	Tot. Vm	U#	Ref	Comments and Aliases
SL 646	cl	05 39 53.9	−71 09 48	Men	1.0		212	11	KMHK: Loose cluster. Alias: KMHK 1205
LH 105	cl	05 39 54	−69 44.9	Dor		8.73	212	5	
[H60b] 5	cl	05 39 56.7	−72 15 01	Men			212	99	Archinal: Slight condensation in rich field.
KMHK 1204	cl	05 39 59.3	−70 27 28	Men	0.6		212	11	KMHK: Compact cluster.
LH 102	cl	05 40.0	−67 24	Dor			212	5	
LH 103	cl	05 40 00	−69 39.8	Dor		8.09	212	5	
[HS66] 380	cl	05 40 02.0	−65 00 11	Dor	0.4		212	11	KMHK: Loose cluster. Alias: KMHK 1192
KMHK 1201	cl	05 40 02.8	−68 20 15	Dor	0.7		212	11	KMHK: Loose cluster.
KMHK 1213	cl	05 40 02.8	−71 22 50	Men	0.7		212	11	KMHK: Loose cluster.
NGC 2062	cl	05 40 03.3	−66 52 36	Dor	0.9		212	99	DSFG: Faint.; KMHK: Compact cluster. Alias: KMHK 1194
KMHK 1210	cl	05 40 07.8	−70 39 25	Men	0.9		212	11	KMHK: Loose cluster.
NGC 2085	cl	05 40 09.2	−69 40 21	Dor			212	99	Archinal: NGC 2086 just to E. Aliases: BRHT 19a; h 2954
SL 648	cl	05 40 10.4	−72 11 29	Men	1.7		212	11	KMHK: Compact cluster. Alias: KMHK 1219
KMHK 1220	cl	05 40 12.7	−72 02 26	Men	0.8		212	11	KMHK: Loose cluster.
[HS66] 383	cl	05 40 14.2	−70 51 27	Men	0.6		212	11	KMHK: Compact cluster. Alias: KMHK 1215
KMHK 1217	cl	05 40 16.9	−71 18 29	Men	0.8		212	11	KMHK: Loose cluster.
SL 643	cl	05 40 22.4	−67 02 45	Dor	1.5		212	11	KMHK: Loose cluster. Alias: KMHK 1202
LW 270	cl	05 40 23.4	−75 18 02	Men	0.6		219	11	KMHK: Loose cluster. Alias: KMHK 1243
KMHK 1195	cl	05 40 23.5	−64 15 00	Dor	0.7		212	11	KMHK: Loose cluster.
IC 2145	cl	05 40 24	−69 40.2	Dor			212	5	Alias: BRHT 19b
LW 266	cl	05 40 30.7	−64 17 51	Dor	0.6		212	11	KMHK: Incorrect on Hodge-Wright Atlas (1967). Alias: KMHK 1198
KMHK 1206	cl	05 40 33.6	−66 53 38	Dor	0.6		212	99	KMHK: Loose cluster.
[HS66] 382	cl	05 40 36.1	−67 25 27	Dor	0.9		212	11	KMHK: Loose cluster. Alias: KMHK 1209
KMHK 1236	cl	05 40 37.8	−73 28 06	Men	0.8		212	11	KMHK: Loose cluster.
OHSC 24	cl	05 40 38.7	−74 03 09	Men			219	5	
KMHK 1228	cl	05 40 39.3	−70 38 31	Men	0.7		212	11	KMHK: Compact cluster.
KMHK 1211	cl	05 40 40.6	−67 21 14	Dor	0.7		212	11	KMHK: Compact cluster.
KMHK 1212	cl	05 40 40.7	−67 21 12	Dor	0.9		212	11	KMHK: Loose cluster.
LH 107	cl	05 40.7	−71 15	Men			212	5	
LH 106	cl	05 40.8	−69 35	Dor			212	5	
[HS66] 385	cl	05 40 47.5	−69 33 35	Dor			212	99	Larger than 15", stars brighter than V=17.
SL 655	cl	05 40 53.6	−71 48 04	Men	0.9		212	11	KMHK: Loose cluster. Alias: KMHK 1234
[HS66] 386	cl	05 40 57.4	−67 26 25	Dor	0.8		212	11	KMHK: Compact cluster. Aliases: BRHT 55a; KMHK 1218
NGC 2091	cl	05 40 58.0	−69 26 11	Dor	1.7		212	11	DSFG: Relatively faint; somewhat extended E-W.; KMHK: Compact cluster. Aliases: SL 653; KMHK 1229
SL 651	cl	05 40 59.2	−68 06 03	Dor	1.6		212	99	KMHK: Loose cluster. Archinal: Faint fiber/hair going through image of cluster on DSS. Alias: KMHK 1222
NGC 2088	cl	05 40 59.7	−68 27 51	Dor	1.7		212	56	See notes. Declination is wrong in many catalogs. DSFG: Relatively faint. Alias: KMHK 1227
KMHK 1232	cl	05 41 01.9	−70 50 54	Men	0.7		212	11	KMHK: Compact cluster.
KMHK 1221	cl	05 41 04.6	−67 25 34	Dor	0.6		212	99	KMHK: Compact cluster. Alias: BRHT 55b
SL 656	cl	05 41 05.8	−71 20 33	Men	0.8		212	11	KMHK: Compact cluster. Alias: KMHK 1237

Table C.1: Tables of LMC Objects

Name	Type	2000.0 R.A.	2000.0 Dec.	Con	Diam (′)	Tot. Vm	U#	Ref	Comments and Aliases
KMHK 1224	cl	05 41 08.1	–67 19 36	Dor	1.0		212	11	KMHK: Compact cluster.
[HS66] 387	cl	05 41 08.3	–67 16 42	Dor	0.9		212	99	KMHK: Loose cluster. Alias: KMHK 1226
SL 650	cl	05 41 08.3	–67 19 35	Dor	1.2		212	11	KMHK: Compact cluster. Alias: KMHK 1225
SL 649	cl	05 41 08.6	–63 46 21	Dor	0.7		212	11	KMHK: Compact cluster. Aliases: LW 269; KMHK 1214
SL 654	cl	05 41 10.3	–69 54 17	Dor?	1.3		212	11	KMHK: Compact cluster. Alias: KMHK 1231
KMHK 1230	cl	05 41 12.6	–68 51 58	Dor	0.8		212	11	KMHK: Compact cluster.
NGC 2092	cl	05 41 22.2	–69 13 25	Dor	1.2		212	11	DSFG: Relatively faint.; KMHK: Compact cluster. Aliases: NGC 2100; SL 662; KMHK 1235
[HS66] 391	cl	05 41 28.8	–70 14 01	Men	0.9		212	11	KMHK: Loose cluster. Alias: KMHK 1242
[HS66] 390	cl	05 41 30.6	–69 11 06	Dor	0.7		212	11	KMHK: Compact cluster. Alias: KMHK 1239
KMHK 1240	cl	05 41 31.7	–69 40 07	Dor	0.7		212	99	KMHK: Compact cluster. Archinal: Nearly on DSS overlap boundary.
KMHK 1238	cl	05 41 32.7	–68 50 19	Dor	0.7		212	11	KMHK: Loose cluster.
LH 108	cl	05 41.6	–69 40	Dor			212	99	Archinal: On DSS overlap boundary, so not obvious on DSS image.
SL 658	cl	05 41 39.3	–71 05 08	Men	1.0		212	11	KMHK: Loose cluster. Alias: KMHK 1249
LH 110	cl	05 41.7	–71 21	Men			212	5	
SL 661	cl	05 41 41.3	–71 26 32	Men	1.6		212	11	KMHK: Loose cluster. Alias: KMHK 1252
KMHK 1233	cl	05 41 42.1	–66 27 01	Dor	0.7		212	11	KMHK: Compact cluster.
NGC 2093	cl	05 41 49.1	–68 55 14	Dor	1.7		212	11	KMHK: Loose cluster. Aliases: LH 109; KMHK 1245
[HS66] 393	cl	05 41 57.2	–70 51 01	Men	0.9		212	11	KMHK: Loose cluster. Alias: KMHK 1261
KMHK 1262	cl	05 41 57.8	–71 11 09	Men	0.6		212	11	KMHK: Loose cluster.
KMHK 1248	cl	05 41 58.9	–69 02 51	Dor	0.8		212	11	KMHK: Loose cluster.
KMHK 1244	cl	05 41 59.8	–67 20 35	Dor	0.7		212	11	KMHK: Compact cluster.
KMHK 1246	cl	05 42 01.4	–67 29 19	Dor	0.6		212	11	KMHK: Loose cluster.
KMHK 1247	cl	05 42 01.6	–67 29 20	Dor	0.7		212	11	KMHK: Loose cluster.
KMHK 1266	cl	05 42 03.0	–71 18 24	Men	0.6		212	11	KMHK: Compact cluster.
[HS66] 395	cl	05 42 03.5	–71 26 08	Men	0.6		212	11	KMHK: Compact cluster. Alias: KMHK 1267
NGC 2094	cl	05 42 07.2	–68 21 47	Dor	0.4		212	99	See notes. DSFG: Relatively faint; slightly extended N-S.; KMHK: Compact cluster. Alias: KMHK 1251
LH 111	cl	05 42 08.3	–69 12 44	Dor		8.94	212	99	
NGC 2100	cl	05 42 08.3	–69 12 44	Dor	2.8	9.6	212	99	DSFG: Only a few stars brighter than magnitude 13.5.; KMHK: Compact cluster. Alias: KMHK 1257
KMHK 1260	cl	05 42 13.7	–68 55 02	Dor	0.4		212	56	See notes. KMHK: Loose cluster. Alias: KMHK 1260
SL 666	cl	05 42 15.5	–68 10 34	Dor	1.3		212	11	KMHK: Loose cluster. Alias: KMHK 1254
NGC 2096	cl	05 42 16.5	–68 27 29	Dor	1.2		212	11	DSFG: Relatively faint.; KMHK: Compact cluster. Alias: KMHK 1259
KMHK 1256	cl	05 42 17.0	–68 05 03	Dor	0.6		212	11	KMHK: Compact cluster.
[HS66] 397	cl	05 42 17.3	–70 39 39	Men	0.8		212	99	KMHK: Loose cluster. Alias: KMHK 1270
SL 668	cl	05 42 17.6	–71 35 28	Men	2.6		212	11	KMHK: Compact cluster. Alias: KMHK 1275
NGC 2102	cl	05 42 19.7	–69 29 14	Dor	1.0		212	11	DSFG: Relatively faint.; KMHK: Compact cluster. Aliases: SL 665; KMHK 1264
KMHK 1253	cl	05 42 21.1	–67 18 51	Dor	0.9		212	11	KMHK: Loose cluster.
LW 272	cl	05 42 25.7	–62 30 07	Dor	0.8		212	11	KMHK: Compact cluster. Alias: KMHK 1241
[H60b] 6	cl	05 42 27.4	–71 38 23	Men			212	99	
[HS66] 396	cl	05 42 28.2	–66 56 32	Dor	0.8		212	11	KMHK: Loose cluster. Alias: KMHK 1258

Table C.1: Tables of LMC Objects

Name	Type	2000.0 R.A.	2000.0 Dec.	Con	Diam (′)	Tot. Vm	U#	Ref	Comments and Aliases
LH 112	cl	05 42 29.1	−67 19 40	Dor			212	99	
SL 663	cl	05 42 29.5	−65 21 48	Dor	1.0		212	11	KMHK: Loose cluster. Alias: KMHK 1250
NGC 2098	cl	05 42 29.8	−68 16 26	Dor	1.6		212	11	KMHK: Compact cluster. Alias: KMHK 1263
KMHK 1255	cl	05 42 36.7	−65 26 21	Dor	0.4		212	11	KMHK: Compact cluster.
KMHK 1277	cl	05 42 36.7	−69 57 11	Men?	0.9		212	11	KMHK: Loose cluster.
BRHT 20b	cl	05 42 38	−67 19.6	Dor			212	5	
SL 672	cl	05 42 41.7	−72 03 39	Men	0.8		212	11	KMHK: Compact cluster. Alias: KMHK 1285
[HS66] 397A	cl	05 42 42.0	−69 03 39	Dor	1.7		212	11	KMHK: Compact cluster. Aliases: LH 113; KMHK 1274
[HS66] 398	cl	05 42 42.0	−70 29 44	Men	1.0		212	99	KMHK: Loose cluster. Alias: KMHK 1280
KMHK 1271	cl	05 42 45.5	−68 04 06	Dor	1.3		212	11	KMHK: Loose cluster.
KMHK 1273	cl	05 42 46.2	−68 06 33	Dor	1.0		212	11	KMHK: Loose cluster.
KMHK 1279	cl	05 42 51.2	−68 47 26	Dor	0.7		212	11	KMHK: Loose cluster.
NGC 2095	cl	05 42 51.7	−67 19 16	Dor	0.8		212	11	KMHK: Compact cluster. Aliases: BRHT 20a; KMHK 1272
SL 671	cl	05 42 57.3	−67 39 03	Dor	1.0		212	11	KMHK: Loose cluster. Alias: KMHK 1276
[HS66] 399	cl	05 43 06.1	−70 16 43	Men	0.8		212	11	KMHK: Loose cluster. Alias: KMHK 1287
[HS66] 400	cl	05 43 06.5	−69 45 37	Dor	1.0		212	11	KMHK: Loose cluster. Alias: KMHK 1284
[HS66] 401	cl	05 43 07.6	−70 25 02	Men	0.8		212	11	KMHK: Compact cluster. Alias: KMHK 1288
SL 676	cl	05 43 08.8	−70 34 19	Men	1.2		212	11	KMHK: Compact cluster. Alias: KMHK 1289
LW 278	cl	05 43 11.9	−62 28 30	Dor	1.6		201	11	KMHK: Compact cluster. Alias: KMHK 1265
LW 276	cl	05 43 11.9	−63 37 02	Dor	0.7		212	11	KMHK: Loose cluster. Alias: KMHK 1269
NGC 2107	cl	05 43 11.9	−70 38 27	Men	2.1	11.5	212	11	KMHK: Compact cluster. Aliases: SL 679; KMHK 1291
SL 670	cl	05 43 14.3	−62 50 02	Dor	0.7		212	11	KMHK: Loose cluster. Aliases: ESO 86-25; LW 277; KMHK 1268
SL 675	cl	05 43 15.6	−67 35 22	Dor	0.9		212	11	KMHK: Compact cluster. Alias: KMHK 1282
KMHK 1296	cl	05 43 16.2	−71 29 51	Men	1.0		212	11	KMHK: Loose cluster.
LH 114	cl	05 43 18	−67 51.5	Dor			212	5	
SL 674	cl	05 43 20.2	−66 15 47	Dor	1.6		212	11	KMHK: Loose cluster. Alias: KMHK 1281
KMHK 1278	cl	05 43 28.0	−63 24 47	Dor	0.4		212	11	KMHK: Loose cluster.
KMHK 1299	cl	05 43 33.9	−70 30 42	Men	0.7		212	11	KMHK: Compact cluster.
SL 678	cl	05 43 35.9	−66 12 31	Dor	0.9		212	11	KMHK: Loose cluster. Alias: KMHK 1283
SL 684	cl	05 43 37.8	−70 33 59	Men	0.8		212	11	KMHK: Compact cluster. Alias: KMHK 1302
KMHK 1295	cl	05 43 39.0	−69 15 51	Dor	1.0		212	11	KMHK: Loose cluster.
KMHK 1317	cl	05 43 40.0	−73 05 47	Men	0.6		212	11	KMHK: Loose cluster.
KMHK 1297	cl	05 43 44.1	−69 13 24	Dor	0.9		212	11	KMHK: Loose cluster.
KMHK 1292	cl	05 43 44.8	−67 10 27	Dor	1.7		212	11	KMHK: Compact cluster.
KMHK 1293	cl	05 43 44.9	−67 10 27	Dor	0.8		212	11	KMHK: Compact cluster.
KMHK 1307	cl	05 43 45.3	−70 51 17	Men	0.6		212	11	KMHK: Loose cluster.
SL 683	cl	05 43 49.8	−69 47 19	Dor	1.3		212	11	KMHK: Compact cluster. Alias: KMHK 1303
SL 677	cl	05 43 55.6	−63 22 23	Dor	0.7		212	11	KMHK: Loose cluster. Aliases: LW 280; KMHK 1286
NGC 2108	cl	05 43 56.9	−69 10 50	Dor	2.0		212	11	KMHK: Compact cluster. Aliases: SL 686; KMHK 1304

Table C.1: Tables of LMC Objects

Name	Type	2000.0 R.A.	2000.0 Dec.	Con	Diam (′)	Tot. Vm	U#	Ref	Comments and Aliases
[HS66] 403	cl	05 43 59.9	−69 59 45	Men?	0.8		212	11	KMHK: Compact cluster. Alias: KMHK 1312
KMHK 1300	cl	05 44 03.5	−67 31 30	Dor	0.7		212	11	KMHK: Loose cluster.
KMHK 1301	cl	05 44 03.6	−67 31 31	Dor	0.6		212	11	KMHK: Loose cluster.
SL 680	cl	05 44 03.8	−63 55 34	Dor	1.0		212	11	KMHK: Loose cluster. Aliases: LW 281; KMHK 1290
OHSC 25	cl	05 44 05.1	−74 27 11	Men	0.6		219	11	KMHK: Loose cluster. Alias: KMHK 1338
[HS66] 402	cl	05 44 07.5	−68 21 25	Dor	0.7		212	11	KMHK: Loose cluster. Alias: KMHK 1305
LH 115	cl	05 44.1	−66 19	Dor			212	5	
KMHK 1309	cl	05 44 09.2	−68 46 26	Dor	0.9		212	11	KMHK: Loose cluster.
KMHK 1313	cl	05 44 12.1	−69 20 01	Dor	0.8		212	11	KMHK: Compact cluster.
[HS66] 405	cl	05 44 12.7	−71 19 44	Men	0.8		212	11	KMHK: Loose cluster. Alias: KMHK 1321
SL 691	cl	05 44 13.5	−70 39 22	Men	0.7		212	11	KMHK: Loose cluster. Aliases: BRHT 40a; KMHK 1319
SL 692	cl	05 44 13.7	−70 40 09	Men	0.7		212	11	KMHK: Loose cluster. Aliases: BRHT 40b; KMHK 1320
SL 685	cl	05 44 15.1	−65 18 10	Dor	1.5		212	11	KMHK: Loose cluster. Alias: KMHK 1298
NGC 2097	cl	05 44 15.5	−62 47 05	Dor	1.8		212	11	KMHK: Compact cluster. Aliases: LW 282; ESO 86-28; SL 682; KMHK 1294
NGC 2105	cl	05 44 19.8	−66 55 02	Dor	1.7		212	56	See notes. Declination is 30' too far north in many catalogs. DSFG: Faint.; KMHK: Compact cluster. Aliases: SL 687; KMHK 1306
NGC 2109	cl	05 44 22.7	−68 32 54	Dor	2.0		212	11	KMHK: Compact cluster. Alias: KMHK 1314
[HS66] 404	cl	05 44 24.2	−67 10 03	Dor	0.8		212	11	Smaller than 15", stars fainter than V=17.; KMHK: Loose cluster. Aliases: (3) LH 116; KMHK 1311
KMHK 1315	cl	05 44 26.5	−68 44 28	Dor	0.6		212	11	KMHK: Compact cluster.
KMHK 1340	cl	05 44 27.3	−73 29 01	Men	1.0		212	11	KMHK: Loose cluster.
NGC 2111	cl	05 44 32.5	−70 59 37	Men	1.6		212	11	DSFG: Relatively faint.; KMHK: Compact cluster. Aliases: BRHT 21a; KMHK 1328
LW 285	cl	05 44 35.4	−64 55 50	Dor	0.6		212	11	KMHK: Loose cluster. Alias: KMHK 1308
SL 689	cl	05 44 38.8	−65 00 09	Dor	0.9		212	11	KMHK: Loose cluster. Alias: KMHK 1310
SL 697	cl	05 44 40.9	−67 07 57	Dor	0.8		212	11	Part of association LH 116.; KMHK: Loose cluster. Aliases: KMHK 1316; (3) LH 116
[HS66] 407	cl	05 44 44.7	−71 00 22	Men	0.7		212	11	KMHK: Loose cluster. Aliases: BRHT 21b; KMHK 1334
KMHK 1331	cl	05 44 45.9	−70 17 20	Men	0.6		212	11	KMHK: Compact cluster.
[HS66] 406	cl	05 44 46.1	−70 24 24	Men	0.7		212	11	KMHK: Compact cluster. Alias: KMHK 1332
KMHK 1325	cl	05 44 48.0	−68 44 08	Dor	1.0		212	11	KMHK: Loose cluster.
SL 690	cl	05 44 50.6	−67 46 45	Dor	1.1		212	11	KMHK: Compact cluster. Alias: KMHK 1323
SL 703	cl	05 44 54.3	−74 50 50	Men	1.0		219	11	KMHK: Loose cluster. Aliases: LW 290; KMHK 1352
KMHK 1341	cl	05 44 54.5	−71 42 04	Men	0.7		212	11	KMHK: Loose cluster.
[HS66] 409	cl	05 44 56.4	−70 19 58	Men	0.6		212	11	KMHK: Compact cluster. Alias: KMHK 1336
KMHK 1337	cl	05 44 57.7	−70 13 06	Men	0.7		212	11	KMHK: Loose cluster.
SL 693	cl	05 44 59.1	−67 42 26	Dor	1.0		212	11	KMHK: Compact cluster. Alias: KMHK 1326
LH 116	ass	05 45.0	−67 13	Dor	9.0		212	54	Includes SL 697, [HS66] 404, and nebula Hen N 74. Aliases: (2) SL 697; (2) [HS66] 404; (2) Hen N 74
SL 695	cl	05 45 03.1	−67 49 30	Dor	0.9		212	11	KMHK: Loose cluster. Alias: KMHK 1329
SL 702	cl	05 45 06.4	−70 14 30	Men	1.6		212	11	KMHK: Loose cluster. Alias: KMHK 1339
SL 694	cl	05 45 06.5	−63 40 35	Dor	0.6		212	11	KMHK: Loose cluster. Aliases: LW 287; KMHK 1318
[HS66] 408	cl	05 45 06.8	−66 57 56	Dor	1.0		212	11	KMHK: Compact cluster. Alias: KMHK 1327

Table C.1: Tables of LMC Objects

Name	Type	2000.0 R.A.	2000.0 Dec.	Con	Diam (′)	Tot. Vm	U#	Ref	Comments and Aliases
KMHK 1322	cl	05 45 09.2	−64 47 51	Dor	0.4		212	11	KMHK: Loose cluster.
SL 698	cl	05 45 12.6	−68 08 45	Dor	1.8		212	11	KMHK: Loose cluster. Aliases: BRHT 41a; KMHK 1335
SL 696	cl	05 45 14.1	−64 46 23	Dor	0.7		212	11	KMHK: Loose cluster. Alias: KMHK 1324
BRHT 41b	cl	05 45 17	−68 08.6	Dor			212	99	Archinal: The BRHT paper has this object reversed with SL 698 = BRHT 41a in their figure on p. 347.
SL 700	cl	05 45 24.1	−66 07 15	Dor	1.7		212	11	KMHK: Incorrect on Hodge-Wright Atlas (1967). Alias: KMHK 1333
SL 704	cl	05 45 24.3	−70 24 04	Men	0.9		212	11	KMHK: Compact cluster. Alias: KMHK 1343
NGC 2113	cl	05 45 24.5	−69 46 27	Dor	1.8		212	11	KMHK: Compact cluster. Alias: KMHK 1342
[HS66] 410	cl	05 45 31.0	−70 45 33	Men	0.8		212	11	KMHK: Loose cluster. Alias: KMHK 1344
SL 701	cl	05 45 32.7	−63 42 54	Dor	1.3		212	11	KMHK: Loose cluster. Aliases: ESO 86-30; LW 289; KMHK 1330
[HS66] 411	cl	05 45 50.0	−69 22 50	Dor	0.6		212	11	KMHK: Loose cluster. Alias: KMHK 1345
[HS66] 412	cl	05 45 56.4	−69 16 19	Dor	0.6		212	99	KMHK: Loose cluster. Archinal: DSS overlap region. Alias: KMHK 1347
LW 294	cl	05 46 02.5	−71 44 40	Men	0.7		212	11	KMHK: Loose cluster. Alias: KMHK 1357
LW 297	cl	05 46 07.5	−74 31 22	Men	1.5		219	11	KMHK: Loose cluster. Alias: KMHK 1372
KMHK 1348	cl	05 46 09.6	−68 00 22	Dor	0.7		212	11	KMHK: Loose cluster.
NGC 2114	cl	05 46 12.3	−68 02 56	Dor	1.0		212	11	DSFG: Faint extended NW-SE.; KMHK: Loose cluster. Alias: KMHK 1351
SL 707	cl	05 46 12.3	−69 04 57	Dor	1.6		212	99	KMHK: Loose cluster. Archinal: Very faint, in DSS overlap region. Alias: KMHK 1353
SL 709	cl	05 46 14.7	−67 34 06	Dor	1.0		212	11	KMHK: Compact cluster. Alias: KMHK 1350
KMHK 1349	cl	05 46 16.4	−67 15 39	Dor	0.7		212	11	KMHK: Compact cluster.
LW 295	cl	05 46 18.7	−73 07 02	Men	0.3		212	11	KMHK: Incorrect on Hodge-Wright Atlas (1967). Alias: KMHK 1368
[HS66] 413	cl	05 46 22.3	−70 08 49	Men	1.3		212	11	KMHK: Compact cluster. Alias: KMHK 1358
SL 708	cl	05 46 22.6	−65 26 11	Dor	1.0		212	11	KMHK: Compact cluster. Alias: KMHK 1346
SL 713	cl	05 46 26.1	−71 33 13	Men	1.0		212	11	KMHK: Compact cluster. Alias: KMHK 1362
KMHK 1354	cl	05 46 30.8	−67 41 04	Dor	0.6		212	11	KMHK: Loose cluster.
[HS66] 414	cl	05 46 41.0	−70 50 50	Men	0.6		212	11	KMHK: Compact cluster. Aliases: BRHT 42b; KMHK 1365
SL 716	cl	05 46 46.3	−70 49 59	Men	0.6		212	11	KMHK: Compact cluster. Aliases: BRHT 42a; KMHK 1367
KMHK 1355	cl	05 46 49.1	−65 17 12	Dor	0.4		212	11	KMHK: Loose cluster.
KMHK 1364	cl	05 46 51.0	−69 25 18	Dor	1.0		212	11	KMHK: Loose cluster.
KMHK 1363	cl	05 46 51.9	−69 11 23	Dor	0.7		212	99	KMHK: Loose cluster. Archinal: DSS overlap region.
SL 711	cl	05 46 55.0	−66 40 01	Dor	0.7		212	99	KMHK: Compact cluster. Archinal: Bright, but on DSS overlap boundary. Alias: KMHK 1359
SL 710	cl	05 46 58.1	−63 52 43	Dor	1.3		212	11	KMHK: Compact cluster. Aliases: ESO 86-32; LW 298; KMHK 1356
SL 712	cl	05 46 58.7	−66 46 05	Dor	0.9		212	99	KMHK: Loose cluster. Archinal: Very faint, on DSS overlap region. Alias: KMHK 1360
[HS66] 415	cl	05 47 00.1	−66 59 59	Dor	0.7		212	11	KMHK: Compact cluster. Alias: KMHK 1361
[HS66] 416	cl	05 47 01.9	−69 57 47	Men?	0.6		212	11	KMHK: Loose cluster. Aliases: BRHT 56a; KMHK 1371
[HS66] 417	cl	05 47 10.2	−69 57 20	Dor?	0.8		212	11	KMHK: Compact cluster. Aliases: BRHT 56b; KMHK 1374
KMHK 1369	cl	05 47 12.6	−68 10 45	Dor	0.4		212	11	KMHK: Loose cluster.
NGC 2116	cl	05 47 14.5	−68 30 24	Dor	1.0		212	11	DSFG: Faint.; KMHK: Compact cluster. Alias: KMHK 1370
SL 714	cl	05 47 17.0	−66 52 59	Dor	1.0		212	11	KMHK: Loose cluster. Alias: KMHK 1366
OHSC 26	cl	05 47 23.6	−62 37 21	Dor			212	5	
KMHK 1375	cl	05 47 29.8	−68 11 28	Dor	0.4		212	11	KMHK: Loose cluster.

Table C.1: Tables of LMC Objects

Name	Type	2000.0 R.A.	2000.0 Dec.	Con	Diam (′)	Tot. Vm	U#	Ref	Comments and Aliases
SL 721	cl	05 47 30.9	−72 29 11	Men	0.3		212	99	KMHK: Loose cluster. Alias: KMHK 1387
KMHK 1383	cl	05 47 33.2	−70 57 54	Men	0.7		212	11	KMHK: Loose cluster.
KMHK 1376	cl	05 47 36.4	−68 34 07	Dor	0.7		212	11	KMHK: Loose cluster.
SL 719	cl	05 47 36.7	−69 19 39	Dor	0.9		212	11	KMHK: Compact cluster. Alias: KMHK 1379
KMHK 1382	cl	05 47 37.7	−69 35 17	Dor	0.9		212	11	KMHK: Loose cluster.
NGC 2118	cl	05 47 39.6	−69 07 54	Dor	1.3	12.0	212	11	DSFG: Relatively faint.; KMHK: Compact cluster. Alias: KMHK 1380
SL 722	cl	05 47 41.5	−71 12 25	Men	1.0		212	11	KMHK: Compact cluster. Alias: KMHK 1384
SL 723	cl	05 47 44.8	−73 10 08	Men	0.9		212	11	KMHK: Compact cluster. Alias: KMHK 1394
SL 720	cl	05 47 46.9	−65 00 40	Dor	0.7		212	11	KMHK: Loose cluster. Alias: KMHK 1373
NGC 2117	cl	05 47 47.2	−67 27 07	Dor	1.3		212	11	DSFG: Relatively bright.; KMHK: Compact cluster. Alias: KMHK 1377
KMHK 1378	cl	05 47 53.6	−67 03 45	Dor	1.1		212	11	KMHK: Loose cluster.
KMHK 1386	cl	05 48 02.3	−69 34 59	Dor	1.7		212	11	KMHK: Loose cluster.
KMHK 1389	cl	05 48 12.4	−70 27 59	Men	0.7		212	11	KMHK: Compact cluster.
NGC 2121	cl	05 48 12.8	−71 28 47	Men	2.7		212	11	KMHK: Compact cluster. Alias: KMHK 1398
KMHK 1392	cl	05 48 15.4	−70 26 35	Men	0.7		212	11	KMHK: Loose cluster.
KMHK 1405	cl	05 48 15.6	−71 59 21	Men	0.7		212	11	KMHK: Loose cluster.
[HS66] 419	cl	05 48 19.7	−67 14 30	Dor	1.0		212	11	KMHK: Compact cluster. Alias: KMHK 1385
KMHK 1381	cl	05 48 21.4	−63 35 50	Dor	0.7		212	11	KMHK: Loose cluster.
[HS66] 420	cl	05 48 28.9	−70 32 53	Men	0.9		212	11	KMHK: Compact cluster. Alias: KMHK 1403
SL 737	cl	05 48 44.1	−75 44 02	Men	0.7		219	11	KMHK: Loose cluster. Aliases: LW 312; KMHK 1432
SL 733	cl	05 48 44.7	−71 38 45	Men	0.9		212	11	KMHK: Compact cluster. Alias: KMHK 1412
KMHK 1408	cl	05 48 46.8	−70 28 23	Men	0.7		212	11	KMHK: Loose cluster.
KMHK 1395	cl	05 48 52.6	−66 25 58	Dor	0.6		212	11	KMHK: Loose cluster.
SL 724	cl	05 48 53.0	−64 38 04	Dor	0.9		212	11	KMHK: Loose cluster. Alias: KMHK 1388
KMHK 1410	cl	05 48 53.5	−70 14 20	Men	0.8		212	11	KMHK: Loose cluster.
LH 117	cl	05 48 53.8	−70 04 23	Men			212	99	
SL 734	cl	05 48 54.2	−71 03 36	Men	1.3		212	11	KMHK: Compact cluster. Alias: KMHK 1413
NGC 2122	cl	05 48 55	−70 04.0	Men	4.5		212	99	KMHK: Compact cluster. Archinal: Stars mostly hidden by very bright nebula on DSS image. Aliases: KMHK 1414; h 2981
[HS66] 421	cl	05 48 56.2	−67 05 40	Dor	0.4		212	11	KMHK: Compact cluster. Alias: KMHK 1401
SL 726	cl	05 48 59.4	−64 43 58	Dor	0.6		212	11	KMHK: Compact cluster. Alias: KMHK 1390
KMHK 1400	cl	05 48 59.5	−66 29 30	Dor	0.4		212	11	KMHK: Loose cluster.
KMHK 1391	cl	05 49 01.8	−64 20 48	Dor	0.8		212	11	KMHK: Compact cluster.
SL 727	cl	05 49 01.9	−65 00 44	Dor	0.7		212	11	KMHK: Loose cluster. Alias: KMHK 1393
SL 728	cl	05 49 02.7	−65 41 42	Dor	0.8		212	11	KMHK: Incorrect on Hodge-Wright Atlas (1967). Alias: KMHK 1397
KMHK 1411	cl	05 49 04.5	−69 33 23	Dor	0.6		212	11	KMHK: Loose cluster.
LW 309	cl	05 49 04.6	−65 12 14	Dor	0.8		212	99	KMHK: Loose cluster. Alias: KMHK 1396
KMHK 1404	cl	05 49 04.6	−66 47 10	Dor	0.4		212	11	KMHK: Compact cluster.
KMHK 1402	cl	05 49 09.5	−65 42 51	Dor	0.4		212	11	KMHK: Loose cluster.
SL 730	cl	05 49 11.5	−67 30 44	Dor	0.9		212	11	KMHK: Loose cluster. Alias: KMHK 1407

Table C.1: Tables of LMC Objects

Name	Type	2000.0 R.A.	2000.0 Dec.	Con	Diam (′)	Tot. Vm	U#	Ref	Comments and Aliases
[HS66] 422	cl	05 49 14.2	–66 46 37	Dor	0.6		212	11	KMHK: Compact cluster. Alias: KMHK 1406
SL 736	cl	05 49 16.6	–70 47 52	Men	0.8		212	11	KMHK: Loose cluster. Alias: KMHK 1420
SL 729	cl	05 49 20.6	–63 07 44	Dor	1.2		212	11	KMHK: Loose cluster. Aliases: LW 311; KMHK 1399
LW 315	cl	05 49 27.0	–74 42 04	Men	1.1		219	11	KMHK: Loose cluster. Alias: KMHK 1446
KMHK 1409	cl	05 49 33.4	–65 17 10	Dor	0.6		212	11	KMHK: Loose cluster.
SL 732	cl	05 49 35.9	–67 38 48	Dor	1.0		212	11	KMHK: Loose cluster. Alias: KMHK 1415
[HS66] 424	cl	05 49 35.9	–70 41 36	Men	0.9		212	11	KMHK: Loose cluster. Alias: KMHK 1425
KMHK 1421	cl	05 49 38.5	–70 04 44	Men	0.6		212	11	KMHK: Loose cluster.
KMHK 1419	cl	05 49 42.2	–68 05 33	Dor	0.7		212	99	KMHK: Loose cluster. Archinal: In DSS overlap region.
SL 740	cl	05 49 45.7	–70 12 39	Men	1.8		212	11	KMHK: Compact cluster. Alias: KMHK 1427
KMHK 1416	cl	05 49 46.7	–67 02 54	Dor	0.7		212	11	KMHK: Loose cluster.
LH 118	cl	05 49.8	–70 04	Men			212	5	Alias: [HS66] 423
KMHK 1422	cl	05 49 50.6	–68 58 09	Dor	0.7		212	11	KMHK: Loose cluster.
SL 744	cl	05 49 56.1	–70 51 17	Men	1.0		212	11	KMHK: Compact cluster. Alias: KMHK 1434
KMHK 1435	cl	05 49 56.4	–71 12 49	Men	1.0		212	11	KMHK: Loose cluster.
LH 119	cl	05 49 59.5	–68 15 02	Dor			212	99	
SL 749	cl	05 50 00.1	–73 02 52	Men	1.0		212	11	KMHK: Loose cluster. Alias: KMHK 1449
SL 739	cl	05 50 00.4	–65 30 36	Dor	0.9		212	11	KMHK: Compact cluster. Alias: KMHK 1418
[HS66] 425	cl	05 50 02.1	–70 04 51	Men	0.7		212	11	KMHK: Loose cluster. Alias: KMHK 1431
[H60b] 7	cl	05 50 03.2	–67 43 07	Dor	2.1	12.26	212	99	KMHK: Compact cluster. Aliases: SL 735; KMHK 1424
KMHK 1428	cl	05 50 07.9	–68 14 45	Dor	0.8		212	11	KMHK: Compact cluster.
SL 738	cl	05 50 08.2	–64 09 17	Dor	0.8		212	99	KMHK: Loose cluster. Alias: KMHK 1417
SL 747	cl	05 50 09.9	–71 09 39	Men	1.7		212	11	KMHK: Compact cluster. Alias: KMHK 1441
SL 748	cl	05 50 15.5	–70 25 41	Men	1.2		212	11	KMHK: Compact cluster. Alias: KMHK 1437
[HS66] 427	cl	05 50 17.6	–70 36 57	Men	0.8		212	11	KMHK: Compact cluster. Alias: KMHK 1443
KMHK 1423	cl	05 50 22.6	–65 01 02	Dor	0.3		212	11	KMHK: Loose cluster.
SL 743	cl	05 50 23.7	–67 14 19	Dor	0.7		212	99	KMHK: Loose cluster. Alias: KMHK 1430
[HS66] 426	cl	05 50 25.2	–66 51 41	Dor	1.0		212	11	KMHK: Compact cluster. Alias: KMHK 1429
KMHK 1448	cl	05 50 28.2	–70 32 34	Men	0.7		212	11	KMHK: Loose cluster.
LH 120	cl	05 50 31	–68 10.7	Dor			212	99	
NGC 2120	cl	05 50 34.8	–63 40 33	Dor	2.0		212	11	KMHK: Compact cluster. Aliases: LW 316; ESO 86-34; SL 742; KMHK 1426
SL 754	cl	05 50 35.6	–75 22 19	Men	0.7		219	11	KMHK: Loose cluster. Aliases: LW 322; KMHK 1473
KMHK 1464	cl	05 50 36.0	–73 47 02	Men	0.4		219	11	KMHK: Compact cluster.
SL 745	cl	05 50 38.2	–68 00 47	Dor	0.8		212	99	KMHK: Loose cluster. Archinal: On DSS overlap boundary. Alias: KMHK 1438
LW 318	cl	05 50 43.0	–65 18 14	Dor	0.8		212	11	KMHK: Compact cluster. Alias: KMHK 1433
KMHK 1440	cl	05 50 44.1	–67 23 07	Dor	0.8		212	11	KMHK: Loose cluster.
KMHK 1445	cl	05 50 45.1	–67 54 39	Dor	0.8		212	11	KMHK: Loose cluster.
SL 746	cl	05 50 45.3	–67 34 55	Dor	0.8		212	11	KMHK: Compact cluster. Alias: KMHK 1442
KMHK 1436	cl	05 50 47.4	–65 37 15	Dor	0.7		212	11	KMHK: Compact cluster.

Table C.1: Tables of LMC Objects

Name	Type	2000.0 R.A.	2000.0 Dec.	Con	Diam (′)	Tot. Vm	U#	Ref	Comments and Aliases
[HS66] 430	cl	05 50 48.4	−71 02 46	Men	0.9		212	11	KMHK: Loose cluster. Alias: KMHK 1456
KMHK 1454	cl	05 50 48.8	−70 14 08	Men	0.6		212	11	KMHK: Loose cluster.
[HS66] 428	cl	05 50 50.3	−67 10 07	Dor	0.4		212	11	KMHK: Loose cluster. Alias: KMHK 1444
[HS66] 429	cl	05 50 52.6	−69 42 20	Dor	0.7		212	99	KMHK: Loose cluster. Alias: KMHK 1453
NGC 2125	cl	05 50 53.0	−69 28 42	Dor	1.0		212	11	KMHK: Compact cluster. Alias: KMHK 1451
KMHK 1460	cl	05 50 59.6	−71 02 25	Men	0.7		212	99	KMHK: Loose cluster.
[HS66] 432	cl	05 51 03.5	−69 48 35	Dor	0.9		212	99	KMHK: Loose cluster. Alias: KMHK 1457
LW 319	cl	05 51 06.1	−64 11 16	Dor	0.7		212	11	KMHK: Incorrect on Hodge-Wright Atlas (1967). Alias: KMHK 1439
[HS66] 431	cl	05 51 12.1	−67 11 27	Dor	0.7		212	99	KMHK: Loose cluster. Alias: KMHK 1450
KMHK 1459	cl	05 51 14.1	−69 07 29	Dor	0.8		212	11	KMHK: Loose cluster.
LW 321	cl	05 51 18.4	−66 35 35	Dor	0.8		212	99	KMHK: Loose cluster. Alias: KMHK 1452
LW 320	cl	05 51 21.2	−62 59 32	Dor	1.0		212	11	KMHK: Loose cluster. Alias: KMHK 1447
NGC 2127	cl	05 51 21.7	−69 21 38	Dor	1.2		212	11	DSFG: Relatively faint.; KMHK: Compact cluster. Alias: KMHK 1462
SL 756	cl	05 51 29.1	−70 27 27	Men	1.0		212	99	KMHK: Compact cluster. Alias: KMHK 1467
NGC 2133	cl	05 51 29.3	−71 10 24	Men	1.7		212	99	KMHK: Compact cluster. Aliases: SL 757; KMHK 1471
[HS66] 435	cl	05 51 35.9	−71 01 20	Men	0.6		212	11	KMHK: Compact cluster. Alias: KMHK 1472
[HS66] 434	cl	05 51 36.6	−69 15 25	Dor	0.7		212	11	KMHK: Compact cluster. Alias: KMHK 1466
SL 752	cl	05 51 37.3	−68 09 52	Dor	0.8		212	11	KMHK: Compact cluster. Alias: KMHK 1463
NGC 2123	cl	05 51 43.5	−65 19 17	Dor	1.2		212	11	DSFG: Relatively bright and compact group.; KMHK: Compact cluster. Alias: KMHK 1458
LW 323	cl	05 51 45.9	−63 51 19	Dor	0.8		212	11	KMHK: Loose cluster. Alias: KMHK 1455
[HS66] 433	cl	05 51 47.3	−67 35 36	Dor	0.9		212	11	KMHK: Loose cluster. Alias: KMHK 1465
[HS66] 436	cl	05 51 47.8	−69 18 27	Dor	0.6		212	99	KMHK: Compact cluster. Alias: KMHK 1470
SL 753	cl	05 51 48.8	−65 52 29	Dor	1.0		212	99	KMHK: Compact cluster. Alias: KMHK 1461
[HS66] 438	cl	05 51 53.1	−70 51 09	Men	0.8		212	11	KMHK: Loose cluster. Aliases: BRHT 57a; KMHK 1477
BRHT 57b	cl	05 51 53	−70 51.1	Men			212	5	
NGC 2134	cl	05 51 56.5	−71 05 52	Men	2.5	11.1	212	11	See notes. KMHK: Compact cluster. Aliases: SL 760; KMHK 1480
KMHK 1468	cl	05 52 02.2	−67 16 37	Dor	0.7		212	11	KMHK: Compact cluster.
[HS66] 439	cl	05 52 07.1	−69 32 54	Dor	1.0		212	11	KMHK: Loose cluster. Alias: KMHK 1478
KMHK 1475	cl	05 52 07.4	−69 01 02	Dor	0.7		212	11	KMHK: Loose cluster.
SL 759	cl	05 52 09.4	−69 40 37	Dor	0.9		212	11	KMHK: Loose cluster. Alias: KMHK 1479
SL 761	cl	05 52 10.1	−70 54 19	Men	0.8		212	11	KMHK: Compact cluster. Alias: KMHK 1482
[HS66] 437	cl	05 52 15.5	−68 13 36	Dor	1.0		212	99	KMHK: Loose cluster. Archinal: With possible previously uncatalogued cluster (17" diameter) just to N at 05 52 14.5 -68 12 15. Aliases: LH 121; KMHK 1474
NGC 2130	cl	05 52 23.7	−67 20 03	Dor	1.2		212	11	DSFG: Relatively faint.; KMHK: Compact cluster. Alias: KMHK 1476
OHSC 27	cl	05 52 29.7	−63 36 04	Dor	0.3		212	11	KMHK: Loose cluster. Alias: KMHK 1469
KMHK 1481	cl	05 52 32.0	−68 09 48	Dor	0.7		212	11	KMHK: Loose cluster.
[HS66] 440	cl	05 52 35.7	−68 17 17	Dor	0.7		212	11	KMHK: Loose cluster. Alias: KMHK 1483
[HS66] 441	cl	05 52 37.8	−69 08 57	Dor	0.6		212	11	KMHK: Loose cluster. Alias: KMHK 1485
[HS66] 443	cl	05 52 53.5	−70 53 16	Men	0.8		212	11	KMHK: Loose cluster. Alias: KMHK 1492

Table C.1: Tables of LMC Objects

Name	Type	2000.0 R.A.	2000.0 Dec.	Con	Diam (′)	Tot. Vm	U#	Ref	Comments and Aliases
SL 763	cl	05 52 53.7	−69 47 06	Dor	1.2		212	11	KMHK: Compact cluster. Alias: KMHK 1488
KMHK 1489	cl	05 52 57.3	−69 31 51	Dor	0.8		212	11	KMHK: Loose cluster.
NGC 2136	cl	05 52 58.9	−69 29 30	Dor	1.9	10.5	212	99	DSFG: Bright.; KMHK: Compact cluster. Aliases: BRHT 22a; SL 762; KMHK 1490
SL 766	cl	05 53 00.3	−70 32 08	Men	0.6		212	11	KMHK: Loose cluster. Alias: KMHK 1494
[HS66] 442	cl	05 53 04.6	−67 42 37	Dor	0.6		212	99	KMHK: Compact cluster. Alias: KMHK 1487
KMHK 1486	cl	05 53 06.4	−67 21 44	Dor	0.6		212	11	KMHK: Compact cluster.
NGC 2137	cl	05 53 11.9	−69 28 58	Dor	0.8		212	11	DSFG: Faint.; KMHK: Compact cluster. Aliases: BRHT 22b; SL 764; KMHK 1495
KMHK 1484	cl	05 53 12.1	−63 48 27	Dor	0.4		212	11	KMHK: Loose cluster.
SL 767	cl	05 53 12.2	−70 30 31	Men	0.7		212	11	KMHK: Loose cluster. Alias: KMHK 1498
KMHK 1504	cl	05 53 15.7	−71 53 32	Men	0.7		212	11	KMHK: Loose cluster.
KMHK 1491	cl	05 53 23.0	−67 25 43	Dor	0.7		212	11	KMHK: Loose cluster.
SL 769	cl	05 53 23.9	−70 04 16	Men	2.1		212	11	KMHK: Loose cluster. Alias: KMHK 1499
SL 775	cl	05 53 27.0	−71 42 57	Men	1.1		212	11	KMHK: Compact cluster. Alias: KMHK 1506
KMHK 1507	cl	05 53 28.2	−71 41 10	Men	0.7		212	11	KMHK: Loose cluster.
NGC 2135	cl	05 53 35.1	−67 25 43	Dor	1.0		212	11	DSFG: Relatively faint.; KMHK: Compact cluster. Alias: KMHK 1496
SL 776	cl	05 53 38.9	−73 03 25	Men	1.5		212	11	KMHK: Compact cluster. Alias: KMHK 1515
KMHK 1501	cl	05 53 39.4	−68 30 30	Dor	0.7		212	11	KMHK: Compact cluster.
[HS66] 444	cl	05 53 39.5	−67 18 45	Dor	0.7		212	99	KMHK: Compact cluster. Archinal: DSS overlap region. The BRHT paper has this object reversed with BRHT 58b in their p. 350 figure. Aliases: BRHT 58a; KMHK 1497
SL 770	cl	05 53 42.8	−69 20 37	Dor	0.9		212	99	KMHK: Compact cluster. Alias: KMHK 1503
BRHT 58b	cl	05 53 47	−67 19.4	Dor			212	99	Archinal: DSS overlap region. The BRHT paper has this object reversed with [HS66] 444 = BRHT 58a in their figure on p. 350.
KMHK 1500	cl	05 53 49.0	−67 19 25	Dor	0.4		212	99	KMHK: Loose cluster. Archinal: Very faint, in DSS overlap region.
[HS66] 445	cl	05 53 50.2	−67 23 09	Dor	0.7		212	99	KMHK: Compact cluster. Archinal: In DSS overlap region. Alias: KMHK 1502
SL 772	cl	05 53 53.0	−69 38 54	Dor	1.0		212	11	KMHK: Loose cluster. Alias: KMHK 1508
SL 768	cl	05 53 54.5	−63 36 56	Dor	2.4		212	11	KMHK: Loose cluster. Aliases: ESO 86-38; LW 326; KMHK 1493
[H60b] 8	cl	05 54.0	−67 48	Dor			212	99	Archinal: Very faint on DSS image, not much different from surrounding area.
SL 771	cl	05 54 02.6	−67 44 02	Dor	1.9		212	99	KMHK: Loose cluster. Archinal: In DSS overlap region. Alias: KMHK 1505
KMHK 1514	cl	05 54 06.5	−70 44 47	Men	1.0		212	11	KMHK: Loose cluster.
SL 779	cl	05 54 11.8	−71 05 31	Men	0.7		212	11	KMHK: Loose cluster. Alias: KMHK 1517
SL 774	cl	05 54 14.6	−69 01 00	Dor	1.2		212	11	KMHK: Compact cluster. Alias: KMHK 1512
NGC 2140	cl	05 54 16.0	−68 35 58	Dor	1.7		212	11	DSFG: Relatively faint, extended NW-SE.; KMHK: Loose cluster. Alias: KMHK 1511
NGC 2145	cl	05 54 22.6	−70 54 03	Men	1.7		212	11	DSFG: Relatively faint.; KMHK: Compact cluster. Alias: KMHK 1520
KMHK 1513	cl	05 54 30.5	−67 42 41	Dor	0.8		212	99	KMHK: Loose cluster. Archinal: In DSS overlap region.
KMHK 1510	cl	05 54 33.9	−65 44 27	Dor	0.4		212	11	KMHK: Loose cluster.
LW 329	cl	05 54 37.6	−64 53 14	Dor	0.8		212	11	KMHK: Incorrect on Hodge-Wright Atlas (1967). Alias: KMHK 1509
[HS66] 446	cl	05 54 38.5	−70 45 58	Men	0.7		212	11	KMHK: Loose cluster. Alias: KMHK 1523
SL 783	cl	05 54 39.1	−74 36 20	Men	1.6		219	11	KMHK: Compact cluster. Aliases: LW 333; KMHK 1535
SL 781	cl	05 54 42.2	−70 42 01	Men	0.8		212	11	KMHK: Loose cluster. Alias: KMHK 1524

Table C.1: Tables of LMC Objects

Name	Type	2000.0 R.A.	2000.0 Dec.	Con	Diam (′)	Tot. Vm	U#	Ref	Comments and Aliases
NGC 2138	cl	05 54 49.7	−65 50 17	Dor	1.0		212	11	DSFG: Extremely faint; nearly stellar.; KMHK: Loose cluster. Alias: KMHK 1516
[HS66] 448	cl	05 54 54.0	−70 09 33	Men	0.8		212	11	KMHK: Loose cluster. Alias: KMHK 1526
SL 778	cl	05 54 55.4	−66 42 50	Dor	0.8		212	11	KMHK: Loose cluster. Alias: KMHK 1519
KMHK 1528	cl	05 54 57.7	−71 05 06	Men	0.6		212	11	KMHK: Loose cluster.
[HS66] 447	cl	05 54 58.5	−67 06 50	Dor	0.9		212	11	KMHK: Loose cluster. Alias: KMHK 1521
LW 332	cl	05 55 08.1	−64 39 16	Dor	1.3		212	11	KMHK: Loose cluster. Alias: KMHK 1518
SL 782	cl	05 55 09.1	−68 29 33	Dor	1.7		212	11	KMHK: Loose cluster. Alias: KMHK 1525
KMHK 1522	cl	05 55 10.7	−67 01 56	Dor	0.4		212	11	KMHK: Loose cluster.
KMHK 1529	cl	05 55 33.2	−68 01 58	Dor	0.7		212	11	KMHK: Loose cluster.
OHSC 28	cl	05 55 35.4	−62 20 44	Dor			201	5	
KMHK 1527	cl	05 55 40.6	−65 37 23	Dor	0.4		212	11	KMHK: Loose cluster.
NGC 2161	cl	05 55 42.3	−74 21 14	Men	2.2	12.95	219	56	= GSC 09175-00406. Position from GSC, diameter from Archinal via DSS. V magnitude from Bica, et al. [1996].; KMHK: Compact cluster. Aliases: LW 337; ESO 33-31; SL 789; KMHK 1544
SL 788	cl	05 55 45.8	−71 11 28	Men	0.9		212	11	KMHK: Compact cluster. Alias: KMHK 1536
NGC 2147	cl	05 55 46.4	−68 12 14	Dor	1.1		212	11	KMHK: Compact cluster. Alias: KMHK 1531
KMHK 1533	cl	05 55 52.6	−67 52 09	Dor	1.0		212	11	KMHK: Loose cluster.
KMHK 1534	cl	05 55 54.2	−68 07 50	Dor	0.9		212	11	KMHK: Loose cluster.
LH 122	cl	05 55 55	−68 13.6	Dor			212	99	Alias: Hen N 75B
LW 335	cl	05 55 57.1	−66 57 04	Dor	0.7		212	11	KMHK: Loose cluster. Alias: KMHK 1532
SL 787	cl	05 55 59.2	−70 00 47	Men?	0.8		212	99	KMHK: Loose cluster. Alias: KMHK 1538
[H60b] 9	cl	05 56 01.3	−70 20 21	Men	2.1	12.67	212	99	KMHK: Loose cluster. Aliases: SL 790; KMHK 1540
KMHK 1537	cl	05 56 06.4	−69 11 49	Dor	0.7		212	11	KMHK: Loose cluster.
KMHK 1530	cl	05 56 08.6	−63 38 33	Dor	0.6		212	11	KMHK: Loose cluster.
NGC 2151	cl	05 56 20.8	−69 01 05	Dor	1.0		212	11	KMHK: Incorrect on Hodge-Wright Atlas (1967). Alias: KMHK 1541
KMHK 1542	cl	05 56 24.7	−70 38 01	Men	0.8		212	11	KMHK: Loose cluster.
KMHK 1539	cl	05 56 39.9	−65 21 57	Dor	0.7		212	11	KMHK: Compact cluster.
KMHK 1547	cl	05 56 52.5	−69 30 41	Dor	0.8		212	11	KMHK: Loose cluster.
KMHK 1543	cl	05 56 53.5	−67 58 06	Dor	0.7		212	11	KMHK: Compact cluster.
SL 791	cl	05 56 55.0	−68 36 45	Dor	1.0		212	99	KMHK: Loose cluster. Alias: KMHK 1545
KMHK 1549	cl	05 57 15.9	−68 36 51	Dor	0.7		212	11	KMHK: Loose cluster.
KMHK 1546	cl	05 57 19.1	−65 32 05	Dor	0.6		212	11	KMHK: Loose cluster.
SL 797	cl	05 57 23.1	−70 23 37	Men	1.2		212	11	KMHK: Loose cluster. Alias: KMHK 1557
KMHK 1554	cl	05 57 23.3	−69 37 32	Dor	0.7		212	11	KMHK: Loose cluster.
KMHK 1550	cl	05 57 23.5	−68 58 49	Dor	0.7		212	99	KMHK: Compact cluster.
IC 2161	cl	05 57 25.5	−75 08 24	Men	1.5		219	11	KMHK: Compact cluster. Alias: KMHK 1572
NGC 2157	cl	05 57 34.8	−69 11 47	Dor	2.7	10.2	212	11	KMHK: Compact cluster. Aliases: SL 794; KMHK 1558
KMHK 1548	cl	05 57 35.1	−64 59 49	Dor	1.2		212	11	KMHK: Loose cluster.
SL 804	cl	05 57 38.1	−74 10 25	Men	1.6		218	11	KMHK: Loose cluster. Aliases: LW 346; KMHK 1569
NGC 2154	cl	05 57 38.5	−67 15 44	Dor	2.4		212	11	KMHK: Compact cluster. Alias: KMHK 1551

Table C.1: Tables of LMC Objects

Name	Type	2000.0 R.A.	2000.0 Dec.	Con	Diam (′)	Tot. Vm	U#	Ref	Comments and Aliases
KMHK 1553	cl	05 57 40.2	−67 39 34	Dor	0.8		212	99	KMHK: Loose cluster. Alias: BRHT 64b
SL 805	cl	05 57 43.0	−71 26 58	Men	1.0		212	11	KMHK: Compact cluster. Alias: KMHK 1565
[H60b] 10	cl	05 57.7	−67 06	Dor			212	99	Archinal: Not obvious on DSS image. Only rich field here.
NGC 2156	cl	05 57 50.0	−68 27 40	Dor	1.1	11.4	212	11	DSFG: Relatively bright.; KMHK: Compact cluster. Alias: KMHK 1560
KMHK 1559	cl	05 57 50.5	−67 39 18	Dor	1.2		212	99	KMHK: Loose cluster. Alias: BRHT 64a
SL 795	cl	05 57 52.1	−65 56 51	Dor	1.0		212	11	KMHK: Incorrect on Hodge-Wright Atlas (1967). Alias: KMHK 1552
NGC 2153	cl	05 57 52.3	−66 24 04	Dor	1.3		212	11	KMHK: Compact cluster. Alias: KMHK 1555
NGC 2173	cl	05 57 58.0	−72 58 44	Men	2.4		212	11	KMHK: Compact cluster. Aliases: LW 348; SL 807; KMHK 1570
NGC 2159	cl	05 58 02.7	−68 37 26	Dor	0.9	11.4	212	11	DSFG: Relatively bright.; KMHK: Loose cluster. Alias: KMHK 1561
SL 798	cl	05 58 12.2	−63 53 38	Dor	0.9		212	11	KMHK: Loose cluster. Alias: KMHK 1556
NGC 2160	cl	05 58 13.0	−68 17 27	Dor	1.2		212	11	DSFG: Relatively faint; irregular in shape.; KMHK: Compact cluster. Alias: KMHK 1564
SL 800	cl	05 58 20.2	−67 06 27	Dor	2.0		212	11	KMHK: Incorrect on Hodge-Wright Atlas (1967). Alias: KMHK 1562
KMHK 1566	cl	05 58 20.8	−68 21 18	Dor	0.3		212	11	KMHK: Compact cluster.
KMHK 1571	cl	05 58 26.2	−70 39 15	Men	0.7		212	11	KMHK: Compact cluster.
NGC 2155	cl	05 58 32.3	−65 28 40	Dor	2.1		212	11	KMHK: Compact cluster. Alias: KMHK 1563
KMHK 1568	cl	05 58 46.9	−66 50 40	Dor	0.6		212	11	KMHK: Loose cluster.
SL 806	cl	05 58 49.9	−66 03 28	Dor	0.7		212	11	KMHK: Incorrect on Hodge-Wright Atlas (1967). Alias: KMHK 1567
NGC 2171	cl	05 58 52.9	−67 53 51	Dor	0.7		212	11	KMHK: Incorrect on Hodge-Wright Atlas (1967). Alias: KMHK 1573
NGC 2164	cl	05 58 55.6	−68 31 01	Dor	2.5	10.3	212	11	KMHK: Compact cluster. Aliases: SL 808; KMHK 1574
SL 810	cl	05 59 10.8	−68 38 20	Dor	0.8		212	11	KMHK: Loose cluster. Alias: KMHK 1575
NGC 2166	cl	05 59 33.0	−67 56 33	Dor	1.2		212	11	DSFG: Relatively faint; compact group.; KMHK: Compact cluster. Alias: KMHK 1576
KMHK 1577	cl	05 59 50.2	−66 46 08	Dor	1.0		212	11	KMHK: Loose cluster.
KMHK 1578	cl	05 59 58.9	−66 26 37	Dor	0.7		212	11	KMHK: Loose cluster.
NGC 2172	cl	06 00 05.6	−68 38 14	Dor	1.7	11.8	211	11	DSFG: Relatively bright.; KMHK: Compact cluster. Alias: KMHK 1580
KMHK 1583	cl	06 00 16.0	−68 55 59	Dor	0.7		211	11	KMHK: Loose cluster.
LW 352	cl	06 00 19.7	−67 45 54	Dor	1.0		211	99	KMHK: Loose cluster. Alias: KMHK 1582
NGC 2162	cl	06 00 31.4	−63 43 18	Dor?	2.1		211	11	KMHK: Compact cluster. Alias: KMHK 1579
KMHK 1587	cl	06 00 31.5	−70 33 08	Men	0.7		211	11	KMHK: Loose cluster.
SL 813	cl	06 00 32.7	−67 07 30	Dor	0.8		211	11	KMHK: Incorrect on Hodge-Wright Atlas (1967). Alias: KMHK 1584
LW 354	cl	06 00 37.7	−64 45 00	Dor	1.0		211	11	KMHK: Incorrect on Hodge-Wright Atlas (1967). Alias: KMHK 1581
SL 817	cl	06 00 37.9	−70 04 12	Men?	0.8		211	99	KMHK: Compact cluster. Alias: KMHK 1588
KMHK 1585	cl	06 00 50.0	−66 54 48	Dor	0.7		211	11	KMHK: Loose cluster.
KMHK 1586	cl	06 00 52.9	−67 41 26	Dor	0.7		211	11	KMHK: Loose cluster.
NGC 2190	cl	06 01 02.3	−74 43 34	Men	2.0		218	11	KMHK: Compact cluster. Aliases: LW 357; ESO 33-36; SL 819; KMHK 1601
OHSC 29	cl	06 01 12.3	−74 31 14	Men	0.4		218	11	KMHK: Loose cluster. Alias: KMHK 1604
NGC 2177	cl	06 01 15.7	−67 44 06	Dor	1.2		211	11	KMHK: Loose cluster. Alias: KMHK 1590
NGC 2176	cl	06 01 19.4	−66 51 19	Dor	1.3		211	11	DSFG: Very faint and diffuse.; KMHK: Loose cluster. Alias: KMHK 1589
SL 821	cl	06 01 23.7	−72 30 36	Men	0.9		211	11	KMHK: Compact cluster. Alias: KMHK 1599
KMHK 1594	cl	06 01 25.9	−68 50 46	Dor	0.6		211	11	KMHK: Loose cluster.

Table C.1: Tables of LMC Objects

Name	Type	2000.0 R.A.	2000.0 Dec.	Con	Diam (′)	Tot. Vm	U#	Ref	Comments and Aliases
LW 360	cl	06 01 30.0	−74 22 57	Men	0.7		218	11	KMHK: Loose cluster. Alias: KMHK 1608
KMHK 1592	cl	06 01 30.3	−66 59 13	Dor	1.7		211	11	KMHK: Loose cluster.
SL 818	cl	06 01 38.9	−68 00 04	Dor	1.1		211	11	KMHK: Loose cluster. Alias: KMHK 1595
KMHK 1593	cl	06 01 52.4	−64 07 58	Dor	0.6		211	11	KMHK: Loose cluster.
SL 826	cl	06 01 53.5	−72 21 19	Men	1.2		211	99	KMHK: Loose cluster. Alias: KMHK 1606
KMHK 1591	cl	06 02 02.6	−60 31 25	Pic	1.3		201	11	KMHK: Compact cluster.
SL 822	cl	06 02 06.9	−68 20 09	Dor	1.3		211	11	KMHK: Loose cluster. Alias: KMHK 1598
LW 361	cl	06 02 09.5	−65 46 32	Dor	0.8		211	11	KMHK: Loose cluster. Alias: KMHK 1597
SL 828	cl	06 02 13.6	−74 11 24	Men	1.3		218	11	KMHK: Compact cluster. Alias: KMHK 1616
LW 367	cl	06 02 14.3	−74 11 25	Men			218	5	Alias: ESO 34-1
SL 823	cl	06 02 18.1	−64 19 46	Dor	1.6		211	11	KMHK: Incorrect on Hodge-Wright Atlas (1967). Alias: KMHK 1596
SL 824	cl	06 02 28.4	−66 55 10	Dor	0.8		211	11	KMHK: Compact cluster. Alias: KMHK 1600
KMHK 1605	cl	06 02 28.9	−68 52 29	Dor	0.7		211	11	KMHK: Loose cluster.
KMHK 1603	cl	06 02 30.6	−67 12 56	Dor	1.3		211	11	KMHK: Loose cluster.
OHSC 30	cl	06 02 31.5	−74 05 24	Men	0.7		218	11	KMHK: Loose cluster. Alias: KMHK 1620
NGC 2181	cl	06 02 43.1	−65 15 54	Dor	1.6		211	11	DSFG: Very faint; very compact.; KMHK: Compact cluster. Alias: KMHK 1602
KMHK 1607	cl	06 02 51.7	−66 39 32	Dor	0.9		211	11	KMHK: Loose cluster.
LW 369	cl	06 02 56.0	−71 27 28	Men	1.0		211	11	KMHK: Loose cluster. Alias: KMHK 1618
LW 368	cl	06 03 02.0	−67 23 58	Dor	1.6		211	11	KMHK: Loose cluster. Alias: KMHK 1610
SL 827	cl	06 03 11.0	−65 40 31	Dor	1.6		211	11	KMHK: Incorrect on Hodge-Wright Atlas (1967). Alias: KMHK 1609
LW 373	cl	06 03 14.0	−74 44 28	Men	0.3		218	11	KMHK: Loose cluster. Alias: KMHK 1625
[HS66] 450	cl	06 03 20.5	−67 03 23	Dor	0.7		211	99	KMHK: Compact cluster. Alias: KMHK 1613
KMHK 1611	cl	06 03 20.7	−66 07 33	Dor	0.7		211	11	KMHK: Loose cluster.
KMHK 1614	cl	06 03 29.2	−66 40 54	Dor	0.3		211	11	KMHK: Loose cluster.
KMHK 1621	cl	06 03 30.1	−71 30 05	Men	0.7		211	11	KMHK: Loose cluster.
SL 829	cl	06 03 31.3	−65 20 41	Dor	0.7		211	11	KMHK: Incorrect on Hodge-Wright Atlas (1967). Alias: KMHK 1612
KMHK 1619	cl	06 03 42.7	−67 09 17	Dor	0.9		211	99	KMHK: Loose cluster.
KMHK 1615	cl	06 03 43.7	−64 43 54	Dor	0.7		211	11	KMHK: Loose cluster.
KMHK 1617	cl	06 03 43.8	−65 29 53	Dor	0.6		211	11	KMHK: Loose cluster.
KMHK 1622	cl	06 03 54.3	−69 14 48	Dor	0.6		211	11	KMHK: Loose cluster.
KMHK 1626	cl	06 04 11.1	−70 38 50	Men	0.8		211	11	KMHK: Loose cluster.
SL 830	cl	06 04 13.0	−69 12 05	Dor	1.0		211	11	KMHK: Loose cluster. Alias: KMHK 1624
SL 832	cl	06 04 24.5	−73 30 37	Men	0.9		218	11	KMHK: Loose cluster. Alias: KMHK 1628
SL 831	cl	06 04 34.2	−66 26 31	Dor	0.9		211	11	KMHK: Loose cluster. Alias: KMHK 1623
NGC 2203	cl	06 04 41.6	−75 26 13	Men	3.3		218	11	KMHK: Compact cluster. Aliases: LW 380; ESO 34-4; SL 836; KMHK 1639
SL 835	cl	06 04 48.1	−75 06 10	Men	0.6		218	11	KMHK: Loose cluster. Aliases: LW 379; KMHK 1640
SL 833	cl	06 05 03.6	−67 39 30	Dor	0.9		211	99	KMHK: Compact cluster. Alias: KMHK 1627
KMHK 1637	cl	06 05 09.5	−73 19 49	Men	0.4		211	11	KMHK: Loose cluster.
KMHK 1634	cl	06 05 26.1	−71 12 38	Men	0.6		211	11	KMHK: Loose cluster.

Table C.1: Tables of LMC Objects

Name	Type	2000.0 R.A.	2000.0 Dec.	Con	Diam (′)	Tot. Vm	U#	Ref	Comments and Aliases
LW 384	cl	06 05 35.4	−71 45 11	Men	1.7		211	11	KMHK: Loose cluster. Alias: KMHK 1638
LW 383	cl	06 05 38.7	−69 16 07	Dor	0.9		211	11	KMHK: Loose cluster. Alias: KMHK 1631
LW 381	cl	06 05 43.6	−68 09 36	Dor	1.0		211	11	KMHK: Incorrect on Hodge-Wright Atlas (1967). Alias: KMHK 1630
SL 837	cl	06 05 52.2	−65 24 20	Dor	0.8		211	11	KMHK: Loose cluster. Alias: KMHK 1629
KMHK 1632	cl	06 05 56.2	−67 53 47	Dor	0.9		211	11	KMHK: Loose cluster.
NGC 2197	cl	06 06 07.4	−67 05 54	Dor	1.7		211	11	DSFG: Faint and compact.; KMHK: Compact cluster. Alias: KMHK 1636
LW 389	cl	06 06 09.3	−70 27 55	Men	0.9		211	11	KMHK: Loose cluster. Alias: KMHK 1643
NGC 2193	cl	06 06 17.4	−65 05 53	Dor	1.9		211	11	KMHK: Compact cluster. Alias: KMHK 1633
LW 386	cl	06 06 17.5	−65 35 14	Dor	0.7		211	11	KMHK: Loose cluster. Alias: KMHK 1635
LW 388	cl	06 06 19.9	−68 15 12	Dor	1.2		211	11	KMHK: Loose cluster. Alias: KMHK 1641
KMHK 1649	cl	06 06 20.9	−73 32 13	Men	0.4		218	11	KMHK: Loose cluster.
LW 390	cl	06 06 26.9	−67 52 22	Dor	0.6		211	11	KMHK: Compact cluster. Alias: KMHK 1642
SL 840	cl	06 06 28.8	−69 21 27	Dor	1.0		211	99	KMHK: Compact cluster. Alias: KMHK 1645
LW 393	cl	06 06 32.2	−72 13 34	Men	0.7		211	99	KMHK: Incorrect on Hodge-Wright Atlas (1967). Alias: KMHK 1648
LW 394	cl	06 07 00.3	−71 44 24	Men	1.8		211	11	KMHK: Loose cluster. Alias: KMHK 1651
LW 392	cl	06 07 00.9	−65 19 35	Dor	1.0		211	99	KMHK: Loose cluster. Alias: KMHK 1644
KMHK 1646	cl	06 07 12.0	−66 59 51	Dor	0.3		211	11	KMHK: Loose cluster.
LW 397	cl	06 07 28.9	−72 29 39	Men	0.7		211	99	KMHK: Loose cluster. Archinal: Double with possible new previously uncatalogued cluster (15" diameter) just to S at 06 07 30.5 -72 30 24. Alias: KMHK 1657
SL 834	cl	06 07 30.6	−70 52 00	Men	0.7		211	11	KMHK: Incorrect on Hodge-Wright Atlas (1967). Alias: KMHK 1654
LW 395	cl	06 07 30.7	−65 19 30	Dor	0.7		211	99	KMHK: Loose cluster. Alias: KMHK 1647
KMHK 1650	cl	06 07 51.8	−65 26 04	Dor	0.6		211	11	KMHK: Loose cluster.
SL 841	cl	06 08 01.6	−67 30 09	Dor	1.7		211	11	KMHK: Loose cluster. Alias: KMHK 1653
SL 843	cl	06 08 08.5	−67 58 21	Dor	1.0		211	11	KMHK: Loose cluster. Alias: KMHK 1655
SL 842	cl	06 08 15.5	−62 59 15	Pic	1.3		211	11	KMHK: Loose cluster. Alias: KMHK 1652
LW 399	cl	06 08 15.7	−62 59 15	Pic			211	5	Alias: ESO 86-61
SL 848	cl	06 08 17.5	−74 01 38	Men	1.1		218	99	KMHK: Loose cluster. Aliases: LW 405; KMHK 1664
LW 404	cl	06 08 32.3	−70 23 21	Men	0.6		211	11	KMHK: Loose cluster. Alias: KMHK 1661
SL 844	cl	06 08 32.8	−67 18 52	Dor	1.2		211	11	KMHK: Incorrect on Hodge-Wright Atlas (1967). Alias: KMHK 1658
NGC 2209	cl	06 08 34.8	−73 50 22	Men	2.8		218	11	KMHK: Loose cluster. Aliases: LW 408; SL 849; KMHK 1669
SL 845	cl	06 08 38.6	−64 48 09	Dor	0.7		211	11	KMHK: Incorrect on Hodge-Wright Atlas (1967). Alias: KMHK 1656
SL 846	cl	06 08 39.2	−66 35 27	Dor	0.7		211	11	KMHK: Loose cluster. Alias: KMHK 1659
KMHK 1668	cl	06 08 53.1	−72 23 03	Men	0.6		211	11	KMHK: Loose cluster.
LW 410	cl	06 08 56.4	−71 39 31	Men	1.7		211	11	KMHK: Loose cluster. Alias: KMHK 1666
LW 407	cl	06 08 58.3	−68 08 04	Dor	0.6		211	11	KMHK: Loose cluster. Alias: KMHK 1662
LW 406	cl	06 09 01.4	−66 49 09	Dor	1.3		211	11	KMHK: Loose cluster. Alias: KMHK 1660
LW 409	cl	06 09 03.5	−67 34 51	Dor	1.0		211	11	KMHK: Loose cluster. Alias: KMHK 1663
KMHK 1665	cl	06 09 25.0	−68 31 50	Dor	0.7		211	99	KMHK: Loose cluster.
LW 411	cl	06 09 30.1	−68 48 20	Dor	1.2		211	99	KMHK: Loose cluster. Archinal: On DSS image appears in glare of very bright star to SW. Alias: KMHK 1667

Table C.1: Tables of LMC Objects

Name	Type	2000.0 R.A.	2000.0 Dec.	Con	Diam (′)	Tot. Vm	U#	Ref	Comments and Aliases
KMHK 1676	cl	06 09 46.4	−73 02 11	Men	0.7		211	11	KMHK: Loose cluster.
KMHK 1670	cl	06 09 51.5	−68 36 09	Dor	0.6		211	11	KMHK: Compact cluster.
LW 414	cl	06 10 03.5	−68 21 03	Dor	0.7		211	11	KMHK: Loose cluster. Alias: KMHK 1672
SL 853	cl	06 10 11.0	−70 17 43	Men	0.9		211	11	KMHK: Loose cluster. Alias: KMHK 1675
SL 850	cl	06 10 12.7	−65 57 36	Dor	1.5		211	11	KMHK: Incorrect on Hodge-Wright Atlas (1967). Alias: KMHK 1671
SL 852	cl	06 10 21.5	−68 25 41	Dor	1.2		211	11	KMHK: Loose cluster. Alias: KMHK 1673
NGC 2213	cl	06 10 42.2	−71 31 46	Men	2.1		211	11	KMHK: Compact cluster. Alias: KMHK 1681
SL 855	cl	06 10 53.5	−65 02 35	Dor	2.1		211	11	KMHK: Loose cluster. Alias: KMHK 1674
LW 421	cl	06 10 53.8	−69 08 24	Dor	0.7		211	11	KMHK: Loose cluster. Alias: KMHK 1679
SL 854	cl	06 10 55.2	−67 06 49	Dor	1.0		211	99	KMHK: Incorrect on Hodge-Wright Atlas (1967). Alias: KMHK 1677
OHSC 31	cl	06 11 16.8	−74 11 16	Men	0.3		218	11	KMHK: Loose cluster. Alias: KMHK 1685
KMHK 1678	cl	06 11 21.5	−64 40 50	Dor	0.9		211	11	KMHK: Loose cluster.
LW 422	cl	06 11 23.2	−71 54 14	Men	0.7		211	11	KMHK: Loose cluster. Alias: KMHK 1684
KMHK 1680	cl	06 11 28.7	−66 22 27	Dor	2.4		211	11	KMHK: Loose cluster.
NGC 2210	gcl	06 11 31.3	−69 07 22	Dor	2.1		211	99	KMHK: Compact cluster. Aliases: LW 423; SL 858; KMHK 1682
KMHK 1683	cl	06 11 45.2	−69 20 31	Dor	0.7		211	11	KMHK: Loose cluster.
SL 859	cl	06 12 35.7	−67 04 29	Dor	1.2		211	11	KMHK: Compact cluster. Alias: KMHK 1686
LW 425	cl	06 12 45.1	−68 25 13	Dor	0.6		211	11	KMHK: Loose cluster. Alias: KMHK 1687
NGC 2214	cl	06 12 56.1	−68 15 38	Dor	3.6	10.9	211	11	DSFG: Somewhat extended E-W.; KMHK: Compact cluster. Aliases: LW 426; SL 860; KMHK 1688
LW 427	cl	06 13 07.1	−68 21 34	Dor	0.7		211	11	KMHK: Loose cluster. Alias: KMHK 1689
LW 430	cl	06 13 14.7	−69 25 07	Dor	0.9		211	11	KMHK: Loose cluster. Alias: KMHK 1690
SL 861	cl	06 13 16.6	−70 10 49	Men	1.2		211	11	KMHK: Loose cluster. Alias: KMHK 1691
SL 862	cl	06 13 27.4	−70 41 48	Men	1.7		211	11	KMHK: Compact cluster. Alias: KMHK 1692
KMHK 1702	cl	06 13 56.2	−72 30 19	Men	0.6		211	11	KMHK: Loose cluster.
SL 864	cl	06 13 57.0	−68 05 01	Dor	1.0		211	11	KMHK: Loose cluster. Alias: KMHK 1694
SL 863	cl	06 13 57.6	−67 58 53	Dor	1.2		211	11	KMHK: Incorrect on Hodge-Wright Atlas (1967). Alias: KMHK 1693
KMHK 1703	cl	06 14 03.5	−71 53 07	Men	0.6		211	99	KMHK: Compact cluster.
SL 867	cl	06 14 03.6	−71 53 07	Men	1.0		211	99	KMHK: Compact cluster. Alias: KMHK 1701
KMHK 1695	cl	06 14 04.1	−67 36 17	Dor	0.9		211	11	KMHK: Loose cluster.
SL 865	cl	06 14 07.8	−68 16 56	Dor	0.8		211	11	KMHK: Loose cluster. Alias: KMHK 1696
OHSC 32	cl	06 14 21.9	−73 51 37	Men			218	5	
SL 868	cl	06 14 22.5	−69 50 55	Dor	2.5		211	11	KMHK: Compact cluster. Alias: KMHK 1700
[H60b] 11	gcl	06 14 23.4	−69 50 50	Dor			211	99	
LW 436	cl	06 14 26.3	−66 26 43	Dor	2.0		211	11	KMHK: Loose cluster. Alias: KMHK 1697
SL 870	cl	06 14 28.5	−72 36 34	Men	1.2		211	11	KMHK: Compact cluster. Alias: KMHK 1705
KMHK 1707	cl	06 14 28.8	−72 36 36	Men	1.0		211	11	KMHK: Compact cluster.
SL 866	cl	06 14 32.4	−65 58 56	Dor	1.6		211	11	KMHK: Compact cluster. Alias: KMHK 1698
KMHK 1699	cl	06 14 40.9	−66 25 14	Dor	0.7		211	11	KMHK: Loose cluster.
SL 869	cl	06 14 41.1	−69 48 07	Dor	1.2		211	11	KMHK: Incorrect on Hodge-Wright Atlas (1967). Alias: KMHK 1704

Table C.1: Tables of LMC Objects

Name	Type	2000.0 R.A.	2000.0 Dec.	Con	Diam (′)	Tot. Vm	U#	Ref	Comments and Aliases
KMHK 1706	cl	06 14 44.8	–71 14 10	Men	0.8		211	99	KMHK: Loose cluster.
SL 872	cl	06 15 02.1	–71 19 45	Men	1.0		211	11	KMHK: Loose cluster. Alias: KMHK 1709
OHSC 33	cl	06 15 17.1	–73 47 08	Men	0.3		218	11	KMHK: Compact cluster. Alias: KMHK 1714
SL 871	cl	06 15 25.6	–67 58 57	Dor	1.0		211	11	KMHK: Loose cluster. Alias: KMHK 1708
KMHK 1711	cl	06 15 40.2	–68 20 13	Dor	0.6		211	99	KMHK: Loose cluster.
LW 445	cl	06 15 47.3	–70 26 45	Men	1.0		211	11	KMHK: Loose cluster. Alias: KMHK 1712
LW 444	cl	06 15 57.5	–64 58 20	Dor	0.7		211	11	KMHK: Loose cluster. Alias: KMHK 1710
SL 874	cl	06 15 57.8	–70 04 25	Men?	1.7		211	11	KMHK: Compact cluster. Alias: KMHK 1713
SL 873	cl	06 16 15.4	–69 07 32	Dor	0.7		211	11	KMHK: Compact cluster. Alias: KMHK 1715
LW 448	cl	06 16 36.2	–68 07 12	Dor	0.6		211	11	KMHK: Loose cluster. Alias: KMHK 1716
LW 449	cl	06 16 48.2	–68 51 08	Dor	1.0		211	11	KMHK: Loose cluster. Alias: KMHK 1717
KMHK 1718	cl	06 17 05.2	–68 23 47	Dor	0.7		211	11	KMHK: Loose cluster.
KMHK 1719	cl	06 17 19.3	–70 03 40	Men?	0.7		211	11	KMHK: Loose cluster.
LW 450	cl	06 17 42.8	–70 34 43	Men	0.7		211	11	KMHK: Incorrect on Hodge-Wright Atlas (1967). Alias: KMHK 1722
LW 451	cl	06 17 44.2	–69 13 31	Dor	0.6		211	11	KMHK: Compact cluster. Alias: KMHK 1720
SL 877	cl	06 17 46.3	–71 44 57	Men	1.6		211	11	KMHK: Loose cluster. Alias: KMHK 1724
SL 876	cl	06 18 07.9	–67 29 01	Dor	0.9		211	11	KMHK: Loose cluster. Alias: KMHK 1721
LW 454	cl	06 18 11.1	–68 04 20	Dor	1.3		211	11	KMHK: Loose cluster. Alias: KMHK 1723
SL 881	cl	06 18 44.9	–71 34 44	Men	1.0		211	11	KMHK: Loose cluster. Alias: KMHK 1726
SL 882	cl	06 19 04.1	–72 23 09	Men	0.9		211	11	KMHK: Loose cluster. Alias: KMHK 1728
KMHK 1729	cl	06 19 04.9	–72 23 09	Men	0.6		211	99	KMHK: Compact cluster.
LW 458	cl	06 19 11.2	–67 29 37	Dor	1.0		211	11	KMHK: Loose cluster. Alias: KMHK 1725
LW 460	cl	06 19 15.2	–71 43 37	Men	0.6		211	99	KMHK: Incorrect on Hodge-Wright Atlas (1967). Archinal: Satellite or meteor trail crosses just W of cluster on DSS image. Alias: KMHK 1730
LW 459	cl	06 19 17.6	–68 19 40	Dor	0.9		211	11	KMHK: Loose cluster. Alias: KMHK 1727
LW 462	cl	06 19 40.8	–72 16 03	Men	0.7		211	11	KMHK: Incorrect on Hodge-Wright Atlas (1967). Alias: KMHK 1734
KMHK 1735	cl	06 19 41.5	–72 16 00	Men	0.6		211	11	KMHK: Loose cluster.
LW 463	cl	06 19 46.4	–71 18 48	Men	1.0		211	11	KMHK: Loose cluster. Alias: KMHK 1733
KMHK 1732	cl	06 19 46.8	–69 47 28	Dor	1.2		211	99	KMHK: Loose cluster. Archinal: On the DSS image, this cluster appears to be separated on the N side (i.e. as a possible double cluster).
SL 883	cl	06 19 56.0	–68 15 09	Dor	1.0		211	11	KMHK: Loose cluster. Alias: KMHK 1731
KMHK 1736	cl	06 20 22.3	–68 22 35	Dor	0.6		211	99	KMHK: Loose cluster.
NGC 2231	cl	06 20 43.7	–67 31 04	Dor	2.0		211	11	KMHK: Compact cluster. Alias: KMHK 1737
KMHK 1739	cl	06 21 03.6	–71 02 01	Men	0.3		211	11	KMHK: Compact cluster.
SL 885	cl	06 21 11.5	–67 28 29	Dor	1.2		211	11	KMHK: Loose cluster. Alias: KMHK 1738
SL 886	cl	06 21 26.3	–69 17 56	Dor	1.0		211	11	KMHK: Loose cluster. Alias: KMHK 1740
KMHK 1741	cl	06 21 33.6	–72 47 21	Men	0.8		211	11	KMHK: Compact cluster.
LW 469	cl	06 21 34.0	–72 47 24	Men	1.0		211	11	KMHK: Compact cluster. Alias: KMHK 1742
LW 470	cl	06 22 24.0	–72 14 15	Men	1.0		211	11	KMHK: Loose cluster. Alias: KMHK 1744

Table C.1: Tables of LMC Objects

Name	Type	2000.0 R.A.	2000.0 Dec.	Con	Diam (′)	Tot. Vm	U#	Ref	Comments and Aliases
KMHK 1745	cl	06 22 24.8	−72 14 16	Men	0.6		211	11	KMHK: Loose cluster.
NGC 2241	cl	06 22 52.0	−68 55 31	Dor	1.3		211	11	DSFG: Faint; very compact group.; KMHK: Compact cluster. Alias: KMHK 1743
SL 890	cl	06 23 02.9	−71 41 11	Men	0.7		211	11	KMHK: Loose cluster. Alias: KMHK 1749
LW 472	cl	06 23 11.8	−68 19 09	Dor	0.6		211	11	KMHK: Loose cluster. Alias: KMHK 1746
LW 475	cl	06 23 23.2	−70 33 14	Men	0.9		211	11	KMHK: Loose cluster. Alias: KMHK 1750
LW 474	cl	06 23 29.7	−68 59 50	Dor	0.6		211	11	KMHK: Incorrect on Hodge-Wright Atlas (1967). Alias: KMHK 1748
KMHK 1747	cl	06 23 34.4	−68 22 50	Dor	0.9		211	11	KMHK: Loose cluster.
OHSC 34	cl	06 24 28.7	−66 30 23	Dor	0.4		211	11	KMHK: Loose cluster. Alias: KMHK 1751
SL 891	cl	06 24 49.6	−71 39 33	Men	1.2		211	11	KMHK: Compact cluster. Alias: KMHK 1752
SL 892	cl	06 25 16.0	−71 06 09	Men	0.8		211	11	KMHK: Compact cluster. Alias: KMHK 1753
OHSC 35	cl	06 25 42.0	−67 59 45	Dor	0.6		211	11	KMHK: Loose cluster. Alias: KMHK 1754
NGC 2249	cl	06 25 49.5	−68 55 13	Dor	1.7	12.23	211	99	See notes. Many references give a position 5′ too far north. Aliases: SL 893; LW 479; KMHK 1755
OHSC 36	cl	06 29 41.9	−70 35 26	Men	1.2		211	11	KMHK: Loose cluster. Alias: KMHK 1757
SL 896	cl	06 29 57.7	−69 20 00	Dor	0.9		211	11	KMHK: Compact cluster. Aliases: LW 480; KMHK 1758
NGC 2257	gcl	06 30 12.4	−64 19 34	Dor	2.2		211	99	KMHK: Compact cluster. Aliases: LW 481; ESO 87-24; SL 895; KMHK 1756
LW 482	cl	06 32 23.6	−72 28 19	Men?	0.6		211	99	KMHK: Loose cluster. Alias: KMHK 1759
KMHK 1761	cl	06 33 00.1	−72 26 02	Vol?	0.8		211	11	KMHK: Loose cluster.
SL 897	cl	06 33 01.2	−71 07 40	Men	1.5		211	11	KMHK: Loose cluster. Alias: KMHK 1760
OHSC 37	cl	07 07 39.9	−69 59 02	Vol	0.4		211	11	KMHK: Loose cluster. Alias: KMHK 1762

Table C.2: Tables of SMC Objects

Name	Type	2000.0 R.A.	2000.0 Dec.	Con	Diam (′)	Tot Vm	# Str	Bt* Vm	V sur	2 U#	Ref	Comments and Aliases
Lindsay 1	cl	00 03 53.2	−73 28 22	Tuc						204	12	
Lindsay 2	cl	00 12 56.1	−73 29 28	Tuc						204	12	
Lindsay 3	cl	00 18 25.3	−74 19 07	Hyi?						214	12	
HW 1	cl	00 18 25.7	−73 23 39	Tuc						204	12	
Kron 1	cl	00 21 26.7	−73 44 54	Tuc						214	12	Alias: Lind 4
Lindsay 5	cl	00 22 41.1	−75 04 30	Hyi						214	12	
Kron 4	cl	00 23 03.5	−73 40 11	Tuc						214	12	Alias: Lind 6
Kron 5	cl	00 24 42.8	−73 45 19	Tuc	11.3					214	12	Alias: Lind 7
Kron 3	cl	00 24 46.4	−72 47 37	Tuc						204	12	Alias: Lind 8
Kron 6	cl	00 25 26.3	−74 04 32	Tuc	4.5					214	12	Alias: Lind 9
NGC 121	gcl	00 26 48.7	−71 32 07	Tuc						204	99	The only globular cluster in the SMC [van den Bergh, 1999, p. 300] Aliases: Kron 2; Lind 10
Kron 7	cl	00 27 45.1	−72 46 55	Tuc						204	12	Alias: Lind 11
HW 2	cl	00 28 01.1	−73 59 47	Tuc	0.3					214	99	Archinal: Not an obvious cluster on DSS image. HW: Loose, certain cluster, 0.3′.
Kron 8	cl	00 28 01.9	−73 18 16	Tuc						204	12	Alias: Lind 12
HW 3	cl	00 29 54.9	−73 42 04	Tuc	0.4					214	99	Archinal: Faintly visible on (short exposure) DSS image. HW: Faint, 0.4′.
Kron 9	cl	00 30 00.7	−73 22 46	Tuc						204	99	Archinal: Faintly visible on (short exposure) DSS image. Alias: Lind 13
HW 4	cl	00 30 32.3	−73 48 32	Tuc	0.2					214	99	Archinal: Not an obvious cluster on DSS image. HW: Loose, certain cluster, 0.3′.
HW 5	cl	00 31 02.5	−72 20 28	Tuc	0.2					204	99	
Lindsay 14	cl	00 32 41.6	−72 34 53	Tuc						204	12	
NGC 152	cl	00 32 55.5	−73 06 59	Tuc						204	12	Aliases: Kron 10; Lind 15
HW 6	cl	00 33 10.5	−72 37 59	Tuc	0.3					204	99	Archinal: Faint sparse group on DSS. HW: Faint, 0.3′.
HW 7	cl	00 33 37.3	−72 22 43	Tuc	0.2					204	99	Archinal: Barely visible on DSS, using histogram equalization stretch of image. HW: Concentrated, 0.2′.
HW 8	cl	00 33 46.5	−73 38 00	Tuc	0.3					214	99	
Kron 13	cl	00 35 41.4	−73 35 53	Tuc						214	12	Alias: Lind 17
NGC 176	cl	00 35 58.6	−73 09 57	Tuc		12.7				204	12	Aliases: Kron 12; Lind 16
Kron 11	cl	00 36 27.9	−72 28 42	Tuc						204	12	Alias: Lind 20
HW 9	cl	00 36 31.3	−72 59 09	Tuc	0.3					204	99	Archinal: May be fainter group just to SW? HW: Faint, 0.3′.
HW 10	cl	00 36 31.9	−72 59 14	Tuc						204	12	
[H86] 35	cl	00 36 38.4	−73 05 09	Tuc	0.4	14.81	11	15.19	12.8	204	13	OGLE: Very probably cluster. Alias: OGLE-CL SMC0001
Kron 14	cl	00 37 21	−72 59.5	Tuc	2.0					204	99	Archinal: Sparse obvious 2′ group on DSS image. Lindsay's 26.1′ size (this is Lindsay 18) is apparently spurious. Alias: Lind 18
HW 11	cl	00 37 33.1	−73 36 42	Tuc	1.0	13.35	127	15.03	13.4	214	13	OGLE: Certain cluster. Alias: OGLE-CL SMC0002
Lindsay 19	cl	00 37 42.3	−73 54 29	Tuc	1.4	13.08	223	16.09	13.8	214	13	OGLE: Certain cluster. Alias: OGLE-CL SMC0003
Bruck 10	cl	00 37 44.1	−73 12 39	Tuc	1.2	13.00	30	13.89	13.4	204	13	OGLE: Very probably cluster. Alias: OGLE-CL SMC0004
Bruck 14	cl?	00 38 37.1	−73 48 20	Tuc	0.4	14.25	25	15.38	12.4	214	99	Archinal: Appears as 24" north-south double star on DSS image. Confirmed against Bruck chart 6. Alias: OGLE-CL SMC0162
HW 12	cl?	00 38 51.3	−73 22 27	Tuc	0.7	14.38	21	16.59	13.6	204	99	Archinal: Only faintly visible on DSS image, sparse group of faint stars. HW: Loose, 0.4′. Alias: OGLE-CL SMC0163

Table C.2: Tables of SMC Objects

Name	Type	2000.0 R.A.	2000.0 Dec.	Con	Diam (′)	Tot Vm	# Str	Bt* Vm	V sur	2 U#	Ref	Comments and Aliases
OGLE-CL SMC0164	cl?	00 38 55.6	−73 24 31	Tuc	0.3	15.97	15	17.80	13.1	204	13	
OGLE-CL SMC0165	cl?	00 39 11.6	−73 14 45	Tuc	0.4	15.52	10	17.40	13.5	204	13	
OGLE-CL SMC0005	cl	00 39 21.7	−73 15 28	Tuc	0.4	16.23	16	18.55	14.1	204	13	OGLE: Very probably cluster.
[H86] 55	cl?	00 39 25.6	−73 06 23	Tuc	0.2	17.42	8	19.00	13.6	204	13	Alias: OGLE-CL SMC0167
HW 13	cl	00 39 30.4	−73 25 33	Tuc						204	12	
OGLE-CL SMC0168	cl?	00 39 30.6	−73 25 25	Tuc	0.5	14.79	11	16.92	13.4	204	13	
OGLE-CL SMC0006	cl	00 39 33.1	−73 10 37	Tuc	0.5	15.22	15	17.16	13.8	204	13	OGLE: Probable cluster.
Kron 15	cl	00 40 13.3	−72 41 56	Tuc						204	12	Alias: Lind 21
HW 14	cl	00 40 15.3	−73 52 20	Tuc						214	12	
OGLE-CL SMC0007	cl	00 40 30.5	−73 13 50	Tuc	0.4	15.17	17	16.76	13.2	204	13	OGLE: Probable cluster.
NGC 220	cl	00 40 30.6	−73 24 10	Tuc	0.8	12.4	256	14.75	11.9	204	13	See notes. Part of association [H85] 2.; OGLE: Certain cluster. Aliases: Kron 18; Lind 22; (3) [H85] 2; OGLE-CL SMC0008
Kron 16	cl	00 40 33.8	−72 44 24	Tuc						204	12	Alias: Lind 23
NGC 222	cl	00 40 44.1	−73 23 00	Tuc	0.6	12.2	128	15.30	11.1	204	13	See notes. Part of association [H85] 2.; OGLE: Certain cluster. Aliases: Kron 19; Lind 24; (3) [H85] 2; OGLE-CL SMC0009
[H86] 60	ast?	00 40 44.3	−73 07 03	Tuc	0.1					204	99	Archinal: Appears as 3 stars, aligned E-W, on DSS image.
Bruck 26	cl?	00 40 44.8	−73 44 26	Tuc	0.5	15.18	27	17.69	13.8	214	13	Alias: OGLE-CL SMC0169
[H86] 62	cl	00 40 47.6	−73 05 16	Tuc	0.4	15.35	15	17.86	13.4	204	13	OGLE: Very probably cluster. Alias: OGLE-CL SMC0010
HW 15	cl	00 40 47.6	−74 01 19	Tuc						214	12	
OGLE-CL SMC0170	cl?	00 40 55.5	−73 24 06	Tuc	0.3	14.76	21	16.11	12.4	204	13	
[H86] 64	cl	00 40 59.2	−73 12 01	Tuc	0.1					204	99	Archinal: Very faint on DSS image, found by comparison with [H86] figure 1.
Kron 17	cl	00 41 01.0	−72 34 20	Tuc						204	12	Alias: Lind 26
NGC 231	cl	00 41 06.2	−73 21 07	Tuc	0.8	12.7	131	15.04	12.2	204	13	See notes. Outer diameter of 100″. Part of association [H85] 2.; OGLE: Certain cluster. Aliases: Dunlop 2; Kron 20; Lind 25; (3) [H85] 2; OGLE-CL SMC0011
Bruck 21	cl?	00 41 15.3	−72 49 54	Tuc	0.2	15.82	6	16.72	12.6	204	99	Archinal: Almost stellar on DSS image. Confirmed against Bruck chart 6. Alias: OGLE-CL SMC0171
Kron 21	cl	00 41 23.8	−72 53 27	Tuc	1.2	13.14	240	16.64	13.5	204	13	OGLE: Certain cluster. Aliases: Lind 27; OGLE-CL SMC0012
OGLE-CL SMC0172	cl?	00 41 48.4	−73 23 27	Tuc	0.2	16.49	12	18.37	13.0	204	13	
OGLE-CL SMC0166	cl?	00 41 56	−73 29.3	Tuc	0.3	15.05	14	16.64	12.4	204	57	See notes. Position is incorrect in OGLE-CL listing. Position here from Bica and Dutra [2000].
OGLE-CL SMC0173	cl?	00 42 11.6	−73 16 02	Tuc	0.2	16.59	6	17.60	13.1	204	13	
HW 17	cl	00 42 17.7	−72 28 14	Tuc						204	12	
HW 16	cl	00 42 22.4	−73 44 03	Tuc	0.5	13.95	30	15.70	12.6	214	13	OGLE: Certain cluster. Alias: OGLE-CL SMC0013
OGLE-CL SMC0014	cl	00 42 27.9	−73 32 49	Tuc	0.4	15.10	17	16.97	13.1	214	13	OGLE: Probable cluster.
OGLE-CL SMC0015	cl	00 42 54.2	−73 17 37	Tuc	0.4	14.39	23	16.08	12.2	204	13	OGLE: Certain cluster.
[BS95] 16	cl	00 42 58.5	−73 10 07	Tuc	1.0	12.00	130	12.62	11.9	204	13	OGLE: Certain cluster. Alias: OGLE-CL SMC0016
HW 18	cl	00 42 59.5	−72 24 40	Tuc						204	12	
Lindsay 28	cl	00 42 59.7	−72 35 20	Tuc						204	12	
[BS95] 17	cl?	00 43 14.3	−73 00 42	Tuc	0.7	14.59	11	17.73	13.8	204	13	Alias: OGLE-CL SMC0174
HW 19	cl	00 43 28.3	−74 11 05	Tuc						214	12	
NGC 241	ass	00 43 28.5	−73 35 36	Tuc	7.5		60			214	99	This is NOT NGC 242 or part of NGC 242, which is about 10′ to the north. Archinal: Large (7.5′) scattered group.

Table C.2: Tables of SMC Objects

Name	Type	2000.0 R.A.	2000.0 Dec.	Con	Diam (′)	Tot Vm	# Str	Bt* Vm	V sur	2 U#	Ref	Comments and Aliases
OGLE-CL SMC0017	cl	00 43 32.8	−73 26 25	Tuc	0.7	12.0	261	14.18	11.1	204	57	OGLE: Certain cluster. Western part of NGC 242 double cluster. Alias: (3) NGC 242
NGC 242	2cl	00 43 33.9	−73 26 28	Tuc	0.9					204	57	This is NOT and does NOT contain NGC 241. Its component clusters are OGLE-CL SMC0017 and [HB90] 1. Aliases: Kron 22; Lind 29; ESO 29-SC6; (2) OGLE-CL SMC0017; (2) [HB90] 1
Bruck 31	cl	00 43 37.6	−72 57 30	Tuc	0.3	15.31	30	17.36	12.9	204	57	See notes. Included twice in OGLE-CL catalogue, as OGLE-CL SMC0019 and OGLE-CL SMC0175. Aliases: OGLE-CL SMC0019; OGLE-CL SMC0175
[HB90] 1	cl	00 43 37.6	−73 26 37	Tuc	0.5	12.0	110	14.18	10.4	204	57	OGLE: Certain cluster. Southeastern part of NGC 242 double cluster. Aliases: OGLE-CL SMC0018; (3) NGC 242
[BS95] 20	cl	00 43 37.9	−72 58 48	Tuc	0.3	15.82	6	17.94	13.2	204	13	OGLE: Probable cluster. Alias: OGLE-CL SMC0020
[H86] 70	cl	00 43 44.4	−72 58 35	Tuc	0.6	14.32	41	16.36	13.2	204	13	OGLE: Certain cluster. Alias: OGLE-CL SMC0021
OGLE-CL SMC0022	cl	00 43 58.0	−73 09 07	Tuc	0.4	14.98	17	17.38	13.0	204	13	OGLE: Probable cluster.
Bruck 33	cl	00 44 12.6	−73 37 08	Tuc	0.4	15.32	27	18.04	13.3	214	13	OGLE: Probable cluster. Alias: OGLE-CL SMC0023
HW 20	cl	00 44 48.1	−74 21 46	Hyi?						214	12	
Bruck 34	cl?	00 44 51.6	−73 00 07	Tuc	0.5	14.51	20	16.70	12.9	204	13	Alias: OGLE-CL SMC0176
[BS95] 27	cl?	00 44 55.1	−73 10 27	Tuc	0.3	14.37	23	16.65	11.8	204	13	Alias: OGLE-CL SMC0177
OGLE-CL SMC0024	cl	00 45 01.2	−72 55 17	Tuc	1.0	12.18	92	13.17	12.2	204	99	OGLE: Very probably cluster. Archinal: Appears as several brighter stars and some fainter background stars on DSS image.
OGLE-CL SMC0178	cl?	00 45 10.9	−72 52 31	Tuc	0.3	15.39	17	17.77	12.8	204	13	
[H86] 74	cl	00 45 13.9	−73 13 09	Tuc	0.5	12.94	65	14.86	11.3	204	13	OGLE: Very probably cluster. Alias: OGLE-CL SMC0025
OGLE-CL SMC0179	cl?	00 45 20.9	−73 02 07	Tuc	0.3	15.09	15	16.68	12.7	204	13	
OGLE-CL SMC0180	cl?	00 45 23.1	−72 55 42	Tuc	0.2	16.36	12	18.60	13.2	204	13	
NGC 248	cl	00 45 24.1	−73 22 44	Tuc	0.8	13.55	20	14.82	13.1	204	99	OGLE: Certain cluster. Archinal: Possibly nebulous and (as noted by J. Herschel) binuclear cluster. Aliases: L61 67; OGLE-CL SMC0026; h 2344; GC 133
Bruck 39	cl	00 45 25.7	−73 28 52	Tuc	0.8	13.53	79	16.79	13.0	204	13	OGLE: Certain cluster. Alias: OGLE-CL SMC0027
OGLE-CL SMC0181	cl?	00 45 27.5	−72 53 08	Tuc	0.4	14.50	20	16.02	12.7	204	13	
OGLE-CL SMC0028	cl	00 45 27.9	−72 49 09	Tuc	0.3	15.82	16	17.51	13.0	204	13	OGLE: Very probably cluster.
Lindsay [1961] 68	cl	00 45 29.8	−73 04 40	Tuc	0.6	13.57	18	14.50	12.5	204	13	OGLE: Certain cluster. Alias: OGLE-CL SMC0029
OGLE-CL SMC0030	cl	00 45 32.9	−73 06 26	Tuc	0.4	15.21	14	16.68	13.2	204	13	OGLE: Probable cluster.
HW 21	cl	00 45 39.6	−74 00 32	Tuc						214	12	
Bruck 36	cl	00 45 43.1	−72 50 26	Tuc	0.4	15.84	42	18.52	13.9	204	99	OGLE: Probable cluster. Archinal: Binuclear. Confirmed on Bruck chart 6. OGLE SMC position is too far east by 8 time seconds. Alias: OGLE-CL SMC0031
NGC 256	cl	00 45 54.4	−73 30 24	Tuc	0.6	12.74	142	14.74	11.7	214	13	OGLE: Certain cluster. Aliases: Kron 23; Lind 30; OGLE-CL SMC0032
[H86] 76	cl?	00 46 01.7	−73 23 44	Tuc	0.2	15.09	10	17.10	11.9	204	13	Alias: OGLE-CL SMC0182
OGLE-CL SMC0183	cl?	00 46 10.4	−73 03 55	Tuc	0.3	14.64	16	16.23	12.2	204	13	
[H86] 80	cl?	00 46 11.2	−72 49 02	Tuc	0.2	16.28	12	17.67	12.8	204	13	Alias: OGLE-CL SMC0184
[H86] 78	cl	00 46 12.3	−73 23 34	Tuc	0.4	13.47	10	14.54	11.5	204	13	OGLE: Probable cluster. Alias: OGLE-CL SMC0033
NGC 261	cl	00 46 33.0	−73 05 55	Tuc	0.4	13.40	16	13.85	11.4	204	13	OGLE: Probable cluster. Aliases: Bruck 42; OGLE-CL SMC0034
[H86] 83	cl	00 46 33.7	−72 46 25	Tuc	0.4	14.37	8	16.05	12.5	204	13	OGLE: Probable cluster. Alias: OGLE-CL SMC0035
[H86] 84	cl?	00 46 34.1	−72 45 55	Tuc	0.1	16.49	11	17.83	12.1	204	13	Alias: OGLE-CL SMC0185
Lindsay 31	cl	00 46 35.0	−72 44 32	Tuc	0.7	13.16	86	14.56	12.3	204	13	OGLE: Certain cluster. Alias: OGLE-CL SMC0036
OGLE-CL SMC0037	cl	00 46 41.1	−72 59 59	Tuc	0.4	14.18	31	14.89	12.0	204	13	OGLE: Probable cluster.

Table C.2: Tables of SMC Objects

Name	Type	2000.0 R.A.	2000.0 Dec.	Con	Diam (′)	Tot Vm	# Str	Bt* Vm	V sur	2 U#	Ref	Comments and Aliases
HW 23	cl	00 46 42.1	−73 46 30	Tuc						214	12	
HW 22	cl	00 46 44.5	−72 03 48	Tuc						204	12	
[H86] 85	cl?	00 46 56.3	−73 25 24	Tuc	0.2	14.84	15	15.63	11.6	204	13	Alias: OGLE-CL SMC0186
[H86] 86	cl	00 47 01.2	−73 23 34	Tuc	0.5	13.69	13	14.75	12.1	204	13	OGLE: Very probably cluster. Alias: OGLE-CL SMC0040
[H86] 89	ast?	00 47 03.7	−73 15 35	Tuc	0.1	13.57	48	15.93	8.6	204	99	OGLE: Probable cluster. Archinal: Possibly just 3 faint stars on DSS. Found via comparison with [H86] figure 3. Alias: OGLE-CL SMC0038
OGLE-CL SMC0187	cl?	00 47 05.9	−73 22 16	Tuc	0.5	13.63	37	14.45	12.0	204	13	
NGC 265	cl	00 47 11.6	−73 28 38	Tuc	1.0	12.21	301	14.99	12.2	204	13	OGLE: Certain cluster. Aliases: Kron 24; Lind 34; OGLE-CL SMC0039
[H86] 93	cl?	00 47 24.4	−73 12 19	Tuc	0.3	14.08	7	15.85	11.7	204	13	Alias: OGLE-CL SMC0188
Lindsay 32	cl	00 47 24.8	−68 55 13	Tuc						204	12	
Lindsay 33	cl	00 47 24.9	−72 50 26	Tuc	0.4	13.92	41	15.96	12.1	204	13	OGLE: Very probably cluster. Alias: OGLE-CL SMC0041
HW 24	cl	00 47 29.3	−72 28 30	Tuc						204	12	
[BS95] 35	cl	00 47 49.7	−73 28 42	Tuc	0.5	14.61	8	16.76	13.0	204	13	OGLE: Doubtful cluster. Alias: OGLE-CL SMC0042
[H86] 97	cl	00 47 52.4	−73 13 20	Tuc	0.5	13.08	74	15.47	11.7	204	13	OGLE: Certain cluster. Alias: OGLE-CL SMC0043
[H86] 98	cl	00 47 54.3	−72 57 02	Tuc	1.0	13.19	50	15.04	13.2	204	99	OGLE: Very probably cluster. Archinal: 10 brighter stars in 1′ group, with fainter background stars. Confirmed against [H86] figure 3. Alias: OGLE-CL SMC0044
Kron 25	cl	00 48 00.7	−73 29 10	Tuc	1.1	12.54	173	15.66	12.7	204	13	OGLE: Certain cluster. Aliases: Lind 35; OGLE-CL SMC0045
OGLE-CL SMC0189	cl?	00 48 09.1	−73 14 19	Tuc	0.4	13.87	14	14.40	11.9	204	13	
[H86] 99	cl?	00 48 13.2	−72 47 34	Tuc	0.4	14.68	7	16.05	12.7	204	13	Alias: OGLE-CL SMC0190
Kron 27	cl	00 48 13.7	−73 51 46	Tuc						214	12	Alias: Lind 36
[H86] 100	cl?	00 48 20.2	−72 47 42	Tuc	0.7	13.67	27	15.01	12.8	204	13	Alias: OGLE-CL SMC0191
NGC 269	cl	00 48 21.3	−73 31 49	Tuc	0.6	13.35	218	15.20	12.2	214	13	OGLE: Certain cluster. Aliases: Kron 26; Lind 37; OGLE-CL SMC0046
OGLE-CL SMC0192	cl?	00 48 26.1	−73 00 25	Tuc	0.3	15.28	9	17.86	12.9	204	13	
OGLE-CL SMC0047	cl	00 48 28.2	−72 59 00	Tuc	0.8	12.64	23	13.61	12.2	204	13	OGLE: Very probably cluster.
Bruck 47	cl	00 48 33.3	−73 18 25	Tuc	0.8	12.53	119	13.79	12.0	204	13	OGLE: Certain cluster. Alias: OGLE-CL SMC0048
OGLE-CL SMC0193	cl?	00 48 36.6	−73 10 45	Tuc	0.5	14.06	26	16.52	12.6	204	13	
Bruck 48	cl	00 48 37.5	−73 24 53	Tuc	0.8	12.55	64	14.22	12.1	204	13	OGLE: Very probably cluster. Alias: OGLE-CL SMC0049
HW 25	cl	00 48 44.5	−74 18 11	Tuc?						214	12	
Lindsay 38	cl	00 48 51.0	−69 52 14	Tuc						204	12	
Bruck 49	**	00 48 55.7	−73 33 37	Tuc						214	99	Double star identification from Brian Skiff. Aliases: HD 4852; CPD−74 66; CD−74 36
OGLE-CL SMC0050	cl	00 48 59.0	−73 09 03	Tuc	0.4	14.37	22	16.70	12.4	204	13	OGLE: Probable cluster.
[H86] 103	cl	00 49 04.8	−73 03 03	Tuc	0.4	13.91	34	15.54	11.8	204	13	OGLE: Probable cluster. Alias: OGLE-CL SMC0051
[BS95] 41	cl?	00 49 05.6	−73 21 09	Tuc	0.4	13.66	13	14.90	11.7	204	13	Alias: OGLE-CL SMC0194
[H86] 104	cl	00 49 12.2	−73 06 30	Tuc	0.3	15.51	31	17.87	12.7	204	13	OGLE: Very probably cluster. Alias: OGLE-CL SMC0052
[BS95] 42	cl?	00 49 16.5	−73 14 56	Tuc	0.9	12.08	4	13.42	11.9	204	13	Alias: OGLE-CL SMC0195
OGLE-CL SMC0053	cl	00 49 17.5	−73 12 41	Tuc	0.4	14.10	20	15.57	12.1	204	13	OGLE: Probable cluster.
Lindsay 39	cl	00 49 17.6	−73 22 19	Tuc	0.6	13.10	87	15.21	12.0	204	13	OGLE: Certain cluster. Alias: OGLE-CL SMC0054
OGLE-CL SMC0055	cl	00 49 21.3	−73 11 01	Tuc	0.4	14.41	17	16.27	12.4	204	13	OGLE: Probable cluster.
OGLE-CL SMC0196	cl?	00 49 26.8	−73 23 55	Tuc	0.3	15.00	11	17.23	12.6	204	13	

Table C.2: Tables of SMC Objects

Name	Type	2000.0 R.A.	2000.0 Dec.	Con	Diam (′)	Tot Vm	# Str	Bt* Vm	V sur	2 U#	Ref	Comments and Aliases
OGLE-CL SMC0056	cl	00 49 36.3	−72 50 12	Tuc	0.4	15.05	7	17.54	13.1	204	13	OGLE: Probable cluster.
Bruck 52	cl	00 49 39.8	−73 03 31	Tuc	1.0	12.27	150	14.19	12.3	204	13	OGLE: Certain cluster. Alias: OGLE-CL SMC0057
HW 26	cl	00 49 42.3	−73 42 36	Tuc						214	12	
[H86] 109	cl	00 49 45.5	−72 51 58	Tuc	0.7	13.61	32	16.34	12.7	204	13	OGLE: Certain cluster. Alias: OGLE-CL SMC0058
[H86] 107	cl	00 50 00.3	−73 15 17	Tuc	0.6	12.99	37	14.55	11.9	204	13	OGLE: Very probably cluster. Alias: OGLE-CL SMC0061
Bruck 53	cl?	00 50 03.8	−73 23 03	Tuc	0.8	13.12	37	16.03	12.6	204	13	Alias: OGLE-CL SMC0197
[H86] 112	cl?	00 50 07.5	−73 11 25	Tuc	0.7	12.38	60	14.48	11.7	204	13	Alias: OGLE-CL SMC0198
OGLE-CL SMC0199	cl?	00 50 15.1	−73 03 14	Tuc	0.2	15.51	6	17.30	12.3	204	13	
[BS95] 45	cl	00 50 16.1	−73 01 59	Tuc	0.8	12.91	62	14.51	12.5	204	13	OGLE: Probable cluster. Alias: OGLE-CL SMC0059
Bruck 55	cl	00 50 22.0	−73 23 16	Tuc	0.6	13.05	91	15.22	11.9	204	13	OGLE: Certain cluster. Alias: OGLE-CL SMC0060
Bruck 54	cl	00 50 28.1	−73 12 11	Tuc	0.4	14.58	28	17.52	12.4	204	13	OGLE: Certain cluster. Alias: OGLE-CL SMC0062
HW 27	cl	00 50 32.8	−74 36 51	Tuc						214	12	
[H86] 115	cl	00 50 36.9	−73 03 28	Tuc	0.8	12.91	34	15.26	12.4	204	13	OGLE: Probable cluster. Alias: OGLE-CL SMC0063
Lindsay 40	ass	00 50 38.5	−72 58 08	Tuc	2.0					204	99	Archinal: Lindsay diameter of 12.5′ is far too large a size for this 2′ association. Alias: (2) [H86] 116
[BS95] 46	cl?	00 50 39.0	−72 58 43	Tuc	0.4	13.39	27	15.04	11.2	204	13	Alias: OGLE-CL SMC0200
[H86] 116	cl	00 50 39.6	−72 57 54	Tuc	0.6	12.73	121	14.89	11.7	204	99	OGLE: Certain cluster. Aliases: OGLE-CL SMC0064; (3) Lind 40
HW 28	cl	00 50 40.2	−74 07 02	Tuc						214	12	
[BS95] 48	cl?	00 50 42.5	−73 23 49	Tuc	0.6	13.58	52	16.02	12.6	204	13	Alias: OGLE-CL SMC0201
OGLE-CL SMC0065	cl	00 50 54.6	−73 03 26	Tuc	0.4	14.56	30	17.24	12.6	204	13	OGLE: Probable cluster.
Bruck 56	cl	00 50 55.4	−73 12 11	Tuc	0.5	12.85	28	14.36	11.2	204	13	OGLE: Probable cluster. Alias: OGLE-CL SMC0066
Lindsay 41	cl	00 50 55.6	−72 43 39	Tuc	0.6	12.54	154	14.80	11.4	204	13	OGLE: Certain cluster. Alias: OGLE-CL SMC0067
[BS95] 40	cl	00 50 56.3	−73 17 21	Tuc	0.8	12.15	132	13.98	11.7	204	13	OGLE: Probable cluster. Alias: OGLE-CL SMC0068
OGLE-CL SMC0202	cl?	00 50 58.7	−73 30 13	Tuc	0.3	14.72	16	16.41	12.3	214	13	
OGLE-CL SMC0203	cl?	00 51 10.3	−73 35 23	Tuc	0.2	14.96	13	16.68	11.5	214	13	
NGC 290	cl	00 51 14.2	−73 09 41	Tuc	0.8	12.0	228	13.77	11.5	204	13	OGLE: Certain cluster. Aliases: Lind 42; OGLE-CL SMC0069
[H86] 121	cl?	00 51 21.4	−73 08 18	Tuc	0.3	13.22	31	14.58	10.8	204	13	Alias: OGLE-CL SMC0204
[BS95] 251	cl	00 51 26.2	−73 16 59	Tuc	0.5	13.45	27	14.53	11.8	204	13	OGLE: Very probably cluster. Alias: OGLE-CL SMC0070
[H86] 124	cl?	00 51 31.3	−72 58 43	Tuc	0.6	13.49	12	15.94	12.4	204	13	Alias: OGLE-CL SMC0205
OGLE-CL SMC0071	cl	00 51 31.8	−73 00 38	Tuc	0.8	12.30	61	14.07	11.8	204	13	OGLE: Certain cluster.
Kron 28	cl	00 51 40.6	−71 59 59	Tuc						204	99	Alias: Lind 43
OGLE-CL SMC0072	cl	00 51 41.7	−73 13 46	Tuc	0.6	12.65	36	14.54	11.5	204	13	OGLE: Probable cluster.
Lindsay [1961] 184	cl	00 51 44.1	−72 50 25	Tuc	0.8	12.40	131	15.48	11.9	204	13	OGLE: Certain cluster. Alias: OGLE-CL SMC0073
[H86] 123	cl?	00 51 44.4	−73 10 01	Tuc	0.5	13.07	23	14.63	11.7	204	13	Alias: OGLE-CL SMC0206
[H86] 127	cl?	00 51 48.8	−72 32 27	Tuc	0.4	14.92	22	16.83	12.9	204	13	Alias: OGLE-CL SMC0207
Kron 29	cl	00 51 52.9	−72 57 13	Tuc	0.9	11.99	187	15.47	11.8	204	13	OGLE: Certain cluster. Aliases: Lind 44; OGLE-CL SMC0074
[H86] 126	cl	00 51 54.3	−73 05 52	Tuc	0.5	13.56	32	15.51	11.9	204	13	OGLE: Probable cluster. Alias: OGLE-CL SMC0075
OGLE-CL SMC0208	cl?	00 52 02.8	−72 49 03	Tuc	0.3	14.42	27	16.02	11.6	204	13	
[H86] 129	cl	00 52 12.5	−72 31 51	Tuc	0.6	13.33	60	15.85	12.1	204	13	OGLE: Certain cluster. Alias: OGLE-CL SMC0076

Table C.2: Tables of SMC Objects

Name	Type	2000.0 R.A.	2000.0 Dec.	Con	Diam (′)	Tot Vm	# Str	Bt* Vm	V sur	2 U#	Ref	Comments and Aliases
[BS95] 56	cl	00 52 13.4	−73 00 12	Tuc	0.5	13.48	8	14.97	12.1	204	13	OGLE: Probable cluster. Alias: OGLE-CL SMC0077
OGLE-CL SMC0209	cl?	00 52 15.3	−72 45 58	Tuc	0.4	12.42	8	12.70	10.4	204	13	
[H86] 130	cl	00 52 16.6	−73 01 04	Tuc	0.7	12.63	41	14.72	11.8	204	13	OGLE: Probable cluster. Alias: OGLE-CL SMC0078
[H86] 125	cl	00 52 16.8	−73 22 32	Tuc	0.7	13.57	53	15.90	12.8	204	13	OGLE: Very probably cluster. Alias: OGLE-CL SMC0079
Bruck 64	cl?	00 52 30.3	−73 02 59	Tuc	0.7	12.99	5	14.49	12.2	204	13	Alias: OGLE-CL SMC0210
[H86] 132	cl	00 52 31.5	−72 37 46	Tuc	0.3	15.23	23	17.12	12.4	204	13	OGLE: Probable cluster. Alias: OGLE-CL SMC0080
[BS95] 57	cl?	00 52 32.2	−73 02 10	Tuc	0.5	13.13	6	14.01	11.5	204	13	Alias: OGLE-CL SMC0211
[H86] 133	cl	00 52 33.7	−72 40 53	Tuc	0.6	13.85	97	15.80	12.7	204	13	OGLE: Certain cluster. Alias: OGLE-CL SMC0081
Kron 30	cl	00 52 35.4	−72 11 35	Tuc						204	12	Alias: Lind 45
[BS95] 60	cl	00 52 42.1	−72 55 31	Tuc	0.6	13.47	53	15.72	12.2	204	13	OGLE: Very probably cluster. Alias: OGLE-CL SMC0082
Bruck 65	cl	00 52 44.3	−72 58 47	Tuc	0.6	12.52	80	14.76	11.4	204	13	OGLE: Certain cluster. Alias: OGLE-CL SMC0083
OGLE-CL SMC0212	cl?	00 52 44.5	−72 59 24	Tuc	0.3	14.59	8	15.89	12.0	204	57	See notes. According to [H86] figure 3, this is NOT [H86] 134 as OGLE-CL SMC catalogue inci-cates.
[BS95] 63	cl	00 52 46.7	−73 24 25	Tuc	0.4	14.36	28	16.55	12.4	204	13	OGLE: Probable cluster. Alias: OGLE-CL SMC0084
Bruck 66	cl	00 52 47.7	−72 47 45	Tuc	0.4	14.13	38	15.93	12.1	204	13	OGLE: Very probably cluster. Alias: OGLE-CL SMC0085
[H86] 135	cl	00 52 48.2	−72 30 38	Tuc	0.4	14.82	40	16.46	12.8	204	13	OGLE: Very probably cluster. Alias: OGLE-CL SMC0086
[H86] 134	cl?	00 52 48.3	−72 59 22	Tuc	0.4	14.25	28	16.86	12.3	204	57	See notes. Comparison of [H86] figure 3 with OGLE-CL SMC catalogue shows this is OGLE-CL SMC0213. Alias: OGLE-CL SMC0213
Bruck 67	cl	00 52 49.0	−73 24 43	Tuc	0.6	13.60	123	16.33	12.4	204	13	OGLE: Certain cluster. Alias: OGLE-CL SMC0087
Kron 31	cl	00 53 00.6	−72 53 48	Tuc	1.0	12.34	440	15.85	12.3	204	13	OGLE: Certain cluster. Aliases: Lind 46; OGLE-CL SMC0088
Bruck 69	cl	00 53 05.3	−72 37 27	Tuc	0.6	12.66	87	14.23	11.6	204	13	OGLE: Certain cluster. Alias: OGLE-CL SMC0089
NGC 294	cl	00 53 05.6	−73 22 49	Tuc	0.8	12.68	410	16.08	12.2	204	13	OGLE: Certain cluster. Aliases: Lind 47; OGLE-CL SMC0090
OGLE-CL SMC0214	cl?	00 53 08.6	−72 49 57	Tuc	0.3	14.62	9	15.30	11.8	204	13	
[H86] 138	cl	00 53 09.6	−72 34 24	Tuc	0.6	14.09	59	17.38	13.0	204	13	OGLE: Very probably cluster. Alias: OGLE-CL SMC0091
OGLE-CL SMC0215	cl?	00 53 16.9	−72 44 02	Tuc	0.4	13.32	7	14.12	11.3	204	13	
Bruck 71	cl	00 53 17.9	−72 45 59	Tuc	0.7	11.77	93	13.24	10.9	204	13	OGLE: Certain cluster. Alias: OGLE-CL SMC0092
NGC 299	cl	00 53 24.8	−72 11 47	Tuc						204	12	Aliases: Kron 32; Lind 49
Lindsay 48	cl	00 53 27.9	−71 23 56	Tuc						204	12	
[H86] 143	cl	00 53 31.3	−72 40 04	Tuc	0.6	14.14	25	16.27	13.0	204	13	OGLE: Very probably cluster. Alias: OGLE-CL SMC0093
[H86] 140	cl	00 53 40.1	−72 39 35	Tuc	0.3	15.01	9	16.55	12.2	204	13	OGLE: Probable cluster. Alias: OGLE-CL SMC0094
[BS95] 68	cl	00 53 42.1	−73 21 31	Tuc	0.8	13.66	45	17.08	13.2	204	13	OGLE: Probable cluster. Alias: OGLE-CL SMC0095
Lindsay [1961] 244	cl	00 53 42.3	−72 39 14	Tuc	0.3	14.31	34	15.69	11.9	204	13	OGLE: Very probably cluster. Aliases: Bruck 73; OGLE-CL SMC0096
HW 29	cl	00 53 49.4	−74 08 33	Tuc						214	12	
[H86] 147	cl?	00 53 50.2	−72 53 47	Tuc	1.3	11.62	85	12.97	12.2	204	13	Alias: OGLE-CL SMC0216
[BS95] 69	cl?	00 53 56.5	−72 51 23	Tuc	0.3	15.50	15	17.18	12.7	204	13	Alias: OGLE-CL SMC0217
[BS95] 72	cl	00 54 11.0	−72 51 54	Tuc	0.7	14.06	22	16.86	13.2	204	13	OGLE: Probable cluster. Alias: OGLE-CL SMC0097
NGC 306	cl	00 54 14.8	−72 14 28	Tuc						204	12	Aliases: Kron 33; Lind 50
[H86] 152	cl?	00 54 22.8	−72 41 41	Tuc	0.4	14.09	63	17.18	12.1	204	13	Alias: OGLE-CL SMC0218
HW 30	cl	00 54 28.3	−73 37 05	Tuc						214	12	

Table C.2: Tables of SMC Objects

Name	Type	2000.0 R.A.	2000.0 Dec.	Con	Diam (′)	Tot Vm	# Str	Bt* Vm	V sur	2 U#	Ref	Comments and Aliases
Bruck 80	cl	00 54 46.8	–73 13 24	Tuc	0.8	13.04	120	15.25	12.6	204	13	OGLE: Certain cluster. Alias: OGLE-CL SMC0098
Bruck 79	cl	00 54 48.3	–72 27 57	Tuc	0.8	12.19	137	13.68	11.6	204	13	OGLE: Certain cluster. Alias: OGLE-CL SMC0099
Bruck 76	cl?	00 54 51.5	–72 54 59	Tuc	0.2	15.60	7	17.73	12.4	204	13	Alias: OGLE-CL SMC0219
Lindsay 51	cl	00 54 54.8	–72 06 46	Tuc						204	12	
[H86] 158	cl	00 55 08.6	–72 48 40	Tuc	0.5	14.63	32	17.12	13.0	204	13	OGLE: Probable cluster. Alias: OGLE-CL SMC0100
[H86] 155	cl	00 55 11.7	–73 17 47	Tuc	0.5	14.34	43	17.30	13.0	204	13	OGLE: Very probably cluster. Alias: OGLE-CL SMC0101
[H86] 159	cl	00 55 12.1	–72 40 60	Tuc	0.6	13.67	97	15.20	12.6	204	13	OGLE: Probable cluster. Alias: OGLE-CL SMC0102
OGLE-CL SMC0220	cl?	00 55 14.1	–72 36 03	Tuc	0.3	15.05	21	17.17	12.6	204	99	Archinal: DSS plate defect (vertical line) to NE.
Lindsay 52	cl	00 55 17.7	–73 30 30	Tuc						214	12	
Bruck 83	cl	00 55 29.7	–73 04 17	Tuc	0.8	12.35	93	12.94	11.9	204	13	OGLE: Certain cluster. Alias: OGLE-CL SMC0103
Kron 34	cl	00 55 33.0	–72 49 58	Tuc	0.9	12.65	366	16.31	12.5	204	13	OGLE: Certain cluster. Aliases: Lind 53; OGLE-CL SMC0104
HW 31	cl	00 55 33.9	–74 03 49	Tuc						214	12	
[H86] 165	cl	00 55 43.0	–72 52 48	Tuc	1.0	12.71	52	15.61	12.6	204	13	OGLE: Very probably cluster. Alias: OGLE-CL SMC0105
OGLE-CL SMC0221	cl?	00 55 44.8	–72 42 18	Tuc	0.2	15.82	23	17.89	12.3	204	13	
OGLE-CL SMC0106	cl	00 56 08.9	–73 12 22	Tuc	0.6	14.25	19	15.90	13.1	204	13	OGLE: Probable cluster.
Bruck 86	cl?	00 56 15.9	–72 30 58	Tuc	0.3	14.89	14	15.93	12.0	204	13	Alias: OGLE-CL SMC0222
NGC 330	cl	00 56 18.7	–72 27 50	Tuc	1.4	9.6	874	12.62	10.4	204	13	OGLE: Certain cluster. Aliases: Kron 35; Lind 54; OGLE-CL SMC0107
[BS95] 81	cl?	00 56 25.6	–72 29 45	Tuc	0.2	15.36	12	15.87	11.9	204	13	Alias: OGLE-CL SMC0223
[H86] 172	cl	00 56 34.5	–72 30 08	Tuc	0.5	14.47	36	16.49	13.0	204	13	OGLE: Probable cluster. Alias: OGLE-CL SMC0108
Lindsay 55	cl	00 56 44.8	–73 53 56	Tuc						214	12	
OGLE-CL SMC0224	cl?	00 56 45.9	–72 45 06	Tuc	0.4	14.91	17	16.99	12.9	204	13	
[H86] 174	cl?	00 57 17.8	–72 56 01	Tuc	0.5	14.72	26	17.75	13.1	204	13	Alias: OGLE-CL SMC0225
HW 32	cl	00 57 20.8	–71 10 14	Tuc						204	12	
HW 33	cl	00 57 23.6	–70 48 33	Tuc						204	12	
Lindsay 56	cl	00 57 29.8	–72 15 51	Tuc	0.6	13.09	270	14.17	12.0	204	99	OGLE: Probable cluster. Archinal: Fairly bright condensed cluster, with extension to NE. OGLE-CL SMC catalogue missed identification. Alias: OGLE-CL SMC0109
NGC 339	cl	00 57 45.4	–74 28 20	Tuc						214	12	Aliases: Kron 36; Lind 59
[H86] 178	cl	00 57 46.2	–72 42 20	Tuc	0.4	12.74	36	13.07	10.8	204	13	OGLE: Certain cluster. Alias: OGLE-CL SMC0110
Kron 37	cl	00 57 47.5	–74 19 37	Tuc						214	12	Alias: Lind 58
Kron 38	cl	00 57 48.3	–73 25 19	Tuc						204	12	Alias: Lind 57
[H86] 177	cl?	00 57 49.8	–72 30 29	Tuc	0.5	13.78	12	14.66	12.1	204	13	Alias: OGLE-CL SMC0226
[H86] 175	cl?	00 57 50.3	–72 26 23	Tuc	0.2	14.43	15	15.00	11.2	204	13	Alias: OGLE-CL SMC0227
[BS95] 88	cl	00 57 50.3	–72 56 36	Tuc	0.3	15.60	22	18.03	13.0	204	13	OGLE: Very probably cluster. Alias: OGLE-CL SMC0111
HW 34	cl	00 57 52.1	–73 32 44	Tuc						214	12	
[H86] 179	cl	00 57 57.2	–72 26 42	Tuc	0.6	14.25	43	16.85	13.1	204	13	OGLE: Very probably cluster. Alias: OGLE-CL SMC0112
Lindsay [1961] 331	cl	00 58 16.3	–72 38 46	Tuc	0.5	14.41	5	15.25	12.8	204	99	OGLE: Probable cluster. Archinal: Tiny cluster in center of circular HII region. Alias: OGLE-CL SMC0113
[H86] 181	cl?	00 58 19.4	–72 17 56	Tuc	0.3	13.38	21	14.45	11.0	204	13	Alias: OGLE-CL SMC0228
Lindsay [1961] 335	cl	00 58 25.8	–72 39 56	Tuc	0.4	13.71	51	15.12	11.7	204	13	OGLE: Certain cluster. Alias: OGLE-CL SMC0114

Table C.2: Tables of SMC Objects

Name	Type	2000.0 R.A.	2000.0 Dec.	Con	Diam (′)	Tot Vm	# Str	Bt* Vm	V sur	2 U#	Ref	Comments and Aliases
[H86] 183	cl	00 58 33.7	−72 16 51	Tuc	0.5	14.08	24	15.75	12.6	204	13	OGLE: Probable cluster. Alias: OGLE-CL SMC0115
[BS95] 272	cl?	00 58 38.1	−72 14 04	Tuc	0.7	13.35	6	14.90	12.5	204	13	Alias: OGLE-CL SMC0229
HW 35	cl	00 58 42.4	−73 35 03	Tuc						214	12	
HW 36	cl	00 59 03.7	−73 50 31	Tuc						214	12	
OGLE-CL SMC0116	cl	00 59 04.6	−72 47 11	Tuc	0.4	14.11	21	14.98	12.3	204	13	OGLE: Probable cluster.
NGC 346	cl	00 59.1	−72 11	Tuc	5.2	10.3			13.9	204	99	DSFG: Involved in nebulosity which also carries the same designation. Archinal: Impressive cluster and nebula on DSS image. Aliases: Lind 60; LHA 115-N 66A
Bruck 96	cl	00 59 13.9	−72 36 29	Tuc	0.9	13.10	130	15.99	12.9	204	13	OGLE: Certain cluster. Alias: OGLE-CL SMC0117
HW 37	cl	00 59 15.4	−71 46 08	Tuc						204	12	
HW 38	cl	00 59 26.1	−73 49 02	Tuc						214	12	
HW 39	cl	00 59 30.9	−71 40 10	Tuc						204	12	
IC 1611	cl	00 59 48.1	−72 20 02	Tuc	1.0	11.96	336	14.74	11.9	204	13	OGLE: Certain cluster. Aliases: Lind 61; Kron 40; OGLE-CL SMC0118
[H86] 186	cl	00 59 56.9	−72 22 24	Tuc	0.3	13.84	22	15.58	11.2	204	13	OGLE: Probable cluster. Alias: OGLE-CL SMC0119
IC 1612	cl	01 00 01.4	−72 22 08	Tuc	0.7	12.48	104	14.40	11.7	204	13	OGLE: Certain cluster. Aliases: Lind 62; Kron 41; OGLE-CL SMC0120
[H86] 188	cl	01 00 13.1	−72 27 43	Tuc	0.8	13.26	45	15.11	12.8	204	13	OGLE: Very probably cluster. Alias: OGLE-CL SMC0121
HW 40	cl	01 00 25.6	−71 17 41	Tuc						204	12	
Bruck 99	cl	01 00 26.8	−73 05 11	Tuc	0.9	13.37	44	16.39	13.1	204	13	OGLE: Certain cluster. Alias: OGLE-CL SMC0122
[H86] 189	cl	01 00 33.1	−72 14 23	Tuc	0.8	13.35	78	15.46	12.9	204	13	OGLE: Certain cluster. Alias: OGLE-CL SMC0123
OGLE-CL SMC0230	cl?	01 00 33.2	−72 15 30	Tuc	0.3	14.83	19	16.47	12.2	204	13	
Kron 42	cl	01 00 34.4	−72 21 55	Tuc	0.8	12.40	130	13.94	11.9	204	13	OGLE: Certain cluster. Aliases: Lind 63; OGLE-CL SMC0124
HW 41	cl	01 00 35.8	−71 27 40	Tuc	0.8					204	99	Archinal: Faint, extended, on DSS image. HW: Loose, 0.8′.
OGLE-CL SMC0125	cl	01 00 46.8	−72 55 41	Tuc	0.4	14.13	20	15.12	12.3	204	13	OGLE: Probable cluster.
Kron 43	cl	01 00 49.7	−73 20 57	Tuc						204	12	Alias: Lind 64
[H86] 191	cl?	01 00 58.2	−72 32 24	Tuc	0.7	13.82	49	16.17	13.0	204	13	Alias: OGLE-CL SMC0231
Lindsay 65	cl	01 01 02.0	−72 45 05	Tuc	1.0	12.99	95	15.73	12.9	204	13	OGLE: Certain cluster. Aliases: [H86] 192; OGLE-CL SMC0126
HW 43	cl	01 01 08.2	−71 45 17	Tuc						204	12	
HW 42	cl	01 01 08.7	−74 04 25	Tuc						214	12	
OGLE-CL SMC0232	cl?	01 01 13.6	−72 33 03	Tuc	0.3	15.44	13	16.77	12.6	204	13	
[H86] 193	cl	01 01 17.8	−72 13 42	Tuc	0.4	14.31	39	15.98	12.5	204	13	OGLE: Certain cluster. Alias: OGLE-CL SMC0127
HW 44	cl	01 01 22.5	−73 47 16	Tuc						214	12	
Bruck 105	cl	01 01 37.2	−72 24 24	Tuc	0.8	13.52	54	16.43	13.1	204	13	OGLE: Certain cluster. Alias: OGLE-CL SMC0128
Lindsay 66	cl	01 01 45.1	−72 33 51	Tuc	0.7	11.71	163	12.76	10.8	204	13	OGLE: Certain cluster. Alias: OGLE-CL SMC0129
Bruck 108	cl	01 01 52.3	−72 10 57	Tuc	0.9	13.46	79	15.80	13.3	204	99	OGLE: Certain cluster. Archinal: Three component cluster. Identity confirmed on Bruck plate 7. Alias: OGLE-CL SMC0130
OGLE-CL SMC0131	cl	01 02 03.3	−72 31 18	Tuc	0.3	15.08	19	16.11	12.2	204	13	OGLE: Probable cluster.
Kron 44	cl	01 02 05.2	−73 55 33	Tuc						214	12	Alias: Lind 68
NGC 361	cl	01 02 11.3	−71 36 25	Tuc						204	12	Aliases: Kron 46; Lind 67
OGLE-CL SMC0132	cl	01 02 13.2	−72 57 59	Tuc	0.4	14.78	42	16.92	12.9	204	13	OGLE: Very probably cluster.
OGLE-CL SMC0133	cl	01 02 30.9	−72 19 05	Tuc	0.7	14.28	62	16.72	13.4	204	13	OGLE: Certain cluster.

Table C.2: Tables of SMC Objects

Name	Type	2000.0 R.A.	2000.0 Dec.	Con	Diam (′)	Tot Vm	# Str	Bt* Vm	V sur	2 U#	Ref	Comments and Aliases
OGLE-CL SMC0233	cl?	01 02 40.0	–72 23 50	Tuc	0.4	14.18	25	15.91	12.2	204	13	
Kron 45	cl	01 02 47.9	–73 44 22	Tuc						214	99	Archinal: On DSS overlap boundary. Alias: Lind 69
OGLE-CL SMC0234	cl?	01 02 53.2	–72 24 53	Tuc	0.5	13.65	18	15.25	12.1	204	13	
Kron 47	cl	01 03 11.5	–72 16 21	Tuc	0.6	12.83	95	14.96	11.7	204	13	OGLE: Certain cluster. Aliases: Lind 70; OGLE-CL SMC0134
OGLE-CL SMC0135	cl	01 03 16.7	–72 44 26	Tuc	0.9	14.06	70	16.91	13.9	204	13	OGLE: Probable cluster.
NGC 371	cl	01 03.3	–72 05	Tuc	7.5					204	99	Archinal: Large sparse star cloud or association. Aliases: Mel 5; Lind 71
OGLE-CL SMC0136	cl	01 03 22.1	–72 27 57	Tuc	0.5	14.61	12	16.30	13.0	204	13	OGLE: Probable cluster.
OGLE-CL SMC0137	cl	01 03 22.7	–72 39 05	Tuc	0.6	13.17	89	15.15	12.1	204	13	OGLE: Certain cluster.
HW 45	cl	01 03 49.2	–71 47 31	Tuc						204	12	
Lindsay [1961] 420	cl	01 03 53.0	–72 06 10	Tuc	0.4	13.69	35	15.87	11.5	204	13	OGLE: Certain cluster. Alias: OGLE-CL SMC0138
NGC 376	cl	01 03 53.5	–72 49 34	Tuc	1.0	10.88	470	12.75	10.9	204	13	See notes. OGLE: Certain cluster. Aliases: h 2378; Kron 49; Lind 72; ESO 010219–7305.5; ESO 29-SC29; OGLE-CL SMC0139
OGLE-CL SMC0235	cl?	01 03 59.0	–72 48 18	Tuc	0.3	14.60	20	15.26	11.8	204	13	
HW 46	cl	01 03 59.7	–73 41 58	Tuc						214	12	
HW 47	cl	01 04 04.4	–74 37 10	Tuc						214	12	
OGLE-CL SMC0144	cl	01 04 05.3	–72 07 14	Tuc	0.5	14.37	6	15.85	12.7	204	57	See notes. Included twice in OGLE-CL catalogue, as OGLE-CL SMC0144 and OGLE-CL SMC0236. Alias: OGLE-CL SMC0236
OGLE-CL SMC0140	cl	01 04 14.1	–72 38 49	Tuc	0.6	13.55	38	14.73	12.4	204	13	OGLE: Probable cluster.
OGLE-CL SMC0237	cl?	01 04 22.5	–72 50 51	Tuc	0.9	13.24	70	15.24	12.9	204	13	
Lindsay 73	cl	01 04 25.1	–70 20 43	Tuc						204	12	
Bruck 121	cl	01 04 30.2	–72 37 09	Tuc	0.8	13.29	92	15.29	12.8	204	13	OGLE: Certain cluster. Alias: OGLE-CL SMC0141
Kron 50	cl	01 04 36.2	–72 09 38	Tuc	0.8	12.41	155	14.29	11.9	204	13	OGLE: Certain cluster. Aliases: Lind 74; OGLE-CL SMC0142
[BS95] 125	cl	01 04 39.6	–72 32 59	Tuc	0.8	13.57	76	15.73	13.0	204	13	OGLE: Very probably cluster. Alias: OGLE-CL SMC0143
HW 48	cl	01 04 58.8	–73 38 16	Tuc						214	12	
OGLE-CL SMC0147	cl	01 05 08.0	–71 59 45	Tuc	0.5	13.32	102	15.00	11.7	204	99	OGLE: Certain cluster. Archinal: E nearly stellar (on DSS) "clump" in NGC 395.
Lindsay [1961] 439	ptcl	01 05 08.1	–71 59 43	Tuc	0.5	13.69	86	16.39	12.3	204	99	OGLE: Certain cluster. Archinal: Center/west "clump" of stars in NGC 395, identified via Lindsay [1961] figure 3. Aliases: OGLE-CL SMC0145; (3) NGC 395
OGLE-CL SMC0148	cl	01 05 09.7	–72 36 07	Tuc	0.6	14.43	23	16.17	13.4	204	13	OGLE: Probable cluster.
NGC 395	ass	01 05 11	–71 59.3	Tuc						204	99	Archinal: Large (2′) association as described by John Herschel. Position here measured from DSS. Aliases: Kron 51; Lind 75; h 2379; GC 216; (2) L61 439
OGLE-CL SMC0146	cl	01 05 13.4	–71 59 41	Tuc	0.4	13.12	20	13.86	11.1	204	99	OGLE: Very probably cluster. Archinal: S central "clump" of stars in NGC 395.
IC 1624	cl	01 05 21.5	–72 02 34	Tuc	0.7	12.94	130	15.73	12.1	204	13	OGLE: Certain cluster. Aliases: Kron 52; Lind 76; OGLE-CL SMC0149
HW 49	cl	01 05 56.9	–73 23 20	Tuc						204	12	
[BS95] 131	cl	01 05 59.6	–72 20 29	Tuc	0.4	14.04	46	15.85	12.1	204	13	OGLE: Certain cluster. Alias: OGLE-CL SMC0150
HW 50	cl	01 06 03.5	–71 42 41	Tuc	0.9					204	99	Archinal: Faint on DSS image. HW: Loose, 0.9′.
OGLE-CL SMC0151	cl	01 06 12.6	–72 47 38	Tuc	0.9	13.90	20	16.20	13.7	204	13	OGLE: Probable cluster.
IC 1626	cl	01 06 13.8	–73 17 52	Tuc						204	12	Aliases: Kron 53; Lind 77
HW 51	cl	01 06 18.3	–74 38 04	Tuc						214	12	
OGLE-CL SMC0152	cl	01 06 21.1	–72 49 48	Tuc	0.3	15.37	13	16.32	12.8	204	13	OGLE: Probable cluster.
Kron 54	cl	01 06 47.8	–72 16 24	Tuc	0.6	12.65	91	14.78	11.6	204	13	OGLE: Certain cluster. Aliases: Lind 79; OGLE-CL SMC0153

Table C.2: Tables of SMC Objects

Name	Type	2000.0 R.A.	2000.0 Dec.	Con	Diam (′)	Tot Vm	# Str	Bt* Vm	V sur	2 U#	Ref	Comments and Aliases
Lindsay 78	cl	01 06 53.7	−71 41 28	Tuc						204	12	
HW 52	cl	01 06 57.3	−73 14 09	Tuc						204	12	
HW 53	cl	01 06 59.0	−73 34 42	Tuc						214	12	
Bruck 129	cl	01 07 02.3	−72 37 18	Tuc	0.8	13.22	70	14.61	12.7	204	13	OGLE: Probable cluster. Alias: OGLE-CL SMC0154
HW 54	cl	01 07 16.0	−72 06 08	Tuc						204	12	
HW 55	cl	01 07 20.0	−73 22 40	Tuc						204	12	
Kron 56	cl	01 07 27.9	−72 29 35	Tuc	0.9	12.95	99	15.42	12.8	204	13	OGLE: Certain cluster. Alias: OGLE-CL SMC0155
Lindsay 80	cl	01 07 28.5	−72 46 09	Tuc	1.1	12.44	130	13.79	12.7	204	13	OGLE: Certain cluster. Alias: OGLE-CL SMC0156
Kron 55	cl	01 07 32.4	−73 07 11	Tuc	0.7	14.26	100	16.91	13.6	204	13	OGLE: Certain cluster. Aliases: Lind 81; OGLE-CL SMC0157
HW 56	cl	01 07 42.1	−70 56 10	Tuc						204	12	
HW 57	cl	01 07 44.0	−71 52 51	Tuc						204	12	
OGLE-CL SMC0238	cl?	01 07 52.3	−72 31 54	Tuc	0.3	14.92	20	15.76	12.5	204	13	
NGC 411	cl	01 07 55.7	−71 46 09	Tuc						204	12	Aliases: Kron 60; Lind 82
NGC 416	cl	01 07 59.0	−72 21 19	Tuc	1.2	12.56	985	15.26	13.0	204	13	OGLE: Certain cluster. Aliases: Kron 59; Lind 83; OGLE-CL SMC0158
HW 58	cl	01 08 05.6	−73 41 50	Tuc	0.3					214	99	Archinal: Appears as 3 stars in DSS overlap region. HW: Loose, certain cluster, 0.3′.
Kron 57	cl	01 08 14.5	−73 15 27	Tuc						204	12	Alias: Lind 86
NGC 419	cl	01 08 17.7	−72 53 03	Tuc	2.4	11.20	1762	15.35	13.1	204	99	OGLE: Certain cluster. Aliases: Kron 58; Lind 85; OGLE-CL SMC0159
Lindsay 84	cl	01 08 28.2	−71 59 56	Tuc						204	12	
OGLE-CL SMC0160	cl	01 08 37.5	−72 26 20	Tuc	0.5	13.68	22	15.93	12.2	204	13	OGLE: Probable cluster.
HW 59	cl	01 08 53.9	−73 14 31	Tuc						204	12	
Kron 61	cl	01 09 03.5	−73 05 12	Tuc	0.5	13.89	44	15.57	12.4	204	13	OGLE: Certain cluster. Alias: OGLE-CL SMC0161
NGC 422	cl	01 09 25.4	−71 46 01	Tuc	2.0	13.4			14.9	204	99	Archinal: Aliases: Kron 62; Lind 87; h [162]; GC 231
HW 62	cl	01 09 39.1	−71 46 08	Tuc						204	12	
HW 61	cl	01 09 42.8	−72 17 44	Tuc						204	12	
HW 63	cl	01 10 12.7	−73 12 33	Tuc						204	12	Position measured from DSS.
HW 64	cl	01 10 45.5	−71 20 18	Tuc						204	12	
Kron 63	cl	01 10 47.9	−72 47 37	Tuc						204	12	Alias: Lind 88
IC 1655	cl	01 11 54.4	−71 19 48	Tuc						204	12	Alias: Lind 90
HW 65	cl	01 11 58.5	−72 16 16	Tuc						204	12	
HW 66	cl	01 12 04.8	−75 11 54	Tuc						214	12	
IC 1662	cl	01 12 33.4	−73 27 25	Tuc						213	12	Alias: Lind 92
IC 1660	cl	01 12 38.4	−71 45 41	Tuc						213	99	Archinal: Possible “tidal arm” of stars trailing to NE on DSS image. Aliases: Kron 64; Lind 89
Lindsay 93	cl	01 12 48.6	−73 28 27	Tuc						213	12	
Lindsay 91	cl	01 12 52.4	−73 07 10	Tuc						213	12	
HW 67	cl	01 13 01.9	−70 57 46	Tuc						213	12	
NGC 456	cl	01 13 43.9	−73 17 35	Tuc						213	99	DSFG: Involved in nebulosity which also carries the same designation. Aliases: Lind 94; h 2399; GC 255
HW 68	cl	01 13 52.6	−73 24 59	Tuc						213	12	
HW 69	cl	01 14 16.3	−73 22 42	Tuc						213	12	

Table C.2: Tables of SMC Objects

Name	Type	2000.0 R.A.	2000.0 Dec.	Con	Diam (′)	Tot Vm	# Str	Bt* Vm	V sur	2 U#	Ref	Comments and Aliases
NGC 460	cl	01 14 37.9	−73 18 28	Tuc	1.0	12.5			12.5	213	99	See notes. Part of association [H85] 62. Involved nebula is Henize N 84A. Aliases: ESO 011316−7332.3; ESO 29-SC39; (3) [H85] 62; (4) Hen N 84A; Lind 97; Kron 66
Lindsay 95	cl	01 14 45.8	−71 20 49	Tuc						213	12	
NGC 458	cl	01 14 53.2	−71 33 02	Tuc						213	99	Aliases: Kron 69; Lind 96
HW 70	cl	01 14 56.1	−72 12 22	Tuc						213	12	
HW 71	cl	01 15 32.7	−72 22 44	Tuc						213	12	
Kron 68	cl	01 15 33.9	−72 37 26	Tuc						213	12	Alias: Lind 98
HW 72	cl	01 15 41.9	−73 10 00	Tuc						213	12	
NGC 465	ass	01 15 42.7	−73 19 27	Tuc		11.5				213	99	Archinal: Large sparse starcloud or association. On DSS overlap boundary. Aliases: Kron 67; Lind 99
HW 73	cl	01 16 25.0	−71 19 38	Tuc	0.3					213	99	
HW 74	cl	01 16 48.3	−73 09 36	Tuc						213	12	
HW 75	cl	01 17 29.7	−73 34 09	Tuc						214	12	
HW 76	cl	01 17 35.1	−74 20 46	Tuc						214	12	
Lindsay 100	cl	01 18 17.1	−72 00 05	Tuc						213	12	
HW 77	cl	01 20.0	−72 36	Tuc	0.6					213	99	Archinal: Faint on DSS image.
HW 78	cl	01 21 20.9	−73 05 41	Tuc						213	12	
HW 79	cl	01 22 45.0	−75 00 21	Hyi?	0.9					214	99	
HW 80	cl	01 23 26.3	−73 13 26	Hyi?						213	12	
Lindsay 101	cl	01 23 44.2	−73 12 25	Hyi						213	12	
HW 81	cl	01 24 10.3	−73 09 16	Hyi						213	12	
HW 82	cl	01 24 28.1	−73 10 15	Hyi						213	12	
Lindsay 102	cl	01 24 55.8	−71 11 05	Hyi						213	99	
Lindsay 104	cl	01 25 27.8	−73 23 10	Hyi						213	99	Archinal: Large cluster involved in impressive nebulosity on DSS image.
Lindsay 103	ass	01 25 48	−73 14.6	Hyi	20.0					213	99	Archinal: By Lindsay's diameter of 34′, clearly the large association here is the correct object. Numerous objects contained. Alias: (4) IRAS 01241−7332
Lindsay 106	cl	01 30 37.9	−76 03 15	Hyi	1.5					214	99	Archinal: Impressive cluster identified from Lindsay's position and diameter.
Lindsay 107	cl	01 31.1	−73 25	Hyi						213	5	
Lindsay 108	cl	01 31 38.5	−71 56 50	Hyi	1.1					213	99	Archinal: Impressive cluster identified from Lindsay's position (her diameter of 5.7′ too large).
Lindsay 109	cl	01 33 13.4	−74 10 01	Hyi						214	12	
Lindsay 110	cl	01 34 26.2	−72 52 31	Hyi						213	99	
NGC 643	cl	01 35 00.8	−75 33 26	Hyi						214	12	Do not confuse with the galaxy "NGC 643B". Alias: Lind 111
Lindsay 112	cl	01 35 58.3	−75 27 29	Hyi						214	12	
HW 83	cl	01 38 36.8	−74 32 54	Hyi	0.3					214	99	Archinal: Brighter star, and fainter pair, on NW side of faint cluster? HW: Faint, certain cluster, 0.3′.
HW 84	cl	01 41 41.4	−71 09 41	Hyi	0.8					213	99	Archinal: Nice cluster. HW: Loose, 0.8′
HW 86	cl	01 42 22.2	−74 10 24	Hyi						214	12	
HW 85	cl	01 42 28.1	−71 16 42	Hyi	0.2					213	99	
[WG71] Cl* 1	cl	01 42 52.9	−73 20 11	Hyi						213	12	
[WG71] Cl* 2	cl	01 45 14.6	−74 41 16	Hyi						214	99	

Table C.2: Tables of SMC Objects

Name	Type	2000.0 R.A.	2000.0 Dec.	Con	Diam (′)	Tot Vm	# Str	Bt* Vm	V sur	2 U#	Ref	Comments and Aliases
Lindsay 113	cl	01 49 28.6	–73 43 39	Hyi						214	12	
[WG71] Cl* 3	cl	01 49 43.0	–74 36 50	Hyi						214	12	
Lindsay 114	cl	01 50 19.4	–74 21 23	Hyi						214	12	Alias: WG71 4
[WG71] Cl* 5	cl	01 50 51.6	–74 08 39	Hyi						214	99	Archinal: Sparse cluster. Faint diagonal streak running across DSS image, NNE to SSW.
[WG71] Cl* 6	cl	01 53 13.1	–73 58 39	Hyi						214	99	Archinal: Compact cluster or group of stars. Difficult to identify for certain from Westerlund and Glaspy [1971] position.
[WG71] Cl* 7	cl	01 53 34.3	–73 58 17	Hyi						214	99	Archinal: Large sparse group.
[WG71] Cl* 8	cl	01 56 35.5	–74 17 01	Hyi						214	12	
NGC 796	cl	01 56 44.5	–74 13 09	Hyi						214	12	Aliases: Lind 115; ESO 30-6; WG71 9
[WG71] Cl* 10	cl	02 00 01.7	–74 22 57	Hyi						219	12	
[WG71] Cl* 11	cl	02 00 37.3	–74 33 30	Hyi						219	12	
[WG71] Cl* 12	cl	02 01 02.7	–74 54 11	Hyi						219	12	
[WG71] Cl* 13	cl	02 02 42.0	–73 56 21	Hyi						214	12	
[WG71] Cl* 14	cl	02 04 49.0	–74 31 03	Hyi						219	99	Archinal: 4 stars only? Oriented E-W. Difficult to identify for certain from poor Westerlund and Glaspy [1971] position.
[WG71] Cl* 15	cl	02 07 44.8	–74 38 17	Hyi						219	99	Archinal: Asterism of 6 stars only? Difficult to identify for certain from poor Westerlund and Glaspy [1971] position.
[WG71] Cl* 16	cl	02 08 08.4	–74 47 59	Hyi						219	12	
[WG71] Cl* 17	cl	02 08 10.8	–74 32 42	Hyi						219	12	
[WG71] Cl* 18	cl	02 15 41.4	–74 02 16	Hyi						219	12	
AM 3	cl	23 48 59.5	–72 56 44	Tuc						204	99	See photo in Arp and Madore, 1987, volume 2, page 22.3. Aliases: AM 2346–731; C2346–732; ESO 28-SC4

Table C.3: Tables of Objects in M31, the Andromeda Galaxy

Name	Type	2000.0 RA	2000.0 DEC	Tot Vm	2U#	Ref	Comments and Aliases
[S73] 1	gcl?	00 32 41.3	+40 01 33	15.62	45	5	
[ME53] II	gcl	00 32 46.9	+39 34 42	13.7	45	99	Intrinsically brightest globular cluster in the Local Group. Also known as Mayall II or G1. Aliases: Mayall II; SKHB 1; HBK 0-1
SKHB 2	gcl	00 33 33.9	+39 31 20	15.81	45	18	Alias: [BHB2000] 000-002
Bol 290	gcl	00 34 20.9	+41 28 17	17.14	30	18	Alias: [BHB2000] 290-000
Bol 289	gcl	00 34 20.9	+41 47 51	16.09	30	99	Barmby, *et al.* [2000] give the wrong position for this cluster. Alias: [BHB2000] 289-000
[CCS85] 1	gal	00 35 18.8	+40 09 11	19.7	45	18	Alias: [BHB2000] DA0001
[CCS85] 2	gal	00 35 32.5	+40 22 45	18.9	45	18	Alias: [BHB2000] DA0002
[CCS85] 3	gal	00 35 52.1	+40 21 01	18.9	45	18	Alias: [BHB2000] DA0003
Bol 291	gcl	00 36 05.0	+42 02 09	16.59	30	18	Aliases: SKHB 9; [BHB2000] 291-009
[CCS85] 4	gal	00 36 08.8	+39 58 10	19.2	45	18	Alias: [BHB2000] DA0004
Bol 292	gcl	00 36 16.7	+40 58 26	17.00	30	18	Aliases: SKHB 10; [BHB2000] 292-010
Bol 293	*?	00 36 20.5	+40 53 37	16.30	30	18	Barmby, *et al.* [2000]: Object type unknown, but not a globular cluster. Aliases: SKHB 11; [BHB2000] 293-011; [BHB2000] 293-000
Bol 294	gal	00 36 33.0	+40 24 54	16.9	45	18	Aliases: SKHB 12; [BHB2000] 294-012
[CCS85] 5	gal	00 36 35.6	+40 28 15	18.9	45	18	Aliases: Bol D143; [BHB2000] DA0005
Bol 295	gcl	00 36 46.4	+40 19 42	16.72	45	18	Aliases: SKHB 14; [BHB2000] 295-014
[CCS85] 6	*?	00 36 56.1	+40 08 52	17.92	45	18	Barmby, *et al.* [2000]: Object type unknown, but not a globular cluster. Aliases: Bol D149; [BHB2000] DA0006
Bol D150	gcl	00 36 59.8	+41 25 30	17.67	30	18	Alias: [BHB2000] 150D-000
Bol 416	gcl	00 37 01.4	+39 48 35	18.07	45	18	Aliases: CCS85 7; [BHB2000] 416-D007
Bol D151	gcl	00 37 02.2	+39 48 05	18.20	45	18	Aliases: CCS85 8; CCS85 D08; [BHB2000] 151D-D08
Bol 418	gcl	00 37 17.8	+40 06 51	18.43	45	18	Alias: [BHB2000] 418-000
SKHB 18	*	00 37 18.5	+40 21 19		45	18	Alias: [BHB2000] 000-018
[CCS85] 9	gal	00 37 25.7	+40 04 55	17.99	45	18	Aliases: Bol D155; [BHB2000] DA0009
Bol 419	gcl	00 37 27.2	+39 43 08	18.4	45	18	Aliases: CCS85 10; [BHB2000] 419-D010
[CCS85] 11	gcl	00 37 29.6	+39 57 04	19.7	45	18	Alias: [BHB2000] DA0011
Bol 421	gal	00 37 32.8	+41 07 31	18.1	30	18	Aliases: SKHB 19; [BHB2000] 421-019
Bol 422	gcl	00 37 38.4	+41 59 59	18.11	30	18	Alias: [BHB2000] 422-000
Bol 423	gcl	00 37 56.6	+40 57 35	17.87	30	18	Alias: [BHB2000] 423-000
[CCS85] 16	gcl	00 37 56.9	+40 24 45	18.5	45	18	Alias: [BHB2000] DA0016
SKHB 20	gcl	00 37 58.1	+42 31 48		30	5	
Bol 298	gcl	00 38 00.3	+40 43 56	16.59	30	18	Aliases: SKHB 21; [BHB2000] 298-021
Bol 299	gal	00 38 02.0	+40 41 46		30	18	Alias: [BHB2000] 299-000
Bol 424	gcl	00 38 03.1	+39 45 23	18.38	45	18	Aliases: CCS85 17; [BHB2000] 424-D017
Bol 426	gal	00 38 19.8	+41 14 31	17.0	30	18	Barmby, *et al.* [2000]: star and galaxy. Aliases: CCS85 18; [BHB2000] 426-000
[CCS85] 18	*	00 38 19.8	+41 14 31	17.0	30	18	Aliases: Bol 426; [BHB2000] DA0018
Bol 301	gcl	00 38 21.6	+40 03 37	17.12	45	18	Aliases: [S73] 4; BA 3- 15; SKHB 22; [BHB2000] 301-022
Bol D167	gcl	00 38 22.4	+41 54 35	17.95	30	18	Alias: [BHB2000] 167D-000
Bol 427	gcl	00 38 22.7	+39 58 10	18.18	45	18	Aliases: CCS85 19; [BHB2000] 427-D019
Bol D168	gcl	00 38 25.0	+39 40 52	18.7	45	18	Aliases: CCS85 20; CCS85 D20; [BHB2000] 168D-D20
Bol D170	gcl	00 38 28.1	+39 44 06	18.85	45	18	Aliases: CCS85 21; CCS85 D21; [BHB2000] 170D-D21

Table C.3: Tables of Objects in M31, the Andromeda Galaxy

Name	Type	2000.0 RA	2000.0 DEC	Tot Vm	2U#	Ref	Comments and Aliases
Bol 302	gcl	00 38 33.4	+41 20 52	16.68	30	18	Aliases: SKHB 23; [BHB2000] 302-023
Bol 429	gal	00 38 38.6	+41 09 10	18.03	30	18	Aliases: SKHB 24; [BHB2000] 429-024
Bol 430	gcl	00 38 42.9	+41 44 01	18.52	30	18	Aliases: SKHB 25; [BHB2000] 430-025
Bol 303	gcl	00 38 50.5	+40 27 31	18.22	45	18	Aliases: SKHB 26; [BHB2000] 303-026
Bol D176	gcl	00 38 53.0	+41 29 04	18.14	30	5	
[CCS85] 22	gal	00 38 53.7	+39 51 29	18.6	45	18	Alias: [BHB2000] DAO022
[CCS85] 23	gcl	00 38 54.3	+40 26 46	18.4	45	18	Alias: [BHB2000] DAO023
Bol 431	gcl	00 38 54.9	+40 34 57	17.73	30	18	Aliases: SKHB 27; [BHB2000] 431-027
[S73] 5	gcl?	00 38 55.2	+41 10 29	17.24	30	5	
Bol 304	gcl	00 38 56.8	+41 10 28	16.83	30	18	Aliases: SKHB 28; [BHB2000] 304-028
Bol 305	gcl	00 38 58.9	+40 16 32	18.11	45	18	Aliases: CCS85 24; [BHB2000] 305-D024
Bol 432	*?	00 38 59.1	+41 43 15		30	18	Barmby, *et al.* [2000]: Object type unknown, but not a globular cluster. Alias: [BHB2000] 432-000
Bol 433	gcl	00 39 02.4	+40 00 09	18.28	45	18	Alias: [BHB2000] 433-000
Bol 306	gcl	00 39 08.8	+40 34 20	16.29	30	18	Aliases: SKHB 29; [BHB2000] 306-029
[CCS85] 25	gcl	00 39 13.4	+40 07 31	18.8	45	18	Alias: [BHB2000] DAO025
Bol 434	gal	00 39 15.1	+41 29 15	18.10	30	18	Aliases: CCS85 26; [BHB2000] 434-D026; [BHB2000] 434-000
[CCS85] 27	gcl	00 39 16.5	+40 41 05	18.0	30	18	Alias: [BHB2000] DAO027
Bol 435	gcl	00 39 18.4	+40 48 25	18.61	30	18	Aliases: CCS85 28; [BHB2000] 435-D028
Bol 307	gcl	00 39 18.6	+40 32 58	17.31	30	18	Aliases: [V62] 3; SKHB 30; [H32] 3; [BHB2000] 307-030
[S73] 6	gcl?	00 39 19.3	+41 10 28	16.67	30	5	
Bol 309	gcl	00 39 23.5	+40 14 41	17.50	45	18	Aliases: SKHB 31; [BHB2000] 309-031
Bol 310	gcl	00 39 25.8	+41 23 33	17.04	30	18	Aliases: SKHB 32; [BHB2000] 310-032
[CCS85] 29	gal	00 39 27.4	+41 54 14	17.5	30	18	Aliases: Bol D180; [BHB2000] DAO029
Bol 436	gcl	00 39 30.6	+40 18 21	18.41	45	18	Alias: [BHB2000] 436-000
Bol 311	gcl	00 39 33.9	+40 31 14	15.48	30	18	Aliases: SKHB 33; [BHB2000] 311-033
[S73] 7	gcl?	00 39 37.7	+42 09 28	16.84	30	5	
SKHB 34	gal	00 39 40.1	+41 02 14	17.48	30	18	Aliases: Bol 439; [BHB2000] 000-034
Bol 312	gcl	00 39 40.4	+40 57 03	15.58	30	18	Aliases: SKHB 35; [BHB2000] 312-035
Bol 313	gcl	00 39 44.5	+40 52 56	16.36	30	18	Aliases: SKHB 36; [BHB2000] 313-036
Bol 314	gcl	00 39 44.6	+40 14 08	17.63	45	18	Barmby, *et al.* [2000]: Possible young cluster. Aliases: SKHB 37; [BHB2000] 314-037
Bol 315	gcl	00 39 48.6	+40 31 31	16.32	30	18	Aliases: SKHB 38; [BHB2000] 315-038
[CCS85] 30	gcl	00 39 50.8	+40 18 15	18.4	45	18	Alias: [BHB2000] DAO030
Bol 1	gcl	00 39 51.4	+40 58 12	17.06	30	18	Aliases: SKHB 39; [BHB2000] 001-039
Bol 316	gcl	00 39 53.8	+40 41 40	16.82	30	18	Aliases: [V62] 10; SKHB 40; [H32] 10; [BHB2000] 316-040
Bol 317	gcl	00 39 55.5	+41 47 47	16.55	30	18	Barmby, *et al.* [2000]: Possibly in NGC 205 = M 110. Aliases: SKHB 41; [BHB2000] 317-041
Bol 318	gcl	00 40 01.0	+40 34 09	16.89	30	18	Aliases: SKHB 42; [BHB2000] 318-042
Bol 2	gcl	00 40 02.5	+41 11 54	17.54	30	18	Aliases: SKHB 43; [BHB2000] 002-043
Bol 319	gcl	00 40 03.2	+40 33 59	17.49	30	18	Aliases: [V62] 8; SKHB 44; [H32] 8; [BHB2000] 319-044
Bol 3	gcl	00 40 09.4	+41 11 05	17.57	30	18	Aliases: SKHB 45; [BHB2000] 003-045
Bol 321	gcl	00 40 15.3	+40 27 46	17.78	45	18	Barmby, *et al.* [2000]: Possible young cluster. Aliases: SKHB 46; [BHB2000] 321-046
SKHB 47	gcl	00 40 15.5	+40 39 59		30	18	Aliases: Bol D189; [BHB2000] 189D-047

Table C.3: Tables of Objects in M31, the Andromeda Galaxy

Name	Type	2000.0 RA	2000.0 DEC	Tot Vm	2U#	Ref	Comments and Aliases
Bol 320	gcl	00 40 15.5	+41 48 30	18.2	30	18	Barmby, *et al.* [2000]: Possibly in NGC 205 = M 110. Alias: [BHB2000] 320-000
SKHB 48	gcl	00 40 16.9	+40 39 30	18.38	30	18	Aliases: Bol D190; [BHB2000] 190D-048
Bol 322	gcl	00 40 17.3	+40 39 05	17.92	30	18	Barmby, *et al.* [2000]: Possible young cluster. Aliases: SKHB 49; [BHB2000] 322-049
Bol 323	gcl	00 40 18.3	+40 32 44	17.74	30	18	Alias: [BHB2000] 323-000
Bol 4	gcl	00 40 18.4	+41 22 41	16.95	30	18	Aliases: SKHB 50; [BHB2000] 004-050
[CCS85] 32	gcl	00 40 19.2	+40 32 47	18.3	30	18	Alias: [BHB2000] DAO032
Bol 442	gcl	00 40 19.4	+40 37 28	18.62	30	18	Aliases: CCS85 33; [BHB2000] 442-D033
Bol 5	gcl	00 40 20.6	+40 43 30	15.71	30	18	Aliases: SKHB 52; [BHB2000] 005-052
Bol 324	gcl	00 40 20.8	+41 40 50	16.91	30	18	Barmby, *et al.* [2000]: In NGC 205 = M 110. Aliases: [H32] V; SKHB 51; [BHB2000] 324-051
Bol 443	gcl	00 40 21.4	+40 33 19	18.43	30	18	Aliases: CCS85 34; [BHB2000] 443-D034
Bol 325	gcl	00 40 23.1	+40 30 46		30	18	Alias: [BHB2000] 325-000
Bol 326	gcl	00 40 23.6	+41 41 10	17.98	30	18	Barmby, *et al.* [2000]: Possibly in NGC 205 = M 110. Alias: [BHB2000] 326-000
Bol 327	gcl	00 40 24.1	+40 36 22	16.58	30	18	Barmby, *et al.* [2000]: Possible young cluster. Aliases: SKHB 53; [BHB2000] 327-053
Bol 329	gcl	00 40 24.5	+41 47 22	18.39	30	18	Barmby, *et al.* [2000]: Possibly in NGC 205 = M 110. Alias: [BHB2000] 329-000
Bol 328	gcl	00 40 24.9	+41 40 23	17.57	30	18	Barmby, *et al.* [2000]: Possibly in NGC 205 = M 110. Aliases: SKHB 54; [BHB2000] 328-054
SKHB 55	gcl	00 40 25.1	+41 42 54		30	18	Aliases: Bol D193; [BHB2000] 193D-055
Bol 330	gcl	00 40 25.6	+41 42 53	17.69	30	18	Barmby, *et al.* [2000]: In NGC 205 = M 110. Aliases: SKHB 56; [BHB2000] 330-056
Bol 331	gcl	00 40 26.4	+41 42 05	18.20	30	18	Barmby, *et al.* [2000]: In NGC 205 = M 110. Aliases: SKHB 57; [BHB2000] 331-057
Bol 244	gcl	00 40 26.7	+41 18 35	18.26	30	18	Alias: [BHB2000] 244-000
Bol 6	gcl	00 40 26.8	+41 27 27	15.52	30	18	Aliases: SKHB 58; [BHB2000] 006-058
Bol 7	gal	00 40 27.6	+41 29 11	16.98	30	18	Aliases: SKHB 59; [V62] 238; [BHB2000] 007-059
Cl vdB 0	gcl	00 40 29.4	+40 35 57	14.94	30	99	Aliases: [V62] 0; [BHB2000] VDB0
Bol 333	gcl	00 40 29.6	+41 40 26	19.13	30	18	Barmby, *et al.* [2000]: Possibly in NGC 205 = M 110. Alias: [BHB2000] 333-000
Bol 8	gcl	00 40 30.6	+41 16 09	16.52	30	18	Aliases: SKHB 60; [V62] 224; [BHB2000] 008-060
Bol 9	gcl	00 40 31.2	+41 36 57	16.91	30	18	Barmby, *et al.* [2000]: Possibly in NGC 205 = M 110. Aliases: SKHB 61; [BHB2000] 009-061
[S73] 8	gcl?	00 40 31.4	+40 26 28	18.2	45	5	
Bol 10	gcl	00 40 31.9	+41 14 23	16.66	30	18	Aliases: SKHB 62; [BHB2000] 010-062
Bol 11	gcl	00 40 32.6	+41 39 19	16.79	30	18	Barmby, *et al.* [2000]: In NGC 205 = M 110. Aliases: SKHB 63; [BHB2000] 011-063
Bol 12	gcl	00 40 32.8	+41 21 44	15.12	30	18	Aliases: SKHB 64; [BHB2000] 012-064
Bol 448	gcl	00 40 36.5	+40 40 14	18.41	30	18	Aliases: CCS85 35; [BHB2000] 448-D035
Bol D6	gcl	00 40 37.3	+40 48 45	18.0	30	18	Aliases: CCS85 36; CCS85 D36; [BHB2000] 006D-D36
[V62] B22	gcl	00 40 38.8	+41 12 45	18.08	30	18	Aliases: Bol 14; [BHB2000] 014-B222
Bol 13	gcl	00 40 38.8	+41 25 24	17.18	30	18	Aliases: [V62] 54; SKHB 65; [H32] 54; [BHB2000] 013-065
[H32] 13	gcl	00 40 42.0	+40 38 28	18.08	30	18	Aliases: [V62] 13; Bol 335; [BHB2000] 335-H13
[H32] 11	gcl	00 40 42.5	+40 36 04	18.84	30	18	Aliases: [V62] 11; Bol 449; [BHB2000] 449-H11
[V62] B20	gcl	00 40 45.1	+40 59 56	17.79	30	18	Aliases: Bol 15; [BHB2000] 015-B204
Bol 16	gcl	00 40 45.2	+41 22 10	17.58	30	18	Aliases: SKHB 66; [BHB2000] 016-066
Bol 451	gcl	00 40 46.4	+40 51 40	18.95	30	18	Aliases: CCS85 37; [BHB2000] 451-D037
Bol 450	gcl	00 40 47.0	+41 40 32	19.04	30	18	Barmby, *et al.* [2000]: Possibly in NGC 205 = M 110. Alias: [BHB2000] 450-000

Table C.3: Tables of Objects in M31, the Andromeda Galaxy

Name	Type	2000.0 RA	2000.0 DEC	Tot Vm	2U#	Ref	Comments and Aliases
Bol 336	gcl	00 40 47.7	+42 08 41	17.81	30	18	Aliases: SKHB 67; [BHB2000] 336-067
Bol 452	gcl	00 40 48.3	+40 35 07	17.87	30	18	Aliases: SKHB 69; [BHB2000] 452-069
Bol 337	gcl	00 40 48.5	+42 12 10	16.73	30	18	Aliases: SKHB 68; [BHB2000] 337-068
Bol 17	gcl	00 40 48.9	+41 12 09	15.95	30	18	Aliases: SKHB 70; [BHB2000] 017-070
Bol 18	gcl	00 40 49.6	+40 41 32	17.51	30	18	Aliases: [V62] 17; SKHB 71; [H32] 17; [BHB2000] 018-071
[CCS85] 40	gcl	00 40 52.2	+40 36 03	18.0	30	18	Alias: [BHB2000] DAO040
Bol D12	gcl	00 40 52.3	+40 58 41	18.4	30	18	Aliases: CCS85 39; CCS85 D39; [BHB2000] 012D-D39
Bol 19	gcl	00 40 52.9	+41 18 43	14.92	30	18	Aliases: SKHB 72; [BHB2000] 019-072
Bol 20	gcl	00 40 55.6	+41 41 27	14.91	30	18	Aliases: SKHB 73; [BHB2000] 020-073
Bol 338	gcl	00 40 59.1	+40 35 48	14.26	30	18	Aliases: SKHB 76; [BHB2000] 338-076
Bol 21	gcl	00 40 59.1	+41 05 39	17.54	30	18	Aliases: SKHB 75; [V62] 214; [BHB2000] 021-075
Bol 22	gcl	00 40 59.1	+41 24 41	17.35	30	18	Aliases: SKHB 74; [BHB2000] 022-074
Bol 339	gcl	00 41 00.6	+39 55 54	16.87	62	18	Aliases: SKHB 77; [BHB2000] 339-077
Bol 23	gcl	00 41 01.3	+41 13 45	14.22	30	18	Aliases: SKHB 78; [BHB2000] 023-078
[V62] 211	gcl	00 41 02.1	+41 02 55		30	5	Aliases: BA 1- 435; [PAV78] 283; MLA 303
Bol D15	gcl	00 41 02.7	+41 06 36	17.8	30	18	Aliases: CCS85 41; CCS85 D41; [BHB2000] 015D-D41
Bol 453	gcl	00 41 03.3	+41 00 55	17.30	30	18	Aliases: CCS85 42; [BHB2000] 453-D042
Bol 455	gal	00 41 05.7	+39 41 58	17.5	62	18	Aliases: SKHB 80; [BHB2000] 455-080
Bol D200	gcl	00 41 06.9	+40 34 29	17.60	30	18	Aliases: CCS85 43; CCS85 D43; [BHB2000] 200D-D43
Bol D201	gcl	00 41 08.3	+40 32 52	18.30	30	18	Aliases: CCS85 44; CCS85 D44; [BHB2000] 201D-D44
SKHB 83	gcl	00 41 08.8	+41 09 55		30	18	Aliases: [PAV78] 319; [V62] 225; [BHB2000] 000-083
Bol 341	*	00 41 09.2	+40 35 54	16.38	30	18	Aliases: SKHB 81; [BHB2000] 341-081
Bol 24	gcl	00 41 12.1	+41 45 50	16.79	30	18	Aliases: SKHB 82; [BHB2000] 024-082
[H32] 31	gcl	00 41 12.2	+41 05 32		30	18	Aliases: [V62] 31; [BHB2000] VH31
Bol 25	gcl	00 41 12.7	+41 00 28	16.85	30	18	Aliases: SKHB 84; [V62] 210; [BHB2000] 025-084
[V62] 15	gcl	00 41 12.8	+40 34 17		30	5	Alias: SKHB 85
Bol 27	gcl	00 41 14.6	+40 55 51	15.63	30	18	Aliases: SKHB 87; [BHB2000] 027-087
Bol 26	gcl	00 41 14.6	+41 24 41	17.53	30	18	Aliases: SKHB 86; [BHB2000] 026-086
Bol 28	gcl	00 41 16.6	+40 59 03	16.86	30	18	Aliases: SKHB 88; [V62] 209; [BHB2000] 028-088
SKHB 89	gcl	00 41 17.4	+41 08 10	17.6	30	18	Aliases: Bol D20; [V62] 221; [BHB2000] 020D-089
Bol 29	gcl	00 41 17.9	+41 00 23	16.58	30	18	Aliases: SKHB 90; [BHB2000] 029-090
Bol 30	gcl	00 41 19.0	+40 57 16	17.40	30	18	Aliases: SKHB 91; [V62] 207; [BHB2000] 030-091
Bol 31	gcl	00 41 21.1	+40 59 05	17.71	30	18	Aliases: SKHB 92; [V62] 208; [BHB2000] 031-092
Bol 456	gcl	00 41 21.4	+40 15 09	18.09	62	18	Aliases: CCS85 45; [BHB2000] 456-D045
Bol 32	gcl	00 41 21.7	+41 17 31	17.60	30	18	Aliases: SKHB 93; [V62] 237; [BHB2000] 032-093
[CCS85] 46	gcl	00 41 23.0	+40 28 33	18.4	62	18	Alias: [BHB2000] DAO046
Bol 342	gcl	00 41 24.4	+40 36 49	18.35	30	18	Aliases: SKHB 94; [BHB2000] 342-094
[S73] 9	gcl?	00 41.4	+42 18	17.09	30	5	
Bol 33	gcl	00 41 26.4	+41 00 14	17.86	30	18	Aliases: SKHB 95; [V62] 215; [BHB2000] 033-095

Table C.3: Tables of Objects in M31, the Andromeda Galaxy

Name	Type	2000.0 RA	2000.0 DEC	Tot Vm	2U#	Ref	Comments and Aliases
Bol 34	gcl	00 41 28.2	+40 53 49	15.47	30	18	Aliases: SKHB 96; [BHB2000] 034-096
Bol 457	gcl	00 41 29.2	+42 18 36	16.91	30	18	Aliases: SKHB 97; [BHB2000] 457-097
[CCS85] 47	gcl	00 41 29.4	+40 45 16	19.0	30	18	Alias: [BHB2000] DA0047
Bol 35	gcl	00 41 32.8	+41 38 33	17.47	30	18	Alias: [BHB2000] 035-000
Bol 36	gcl	00 41 32.9	+41 26 04	17.31	30	18	Alias: [BHB2000] 036-000
[V62] B21	gcl	00 41 34.5	+41 01 06		30	18	Aliases: Bol D25; [BHB2000] 025D-B217
[V62] B21	gcl	00 41 34.6	+41 00 50		30	18	Aliases: Bol D26; [BHB2000] 026D-B216
[V62] B32	gcl	00 41 35.0	+41 14 54	16.81	30	18	Aliases: Bol 37; [BHB2000] 037-B327
Bol 38	gcl	00 41 36.1	+41 19 14	16.49	30	18	Aliases: SKHB 98; [BHB2000] 038-098
SKHB 99	gal	00 41 36.3	+40 47 25		30	18	Aliases: [V62] 22; BA 2- 16; [H32] 22; [BHB2000] 000-099
SKHB 100	*	00 41 37.9	+40 52 06		30	18	Aliases: [V62] 28; Bol D28; [H32] 28; [BHB2000] 000-100
Bol 39	gcl	00 41 38.1	+41 20 50	15.97	30	18	Aliases: SKHB 101; [BHB2000] 039-101
Bol 40	gcl	00 41 39.0	+40 40 54	17.46	30	18	Aliases: [V62] 20; SKHB 102; [H32] 20; [BHB2000] 040-102
Bol D206	gcl	00 41 40.6	+40 50 06	19.40	30	18	Aliases: CCS85 48; CCS85 D48; [BHB2000] 206D-D48
Bol 41	gcl	00 41 41.1	+41 14 46	17.64	30	18	Aliases: [V62] 51; SKHB 103; [H32] 51; [BHB2000] 041-103
Bol 42	gcl	00 41 41.8	+41 07 27	16.28	30	18	Aliases: SKHB 104; [BHB2000] 042-104
Bol 343	gcl	00 41 42.2	+40 12 22	16.34	62	18	Aliases: SKHB 105; [V62] 199; [BHB2000] 343-105
Bol 43	gcl	00 41 42.5	+40 42 40	16.96	30	18	Aliases: SKHB 106; [BHB2000] 043-106
Bol 44	gcl	00 41 42.9	+41 20 05	16.70	30	18	Aliases: SKHB 107; [BHB2000] 044-107
Bol 45	gcl	00 41 43.3	+41 34 21	15.78	30	18	Aliases: SKHB 108; [BHB2000] 045-108
Bol 458	gcl	00 41 44.6	+40 51 21	17.84	30	18	Aliases: CCS85 49; [BHB2000] 458-D049
Bol D207	gcl	00 41 45.0	+40 16 06	17.54	62	18	Aliases: CCS85 50; CCS85 D50; [BHB2000] 207D-D50
Bol 46	gcl	00 41 45.0	+41 46 29	17.80	30	18	Aliases: SKHB 109; [BHB2000] 046-109
Bol 48	gcl	00 41 45.6	+41 13 30	16.64	30	18	Aliases: SKHB 110; [BHB2000] 048-110
Bol 47	gcl	00 41 45.7	+41 42 05	17.50	30	18	Aliases: SKHB 111; [BHB2000] 047-111
Bol 49	gcl	00 41 45.8	+40 49 55	17.56	30	18	Aliases: [V62] 24; SKHB 112; [H32] 24; [BHB2000] 049-112
Bol 50	gcl	00 41 46.4	+41 32 18	16.84	30	18	Aliases: SKHB 113; [V62] 260; [BHB2000] 050-113
Bol 51	gcl	00 41 46.7	+41 25 18	16.08	30	18	Aliases: SKHB 114; [BHB2000] 051-114
Bol 53	gcl	00 41 47.3	+41 22 45	17.82	30	18	Alias: [BHB2000] 053-000
[V62] B26	gcl	00 41 47.3	+41 38 10	17.21	30	18	Aliases: Bol 52; [BHB2000] 052-B266
Bol 54	gcl	00 41 47.9	+41 00 56	18.34	30	18	Aliases: SKHB 115; [V62] 220; [BHB2000] 054-115
Bol 55	*	00 41 50.5	+41 12 11	16.7	30	18	Aliases: [V62] 47; SKHB 116; [H32] 47; [BHB2000] 055-116
Bol 56	gcl	00 41 51.2	+40 57 39	17.30	30	18	Aliases: SKHB 117; [V62] 218; [BHB2000] 056-117
Bol 58	gcl	00 41 53.0	+40 47 10	15.00	30	18	Aliases: SKHB 119; [BHB2000] 058-119
Bol 57	gcl	00 41 53.0	+40 52 06	17.64	30	18	Aliases: SKHB 118; [V62] 206; [BHB2000] 057-118
Bol 59	gcl	00 41 54.3	+41 11 02	17.05	30	18	Aliases: SKHB 120; [V62] 236; [BHB2000] 059-120
Bol 60	gcl	00 41 57.1	+41 05 13	16.74	30	18	Aliases: [V62] 41; SKHB 121; [H32] 41; [BHB2000] 060-121
Bol 61	gcl	00 42 00.2	+41 29 35	16.60	30	18	Aliases: SKHB 122; [BHB2000] 061-122
Bol 62	gcl	00 42 00.6	+41 38 33	17.23	30	18	Aliases: SKHB 123; [V62] 267; [BHB2000] 062-123

Table C.3: Tables of Objects in M31, the Andromeda Galaxy

Name	Type	2000.0 RA	2000.0 DEC	Tot Vm	2U#	Ref	Comments and Aliases
Bol 63	gcl	00 42 00.8	+41 29 09	15.66	30	18	Aliases: SKHB 124; [BHB2000] 063-124
Bol 64	gcl	00 42 02.0	+41 11 07	16.31	30	18	Aliases: SKHB 125; [BHB2000] 064-125
Bol 65	gcl	00 42 02.1	+40 40 11	16.93	30	18	Aliases: SKHB 126; [BHB2000] 065-126
Bol 66	gcl	00 42 03.1	+40 44 48	17.42	30	18	Aliases: SKHB 128; [BHB2000] 066-128
Bol 68	gcl	00 42 03.3	+40 58 49	16.37	30	18	Aliases: SKHB 130; [BHB2000] 068-130
Bol 344	gcl	00 42 03.3	+41 52 03	15.95	30	18	Aliases: SKHB 127; [BHB2000] 344-127
Bol 67	gcl	00 42 03.4	+41 04 25	17.24	30	18	Aliases: [V62] 40; SKHB 129; [H32] 40; [BHB2000] 067-129
Bol 461	gcl	00 42 04.2	+42 03 26	17.52	30	18	Aliases: SKHB 131; [BHB2000] 461-131
Bol 69	gcl	00 42 05.7	+41 26 10	18.15	30	18	Aliases: [V62] 85; SKHB 132; [H32] 85; [BHB2000] 069-132
[V62] B24	gcl	00 42 06.8	+41 18 06		30	18	Aliases: Bol D43; [BHB2000] 043D-B246
Bol 70	gcl	00 42 06.9	+41 07 55	16.88	30	18	Aliases: [V62] 45; SKHB 133; [H32] 45; [BHB2000] 070-133
Bol 71	gcl	00 42 07.1	+41 12 11	17.78	30	18	Alias: [BHB2000] 071-000
[V62] B22	gcl	00 42 07.3	+41 00 17		30	18	Aliases: Bol D44; [BHB2000] 044D-B228
Bol 73	gcl	00 42 07.4	+40 59 21	15.99	30	18	Aliases: SKHB 134; [BHB2000] 073-134
Bol 72	gcl	00 42 07.4	+41 22 47	17.23	30	18	Alias: [BHB2000] 072-000
Bol 74	gcl	00 42 08.1	+41 43 23	16.65	30	18	Aliases: SKHB 135; [BHB2000] 074-135
[CCS85] 52	gcl	00 42 08.8	+40 50 52	18.42	30	18	Alias: [BHB2000] DAO052
Bol 75	gcl	00 42 09.0	+41 20 22	17.32	30	18	Aliases: SKHB 136; [V62] 250; [BHB2000] 075-136
SKHB 137	gcl	00 42 09.5	+41 28 32		30	5	Aliases: BA 1- 513; [PAV78] 464
[CCS85] 53	gcl	00 42 09.9	+40 38 03	18.8	30	18	Alias: [BHB2000] DAO053
Bol 76	gcl	00 42 10.2	+41 05 21	16.89	30	18	Aliases: SKHB 138; [BHB2000] 076-138
[CCS85] 54	gcl	00 42 10.9	+40 18 55	18.7	62	18	Alias: [BHB2000] DAO054
Bol 77	gcl	00 42 11.3	+41 07 34	17.25	30	18	Aliases: SKHB 139; [V62] 235; [BHB2000] 077-139
Bol 79	gcl	00 42 12.3	+41 29 28	17.82	30	18	Alias: [BHB2000] 079-000
Bol 78	gcl	00 42 12.4	+41 17 59	17.41	30	18	Aliases: SKHB 140; [PFJ93] 8; [V62] 247; [BHB2000] 078-140
Bol 80	gcl	00 42 12.5	+41 19 00	17.20	30	18	Aliases: [V62] 68; SKHB 141; [H32] 68; [BHB2000] 080-141
Bol 81	gcl	00 42 13.6	+40 48 38	16.80	30	18	Aliases: SKHB 142; [V62] 205; [BHB2000] 081-142
Bol 345	gcl	00 42 14.2	+40 17 37	16.51	62	18	Aliases: SKHB 143; [BHB2000] 345-143
Bol 462	gcl	00 42 14.7	+42 01 38	18.05	30	18	Alias: [BHB2000] 462-000
Bol 82	gcl	00 42 15.8	+41 01 14	15.53	30	18	Aliases: SKHB 144; [BHB2000] 082-144
Bol 83	gcl	00 42 16.5	+41 45 22	17.09	30	18	Aliases: SKHB 146; [BHB2000] 083-146
Bol 84	gcl	00 42 17.4	+41 18 55	17.62	30	18	Alias: [BHB2000] 084-000
Bol 85	gcl	00 42 18.4	+40 39 57	16.84	30	18	Aliases: SKHB 147; [BHB2000] 085-147
Bol 86	gcl	00 42 18.7	+41 14 01	15.04	30	18	Aliases: SKHB 148; [BHB2000] 086-148
Bol 346	gcl	00 42 20.2	+40 30 32	17.51	30	18	Aliases: SKHB 149; [BHB2000] 346-149
Bol 90	gcl	00 42 21.1	+41 02 57	18.79	30	18	Alias: [BHB2000] 090-000
Bol 88	gcl	00 42 21.1	+41 32 16	15.42	30	18	Aliases: SKHB 150; [BHB2000] 088-150
Bol 89	gcl	00 42 21.3	+41 39 49	18.18	30	18	Alias: [BHB2000] 089-000
Bol 91	gcl	00 42 22.0	+41 22 06	17.56	30	18	Aliases: SKHB 151; [V62] 251; [BHB2000] 091-151

Table C.3: Tables of Objects in M31, the Andromeda Galaxy

Name	Type	2000.0 RA	2000.0 DEC	Tot Vm	2U#	Ref	Comments and Aliases
Bol 92	gcl	00 42 22.4	+41 08 08	16.92	30	18	Aliases: SKHB 152; [BHB2000] 092-152
Bol 348	gcl	00 42 23.0	+41 52 28	16.79	30	18	Aliases: SKHB 153; [BHB2000] 348-153
Bol 347	gcl	00 42 23.0	+41 54 28	16.49	30	18	Barmby, *et al.* [2000]: Possible young cluster. Aliases: SKHB 154; [BHB2000] 347-154
Bol 93	gcl	00 42 23.2	+41 21 43	16.87	30	18	Aliases: SKHB 155; [BHB2000] 093-155
Bol 349	gcl	00 42 24.0	+40 37 43	18.00	30	18	Alias: [BHB2000] 349-000
Bol D53	*	00 42 24.8	+41 12 35	18.4	30	18	Aliases: ACH 1; NBol 20; [BHB2000] 053D-NB20
Bol 94	gcl	00 42 25.0	+40 57 21	15.54	30	18	Aliases: SKHB 156; [BHB2000] 094-156
[S73] 11	gcl?	00 42.4	+40 25	16.57	62	5	
Bol 95	gcl	00 42 25.9	+41 05 27	15.81	30	18	Aliases: SKHB 157; [BHB2000] 095-157
Bol 96	gcl	00 42 26.2	+41 19 14	16.61	30	18	Aliases: [V62] 78; SKHB 158; TF 26; NBol 2; [PFJ93] 23; C84 29; [H32] 78; [BHB2000] 096-158
NBol 23	gcl	00 42 26.7	+41 18 04	17.17	30	18	Aliases: NBol 60; WSTB 36W188; WSTB 37W125; [B90] 70; [BHB2000] NB23
NBol 83	gcl	00 42 26.9	+41 13 20	16.67	30	18	Alias: [BHB2000] NB83
Bol 463	gcl	00 42 27.5	+40 35 54	18.30	30	18	Aliases: SKHB 160; [BHB2000] 463-160
Bol 98	gcl	00 42 27.5	+40 59 36	16.21	30	18	Alias: [BHB2000] 098-000
Bol 97	gcl	00 42 27.5	+41 25 32	16.84	30	18	Aliases: [V62] 139; SKHB 159; [H32] 139; [BHB2000] 097-159
Bol 99	gcl	00 42 27.6	+41 10 02	16.73	30	18	Aliases: [V62] 53; SKHB 161; [H32] 53; [BHB2000] 099-161
Bol 350	gcl	00 42 28.5	+40 24 52	16.74	62	18	Aliases: SKHB 162; [BHB2000] 350-162
Bol 100	gcl	00 42 29.1	+40 49 56	17.91	30	18	Aliases: [V62] 25; SKHB 163; [H32] 25; [BHB2000] 100-163
Bol 101	gcl	00 42 29.1	+41 08 15	16.86	30	18	Aliases: SKHB 164; [V62] 240; [BHB2000] 101-164
NBol 65	gcl	00 42 29.7	+41 19 53		30	18	Alias: [BHB2000] NB65
Bol 103	gcl	00 42 29.8	+41 17 29	15.23	30	18	Aliases: SKHB 165; [BHB2000] 103-165
Bol 102	gcl	00 42 29.9	+41 34 18	16.58	30	18	Alias: [BHB2000] 102-000
Bol 104	gcl	00 42 30.0	+41 17 25	17.51	30	18	Aliases: NBol 5; [BHB2000] 104-NB5
[V62] 234	gcl	00 42 30.1	+41 05 52		30	18	Alias: [BHB2000] VB234
NBol 70	gcl	00 42 30.2	+41 18 41		30	18	Alias: [BHB2000] NB70
Bol 105	gcl	00 42 31.1	+41 30 28	17.19	30	18	Aliases: SKHB 166; [V62] 261; [BHB2000] 105-166
Bol 106	gcl	00 42 31.2	+41 12 18	16.03	30	18	Aliases: SKHB 168; [BHB2000] 106-168
Bol 108	gcl	00 42 31.3	+41 08 52	17.47	30	18	Aliases: [V62] 52; SKHB 167; [H32] 52; [BHB2000] 108-167
Bol 107	gcl	00 42 31.3	+41 19 39	15.94	30	18	Aliases: SKHB 169; [BHB2000] 107-169
NBol 63	gcl	00 42 31.3	+41 20 12		30	18	Alias: [BHB2000] NB63
NBol 81	gcl	00 42 31.5	+41 13 37	16.03	30	18	Alias: [BHB2000] NB81
NBol 61	gcl	00 42 31.7	+41 19 48	>19	30	18	Alias: [BHB2000] NB61
Bol 109	gcl	00 42 32.2	+41 10 28	16.24	30	18	Aliases: SKHB 170; [BHB2000] 109-170
Bol 110	gcl	00 42 33.2	+41 03 26	15.19	30	18	Aliases: SKHB 172; [BHB2000] 110-172
NBol 75	gcl	00 42 33.2	+41 16 28		30	18	Alias: [BHB2000] NB75
NBol 16	gcl	00 42 33.2	+41 20 17	17.54	30	18	Barmby, *et al.* [2000]: Possible young cluster. Alias: [BHB2000] NB16
Bol 112	gcl	00 42 33.3	+41 17 42	16.26	30	18	Aliases: SKHB 174; [BHB2000] 112-174
Bol 260	gcl	00 42 33.3	+41 31 25	18.49	30	18	Alias: [BHB2000] 260-000
Bol 111	gcl	00 42 33.4	+41 00 27	16.80	30	18	Aliases: SKHB 173; [V62] 230; [BHB2000] 111-173

Table C.3: Tables of Objects in M31, the Andromeda Galaxy

Name	Type	2000.0 RA	2000.0 DEC	Tot Vm	2U#	Ref	Comments and Aliases
SKHB 171	gal	00 42 33.7	+43 02 06	17.3	30	18	Aliases: [S73] 12; [BHB2000] 000-171
ACH 3	gcl	00 42 33.9	+41 19 29	18.75	30	5	Alias: NBol 47
ACH 13	gcl	00 42 34.2	+41 19 47	16.13	30	99	Aliases: NBol 67; [BHB2000] NB67
Bol 117	gcl	00 42 34.4	+40 57 09	16.33	30	18	Aliases: SKHB 176; [BHB2000] 117-176
Bol 114	gcl	00 42 34.4	+41 12 44	17.13	30	18	Aliases: SKHB 175; [BHB2000] 114-175
Bol 115	gcl	00 42 34.5	+41 14 02	16.06	30	18	Aliases: SKHB 177; [BHB2000] 115-177
[WSB85] W 4	gcl	00 42 34.5	+41 17 31	18.26	30	99	Aliases: ACH 14; NBol 17; [BHB2000] NB17
ACH 4	gcl	00 42 34.5	+41 18 40		30	5	Alias: NBol 35
[V62] 229	gcl	00 42 34.6	+40 55 44		30	18	Alias: [BHB2000] VB229
Bol 116	gcl	00 42 34.7	+41 32 49	16.79	30	18	Aliases: SKHB 178; [BHB2000] 116-178
NBol 53	gcl	00 42 35.3	+41 14 50		30	18	Alias: [BHB2000] NB53
NBol 29	gcl	00 42 35.4	+41 17 47	18.43	30	18	Alias: [BHB2000] NB29
Bol 118	gcl	00 42 35.6	+41 14 34	16.50	30	18	Aliases: NBol 6; [V64] 5; [BHB2000] 118-NB6
Bol 261	gcl	00 42 36.1	+41 17 40	17.63	30	5	Aliases: NBol 72; [WSB85] W 5
NBol 57	cl	00 42 36.2	+41 13 14		30	18	Alias: [BHB2000] NB57
Bol 119	gcl	00 42 36.2	+41 17 35	17.27	30	18	Aliases: NBol 14; [WSB85] W 6; [BHB2000] 119-NB14
NBol 68	gcl	00 42 37.5	+41 19 18	15.59	30	18	Alias: [BHB2000] NB68
NBol 38	gal	00 42 37.6	+41 13 27		30	18	Alias: [BHB2000] NB38
[WSB85] W 7	gcl	00 42 38.0	+41 15 58	17.69	30	99	Aliases: C84 46; ACH 5; NBol 21; [BHB2000] NB21
Bol 351	gcl	00 42 38.0	+42 11 32	17.55	30	18	Aliases: SKHB 179; [BHB2000] 351-179
Bol 352	gcl	00 42 38.3	+42 02 14	16.53	30	18	Aliases: SKHB 180; [BHB2000] 352-180
NBol 74	gcl	00 42 38.5	+41 16 46	15.55	30	18	Alias: [BHB2000] NB74
NBol 25	gcl	00 42 39.4	+41 13 40	18.21	30	18	Alias: [BHB2000] NB25
NBol 91	gcl	00 42 39.7	+41 13 06	15.65	30	18	Alias: [BHB2000] NB91
Bol 122	gcl	00 42 40.3	+41 33 47	17.91	30	18	Aliases: SKHB 181; [V62] 274; [BHB2000] 122-181
Bol 123	gcl	00 42 40.9	+41 10 34	17.45	30	18	Aliases: [V62] 60; SKHB 182; [H32] 60; [BHB2000] 123-182
Bol 124	gcl	00 42 41.1	+41 15 26	14.71	30	18	Aliases: TF 45; NBol 10; C84 51; C84 53; [V64] 2; [BHB2000] 124-NB10
NBol 58	gcl	00 42 42.1	+41 15 12		30	18	Alias: [BHB2000] NB58
Bol 125	gcl	00 42 42.4	+41 05 30	16.53	30	18	Aliases: [V62] 48; SKHB 183; [H32] 48; [BHB2000] 125-183
[CCS85] 55	gcl	00 42 42.5	+40 29 27	18.68	62	18	Alias: [BHB2000] DAO055
Bol D215	gcl	00 42 43.3	+41 12 02		30	18	Aliases: CCS85 D56; [BHB2000] 215D-D56
Bol 126	gcl	00 42 43.8	+41 12 43	17.09	30	18	Aliases: SKHB 184; [BHB2000] 126-184
Bol 127	gcl	00 42 44.5	+41 14 28	14.47	30	18	Aliases: SKHB 185; [BHB2000] 127-185
NBol 89	gcl	00 42 44.7	+41 14 42	>19	30	18	Alias: [BHB2000] NB89
NBol 87	gcl	00 42 45.6	+41 19 05	15.58	30	18	Alias: [BHB2000] NB87
NBol 42	gcl	00 42 47.0	+41 17 39	18.49	30	18	Alias: [BHB2000] NB42
Bol 353	gcl	00 42 47.2	+41 15 38		30	18	Alias: [BHB2000] 353-CFA
NBol 18	gcl	00 42 47.2	+41 18 35	18.43	30	18	Alias: [BHB2000] NB18
Bol 354	gcl	00 42 47.6	+42 00 26	17.81	30	18	Aliases: SKHB 186; [BHB2000] 354-186

Table C.3: Tables of Objects in M31, the Andromeda Galaxy

Name	Type	2000.0 RA	2000.0 DEC	Tot Vm	2U#	Ref	Comments and Aliases
Bol 128	gcl	00 42 47.8	+41 11 12	16.88	30	18	Aliases: [PFJ93] 51; SKHB 187; [BHB2000] 128-187
NBol 95	*	00 42 47.9	+41 15 37		30	18	Alias: [BHB2000] NB95
ACH 6	gcl	00 42 48.4	+41 15 48	18.04	30	5	Aliases: NBol 39; C84 72; [WSB85] C 11
Bol 129	gcl	00 42 48.4	+41 25 06	17.40	30	18	Alias: [BHB2000] 129-000
ACH 7	gcl	00 42 48.6	+41 16 43		30	5	Alias: [WSB85] C 14
Bol 130	gcl	00 42 48.9	+41 29 52	16.93	30	18	Aliases: SKHB 188; [V62] 262; [BHB2000] 130-188
ACH 8	gcl	00 42 49.1	+41 18 11		30	5	
NBol 94	*	00 42 49.4	+41 15 40		30	18	Alias: [BHB2000] NB94
ACH 9	*	00 42 49.5	+41 13 39		30	99	Aliases: NBol 45; [BHB2000] NB45
Bol 262	gcl	00 42 50.1	+41 19 28	17.4	30	5	
Bol 131	gcl	00 42 50.6	+41 16 29	15.07	30	18	Aliases: SKHB 189; [BHB2000] 131-189
Bol 132	*	00 42 51.4	+41 15 40	17.78	30	18	Aliases: NBol 15; [WSB85] C 19; [BHB2000] 132-000
Bol 134	gcl	00 42 51.7	+41 14 02	16.57	30	18	Aliases: [V62] 71; SKHB 190; NBol 13; [H32] 71; [BHB2000] 134-190
Bol 133	gcl	00 42 52.1	+41 23 28	17.51	30	18	Aliases: SKHB 191; [BHB2000] 133-191
Bol 135	gcl	00 42 52.1	+41 31 09	16.04	30	18	Aliases: SKHB 192; [BHB2000] 135-192
Bol 355	gcl	00 42 52.9	+41 57 56	17.76	30	18	Aliases: SKHB 193; [BHB2000] 355-193
Bol 264	*	00 42 53.2	+41 16 13	18.0	30	18	Aliases: NBol 19; [BHB2000] 264-000
Bol 136	gcl	00 42 53.7	+41 19 33	17.21	30	18	Aliases: SKHB 194; [BHB2000] 136-194
Bol D80	*	00 42 54.2	+41 16 13		30	18	Aliases: NBol 93; [BHB2000] 080D-NB93
Bol 137	gcl	00 42 54.3	+41 32 14	17.63	30	18	Aliases: SKHB 195; [V62] 273; [BHB2000] 137-195
Bol 138	gcl	00 42 55.7	+41 18 34	16.84	30	18	Aliases: [PFJ93] 62; [BHB2000] 138-000
NBol 97	gcl	00 42 55.8	+41 14 32	18.16	30	5	Alias: H81 B- 451
ACH 15	HII	00 42 58.5	+41 14 55		30	99	Aliases: NBol 34; [BHB2000] NB34
Bol 140	gal	00 42 58.8	+41 08 52	17.4	30	18	Aliases: [V62] 63; SKHB 196; [H32] 63; [BHB2000] 140-196
Bol D218	gcl	00 42 59.3	+42 06 47	18.40	30	5	
Bol 141	gcl	00 42 59.4	+41 32 47	16.90	30	18	Aliases: SKHB 197; [V62] 278; [BHB2000] 141-197
Bol 143	gcl	00 42 59.7	+41 19 18	16.04	30	18	Aliases: SKHB 198; [BHB2000] 143-198
Bol 144	gcl	00 42 59.9	+41 16 05	16.71	30	18	Aliases: TF 77; [PFJ93] 67; C84 90; [BHB2000] 144-000
Bol 465	gcl	00 43 00.7	+41 14 43	16.5	30	18	Aliases: CCS85 57; [BHB2000] 465-D057
Bol 466	*	00 43 01.4	+40 24 14	18.1	62	18	Aliases: CCS85 59; [BHB2000] 466-D059; [BHB2000] 466-000
Bol D91	gcl	00 43 01.5	+41 30 16		30	18	Aliases: CCS85 D58; [BHB2000] 091D-D58
Bol 145	gcl	00 43 01.7	+41 12 26	18.10	30	18	Alias: [BHB2000] 145-000
ACH 12	gcl	00 43 02.0	+41 12 26		30	5	
Bol 146	gcl	00 43 03.0	+41 15 21	16.94	30	18	Alias: [BHB2000] 146-000
Bol 147	*	00 43 03.4	+41 21 21		30	18	Aliases: SKHB 199; [BHB2000] 147-199
Bol 148	gcl	00 43 03.9	+41 18 04	15.98	30	18	Aliases: SKHB 200; [BHB2000] 148-200
Bol D220	gcl	00 43 04.3	+39 50 05	16.97	62	18	Alias: [BHB2000] 220D-000
Bol 149	gcl	00 43 05.5	+41 34 27	17.03	30	18	Aliases: SKHB 201; [V62] 279; [BHB2000] 149-201
Bol 467	gcl	00 43 06.5	+42 01 48	17.43	30	18	Aliases: SKHB 202; [BHB2000] 467-202

Table C.3: Tables of Objects in M31, the Andromeda Galaxy

Name	Type	2000.0		Tot	2U#	Ref	Comments and Aliases
		RA	DEC	Vm			
Bol 268	gcl	00 43 07.3	+41 11 47	18.20	30	18	Alias: [BHB2000] 268-000
Bol 150	gcl	00 43 07.6	+41 20 19	16.80	30	18	Aliases: SKHB 203; [V62] 256; [BHB2000] 150-203
SKHB 204	gcl	00 43 08.1	+41 16 53		30	5	
Bol 151	gcl	00 43 09.7	+41 21 26	14.83	30	18	Aliases: SKHB 205; [BHB2000] 151-205
Bol 152	gcl	00 43 10.1	+41 18 15	16.16	30	18	Aliases: SKHB 207; [BHB2000] 152-207
Bol 356	gcl	00 43 10.3	+41 50 30	17.34	30	18	Aliases: SKHB 206; [BHB2000] 356-206
Bol 153	gcl	00 43 10.6	+41 14 50	16.24	30	18	Alias: [BHB2000] 153-000
Bol 468	gcl	00 43 12.5	+39 47 56	18.12	62	18	Alias: [BHB2000] 468-000
Bol 154	gcl	00 43 12.5	+41 16 04	17.02	30	18	Aliases: SKHB 208; [BHB2000] 154-208
Bol 357	gcl	00 43 13.2	+40 10 56	16.61	62	18	Aliases: SKHB 209; [BHB2000] 357-209
Bol D225	gcl	00 43 13.4	+40 01 14	18.36	62	18	Alias: [BHB2000] 225D-000
Bol 155	gcl	00 43 13.6	+41 03 29	17.92	30	18	Aliases: SKHB 210; [V62] 243; [BHB2000] 155-210
Bol 156	gcl	00 43 14.0	+41 01 18	16.84	30	18	Aliases: SKHB 211; [V62] 241; [BHB2000] 156-211
Bol 157	gcl	00 43 14.1	+41 11 20	17.73	30	18	Aliases: [V62] 72; SKHB 212; [H32] 72; [BHB2000] 157-212
Bol 158	gcl	00 43 14.5	+41 07 20	14.70	30	18	Aliases: SKHB 213; [BHB2000] 158-213
Bol 159	gcl	00 43 14.7	+41 25 13	17.20	30	18	Alias: [BHB2000] 159-000
Bol 160	gcl	00 43 15.2	+41 01 37	17.95	30	18	Aliases: SKHB 214; [V62] 242; [BHB2000] 160-214
Bol 161	gcl	00 43 15.5	+41 11 24	16.33	30	18	Aliases: SKHB 215; [BHB2000] 161-215
Bol 162	gcl	00 43 16.5	+41 24 04	17.47	30	18	Aliases: SKHB 216; [V62] 265; [BHB2000] 162-216
Bol 163	gcl	00 43 17.7	+41 27 45	15.04	30	18	Aliases: SKHB 217; [BHB2000] 163-217
Bol 358	gcl	00 43 18.0	+39 49 13	15.12	62	18	Aliases: SKHB 219; [BHB2000] 358-219
[V62] B25	gcl	00 43 18.2	+41 12 29	17.94	30	18	Aliases: Bol 164; [V62] 253; [BHB2000] 164-B253
Bol 165	gcl	00 43 18.3	+41 10 54	16.47	30	18	Aliases: SKHB 218; [BHB2000] 165-218
Bol 469	gcl	00 43 19.4	+42 10 17	17.58	30	18	Aliases: BA 4- 1; SKHB 220; [BHB2000] 469-220
Bol 166	gcl	00 43 20.6	+41 12 33	16.76	30	18	Alias: [BHB2000] 166-000
Bol 167	gcl	00 43 21.3	+41 14 08	17.40	30	18	Alias: [BHB2000] 167-000
Bol 168	gcl	00 43 22.5	+41 44 07	17.63	30	18	Alias: [BHB2000] 168-000
Bol 169	gcl	00 43 23.1	+41 15 25	17.08	30	18	Alias: [BHB2000] 169-000
Bol 170	gcl	00 43 23.5	+40 50 41	17.39	30	18	Aliases: SKHB 221; [BHB2000] 170-221
[CCS85] 60	gcl	00 43 24.4	+41 45 54	16.64	30	18	Alias: [BHB2000] DAO060
Bol 171	gcl	00 43 25.7	+41 15 37	15.24	30	18	Aliases: SKHB 222; [BHB2000] 171-222
[V62] B29	gcl	00 43 25.8	+41 37 12		30	18	Aliases: Bol 272; [BHB2000] 272-B294
Bol 172	gcl	00 43 26.1	+41 21 31	16.69	30	18	Aliases: SKHB 223; [V62] 263; [BHB2000] 172-223
[CCS85] 62	gcl	00 43 27.0	+40 47 27	17.60	30	18	Alias: [BHB2000] DAO062
Bol 173	gcl	00 43 28.9	+41 22 36	18.26	30	18	Aliases: SKHB 224; [V62] 264; [BHB2000] 173-224
Bol 174	gcl	00 43 30.4	+41 38 57	15.47	30	18	Aliases: SKHB 226; [BHB2000] 174-226
Bol 176	gcl	00 43 30.6	+40 49 11	16.52	30	18	Aliases: SKHB 227; [BHB2000] 176-227
Bol 177	gcl	00 43 30.8	+41 05 42	18.05	30	18	Aliases: SKHB 228; [V62] 248; [BHB2000] 177-228
Bol 178	gcl	00 43 31.0	+41 21 18	15.02	30	18	Aliases: SKHB 229; [BHB2000] 178-229

Table C.3: Tables of Objects in M31, the Andromeda Galaxy

Name	Type	2000.0 RA	2000.0 DEC	Tot Vm	2U#	Ref	Comments and Aliases
Bol 179	gcl	00 43 31.2	+41 18 14	15.38	30	18	Aliases: SKHB 230; [BHB2000] 179-230
Bol 180	gcl	00 43 31.9	+41 07 46	16.02	30	18	Aliases: SKHB 231; [BHB2000] 180-231
Bol 181	gcl	00 43 32.7	+41 29 08	16.95	30	18	Aliases: SKHB 232; [V62] 289; [BHB2000] 181-232
Bol 182	gcl	00 43 36.8	+41 08 12	15.43	30	18	Aliases: SKHB 233; [BHB2000] 182-233
Bol 183	gcl	00 43 37.1	+41 01 29	15.95	30	18	Aliases: SKHB 234; [BHB2000] 183-234
Bol 185	gcl	00 43 37.4	+41 14 27	15.54	30	18	Aliases: SKHB 235; [BHB2000] 185-235
Bol 470	gcl	00 43 37.5	+42 09 55	17.89	30	18	Aliases: CCS85 63; [BHB2000] 470-D063
Bol 184	gcl	00 43 37.8	+41 36 35	17.23	30	18	Aliases: SKHB 236; [V62] 293; [BHB2000] 184-236
Bol 186	gcl	00 43 38.2	+41 36 23	18.01	30	18	Alias: [BHB2000] 186-000
Bol 187	gcl	00 43 38.8	+41 29 47	17.17	30	18	Aliases: [V62] 104; SKHB 237; [H32] 104; [BHB2000] 187-237
Bol 188	gcl	00 43 41.6	+41 24 25	17.03	30	18	Aliases: SKHB 239; [V62] 277; [BHB2000] 188-239
Bol 471	gcl	00 43 41.7	+42 07 57	17.12	30	18	Aliases: SKHB 238; [BHB2000] 471-238
Bol 189	gcl	00 43 42.5	+41 35 24	16.99	30	18	Aliases: [V62] 113; SKHB 240; [H32] 113; [BHB2000] 189-240
Bol 190	gcl	00 43 43.5	+41 34 06	16.82	30	18	Aliases: [V62] 109; SKHB 241; [H32] 109; [BHB2000] 190-241
Bol 191	gal	00 43 43.7	+40 43 41		30	18	Alias: [BHB2000] 191-000
Bol 192	gcl	00 43 44.5	+41 37 26	18.28	30	18	Aliases: SKHB 242; [BHB2000] 192-242
Bol 194	gcl	00 43 45.3	+41 06 08	17.18	30	18	Aliases: [V62] 69; SKHB 243; [H32] 69; [BHB2000] 194-243
Bol 193	gcl	00 43 45.7	+41 36 58	15.32	30	18	Aliases: SKHB 244; [BHB2000] 193-244
SKHB 245	*	00 43 47.8	+41 27 09	17.8	30	18	Aliases: Bol D103; [V62] 287; [BHB2000] 000-245
Bol 196	gcl	00 43 48.6	+40 42 37	17.40	30	18	Aliases: SKHB 246; [BHB2000] 196-246
Bol 195	gcl	00 43 48.7	+41 02 27	18.56	30	18	Alias: [BHB2000] 195-000
Bol 472	gcl	00 43 48.9	+41 26 57	15.19	30	18	Aliases: CCS85 64; [BHB2000] 472-D064
Bol 199	gcl	00 43 49.9	+40 58 14	17.60	30	18	Aliases: SKHB 248; [BHB2000] 199-248
Bol 197	gcl	00 43 50.0	+41 30 10	17.63	30	18	Aliases: SKHB 247; [V62] 290; [BHB2000] 197-247
Bol 198	gcl	00 43 50.4	+41 31 53	17.54	30	18	Aliases: SKHB 249; [V62] 291; [BHB2000] 198-249
Bol 200	gcl	00 43 50.5	+41 29 23	18.54	30	18	Alias: [BHB2000] 200-000
Bol 201	gcl	00 43 53.1	+41 09 58	16.20	30	18	Aliases: SKHB 250; [BHB2000] 201-250
Bol 202	gcl	00 43 54.7	+41 00 32	17.78	30	18	Aliases: SKHB 251; [BHB2000] 202-251
SKHB 253	gcl	00 43 56.0	+41 26 34		30	5	Aliases: BA 1- 74; [PAV78] 563
Bol 203	gcl	00 43 56.0	+41 32 36	16.68	30	18	Aliases: [V62] 110; SKHB 252; [H32] 110; [BHB2000] 203-252
Bol 204	gcl	00 43 56.6	+41 22 03	15.74	30	18	Aliases: SKHB 254; [BHB2000] 204-254
Bol 361	gcl	00 43 57.2	+40 14 02	17.10	62	18	Aliases: SKHB 255; [BHB2000] 361-255
Bol 205	gcl	00 43 58.3	+41 24 38	15.45	30	18	Aliases: SKHB 256; [BHB2000] 205-256
Bol 206	gcl	00 43 58.7	+41 30 18	15.06	30	18	Aliases: SKHB 257; [BHB2000] 206-257
[V62] B29	gcl	00 43 59.5	+41 36 42	18.20	30	18	Aliases: Bol D110; [BHB2000] 110D-B296; Bol 272; [BHB2000] 272-B294
Bol 207	gcl	00 43 59.7	+41 06 11	17.33	30	18	Aliases: SKHB 258; [BHB2000] 207-258
Bol 208	gcl	00 44 00.4	+41 23 13	17.80	30	18	Aliases: SKHB 259; [V62] 276; [BHB2000] 208-259
SKHB 260	gcl	00 44 00.9	+42 34 48	17.01	30	18	Alias: [BHB2000] 000-260
Bol 209	gcl	00 44 02.8	+41 25 26	16.64	30	18	Aliases: SKHB 261; [BHB2000] 209-261

Table C.3: Tables of Objects in M31, the Andromeda Galaxy

Name	Type	2000.0 RA	2000.0 DEC	Tot Vm	2U#	Ref	Comments and Aliases
Bol 210	gcl	00 44 02.9	+41 14 24	17.57	30	18	Alias: [BHB2000] 210-000
Bol 211	gcl	00 44 03.2	+41 20 04	16.61	30	18	Aliases: SKHB 262; [BHB2000] 211-262
Bol 212	gcl	00 44 03.3	+41 04 56	15.48	30	18	Aliases: SKHB 263; [BHB2000] 212-263
Bol 213	gcl	00 44 03.6	+41 30 38	16.77	30	18	Aliases: SKHB 264; [BHB2000] 213-264
Bol 214	gcl	00 44 04.1	+41 26 19	17.65	30	18	Aliases: SKHB 265; [V62] 286; [BHB2000] 214-265
Bol D111	gcl	00 44 04.9	+41 39 05	18.1	30	18	Aliases: CCS85 65; CCS85 D65; [BHB2000] 111D-D65
Bol 215	gcl	00 44 06.5	+41 31 42	17.13	30	18	Aliases: SKHB 266; [BHB2000] 215-266
Bol D240	gcl	00 44 06.9	+41 40 27	17.20	30	18	Aliases: CCS85 66; CCS85 D66; [BHB2000] 240D-D66
Bol 216	gcl	00 44 09.0	+41 37 56	17.25	30	18	Aliases: SKHB 267; [BHB2000] 216-267
Bol 362	gcl	00 44 09.3	+41 41 39	17.60	30	18	Alias: [BHB2000] 362-000
SKHB 268	gcl	00 44 10.1	+42 46 56	16.63	30	18	Alias: [BHB2000] 000-268
Bol 217	gcl	00 44 10.6	+41 23 50	16.51	30	18	Aliases: SKHB 269; [BHB2000] 217-269
SKHB 270	gcl	00 44 12.0	+41 33 20		30	5	Alias: BA 1- 118
Bol D242	gcl	00 44 13.3	+39 48 52	17.81	62	18	Alias: [BHB2000] 242D-000
Bol 218	gcl	00 44 14.5	+41 19 19	14.79	30	18	Aliases: SKHB 272; [BHB2000] 218-272
[S73] 14	gcl?	00 44 14.8	+41 55 25	16.53	30	5	
Bol 219	gcl	00 44 15.2	+40 56 47	16.39	30	18	Aliases: SKHB 271; [BHB2000] 219-271
Bol 277	gcl	00 44 17.1	+41 14 15	18.50	30	18	Alias: [BHB2000] 277-000
Bol 363	gcl	00 44 17.2	+40 33 35	17.86	30	18	Aliases: SKHB 274; [BHB2000] 363-274
Bol 220	gcl	00 44 19.5	+41 30 35	16.55	30	18	Aliases: SKHB 275; [BHB2000] 220-275
Bol 221	gcl	00 44 23.1	+41 33 07	16.86	30	18	Aliases: SKHB 276; [BHB2000] 221-276
Bol 278	gcl	00 44 23.4	+41 35 04	18.83	30	18	Alias: [BHB2000] 278-000
Bol 222	gcl	00 44 25.5	+41 14 12	17.43	30	18	Aliases: [V62] 96; SKHB 277; [H32] 96; [BHB2000] 222-277
Bol 223	gcl	00 44 27.1	+41 34 36	17.81	30	18	Aliases: SKHB 278; [BHB2000] 223-278
Bol 224	gcl	00 44 27.2	+41 28 50	15.45	30	18	Aliases: SKHB 279; [BHB2000] 224-279
Bol 473	gcl	00 44 27.4	+41 11 34	17.46	30	18	Alias: [BHB2000] 473-000
Bol 279	gcl	00 44 28.0	+41 44 10	18.40	30	18	Aliases: CCS85 68; [BHB2000] 279-D068
Bol 225	gcl	00 44 29.8	+41 21 36	14.15	30	18	Aliases: SKHB 280; [BHB2000] 225-280
Bol 226	gcl	00 44 30.7	+41 10 59	17.65	30	18	Alias: [BHB2000] 226-000
Bol 227	gcl	00 44 31.4	+40 44 19	17.79	30	18	Alias: [BHB2000] 227-000
Bol 228	gcl	00 44 33.2	+41 41 29	16.77	30	18	Aliases: SKHB 281; [BHB2000] 228-281
Bol 229	gcl	00 44 33.8	+41 38 29	16.47	30	18	Aliases: SKHB 282; [BHB2000] 229-282
[CCS85] 69	gcl	00 44 34.8	+41 53 27	16.6	30	18	Alias: [BHB2000] DA0069
Bol 230	gcl	00 44 35.4	+40 57 14	16.04	30	18	Aliases: SKHB 283; [BHB2000] 230-283
Bol 365	gcl	00 44 36.8	+42 17 20	16.73	30	18	Aliases: [S73] 16; BA 3- 27; SKHB 284; [BHB2000] 365-284
Bol 231	gcl	00 44 38.7	+41 27 47	17.29	30	18	Aliases: SKHB 285; [BHB2000] 231-285
Bol 232	gcl	00 44 40.5	+41 15 03	15.69	30	18	Aliases: SKHB 286; [BHB2000] 232-286
Bol D248	gcl	00 44 41.3	+41 40 44	18.60	30	18	Aliases: CCS85 70; CCS85 D70; [BHB2000] 248D-D70
Bol 233	gcl	00 44 42.0	+41 43 27	15.80	30	18	Aliases: SKHB 287; [BHB2000] 233-287

Table C.3: Tables of Objects in M31, the Andromeda Galaxy

Name	Type	2000.0 RA	2000.0 DEC	Tot Vm	2U#	Ref	Comments and Aliases
Bol 281	gcl	00 44 43.1	+41 20 09	17.66	30	18	Aliases: SKHB 288; [V62] 283; [BHB2000] 281-288
Bol 282	gcl	00 44 43.9	+40 44 16	18.20	30	18	Alias: [BHB2000] 282-000
SKHB 289	gcl	00 44 45.7	+41 17 07		30	5	
Bol 234	gcl	00 44 46.5	+41 29 18	16.82	30	18	Aliases: SKHB 290; [V62] 297; [BHB2000] 234-290
Bol 366	gcl	00 44 46.9	+42 03 51	16.23	30	18	Aliases: SKHB 291; [BHB2000] 366-291
Bol 367	gcl	00 44 47.5	+42 05 32	18.45	30	18	Aliases: BA 3- 25; SKHB 292; [BHB2000] 367-292
Bol 368	gcl	00 44 48.1	+41 51 08	18.04	30	18	Aliases: [V62] 123; SKHB 293; [H32] 123; [BHB2000] 368-293
Bol D255	gcl	00 44 48.6	+42 06 13	18.10	30	18	Aliases: CCS85 72; CCS85 D72; [BHB2000] 255D-D72
SKHB 295	gcl	00 44 52.6	+41 25 10		30	5	
Bol 283	gcl	00 44 55.4	+41 17 00	17.64	30	18	Aliases: SKHB 296; [BHB2000] 283-296
[H32] 128	gcl	00 44 56.2	+41 54 00	17.67	30	18	Aliases: [V62] 128; Bol 475; [BHB2000] 475-H128
Bol 284	gcl	00 44 56.3	+40 57 59	19.23	30	18	Alias: [BHB2000] 284-000
Bol 235	gcl	00 44 58.2	+41 29 24	16.26	30	18	Aliases: SKHB 297; [BHB2000] 235-297
Bol D257	gcl	00 44 59.5	+41 54 47	17.50	30	18	Aliases: CCS85 73; CCS85 D73; [BHB2000] 257D-D73
Bol 476	gcl	00 45 07.2	+41 40 32	18.11	30	18	Aliases: CCS85 74; [BHB2000] 476-D074
Bol 477	gcl	00 45 08.4	+41 39 39	18.45	30	18	Aliases: CCS85 75; [BHB2000] 477-D075
Bol 236	gcl	00 45 08.9	+40 50 29	17.38	30	18	Aliases: SKHB 298; [BHB2000] 236-298
Bol 237	gcl	00 45 09.5	+41 22 35	17.10	30	18	Aliases: [V62] 111; SKHB 299; [S73] 17; [H32] 111; [BHB2000] 237-299
Bol 478	gcl	00 45 12.8	+42 24 09	17.50	30	18	Aliases: CCS85 76; [BHB2000] 478-D076
Bol 370	gcl	00 45 14.6	+41 57 41	16.24	30	18	Aliases: SKHB 300; [BHB2000] 370-300
Bol 238	gcl	00 45 15.0	+41 19 38	16.42	30	18	Aliases: SKHB 301; [BHB2000] 238-301
Bol 239	gcl	00 45 15.7	+41 35 17	17.08	30	18	Alias: [BHB2000] 239-000
Bol D262	gcl	00 45 20.0	+41 19 11	18.80	30	18	Aliases: CCS85 77; CCS85 D77; [BHB2000] 262D-D77
Bol D263	gcl	00 45 22.2	+42 20 56	17.65	30	18	Aliases: CCS85 78; CCS85 D78; [BHB2000] 263D-D78
Bol D128	gcl	00 45 23.4	+41 21 27	18.5	30	18	Aliases: CCS85 79; CCS85 D79; [BHB2000] 128D-D79
Bol 240	gcl	00 45 25.2	+41 06 24	15.23	30	18	Aliases: SKHB 302; [BHB2000] 240-302
Bol 286	gcl	00 45 25.9	+40 59 26	18.70	30	5	
Bol 371	gcl	00 45 27.4	+41 43 44	17.54	30	18	Aliases: [V62] 122; SKHB 303; [H32] 122; [BHB2000] 371-303
Bol 479	gcl	00 45 27.9	+42 07 07	17.35	30	18	Aliases: CCS85 80; [BHB2000] 479-D080
Bol 372	gcl	00 45 33.5	+42 00 25	16.60	30	18	Aliases: SKHB 304; [BHB2000] 372-304
Bol 373	gcl	00 45 42.1	+41 45 34	15.64	30	18	Aliases: SKHB 305; [BHB2000] 373-305
Bol D268	gcl	00 45 44.1	+41 40 06	18.13	30	18	Aliases: CCS85 82; MLA 1186; CCS85 D82; [BHB2000] 268D-D82
Bol 374	gcl	00 45 44.5	+41 41 54	18.31	30	18	Aliases: SKHB 306; [BHB2000] 374-306
Bol 375	gcl	00 45 45.6	+41 39 41	17.61	30	18	Aliases: SKHB 307; [BHB2000] 375-307
[H32] 127	gcl	00 45 45.7	+41 45 52	17.91	30	18	Aliases: [V62] 127; Bol 480; [BHB2000] 480-H127
Bol 377	gcl	00 45 48.2	+40 38 05	17.14	30	18	Aliases: SKHB 308; [BHB2000] 377-308
Bol 376	gcl	00 45 48.7	+41 42 40	18.06	30	18	Aliases: SKHB 309; [BHB2000] 376-309
[CCS85] 83	gcl	00 45 49.9	+41 48 18	19.8	30	18	Alias: [BHB2000] DA0083
[S73] 18	gcl?	00 45 50.7	+40 30 23	16.89	30	5	

Table C.3: Tables of Objects in M31, the Andromeda Galaxy

Name	Type	2000.0 RA	2000.0 DEC	Tot Vm	2U#	Ref	Comments and Aliases
[CCS85] 84	gcl	00 45 52.4	+41 42 49	18.7	30	18	Alias: [BHB2000] DAO084
Bol 483	gcl	00 45 53.8	+42 02 21	18.71	30	18	Aliases: CCS85 85; [BHB2000] 483-D085
Bol 484	gcl	00 45 53.9	+41 47 37	18.10	30	18	Aliases: SKHB 310; [BHB2000] 484-310
[S73] 19	gcl?	00 45.9	+40 42	16.12	30	5	
Bol 378	gcl	00 45 57.4	+41 53 31	17.64	30	18	Aliases: [V62] 132; SKHB 311; BA 3- 5; [H32] 132; [BHB2000] 378-311
Bol 379	gcl	00 45 58.8	+40 42 32	16.13	30	18	Aliases: SKHB 312; [BHB2000] 379-312
Bol 380	gcl	00 46 06.4	+42 00 53	16.95	30	18	Barmby, *et al.* [2000]: Possible young cluster. Aliases: [V62] 137; SKHB 313; BA 3- 6; [H32] 137; [BHB2000] 380-313
Bol 381	gcl	00 46 07.3	+41 20 58	15.76	30	18	Aliases: SKHB 315; [BHB2000] 381-315
Bol 486	gcl	00 46 08.5	+40 58 04	17.52	30	18	Aliases: SKHB 316; [BHB2000] 486-316
Bol 382	gcl	00 46 10.3	+41 37 41	17.36	30	18	Aliases: SKHB 317; [BHB2000] 382-317
Bol 383	gcl	00 46 11.9	+41 19 42	15.33	30	18	Aliases: SKHB 318; [BHB2000] 383-318
Bol 384	gcl	00 46 22.1	+40 16 60	15.79	62	18	Aliases: SKHB 319; [BHB2000] 384-319
Bol 385	gcl	00 46 25.0	+41 35 09	17.67	30	18	Aliases: SKHB 321; [BHB2000] 385-321
[S73] 20	gcl?	00 46 27.0	+41 03 23	16.80	30	5	
Bol 386	gcl	00 46 27.2	+42 01 53	15.64	30	18	Aliases: SKHB 322; [BHB2000] 386-322
[S73] 21	gcl?	00 46 32.4	+39 24 23	16.58	62	5	
Bol 387	gcl	00 46 33.7	+40 44 13	16.98	30	18	Aliases: SKHB 323; [BHB2000] 387-323
SKHB 325	gcl	00 46 41.2	+41 50 02		30	5	
Bol 389	gcl	00 46 43.8	+41 49 10	17.38	30	18	Aliases: SKHB 326; [BHB2000] 389-326
[CCS85] 89	gal	00 46 46.4	+42 48 40	18.60	30	18	Alias: [BHB2000] DAO089
SKHB 327	gcl	00 46 49.5	+42 44 48	15.94	30	18	Alias: [BHB2000] 000-327
Bol 391	gcl	00 46 58.1	+41 33 57	17.28	30	18	Aliases: SKHB 328; [BHB2000] 391-328
Bol 392	*	00 47 00.8	+41 54 44	17.05	30	18	Aliases: [V62] 138; SKHB 329; BA 3- 7; [H32] 138; [BHB2000] 392-329
Bol 393	gcl	00 47 01.2	+41 24 06	16.93	30	18	Aliases: [S73] 22; SKHB 330; [BHB2000] 393-330
Bol 395	gal	00 47 06.2	+41 12 25	17.0	30	18	Aliases: SKHB 332; [BHB2000] 395-332
Bol 493	gcl	00 47 14.5	+42 17 08	18.11	30	18	Aliases: CCS85 90; [BHB2000] 493-D090
Bol 494	gcl	00 47 20.5	+41 54 58	17.39	30	18	Aliases: SKHB 333; [BHB2000] 494-333
Bol 495	gcl	00 47 24.8	+41 55 11	18.10	30	18	Aliases: SKHB 334; [BHB2000] 495-334
[CCS85] 91	gal	00 47 24.8	+42 39 50	18.80	30	18	Alias: [BHB2000] DAO091
Bol 396	gcl	00 47 25.2	+40 21 41	17.38	62	18	Aliases: SKHB 335; [BHB2000] 396-335
Bol 397	gcl	00 47 27.5	+41 12 11	16.53	30	18	Aliases: SKHB 336; [BHB2000] 397-336
SKHB 337	gal	00 47 29.7	+41 43 21		30	18	Aliases: Bol D311; [BHB2000] 311D-337
[CCS85] 92	gal	00 47 37.6	+42 48 00	18.00	30	18	Alias: [BHB2000] DAO092
[CCS85] 93	gal	00 47 46.2	+42 45 01	18.20	30	18	Alias: [BHB2000] DAO093
SKHB 339	*?	00 47 49.0	+43 09 17	17.19	30	18	Barmby, *et al.* [2000]: Object type unknown, but not a globular cluster. Aliases: BA 3- 30; [BHB2000] 000-339
Bol D324	gcl	00 47 54.2	+41 45 33	19.04	30	5	
[CCS85] 94	gcl	00 47 54.4	+42 44 06	18.58	30	18	Alias: [BHB2000] DAO094
[CCS85] 95	gal	00 47 57.3	+42 06 57	18.5	30	18	Aliases: Bol D325; Bol D327; [BHB2000] DAO095
Bol 398	gcl	00 47 57.9	+41 48 44	17.46	30	18	Aliases: SKHB 341; [BHB2000] 398-341

Table C.3: Tables of Objects in M31, the Andromeda Galaxy

Name	Type	2000.0 RA	2000.0 DEC	Tot Vm	2U#	Ref	Comments and Aliases
Bol 399	gcl	00 47 59.6	+41 35 28	17.28	30	18	Aliases: SKHB 342; [BHB2000] 399-342
Bol 400	gcl	00 48 01.3	+42 25 32	16.46	44	18	Aliases: BA 3- 9; SKHB 343; [BHB2000] 400-343
Bol 401	gcl	00 48 08.5	+41 40 42	16.83	44	18	Aliases: [S73] 23; SKHB 344; [BHB2000] 401-344
[CCS85] 96	gal	00 48 08.9	+42 57 49	18.50	44	18	Alias: [BHB2000] DAO096
[CCS85] 97	gal	00 48 09.1	+42 55 25	18.0	44	18	Alias: [BHB2000] DAO097
[S73] 24	gcl?	00 48 10.0	+42 25 21	17.27	44	5	
[CCS85] 98	gal	00 48 29.2	+42 18 40		44	18	Alias: [BHB2000] DAO098
Bol 402	gcl	00 48 36.1	+42 01 34	17.27	44	18	Aliases: SKHB 346; [BHB2000] 402-346
BA 3- 11	gcl	00 48 45.6	+42 23 37	17.66	44	18	Alias: [BHB2000] BA11
[CCS85] 99	gcl	00 48 48.3	+42 32 44	19.03	44	18	Alias: [BHB2000] DAO099
[CCS85] 101	gal	00 49 06.6	+42 30 32	18.90	44	18	Alias: [BHB2000] DAO101
Bol D336	gcl	00 49 09.7	+41 17 25	18.51	44	5	
Bol D337	gcl	00 49 11.4	+41 07 21	18.23	44	18	Alias: [BHB2000] 337D-000
[CCS85] 102	gal	00 49 14.0	+42 53 08	17.2	44	18	Alias: [BHB2000] DAO102
Bol 505	gal	00 49 15.4	+42 19 00	17.4	44	18	Aliases: CCS85 103; [BHB2000] 505-D103
Bol 403	gcl	00 49 18.0	+41 35 08	16.22	44	18	Aliases: SKHB 348; [BHB2000] 403-348
[CCS85] 104	gcl	00 49 21.4	+42 16 12	18.79	44	18	Alias: [BHB2000] DAO104
Bol 404	gal	00 49 32.6	+40 41 18	18.1	44	18	Aliases: SKHB 350; [BHB2000] 404-350
[CCS85] 105	gal	00 49 35.5	+42 50 56	17.6	44	18	Alias: [BHB2000] DAO105
[CCS85] 106	gal	00 49 36.0	+42 16 14	18.4	44	18	Aliases: Bol D342; [BHB2000] DAO106
Bol 405	gcl	00 49 39.7	+41 35 31	15.20	44	18	Aliases: SKHB 351; [BHB2000] 405-351
[CCS85] 107	gal	00 49 41.4	+42 45 30	18.2	44	18	Alias: [BHB2000] DAO107
Bol D344	gcl	00 49 52.1	+41 36 38	17.05	44	18	Alias: [BHB2000] 344D-000
Bol 509	gal	00 49 52.9	+42 09 36	17.77	44	18	Aliases: CCS85 108; [BHB2000] 509-D108; [BHB2000] 509-000
Bol 406	gal	00 49 59.4	+42 15 49	17.4	44	18	Aliases: CCS85 109; [BHB2000] 406-D109; [BHB2000] 406-000
Bol 407	gcl	00 50 10.1	+41 41 00	16.09	44	18	Aliases: SKHB 352; [BHB2000] 407-352
SKHB 353	gcl	00 50 18.2	+42 35 45	17.15	44	18	Aliases: BA 3- 13; [BHB2000] 000-353
[S73] 25	gcl?	00 51 58.6	+41 35 18	16.84	44	5	
[BHB2000] EX8	gcl	00 53 14.4	+41 33 23		44	18	
Cl vdB	**	01 16 04.1	+49 36 32	16.17	44	99	See notes. Barmby, *et al.* [2000] incorrectly list this as a star. Alias: [BHB2000] GS-SET

Table C.4: Table of Fornax Objects

Name	Type	2000.0 R.A.	2000.0 Dec	Diam (′)	Tot. Vm	Bt * Vm	V Sur	U#	Ref	Comments and Aliases
Fornax 1	gcl	02 37 02	–34 11.0	0.9	15.6	18.3	15.4	175	7	
Fornax 2	gcl	02 38 44	–34 48.5		13.5	19.0		175	54	This cluster in the Fornax Dwarf has been listed incorrectly as a galaxy, i.e., as MCG –06-06-016. [Lederman and Gottlieb, 1996] Alias: (5) MCG –06-06-016
NGC 1049	gcl	02 39 48	–34 15.5		12.6	18.4		175	99	This cluster in the Fornax Dwarf has been listed incorrectly as a galaxy, i.e., as MCG –06-06-017. [Lederman and Gottlieb, 1996] Aliases: Fornax 3; (5) MCG –06-06-017
Fornax 6	gcl	02 40 06.8	–34 25 14					175	99	Alias: C0238–34
Fornax 4	gcl	02 40 07.7	–34 32 10		13.6	18.6		175	99	Alias: Fornax 6 C4
Fornax 5	gcl	02 42 21	–34 06.1	1.7	13.4	18.6	14.6	175	54	This cluster in the Fornax Dwarf has been listed incorrectly as a galaxy, i.e., as MCG –06-07-002. [Lederman and Gottlieb, 1996] Alias: (5) MCG –06-07-002

Appendix D
Names and Alias Names

If you don't find it in the index, look carefully through the entire catalogue.
—Introduction to the 1897 edition of the Sears, Roebuck and Co. Catalogue

This Appendix contains three lists of alias names for the objects included in the main catalog tables of Chapter 4, Chapter 7, and Appendix C.Table D.1 lists the Messier objects which are known to be (or known to be associated with) star clusters or asterisms. The table shows for each object, the Messier name, the primary (NGC or other) name by which the cluster is known in the catalog and the 2000.0 right ascension. The latter position may be used to locate the object in the main catalog.

Table D.2 lists "special" or "common" names for many star clusters and asterisms. These names are provided due to their use in various publications. Their further use, however, is discouraged—unless the primary name and/or position is also given—in order to avoid confusion in the future. However, they are listed here separately for convenience, include names completely spelled out for clarity, and include some additional particularly long or unusual names that are not appropriate to include in the main list. It also includes names based on the shape of the cluster or the colors of the stars (as noted here with the listed names). Relatively insignificant names (already in the general list below) and most unnumbered clusters with a discoverer's (or re-discoverer's) name are not included. For some names, "[star]" has been added, in order to differentiate the name from that of a similarly named *galaxy* cluster. The table shows for each object, the special name, the primary name by which the cluster is known in the catalog, the 2000.0 right ascension, and a source for the name. The position may be used to locate the object in the main catalog tables of Chapters 4 and 7 and Appendix C. The possible sources for these names are "common knowledge" (i.e., known to the authors, e.g. the Beehive is M 44 = NGC 2632), Collinder [1931], Eicher (see Appendix E for Web address), Frommert (Appendix E), Goldstein ([1981]; (Appendix E), Markarian [1951] (Tau Canis Majoris cluster), Moore and Pepin [1995], Lyngå [1987], McNeil (Appendix E), O'Meara [1998a], O'Meara and Green [2003], Pensack (Appendix E), Pommier [2000], SAC Database (Appendix E), "SC2," meaning Sky Catalogue 2000.0 (Hirshfeld and Sinnott [1985]), Shapley [1944] (the "Intergalactic Tramp"), SIMBAD, and Smyth [1844] (the "Wild Duck cluster"). "See Section 4" means that this object and (at least partially) its name are covered individually in Section 4.4.

Table D.3 is the main table of names for objects in our catalog. The first column includes all names, including preferred object names, alias names for those objects, and names of associated objects (e.g., the nebula a cluster is involved in). These are given in alphabetical order, ignoring case and any leading bracket characters. Note that a few names begin with "Cl" in order to distinguish them from objects of other types with similar names. Names, their abbreviations, and references for them are given in Appendix A. Included here are 13,949 names for the 5,045 objects in the catalog.

If a name is an alias or an associated object, the second column contains the preferred name or at least the name the catalog entry is under.

The third column is a single character that indicates what Table the entry is in here in the book. If blank, see the list of Milky Way objects in Table 4.1 on page 162. If "g", see either Table 4.1 or the list of Milky Way globular clusters in Table 7.1 on page 227. If "L", see the list of objects in the Large Magellanic Cloud in Table C.1 on page 291. If "S", see the list of objects in the Small Magellanic Cloud in Table C.2 on page 345. If "A" see the list of objects in the Andromeda Galaxy (NGC 224 = M 31) in Table C.3 on page 357. And if "F" see the list of objects in the Fornax Galaxy in Table C.4 and page 372.

The fourth column is the 2000 right ascension of the object.

Thus, as an example, to find the cluster "Ru 93", one must either know that "Ru" is an abbreviation for "Ruprecht", or else this can be looked up in Appendix A. Next, the first column of Table D.3 is searched for the name "Ruprecht 93" and this is found on page 444. The second column contains "NGC 3519" showing that either Ruprecht 93 is an alias name for NGC 3519, or it is associated with NGC 3519 (in this case the former is true, as the user will eventually see from the catalog comment field or the entry for NGC 3519 in the Extended Notes Section 4.4). In either case it is now clear the entry for NGC 3519 is what must be found. The next (single character) column is blank, showing this is in Table 4.1 of Milky Way objects starting on page 49. The final column gives the 2000.0 right ascension of this object, "11 04 03", in hours, minutes, and seconds, to the approximate accuracy with which it is known. The object can finally be found under this right ascension in Table 4.1 beginning on page 78.

The preferred name for each object, so far as we have been able to determine, is that by which the object was first historically known, or, in a few cases, is that name by which an object has most popularly (and legitimately) come to be known. NGC and IC names have been used in preference over earlier names (e.g. by Messier and the Herschels). Note that where the original discovery name for an object may have referred to both a cluster and nebula, that name has been kept here, even if later alias names refer only to the cluster. There are for example, many NGC objects (including many Messier objects) that refer to both a cluster and a nebula, while later names, e.g. by Melotte and Collinder, refer only to the cluster. There are also a number of objects (e.g. Messier, NGC, and IC) originally discovered as *only* a nebula, but later found to be associated with a star cluster. These objects are listed here under their discovery name as a star cluster, not their name as a nebula. Numerous cases where a current name in wide use is not the historically correct one—or was supposed to be the name of nebula only—are documented here in the extended notes of Section 4.4, beginning on page 111, and the corrected names have been used in the catalog here.

Appendix A lists the origin of the various object (and earlier catalog) names, i.e., the discovery references of the objects included here. The references themselves are listed in the back of this book. To check whether a "complete" discovery list or previous catalog has been included in the main catalog here, one should check Appendix A to see how many objects were in the discovery list, and then check the list below to see if all the numbered/named objects are included. E.g. Appendix A, under "Collinder" shows that Collinder [1931] listed 471 objects, and indeed it can be seen from column 1 in Table D.3 below that all of these are included.

Table D.1: Messier Names

Messier Name	Primary Name	2000 RA hh mm ss.s	Messier Name	Primary Name	2000 RA hh mm ss.s
M 2	NGC 7089	21 33 29.3	M 37	NGC 2099	05 52 19
M 3	NGC 5272	13 42 11.2	M 38	NGC 1912	05 28 43
M 4	NGC 6121	16 23 35.5	M 39	NGC 7092	21 31 52
M 5	NGC 5904	15 18 33.8	M 41	NGC 2287	06 46 00
M 6	NGC 6405	17 40 17	M 42	NGC 1976	05 35 16
M 7	NGC 6475	17 53 46	M 44	NGC 2632	08 40 22
M 8	NGC 6523	18 04 25	M 45	Pleiades	03 47 29
M 9	NGC 6333	17 19 11.8	M 46	NGC 2437	07 41 47
M 10	NGC 6254	16 57 08.9	M 47	NGC 2422	07 36 36
M 11	NGC 6705	18 51 04	M 48	NGC 2548	08 13 44
M 12	NGC 6218	16 47 14.5	M 50	NGC 2323	07 02 47.8
M 13	NGC 6205	16 41 41.5	M 52	NGC 7654	23 24 51
M 14	NGC 6402	17 37 36.1	M 53	NGC 5024	13 12 55.3
M 15	NGC 7078	21 29 58.3	M 54	NGC 6715	18 55 03.3
M 16	NGC 6611	18 18 45	M 55	NGC 6809	19 39 59.4
M 17	NGC 6618	18 21 09	M 56	NGC 6779	19 16 35.5
M 18	NGC 6613	18 20 00	M 62	NGC 6266	17 01 12.6
M 19	NGC 6273	17 02 37.7	M 67	NGC 2682	08 51 24
M 20	NGC 6514	18 02 31	M 68	NGC 4590	12 39 28.0
M 21	NGC 6531	18 04 13	M 69	NGC 6637	18 31 23.2
M 22	NGC 6656	18 36 24.2	M 70	NGC 6681	18 43 12.7
M 23	NGC 6494	17 56 56	M 71	NGC 6838	19 53 46.1
M 24	IC 4715	18 17	M 72	NGC 6981	20 53 27.9
M 25	IC 4725	18 31 45	M 73	NGC 6994	20 58 56
M 26	NGC 6694	18 45 15	M 75	NGC 6864	20 06 04.8
M 28	NGC 6626	18 24 32.9	M 79	NGC 1904	05 24 10.6
M 29	NGC 6913	20 24 06	M 80	NGC 6093	16 17 02.5
M 30	NGC 7099	21 40 22.0	M 92	NGC 6341	17 17 07.3
M 34	NGC 1039	02 42 08	M 93	NGC 2447	07 44 30
M 35	NGC 2168	06 09.0	M 103	NGC 581	01 33 22
M 36	NGC 1960	05 36 18			

Table D.2: Special Alias Names

Special Name	Primary Name	2000.0 RA hh mm ss	Source for Special Name
20 Vulpeculae Cluster	NGC 6885	20 12 01	common knowledge
30 Doradus Cluster	NGC 2070	05 38.6	common knowledge, SC2
"37" cluster (due to shape)	NGC 2169	06 08 25	Goldstein
4-5 Vulpeculae Cluster	Cr 399	19 26 12	Collinder, Lyngå
47 Tucanae	NGC 104	00 24 05.2	common knowledge, SAC Database
9-12 Geminorum	Cr 89	06 18.0	Collinder, Lyngå
Al Sûfi's Cluster	Cr 399	19 26 12	Frommert
Alpha Persei Cluster	Mel 20	03 24 19	Lyngå
Alpha Persei Moving Cluster	Mel 20	03 24 19	SC2
Anonymous vdB Cluster	Cl vdB 1	06 37 05	SIMBAD
Antares Cluster	Cr 302	16 26.0	Lyngå
Antares Moving Cluster	Cr 302	16 26.0	SC2
Auriga Salt-and-Pepper (due to shape)	NGC 2099 (M 37)	05 52 19	Frommert
BD+40 4124 stellar group	Do 6	20 20.8	Lyngå
Beehive	NGC 2632 (M 44)	08 40 22	common knowledge, SC2, SAC Database
Black Swan (due to shape and other)	NGC 6613 (M 18)	18 20 00	O'Meara
Black Widow (due to shape)	Lederman 1	02 27 18	See Section 4 (page 143)
Brocchi's "Cluster"	Cr 399	19 26 12	common knowledge, SC2, SAC Database
Butterfly Cluster (due to shape)	NGC 6405 (M 6)	17 40 17	SC2, Frommert
Butterfly Cluster (due to shape)	NGC 2447 (M 93)	07 44 30	Frommert
Capricorn Dwarf	Pal 12	21 46 38.8	Frommert
Crackerjack Cluster	NGC 6656 (M 22)	18 36 24.2	O'Meara
Cassiopeia Salt-and-Pepper (shape)	NGC 7654 (M 52)	23 24 51	Frommert
Cat's Eye (due to shape)	NGC 6121 (M 4)	16 23 35.5	O'Meara
Coalsack Cluster	NGC 4609	12 42 20	Collinder, Lyngå
Coathanger, The (due to shape)	Cr 399	19 26 12	common knowledge
Chi Persei	Double Cluster	02 20 40.6	O'Meara and Green
Christmas Tree Cluster (due to shape)	NGC 2264	06 40 59	SAC Database
Cocoon Nebula Cluster	Cr 470	21 53.5	common knowledge
Coma Berenices [Star] Cluster	Mel 111	12 25.1	Lyngå, SC2
Cooling Tower (due to shape)	NGC 6913 (M 29)	20 24 06	Frommert
CV Monoceros Cluster	Cl vdB 1	06 37 05	SIMBAD
Delta Lyrae Cluster	Ste 1	18 53.6	Lyngå, SC2
Double Cluster, The	NGC 869 and NGC 884	02 20.0	common knowledge
Dragonfly Cluster (due to shape)	NGC 457	01 19 33	Frommert
ET Cluster (due to shape)	NGC 457	01 19 33	Frommert
Eta Carinae Cluster	Tr 16	10 45 10	Collinder, Lyngå, SC2
Flickering Globular	NGC 6266 (M 62)	17 01 12.6	O'Meara
Gem Cluster (due to star colors)	NGC 3293	10 35 49	Frommert
Great Hercules [star] Cluster	NGC 6205 (M 13)	16 41 41.5	O'Meara
Great Pegasus Cluster	NGC 7078 (M 15)	21 29 58.3	O'Meara
Great Sagittarius Cluster	NGC 6656 (M 22)	18 36 24.2	O'Meara
h Persei	HD 13841 and HD 13854	02 16 49	O'Meara and Green
Heart-Shaped Cluster (due to shape)	NGC 2323 (M 50)	07 02 47.8	Frommert
Hercules [star] Cluster	NGC 6205 (M 13)	16 41 41.5	SAC Database
Hole in a Cluster (due to shape)	NGC 6811	19 37 09.6	Frommert (Houston)
Intergalactic Tramp	NGC 2419	07 38 08.5	Shapley [1944]
Intergalactic Wanderer	NGC 2419	07 38 08.5	common knowledge
January Salt-and-Pepper (due to shape)	NGC 2099 (M 37)	05 52 19	Frommert
Jewel Box (due to star colors)	NGC 4755	12 53 38	See Section 4 (page 174)
July Salt-and-Pepper (due to shape)	NGC 6705 (M 11)	18 51 04	Frommert
Kappa Crucis Cluster	NGC 4755	12 53 38	Lyngå, SC2
Kemble's Cascade	Kemble 1	03 57 25.3	See Section 4 (page 141)
King Cobra (due to shape)	NGC 2682 (M 67)	08 51 24	O'Meara
Ksi Tucanae	NGC 104	00 24 05.2	common knowledge
Lagoon Nebula Cluster	NGC 6523 (M 8)	18 04 25	common knowledge, Lyngå
Lamda Centauri Cluster	Cr 249	11 38 20.4	SC2

Table D.2: Special Alias Names

Special Name	Primary Name	2000.0 RA hh mm ss	Source for Special Name
Lamda Orionis Cluster	Cr 69	05 35.0	Collinder, SC2
"LE" Cluster (due to shape)	NGC 2169	06 08 25	McNeil
Little Beehive	NGC 2287 (M 41)	06 46 00	O'Meara
Manger (Praesepe)	NGC 2632 (M 44)	08 40 22	common knowledge
Mexican Jumping Star (due to shape)	NGC 2362	07 18 42	Frommert
Mini Cassiopeia (due to shape)	Kemble 2	18 35.0	See Section 4 (page 141).
Mu Normae Cluster	NGC 6169	16 34.1	Lyngå, SC2
Muscle Man Cluster (due to shape)	St 2	02 15.0	Frommert
October Salt-and-Pepper (due to shape)	NGC 7654 (M 52)	23 24 51	Frommert
Omega Centauri	NGC 5139	13 26 45.9	common knowledge, SAC Database
Omega Nebula Cluster	NGC 6618 (M 17)	18 21 09	common knowledge
Omicron Canis Minorum	Cr 121	06 54.2	SC2
Omicron Velorum	IC 2391	08 40.3	Lyngå, SC2
Orion's Belt	Cr 70	05 35.6	Collinder, Lyngå, SC2
Orion Cluster	Cr 69	05 35.0	Collinder, Lyngå
Owl Cluster (due to shape)	NGC 457	01 19 33	Eicher, Frommert
Pazmino's Cluster	St 23	03 16 10.8	See Section 4 (page 203)
Perseus [star] Cluster	Mel 20	03 24 19	Collinder
Perseus Moving Cluster	Mel 20	03 24 19	Collinder, Lyngå
Phi Cassiopeiae Cluster	NGC 457	01 19 33	Frommert
Pinwheel Cluster (due to shape)	NGC 1960 (M 36)	05 36 18	Frommert
Praesepe	NGC 2632 (M 44)	08 40 22	common knowledge, Lyngå, SC2, SAC Database
Ptolemy's Cluster	NGC 6475 (M 7)	17 53 46	Frommert
Rosette Nebula Cluster	NGC 2244	06 32 19	common knowledge, see Section 4 (page 163)
S Normae Cluster	NGC 6087	16 18.9	Moore and Pepin [1995]
Sailboat Cluster	NGC 225	00 43 36	Pommier [2000, 89]
Scorpion (due to shape)	NGC 7654 (M 52)	23 24 51	O'Meara
Scutum Salt-and-Pepper (due to shape)	NGC 6705 (M 11)	18 51 04	Frommert
Sérsic Cluster	Reticulum	04 36 11.3	See Section 4 (page 196)
Seven Sisters	Pleiades (M 45)	03 47 29	Frommert
Sigma Nu Cluster (due to shape)	NGC 2169	06 08 25	Pensack
Small Sagittarius Star Cloud	IC 4715 (M 24)	18 17	common knowledge
Sorority Cluster (due to sigma nu shape)	NGC 2169	06 08 25	Pensack
Southern Pleiades	IC 2602	10 42 57	Frommert
Spiral Cluster (due to shape)	NGC 1039 (M 34)	02 42 08	Frommert
Starfish Cluster (due to shape)	NGC 1922 (M 38)	05 19.7	Frommert
Subaru	Pleiades (M 45)	03 47 29	Frommert
Summer Beehive (resemblance to NGC 2632)	IC 4665	17 46.2	Pommier [2000, 87]
Table of Scorpius	NGC 6231	16 54 09.8	SAC Database
Tarantula Nebula Cluster	NGC 2070	05 38.6	SIMBAD
Tau Canis Majoris Cluster	NGC 2362	08 40 22	Markarian [1951], Moore and Pepin [1995]
Taurus Cluster	Hyades	04 26.9	Lyngå
Taurus Moving Cluster	Hyades	04 26.9	Collinder, SC2
Theta Carinae Cluster	IC 2602	10 42 57	SC2, Frommert
Theta-1 Orionis Cluster	NGC 1976 (M 42)	05 35 16	common knowledge, SIMBAD
Toadstool (due to shape)	French 1	21 07 22	See Section 4 (page 131)
Tom Thumb Cluster	NGC 6451	17 50 41	SAC Database, Frommert
Trapezium Cluster	NGC 1976 (M 42)	05 35 16	Lyngå
Trifid Nebula Cluster	NGC 6514 (M 20)	18 02 31	Lyngå
Tuft in the Tail of the Dog (shape?)	Cr 140	07 23.9	SAC Database, Frommert
Ursa Major [Star] Cluster	Cr 285	14 40.9	Collinder
Ursa Major Moving Cluster	Cr 285	14 40.9	Lyngå, SC2
V Man Cluster (due to shape)	St 2	02 15.0	Frommert
Wild Duck Cluster (due to shape)	NGC 6705 (M 11)	18 51 04	Smyth [1844, 431]
X-mas Tree Cluster (due to shape)	NGC 2264	06 40 59	Frommert
Zeta Sculptoris Cluster	Bl 1	00 04.2	Lyngå, SC2

Table D.3: Cluster Cross-Reference

Name	Look Under	GX	2000.0 RA
1E 0021.8–7221	NGC 104	g	00 24 05.2
1E 0522.1–2433	NGC 1904	g	05 24 10.6
1E 1042.6–5905	Trumpler 15		10 44 44
1E 1339.8+2837	NGC 5272	g	13 42 11.2
1E 1500.7–3251	NGC 5824	g	15 03 58.5
1E 1804.4–4343	NGC 6541	g	18 08 02.2
1E 1833.3–2357	NGC 6656	g	18 36 24.2
1ES 0021–72.3	NGC 104	g	00 24 05.2
1ES 0532–05.4	NGC 1976		05 35 16
1ES 1333+412	Abell 1763		13 35 20.1
20 Vulpeculae	NGC 6885		20 12 01
2E 82	NGC 104	g	00 24 05.2
2E 0021.8–7221	NGC 104	g	00 24 05.2
2E 0532.6–0526	NGC 1976		05 35 16
2E 1366	NGC 1976		05 35 16
2MASS-GC 1		g	18 08 21.8
2MASS-GC 2		g	18 08 36.5
30 Dor cluster	NGC 2070	L	05 38 42.4
4-5 Vulpeculae	Collinder 399		19 26 12
47 Tucanae	NGC 104	g	00 24 05.2
9-12 Gem	Collinder 89		06 18.0
Abell 1763			13 35 20.1
Abell 2141			15 57 42.3
Abt 1	Markarian 6		02 29 40
ACH 1	Bol D53	A	00 42 24.8
ACH 3		A	00 42 33.9
ACH 4		A	00 42 34.5
ACH 5	[WSB85] W 7	A	00 42 38.0
ACH 6		A	00 42 48.4
ACH 7		A	00 42 48.6
ACH 8		A	00 42 49.1
ACH 9		A	00 42 49.5
ACH 12		A	00 43 02.0
ACH 13		A	00 42 34.2
ACH 14	[WSB85] W 4	A	00 42 34.5
ACH 15		A	00 42 58.5
ADS 4186	NGC 1976		05 35 16
ADS 6366	ADS 6366 cl		07 47 02.4
ADS 6366 cl			07 47 02.4
ADS 13292			20 02 23.6
AH03 J0521.3-6954		L	05 21 23.0
AH03 J0524.4-6958		L	05 24 22.1
AH03 J0535.7-6912		L	05 35 41.9
AH03 J0535.9-6910		L	05 35 55.6
AH03 J0536.1-6912		L	05 36 06.4
AH03 J0536.1-6912	NGC 2044	L	05 36 06.4
AH03 J0537.3-6919		L	05 37 22.8
AH03 J0537.3-6919	LH 97	L	05 37.6
AH03 J0748.6-2656			07 48 40
AH03 J0822.2-3624			08 22 12
AH03 J1725.5-3424			17 25 32
AH03 J2011.9+2644			20 11 56.9
AL 1			13 15 16
AL 2			17 53.0
AL 3			18 14 05.7
AL 4			18 19 05.8
AL 5			18 44 19.1
Al Sufi's cluster	Collinder 399		19 26 12
Alessi 1	LeDrew 1		00 53.3
Alessi 2	LeDrew 4		04 46.4

Table D.3: Cluster Cross-Reference

Name	Look Under	GX	2000.0 RA
Alessi 3			07 16 29
Alessi 4			10 16 13
Alessi 5			10 43 08
Alessi 6			14 40 07
Alessi 8			15 29 33
Alessi 9			17 42 25
Alessi 10	Alessi J20046-1030		20 04.6
Alessi 11			20 21 24
Alessi 12	LeDrew 2		20 44.0
Alessi 14			06 30 27
Alessi 15			06 43 04
Alessi 16			06 43 35
Alessi 17	Alessi J07354-1505		07 35 25
Alessi 18	Alessi J07372-2623		07 37 11
Alessi 19	LeDrew 5		18 18.6
Alessi 20			00 09 23
Alessi J01232–3330			01 23.2
Alessi J03091+2420			03 09 03.2
Alessi J03435–2925			03 43.5
Alessi J06245–3151			06 24.5
Alessi J06594–1027			06 59 29.9
Alessi J07279–5141			07 27.9
Alessi J07354–1505			07 35 25
Alessi J07356–2746			07 35 37
Alessi J07372–2623			07 37 11
Alessi J07405–5155			07 40.5
Alessi J08141–1433			08 14 09.0
Alessi J08154–5808			08 15.4
Alessi J08317–3904			08 31.7
Alessi J11046–3157			11 04 37
Alessi J12130–6242			12 13 02
Alessi J18124–1523			18 12 26.4
Alessi J18350+7223	Kemble 2		18 35.0
Alessi J20046–1030			20 04.6
Alessi J20053+4732			20 05.3
Alessi J21075+1619	French 1		21 07 22
Alessi J21426+1004			21 42.6
Alessi J21430+1027			21 43.0
Alessi J21450+1647			21 45.0
Alessi J23407+0757			23 40.7
Alessi J23506+4149			23 50.6
Alpha Perseus	Melotte 20		03 24 19
Alter	King 14		00 31.9
AM 1		g	03 55 02.7
AM 2			07 38 44
AM 3		S	23 48 59.5
AM 4		g	13 56 21
AM 0430–392			04 32 24
AM 0733–273	Haffner 11		07 35 22
AM 1353–265	AM 4	g	13 56 21
AM 1843–651	NGC 6684		18 48 57.5
AM 2346–731	AM 3	S	23 48 59.5
Anon Platais			21 30 02
Antalova 1			17 28.9
Antalova 2			17 29.7
Antalova 3			17 30 34
Antalova 4			17 32 39
Antares cluster	Collinder 302		16 26.0
[A084] I			10.6
[A084] II			09.6

Table D.3: Cluster Cross-Reference

Name	Look Under	GX	2000.0 RA
[A084] III			23.2
[A084] III	Latysev 1		02 52
[A084] IV			03.4
[A084] V			21.7
[A084] VI			09.5
[A084] VII			06.6
[A084] VIII			00.3
[A084] IX			11.7
Apriamasvili	Apriamasvili 1		18 48.1
Apriamasvili 1			18 48.1
Arches cluster	[NHS93] 17		17 45 50.5
Archinal 1			18 54 49.4
Arcturus group			14 19.5
Arp 1	Palomar 14	g	16 11 00.3
Arp 2		g	19 28 44.1
Auner 1			07 04 15.3
AvdB	Palomar 14	g	16 11 00.3
AvdB gcl	Palomar 14	g	16 11 00.3
Aveni-Hunter 1			23 37 47
[B90] 70	NBol 23	A	00 42 26.7
BA 1- 74	SKHB 253	A	00 43 56.0
BA 1- 118	SKHB 270	A	00 44 12.0
BA 1- 435	[V62] 211	A	00 41 02.1
BA 1- 513	SKHB 137	A	00 42 09.5
BA 2- 16	SKHB 99	A	00 41 36.3
BA 3- 5	Bol 378	A	00 45 57.4
BA 3- 6	Bol 380	A	00 46 06.4
BA 3- 7	Bol 392	A	00 47 00.8
BA 3- 9	Bol 400	A	00 48 01.3
BA 3- 11		A	00 48 45.6
BA 3- 13	SKHB 353	A	00 50 18.2
BA 3- 15	Bol 301	A	00 38 21.6
BA 3- 25	Bol 367	A	00 44 47.5
BA 3- 27	Bol 365	A	00 44 36.8
BA 3- 30	SKHB 339	A	00 47 49.0
BA 4- 1	Bol 469	A	00 43 19.4
Baractova 1			20 53.7
Baractova 2			21 43 38
Basel 1	Apriamasvili 1		18 48.1
Basel 2	King 19		23 08.3
Basel 3	Markarian 50		23 15 14
Basel 4			05 48 54
Basel 5			17 52 28.4
Basel 6	NGC 6874		20 07.8
Basel 7			06 36 19
Basel 8			06 34.2
Basel 9	Ruprecht 148		04 46 35
Basel 10			02 19 28
Basel 11			
Basel 11A	Basel 11a		07 17 08
Basel 11a			07 17 08
Basel 11B	Basel 11b		05 58 10
Basel 11b			05 58 10
Basel 12			21 10.5
Basel 13			21 13 11
Basel 14			21 21 14.0
Basel 15			21 15.9
Basel 17			11 10 32.9
Basel 18			13 27 49
Basel 19	Hogg 16		13 29 11

Table D.3: Cluster Cross-Reference

Name	Look Under	GX	2000.0 RA
Basel 20			09 32.5
BD+40°4124 grp	Dolidze 6		20 20 38.0
Belt of Orion	Collinder 70		05 35.6
Bergeron 1	Reiland 1		23 04 45.3
Berkeley 1			00 09 41
Berkeley 2			00 25 15
Berkeley 3	Stock 24		00 39 50
Berkeley 4			00 45 13
Berkeley 5			01 47 44
Berkeley 6			01 51 12
Berkeley 7			01 54 12
Berkeley 8			02 01 05
Berkeley 9			03 32 38
Berkeley 10			03 39 37
Berkeley 11			04 20 27
Berkeley 12			04 44 24
Berkeley 13			04 55 46.2
Berkeley 14			04 59 44
Berkeley 15			05 02 05
Berkeley 16	NGC 1798		05 11 40
Berkeley 17			05 20 30
Berkeley 18			05 22 12
Berkeley 19			05 24 03
Berkeley 20			05 32 37
Berkeley 21			05 51 46
Berkeley 22			05 58 27
Berkeley 23			06 33 15
Berkeley 24			06 37 47
Berkeley 25			06 41 14
Berkeley 26	Biurakan 12		06 50 16
Berkeley 27	Biurakan 11		06 51 21
Berkeley 28	Biurakan 10		06 52 07
Berkeley 29			06 53 04
Berkeley 30	Biurakan 9		06 57 46
Berkeley 31	Biurakan 7		06 57 37
Berkeley 32	Biurakan 8		06 58 07
Berkeley 33	Ruprecht 7		06 57 50
Berkeley 34	Biurakan 13		07 00 22
Berkeley 35			07 09 54
Berkeley 36			07 16 23
Berkeley 37			07 20 18
Berkeley 38	Ruprecht 34		07 45 54
Berkeley 39			07 46 50
Berkeley 40	Ruprecht 37		07 49 47
Berkeley 41	Ruprecht 42		07 57 37
Berkeley 42	NGC 6749	g	19 05 15.3
Berkeley 43			19 15 30
Berkeley 44			19 17 17
Berkeley 45			19 19 06
Berkeley 46	NGC 6791		19 20 52.7
Berkeley 47			19 28 27.3
Berkeley 48	NGC 6827		19 48 53.2
Berkeley 49			19 59 30.2
Berkeley 50	IC 1310		20 10 01
Berkeley 51			20 11 53
Berkeley 52			20 14 30
Berkeley 53			20 55 59
Berkeley 54			21 03 00
Berkeley 55			21 16 57
Berkeley 56			21 17 34.5

Table D.3: Cluster Cross-Reference

Name	Look Under	GX	2000.0 RA
Berkeley 57	NGC 7423		22 55 06.5
Berkeley 58			00 00 12
Berkeley 59			00 02 10
Berkeley 60			00 17 42
Berkeley 61			00 48 10
Berkeley 62			01 01 12
Berkeley 63			02 19 27
Berkeley 64			02 21 46
Berkeley 65			02 39 06
Berkeley 66			03 04 05
Berkeley 67			04 37 50
Berkeley 68			04 44.5
Berkeley 69			05 24 21
Berkeley 70			05 25 48
Berkeley 71			05 40 57
Berkeley 72			05 50 12
Berkeley 73			06 22 05
Berkeley 74	Ruprecht 4		06 48 57
Berkeley 75			06 49 00
Berkeley 76			07 06 40
Berkeley 77			07 21 28
Berkeley 78			07 23 38
Berkeley 79			18 44 57.5
Berkeley 80			18 54 20.6
Berkeley 81			19 01 39.7
Berkeley 82			19 11 20.3
Berkeley 83			20 01 25.1
Berkeley 84			20 04 42.2
Berkeley 85			20 18 47
Berkeley 86			20 20 21.2
Berkeley 87			20 21 35
Berkeley 88			20 21 16
Berkeley 89			20 24 28.4
Berkeley 90			20 35 16
Berkeley 91			21 10 51
Berkeley 92			21 24 46.3
Berkeley 93			21 55 29
Berkeley 94			22 22 53
Berkeley 95			22 28.3
Berkeley 96			22 29 51.2
Berkeley 97			22 39 22.2
Berkeley 98			22 42 39.2
Berkeley 99			23 21 16.9
Berkeley 100			23 25 58
Berkeley 101			23 32 46.5
Berkeley 102			23 38.7
Berkeley 103			23 45.2
Berkeley 104			00 03 27
[BHB2000] 000-002	SKHB 2	A	00 33 33.9
[BHB2000] 000-018	SKHB 18	A	00 37 18.5
[BHB2000] 000-034	SKHB 34	A	00 39 40.1
[BHB2000] 000-083	SKHB 83	A	00 41 08.8
[BHB2000] 000-099	SKHB 99	A	00 41 36.3
[BHB2000] 000-100	SKHB 100	A	00 41 37.9
[BHB2000] 000-171	SKHB 171	A	00 42 33.7
[BHB2000] 000-245	SKHB 245	A	00 43 47.8
[BHB2000] 000-260	SKHB 260	A	00 44 00.9
[BHB2000] 000-268	SKHB 268	A	00 44 10.1
[BHB2000] 000-327	SKHB 327	A	00 46 49.5
[BHB2000] 000-339	SKHB 339	A	00 47 49.0

Table D.3: Cluster Cross-Reference

Name	Look Under	GX	2000.0 RA
[BHB2000] 000-353	SKHB 353	A	00 50 18.2
[BHB2000] 001-039	Bol 1	A	00 39 51.4
[BHB2000] 002-043	Bol 2	A	00 40 02.5
[BHB2000] 003-045	Bol 3	A	00 40 09.4
[BHB2000] 004-050	Bol 4	A	00 40 18.4
[BHB2000] 005-052	Bol 5	A	00 40 20.6
[BHB2000] 006-058	Bol 6	A	00 40 26.8
[BHB2000] 006D-D36	Bol D6	A	00 40 37.3
[BHB2000] 007-059	Bol 7	A	00 40 27.6
[BHB2000] 008-060	Bol 8	A	00 40 30.6
[BHB2000] 009-061	Bol 9	A	00 40 31.2
[BHB2000] 010-062	Bol 10	A	00 40 31.9
[BHB2000] 011-063	Bol 11	A	00 40 32.6
[BHB2000] 012-064	Bol 12	A	00 40 32.8
[BHB2000] 012D-D39	Bol D12	A	00 40 52.3
[BHB2000] 013-065	Bol 13	A	00 40 38.8
[BHB2000] 014-B222	[V62] B22	A	00 40 38.8
[BHB2000] 015-B204	[V62] B20	A	00 40 45.1
[BHB2000] 015D-D41	Bol D15	A	00 41 02.7
[BHB2000] 016-066	Bol 16	A	00 40 45.2
[BHB2000] 017-070	Bol 17	A	00 40 48.9
[BHB2000] 018-071	Bol 18	A	00 40 49.6
[BHB2000] 019-072	Bol 19	A	00 40 52.9
[BHB2000] 020-073	Bol 20	A	00 40 55.6
[BHB2000] 020D-089	SKHB 89	A	00 41 17.4
[BHB2000] 021-075	Bol 21	A	00 40 59.1
[BHB2000] 022-074	Bol 22	A	00 40 59.1
[BHB2000] 023-078	Bol 23	A	00 41 01.3
[BHB2000] 024-082	Bol 24	A	00 41 12.1
[BHB2000] 025-084	Bol 25	A	00 41 12.7
[BHB2000] 025D-B217	[V62] B21	A	00 41 34.5
[BHB2000] 026-086	Bol 26	A	00 41 14.6
[BHB2000] 026D-B216	[V62] B21	A	00 41 34.6
[BHB2000] 027-087	Bol 27	A	00 41 14.6
[BHB2000] 028-088	Bol 28	A	00 41 16.6
[BHB2000] 029-090	Bol 29	A	00 41 17.9
[BHB2000] 030-091	Bol 30	A	00 41 19.0
[BHB2000] 031-092	Bol 31	A	00 41 21.1
[BHB2000] 032-093	Bol 32	A	00 41 21.7
[BHB2000] 033-095	Bol 33	A	00 41 26.4
[BHB2000] 034-096	Bol 34	A	00 41 28.2
[BHB2000] 035-000	Bol 35	A	00 41 32.8
[BHB2000] 036-000	Bol 36	A	00 41 32.9
[BHB2000] 037-B327	[V62] B32	A	00 41 35.0
[BHB2000] 038-098	Bol 38	A	00 41 36.1
[BHB2000] 039-101	Bol 39	A	00 41 38.1
[BHB2000] 040-102	Bol 40	A	00 41 39.0
[BHB2000] 041-103	Bol 41	A	00 41 41.1
[BHB2000] 042-104	Bol 42	A	00 41 41.8
[BHB2000] 043-106	Bol 43	A	00 41 42.5
[BHB2000] 043D-B246	[V62] B24	A	00 42 06.8
[BHB2000] 044-107	Bol 44	A	00 41 42.9
[BHB2000] 044D-B228	[V62] B22	A	00 42 07.3
[BHB2000] 045-108	Bol 45	A	00 41 43.3
[BHB2000] 046-109	Bol 46	A	00 41 45.0
[BHB2000] 047-111	Bol 47	A	00 41 45.7
[BHB2000] 048-110	Bol 48	A	00 41 45.6
[BHB2000] 049-112	Bol 49	A	00 41 45.8
[BHB2000] 050-113	Bol 50	A	00 41 46.4
[BHB2000] 051-114	Bol 51	A	00 41 46.7

Table D.3: Cluster Cross-Reference

Name	Look Under	GX	2000.0 RA
[BHB2000] 052-B266	[V62] B26	A	00 41 47.3
[BHB2000] 053-000	Bol 53	A	00 41 47.3
[BHB2000] 053D-NB20	Bol D53	A	00 42 24.8
[BHB2000] 054-115	Bol 54	A	00 41 47.9
[BHB2000] 055-116	Bol 55	A	00 41 50.5
[BHB2000] 056-117	Bol 56	A	00 41 51.2
[BHB2000] 057-118	Bol 57	A	00 41 53.0
[BHB2000] 058-119	Bol 58	A	00 41 53.0
[BHB2000] 059-120	Bol 59	A	00 41 54.3
[BHB2000] 060-121	Bol 60	A	00 41 57.1
[BHB2000] 061-122	Bol 61	A	00 42 00.2
[BHB2000] 062-123	Bol 62	A	00 42 00.6
[BHB2000] 063-124	Bol 63	A	00 42 00.8
[BHB2000] 064-125	Bol 64	A	00 42 02.0
[BHB2000] 065-126	Bol 65	A	00 42 02.1
[BHB2000] 066-128	Bol 66	A	00 42 03.1
[BHB2000] 067-129	Bol 67	A	00 42 03.4
[BHB2000] 068-130	Bol 68	A	00 42 03.3
[BHB2000] 069-132	Bol 69	A	00 42 05.7
[BHB2000] 070-133	Bol 70	A	00 42 06.9
[BHB2000] 071-000	Bol 71	A	00 42 07.1
[BHB2000] 072-000	Bol 72	A	00 42 07.4
[BHB2000] 073-134	Bol 73	A	00 42 07.4
[BHB2000] 074-135	Bol 74	A	00 42 08.1
[BHB2000] 075-136	Bol 75	A	00 42 09.0
[BHB2000] 076-138	Bol 76	A	00 42 10.2
[BHB2000] 077-139	Bol 77	A	00 42 11.3
[BHB2000] 078-140	Bol 78	A	00 42 12.4
[BHB2000] 079-000	Bol 79	A	00 42 12.3
[BHB2000] 080-141	Bol 80	A	00 42 12.5
[BHB2000] 080D-NB93	Bol D80	A	00 42 54.2
[BHB2000] 081-142	Bol 81	A	00 42 13.6
[BHB2000] 082-144	Bol 82	A	00 42 15.8
[BHB2000] 083-146	Bol 83	A	00 42 16.5
[BHB2000] 084-000	Bol 84	A	00 42 17.4
[BHB2000] 085-147	Bol 85	A	00 42 18.4
[BHB2000] 086-148	Bol 86	A	00 42 18.7
[BHB2000] 088-150	Bol 88	A	00 42 21.1
[BHB2000] 089-000	Bol 89	A	00 42 21.3
[BHB2000] 090-000	Bol 90	A	00 42 21.1
[BHB2000] 091-151	Bol 91	A	00 42 22.0
[BHB2000] 091D-D58	Bol D91	A	00 43 01.5
[BHB2000] 092-152	Bol 92	A	00 42 22.4
[BHB2000] 093-155	Bol 93	A	00 42 23.2
[BHB2000] 094-156	Bol 94	A	00 42 25.0
[BHB2000] 095-157	Bol 95	A	00 42 25.9
[BHB2000] 096-158	Bol 96	A	00 42 26.2
[BHB2000] 097-159	Bol 97	A	00 42 27.5
[BHB2000] 098-000	Bol 98	A	00 42 27.5
[BHB2000] 099-161	Bol 99	A	00 42 27.6
[BHB2000] 100-163	Bol 100	A	00 42 29.1
[BHB2000] 101-164	Bol 101	A	00 42 29.1
[BHB2000] 102-000	Bol 102	A	00 42 29.9
[BHB2000] 103-165	Bol 103	A	00 42 29.8
[BHB2000] 104-NB5	Bol 104	A	00 42 30.0
[BHB2000] 105-166	Bol 105	A	00 42 31.1
[BHB2000] 106-168	Bol 106	A	00 42 31.2
[BHB2000] 107-169	Bol 107	A	00 42 31.3
[BHB2000] 108-167	Bol 108	A	00 42 31.3
[BHB2000] 109-170	Bol 109	A	00 42 32.2

Table D.3: Cluster Cross-Reference

Name	Look Under	GX	2000.0 RA
[BHB2000] 110-172	Bol 110	A	00 42 33.2
[BHB2000] 110D-B296	[V62] B29	A	00 43 59.5
[BHB2000] 111-173	Bol 111	A	00 42 33.4
[BHB2000] 111D-D65	Bol D111	A	00 44 04.9
[BHB2000] 112-174	Bol 112	A	00 42 33.3
[BHB2000] 114-175	Bol 114	A	00 42 34.4
[BHB2000] 115-177	Bol 115	A	00 42 34.5
[BHB2000] 116-178	Bol 116	A	00 42 34.7
[BHB2000] 117-176	Bol 117	A	00 42 34.4
[BHB2000] 118-NB6	Bol 118	A	00 42 35.6
[BHB2000] 119-NB14	Bol 119	A	00 42 36.2
[BHB2000] 122-181	Bol 122	A	00 42 40.3
[BHB2000] 123-182	Bol 123	A	00 42 40.9
[BHB2000] 124-NB10	Bol 124	A	00 42 41.1
[BHB2000] 125-183	Bol 125	A	00 42 42.4
[BHB2000] 126-184	Bol 126	A	00 42 43.8
[BHB2000] 127-185	Bol 127	A	00 42 44.5
[BHB2000] 128-187	Bol 128	A	00 42 47.8
[BHB2000] 128D-D79	Bol D128	A	00 45 23.4
[BHB2000] 129-000	Bol 129	A	00 42 48.4
[BHB2000] 130-188	Bol 130	A	00 42 48.9
[BHB2000] 131-189	Bol 131	A	00 42 50.6
[BHB2000] 132-000	Bol 132	A	00 42 51.4
[BHB2000] 133-191	Bol 133	A	00 42 52.1
[BHB2000] 134-190	Bol 134	A	00 42 51.7
[BHB2000] 135-192	Bol 135	A	00 42 52.1
[BHB2000] 136-194	Bol 136	A	00 42 53.7
[BHB2000] 137-195	Bol 137	A	00 42 54.3
[BHB2000] 138-000	Bol 138	A	00 42 55.7
[BHB2000] 140-196	Bol 140	A	00 42 58.8
[BHB2000] 141-197	Bol 141	A	00 42 59.4
[BHB2000] 143-198	Bol 143	A	00 42 59.7
[BHB2000] 144-000	Bol 144	A	00 42 59.9
[BHB2000] 145-000	Bol 145	A	00 43 01.7
[BHB2000] 146-000	Bol 146	A	00 43 03.0
[BHB2000] 147-199	Bol 147	A	00 43 03.4
[BHB2000] 148-200	Bol 148	A	00 43 03.9
[BHB2000] 149-201	Bol 149	A	00 43 05.5
[BHB2000] 150-203	Bol 150	A	00 43 07.6
[BHB2000] 150D-000	Bol D150	A	00 36 59.8
[BHB2000] 151-205	Bol 151	A	00 43 09.7
[BHB2000] 151D-D08	Bol D151	A	00 37 02.2
[BHB2000] 152-207	Bol 152	A	00 43 10.1
[BHB2000] 153-000	Bol 153	A	00 43 10.6
[BHB2000] 154-208	Bol 154	A	00 43 12.5
[BHB2000] 155-210	Bol 155	A	00 43 13.6
[BHB2000] 156-211	Bol 156	A	00 43 14.0
[BHB2000] 157-212	Bol 157	A	00 43 14.1
[BHB2000] 158-213	Bol 158	A	00 43 14.5
[BHB2000] 159-000	Bol 159	A	00 43 14.7
[BHB2000] 160-214	Bol 160	A	00 43 15.2
[BHB2000] 161-215	Bol 161	A	00 43 15.5
[BHB2000] 162-216	Bol 162	A	00 43 16.5
[BHB2000] 163-217	Bol 163	A	00 43 17.7
[BHB2000] 164-B253	[V62] B25	A	00 43 18.2
[BHB2000] 165-218	Bol 165	A	00 43 18.3
[BHB2000] 166-000	Bol 166	A	00 43 20.6
[BHB2000] 167-000	Bol 167	A	00 43 21.3
[BHB2000] 167D-000	Bol D167	A	00 38 22.4
[BHB2000] 168-000	Bol 168	A	00 43 22.5

Table D.3: Cluster Cross-Reference

Name	Look Under	GX	2000.0 RA
[BHB2000] 168D-D20	Bol D168	A	00 38 25.0
[BHB2000] 169-000	Bol 169	A	00 43 23.1
[BHB2000] 170-221	Bol 170	A	00 43 23.5
[BHB2000] 170D-D21	Bol D170	A	00 38 28.1
[BHB2000] 171-222	Bol 171	A	00 43 25.7
[BHB2000] 172-223	Bol 172	A	00 43 26.1
[BHB2000] 173-224	Bol 173	A	00 43 28.9
[BHB2000] 174-226	Bol 174	A	00 43 30.4
[BHB2000] 176-227	Bol 176	A	00 43 30.6
[BHB2000] 177-228	Bol 177	A	00 43 30.8
[BHB2000] 178-229	Bol 178	A	00 43 31.0
[BHB2000] 179-230	Bol 179	A	00 43 31.2
[BHB2000] 180-231	Bol 180	A	00 43 31.9
[BHB2000] 181-232	Bol 181	A	00 43 32.7
[BHB2000] 182-233	Bol 182	A	00 43 36.8
[BHB2000] 183-234	Bol 183	A	00 43 37.1
[BHB2000] 184-236	Bol 184	A	00 43 37.8
[BHB2000] 185-235	Bol 185	A	00 43 37.4
[BHB2000] 186-000	Bol 186	A	00 43 38.2
[BHB2000] 187-237	Bol 187	A	00 43 38.8
[BHB2000] 188-239	Bol 188	A	00 43 41.6
[BHB2000] 189-240	Bol 189	A	00 43 42.5
[BHB2000] 189D-047	SKHB 47	A	00 40 15.5
[BHB2000] 190-241	Bol 190	A	00 43 43.5
[BHB2000] 190D-048	SKHB 48	A	00 40 16.9
[BHB2000] 191-000	Bol 191	A	00 43 43.7
[BHB2000] 192-242	Bol 192	A	00 43 44.5
[BHB2000] 193-244	Bol 193	A	00 43 45.7
[BHB2000] 193D-055	SKHB 55	A	00 40 25.1
[BHB2000] 194-243	Bol 194	A	00 43 45.3
[BHB2000] 195-000	Bol 195	A	00 43 48.7
[BHB2000] 196-246	Bol 196	A	00 43 48.6
[BHB2000] 197-247	Bol 197	A	00 43 50.0
[BHB2000] 198-249	Bol 198	A	00 43 50.4
[BHB2000] 199-248	Bol 199	A	00 43 49.9
[BHB2000] 200-000	Bol 200	A	00 43 50.5
[BHB2000] 200D-D43	Bol D200	A	00 41 06.9
[BHB2000] 201-250	Bol 201	A	00 43 53.1
[BHB2000] 201D-D44	Bol D201	A	00 41 08.3
[BHB2000] 202-251	Bol 202	A	00 43 54.7
[BHB2000] 203-252	Bol 203	A	00 43 56.0
[BHB2000] 204-254	Bol 204	A	00 43 56.6
[BHB2000] 205-256	Bol 205	A	00 43 58.3
[BHB2000] 206-257	Bol 206	A	00 43 58.7
[BHB2000] 206D-D48	Bol D206	A	00 41 40.6
[BHB2000] 207-258	Bol 207	A	00 43 59.7
[BHB2000] 207D-D50	Bol D207	A	00 41 45.0
[BHB2000] 208-259	Bol 208	A	00 44 00.4
[BHB2000] 209-261	Bol 209	A	00 44 02.8
[BHB2000] 210-000	Bol 210	A	00 44 02.9
[BHB2000] 211-262	Bol 211	A	00 44 03.2
[BHB2000] 212-263	Bol 212	A	00 44 03.3
[BHB2000] 213-264	Bol 213	A	00 44 03.6
[BHB2000] 214-265	Bol 214	A	00 44 04.1
[BHB2000] 215-266	Bol 215	A	00 44 06.5
[BHB2000] 215D-D56	Bol D215	A	00 42 43.3
[BHB2000] 216-267	Bol 216	A	00 44 09.0
[BHB2000] 217-269	Bol 217	A	00 44 10.6
[BHB2000] 218-272	Bol 218	A	00 44 14.5
[BHB2000] 219-271	Bol 219	A	00 44 15.2

Table D.3: Cluster Cross-Reference

Name	Look Under	GX	2000.0 RA
[BHB2000] 220-275	Bol 220	A	00 44 19.5
[BHB2000] 220D-000	Bol D220	A	00 43 04.3
[BHB2000] 221-276	Bol 221	A	00 44 23.1
[BHB2000] 222-277	Bol 222	A	00 44 25.5
[BHB2000] 223-278	Bol 223	A	00 44 27.1
[BHB2000] 224-279	Bol 224	A	00 44 27.2
[BHB2000] 225-280	Bol 225	A	00 44 29.8
[BHB2000] 225D-000	Bol D225	A	00 43 13.4
[BHB2000] 226-000	Bol 226	A	00 44 30.7
[BHB2000] 227-000	Bol 227	A	00 44 31.4
[BHB2000] 228-281	Bol 228	A	00 44 33.2
[BHB2000] 229-282	Bol 229	A	00 44 33.8
[BHB2000] 230-283	Bol 230	A	00 44 35.4
[BHB2000] 231-285	Bol 231	A	00 44 38.7
[BHB2000] 232-286	Bol 232	A	00 44 40.5
[BHB2000] 233-287	Bol 233	A	00 44 42.0
[BHB2000] 234-290	Bol 234	A	00 44 46.5
[BHB2000] 235-297	Bol 235	A	00 44 58.2
[BHB2000] 236-298	Bol 236	A	00 45 08.9
[BHB2000] 237-299	Bol 237	A	00 45 09.5
[BHB2000] 238-301	Bol 238	A	00 45 15.0
[BHB2000] 239-000	Bol 239	A	00 45 15.7
[BHB2000] 240-302	Bol 240	A	00 45 25.2
[BHB2000] 240D-D66	Bol D240	A	00 44 06.9
[BHB2000] 242D-000	Bol D242	A	00 44 13.3
[BHB2000] 244-000	Bol 244	A	00 40 26.7
[BHB2000] 248D-D70	Bol D248	A	00 44 41.3
[BHB2000] 255D-D72	Bol D255	A	00 44 48.6
[BHB2000] 257D-D73	Bol D257	A	00 44 59.5
[BHB2000] 260-000	Bol 260	A	00 42 33.3
[BHB2000] 262D-D77	Bol D262	A	00 45 20.0
[BHB2000] 263D-D78	Bol D263	A	00 45 22.2
[BHB2000] 264-000	Bol 264	A	00 42 53.2
[BHB2000] 268-000	Bol 268	A	00 43 07.3
[BHB2000] 268D-D82	Bol D268	A	00 45 44.1
[BHB2000] 272-B294	[V62] B29	A	00 43 25.8
[BHB2000] 272-B294	[V62] B29	A	00 43 59.5
[BHB2000] 277-000	Bol 277	A	00 44 17.1
[BHB2000] 278-000	Bol 278	A	00 44 23.4
[BHB2000] 279-D068	Bol 279	A	00 44 28.0
[BHB2000] 281-288	Bol 281	A	00 44 43.1
[BHB2000] 282-000	Bol 282	A	00 44 43.9
[BHB2000] 283-296	Bol 283	A	00 44 55.4
[BHB2000] 284-000	Bol 284	A	00 44 56.3
[BHB2000] 289-000	Bol 289	A	00 34 20.9
[BHB2000] 290-000	Bol 290	A	00 34 20.9
[BHB2000] 291-009	Bol 291	A	00 36 05.0
[BHB2000] 292-010	Bol 292	A	00 36 16.7
[BHB2000] 293-000	Bol 293	A	00 36 20.5
[BHB2000] 293-011	Bol 293	A	00 36 20.5
[BHB2000] 294-012	Bol 294	A	00 36 33.0
[BHB2000] 295-014	Bol 295	A	00 36 46.4
[BHB2000] 298-021	Bol 298	A	00 38 00.3
[BHB2000] 299-000	Bol 299	A	00 38 02.0
[BHB2000] 301-022	Bol 301	A	00 38 21.6
[BHB2000] 302-023	Bol 302	A	00 38 33.4
[BHB2000] 303-026	Bol 303	A	00 38 50.5
[BHB2000] 304-028	Bol 304	A	00 38 56.8
[BHB2000] 305-D024	Bol 305	A	00 38 58.9
[BHB2000] 306-029	Bol 306	A	00 39 08.8

Table D.3: Cluster Cross-Reference

Name	Look Under	GX	2000.0 RA
[BHB2000] 307-030	Bol 307	A	00 39 18.6
[BHB2000] 309-031	Bol 309	A	00 39 23.5
[BHB2000] 310-032	Bol 310	A	00 39 25.8
[BHB2000] 311-033	Bol 311	A	00 39 33.9
[BHB2000] 311D-337	SKHB 337	A	00 47 29.7
[BHB2000] 312-035	Bol 312	A	00 39 40.4
[BHB2000] 313-036	Bol 313	A	00 39 44.5
[BHB2000] 314-037	Bol 314	A	00 39 44.6
[BHB2000] 315-038	Bol 315	A	00 39 48.6
[BHB2000] 316-040	Bol 316	A	00 39 53.8
[BHB2000] 317-041	Bol 317	A	00 39 55.5
[BHB2000] 318-042	Bol 318	A	00 40 01.0
[BHB2000] 319-044	Bol 319	A	00 40 03.2
[BHB2000] 320-000	Bol 320	A	00 40 15.5
[BHB2000] 321-046	Bol 321	A	00 40 15.3
[BHB2000] 322-049	Bol 322	A	00 40 17.3
[BHB2000] 323-000	Bol 323	A	00 40 18.3
[BHB2000] 324-051	Bol 324	A	00 40 20.8
[BHB2000] 325-000	Bol 325	A	00 40 23.1
[BHB2000] 326-000	Bol 326	A	00 40 23.6
[BHB2000] 327-053	Bol 327	A	00 40 24.1
[BHB2000] 328-054	Bol 328	A	00 40 24.9
[BHB2000] 329-000	Bol 329	A	00 40 24.5
[BHB2000] 330-056	Bol 330	A	00 40 25.6
[BHB2000] 331-057	Bol 331	A	00 40 26.4
[BHB2000] 333-000	Bol 333	A	00 40 29.6
[BHB2000] 335-H13	[H32] 13	A	00 40 42.0
[BHB2000] 336-067	Bol 336	A	00 40 47.7
[BHB2000] 337-068	Bol 337	A	00 40 48.5
[BHB2000] 337D-000	Bol D337	A	00 49 11.4
[BHB2000] 338-076	Bol 338	A	00 40 59.1
[BHB2000] 339-077	Bol 339	A	00 41 00.6
[BHB2000] 341-081	Bol 341	A	00 41 09.2
[BHB2000] 342-094	Bol 342	A	00 41 24.4
[BHB2000] 343-105	Bol 343	A	00 41 42.2
[BHB2000] 344-127	Bol 344	A	00 42 03.3
[BHB2000] 344D-000	Bol D344	A	00 49 52.1
[BHB2000] 345-143	Bol 345	A	00 42 14.2
[BHB2000] 346-149	Bol 346	A	00 42 20.2
[BHB2000] 347-154	Bol 347	A	00 42 23.0
[BHB2000] 348-153	Bol 348	A	00 42 23.0
[BHB2000] 349-000	Bol 349	A	00 42 24.0
[BHB2000] 350-162	Bol 350	A	00 42 28.5
[BHB2000] 351-179	Bol 351	A	00 42 38.0
[BHB2000] 352-180	Bol 352	A	00 42 38.3
[BHB2000] 353-CFA	Bol 353	A	00 42 47.2
[BHB2000] 354-186	Bol 354	A	00 42 47.6
[BHB2000] 355-193	Bol 355	A	00 42 52.9
[BHB2000] 356-206	Bol 356	A	00 43 10.3
[BHB2000] 357-209	Bol 357	A	00 43 13.2
[BHB2000] 358-219	Bol 358	A	00 43 18.0
[BHB2000] 361-255	Bol 361	A	00 43 57.2
[BHB2000] 362-000	Bol 362	A	00 44 09.3
[BHB2000] 363-274	Bol 363	A	00 44 17.2
[BHB2000] 365-284	Bol 365	A	00 44 36.8
[BHB2000] 366-291	Bol 366	A	00 44 46.9
[BHB2000] 367-292	Bol 367	A	00 44 47.5
[BHB2000] 368-293	Bol 368	A	00 44 48.1
[BHB2000] 370-300	Bol 370	A	00 45 14.6
[BHB2000] 371-303	Bol 371	A	00 45 27.4

Table D.3: Cluster Cross-Reference

Name	Look Under	GX	2000.0 RA
[BHB2000] 372-304	Bol 372	A	00 45 33.5
[BHB2000] 373-305	Bol 373	A	00 45 42.1
[BHB2000] 374-306	Bol 374	A	00 45 44.5
[BHB2000] 375-307	Bol 375	A	00 45 45.6
[BHB2000] 376-309	Bol 376	A	00 45 48.7
[BHB2000] 377-308	Bol 377	A	00 45 48.2
[BHB2000] 378-311	Bol 378	A	00 45 57.4
[BHB2000] 379-312	Bol 379	A	00 45 58.8
[BHB2000] 380-313	Bol 380	A	00 46 06.4
[BHB2000] 381-315	Bol 381	A	00 46 07.3
[BHB2000] 382-317	Bol 382	A	00 46 10.3
[BHB2000] 383-318	Bol 383	A	00 46 11.9
[BHB2000] 384-319	Bol 384	A	00 46 22.1
[BHB2000] 385-321	Bol 385	A	00 46 25.0
[BHB2000] 386-322	Bol 386	A	00 46 27.2
[BHB2000] 387-323	Bol 387	A	00 46 33.7
[BHB2000] 389-326	Bol 389	A	00 46 43.8
[BHB2000] 391-328	Bol 391	A	00 46 58.1
[BHB2000] 392-329	Bol 392	A	00 47 00.8
[BHB2000] 393-330	Bol 393	A	00 47 01.2
[BHB2000] 395-332	Bol 395	A	00 47 06.2
[BHB2000] 396-335	Bol 396	A	00 47 25.2
[BHB2000] 397-336	Bol 397	A	00 47 27.5
[BHB2000] 398-341	Bol 398	A	00 47 57.9
[BHB2000] 399-342	Bol 399	A	00 47 59.6
[BHB2000] 400-343	Bol 400	A	00 48 01.3
[BHB2000] 401-344	Bol 401	A	00 48 08.5
[BHB2000] 402-346	Bol 402	A	00 48 36.1
[BHB2000] 403-348	Bol 403	A	00 49 18.0
[BHB2000] 404-350	Bol 404	A	00 49 32.6
[BHB2000] 405-351	Bol 405	A	00 49 39.7
[BHB2000] 406-000	Bol 406	A	00 49 59.4
[BHB2000] 406-D109	Bol 406	A	00 49 59.4
[BHB2000] 407-352	Bol 407	A	00 50 10.1
[BHB2000] 416-D007	Bol 416	A	00 37 01.4
[BHB2000] 418-000	Bol 418	A	00 37 17.8
[BHB2000] 419-D010	Bol 419	A	00 37 27.2
[BHB2000] 421-019	Bol 421	A	00 37 32.8
[BHB2000] 422-000	Bol 422	A	00 37 38.4
[BHB2000] 423-000	Bol 423	A	00 37 56.6
[BHB2000] 424-D017	Bol 424	A	00 38 03.1
[BHB2000] 426-000	Bol 426	A	00 38 19.8
[BHB2000] 427-D019	Bol 427	A	00 38 22.7
[BHB2000] 429-024	Bol 429	A	00 38 38.6
[BHB2000] 430-025	Bol 430	A	00 38 42.9
[BHB2000] 431-027	Bol 431	A	00 38 54.9
[BHB2000] 432-000	Bol 432	A	00 38 59.1
[BHB2000] 433-000	Bol 433	A	00 39 02.4
[BHB2000] 434-000	Bol 434	A	00 39 15.1
[BHB2000] 434-D026	Bol 434	A	00 39 15.1
[BHB2000] 435-D028	Bol 435	A	00 39 18.4
[BHB2000] 436-000	Bol 436	A	00 39 30.6
[BHB2000] 442-D033	Bol 442	A	00 40 19.4
[BHB2000] 443-D034	Bol 443	A	00 40 21.4
[BHB2000] 448-D035	Bol 448	A	00 40 36.5
[BHB2000] 449-H11	[H32] 11	A	00 40 42.5
[BHB2000] 450-000	Bol 450	A	00 40 47.0
[BHB2000] 451-D037	Bol 451	A	00 40 46.4
[BHB2000] 452-069	Bol 452	A	00 40 48.3
[BHB2000] 453-D042	Bol 453	A	00 41 03.3

Table D.3: Cluster Cross-Reference

Name	Look Under	GX	2000.0 RA
[BHB2000] 455-080	Bol 455	A	00 41 05.7
[BHB2000] 456-D045	Bol 456	A	00 41 21.4
[BHB2000] 457-097	Bol 457	A	00 41 29.2
[BHB2000] 458-D049	Bol 458	A	00 41 44.6
[BHB2000] 461-131	Bol 461	A	00 42 04.2
[BHB2000] 462-000	Bol 462	A	00 42 14.7
[BHB2000] 463-160	Bol 463	A	00 42 27.5
[BHB2000] 465-D057	Bol 465	A	00 43 00.7
[BHB2000] 466-000	Bol 466	A	00 43 01.4
[BHB2000] 466-D059	Bol 466	A	00 43 01.4
[BHB2000] 467-202	Bol 467	A	00 43 06.5
[BHB2000] 468-000	Bol 468	A	00 43 12.5
[BHB2000] 469-220	Bol 469	A	00 43 19.4
[BHB2000] 470-D063	Bol 470	A	00 43 37.5
[BHB2000] 471-238	Bol 471	A	00 43 41.7
[BHB2000] 472-D064	Bol 472	A	00 43 48.9
[BHB2000] 473-000	Bol 473	A	00 44 27.4
[BHB2000] 475-H128	[H32] 128	A	00 44 56.2
[BHB2000] 476-D074	Bol 476	A	00 45 07.2
[BHB2000] 477-D075	Bol 477	A	00 45 08.4
[BHB2000] 478-D076	Bol 478	A	00 45 12.8
[BHB2000] 479-D080	Bol 479	A	00 45 27.9
[BHB2000] 480-H127	[H32] 127	A	00 45 45.7
[BHB2000] 483-D085	Bol 483	A	00 45 53.8
[BHB2000] 484-310	Bol 484	A	00 45 53.9
[BHB2000] 486-316	Bol 486	A	00 46 08.5
[BHB2000] 493-D090	Bol 493	A	00 47 14.5
[BHB2000] 494-333	Bol 494	A	00 47 20.5
[BHB2000] 495-334	Bol 495	A	00 47 24.8
[BHB2000] 505-D103	Bol 505	A	00 49 15.4
[BHB2000] 509-000	Bol 509	A	00 49 52.9
[BHB2000] 509-D108	Bol 509	A	00 49 52.9
[BHB2000] BA11	BA 3- 11	A	00 48 45.6
[BHB2000] DA0001	[CCS85] 1	A	00 35 18.8
[BHB2000] DA0002	[CCS85] 2	A	00 35 32.5
[BHB2000] DA0003	[CCS85] 3	A	00 35 52.1
[BHB2000] DA0004	[CCS85] 4	A	00 36 08.8
[BHB2000] DA0005	[CCS85] 5	A	00 36 35.6
[BHB2000] DA0006	[CCS85] 6	A	00 36 56.1
[BHB2000] DA0009	[CCS85] 9	A	00 37 25.7
[BHB2000] DA0011	[CCS85] 11	A	00 37 29.6
[BHB2000] DA0016	[CCS85] 16	A	00 37 56.9
[BHB2000] DA0018	[CCS85] 18	A	00 38 19.8
[BHB2000] DA0022	[CCS85] 22	A	00 38 53.7
[BHB2000] DA0023	[CCS85] 23	A	00 38 54.3
[BHB2000] DA0025	[CCS85] 25	A	00 39 13.4
[BHB2000] DA0027	[CCS85] 27	A	00 39 16.5
[BHB2000] DA0029	[CCS85] 29	A	00 39 27.4
[BHB2000] DA0030	[CCS85] 30	A	00 39 50.8
[BHB2000] DA0032	[CCS85] 32	A	00 40 19.2
[BHB2000] DA0040	[CCS85] 40	A	00 40 52.2
[BHB2000] DA0046	[CCS85] 46	A	00 41 23.0
[BHB2000] DA0047	[CCS85] 47	A	00 41 29.4
[BHB2000] DA0052	[CCS85] 52	A	00 42 08.8
[BHB2000] DA0053	[CCS85] 53	A	00 42 09.9
[BHB2000] DA0054	[CCS85] 54	A	00 42 10.9
[BHB2000] DA0055	[CCS85] 55	A	00 42 42.5
[BHB2000] DA0060	[CCS85] 60	A	00 43 24.4
[BHB2000] DA0062	[CCS85] 62	A	00 43 27.0
[BHB2000] DA0069	[CCS85] 69	A	00 44 34.8
[BHB2000] DA0083	[CCS85] 83	A	00 45 49.9
[BHB2000] DA0084	[CCS85] 84	A	00 45 52.4
[BHB2000] DA0089	[CCS85] 89	A	00 46 46.4
[BHB2000] DA0091	[CCS85] 91	A	00 47 24.8
[BHB2000] DA0092	[CCS85] 92	A	00 47 37.6
[BHB2000] DA0093	[CCS85] 93	A	00 47 46.2
[BHB2000] DA0094	[CCS85] 94	A	00 47 54.4
[BHB2000] DA0095	[CCS85] 95	A	00 47 57.3
[BHB2000] DA0096	[CCS85] 96	A	00 48 08.9
[BHB2000] DA0097	[CCS85] 97	A	00 48 09.1
[BHB2000] DA0098	[CCS85] 98	A	00 48 29.2
[BHB2000] DA0099	[CCS85] 99	A	00 48 48.3
[BHB2000] DA0101	[CCS85] 101	A	00 49 06.6
[BHB2000] DA0102	[CCS85] 102	A	00 49 14.0
[BHB2000] DA0104	[CCS85] 104	A	00 49 21.4
[BHB2000] DA0105	[CCS85] 105	A	00 49 35.5
[BHB2000] DA0106	[CCS85] 106	A	00 49 36.0
[BHB2000] DA0107	[CCS85] 107	A	00 49 41.4
[BHB2000] EX8		A	00 53 14.4
[BHB2000] GS-SET	Cl vdB	A	01 16 04.1
[BHB2000] NB16	NBol 16	A	00 42 33.2
[BHB2000] NB17	[WSB85] W 4	A	00 42 34.5
[BHB2000] NB18	NBol 18	A	00 42 47.2
[BHB2000] NB21	[WSB85] W 7	A	00 42 38.0
[BHB2000] NB23	NBol 23	A	00 42 26.7
[BHB2000] NB25	NBol 25	A	00 42 39.4
[BHB2000] NB29	NBol 29	A	00 42 35.4
[BHB2000] NB34	ACH 15	A	00 42 58.5
[BHB2000] NB38	NBol 38	A	00 42 37.6
[BHB2000] NB42	NBol 42	A	00 42 47.0
[BHB2000] NB45	ACH 9	A	00 42 49.5
[BHB2000] NB53	NBol 53	A	00 42 35.3
[BHB2000] NB57	NBol 57	A	00 42 36.2
[BHB2000] NB58	NBol 58	A	00 42 42.1
[BHB2000] NB61	NBol 61	A	00 42 31.7
[BHB2000] NB63	NBol 63	A	00 42 31.3
[BHB2000] NB65	NBol 65	A	00 42 29.7
[BHB2000] NB67	ACH 13	A	00 42 34.2
[BHB2000] NB68	NBol 68	A	00 42 37.5
[BHB2000] NB70	NBol 70	A	00 42 30.2
[BHB2000] NB74	NBol 74	A	00 42 38.5
[BHB2000] NB75	NBol 75	A	00 42 33.2
[BHB2000] NB81	NBol 81	A	00 42 31.5
[BHB2000] NB83	NBol 83	A	00 42 26.9
[BHB2000] NB87	NBol 87	A	00 42 45.6
[BHB2000] NB89	NBol 89	A	00 42 44.7
[BHB2000] NB91	NBol 91	A	00 42 39.7
[BHB2000] NB94	NBol 94	A	00 42 49.4
[BHB2000] NB95	NBol 95	A	00 42 47.9
[BHB2000] VB229	[V62] 229	A	00 42 34.6
[BHB2000] VB234	[V62] 234	A	00 42 30.1
[BHB2000] VDB0	Cl vdB 0	A	00 40 29.4
[BHB2000] VH31	[H32] 31	A	00 41 12.2
Bica 1			17 24 53.5
Biurakan 1			20 07.5
Biurakan 2			20 09 14.3
Biurakan 3	Markarian 50		23 15 14
Biurakan 4	Markarian 6		02 29 40
Biurakan 5	Markarian 38		18 15 16.6
Biurakan 7			06 57 37
Biurakan 8			06 58 07
Biurakan 9			06 57 46
Biurakan 10			06 52 07
Biurakan 11			06 51 21
Biurakan 12			06 50 16
Biurakan 13			07 00 22
Blanco 1			00 04.2
Bochum 1			06 25 24.9
Bochum 2			06 48 50
Bochum 3			07 03 28
Bochum 4	NGC 2409		07 31 37
Bochum 5			07 32.1
Bochum 6			07 31 45.1
Bochum 7			08 44.8
Bochum 8	vdB-Ha 90		10 12 10
Bochum 9			10 35.5
Bochum 10			10 42 08
Bochum 11			10 47 12
Bochum 12			10 57 18
Bochum 13			17 17 20.7
Bochum 14			18 02.0
Bochum 15			07 40 15
Bok 1			
Bok 1	NGC 1901		05 17.8
Bol 1		A	00 39 51.4
Bol 2		A	00 40 02.5
Bol 3		A	00 40 09.4
Bol 4		A	00 40 18.4
Bol 5		A	00 40 20.6
Bol 6		A	00 40 26.8
Bol 7		A	00 40 27.6
Bol 8		A	00 40 30.6
Bol 9		A	00 40 31.2
Bol 10		A	00 40 31.9
Bol 11		A	00 40 32.6
Bol 12		A	00 40 32.8
Bol 13		A	00 40 38.8
Bol 14	[V62] B22	A	00 40 38.8
Bol 15	[V62] B20	A	00 40 45.1
Bol 16		A	00 40 45.2
Bol 17		A	00 40 48.9
Bol 18		A	00 40 49.6
Bol 19		A	00 40 52.9
Bol 20		A	00 40 55.6
Bol 21		A	00 40 59.1
Bol 22		A	00 40 59.1
Bol 23		A	00 41 01.3
Bol 24		A	00 41 12.1
Bol 25		A	00 41 12.7
Bol 26		A	00 41 14.6
Bol 27		A	00 41 14.6
Bol 28		A	00 41 16.6
Bol 29		A	00 41 17.9
Bol 30		A	00 41 19.0
Bol 31		A	00 41 21.1
Bol 32		A	00 41 21.7
Bol 33		A	00 41 26.4
Bol 34		A	00 41 28.2
Bol 35		A	00 41 32.8
Bol 36		A	00 41 32.9

Table D.3: Cluster Cross-Reference

Name	Look Under	GX	2000.0 RA
Bol 37	[V62] B32	A	00 41 35.0
Bol 38		A	00 41 36.1
Bol 39		A	00 41 38.1
Bol 40		A	00 41 39.0
Bol 41		A	00 41 41.1
Bol 42		A	00 41 41.8
Bol 43		A	00 41 42.5
Bol 44		A	00 41 42.9
Bol 45		A	00 41 43.3
Bol 46		A	00 41 45.0
Bol 47		A	00 41 45.7
Bol 48		A	00 41 45.6
Bol 49		A	00 41 45.8
Bol 50		A	00 41 46.4
Bol 51		A	00 41 46.7
Bol 52	[V62] B26	A	00 41 47.3
Bol 53		A	00 41 47.3
Bol 54		A	00 41 47.9
Bol 55		A	00 41 50.5
Bol 56		A	00 41 51.2
Bol 57		A	00 41 53.0
Bol 58		A	00 41 53.0
Bol 59		A	00 41 54.3
Bol 60		A	00 41 57.1
Bol 61		A	00 42 00.2
Bol 62		A	00 42 00.6
Bol 63		A	00 42 00.8
Bol 64		A	00 42 02.0
Bol 65		A	00 42 02.1
Bol 66		A	00 42 03.1
Bol 67		A	00 42 03.4
Bol 68		A	00 42 03.3
Bol 69		A	00 42 05.7
Bol 70		A	00 42 06.9
Bol 71		A	00 42 07.1
Bol 72		A	00 42 07.4
Bol 73		A	00 42 07.4
Bol 74		A	00 42 08.1
Bol 75		A	00 42 09.0
Bol 76		A	00 42 10.2
Bol 77		A	00 42 11.3
Bol 78		A	00 42 12.4
Bol 79		A	00 42 12.3
Bol 80		A	00 42 12.5
Bol 81		A	00 42 13.6
Bol 82		A	00 42 15.8
Bol 83		A	00 42 16.5
Bol 84		A	00 42 17.4
Bol 85		A	00 42 18.4
Bol 86		A	00 42 18.7
Bol 88		A	00 42 21.1
Bol 89		A	00 42 21.3
Bol 90		A	00 42 21.1
Bol 91		A	00 42 22.0
Bol 92		A	00 42 22.4
Bol 93		A	00 42 23.2
Bol 94		A	00 42 25.0
Bol 95		A	00 42 25.9
Bol 96		A	00 42 26.2
Bol 97		A	00 42 27.5

Table D.3: Cluster Cross-Reference

Name	Look Under	GX	2000.0 RA
Bol 98		A	00 42 27.5
Bol 99		A	00 42 27.6
Bol 100		A	00 42 29.1
Bol 101		A	00 42 29.1
Bol 102		A	00 42 29.9
Bol 103		A	00 42 29.8
Bol 104		A	00 42 30.0
Bol 105		A	00 42 31.1
Bol 106		A	00 42 31.2
Bol 107		A	00 42 31.3
Bol 108		A	00 42 31.3
Bol 109		A	00 42 32.2
Bol 110		A	00 42 33.2
Bol 111		A	00 42 33.4
Bol 112		A	00 42 33.3
Bol 114		A	00 42 34.4
Bol 115		A	00 42 34.5
Bol 116		A	00 42 34.7
Bol 117		A	00 42 34.4
Bol 118		A	00 42 35.6
Bol 119		A	00 42 36.2
Bol 122		A	00 42 40.3
Bol 123		A	00 42 40.9
Bol 124		A	00 42 41.1
Bol 125		A	00 42 42.4
Bol 126		A	00 42 43.8
Bol 127		A	00 42 44.5
Bol 128		A	00 42 47.8
Bol 129		A	00 42 48.4
Bol 130		A	00 42 48.9
Bol 131		A	00 42 50.6
Bol 132		A	00 42 51.4
Bol 133		A	00 42 52.1
Bol 134		A	00 42 51.7
Bol 135		A	00 42 52.1
Bol 136		A	00 42 53.7
Bol 137		A	00 42 54.3
Bol 138		A	00 42 55.7
Bol 140		A	00 42 58.8
Bol 141		A	00 42 59.4
Bol 143		A	00 42 59.7
Bol 144		A	00 42 59.9
Bol 145		A	00 43 01.7
Bol 146		A	00 43 03.0
Bol 147		A	00 43 03.4
Bol 148		A	00 43 03.9
Bol 149		A	00 43 05.5
Bol 150		A	00 43 07.6
Bol 151		A	00 43 09.7
Bol 152		A	00 43 10.1
Bol 153		A	00 43 10.6
Bol 154		A	00 43 12.5
Bol 155		A	00 43 13.6
Bol 156		A	00 43 14.0
Bol 157		A	00 43 14.1
Bol 158		A	00 43 14.5
Bol 159		A	00 43 14.7
Bol 160		A	00 43 15.2
Bol 161		A	00 43 15.5
Bol 162		A	00 43 16.5

Table D.3: Cluster Cross-Reference

Name	Look Under	GX	2000.0 RA
Bol 163		A	00 43 17.7
Bol 164	[V62] B25	A	00 43 18.2
Bol 165		A	00 43 18.3
Bol 166		A	00 43 20.6
Bol 167		A	00 43 21.3
Bol 168		A	00 43 22.5
Bol 169		A	00 43 23.1
Bol 170		A	00 43 23.5
Bol 171		A	00 43 25.7
Bol 172		A	00 43 26.1
Bol 173		A	00 43 28.9
Bol 174		A	00 43 30.4
Bol 176		A	00 43 30.6
Bol 177		A	00 43 30.8
Bol 178		A	00 43 31.0
Bol 179		A	00 43 31.2
Bol 180		A	00 43 31.9
Bol 181		A	00 43 32.7
Bol 182		A	00 43 36.8
Bol 183		A	00 43 37.1
Bol 184		A	00 43 37.8
Bol 185		A	00 43 37.4
Bol 186		A	00 43 38.2
Bol 187		A	00 43 38.8
Bol 188		A	00 43 41.6
Bol 189		A	00 43 42.5
Bol 190		A	00 43 43.5
Bol 191		A	00 43 43.7
Bol 192		A	00 43 44.5
Bol 193		A	00 43 45.7
Bol 194		A	00 43 45.3
Bol 195		A	00 43 48.7
Bol 196		A	00 43 48.6
Bol 197		A	00 43 50.0
Bol 198		A	00 43 50.4
Bol 199		A	00 43 49.9
Bol 200		A	00 43 50.5
Bol 201		A	00 43 53.1
Bol 202		A	00 43 54.7
Bol 203		A	00 43 56.0
Bol 204		A	00 43 56.6
Bol 205		A	00 43 58.3
Bol 206		A	00 43 58.7
Bol 207		A	00 43 59.7
Bol 208		A	00 44 00.4
Bol 209		A	00 44 02.8
Bol 210		A	00 44 02.9
Bol 211		A	00 44 03.2
Bol 212		A	00 44 03.3
Bol 213		A	00 44 03.6
Bol 214		A	00 44 04.1
Bol 215		A	00 44 06.5
Bol 216		A	00 44 09.0
Bol 217		A	00 44 10.6
Bol 218		A	00 44 14.5
Bol 219		A	00 44 15.2
Bol 220		A	00 44 19.5
Bol 221		A	00 44 23.1
Bol 222		A	00 44 25.5
Bol 223		A	00 44 27.1

Table D.3: Cluster Cross-Reference

Name	Look Under	GX	2000.0 RA
Bol 224		A	00 44 27.2
Bol 225		A	00 44 29.8
Bol 226		A	00 44 30.7
Bol 227		A	00 44 31.4
Bol 228		A	00 44 33.2
Bol 229		A	00 44 33.8
Bol 230		A	00 44 35.4
Bol 231		A	00 44 38.7
Bol 232		A	00 44 40.5
Bol 233		A	00 44 42.0
Bol 234		A	00 44 46.5
Bol 235		A	00 44 58.2
Bol 236		A	00 45 08.9
Bol 237		A	00 45 09.5
Bol 238		A	00 45 15.0
Bol 239		A	00 45 15.7
Bol 240		A	00 45 25.2
Bol 244		A	00 40 26.7
Bol 260		A	00 42 33.3
Bol 261		A	00 42 36.1
Bol 262		A	00 42 50.1
Bol 264		A	00 42 53.2
Bol 268		A	00 43 07.3
Bol 272	[V62] B29	A	00 43 25.8
Bol 272	[V62] B29	A	00 43 59.5
Bol 277		A	00 44 17.1
Bol 278		A	00 44 23.4
Bol 279		A	00 44 28.0
Bol 281		A	00 44 43.1
Bol 282		A	00 44 43.9
Bol 283		A	00 44 55.4
Bol 284		A	00 44 56.3
Bol 286		A	00 45 25.9
Bol 289		A	00 34 20.9
Bol 290		A	00 34 20.9
Bol 291		A	00 36 05.0
Bol 292		A	00 36 16.7
Bol 293		A	00 36 20.5
Bol 294		A	00 36 33.0
Bol 295		A	00 36 46.4
Bol 298		A	00 38 00.3
Bol 299		A	00 38 02.0
Bol 301		A	00 38 21.6
Bol 302		A	00 38 33.4
Bol 303		A	00 38 50.5
Bol 304		A	00 38 56.8
Bol 305		A	00 38 58.9
Bol 306		A	00 39 08.8
Bol 307		A	00 39 18.6
Bol 309		A	00 39 23.5
Bol 310		A	00 39 25.8
Bol 311		A	00 39 33.9
Bol 312		A	00 39 40.4
Bol 313		A	00 39 44.5
Bol 314		A	00 39 44.6
Bol 315		A	00 39 48.6
Bol 316		A	00 39 53.8
Bol 317		A	00 39 55.5
Bol 318		A	00 40 01.0
Bol 319		A	00 40 03.2

Table D.3: Cluster Cross-Reference

Name	Look Under	GX	2000.0 RA
Bol 320		A	00 40 15.5
Bol 321		A	00 40 15.3
Bol 322		A	00 40 17.3
Bol 323		A	00 40 18.3
Bol 324		A	00 40 20.8
Bol 325		A	00 40 23.1
Bol 326		A	00 40 23.6
Bol 327		A	00 40 24.1
Bol 328		A	00 40 24.9
Bol 329		A	00 40 24.5
Bol 330		A	00 40 25.6
Bol 331		A	00 40 26.4
Bol 333		A	00 40 29.6
Bol 335	[H32] 13	A	00 40 42.0
Bol 336		A	00 40 47.7
Bol 337		A	00 40 48.5
Bol 338		A	00 40 59.1
Bol 339		A	00 41 00.6
Bol 341		A	00 41 09.2
Bol 342		A	00 41 24.4
Bol 343		A	00 41 42.2
Bol 344		A	00 42 03.3
Bol 345		A	00 42 14.2
Bol 346		A	00 42 20.2
Bol 347		A	00 42 23.0
Bol 348		A	00 42 23.0
Bol 349		A	00 42 24.0
Bol 350		A	00 42 28.5
Bol 351		A	00 42 38.0
Bol 352		A	00 42 38.3
Bol 353		A	00 42 47.2
Bol 354		A	00 42 47.6
Bol 355		A	00 42 52.9
Bol 356		A	00 43 10.3
Bol 357		A	00 43 13.2
Bol 358		A	00 43 18.0
Bol 361		A	00 43 57.2
Bol 362		A	00 44 09.3
Bol 363		A	00 44 17.2
Bol 365		A	00 44 36.8
Bol 366		A	00 44 46.9
Bol 367		A	00 44 47.5
Bol 368		A	00 44 48.1
Bol 370		A	00 45 14.6
Bol 371		A	00 45 27.4
Bol 372		A	00 45 33.5
Bol 373		A	00 45 42.1
Bol 374		A	00 45 44.5
Bol 375		A	00 45 45.6
Bol 376		A	00 45 48.7
Bol 377		A	00 45 48.2
Bol 378		A	00 45 57.4
Bol 379		A	00 45 58.8
Bol 380		A	00 46 06.4
Bol 381		A	00 46 07.3
Bol 382		A	00 46 10.3
Bol 383		A	00 46 11.9
Bol 384		A	00 46 22.1
Bol 385		A	00 46 25.0
Bol 386		A	00 46 27.2

Table D.3: Cluster Cross-Reference

Name	Look Under	GX	2000.0 RA
Bol 387		A	00 46 33.7
Bol 389		A	00 46 43.8
Bol 391		A	00 46 58.1
Bol 392		A	00 47 00.8
Bol 393		A	00 47 01.2
Bol 395		A	00 47 06.2
Bol 396		A	00 47 25.2
Bol 397		A	00 47 27.5
Bol 398		A	00 47 57.9
Bol 399		A	00 47 59.6
Bol 400		A	00 48 01.3
Bol 401		A	00 48 08.5
Bol 402		A	00 48 36.1
Bol 403		A	00 49 18.0
Bol 404		A	00 49 32.6
Bol 405		A	00 49 39.7
Bol 406		A	00 49 59.4
Bol 407		A	00 50 10.1
Bol 416		A	00 37 01.4
Bol 418		A	00 37 17.8
Bol 419		A	00 37 27.2
Bol 421		A	00 37 32.8
Bol 422		A	00 37 38.4
Bol 423		A	00 37 56.6
Bol 424		A	00 38 03.1
Bol 426		A	00 38 19.8
Bol 426	[CCS85] 18	A	00 38 19.8
Bol 427		A	00 38 22.7
Bol 429		A	00 38 38.6
Bol 430		A	00 38 42.9
Bol 431		A	00 38 54.9
Bol 432		A	00 38 59.1
Bol 433		A	00 39 02.4
Bol 434		A	00 39 15.1
Bol 435		A	00 39 18.4
Bol 436		A	00 39 30.6
Bol 439	SKHB 34	A	00 39 40.1
Bol 442		A	00 40 19.4
Bol 443		A	00 40 21.4
Bol 448		A	00 40 36.5
Bol 449	[H32] 11	A	00 40 42.5
Bol 450		A	00 40 47.0
Bol 451		A	00 40 46.4
Bol 452		A	00 40 48.3
Bol 453		A	00 41 03.3
Bol 455		A	00 41 05.7
Bol 456		A	00 41 21.4
Bol 457		A	00 41 29.2
Bol 458		A	00 41 44.6
Bol 461		A	00 42 04.2
Bol 462		A	00 42 14.7
Bol 463		A	00 42 27.5
Bol 465		A	00 43 00.7
Bol 466		A	00 43 01.4
Bol 467		A	00 43 06.5
Bol 468		A	00 43 12.5
Bol 469		A	00 43 19.4
Bol 470		A	00 43 37.5
Bol 471		A	00 43 41.7
Bol 472		A	00 43 48.9

Table D.3: Cluster Cross-Reference

Name	Look Under	GX	2000.0 RA
Bol 473		A	00 44 27.4
Bol 475	[H32] 128	A	00 44 56.2
Bol 476		A	00 45 07.2
Bol 477		A	00 45 08.4
Bol 478		A	00 45 12.8
Bol 479		A	00 45 27.9
Bol 480	[H32] 127	A	00 45 45.7
Bol 483		A	00 45 53.8
Bol 484		A	00 45 53.9
Bol 486		A	00 46 08.5
Bol 493		A	00 47 14.5
Bol 494		A	00 47 20.5
Bol 495		A	00 47 24.8
Bol 505		A	00 49 15.4
Bol 509		A	00 49 52.9
Bol D6		A	00 40 37.3
Bol D12		A	00 40 52.3
Bol D15		A	00 41 02.7
Bol D20	SKHB 89	A	00 41 17.4
Bol D25	[V62] B21	A	00 41 34.5
Bol D26	[V62] B21	A	00 41 34.6
Bol D28	SKHB 100	A	00 41 37.9
Bol D43	[V62] B24	A	00 42 06.8
Bol D44	[V62] B22	A	00 42 07.3
Bol D53		A	00 42 24.8
Bol D80		A	00 42 54.2
Bol D91		A	00 43 01.5
Bol D103	SKHB 245	A	00 43 47.8
Bol D110	[V62] B29	A	00 43 59.5
Bol D111		A	00 44 04.9
Bol D128		A	00 45 23.4
Bol D143	[CCS85] 5	A	00 36 35.6
Bol D149	[CCS85] 6	A	00 36 56.1
Bol D150		A	00 36 59.8
Bol D151		A	00 37 02.2
Bol D155	[CCS85] 9	A	00 37 25.7
Bol D167		A	00 38 22.4
Bol D168		A	00 38 25.0
Bol D170		A	00 38 28.1
Bol D176		A	00 38 53.0
Bol D180	[CCS85] 29	A	00 39 27.4
Bol D189	SKHB 47	A	00 40 15.5
Bol D190	SKHB 48	A	00 40 16.9
Bol D193	SKHB 55	A	00 40 25.1
Bol D200		A	00 41 06.9
Bol D201		A	00 41 08.3
Bol D206		A	00 41 40.6
Bol D207		A	00 41 45.0
Bol D215		A	00 42 43.3
Bol D218		A	00 42 59.3
Bol D220		A	00 43 04.3
Bol D225		A	00 43 13.4
Bol D240		A	00 44 06.9
Bol D242		A	00 44 13.3
Bol D248		A	00 44 41.3
Bol D255		A	00 44 48.6
Bol D257		A	00 44 59.5
Bol D262		A	00 45 20.0
Bol D263		A	00 45 22.2
Bol D268		A	00 45 44.1

Table D.3: Cluster Cross-Reference

Name	Look Under	GX	2000.0 RA
Bol D311	SKHB 337	A	00 47 29.7
Bol D324		A	00 47 54.2
Bol D325	[CCS85] 95	A	00 47 57.3
Bol D327	[CCS85] 95	A	00 47 57.3
Bol D336		A	00 49 09.7
Bol D337		A	00 49 11.4
Bol D342	[CCS85] 106	A	00 49 36.0
Bol D344		A	00 49 52.1
BRAN 66A	Ruprecht 32		07 45 06
BRAN 80A	NGC 2467		07 52 30
BRAN 84	Waterloo 3		07 55 06.4
BRAN 115	NGC 2547		08 10 11
BRAN 159	Pismis 4		08 34.6
BRAN 165	Pismis 5		08 37 39
BRAN 316C	NGC 3293		10 35 49
BRAN 333	Collinder 236		10 57 00
BRAN 360	NGC 3766		11 36 15
BRAN 362A	Collinder 249		11 38 20.4
BRAN 380	NGC 4103		12 06 40
BRHT 1b	KMHK 173	L	04 51 53.0
BRHT 2a	NGC 1775	L	04 56 53.6
BRHT 2b	KMHK 340	L	04 56 56.6
BRHT 3a	NGC 1830	L	05 04 39.5
BRHT 3b		L	05 04 30
BRHT 4a	NGC 1836	L	05 05 35.6
BRHT 4b		L	05 05 41
BRHT 5a	NGC 1850	L	05 08 46.7
BRHT 5b		L	05 08 55
BRHT 5b	NGC 1850	L	05 08 46.7
BRHT 6a	NGC 1862	L	05 12 33.6
BRHT 6b		L	05 12 35.2
BRHT 7	NGC 1874	L	05 13 11
BRHT 7a	NGC 1874	L	05 13 11
BRHT 7b		L	05 13 11.5
BRHT 7b	NGC 1874	L	05 13 11
BRHT 8a	NGC 1894	L	05 15 51.4
BRHT 8b	SL 341	L	05 15 36
BRHT 9a	NGC 1903	L	05 17 22.8
BRHT 10a	NGC 1913	L	05 18 19.2
BRHT 10b		L	05 18 10
BRHT 11a	NGC 1938	L	05 21 27.1
BRHT 11b	NGC 1939	L	05 21 24.3
BRHT 12a	NGC 1971	L	05 26 45.0
BRHT 12b	NGC 1972	L	05 26 48.1
BRHT 13a	NGC 2006	L	05 31 19.9
BRHT 13b	SL 538	L	05 31 19.8
BRHT 14a	NGC 2011	L	05 32 19.8
BRHT 14b	KMHK 1040	L	05 32 20.2
BRHT 15a	SL 557	L	05 32 06.8
BRHT 15b		L	05 32 17.8
BRHT 15b	NGC 2015	L	05 31 48
BRHT 16a	SL 601	L	05 36 09.5
BRHT 16b		L	05 36 10.5
BRHT 16b	KMHK 1131	L	05 36 09.6
BRHT 17a		L	05 36 11.9
BRHT 17a	NGC 2044	L	05 36 06.4
BRHT 17b	NGC 2044	L	05 36 06.4
BRHT 17b	SL 602	L	05 35 59.6
BRHT 18a	NGC 2077	L	05 39 34.9
BRHT 18b	NGC 2080	L	05 39 44.6

Table D.3: Cluster Cross-Reference

Name	Look Under	GX	2000.0 RA
BRHT 19a	NGC 2085	L	05 40 09.2
BRHT 19b	IC 2145	L	05 40 24
BRHT 20a	NGC 2095	L	05 42 51.7
BRHT 20b		L	05 42 38
BRHT 21a	NGC 2111	L	05 44 32.5
BRHT 21b	[HS66] 407	L	05 44 44.7
BRHT 22a	NGC 2136	L	05 52 58.9
BRHT 22b	NGC 2137	L	05 53 11.9
BRHT 23a	SL 23	L	04 43 38.0
BRHT 23b		L	04 43 41.8
BRHT 24a	LW 75	L	04 50 14.0
BRHT 24b	LW 76	L	04 50 24.8
BRHT 25a	SL 111	L	04 55 42.3
BRHT 25b	KMHK 312	L	04 55 55.4
BRHT 26a	SL 169	L	05 00 22.9
BRHT 26b	SL 171	L	05 00 32.9
BRHT 27a	SL 222	L	05 05 26.2
BRHT 27b	KMHK 520	L	05 05 24.1
BRHT 28a	SL 228	L	05 06 27.2
BRHT 28b		L	05 06 32
BRHT 29a	SL 229	L	05 06 32.4
BRHT 30a	SL 255	L	05 07 56.7
BRHT 30b		L	05 07 49
BRHT 31a	SL 278	L	05 10 16.3
BRHT 31b		L	05 10 16
BRHT 32a	SL 283	L	05 10 44.7
BRHT 32b	KMHK 617	L	05 10 41.9
BRHT 33a	SL 349	L	05 16 54.6
BRHT 33b	SL 353	L	05 17 10
BRHT 33b	[H60b] 1	L	05 16.0
BRHT 34a	SL 378	L	05 18 57.9
BRHT 34b		L	05 18 58
BRHT 35a	SL 385	L	05 19 25.4
BRHT 35b	SL 387	L	05 19 33
BRHT 36a	SL 485	L	05 27 50.0
BRHT 36b	KMHK 922	L	05 27 44.3
BRHT 37a	SL 550	L	05 31 55.1
BRHT 37b	KMHK 1020	L	05 32 00.0
BRHT 38a	SL 551	L	05 31 51.8
BRHT 38b		L	05 31 59
BRHT 39a	SL 585	L	05 34 30.8
BRHT 39b		L	05 34 30
BRHT 40a	SL 691	L	05 44 13.5
BRHT 40b	SL 692	L	05 44 13.7
BRHT 41a	SL 698	L	05 45 12.6
BRHT 41b		L	05 45 17
BRHT 42a	SL 716	L	05 46 46.3
BRHT 42b	[HS66] 414	L	05 46 41.0
BRHT 43a	[HS66] 60	L	04 54 44.1
BRHT 43b		L	04 54 46
BRHT 44a	[HS66] 62	L	04 54 54
BRHT 44b		L	04 55 07
BRHT 45a	[HS66] 72	L	04 56 54.1
BRHT 45b		L	04 56 52
BRHT 46a	[HS66] 138	L	05 09 57.3
BRHT 46b	[HS66] 144	L	05 09 57
BRHT 47a	[HS66] 139	L	05 09 45.3
BRHT 47b		L	05 09 43
BRHT 48a	[HS66] 153	L	05 10 30
BRHT 48b		L	05 10 20

Table D.3: Cluster Cross-Reference

Name	Look Under	GX	2000.0 RA
BRHT 49a	[HS66] 239	L	05 19 22
BRHT 49b		L	05 19 18
BRHT 50a	[HS66] 255	L	05 22 26
BRHT 50b	[HS66] 256	L	05 22 36
BRHT 51a	[HS66] 270	L	05 23 52.1
BRHT 51b	[HS66] 274	L	05 24 06.2
BRHT 52a	[HS66] 319	L	05 28 47
BRHT 52b		L	05 28 53
BRHT 53a	[HS66] 345	L	05 31 50
BRHT 53b	[HS66] 342	L	05 31 45
BRHT 54a	[HS66] 371	L	05 37 45
BRHT 54b		L	05 37 47
BRHT 54b	LH 97	L	05 37.6
BRHT 55a	[HS66] 386	L	05 40 57.4
BRHT 55b	KMHK 1221	L	05 41 04.6
BRHT 56a	[HS66] 416	L	05 47 01.9
BRHT 56b	[HS66] 417	L	05 47 10.2
BRHT 57a	[HS66] 438	L	05 51 53.1
BRHT 57b		L	05 51 53
BRHT 58a	[HS66] 444	L	05 53 39.5
BRHT 58b		L	05 53 47
BRHT 59a	LW 43	L	04 44 17.0
BRHT 59b		L	04 44 17
BRHT 60a		L	04 56 27
BRHT 60b	KMHK 309	L	04 56 25.5
BRHT 61a		L	04 59 21
BRHT 61b		L	04 59 19
BRHT 62a		L	05 00 06
BRHT 62b		L	04 59 57
BRHT 63a		L	05 34 30
BRHT 63b		L	05 34 27
BRHT 64a	KMHK 1559	L	05 57 50.5
BRHT 64b	KMHK 1553	L	05 57 40.2
Brocchi's cluster	Collinder 399		19 26 12
Bruck 10		S	00 37 44.1
Bruck 14		S	00 38 37.1
Bruck 21		S	00 41 15.3
Bruck 26		S	00 40 44.8
Bruck 31		S	00 43 37.6
Bruck 33		S	00 44 12.6
Bruck 34		S	00 44 51.6
Bruck 36		S	00 45 43.1
Bruck 39		S	00 45 25.7
Bruck 42	NGC 261	S	00 46 33.0
Bruck 47		S	00 48 33.3
Bruck 48		S	00 48 37.5
Bruck 49		S	00 48 55.7
Bruck 52		S	00 49 39.8
Bruck 53		S	00 50 03.8
Bruck 54		S	00 50 28.1
Bruck 55		S	00 50 22.0
Bruck 56		S	00 50 55.4
Bruck 64		S	00 52 30.3
Bruck 65		S	00 52 44.3
Bruck 66		S	00 52 47.7
Bruck 67		S	00 52 49.0
Bruck 69		S	00 53 05.3
Bruck 71		S	00 53 17.9
Bruck 73	Lindsay [1961] 244	S	00 53 42.3
Bruck 76		S	00 54 51.5

Table D.3: Cluster Cross-Reference

Name	Look Under	GX	2000.0 RA
Bruck 79		S	00 54 48.3
Bruck 80		S	00 54 46.8
Bruck 83		S	00 55 29.7
Bruck 86		S	00 56 15.9
Bruck 96		S	00 59 13.9
Bruck 99		S	01 00 26.8
Bruck 105		S	01 01 37.2
Bruck 108		S	01 01 52.3
Bruck 121		S	01 04 30.2
Bruck 129		S	01 07 02.3
[BS95] 16		S	00 42 58.5
[BS95] 17		S	00 43 14.3
[BS95] 20		S	00 43 37.9
[BS95] 27		S	00 44 55.1
[BS95] 35		S	00 47 49.7
[BS95] 40		S	00 50 56.3
[BS95] 41		S	00 49 05.6
[BS95] 42		S	00 49 16.5
[BS95] 45		S	00 50 16.1
[BS95] 46		S	00 50 39.0
[BS95] 48		S	00 50 42.5
[BS95] 56		S	00 52 13.4
[BS95] 57		S	00 52 32.2
[BS95] 60		S	00 52 42.1
[BS95] 63		S	00 52 46.7
[BS95] 68		S	00 53 42.1
[BS95] 69		S	00 53 56.5
[BS95] 72		S	00 54 11.0
[BS95] 81		S	00 56 25.6
[BS95] 88		S	00 57 50.3
[BS95] 125		S	01 04 39.6
[BS95] 131		S	01 05 59.6
[BS95] 251		S	00 51 26.2
[BS95] 272		S	00 58 38.1
C0000+633	Berkeley 104		00 03 27
C0000+671	Berkeley 59		00 02 10
C0001+557	Stock 19		00 04 39
C0001−302	Blanco 1		00 04.2
C0005+611	Czernik 1		00 07 39
C0007+601	Berkeley 1		00 09 41
C0007+609	King 13		00 10 10
C0015+606	Berkeley 60		00 17 42
C0019+614	Mayer 1		00 21 54
C0019+641	King 1		00 21 52
C0021−723	NGC 104	g	00 24 05.2
C0022+601	Berkeley 2		00 25 15
C0022+610	NGC 103		00 25 18
C0022+623	Stock 20		00 25 16
C0024+711	NGC 110		00 27 25.4
C0027+577	Stock 21		00 30 28
C0027+599	NGC 129		00 29 58
C0028+612	NGC 136		00 31 31
C0028+630	NGC 133		00 31 18
C0029+628	King 14		00 31.9
C0030+615	King 15		00 33 07
C0030+630	NGC 146		00 33.1
C0036+608	NGC 189		00 39 36
C0036+616	Stock 24		00 39 50
C0037+605	Dolidze 12		00 40.8
C0039+850	NGC 188		00 47 30

Table D.3: Cluster Cross-Reference

Name	Look Under	GX	2000.0 RA
C0040+598	Czernik 2		00 43 39
C0040+615	NGC 225		00 43 36
C0040+639	King 16		00 43.7
C0042+641	Berkeley 4		00 45 13
C0045+669	Berkeley 61		00 48 10
C0047+638	Dolidze 13		00 50.0
C0048+355	NGC 272		00 51 26
C0048+579	King 2		00 50 57
C0049+563	IC 1590		00 52 49
C0050−268	NGC 288	g	00 52 45.5
C0057+636	Berkeley 62		01 01 12
C0100+625	Czernik 3		01 03 07
C0100−711	NGC 362	g	01 03 14.3
C0103+619	NGC 366		01 06 27
C0104+653	PWM78 1		01 08 04.8
C0105+613	NGC 381		01 08 18
C0109+620	Stock 3		01 12 03
C0112+585	NGC 436		01 15 58
C0112+598	NGC 433		01 15 10
C0115+580	NGC 457		01 19 33
C0126+630	NGC 559		01 29 33
C0129+604	NGC 581		01 33 22
C0132+610	Trumpler 1		01 35 40
C0132+611	Czernik 4		01 35 36.4
C0133+643	NGC 609		01 36 24
C0139+637	NGC 637		01 43 04
C0140+556	NGC 657		01 43 29.8
C0140+604	NGC 659		01 44 24
C0140+616	NGC 654		01 44 00
C0142+610	NGC 663		01 46 17
C0144+626	Berkeley 5		01 47 44
C0144+717	Collinder 463		01 45 45
C0147+270	Collinder 21		01 50 12
C0147+608	Berkeley 6		01 51 12
C0149+568	Stock 4		01 52.7
C0149+615	IC 166		01 52 22
C0149−447	Phoenix dwarf gal		01 51 06.3
C0150+621	Berkeley 7		01 54 12
C0151+610	Czernik 5		01 55 40
C0154+374	NGC 752		01 57 35
C0155+552	NGC 744		01 58 30
C0155+599	NGC 743		01 58 32
C0156+753	Berkeley 8		02 01 05
C0158+620	Czernik 7		02 03 01
C0158+626	Czernik 6		02 02 08
C0200+642	Stock 5		02 04.4
C0211+590	Stock 2		02 14 43
C0215+569	NGC 869		02 19 04
C0215+580	Basel 10		02 19 28
C0215+635	Berkeley 63		02 19 27
C0217+656	Berkeley 64		02 21 46
C0218+568	NGC 884		02 22 05
C0219+636	NGC 886		02 23 28.1
C0225+604	Markarian 6		02 29 40
C0225+615	Tombaugh 4		02 29 10.7
C0228+612	IC 1805		02 32 42
C0229+444	NGC 956		02 32 14.9
C0229+585	Czernik 8		02 32 58
C0229+596	Czernik 9		02 33.6
C0230+573	NGC 957		02 33 20

Table D.3: Cluster Cross-Reference

Name	Look Under	GX	2000.0 RA
C0230+599	Czernik 10		02 33 55
C0232+587	King 4		02 36 02
C0232+594	Czernik 11		02 36 36
C0233+557	Trumpler 2		02 36 53
C0234+209	Dejc 1		02 37 28.3
C0235+547	Czernik 12		02 39 23
C0235+602	Berkeley 65		02 39 06
C0238+425	NGC 1039		02 42 08
C0238+613	NGC 1027		02 42 36
C0238-346	Fornax 6	F	02 40 06.8
C0240+621	Czernik 13		02 44 27
C0244+169	DoDz 1		02 47 27
C0247+602	IC 1848		02 51 11
C0249+272	Latysev 1		02 52
C0255+602	IC 1848		02 51 11
C0257+602	Collinder 34		02 59 23.2
C0300+585	Berkeley 66		03 04 05
C0302+441	NGC 1193		03 05 56
C0307+630	Trumpler 3		03 12 00
C0307-583	NGC 1252		03 10 56
C0308+531	NGC 1220		03 11 41
C0309-583	NGC 1252		03 10 56
C0310-554	NGC 1261	g	03 12 15.3
C0311+470	NGC 1245		03 14 42
C0311+525	King 5		03 14 40
C0312+598	Stock 23		03 16 10.8
C0313+584	Czernik 14		03 16 57
C0318+484	Melotte 20		03 24 19
C0319+520	Czernik 15		03 23 13
C0324+562	King 6		03 28 00
C0325+794	Palomar 1	g	03 33 20.8
C0327+524	Czernik 16		03 31 02
C0328+371	NGC 1342		03 31 40
C0329+525	Berkeley 9		03 32 38
C0330+512	NGC 1348		03 34 09
C0334+663	Berkeley 10		03 39 37
C0341+321	IC 348		03 44 34
C0343+589	Tombaugh 5		03 47 44
C0344+239	Pleiades		03 47 29
C0345+525	NGC 1444		03 49 27
C0348+618	Czernik 17		03 52 20
C0354-498	AM 1	g	03 55 02.7
C0355+516	King 7		03 59 10
C0400+524	NGC 1496		04 04 32
C0403+273	Dolidze 14		04 06 41
C0403+622	NGC 1502		04 07 50
C0406+493	NGC 1513		04 09 55
C0411+511	NGC 1528		04 15 19
C0414+581	IC 361		04 18 51
C0415+530	Mayer 2		04 19 51
C0417+368	NGC 1548		04 21 20
C0417+448	Berkeley 11		04 20 27
C0417+501	NGC 1545		04 20 57
C0422-213	Eridanus	g	04 24 44.5
C0424+157	Hyades		04 26.9
C0424+308	Czernik 18		04 27 48
C0428+437	NGC 1582		04 31 39
C0431+451	NGC 1605		04 34 53
C0434+506	Berkeley 67		04 37 50
C0436+503	NGC 1624		04 40 37

Table D.3: Cluster Cross-Reference

Name	Look Under	GX	2000.0 RA
C0441+419	Berkeley 68		04 44.5
C0441+425	Berkeley 12		04 44 24
C0442+446	Ruprecht 148		04 46 35
C0443+189	NGC 1647		04 45 42.2
C0443+313	Palomar 2	g	04 46 05.9
C0444+840	NGC 1841	L	04 45 24.2
C0445+108	NGC 1662		04 48 29
C0445+130	NGC 1663		04 49 24.3
C0447+436	NGC 1664		04 51 06
C0451+526	Berkeley 13		04 55 46.2
C0453+287	Czernik 19		04 56 56
C0456+434	Berkeley 14		04 59 44
C0458+443	Berkeley 15		05 02 05
C0459+494	NGC 1724		05 03 33
C0500+235	NGC 1746		05 03.6
C0500+235	NGC 1750		05 03.9
C0500+237	NGC 1746		05 03.6
C0500+237	NGC 1750		05 03.9
C0501+237	NGC 1758		05 04.4
C0501+347	Dolidze 15		05 04.6
C0504+369	NGC 1778		05 08 06
C0505+390	King 17		05 08 24
C0507+164	NGC 1807		05 10 46
C0508+475	NGC 1798		05 11 40
C0509+166	NGC 1817		05 12 27
C0511+326	Dolidze 16		05 14.6
C0512-400	NGC 1851	g	05 14 06.3
C0512-684		L	05 12 08.3
C0516+393	NGC 1857		05 20 06
C0516+394	Czernik 20		05 20 32.5
C0516+732	Collinder 464		05 12 39.0
C0517+305	Berkeley 17		05 20 30
C0518+453	Berkeley 18		05 22 12
C0518-685	NGC 1901		05 17.8
C0519+070	Dolidze 17		05 22.4
C0519+333	NGC 1893		05 22 46
C0519+334	IC 410		05 22.0
C0519+409	Collinder 62		05 20 53.0
C0519+454	Berkeley 18		05 22 12
C0520+295	Berkeley 19		05 24 03
C0520+332	Dolidze 18		05 24 09
C0521+081	Dolidze 19		05 23.7
C0521+114	DoDz 2		05 23.2
C0521+326	Berkeley 69		05 24 21
C0522+418	Berkeley 70		05 25 48
C0522+465	NGC 1883		05 25 55
C0522-245	NGC 1904	g	05 24 10.6
C0523+160	Collinder 65		05 26 05.7
C0523+359	Czernik 21		05 26 40
C0524+070	Dolidze 21		05 27.4
C0524+343	Stock 8		05 28 07
C0524+352	NGC 1907		05 28 05
C0525+337	Dolidze 20		05 28 33
C0525+358	NGC 1912		05 28 43
C0528+342	NGC 1931		05 31 26
C0530+001	Berkeley 20		05 32 37
C0530+264	DoDz 3		05 33.5
C0532+099	Collinder 69		05 35.0
C0532+259	DoDz 4		05 35.9
C0532+341	NGC 1960		05 36 18

Table D.3: Cluster Cross-Reference

Name	Look Under	GX	2000.0 RA
C0532-044	NGC 1981		05 35.2
C0532-048	NGC 1977		05 35.3
C0532-054	NGC 1976		05 35 16
C0532-059	NGC 1980		05 35 26
C0533-011	Collinder 70		05 35.6
C0535+379	Stock 10		05 39.0
C0535-618	ESO 120-8		05 36 21.8
C0536-026	Sigma Ori		05 38 45
C0538+323	Berkeley 71		05 40 57
C0545+073	Collinder 74		05 48 40
C0545+302	Basel 4		05 48 54
C0546+289	Czernik 23		05 50 08
C0546+336	King 8		05 49 17
C0547+221	Berkeley 72		05 50 12
C0548+217	Berkeley 21		05 51 46
C0549+325	NGC 2099		05 52 19
C0551+003	NGC 2112		05 53 46
C0552+208	Czernik 24		05 55 26
C0555+078	Berkeley 22		05 58 27
C0555+219	Basel 11b		05 58 10
C0556+215	Basel 11		
C0558+233	NGC 2129		06 01 06
C0559+499	NGC 2126		06 02 34
C0600+104	NGC 2141		06 02 56
C0601+240	IC 2157		06 04 49.8
C0604+241	NGC 2158		06 07 26
C0605+139	NGC 2169		06 08 25
C0605+243	NGC 2168		06 09.0
C0606+203	Collinder 84		06 09 39
C0607+206	NGC 2175.1		06 10 53
C0609+054	NGC 2186		06 12 08
C0610+070	Czernik 25		06 13 41
C0611+128	NGC 2194		06 13 46
C0611+398	NGC 2192		06 15 18
C0613-186	NGC 2204		06 15 33
C0615+236	Collinder 89		06 18.0
C0618-072	NGC 2215		06 20 50
C0619+023	Collinder 91		06 21 33
C0619-063	Berkeley 73		06 22 05
C0620+046	Dolidze 22		06 23.3
C0620+051	Collinder 92		06 22.9
C0622+198	Bochum 1		06 25 24.9
C0624-047	NGC 2232		06 27 15
C0627+029	Collinder 96		06 30.3
C0627+050	NGC 2237		06 31 55.5
C0627+068	NGC 2236		06 29 40
C0627+099	Collinder 95		06 30 51.2
C0627-312	NGC 2243		06 29 35
C0628+059	Collinder 97		06 30 58.1
C0628-041	Czernik 26		06 30 58
C0628-096	Cl van den Bergh		06 30 50
C0629+049	NGC 2237		06 31 55.5
C0629+049	NGC 2244		06 32 19
C0630+205	Berkeley 23		06 33 15
C0631+081	Basel 8		06 34.2
C0632+054	NGC 2252		06 34 19.8
C0632+084	NGC 2251		06 34 39
C0633+048	Collinder 104		06 36.5
C0633+077	NGC 2254		06 35 46.6
C0633+084	Basel 7		06 36 19

Table D.3: Cluster Cross-Reference

Name	Look Under	GX	2000.0 RA
C0634+031	Cl van den Bergh		06 37 05
C0634+060	Collinder 106		06 37.1
C0634+094	Trumpler 5		06 36 31
C0634–141	Ruprecht 1		06 36.4
C0635+012	NGC 2262		06 39 38.7
C0635+020	Collinder 110		06 38 39
C0635+047	Collinder 107		06 37.7
C0635+109	NGC 2259		06 38 33.3
C0635–008	Berkeley 24		06 37 47
C0636+069	Collinder 111		06 38.7
C0638+099	NGC 2264		06 40 59
C0638–164	Berkeley 25		06 41 14
C0638–272	Cl van den Bergh		06 40.0
C0639–295	Ruprecht 2		06 41 01
C0640+000	Dolidze 23		06 43 05.7
C0640+270	NGC 2266		06 43 20
C0640–294	Ruprecht 3		06 42 06
C0641+016	Dolidze 24		06 44 44
C0641+046	NGC 2269		06 43 16.8
C0642+003	Dolidze 25		06 45.0
C0643+018	Collinder 115		06 46 40
C0644+013	Cl van den Bergh		06 46 52
C0644–206	NGC 2287		06 46.1
C0645+411	NGC 2281		06 48 18
C0645–031	NGC 2286		06 47 41
C0646+004	Bochum 2		06 48 50
C0646–104	Ruprecht 4		06 48 57
C0647+058	Biurakan 12		06 50 16
C0647–239	Berkeley 75		06 49 00
C0647–359	NGC 2298	g	06 48 59.2
C0648+058	Biurakan 11		06 51 21
C0649+005	NGC 2301		06 51 46
C0649+030	Biurakan 10		06 52 07
C0649–070	NGC 2302		06 51 54
C0650+169	Berkeley 29		06 53 04
C0650–235	Ruprecht 149		06 52.2
C0652+180	NGC 2304		06 55 12
C0652–245	Collinder 121		06 56 20.0
C0653–071	NGC 2309		06 56 04
C0653–132	Ruprecht 6		06 56 05
C0653–186	Ruprecht 5		06 55 24
C0654+083	Biurakan 7		06 57 37
C0655+032	Biurakan 9		06 57 46
C0655+065	Biurakan 8		06 58 07
C0655–045	NGC 2311		06 57 48
C0655–131	Ruprecht 7		06 57 50
C0657–001	Biurakan 13		07 00 22
C0658–204	Tombaugh 1		07 00 27
C0659–135	Ruprecht 8		07 01 46
C0659–218	Ruprecht 9		07 01.9
C0700+064	Czernik 27		07 03 19
C0700–050	Bochum 3		07 03 28
C0700–082	NGC 2323		07 02 47.8
C0701+011	NGC 2324		07 04 08
C0701–060	Haffner 3		07 04 08
C0701–114	Cl van den Bergh		07 03 55
C0701–207	Tombaugh 2		07 03 06
C0702–196	Auner 1		07 04 15.3
C0703+753	NGC 2314		07 10 32.4
C0703–149	Haffner 4		07 06 04
C0703–283	Ruprecht 150		07 05 55
C0704+274	NGC 2331		07 07 01
C0704–100	NGC 2335		07 06 50
C0704–105	Collinder 465		07 06 52
C0704–107	Collinder 466		07 06 56
C0704–115	Berkeley 76		07 06 40
C0704–200	Ruprecht 10		07 06 27.6
C0705–105	NGC 2343		07 08 07
C0705–207	Ruprecht 11		07 07 23
C0705–257	Ruprecht 13		07 08.0
C0705–281	Ruprecht 12		07 07 10
C0706–130	NGC 2345		07 08 19
C0707–168	Haffner 23		07 09.5
C0708+028	Berkeley 35		07 09 54
C0712–102	NGC 2353		07 14 31
C0712–256	NGC 2354		07 14 16
C0712–310	Collinder 132		07 15 21.1
C0713–130	Berkeley 36		07 16 23
C0713–312	Ruprecht 14		07 14 55
C0714+138	NGC 2355		07 17 00
C0714–138	Basel 11a		07 17 08
C0715–155	NGC 2360		07 17 44
C0715–367	Collinder 135		07 17 24.5
C0716–225	Haffner 5		07 18.1
C0716–248	NGC 2362		07 18 42
C0717–010	Berkeley 37		07 20 18
C0717–130	Haffner 6		07 20 01
C0717–195	Ruprecht 15		07 19 34
C0718–102	NGC 2368		07 21 02.2
C0718–218	NGC 2367		07 20 05
C0719–008	Czernik 28		07 21.8
C0719–032	Berkeley 77		07 21 28
C0721+054	Berkeley 78		07 23 38
C0721–122	Haffner 8		07 23 03
C0721–131	NGC 2374		07 23 57
C0721–193	Ruprecht 16		07 23 09
C0721–231	Ruprecht 17		07 23 35
C0721–294	Haffner 7		07 22 54
C0722–169	Haffner 9		07 24 42
C0722–208	NGC 2383		07 24 40
C0722–209	NGC 2384		07 25 12
C0722–261	Ruprecht 18		07 24 39
C0722–321	Collinder 140		07 24 26.7
C0723–214	Ruprecht 19		07 25.6
C0724+136	NGC 2395		07 27 13
C0724–242	Trumpler 6		07 26 23
C0724–287	Ruprecht 20		07 26 41
C0724–476	Melotte 66		07 26 19
C0725–116	NGC 2396		07 28.0
C0725–239	Trumpler 7		07 27 21
C0725–310	Ruprecht 21		07 27.1
C0726–152	Haffner 10		07 28 36
C0726–153	Czernik 29		07 28 24
C0726–182	Haffner 24		07 28.8
C0727+120	Dolidze 26		07 30 02
C0727–138	NGC 2401		07 29 25
C0727–184	Mayer 3		07 30 04
C0727–291	Ruprecht 22		07 29 17
C0728–098	Czernik 30		07 31 11
C0728–168	NGC 2409		07 31 37
C0728–169	Bochum 5		07 32.1
C0728–232	Ruprecht 23		07 30 40
C0729–126	Ruprecht 24		07 31 51
C0729–193	Bochum 6		07 31 45.1
C0731–153	NGC 2414		07 33 13
C0731–203	Ruprecht 40		07 33 27
C0733–276	Haffner 11		07 35 22
C0734+390	NGC 2419	g	07 38 08.5
C0734–137	NGC 2423		07 37 07
C0734–143	NGC 2422		07 36 36
C0734–155	Ruprecht 26		07 37 13
C0734–203	Czernik 31		07 36 58
C0734–205	NGC 2421		07 36 12
C0734–232	Ruprecht 25		07 36 47
C0735+216	NGC 2420		07 38 24
C0735–119	Melotte 71		07 37 30
C0735–264	Ruprecht 27		07 37.6
C0736–104	Melotte 72		07 38 29
C0736–105	Melotte 72		07 38 29
C0736–147	NGC 2425		07 38 18
C0736–359	vdB-Ha 4		07 37 45
C0737–308	Ruprecht 28		07 39 36
C0738–189	NGC 2432		07 40 54
C0738–300	Haffner 13		07 40 26
C0738–315	NGC 2439		07 40 46
C0738–334	Bochum 15		07 40 15
C0739–147	NGC 2437		07 41 47
C0739–161	Ruprecht 151		07 41.3
C0739–242	Ruprecht 29		07 41.1
C0740–313	Ruprecht 30		07 42 22
C0740–354	Ruprecht 31		07 43 00
C0742–237	NGC 2447		07 44 30
C0742–254	Ruprecht 32		07 45 06
C0742–282	Haffner 14		07 44 48
C0743–202	Ruprecht 34		07 45 54
C0743–218	Ruprecht 33		07 45.8
C0743–326	Haffner 15		07 45 30
C0743–378	NGC 2451		07 45.4
C0744–044	Berkeley 39		07 46 50
C0744–311	Ruprecht 35		07 46 14
C0745–271	NGC 2453		07 47 35
C0746–211	NGC 2455		07 48 59
C0746–257	Haffner 25		07 48 40
C0746–261	Ruprecht 36		07 48 24
C0747–171	Ruprecht 37		07 49 47
C0748–200	Ruprecht 38		07 50 31
C0748–253	Haffner 16		07 50 21
C0748–297	Czernik 32		07 50 28
C0749–317	Haffner 17		07 51 36
C0750–223	Ruprecht 39		07 52 20
C0750–261	Haffner 19		07 52 46
C0750–262	Haffner 18		07 52 44
C0750–263	NGC 2467		07 52 30
C0750–384	NGC 2477		07 52 10
C0751–268	Ruprecht 41		07 53 48
C0752–175	NGC 2479		07 55 06
C0752–241	NGC 2482		07 55 10
C0752–381	Ruprecht 152		07 54 29
C0753–258	Trumpler 9		07 55 40
C0753–278	NGC 2483		07 55 39

Table D.3: Cluster Cross-Reference

Name	Look Under	GX	2000.0 RA
C0754–299	NGC 2489		07 56 16
C0754–302	Haffner 20		07 56 15
C0755–257	Ruprecht 42		07 57 37
C0756–287	Ruprecht 43		07 58.8
C0757–106	NGC 2506		08 00 02
C0757–161	Ruprecht 45		07 59.6
C0757–284	Ruprecht 44		07 58 50
C0757–607	NGC 2516		07 58.0
C0758–189	NGC 2509		08 00 48
C0758–301	Ruprecht 153		08 00 18
C0759–193	Ruprecht 46		08 02 10
C0759–270	Haffner 21		08 01 11
C0800–309	Ruprecht 47		08 02 18
C0800–318	Ruprecht 48		08 02 42
C0800–442	Ruprecht 154		08 01.7
C0801–266	Ruprecht 49		08 03 17
C0801–305	Ruprecht 51		08 03.6
C0801–307	Ruprecht 50		08 03.4
C0802–461	Collinder 173		08 03.5
C0803–280	NGC 2527		08 04 53
C0803–316	Ruprecht 155		08 04.9
C0803–318	Ruprecht 52		08 05.0
C0805–297	NGC 2533		08 07.0
C0805–322	vdB-Ha 19		08 07 04.0
C0808–126	NGC 2539		08 10 38
C0808–268	Ruprecht 53		08 10 50
C0809–318	Ruprecht 54		08 11 23
C0809–491	NGC 2547		08 10 11
C0810–277	Haffner 22		08 12.6
C0810–324	Ruprecht 55		08 12 19
C0810–374	NGC 2546		08 12.4
C0810–403	Ruprecht 56		08 12.6
C0811–056	NGC 2548		08 13 44
C0812–268	Ruprecht 57		08 14.8
C0812–318	Ruprecht 58		08 14 49
C0812–362	vdB-Ha 23		08 14.4
C0813–306	Haffner 26		08 15.4
C0815–369	NGC 2568		08 18 19
C0816–295	NGC 2571		08 18 57
C0816–304	NGC 2567		08 18 30
C0816–414	Pismis 2		08 17 54
C0817–343	Ruprecht 59		08 19 22.0
C0817–452	Ruprecht 156		08 19 28.8
C0819–301	NGC 2580		08 21 28
C0819–360	NGC 2579		08 20 53
C0820–360	Collinder 185		08 23 19
C0821–293	NGC 2587		08 23 25
C0821–328	NGC 2588		08 23 10
C0822–289	Collinder 187		08 24 12
C0822–470	Ruprecht 60		08 24 26
C0823–340	Ruprecht 61		08 25 15
C0827–189	Ruprecht 157		08 29 52
C0829–385	Pismis 3		08 31 21
C0829–443	vdB-Ha 34		08 31 12
C0830–194	Ruprecht 62		08 32 30
C0831–481	Ruprecht 63		08 32 40
C0832–441	Pismis 4		08 34.6
C0834–434	vdB-Ha 37		08 35 48
C0835–297	NGC 2627		08 37 15
C0835–394	Pismis 5		08 37 39

Table D.3: Cluster Cross-Reference

Name	Look Under	GX	2000.0 RA
C0835–399	Ruprecht 64		08 37.4
C0836–345	NGC 2635		08 38 27
C0837+201	NGC 2632		08 40 22
C0837–438	Ruprecht 65		08 39 22
C0837–460	NGC 2645		08 39 04
C0838–378	Ruprecht 66		08 40 32
C0838–459	Waterloo 6		08 40 20.7
C0838–528	IC 2391		08 40.3
C0839–385	Pismis 7		08 41 09
C0839–461	Pismis 8		08 41 35
C0839–480	IC 2395		08 42 31
C0840–432	Ruprecht 67		08 41 45
C0840–447	NGC 2659		08 42 34
C0840–469	NGC 2660		08 42 39
C0841–324	NGC 2658		08 43 28
C0841–479	IC 2395		08 42 31
C0842–357	Ruprecht 68		08 44.5
C0842–411	Collinder 197		08 44 40
C0843–314	Collinder 196		08 45.1
C0843–315	Collinder 198		08 45.4
C0843–458	Bochum 7		08 44.8
C0843–474	Ruprecht 69		08 44 49.1
C0843–486	NGC 2670		08 45 30
C0843–527	NGC 2669		08 46 19
C0844–417	NGC 2671		08 46 12
C0845–527	Harvard 3		08 46.5
C0846–423	Trumpler 10		08 47 45
C0847+120	NGC 2682		08 51 24
C0847–465	Ruprecht 71		08 49.5
C0847–466	Ruprecht 70		08 49.1
C0848–442	vdB-Ha 54		08 49 41
C0850–373	Ruprecht 158		08 52 23
C0850–374	Ruprecht 72		08 52 05
C0854–393	vdB-Ha 55		08 56 10.9
C0855–430	vdB-Ha 56		08 57 08
C0855–475	Muzzio 1		08 57.2
C0858–487	Markarian 18		09 00 31
C0859–507	Ruprecht 73		09 01 12
C0900–434	Pismis 10		09 02.6
C0908–560	vdB-Ha 58		09 10 28
C0911–646	NGC 2808	g	09 12 02.6
C0914–364	NGC 2818		09 16 10
C0914–498	Pismis 11		09 15 53
C0915–495	Pismis 11		09 15 53
C0917–403	NGC 2849		09 19 23
C0918–449	Pismis 12		09 20 00
C0918–490	vdB-Ha 63		09 20 38
C0919–368	Ruprecht 74		09 21.0
C0919–601	Ruprecht 159		09 20 08
C0920–509	Pismis 13		09 22 06.5
C0920–560	Ruprecht 75		09 21 54
C0921–770	E 3	g	09 20 59.3
C0922–515	Ruprecht 76		09 24 18
C0923–545	vdB-Ha 66		09 25 16
C0925–511	vdB-Ha 67		09 26 43
C0925–549	Ruprecht 77		09 27 02
C0926–567	IC 2488		09 27 27
C0927–525	Pismis 14		09 29.3
C0927–534	Ruprecht 78		09 29 07.9
C0928–526	NGC 2910		09 30 30

Table D.3: Cluster Cross-Reference

Name	Look Under	GX	2000.0 RA
C0929–527	vdB-Ha 72		09 31 23
C0930–499	vdB-Ha 73		09 31 56
C0931–561	Basel 20		09 32.5
C0932–479	Pismis 15		09 34 45
C0932–532	NGC 2925		09 33 11
C0933–545	vdB-Ha 75		09 34 42
C0938–501	NGC 2972		09 40 12
C0938–503	Hogg 1		09 40 33
C0939–536	Ruprecht 79		09 41 03
C0940–438	NGC 2982		09 42 01
C0942–530	vdB-Ha 79		09 44.1
C0942–563	vdB-Ha 78		09 43 48
C0943–439	Ruprecht 81		09 45 13
C0943–537	Ruprecht 82		09 45 49
C0947–543	Ruprecht 83		09 49 15
C0947–561	NGC 3033		09 48 40
C0947–650	Ruprecht 84		09 49 04
C0949–529	Pismis 16		09 51 14
C0949–560	Hogg 2		09 51.5
C0952–504	Collinder 213		09 55 00
C0953–467	Ruprecht 160		09 55.5
C0956–543	Hogg 4		09 57 53
C0956–544	Hogg 3		09 57 40
C0959–545	NGC 3105		10 00 40
C0959–548	Ruprecht 85		10 01 26
C0959–579	vdB-Ha 84		10 01 19
C1000–494	vdB-Ha 85		10 02.0
C1000–592	Ruprecht 86		10 01 27.7
C1001–598	NGC 3114		10 02.7
C1002–552	vdB-Ha 87		10 04 34
C1002–556	Schuster 1		10 04 39.0
C1003+003	Palomar 3	g	10 05 31.4
C1003–613	Trumpler 11		10 04.9
C1004–513	vdB-Ha 88		10 06 15
C1004–600	Trumpler 12		10 06.5
C1004–601	Hogg 5		10 06 09
C1004–602	Hogg 6		10 06 28
C1007–609	Ruprecht 161		10 08.8
C1009–563	Loden 27		10 11.1
C1010–578	vdB-Ha 90		10 12 10
C1013–504	Ruprecht 87		10 15 30
C1015–461	NGC 3201	g	10 17 36.8
C1015–584	vdB-Ha 91		10 17.3
C1017–561	vdB-Ha 92		10 19 04
C1017–628	Ruprecht 88		10 18 48
C1019–514	NGC 3228		10 21 23
C1022–575	NGC 3247		10 24 01
C1022–598	Trumpler 13		10 23 48
C1024–576	NGC 3247		10 24 01
C1024–604	NGC 3255		10 26 32
C1025–573	IC 2581		10 27 27
C1026–579	Ruprecht 89		10 28.5
C1027–585	Loden 143		10 28 44
C1027–604	Hogg 7		10 29.1
C1027–606	Hogg 8		10 29 09
C1028–538	Loden 59		10 30 22
C1028–595	Collinder 223		10 30.4
C1029–579	Ruprecht 90		10 31.0
C1030–564	Loden 112		10 32 40
C1032–578	Loden 153		10 34 46.7

Table D.3: Cluster Cross-Reference

Name	Look Under	GX	2000.0 RA
C1033–579	NGC 3293		10 35 49
C1033–598	Bochum 9		10 35.5
C1035–583	NGC 3324		10 37 19
C1035–584	Loden 165		10 35 56
C1036–538	NGC 3330		10 38 48
C1036–589	vdB-Ha 99		10 38 45.0
C1040–588	Bochum 10		10 42 08
C1040–648	Melotte 101		10 42 00
C1041–593	Trumpler 14		10 43 57
C1041–597	Collinder 228		10 44 00
C1041–641	IC 2602		10 42 57
C1042–591	Trumpler 15		10 44 44
C1042–593	Collinder 232		10 44 39
C1042–640	IC 2602		10 42 57
C1043–594	Trumpler 16		10 45 10
C1045–572	Ruprecht 91		10 47 38.4
C1045–598	Bochum 11		10 47 12
C1050–539	vdB-Ha 106		10 52 38.6
C1051–614	Ruprecht 92		10 53 49
C1051–620	Ruprecht 162		10 53.0
C1052+407	Shakhbazian 1		10 55 06.0
C1054–589	Trumpler 17		10 56 24
C1054–627	Graham 1		10 56 32
C1055–607	Collinder 236		10 57 00
C1055–614	Bochum 12		10 57 18
C1056–587	Hogg 9		10 58 22
C1057–600	NGC 3496		10 59 34
C1058–601	Sher 1		11 01 03
C1059–595	NGC 3503		11 01 18
C1102–611	NGC 3519		11 04 03
C1102–676	Ruprecht 163		11 04 47
C1103–595	Feinstein 1		11 06.0
C1104–584	NGC 3532		11 05.5
C1105–612	vdB-Ha 110		11 07.3
C1107–588	Loden 280		11 09.5
C1107–602	Loden 309		11 09.5
C1107–635	vdB-Ha 111		11 09.5
C1108–231	Bok 1		
C1108–231	NGC 1901		05 17.8
C1108–587	Basel 17		11 10 32.9
C1108–599	NGC 3572		11 10 26.6
C1108–601	Hogg 10		11 10 42.1
C1109–600	Collinder 240		11 11 40.2
C1109–601	Hogg 11		11 11 32.6
C1109–604	Trumpler 18		11 11.4
C1110–586	Stock 13		11 13.1
C1110–604	Hogg 12		11 12 15
C1110–605	NGC 3590		11 13 00
C1112–573	Trumpler 19		11 14.3
C1112–609	NGC 3603		11 15 07
C1114–600	Hogg 13		11 16.3
C1115–624	IC 2714		11 17 18
C1117–586	Loden 336		11 19.8
C1117–632	Melotte 105		11 19 41
C1120–582	vdB-Ha 118		11 22.9
C1123–429	NGC 3680		11 25 38
C1126+292	Palomar 4	g	11 29 16.8
C1128–582	Loden 372		11 30 52
C1128–605	Ruprecht 164		11 31.1
C1128–631	Ruprecht 94		11 30.4

Table D.3: Cluster Cross-Reference

Name	Look Under	GX	2000.0 RA
C1133–613	NGC 3766		11 36 15
C1134–627	Collinder 249		11 38 20.4
C1135–630	Collinder 249		11 38 20.4
C1136–632	IC 2948		11 38 58
C1140–622	Lynga 15		11 42.4
C1141–608	Ruprecht 95		11 43 40
C1141–622	Stock 14		11 43 51
C1148–554	NGC 3960		11 50 34
C1148–618	Ruprecht 96		11 50 53
C1153–581	Loden 480		11 56 06
C1154–623	Ruprecht 97		11 57 23
C1155–642	Ruprecht 98		11 58.8
C1159–629	NGC 4052		12 02 01
C1200–635	Ruprecht 99		12 03 20
C1203–622	Ruprecht 100		12 05.7
C1204–592	Stock 15		12 10.5
C1204–609	NGC 4103		12 06 40
C1206–606	Loden 565		12 08 24.4
C1206–626	Ruprecht 101		12 09 40
C1207+188	NGC 4147	g	12 10 06.2
C1210–623	NGC 4184		12 13.6
C1213–581	Ruprecht 103		12 15.9
C1214–548	NGC 4230		12 17 16
C1217–645	Loden 615		12 20 37.2
C1221–578	NGC 4337		12 24 04
C1221–616	NGC 4349		12 24 07
C1222+263	Melotte 111		12 25.1
C1222–601	Ruprecht 104		12 24 51
C1223–631	vdB-Ha 131		12 26 25.7
C1223–724	NGC 4372	g	12 25 45.4
C1224–605	Harvard 5		12 27 16.3
C1224–638	vdB-Ha 132		12 26 58
C1225–561	Ruprecht 165		12 28.6
C1225–595	Hogg 14		12 28 39
C1225–598	NGC 4439		12 28 27
C1226–604	Harvard 5		12 27 16.3
C1226–606	Hogg 23		12 28 31.6
C1227–645	NGC 4463		12 29 56
C1231–612	Ruprecht 105		12 34.0
C1232+365	Upgren 1		12 35 00
C1234–682	Harvard 6		12 37 54
C1235–509	Ruprecht 106	g	12 38 40.2
C1236–264	NGC 4590	g	12 39 28.0
C1236–508	Ruprecht 106	g	12 38 40.2
C1236–603	Trumpler 20		12 39 32
C1239–627	NGC 4609		12 42 20
C1240–628	Hogg 15		12 43 36
C1250–600	NGC 4755		12 53 38
C1250–669	vdB-Ha 140		12 53.5
C1254–646	NGC 4815		12 57 59
C1256–706	NGC 4833	g	12 59 35.0
C1257–593	NGC 4852		13 00 05
C1309–624	Danks 1		13 12 26.8
C1309–650	Loden 757		13 12.4
C1310+184	NGC 5024	g	13 12 55.3
C1310–624	Danks 2		13 12 53.8
C1311–656	AL 1		13 15 16
C1313+179	NGC 5053	g	13 16 27.0
C1315–623	Stock 16		13 18 38.4
C1315–669	Harvard 8		13 18 12

Table D.3: Cluster Cross-Reference

Name	Look Under	GX	2000.0 RA
C1317–646	Ruprecht 107		13 19 46
C1319–658	Collinder 269		13 22.6
C1321–621	Loden 807		13 24.9
C1322–631	NGC 5120		13 25 39
C1323–472	NGC 5139	g	13 26 45.9
C1324–587	NGC 5138		13 27 16
C1325–610	Hogg 16		13 29 11
C1325–621	Basel 18		13 27 49
C1326–609	Hogg 16		13 29 11
C1326–639	Collinder 271		13 30.0
C1327–606	NGC 5168		13 31 08
C1327–610	Collinder 272		13 30.5
C1328–582	Ruprecht 108		13 32 12
C1328–625	Trumpler 21		13 32 14
C1330–642	Loden 848		13 33.1
C1331–598	Collinder 275		13 35.4
C1333–619	IC 4291		13 36 55
C1334–630	vdB-Ha 150		13 38 02
C1335–640	Loden 894		13 39 44.3
C1336–614	vdB-Ha 151		13 40 12
C1339+286	NGC 5272	g	13 42 11.2
C1341–617	Loden 991		13 45.4
C1342–600	Loden 1010		13 45.4
C1343–511	NGC 5286	g	13 46 26.5
C1343–626	NGC 5281		13 46 36.7
C1345–644	NGC 5288		13 48 45.6
C1345–658	Collinder 277		13 48.4
C1350–595	Loden 1095		13 53.5
C1350–616	NGC 5316		13 54.0
C1350–650	Loden 1002		13 54.3
C1353–269	AM 4	g	13 56 21
C1354–593	vdB-Ha 155		13 57.5
C1354–615	Loden 1101		13 58 40.6
C1355–576	Loden 1177		13 59.4
C1356–581	Loden 1171		13 59 31.4
C1356–591	Loden 1152		13 59.5
C1356–619	Lynga 1		14 00 02
C1357–593	NGC 5381		14 00.6
C1400–584	Loden 1202		14 04.4
C1402–594	Loden 1194		14 05.8
C1402–673	Ruprecht 110		14 06.5
C1403+287	NGC 5466	g	14 05 27.3
C1404–480	NGC 5460		14 07.6
C1405–594	Loden 1225		14 09.2
C1410–576	Loden 1289		14 16 56.9
C1412–589	Loden 1282		14 15.9
C1414–587	Ruprecht 167		14 18.2
C1414–612	Loden 1256		14 18.2
C1420–611	Lynga 2		14 24 24
C1422–545	NGC 5593		14 25 40
C1424–594	NGC 5606		14 27.8
C1426–605	NGC 5617		14 29.7
C1426–607	Pismis 19		14 30 43
C1427–057	NGC 5634	g	14 29 37.3
C1427–609	Trumpler 22		14 31.2
C1429–611	Hogg 17		14 33 50.4
C1429–617	Loden 1339		14 33.5
C1431–563	NGC 5662		14 35 30.8
C1432–597	Ruprecht 111		14 35.8
C1436–263	NGC 5694	g	14 39 36.5

Table D.3: Cluster Cross-Reference

Name	Look Under	GX	2000.0 RA
C1437–626	Loden 1373		14 41.7
C1439–573	NGC 5715		14 43 39.0
C1439–661	vdB-Ha 164		14 44.1
C1440+697	Collinder 285		14 40.9
C1440–615	Loden 1409		14 44.7
C1440–631	Loden 1375		14 44 33
C1445–543	NGC 5749		14 48 48.8
C1447–520	Hogg 18		14 50 41.4
C1450–524	NGC 5764		14 53 31.8
C1452–820	IC 4499	g	15 00 18.5
C1453–623	Ruprecht 112		14 57.0
C1500–328	NGC 5824	g	15 03 58.5
C1501–541	NGC 5822		15 04 02.3
C1502–554	NGC 5823		15 05 26
C1511–588	Pismis 20		15 15 23.1
C1512–581	Lynga 3		15 16 47
C1512–594	Pismis 21		15 16 47.7
C1513+000	Palomar 5	g	15 16 05.3
C1514–208	NGC 5897	g	15 17 24.5
C1516+022	NGC 5904	g	15 18 33.8
C1523–543	NGC 5925		15 27.7
C1524–505	NGC 5927	g	15 28 00.5
C1529–550	Lynga 4		15 33 20
C1530–534	Harvard 9		15 33.8
C1531–504	NGC 5946	g	15 35 28.5
C1535–499	vdB-Ha 176	g	15 39 07.3
C1538–564	Lynga 5		15 41 57.1
C1542–376	NGC 5986	g	15 46 03.5
C1546–575	Collinder 292		15 50.8
C1548–563	NGC 5999		15 52 14
C1551–572	NGC 6005		15 55 47.4
C1553–593	Ruprecht 113		15 57.2
C1556–533	Trumpler 23		16 00 50.7
C1557–540	Moffat 1		16 01 36.1
C1559–603	NGC 6025		16 03 18
C1601–517	Lynga 6		16 04 51
C1602–567	Ruprecht 114		16 06 31
C1603–539	NGC 6031		16 07 34.4
C1607–551	Lynga 7	g	16 11 03.0
C1608+150	Palomar 14	g	16 11 00.3
C1609–517	Pismis 22		16 14 07.9
C1609–522	Ruprecht 115		16 12 51.1
C1609–540	NGC 6067		16 13 09
C1611–512	Ruprecht 176		16 14 45
C1614–228	NGC 6093	g	16 17 02.5
C1614–550	Harvard 10		16 19.9
C1614–577	NGC 6087		16 18 51.8
C1615–501	Lynga 8		16 22 57.0
C1615–548	Harvard 10		16 19.9
C1616–484	Lynga 9		16 20 39
C1619–517	Ruprecht 117		16 23 30.7
C1619–518	Ruprecht 116		16 23 24.3
C1620–264	NGC 6121	g	16 23 35.5
C1620–488	Pismis 23		16 23 58
C1620–518	NGC 6115		16 24 26.8
C1620–720	NGC 6101	g	16 25 48.6
C1622–243	Grasdalen 1		16 23.8
C1622–405	NGC 6124		16 25 17.2
C1623–261	Collinder 302		16 26.0
C1624–259	NGC 6144	g	16 27 14.1

Table D.3: Cluster Cross-Reference

Name	Look Under	GX	2000.0 RA
C1624–387	NGC 6139	g	16 27 40.4
C1624–490	NGC 6134		16 27 43.6
C1624–514	Ruprecht 119		16 28 09.3
C1625+381	DoDz 5		16 27.4
C1625–490	Hogg 19		16 28 51.7
C1628–525	NGC 6152		16 32.7
C1629–129	NGC 6171	g	16 32 31.9
C1630–439	NGC 6169		16 34 05.0
C1630–495	NGC 6167		16 34 35
C1631–482	Ruprecht 120		16 35 12.2
C1631–508	Collinder 307		16 35.3
C1632–455	NGC 6178		16 35 50.8
C1633–088	Dolidze 27		16 36.5
C1634–462	Lynga 11		16 38 10
C1636–283	ESO 452-SC11	g	16 39 25
C1636–432	NGC 6192		16 40 20.8
C1637–486	NGC 6193		16 41 20.3
C1638–460	Ruprecht 121		16 41 47.6
C1639+365	NGC 6205	g	16 41 41.5
C1640–473	NGC 6200		16 44 08.6
C1640–474	Hogg 20		16 44.4
C1642–469	NGC 6204		16 46 07.9
C1642–476	Hogg 21		16 45 36.9
C1642–507	Lynga 12		16 46 03
C1643+383	DoDz 6		16 45 28.6
C1643–457	vdB-Ha 197		16 46 30.3
C1643–470	Hogg 22		16 46 35
C1644–018	NGC 6218	g	16 47 14.5
C1644–457	Westerlund 1		16 47 04
C1645+476	NGC 6229	g	16 46 58.9
C1645–433	Lynga 13		16 48 54
C1645–446	NGC 6216		16 49 23.6
C1645–537	NGC 6208		16 49 25.8
C1646–441	vdB-Ha 200		16 50.0
C1646–446	NGC 6222		16 50.7
C1650–220	NGC 6235	g	16 53 25.4
C1650–417	NGC 6231		16 54 09.8
C1651–408	Ruprecht 122		16 55 08.3
C1651–452	Lynga 14		16 55 05
C1652–394	NGC 6242		16 55 30.6
C1652–405	vdB-Ha 205		16 56 11.3
C1652–407	Collinder 316		16 55.5
C1653–405	Trumpler 24		16 57.0
C1654–040	NGC 6254	g	16 57 08.9
C1654–447	NGC 6249		16 57 41.7
C1654–457	NGC 6250		16 57 55
C1655–526	NGC 6253		16 59 06.1
C1656–370	NGC 6256	g	16 59 32.6
C1657–004	Palomar 15	g	16 59 50.9
C1657–446	NGC 6259		17 00.7
C1658–300	NGC 6266	g	17 01 12.6
C1658–396	NGC 6268		17 02 04.1
C1658–410	vdB-Ha 211		17 02 07.9
C1659–262	NGC 6273	g	17 02 37.7
C1701–246	NGC 6284	g	17 04 28.8
C1701–378	NGC 6281		17 04 47.2
C1701–481	Harvard 13		17 03 57
C1702–226	NGC 6287	g	17 05 09.4
C1702–366	vdB-Ha 214		17 05 50.3
C1707–265	NGC 6293	g	17 10 10.4

Table D.3: Cluster Cross-Reference

Name	Look Under	GX	2000.0 RA
C1708+156	DoDz 7		17 11 23
C1708–271	Terzan N 5		17 11 15
C1709–251	Terzan N 33		17 12 36.2
C1710–250	Terzan N 34		17 13 15.4
C1711–248	Terzan N 35		17 14 01.5
C1711–294	NGC 6304	g	17 14 32.5
C1712–393	NGC 6318		17 16 13.4
C1712–407	vdB-Ha 217		17 16 20.4
C1713–280	NGC 6316	g	17 16 37.4
C1714–237	NGC 6325	g	17 17 59.2
C1714–355	Bochum 13		17 17 20.7
C1714–394	NGC 6318		17 16 13.4
C1714–429	NGC 6322		17 18.5
C1715+432	NGC 6341	g	17 17 07.3
C1715–262	Terzan N 15		17 18 31
C1715–277	Terzan N 16		17 18 29
C1715–278	Terzan N 17		17 18 41
C1715–323	vdB-Ha 221		17 18 34
C1715–382	vdB-Ha 222		17 18 47.1
C1715–387	Havlen-Moffat 1		17 19 00.5
C1716–184	NGC 6333	g	17 19 11.8
C1717–358	vdB-Ha 223		17 20 42
C1718–195	NGC 6342	g	17 21 10.2
C1718–360	NGC 6334		17 20 58.3
C1720–177	NGC 6356	g	17 23 35.0
C1720–263	NGC 6355	g	17 23 58.6
C1720–378	Ruprecht 123		17 23.4
C1720–499	IC 4651		17 24.7
C1721–389	Trumpler 25		17 24 30.3
C1721–484	NGC 6352	g	17 25 29.2
C1722–343	Pismis 24		17 24 43.4
C1723–346	ESO 392-SC13		17 26 52
C1724+242	DoDz 8		17 26 24
C1724–070	IC 1257	g	17 27 08
C1724–307	Terzan 2	g	17 27 33.4
C1724–407	Ruprecht 124		17 27 55.9
C1725–050	NGC 6366	g	17 27 44.3
C1725–294	Trumpler 26		17 28 29.9
C1725–315	Antalova 1		17 28.9
C1726–324	Antalova 2		17 29.7
C1726–404	Ruprecht 125		17 29.7
C1726–670	NGC 6362	g	17 31 54.8
C1727–299	Haute Provence 1	g	17 31 05.2
C1727–315	Terzan 4	g	17 30 38.9
C1727–370	Collinder 332		17 30.8
C1727–370	Harvard 16		17 31 03
C1728–318	vdB-Ha 231		17 31 55.7
C1728–338	Gri 1		17 31 58
C1728–340	Collinder 333		17 31 31.3
C1728–368	Harvard 16		17 31 03
C1729–325	NGC 6383		17 34 42.2
C1730–293	IRAS 17301–2917		17 33 21.9
C1730–333	Liller 1	g	17 33 24.5
C1731–325	NGC 6383		17 34 42.2
C1731–342	Ruprecht 126		17 35 04.4
C1731–390	NGC 6380	g	17 34 28.0
C1732–304	Terzan 1	g	17 35 47.0
C1732–334	Trumpler 27		17 36 12.7
C1732–385	Tonantzintla 2	g	17 36 10.5
C1732–447	NGC 6388	g	17 36 17.0

Table D.3: Cluster Cross-Reference

Name	Look Under	GX	2000.0 RA
C1733–324	Trumpler 28		17 36 59
C1733–335	Trumpler 27		17 36 12.7
C1733–390	Tonantzintla 2	g	17 36 10.5
C1734–349	NGC 6396		17 37 38
C1734–362	Ruprecht 127		17 37 50.4
C1734–375	Collinder 338		17 38.2
C1735–032	NGC 6402	g	17 37 36.1
C1735–238	NGC 6401	g	17 38 36.9
C1736–321	NGC 6405		17 40 17
C1736–332	NGC 6404		17 39.6
C1736–369	NGC 6400		17 40 10
C1736–536	NGC 6397	g	17 40 41.3
C1737–369	NGC 6400		17 40 10
C1738–400	Trumpler 29		17 41 36.4
C1740–262	Palomar 6	g	17 43 42.2
C1740–342	ESO 393-SC15		17 43 35.2
C1740–348	Ruprecht 128		17 44 19.3
C1741–323	NGC 6416		17 44.3
C1741–328	Terzan N 23		17 45 11
C1741–337	Collinder 345		17 44 35
C1742+031	NGC 6426	g	17 44 54.7
C1743+057	IC 4665		17 46.2
C1743–292	Collinder 347		17 46 18.9
C1743–296	vdB-Ha 245		17 46 14.4
C1743–315	NGC 6425		17 46 53
C1744–295	Ruprecht 129		17 47 08.2
C1744–301	Ruprecht 130		17 47 32
C1745+013	Collinder 350		17 48.2
C1745–247	Terzan 5	g	17 48 04.9
C1745–292	Ruprecht 131		17 49 06.9
C1746–203	NGC 6440	g	17 48 52.6
C1746–287	Collinder 351		17 49 51
C1746–348	NGC 6444		17 49.6
C1746–370	NGC 6441	g	17 50 12.9
C1747–302	NGC 6451		17 50 41
C1747–312	Terzan 6	g	17 50 46.4
C1748–346	NGC 6453	g	17 50 51.8
C1749–223	NGC 6469		17 52 56.5
C1749–284	Ruprecht 168		17 52.8
C1749–287	Ruprecht 133		17 52 34.1
C1749–295	Ruprecht 134		17 52.8
C1749–300	Basel 5		17 52 28.4
C1750–273	Czernik 37		17 53 16.4
C1750–348	NGC 6475		17 53 46
C1751–241	UKS 1	g	17 54 27.2
C1753–190	NGC 6494		17 56 56
C1753–353	Trumpler 30		17 56.4
C1755–050	PWM78 2	g	17 58 39.4
C1755–116	Ruprecht 135		17 58 03.3
C1755–442	NGC 6496	g	17 59 02.0
C1756–174	NGC 6507		17 59 50
C1756–246	Ruprecht 138		17 59.9
C1756–247	Ruprecht 136		17 59 17.8
C1756–248	Ruprecht 169		17 59.5
C1756–251	Ruprecht 137		17 59.9
C1756–281	Trumpler 31		17 59.8
C1758+029	Melotte 186		18 01.1
C1758–235	Ruprecht 139		18 01.2
C1758–237	Bochum 14		18 02.0
C1758–268	Terzan 9	g	18 01 38.8
C1759–089	NGC 6517	g	18 01 50.6
C1759–230	NGC 6514		18 02 31
C1800–243	NGC 6523		18 04 25
C1800–279	NGC 6520		18 03 25
C1800–300	NGC 6522	g	18 03 35.0
C1801–003	NGC 6535	g	18 03 50.7
C1801–225	NGC 6531		18 04 13
C1801–243	NGC 6523		18 04 25
C1801–300	NGC 6528	g	18 04 49.6
C1802–075	NGC 6539	g	18 04 49.8
C1803–274	Collinder 468		18 06 35
C1803–278	NGC 6540	g	18 06 08.6
C1804–233	NGC 6546		18 07.2
C1804–250	NGC 6544	g	18 07 20.6
C1804–437	NGC 6541	g	18 08 02.2
C1805–214	Cl van den Bergh 1		18 08.6
C1806+315	DoDz 9		18 08.8
C1806–240	Collinder 367		18 09 51
C1806–259	NGC 6553	g	18 09 17.3
C1806–317	NGC 6558	g	18 10 17.6
C1808–072	IC 1276	g	18 10 44.2
C1809–216	NGC 6568		18 12 45
C1810–318	NGC 6569	g	18 13 38.9
C1811–286	AL 3		18 14 05.7
C1812–121	Kod 1		18 15 07
C1812–190	Markarian 38		18 15 16.6
C1812–221	NGC 6583		18 15 50
C1813–182	Collinder 469		18 16 33.7
C1814–133	Trumpler 32		18 17 10.4
C1814–149	NGC 6605		18 16 06
C1814–166	NGC 6596		18 17.5
C1814–190			18 16 51
C1814–191a	WZ Sgr cl		18 16 59.6
C1814–191b			18 17 24.6
C1814–199	Collinder 371		18 17 16
C1814–522	NGC 6584	g	18 18 37.7
C1815–122	NGC 6604		18 18.1
C1815–184	NGC 6603		18 18 28
C1816–138	NGC 6611		18 18 45
C1817–162	NGC 6618		18 21 09
C1817–171	NGC 6613		18 20 00
C1818–332	Ruprecht 140		18 21 49.8
C1819–146			18 22.5
C1820–120	NGC 6625		18 23 12.8
C1820–146			18 23.6
C1820–303	NGC 6624	g	18 23 40.5
C1821–197	Trumpler 33		18 24 38.8
C1821–249	NGC 6626	g	18 24 32.9
C1822–100	Ruprecht 170		18 25 10.7
C1822–146	Dolidze 28		18 25 30.0
C1824–120	NGC 6631		18 27 09.5
C1825+065	NGC 6633		18 27 15
C1827–132	NGC 6639		18 30 57.8
C1827–255	NGC 6638	g	18 30 56.2
C1828–066	Dolidze 29		18 31.4
C1828–123	Ruprecht 141		18 31.3
C1828–173	NGC 6647		18 31.5
C1828–192	IC 4725		18 31 45
C1828–235	NGC 6642	g	18 31 54.3
C1828–323	NGC 6637	g	18 31 23.2
C1829–121	Ruprecht 143		18 32 43
C1829–122	Ruprecht 142		18 32 14
C1829–160	Ruprecht 171		18 32 00.7
C1829–169	NGC 6645		18 32 38
C1830–060	Dolidze 30		18 32.9
C1830–104	NGC 6649		18 33 28.3
C1830–114	Ruprecht 144		18 33 32.7
C1832+051	IC 4756		18 38.9
C1832–068	Dolidze 31		18 34.9
C1832–330	NGC 6652	g	18 35 45.7
C1833–239	NGC 6656	g	18 36 24.2
C1834–082	NGC 6664		18 36 30.6
C1836+054	IC 4756		18 38.9
C1837–041	Dolidze 32		18 40.5
C1837–085	Trumpler 34		18 39.8
C1838–044	Dolidze 33		18 40.7
C1838–198	Palomar 8	g	18 41 29.9
C1839–046	Dolidze 34		18 42 03.1
C1839–063	NGC 6683		18 42 12.7
C1840–041	Trumpler 35		18 43 00.5
C1840–323	NGC 6681	g	18 43 12.7
C1842–012	Berkeley 79		18 44 57.5
C1842–094	NGC 6694		18 45 15
C1845–059	Apriamasvili 1		18 48.1
C1846+368	Iskudarian 1		18 48.0
C1846–652	NGC 6684		18 48 57.5
C1847+048	Czernik 38		18 49 47.0
C1847–181	Ruprecht 145		18 50 19.4
C1848–052	NGC 6704		18 50 45.8
C1848–063	NGC 6705		18 51 04
C1849+102	NGC 6709		18 51.5
C1849–211	Ruprecht 146		18 52 30
C1850–087	NGC 6712	g	18 53 04.3
C1850–204	Collinder 394		18 52 16.3
C1851+368	Stephenson 1		18 54 30.6
C1851–013	Berkeley 80		18 54 20.6
C1851–199	NGC 6716		18 54 34
C1851–305	NGC 6715	g	18 55 03.3
C1852–227	NGC 6717	g	18 55 06.2
C1856–367	NGC 6723	g	18 59 33.2
C1859+115	NGC 6738		19 01.4
C1859–005	Berkeley 81		19 01 39.7
C1902+017	NGC 6749	g	19 05 15.3
C1902+018	NGC 6749	g	19 05 15.3
C1905+041	NGC 6755		19 07 49
C1905+042	NGC 6755		19 07 49
C1906+046	NGC 6756		19 08 43
C1906–600	NGC 6752	g	19 10 51.8
C1909+009	NGC 6760	g	19 11 12.1
C1909+129	Berkeley 82		19 11 20.3
C1913+111	Berkeley 43		19 15 30
C1913–163	NGC 6774		19 16.3
C1914+300	NGC 6779	g	19 16 35.5
C1915+194	Berkeley 44		19 17 17
C1916+156	Berkeley 45		19 19 06
C1919+377	NGC 6791		19 20 52.7
C1921+220	NGC 6793		19 23 12.6
C1922+136	King 25		19 24.5
C1923+200	Collinder 399		19 26 12
C1924+115	Dolidze 35		19 25 24

Table D.3: Cluster Cross-Reference

Name	Look Under	GX	2000.0 RA
C1925+250	NGC 6800		19 27 00
C1925–304	Arp 2	g	19 28 44.1
C1926+147	King 26		19 29.0
C1926+173	Berkeley 47		19 28 27.3
C1928+201	NGC 6802		19 30 35
C1933+251	Stock 1		19 35 47
C1935+002	Collinder 401		19 38 21.7
C1936+464	NGC 6811		19 37 09.6
C1936–310	NGC 6809	g	19 39 59.4
C1938+267	NGC 6815		19 40.9
C1938–341	Terzan 8	g	19 41 45.0
C1939+400	NGC 6819		19 41.3
C1940+210	Czernik 40		19 42 38
C1940+229	Collinder 404		19 42 28
C1941+231	NGC 6823		19 43 10
C1942+174	Roslund 1		19 45 06
C1942–081	Palomar 11	g	19 45 14.4
C1943+238	Roslund 2		19 45 24.4
C1946+210	NGC 6827		19 48 53.2
C1947+272			19 49 04
C1948+229	NGC 6830		19 51 00
C1948+250	Czernik 41		19 50 50.8
C1950+182	Harvard 20		19 53 10.3
C1950+292	NGC 6834		19 52 13
C1951+115	NGC 6837		19 53.5
C1951+186	NGC 6838	g	19 53 46.1
C1954+302	NGC 6846		19 56 28.1
C1956+203	Roslund 3		19 58 41.1
C1957+344	Berkeley 49		19 59 30.2
C1959+284	Berkeley 83		20 01 25.1
C2000+419	Dolidze 36		20 02.5
C2001+375	Dolidze 37		20 03.0
C2002+290	Roslund 4		20 04 52
C2002+337	Berkeley 84		20 04 42.2
C2002+438	NGC 6866		20 03 55
C2003–220	NGC 6864	g	20 06 04.8
C2004+356	NGC 6871		20 06 27
C2004+403	DoDz 10		20 05 35
C2004+410	Dolidze 38		20 06 04
C2004–794	Melotte 227		20 15 18
C2005+355	Biurakan 1		20 07.5
C2005+382	NGC 6874		20 07.8
C2006+364	Dolidze 1		20 08.2
C2007+353	Biurakan 2		20 09 14.3
C2008+336	Roslund 5		20 10.0
C2008+347	IC 1310		20 10 01
C2008+410	IC 1311		20 10 47
C2008+412	Dolidze 2		20 09.9
C2009+263	NGC 6885		20 12 01
C2009+264	Collinder 416		20 11 35
C2009+354	Ruprecht 172		20 11 34
C2009+357	NGC 6883		20 11.3
C2010+342	Berkeley 51		20 11 53
C2012+288	Berkeley 52		20 14 30
C2013+366	Dolidze 3		20 15 27
C2014+374	IC 4996		20 16 31.7
C2014+377	Dolidze 39		20 16 12
C2015+365	Dolidze 4		20 17 46.6
C2015+391	Cl van den Bergh 1		20 17 42.2
C2016+375	Berkeley 85		20 18 47

Table D.3: Cluster Cross-Reference

Name	Look Under	GX	2000.0 RA
C2016+376	Dolidze 40		20 18.2
C2016+405	Collinder 419		20 18 07.0
C2017+375	Dolidze 41		20 19.2
C2017+379	Dolidze 42		20 19 39.7
C2018+385	Berkeley 86		20 20 21.2
C2018+392	Dolidze 5		20 20 29
C2019+372	Berkeley 87		20 21 35
C2019+397	Dolidze 43		20 21.7
C2019+412	Dolidze 6		20 20 38.0
C2020+479	Berkeley 88		20 21 16
C2021+406	NGC 6910		20 23 12
C2021+415	Collinder 421		20 23.3
C2022+383	NGC 6913		20 24 06
C2022+421	Dolidze 8		20 24.4
C2023+417	Dolidze 9		20 25 33.4
C2023+458	Berkeley 89		20 24 28.4
C2024+399	Dolidze 10		20 26.3
C2024+412	Dolidze 11		20 26 24.7
C2027+392	Roslund 6		20 28 49
C2027+415	Dolidze 44		20 29.7
C2030+604	NGC 6939		20 31 30
C2031+072	NGC 6934	g	20 34 11.6
C2032+281	NGC 6940		20 34 32.3
C2033+466	Berkeley 90		20 35 16
C2033–048	NGC 6941		20 36 23.5
C2039+353	Ruprecht 173		20 41 41.2
C2039+364	Dolidze 47		20 41 44.2
C2041+368	Ruprecht 174		20 43 28.3
C2043+353	Ruprecht 175		20 45 24
C2049+357	DoDz 11		20 51 04
C2050+377	Roslund 7		20 52 08.5
C2050–127	NGC 6981	g	20 53 27.9
C2052+458	Baractova 1		20 53.7
C2054+444	NGC 6997		20 56.5
C2055+472	h 2091		20 54 43.1
C2055+508	Berkeley 53		20 55 59
C2056–128	NGC 6994		20 58 56
C2058+679	Collinder 427		21 00 36.6
C2059+160	NGC 7006	g	21 01 29.5
C2059+679	Collinder 429		21 01 35.8
C2101+402	Berkeley 54		21 03 00
C2101+443	Collinder 428		21 03.2
C2105+506	NGC 7031		21 06 52
C2107+374	Dolidze 45		21 09.0
C2108+460	Basel 12		21 10.5
C2109+454	NGC 7039		21 11.2
C2110+463	Basel 13		21 13 11
C2110+475	IC 1369		21 12 07
C2110+482	Berkeley 91		21 10 51
C2111+422	NGC 7044		21 13 08
C2114+486	Basel 15		21 15.9
C2115+416	Berkeley 56		21 17 34.5
C2115+515	Berkeley 55		21 16 57
C2119+446	Basel 14		21 21 14.0
C2121+461	NGC 7062		21 23 27
C2122+362	NGC 7063		21 24.5
C2122+478	NGC 7067		21 24 12.3
C2123+572	Berkeley 92		21 24 46.3
C2127+119	NGC 7078	g	21 29 58.3
C2127+468	NGC 7082		21 29 19

Table D.3: Cluster Cross-Reference

Name	Look Under	GX	2000.0 RA
C2128+488	Anon Platais		21 30 02
C2128+513	NGC 7086		21 30 28
C2130+482	NGC 7092		21 31 52
C2130–010	NGC 7089	g	21 33 27.0
C2137+572	IC 1396		21 39.0
C2137–234	NGC 7099	g	21 40 22.0
C2140+658	NGC 7129		21 42 59
C2142+509	Baractova 2		21 43 38
C2142+534	NGC 7128		21 43 58
C2142+543	NGC 7127		21 43 52.9
C2143–214	Palomar 12	g	21 46 38.8
C2144+655	NGC 7142		21 45 09
C2151+470	Collinder 470		21 53.5
C2152+623	NGC 7160		21 53 40
C2154+637	Berkeley 93		21 55 29
C2203+462	NGC 7209		22 05 08
C2206+717	Collinder 471		22 07.1
C2208+525	IC 1434		22 10.5
C2208+551	NGC 7226		22 10 26
C2210+570	NGC 7235		22 12 24
C2211+730	Cl van den Bergh 1		22 12 52.8
C2212+700	Cl van den Bergh 1		22 13 24.5
C2213+496	NGC 7243		22 15 09
C2213+540	NGC 7245		22 15 16
C2213+541	King 9		22 15 31
C2214+538	IC 1442		22 15 59
C2218+578	NGC 7261		22 20 10
C2220+556	Berkeley 94		22 22 53
C2222+575	NGC 7281		22 24 55.7
C2226+520	NGC 7296		22 28 01
C2226+588	Berkeley 95		22 28.3
C2227+551	Berkeley 96		22 29 51.2
C2237+587	Berkeley 97		22 39 22.2
C2237+596	Czernik 42		22 39 35
C2241+521	Berkeley 98		22 42 39.2
C2245+578	NGC 7380		22 47 21
C2250+580	King 18		22 52 08
C2252+589	King 10		22 55.0
C2252+605	NGC 7419		22 54 17
C2253+568	NGC 7423		22 55 06.5
C2253+597	NGC 7429		22 55.9
C2304+124	Palomar 13	g	23 06 44.4
C2305–159	NGC 7492	g	23 08 26.7
C2306+602	King 19		23 08.3
C2306+606	PWM78 3		23 08 10.8
C2309+603	NGC 7510		23 11 04.2
C2313+602	Markarian 50		23 15 14
C2319+555	Dolidze 46		23 21.9
C2319+714	Berkeley 99		23 21 16.9
C2322+613	NGC 7654		23 24 51
C2323+610	Czernik 43		23 25.8
C2324+634	Berkeley 100		23 25 58
C2327+488	NGC 7686		23 30 07
C2330+552	Stock 11		23 30 55
C2331+582	King 20		23 33 14
C2331+616	Czernik 44		23 33 33
C2331+639	Berkeley 101		23 32 46.5
C2334+481	Aveni-Hunter 1		23 37 47
C2334+521	Stock 12		23 36 20
C2336+563	Berkeley 102		23 38.7

Table D.3: Cluster Cross-Reference

Name	Look Under	GX	2000.0 RA
C2342+590	Berkeley 103		23 45.2
C2343+619	Stock 17		23 43 47.0
C2345+683	King 11		23 47 36.6
C2346–732	AM 3	S	23 48 59.5
C2347+624	King 21		23 49.9
C2347+677	NGC 7762		23 49.9
C2348+620	PWM78 4		23 50 53.0
C2349+159	NGC 7772		23 51.8
C2350+616	King 12		23 53.0
C2351+614	Harvard 21		23 54 17.6
C2353+642	Czernik 45		23 55 44.9
C2354+564	NGC 7789		23 57 28.6
C2354+611	NGC 7788		23 56 44
C2354+613	Frolov 1		23 57 26.5
C2355+609	NGC 7790		23 58 24
C2357+606	Berkeley 58		00 00 12
C2359+643	Stock 18		00 01 35
C84 29	Bol 96	A	00 42 26.2
C84 46	[WSB85] W 7	A	00 42 38.0
C84 51	Bol 124	A	00 42 41.1
C84 53	Bol 124	A	00 42 41.1
C84 72	ACH 6	A	00 42 48.4
C84 90	Bol 144	A	00 42 59.9
Caldwell 1	NGC 188		00 47 30
Caldwell 8	NGC 559		01 29 33
Caldwell 10	NGC 663		01 46 17
Caldwell 13	NGC 457		01 19 33
Caldwell 16	NGC 7243		22 15 09
Caldwell 25	NGC 2419	g	07 38 08.5
Caldwell 28	NGC 752		01 57 35
Caldwell 37	NGC 6885		20 12 01
Caldwell 41	Hyades		04 26.9
Caldwell 42	NGC 7006	g	21 01 29.5
Caldwell 47	NGC 6934	g	20 34 11.6
Caldwell 49	NGC 2237		06 31 55.5
Caldwell 50	NGC 2244		06 32 19
Caldwell 54	NGC 2506		08 00 02
Caldwell 58	NGC 2360		07 17 44
Caldwell 64	NGC 2362		07 18 42
Caldwell 66	NGC 5694	g	14 39 36.5
Caldwell 71	NGC 2477		07 52 10
Caldwell 73	NGC 1851	g	05 14 06.3
Caldwell 75	NGC 6124		16 25 17.2
Caldwell 76	NGC 6231		16 54 09.8
Caldwell 78	NGC 6541	g	18 08 02.2
Caldwell 79	NGC 3201	g	10 17 36.8
Caldwell 80	NGC 5139	g	13 26 45.9
Caldwell 81	NGC 6352	g	17 25 29.2
Caldwell 82	NGC 6193		16 41 20.3
Caldwell 84	NGC 5286	g	13 46 26.5
Caldwell 85	IC 2391		08 40.3
Caldwell 86	NGC 6397	g	17 40 41.3
Caldwell 87	NGC 1261	g	03 12 15.3
Caldwell 88	NGC 5823		15 05 26
Caldwell 89	NGC 6087		16 18 51.8
Caldwell 91	NGC 3532		11 05.5
Caldwell 93	NGC 6752	g	19 10 51.8
Caldwell 94	NGC 4755		12 53 38
Caldwell 95	NGC 6025		16 03 18
Caldwell 96	NGC 2516		07 58.0

Table D.3: Cluster Cross-Reference

Name	Look Under	GX	2000.0 RA
Caldwell 97	NGC 3766		11 36 15
Caldwell 98	NGC 4609		12 42 20
Caldwell 102	IC 2602		10 42 57
Caldwell 103	NGC 2070	L	05 38 42.4
Caldwell 104	NGC 362	g	01 03 14.3
Caldwell 105	NGC 4833	g	12 59 35.0
Caldwell 106	NGC 104	g	00 24 05.2
Caldwell 107	NGC 6101	g	16 25 48.6
Caldwell 108	NGC 4372	g	12 25 45.4
Canali			12 35 44.1
Cap gcl	Palomar 12	g	21 46 38.8
Capricorn Dwarf	Palomar 12	g	21 46 38.8
[CCS85] 1		A	00 35 18.8
[CCS85] 2		A	00 35 32.5
[CCS85] 3		A	00 35 52.1
[CCS85] 4		A	00 36 08.8
[CCS85] 5		A	00 36 35.6
[CCS85] 6		A	00 36 56.1
[CCS85] 7	Bol 416	A	00 37 01.4
[CCS85] 8	Bol D151	A	00 37 02.2
[CCS85] 9		A	00 37 25.7
[CCS85] 10	Bol 419	A	00 37 27.2
[CCS85] 11		A	00 37 29.6
[CCS85] 16		A	00 37 56.9
[CCS85] 17	Bol 424	A	00 38 03.1
[CCS85] 18		A	00 38 19.8
[CCS85] 18	Bol 426	A	00 38 19.8
[CCS85] 19	Bol 427	A	00 38 22.7
[CCS85] 20	Bol D168	A	00 38 25.0
[CCS85] 21	Bol D170	A	00 38 28.1
[CCS85] 22		A	00 38 53.7
[CCS85] 23		A	00 38 54.3
[CCS85] 24	Bol 305	A	00 38 58.9
[CCS85] 25		A	00 39 13.4
[CCS85] 26	Bol 434	A	00 39 15.1
[CCS85] 27		A	00 39 16.5
[CCS85] 28	Bol 435	A	00 39 18.4
[CCS85] 29		A	00 39 27.4
[CCS85] 30		A	00 39 50.8
[CCS85] 32		A	00 40 19.2
[CCS85] 33	Bol 442	A	00 40 19.4
[CCS85] 34	Bol 443	A	00 40 21.4
[CCS85] 35	Bol 448	A	00 40 36.5
[CCS85] 36	Bol D6	A	00 40 37.3
[CCS85] 37	Bol 451	A	00 40 46.4
[CCS85] 39	Bol D12	A	00 40 52.3
[CCS85] 40		A	00 40 52.2
[CCS85] 41	Bol D15	A	00 41 02.7
[CCS85] 42	Bol 453	A	00 41 03.3
[CCS85] 43	Bol D200	A	00 41 06.9
[CCS85] 44	Bol D201	A	00 41 08.3
[CCS85] 45	Bol 456	A	00 41 21.4
[CCS85] 46		A	00 41 23.0
[CCS85] 47		A	00 41 29.4
[CCS85] 48	Bol D206	A	00 41 40.6
[CCS85] 49	Bol 458	A	00 41 44.6
[CCS85] 50	Bol D207	A	00 41 45.0
[CCS85] 52		A	00 42 08.8
[CCS85] 53		A	00 42 09.9
[CCS85] 54		A	00 42 10.9

Table D.3: Cluster Cross-Reference

Name	Look Under	GX	2000.0 RA
[CCS85] 55		A	00 42 42.5
[CCS85] 57	Bol 465	A	00 43 00.7
[CCS85] 59	Bol 466	A	00 43 01.4
[CCS85] 60		A	00 43 24.4
[CCS85] 62		A	00 43 27.0
[CCS85] 63	Bol 470	A	00 43 37.5
[CCS85] 64	Bol 472	A	00 43 48.9
[CCS85] 65	Bol D111	A	00 44 04.9
[CCS85] 66	Bol D240	A	00 44 06.9
[CCS85] 68	Bol 279	A	00 44 28.0
[CCS85] 69		A	00 44 34.8
[CCS85] 70	Bol D248	A	00 44 41.3
[CCS85] 72	Bol D255	A	00 44 48.6
[CCS85] 73	Bol D257	A	00 44 59.5
[CCS85] 74	Bol 476	A	00 45 07.2
[CCS85] 75	Bol 477	A	00 45 08.4
[CCS85] 76	Bol 478	A	00 45 12.8
[CCS85] 77	Bol D262	A	00 45 20.0
[CCS85] 78	Bol D263	A	00 45 22.2
[CCS85] 79	Bol D128	A	00 45 23.4
[CCS85] 80	Bol 479	A	00 45 27.9
[CCS85] 82	Bol D268	A	00 45 44.1
[CCS85] 83		A	00 45 49.9
[CCS85] 84		A	00 45 52.4
[CCS85] 85	Bol 483	A	00 45 53.8
[CCS85] 89		A	00 46 46.4
[CCS85] 90	Bol 493	A	00 47 14.5
[CCS85] 91		A	00 47 24.8
[CCS85] 92		A	00 47 37.6
[CCS85] 93		A	00 47 46.2
[CCS85] 94		A	00 47 54.4
[CCS85] 95		A	00 47 57.3
[CCS85] 96		A	00 48 08.9
[CCS85] 97		A	00 48 09.1
[CCS85] 98		A	00 48 29.2
[CCS85] 99		A	00 48 48.3
[CCS85] 101		A	00 49 06.6
[CCS85] 102		A	00 49 14.0
[CCS85] 103	Bol 505	A	00 49 15.4
[CCS85] 104		A	00 49 21.4
[CCS85] 105		A	00 49 35.5
[CCS85] 106		A	00 49 36.0
[CCS85] 107		A	00 49 41.4
[CCS85] 108	Bol 509	A	00 49 52.9
[CCS85] 109	Bol 406	A	00 49 59.4
[CCS85] D08	Bol D151	A	00 37 02.2
[CCS85] D20	Bol D168	A	00 38 25.0
[CCS85] D21	Bol D170	A	00 38 28.1
[CCS85] D36	Bol D6	A	00 40 37.3
[CCS85] D39	Bol D12	A	00 40 52.3
[CCS85] D41	Bol D15	A	00 41 02.7
[CCS85] D43	Bol D200	A	00 41 06.9
[CCS85] D44	Bol D201	A	00 41 08.3
[CCS85] D48	Bol D206	A	00 41 40.6
[CCS85] D50	Bol D207	A	00 41 45.0
[CCS85] D56	Bol D215	A	00 42 43.3
[CCS85] D58	Bol D91	A	00 43 01.5
[CCS85] D65	Bol D111	A	00 44 04.9
[CCS85] D66	Bol D240	A	00 44 06.9
[CCS85] D70	Bol D248	A	00 44 41.3

Table D.3: Cluster Cross-Reference

Name	Look Under	GX	2000.0 RA
[CCS85] D72	Bol D255	A	00 44 48.6
[CCS85] D73	Bol D257	A	00 44 59.5
[CCS85] D77	Bol D262	A	00 45 20.0
[CCS85] D78	Bol D263	A	00 45 22.2
[CCS85] D79	Bol D128	A	00 45 23.4
[CCS85] D82	Bol D268	A	00 45 44.1
CD–69 252	NGC 1743	L	04 54 03.4
CD–69 274	NGC 1835	L	05 05 06.6
CD–74 36	Bruck 49	S	00 48 55.7
Ced 49	NGC 1931		05 31 26
Ced 144	IC 1257	g	17 27 08
Ced 178	IC 1310		20 10 01
Central cluster			17 45 40.0
CGCG 08–35	Palomar 3	g	10 05 31.4
CGCG 21–61	Palomar 5	g	15 16 05.3
CGCG 25–16	Palomar 15	g	16 59 50.9
CGCG 064–073	Leo I		10 08 27.5
CGCG 126–111	Leo II		11 13 29.3
CGCG 430–61	Palomar 13	g	23 06 44.4
CGCG 462–36	Dejc 1		02 37 28.3
CGCG 1005.8+1233	Leo I		10 08 27.5
CGCG 1110.8+2226	Leo II		11 13 29.3
Chi Perseus	Double Cluster		02 20 40.6
Cl van den Bergh		A	01 16 04.1
Cl van den Bergh	Cl vdB	A	01 16 04.1
Cl van den Bergh 0		A	00 40 29.4
Cl van den Bergh 1			06 37 05
Cl van den Bergh 80			06 30 50
Cl van den Bergh 83			06 40.0
Cl van den Bergh 84	Cl vdB 83		06 40.0
Cl van den Bergh 85			06 46 52
Cl van den Bergh 92			07 03 55
Cl van den Bergh 113			18 08.6
Cl van den Bergh 130			20 17 42.2
Cl van den Bergh 150			22 12 52.8
Cl van den Bergh 152			22 13 24.5
Cl Zwicky 1	Palomar 15	g	16 59 50.9
Cl [BW88] 1			04 30 14.3
Coalsack cluster	NGC 4609		12 42 20
Coathanger cluster	Collinder 399		19 26 12
Collinder 1	NGC 103		00 25 18
Collinder 2	NGC 129		00 29 58
Collinder 3	NGC 133		00 31 18
Collinder 4	NGC 136		00 31 31
Collinder 5	NGC 146		00 33.1
Collinder 6	NGC 188		00 47 30
Collinder 7	NGC 225		00 43 36
Collinder 8	IC 1590		00 52 49
Collinder 9	NGC 366		01 06 27
Collinder 10	NGC 381		01 08 18
Collinder 11	NGC 436		01 15 58
Collinder 12	NGC 457		01 19 33
Collinder 13	NGC 559		01 29 33
Collinder 14	NGC 581		01 33 22
Collinder 15	Trumpler 1		01 35 40
Collinder 16	NGC 609		01 36 24
Collinder 17	NGC 637		01 43 04
Collinder 18	NGC 654		01 44 00
Collinder 19	NGC 659		01 44 24
Collinder 20	NGC 663		01 46 17
Collinder 21			01 50 12
Collinder 22	NGC 744		01 58 30
Collinder 23	NGC 752		01 57 35
Collinder 24	NGC 869		02 19 04
Collinder 25	NGC 884		02 22 05
Collinder 26	IC 1805		02 32 42
Collinder 27	NGC 956		02 32 14.9
Collinder 28	NGC 957		02 33 20
Collinder 29	Trumpler 2		02 36 53
Collinder 30	NGC 1027		02 42 36
Collinder 31	NGC 1039		02 42 08
Collinder 32	IC 1848		02 51 11
Collinder 33	IC 1848		02 51 11
Collinder 34			02 59 23.2
Collinder 35	NGC 1193		03 05 56
Collinder 36	Trumpler 3		03 12 00
Collinder 37	NGC 1220		03 11 41
Collinder 38	NGC 1245		03 14 42
Collinder 39	Melotte 20		03 24 19
Collinder 40	NGC 1342		03 31 40
Collinder 41	IC 348		03 44 34
Collinder 42	Pleiades		03 47 29
Collinder 43	NGC 1444		03 49 27
Collinder 44	NGC 1496		04 04 32
Collinder 45	NGC 1502		04 07 50
Collinder 46	NGC 1513		04 09 55
Collinder 47	NGC 1528		04 15 19
Collinder 48	IC 361		04 18 51
Collinder 49	NGC 1545		04 20 57
Collinder 50	Hyades		04 26.9
Collinder 51	NGC 1582		04 31 39
Collinder 52	NGC 1605		04 34 53
Collinder 53	NGC 1624		04 40 37
Collinder 54	NGC 1647		04 45 42.2
Collinder 55	NGC 1662		04 48 29
Collinder 56	NGC 1664		04 51 06
Collinder 57	NGC 1746		05 03.6
Collinder 57	NGC 1750		05 03.9
Collinder 58	NGC 1778		05 08 06
Collinder 59	NGC 1807		05 10 46
Collinder 60	NGC 1817		05 12 27
Collinder 61	NGC 1857		05 20 06
Collinder 62			05 20 53.0
Collinder 63	NGC 1893		05 22 46
Collinder 64	NGC 1883		05 25 55
Collinder 65			05 26 05.7
Collinder 66	NGC 1907		05 28 05
Collinder 67	NGC 1912		05 28 43
Collinder 68	NGC 1931		05 31 26
Collinder 69			05 35.0
Collinder 70			05 35.6
Collinder 71	NGC 1960		05 36 18
Collinder 72	NGC 1980		05 35 26
Collinder 73	NGC 1981		05 35.2
Collinder 74			05 48 40
Collinder 75	NGC 2099		05 52 19
Collinder 76	NGC 2112		05 53 46
Collinder 77	NGC 2129		06 01 06
Collinder 78	NGC 2126		06 02 34
Collinder 79	NGC 2141		06 02 56
Collinder 80	IC 2157		06 04 49.8
Collinder 81	NGC 2158		06 07 26
Collinder 82	NGC 2168		06 09.0
Collinder 83	NGC 2169		06 08 25
Collinder 84			06 09 39
Collinder 85	NGC 2186		06 12 08
Collinder 86	NGC 2192		06 15 18
Collinder 87	NGC 2194		06 13 46
Collinder 88	NGC 2204		06 15 33
Collinder 89			06 18.0
Collinder 90	NGC 2215		06 20 50
Collinder 91			06 21 33
Collinder 92			06 22.9
Collinder 93	NGC 2232		06 27 15
Collinder 94	NGC 2236		06 29 40
Collinder 95			06 30 51.2
Collinder 96			06 30.3
Collinder 97			06 30 58.1
Collinder 98	NGC 2243		06 29 35
Collinder 99	NGC 2237		06 31 55.5
Collinder 99	NGC 2244		06 32 19
Collinder 101	NGC 2251		06 34 39
Collinder 102	NGC 2252		06 34 19.8
Collinder 103	NGC 2254		06 35 46.6
Collinder 104			06 36.5
Collinder 105	Trumpler 5		06 36 31
Collinder 106			06 37.1
Collinder 107			06 37.7
Collinder 108	NGC 2259		06 38 33.3
Collinder 109	NGC 2262		06 39 38.7
Collinder 110			06 38 39
Collinder 111			06 38.7
Collinder 112	NGC 2264		06 40 59
Collinder 113	NGC 2266		06 43 20
Collinder 114	NGC 2269		06 43 16.8
Collinder 115			06 46 40
Collinder 116	NGC 2281		06 48 18
Collinder 117	NGC 2286		06 47 41
Collinder 118	NGC 2287		06 46.1
Collinder 119	NGC 2301		06 51 46
Collinder 120	NGC 2304		06 55 12
Collinder 121			06 56 20.0
Collinder 122	NGC 2309		06 56 04
Collinder 123	NGC 2311		06 57 48
Collinder 124	NGC 2323		07 02 47.8
Collinder 125	NGC 2324		07 04 08
Collinder 126	NGC 2331		07 07 01
Collinder 127	NGC 2335		07 06 50
Collinder 128	NGC 2343		07 08 07
Collinder 129	NGC 2345		07 08 19
Collinder 130	NGC 2353		07 14 31
Collinder 131	NGC 2354		07 14 16
Collinder 132			07 15 21.1
Collinder 133	NGC 2355		07 17 00
Collinder 134	NGC 2360		07 17 44
Collinder 135			07 17 24.5
Collinder 136	NGC 2362		07 18 42
Collinder 137	NGC 2367		07 20 05
Collinder 138	NGC 2368		07 21 02.2
Collinder 139	NGC 2374		07 23 57

Table D.3: Cluster Cross-Reference

Name	Look Under	GX	2000.0 RA
Collinder 140			07 24 26.7
Collinder 141	NGC 2383		07 24 40
Collinder 142	NGC 2384		07 25 12
Collinder 143	NGC 2384		07 25 12
Collinder 144	NGC 2395		07 27 13
Collinder 145	Trumpler 6		07 26 23
Collinder 146	Trumpler 7		07 27 21
Collinder 147	Melotte 66		07 26 19
Collinder 148	NGC 2396		07 28.0
Collinder 149	NGC 2401		07 29 25
Collinder 150	NGC 2414		07 33 13
Collinder 151	NGC 2421		07 36 12
Collinder 152	NGC 2422		07 36 36
Collinder 153	NGC 2423		07 37 07
Collinder 154	NGC 2420		07 38 24
Collinder 155	Melotte 71		07 37 30
Collinder 156	Melotte 72		07 38 29
Collinder 157	NGC 2432		07 40 54
Collinder 158	NGC 2439		07 40 46
Collinder 159	NGC 2437		07 41 47
Collinder 160	NGC 2447		07 44 30
Collinder 161	NGC 2451		07 45.4
Collinder 162	NGC 2453		07 47 35
Collinder 163	NGC 2455		07 48 59
Collinder 164	NGC 2467		07 52 30
Collinder 165	NGC 2477		07 52 10
Collinder 166	NGC 2482		07 55 10
Collinder 167	NGC 2479		07 55 06
Collinder 168	Trumpler 9		07 55 40
Collinder 169	NGC 2489		07 56 16
Collinder 170	NGC 2506		08 00 02
Collinder 171	NGC 2509		08 00 48
Collinder 172	NGC 2516		07 58.0
Collinder 173			08 03.5
Collinder 174	NGC 2527		08 04 53
Collinder 175	NGC 2533		08 07.0
Collinder 176	NGC 2539		08 10 38
Collinder 177	NGC 2547		08 10 11
Collinder 178	NGC 2546		08 12.4
Collinder 179	NGC 2548		08 13 44
Collinder 180	NGC 2567		08 18 30
Collinder 181	NGC 2571		08 18 57
Collinder 182	NGC 2579		08 20 53
Collinder 183	NGC 2580		08 21 28
Collinder 184	NGC 2587		08 23 25
Collinder 185			08 23 19
Collinder 186	NGC 2588		08 23 10
Collinder 187			08 24 12
Collinder 188	NGC 2627		08 37 15
Collinder 189	NGC 2632		08 40 22
Collinder 190	NGC 2635		08 38 27
Collinder 191	IC 2391		08 40.3
Collinder 192	IC 2395		08 42 31
Collinder 193	NGC 2660		08 42 39
Collinder 194	NGC 2659		08 42 34
Collinder 195	NGC 2658		08 43 28
Collinder 196			08 45.1
Collinder 197			08 44 40
Collinder 198			08 45.4
Collinder 199	NGC 2669		08 46 19

Table D.3: Cluster Cross-Reference

Name	Look Under	GX	2000.0 RA
Collinder 200	NGC 2670		08 45 30
Collinder 201	NGC 2671		08 46 12
Collinder 202	Harvard 3		08 46.5
Collinder 203	Trumpler 10		08 47 45
Collinder 204	NGC 2682		08 51 24
Collinder 205	Markarian 18		09 00 31
Collinder 206	NGC 2818		09 16 10
Collinder 207	NGC 2849		09 19 23
Collinder 208	IC 2488		09 27 27
Collinder 209	NGC 2910		09 30 30
Collinder 210	NGC 2925		09 33 11
Collinder 211	NGC 2972		09 40 12
Collinder 212	NGC 3033		09 48 40
Collinder 213			09 55 00
Collinder 214	NGC 3105		10 00 40
Collinder 215	NGC 3114		10 02.7
Collinder 216	Trumpler 11		10 04.9
Collinder 217	Trumpler 12		10 06.5
Collinder 218	NGC 3228		10 21 23
Collinder 219	Trumpler 13		10 23 48
Collinder 220			10 25 52
Collinder 221	NGC 3255		10 26 32
Collinder 222	IC 2581		10 27 27
Collinder 223			10 30.4
Collinder 224	NGC 3293		10 35 49
Collinder 225	NGC 3324		10 37 19
Collinder 226	NGC 3330		10 38 48
Collinder 227	Melotte 101		10 42 00
Collinder 228			10 44 00
Collinder 229	IC 2602		10 42 57
Collinder 230	Trumpler 14		10 43 57
Collinder 231	Trumpler 15		10 44 44
Collinder 232			10 44 39
Collinder 233	Trumpler 16		10 45 10
Collinder 234			10 45 12.9
Collinder 234	Trumpler 16		10 45 10
Collinder 235	Trumpler 17		10 56 24
Collinder 236			10 57 00
Collinder 237	NGC 3496		10 59 34
Collinder 238	NGC 3532		11 05.5
Collinder 239	NGC 3572		11 10 26.6
Collinder 240			11 11 40.2
Collinder 240	Hogg 10		11 10 42.1
Collinder 240	NGC 3572		11 10 26.6
Collinder 241	Trumpler 18		11 11.4
Collinder 242	NGC 3590		11 13 00
Collinder 243	Trumpler 19		11 14.3
Collinder 244	NGC 3603		11 15 07
Collinder 245	IC 2714		11 17 18
Collinder 246	Melotte 105		11 19 41
Collinder 247	NGC 3680		11 25 38
Collinder 248	NGC 3766		11 36 15
Collinder 249			11 38 20.4
Collinder 250	NGC 3960		11 50 34
Collinder 251	NGC 4052		12 02 01
Collinder 252	NGC 4103		12 06 40
Collinder 253	NGC 4230		12 17 16
Collinder 254	NGC 4337		12 24 04
Collinder 255	NGC 4349		12 24 07
Collinder 256	Melotte 111		12 25.1

Table D.3: Cluster Cross-Reference

Name	Look Under	GX	2000.0 RA
Collinder 257			12 24 45.9
Collinder 258	Harvard 5		12 27 16.3
Collinder 259	NGC 4439		12 28 27
Collinder 260	NGC 4463		12 29 56
Collinder 261	Harvard 6		12 37 54
Collinder 262	Trumpler 20		12 39 32
Collinder 263	NGC 4609		12 42 20
Collinder 264	NGC 4755		12 53 38
Collinder 265	NGC 4815		12 57 59
Collinder 266	NGC 4852		13 00 05
Collinder 267	NGC 5053	g	13 16 27.0
Collinder 268	Harvard 8		13 18 12
Collinder 269			13 22.6
Collinder 270	NGC 5138		13 27 16
Collinder 271			13 30.0
Collinder 272			13 30.5
Collinder 273	NGC 5168		13 31 08
Collinder 274	Trumpler 21		13 32 14
Collinder 275			13 35.4
Collinder 276	NGC 5281		13 46 36.7
Collinder 277			13 48.4
Collinder 278	NGC 5288		13 48 45.6
Collinder 279	NGC 5316		13 54.0
Collinder 280	NGC 5460		14 07.6
Collinder 281	NGC 5606		14 27.8
Collinder 282	NGC 5617		14 29.7
Collinder 283	Trumpler 22		14 31.2
Collinder 284	NGC 5662		14 35 30.8
Collinder 285			14 40.9
Collinder 285	[A084] VII		06.6
Collinder 286	NGC 5715		14 43 39.0
Collinder 287	NGC 5749		14 48 48.8
Collinder 288	NGC 5764		14 53 31.8
Collinder 289	NGC 5822		15 04 02.3
Collinder 290	NGC 5823		15 05 26
Collinder 291	NGC 5925		15 27.7
Collinder 292			15 50.8
Collinder 293	NGC 5999		15 52 14
Collinder 294	NGC 6005		15 55 47.4
Collinder 295	Trumpler 23		16 00 50.7
Collinder 296	NGC 6025		16 03 18
Collinder 297	NGC 6031		16 07 34.4
Collinder 298	NGC 6067		16 13 09
Collinder 299	Harvard 10		16 19.9
Collinder 300	NGC 6087		16 18 51.8
Collinder 301	NGC 6124		16 25 17.2
Collinder 302			16 26.0
Collinder 303	NGC 6134		16 27 43.6
Collinder 304	NGC 6152		16 32.7
Collinder 305	NGC 6167		16 34 35
Collinder 306	NGC 6169		16 34 05.0
Collinder 307			16 35.3
Collinder 308	NGC 6178		16 35 50.8
Collinder 309	NGC 6192		16 40 20.8
Collinder 310	NGC 6193		16 41 20.3
Collinder 311	NGC 6200		16 44 08.6
Collinder 312	NGC 6204		16 46 07.9
Collinder 313	NGC 6208		16 49 25.8
Collinder 314	NGC 6216		16 49 23.6
Collinder 315	NGC 6231		16 54 09.8

Table D.3: Cluster Cross-Reference

Name	Look Under	GX	2000.0 RA
Collinder 316			16 55.5
Collinder 317	NGC 6242		16 55 30.6
Collinder 318	Trumpler 24		16 57.0
Collinder 319	NGC 6249		16 57 41.7
Collinder 320	NGC 6250		16 57 55
Collinder 321	NGC 6253		16 59 06.1
Collinder 322	NGC 6259		17 00.7
Collinder 323	NGC 6268		17 02 04.1
Collinder 324	NGC 6281		17 04 47.2
Collinder 325	NGC 6318		17 16 13.4
Collinder 326	NGC 6322		17 18.5
Collinder 327	IC 4651		17 24.7
Collinder 328	NGC 6352	g	17 25 29.2
Collinder 329	Trumpler 25		17 24 30.3
Collinder 330	NGC 6355	g	17 23 58.6
Collinder 331	Trumpler 26		17 28 29.9
Collinder 332			17 30.8
Collinder 332	Harvard 16		17 31 03
Collinder 333			17 31 31.3
Collinder 334	NGC 6383		17 34 42.2
Collinder 335	NGC 6383		17 34 42.2
Collinder 336	Trumpler 27		17 36 12.7
Collinder 337	Trumpler 28		17 36 59
Collinder 338			17 38.2
Collinder 339	NGC 6396		17 37 38
Collinder 340	NGC 6404		17 39.6
Collinder 341	NGC 6405		17 40 17
Collinder 342	NGC 6400		17 40 10
Collinder 343	Trumpler 29		17 41 36.4
Collinder 344	NGC 6416		17 44.3
Collinder 345			17 44 35
Collinder 346	NGC 6426	g	17 44 54.7
Collinder 347			17 46 18.9
Collinder 348	NGC 6425		17 46 53
Collinder 349	IC 4665		17 46.2
Collinder 350			17 48.2
Collinder 351			17 49 51
Collinder 352	NGC 6451		17 50 41
Collinder 353	NGC 6469		17 52 56.5
Collinder 354	NGC 6475		17 53 46
Collinder 355	Trumpler 30		17 56.4
Collinder 356	NGC 6494		17 56 56
Collinder 357	Trumpler 31		17 59.8
Collinder 358	NGC 6507		17 59 50
Collinder 359	Melotte 186		18 01.1
Collinder 360	NGC 6514		18 02 31
Collinder 361	NGC 6520		18 03 25
Collinder 362	NGC 6523		18 04 25
Collinder 363	NGC 6531		18 04 13
Collinder 364	NGC 6540	g	18 06 08.6
Collinder 365	NGC 6546		18 07.2
Collinder 366	NGC 6544	g	18 07 20.6
Collinder 367			18 09 51
Collinder 368	NGC 6558	g	18 10 17.6
Collinder 369	NGC 6568		18 12 45
Collinder 370	NGC 6583		18 15 50
Collinder 371			18 17 16
Collinder 372	Trumpler 32		18 17 10.4
Collinder 373	NGC 6604		18 18.1
Collinder 374	NGC 6603		18 18 28

Table D.3: Cluster Cross-Reference

Name	Look Under	GX	2000.0 RA
Collinder 375	NGC 6611		18 18 45
Collinder 376	NGC 6613		18 20 00
Collinder 377	NGC 6618		18 21 09
Collinder 378	Trumpler 33		18 24 38.8
Collinder 379	NGC 6631		18 27 09.5
Collinder 380	NGC 6633		18 27 15
Collinder 381	NGC 6642	g	18 31 54.3
Collinder 382	IC 4725		18 31 45
Collinder 383	NGC 6645		18 32 38
Collinder 384	NGC 6649		18 33 28.3
Collinder 385	NGC 6664		18 36 30.6
Collinder 386	IC 4756		18 38.9
Collinder 387	Trumpler 34		18 39.8
Collinder 389	NGC 6694		18 45 15
Collinder 390	NGC 6704		18 50 45.8
Collinder 391	NGC 6705		18 51 04
Collinder 392	NGC 6709		18 51.5
Collinder 393	NGC 6716		18 54 34
Collinder 394			18 52 16.3
Collinder 395	NGC 6717	g	18 55 06.2
Collinder 396	NGC 6738		19 01.4
Collinder 397	NGC 6755		19 07 49
Collinder 398	NGC 6756		19 08 43
Collinder 398	Trumpler 35		18 43 00.5
Collinder 399			19 26 12
Collinder 400	NGC 6802		19 30 35
Collinder 401			19 38 21.7
Collinder 402	NGC 6811		19 37 09.6
Collinder 403	NGC 6819		19 41.3
Collinder 404			19 42 28
Collinder 405	NGC 6823		19 43 10
Collinder 406	NGC 6830		19 51 00
Collinder 407	NGC 6834		19 52 13
Collinder 408	Harvard 20		19 53 10.3
Collinder 409	NGC 6838	g	19 53 46.1
Collinder 410	NGC 6846		19 56 28.1
Collinder 411	Melotte 227		20 15 18
Collinder 412	NGC 6866		20 03 55
Collinder 413	NGC 6871		20 06 27
Collinder 414	IC 1311		20 10 47
Collinder 415	NGC 6883		20 11.3
Collinder 416			20 11 35
Collinder 417	NGC 6885		20 12 01
Collinder 418	IC 4996		20 16 31.7
Collinder 419			20 18 07.0
Collinder 420	NGC 6910		20 23 12
Collinder 421			20 23.3
Collinder 422	NGC 6913		20 24 06
Collinder 423	NGC 6939		20 31 30
Collinder 424	NGC 6940		20 34 32.3
Collinder 425	NGC 6997		20 56.5
Collinder 426	NGC 6994		20 58 56
Collinder 427			21 00 36.6
Collinder 427	NGC 7023		21 01 35.8
Collinder 428			21 03.2
Collinder 429			21 01 35.8
Collinder 429	NGC 7023		21 01 35.8
Collinder 430	NGC 7031		21 06 52
Collinder 431	NGC 7039		21 11.2
Collinder 432	IC 1369		21 12 07

Table D.3: Cluster Cross-Reference

Name	Look Under	GX	2000.0 RA
Collinder 433	NGC 7044		21 13 08
Collinder 434	NGC 7062		21 23 27
Collinder 435	NGC 7063		21 24.5
Collinder 436	NGC 7067		21 24 12.3
Collinder 437	NGC 7086		21 30 28
Collinder 438	NGC 7092		21 31 52
Collinder 439	IC 1396		21 39.0
Collinder 440	NGC 7128		21 43 58
Collinder 441	NGC 7129		21 42 59
Collinder 442	NGC 7142		21 45 09
Collinder 443	NGC 7160		21 53 40
Collinder 444	NGC 7209		22 05 08
Collinder 445	IC 1434		22 10.5
Collinder 446	NGC 7226		22 10 26
Collinder 447	NGC 7235		22 12 24
Collinder 448	NGC 7243		22 15 09
Collinder 449	NGC 7245		22 15 16
Collinder 450	NGC 7261		22 20 10
Collinder 451	NGC 7296		22 28 01
Collinder 452	NGC 7380		22 47 21
Collinder 453	NGC 7419		22 54 17
Collinder 454	NGC 7510		23 11 04.2
Collinder 455	NGC 7654		23 24 51
Collinder 456	NGC 7686		23 30 07
Collinder 457	NGC 7762		23 49.9
Collinder 458	Harvard 21		23 54 17.6
Collinder 459	NGC 7788		23 56 44
Collinder 460	NGC 7789		23 57 28.6
Collinder 461	NGC 7790		23 58 24
Collinder 462	NGC 189		00 39 36
Collinder 463			01 45 45
Collinder 464			05 12 39.0
Collinder 465			07 06 52
Collinder 466			07 06 56
Collinder 467	Melotte 72		07 38 29
Collinder 468			18 06 35
Collinder 469			18 16 33.7
Collinder 470			21 53.5
Collinder 471			22 07.1
Coma Berenices	Melotte 111		12 25.1
CPD–69 302	NGC 1743	L	04 54 03.4
CPD–69 330	NGC 1835	L	05 05 06.6
CPD–74 66	Bruck 49	S	00 48 55.7
CSI+16-20591	NGC 7006	g	21 01 29.5
CSI+18-12076	NGC 4147	g	12 10 06.2
CSI+18-19515	NGC 6838	g	19 53 46.1
[CSS95] Cl 1a			06 09 17
[CSS95] Cl 1b			06 09 06
[CSS95] Cl 2			06 08 54
[CSS95] Cl 3			06 09 50
[CSS95] Cl 4a			06 08 41
[CSS95] Cl 4b			06 08 25
CTB 7	IC 1590		00 52 49
CTB 11	IC 1848		02 51 11
CTB 17	IC 410		05 22.0
CTB 23	NGC 2467		07 52 30
CTB 50	NGC 6604		18 18.1
CTB 76	NGC 6823		19 43 10
CTB 105	IC 1396		21 39.0
CV Mon Cluster	Cl vdB 1		06 37 05

Table D.3: Cluster Cross-Reference

Name	Look Under	GX	2000.0 RA
[CV98] 1			08 50 07
[CV98] 2			08 50 30
[CV98] 3			08 51 27
[CV98] 4			08 52 00
[CV98] 5			08 53 01
Czernik 1			00 07 39
Czernik 2			00 43 39
Czernik 3			01 03 07
Czernik 4			01 35 36.4
Czernik 5			01 55 40
Czernik 6			02 02 08
Czernik 7			02 03 01
Czernik 8			02 32 58
Czernik 9			02 33.6
Czernik 10			02 33 55
Czernik 11			02 36 36
Czernik 12			02 39 23
Czernik 13			02 44 27
Czernik 14			03 16 57
Czernik 15			03 23 13
Czernik 16			03 31 02
Czernik 17			03 52 20
Czernik 18			04 27 48
Czernik 19			04 56 56
Czernik 20			05 20 32.5
Czernik 20	NGC 1857		05 20 06
Czernik 21			05 26 40
Czernik 22	Basel 4		05 48 54
Czernik 23			05 50 08
Czernik 24			05 55 26
Czernik 25			06 13 41
Czernik 26			06 30 58
Czernik 27			07 03 19
Czernik 28			07 21.8
Czernik 29			07 28 24
Czernik 30			07 31 11
Czernik 31			07 36 58
Czernik 32			07 50 28
Czernik 33	Leo I		10 08 27.5
Czernik 34	Leo II		11 13 29.3
Czernik 35	Abell 1763		13 35 20.1
Czernik 36	Abell 2141		15 57 42.3
Czernik 37			17 53 16.4
Czernik 38			18 49 47.0
Czernik 39	NGC 6755		19 07 49
Czernik 40			19 42 38
Czernik 41			19 50 50.8
Czernik 42			22 39 35
Czernik 43			23 25.8
Czernik 44			23 33 33
Czernik 45			23 55 44.9
Danks 1			13 12 26.8
Danks 2			13 12 53.8
[DB00] 1			17 46 51.2
[DB00] 2			17 48 01.4
[DB00] 3			17 50 12.4
[DB00] 4			17 47 05.7
[DB00] 5			17 47 07.0
[DB00] 6			17 47 09.6
[DB00] 7			17 50 06.1

Table D.3: Cluster Cross-Reference

Name	Look Under	GX	2000.0 RA
[DB00] 8			17 50 04.7
[DB00] 9			17 56 37.5
[DB00] 10			17 50 17.6
[DB00] 11			17 50 24.1
[DB00] 12			17 50 16.4
[DB00] 13			17 55 20.9
[DB00] 14			17 54 38.9
[DB00] 15			17 51 56.8
[DB00] 16			17 53 58.0
[DB00] 17			17 45 57.7
[DB00] 18			17 42 48.4
[DB00] 19			17 42 40.9
[DB00] 20			17 43 12.4
[DB00] 21			17 43 17.3
[DB00] 22			17 42 58.9
[DB00] 23			17 44 05.2
[DB00] 24			17 55 30.2
[DB00] 25			17 58 54.8
[DB00] 26			17 48 41.5
[DB00] 27			17 54 11.6
[DB00] 28			17 53 28.7
[DB00] 29			17 42 14.1
[DB00] 30			17 56 55.8
[DB00] 31			17 50 49.5
[DB00] 32			17 59 34.6
[DB00] 33			17 45 32.2
[DB00] 34			17 51 07.6
[DB00] 35			17 45 48.6
[DB00] 36			17 45 41.7
[DB00] 37			17 45 38.0
[DB00] 38			17 48 58.7
[DB00] 39			17 55 03.3
[DB00] 40			17 53 15.9
[DB00] 41			17 53 02.8
[DB00] 42			17 50 43.1
[DB00] 43			17 52 07.1
[DB00] 44			17 46 34.9
[DB00] 45			17 47 17.5
[DB00] 46			17 52 44.5
[DB00] 47			17 59 17.5
[DB00] 48			17 58 30.0
[DB00] 49			17 58 34.0
[DB00] 50			17 36 09.9
[DB00] 51			17 49 29.2
[DB00] 52			17 42 28.1
[DB00] 53			17 44 13.4
[DB00] 54			17 44 06.2
[DB00] 55			17 44 24.4
[DB00] 56			17 46 24.2
[DB00] 57			17 50 26.5
[DB00] 58			17 45 00.1
[DB01] 1			17 37 40.7
[DB01] 2			17 39 20.1
[DB01] 3			20 04 52.9
[DB01] 4			20 04 45.4
[DB01] 5			20 21 41.8
[DB01] 6			20 29 36.9
[DB01] 7			20 27 13.0
[DB01] 8			20 31 45.4
[DB01] 9			20 32 27.8

Table D.3: Cluster Cross-Reference

Name	Look Under	GX	2000.0 RA
[DB01] 10			20 32 29.0
[DB01] 11			20 28 09.7
[DB01] 12			20 30 28.0
[DB01] 13			20 39 34.0
[DB01] 14			20 39 33.0
[DB01] 15			20 35 23.0
[DB01] 16			20 38 29.0
[DB01] 17			20 41 15.9
[DB01] 18			20 41 20.1
[DB01] 19			20 38 56.8
[DB01] 20			20 38 37.0
[DB01] 21			20 32 21.8
[DB01] 22			20 42 33.5
[DB01] 23			20 45 37.6
[DB01] 24			05 39 12.5
[DB01] 25			05 52 04.9
[DB01] 26			06 09 28.2
[DB01] 27			06 09 31.0
[DB01] 28			06 09 46.9
[DB01] 29			06 14 45.1
[DB01] 30			06 12 24.9
[DB01] 31			06 12 36.6
[DB01] 32			06 13 28.0
[DB01] 33			06 13 21.2
[DB01] 34			06 13 16.0
[DB01] 35			07 08 39.0
[DB01] 36			08 58 05.0
[DB01] 37			10 45 54.0
[DB01] 38			17 23 23.4
[DB01] 39			17 28 19.1
[DB01] 40			17 30 28.2
[DB01] 41			17 30 24.0
[DB01] 42			17 44 52.7
DDO 74	Leo I		10 08 27.5
DDO 93	Leo II		11 13 29.3
Dejc 1			02 37 28.3
Delta Lyrae cluster	Stephenson 1		18 54 30.6
Djorgovski 1		g	17 47 28.3
Djorgovski 2	ESO 456-SC38	g	18 01 49.1
Djorgovski 3	NGC 6540	g	18 06 08.6
DoDz 1			02 47 27
DoDz 2			05 23.2
DoDz 3			05 33.5
DoDz 4			05 35.9
DoDz 5			16 27.4
DoDz 6			16 45 28.6
DoDz 7			17 11 23
DoDz 8			17 26 24
DoDz 9			18 08.8
DoDz 10			20 05 35
DoDz 11			20 51 04
Dolidze 1			20 08.2
Dolidze 2			20 09.9
Dolidze 3			20 15 27
Dolidze 4			20 17 46.6
Dolidze 5			20 20 29
Dolidze 6			20 20 38.0
Dolidze 7	Berkeley 87		20 21 35
Dolidze 8			20 24.4
Dolidze 9			20 25 33.4

Table D.3: Cluster Cross-Reference

Name	Look Under	GX	2000.0 RA
Dolidze 10			20 26.3
Dolidze 11			20 26 24.7
Dolidze 12			00 40.8
Dolidze 13			00 50.0
Dolidze 14			04 06 41
Dolidze 15			05 04.6
Dolidze 16			05 14.6
Dolidze 17			05 22.4
Dolidze 18			05 24 09
Dolidze 19			05 23.7
Dolidze 20			05 28 33
Dolidze 21			05 27.4
Dolidze 22			06 23.3
Dolidze 23			06 43 05.7
Dolidze 24			06 44 44
Dolidze 25			06 45.0
Dolidze 26			07 30 02
Dolidze 27			16 36.5
Dolidze 28			18 25 30.0
Dolidze 29			18 31.4
Dolidze 30			18 32.9
Dolidze 31			18 34.9
Dolidze 32			18 40.5
Dolidze 33			18 40.7
Dolidze 34			18 42 03.1
Dolidze 35			19 25 24
Dolidze 36			20 02.5
Dolidze 37			20 03.0
Dolidze 38			20 06 04
Dolidze 39			20 16 12
Dolidze 40			20 18.2
Dolidze 41			20 19.2
Dolidze 42			20 19 39.7
Dolidze 43			20 21.7
Dolidze 44			20 29.7
Dolidze 45			21 09.0
Dolidze 46			23 21.9
Dolidze 47			20 41 44.2
Double Cluster			02 20 40.6
Double Cluster	NGC 869		02 19 04
Double Cluster	NGC 884		02 22 05
Dufay 1	Haute Provence 1	g	17 31 05.2
Dunlop 2	NGC 231	S	00 41 06.2
Dunlop 114	NGC 1743	L	04 54 03.4
Dunlop 129	NGC 1910	L	05 18 23.8
Dunlop 213	NGC 1974	L	05 28 00.6
Dunlop 400	NGC 6167		16 34 35
Dunlop 442	NGC 6204		16 46 07.9
Dunlop 562	NGC 1436		03 43 36.9
Dunlop 564	NGC 2818		09 16 10
E	AM 1	g	03 55 02.7
E 1	AM 1	g	03 55 02.7
E 2	ESO 120-8		05 36 21.8
E 3		g	09 20 59.3
[EC95] 1			06 14 37.0
EQ 0001–302	Blanco 1		00 04.2
EQ 0021–723	NGC 104	g	00 24 05.2
EQ 0050–268	NGC 288	g	00 52 45.5
EQ 0100–711	NGC 362	g	01 03 14.3
EQ 0234+209	Dejc 1		02 37 28.3

Table D.3: Cluster Cross-Reference

Name	Look Under	GX	2000.0 RA
EQ 0310–554	NGC 1261	g	03 12 15.3
EQ 0325+794	Palomar 1	g	03 33 20.8
EQ 0422.6–2118	Eridanus	g	04 24 44.5
EQ 0423–21	Eridanus	g	04 24 44.5
EQ 0435–59	Reticulum	L	04 36 11.3
EQ 0443+313	Palomar 2	g	04 46 05.9
EQ 0522–245	NGC 1904	g	05 24 10.6
EQ 0546+336	King 8		05 49 17
EQ 0647–359	NGC 2298	g	06 48 59.2
EQ 0712–1026	NGC 2353		07 14 31
EQ 0734+390	NGC 2419	g	07 38 08.5
EQ 0757–106	NGC 2506		08 00 02
EQ 0911–646	NGC 2808	g	09 12 02.6
EQ 0923–545	vdB-Ha 66		09 25 16
EQ 1003+003	Palomar 3	g	10 05 31.4
EQ 1015–461	NGC 3201	g	10 17 36.8
EQ 1052+407	Shakhbazian 1		10 55 06.0
EQ 1126+292	Palomar 4	g	11 29 16.8
EQ 1207+188	NGC 4147	g	12 10 06.2
EQ 1223–724	NGC 4372	g	12 25 45.4
EQ 1236–264	NGC 4590	g	12 39 28.0
EQ 1256–706	NGC 4833	g	12 59 35.0
EQ 1313+179	NGC 5053	g	13 16 27.0
EQ 1339+286	NGC 5272	g	13 42 11.2
EQ 1343–511	NGC 5286	g	13 46 26.5
EQ 1427–057	NGC 5634	g	14 29 37.3
EQ 1436–263	NGC 5694	g	14 39 36.5
EQ 1452–820	IC 4499	g	15 00 18.5
EQ 1500–328	NGC 5824	g	15 03 58.5
EQ 1513+000	Palomar 5	g	15 16 05.3
EQ 1516+022	NGC 5904	g	15 18 33.8
EQ 1524–505	NGC 5927	g	15 28 00.5
EQ 1531–504	NGC 5946	g	15 35 28.5
EQ 1542–376	NGC 5986	g	15 46 03.5
EQ 1608+150	Palomar 14	g	16 11 00.3
EQ 1614–228	NGC 6093	g	16 17 02.5
EQ 1620–264	NGC 6121	g	16 23 35.5
EQ 1620–720	NGC 6101	g	16 25 48.6
EQ 1624–259	NGC 6144	g	16 27 14.1
EQ 1624–387	NGC 6139	g	16 27 40.4
EQ 1625–352	Terzan 3	g	16 28 40.1
EQ 1629–129	NGC 6171	g	16 32 31.9
EQ 1639+365	NGC 6205	g	16 41 41.5
EQ 1644–018	NGC 6218	g	16 47 14.5
EQ 1645+476	NGC 6229	g	16 46 58.9
EQ 1650–220	NGC 6235	g	16 53 25.4
EQ 1656–370	NGC 6256	g	16 59 32.6
EQ 1657–004	Palomar 15	g	16 59 50.9
EQ 1658–300	NGC 6266	g	17 01 12.6
EQ 1659–262	NGC 6273	g	17 02 37.7
EQ 1702–226	NGC 6287	g	17 05 09.4
EQ 1707–265	NGC 6293	g	17 10 10.4
EQ 1711–294	NGC 6304	g	17 14 32.5
EQ 1713–280	NGC 6316	g	17 16 37.4
EQ 1714–237	NGC 6325	g	17 17 59.2
EQ 1715+432	NGC 6341	g	17 17 07.3
EQ 1716–184	NGC 6333	g	17 19 11.8
EQ 1718–195	NGC 6342	g	17 21 10.2
EQ 1720–177	NGC 6356	g	17 23 35.0
EQ 1720–263	NGC 6355	g	17 23 58.6

Table D.3: Cluster Cross-Reference

Name	Look Under	GX	2000.0 RA
EQ 1721–484	NGC 6352	g	17 25 29.2
EQ 1721–2415	Bica 1		17 24 53.5
EQ 1725–050	NGC 6366	g	17 27 44.3
EQ 1726–670	NGC 6362	g	17 31 54.8
EQ 1727–299	Haute Provence 1	g	17 31 05.2
EQ 1727–315	Terzan 4	g	17 30 38.9
EQ 1730–333	Liller 1	g	17 33 24.5
EQ 1732–447	NGC 6388	g	17 36 17.0
EQ 1733–390	Tonantzintla 2	g	17 36 10.5
EQ 1735–032	NGC 6402	g	17 37 36.1
EQ 1735–238	NGC 6401	g	17 38 36.9
EQ 1736–536	NGC 6397	g	17 40 41.3
EQ 1740–262	Palomar 6	g	17 43 42.2
EQ 1742+031	NGC 6426	g	17 44 54.7
EQ 1748–346	NGC 6453	g	17 50 51.8
EQ 1751–241	UKS 1	g	17 54 27.2
EQ 1755–442	NGC 6496	g	17 59 02.0
EQ 1758–268	Terzan 9	g	18 01 38.8
EQ 1758–278	ESO 456-SC38	g	18 01 49.1
EQ 1759–089	NGC 6517	g	18 01 50.6
EQ 1800–260	Terzan 10	g	18 02 58
EQ 1800–300	NGC 6522	g	18 03 35.0
EQ 1801–003	NGC 6535	g	18 03 50.7
EQ 1801–300	NGC 6528	g	18 04 49.6
EQ 1802–075	NGC 6539	g	18 04 49.8
EQ 1804–250	NGC 6544	g	18 07 20.6
EQ 1804–437	NGC 6541	g	18 08 02.2
EQ 1806–259	NGC 6553	g	18 09 17.3
EQ 1807–317	NGC 6558	g	18 10 17.6
EQ 1808–072	IC 1276	g	18 10 44.2
EQ 1809–227	Terzan 11	g	18 12 15.8
EQ 1810–318	NGC 6569	g	18 13 38.9
EQ 1814–522	NGC 6584	g	18 18 37.7
EQ 1827–255	NGC 6638	g	18 30 56.2
EQ 1828–235	NGC 6642	g	18 31 54.3
EQ 1828–323	NGC 6637	g	18 31 23.2
EQ 1832–330	NGC 6652	g	18 35 45.7
EQ 1833–239	NGC 6656	g	18 36 24.2
EQ 1838–198	Palomar 8	g	18 41 29.9
EQ 1840–323	NGC 6681	g	18 43 12.7
EQ 1851–305	NGC 6715	g	18 55 03.3
EQ 1852–227	NGC 6717	g	18 55 06.2
EQ 1856–367	NGC 6723	g	18 59 33.2
EQ 1902+017	NGC 6749	g	19 05 15.3
EQ 1906–600	NGC 6752	g	19 10 51.8
EQ 1914+300	NGC 6779	g	19 16 35.5
EQ 1914–347	Terzan 7	g	19 17 43.7
EQ 1916+184	Palomar 10	g	19 18 02.1
EQ 1925–304	Arp 2	g	19 28 44.1
EQ 1936–310	NGC 6809	g	19 39 59.4
EQ 1938–341	Terzan 8	g	19 41 45.0
EQ 1942–081	Palomar 11	g	19 45 14.4
EQ 1951+186	NGC 6838	g	19 53 46.1
EQ 2003–220	NGC 6864	g	20 06 04.8
EQ 2031+072	NGC 6934	g	20 34 11.6
EQ 2050–127	NGC 6981	g	20 53 27.9
EQ 2059+160	NGC 7006	g	21 01 29.5
EQ 2130–010	NGC 7089	g	21 33 27.0
EQ 2137–234	NGC 7099	g	21 40 22.0
EQ 2143–214	Palomar 12	g	21 46 38.8

Table D.3: Cluster Cross-Reference

Name	Look Under	GX	2000.0 RA
EQ 2304+124	Palomar 13	g	23 06 44.4
EQ 2305–159	NGC 7492	g	23 08 26.7
Eridanus		g	04 24 44.5
ESO 4-15	NGC 1841	L	04 45 24.2
ESO 28-SC4	AM 3	S	23 48 59.5
ESO 29-SC6	NGC 242	S	00 43 33.9
ESO 29-SC29	NGC 376	S	01 03 53.5
ESO 29-SC39	NGC 460	S	01 14 37.9
ESO 30-6	NGC 796	S	01 56 44.5
ESO 32-19	SL 28	L	04 44 40.8
ESO 33-1	NGC 1777	L	04 55 48.5
ESO 33-19	IC 2134	L	05 23 06.6
ESO 33-26	IC 2146	L	05 37 47.4
ESO 33-31	NGC 2161	L	05 55 42.3
ESO 33-36	NGC 2190	L	06 01 02.3
ESO 34-1	LW 367	L	06 02 14.3
ESO 34-4	NGC 2203	L	06 04 41.6
ESO 54-16	NGC 1466	L	03 44 32.4
ESO 55-SC31	NGC 1649	L	04 38 06.9
ESO 55-SC32	NGC 1652	L	04 38 22.6
ESO 56-G154	[HS66] 356		05 33 59.6
ESO 84-G25	SL 6		04 36 09.5
ESO 85-56	NGC 1868	L	05 14 36.1
ESO 85-63	SL 354	L	05 17 30.9
ESO 85-68	NGC 1900	L	05 19 08.8
ESO 85-72	SL 388	L	05 20 05.5
ESO 85-81	NGC 1942	L	05 24 42.7
ESO 85-SC31	SL 178	L	05 01 44.3
ESO 86-25	SL 670	L	05 43 14.3
ESO 86-28	NGC 2097	L	05 44 15.5
ESO 86-30	SL 701	L	05 45 32.7
ESO 86-32	SL 710	L	05 46 58.1
ESO 86-34	NGC 2120	L	05 50 34.8
ESO 86-38	SL 768	L	05 53 54.5
ESO 86-61	LW 399	L	06 08 15.7
ESO 86-SC9	[H60b] 4	L	05 32 25.4
ESO 87-24	NGC 2257	L	06 30 12.4
ESO 92-18	ESO 92-SC18		10 14 58
ESO 92-SC18			10 14 58
ESO 93-SC8			11 19 42
ESO 96-4	AL 1		13 15 16
ESO 96-SC4	AL 1		13 15 16
ESO 96-SC11	NGC 5120		13 25 39
ESO 008-SC06			14 55.2
ESO 021-SC06			14 15.9
ESO 026-SC02			20 26.6
ESO 043-SC13			17 04.1
ESO 062-SC08			10 21.7
ESO 062-SC11			10 38.9
ESO 064-SC05			12 24.5
ESO 065-SC03			12 51.6
ESO 065-SC07			13 29.3
ESO 085-G087	NGC 1947		05 26 47.5
ESO 092-SC05			10 03.2
ESO 092-SC18	ESO 92-SC18		10 14 58
ESO 093-SC?8	ESO 93-SC8		11 19 42
ESO 097-SC15			14 15.5
ESO 099-SC06			15 29.8
ESO 103-**14			18 20 33
ESO 104-G016	NGC 6684		18 48 57.5

Table D.3: Cluster Cross-Reference

Name	Look Under	GX	2000.0 RA
ESO 118-31	Reticulum	L	04 36 11.3
ESO 119-40	SL 262	L	05 09 21.2
ESO 119-61	LW 195	L	05 22 35.4
ESO 120-8			05 36 21.8
ESO 121-3			06 03 19.7
ESO 123-SC26			07 52.5
ESO 127-SC18	NGC 3247		10 24 01
ESO 127-SC19	Collinder 220		10 25 52
ESO 128-SC16			10 53.7
ESO 129-SC19			11 21.2
ESO 129-SC32			11 44.2
ESO 130-SC13			12 22 49.6
ESO 131-SC09			12 29.6
ESO 132-SC02	NGC 5043		13 16 40
ESO 132-SC14			13 36 31
ESO 132-SC15	IC 4291		13 36 55
ESO 133-?04	NGC 5284		13 47.1
ESO 134-SC12			14 44.8
ESO 137-SC23			16 24.4
ESO 137-SC43			16 48.4
ESO 139-SC13			17 37.7
ESO 139-SC54			18 04.7
ESO 141-SC47			19 18.0
ESO 165-SC09			09 05.2
ESO 166-12	vdB-Ha 66		09 25 16
ESO 166-SC04			09 10.5
ESO 175-SC06			14 18.5
ESO 179-SC1	Harvard 10		16 19.9
ESO 179-SC2	Harvard 10		16 19.9
ESO 201-10	AM 1	g	03 55 02.7
ESO 211-SC01			08 47.2
ESO 211-SC03			08 51.6
ESO 211-SC09			09 16.7
ESO 217-SC8	NGC 3909		11 49 30
ESO 224-8	vdB-Ha 176	g	15 39 07.3
ESO 224-SC8	vdB-Ha 176	g	15 39 07.3
ESO 226-SC5	Pismis 23		16 23 58
ESO 226-SC06			16 24.2
ESO 226-SC06	NGC 6167		16 34 35
ESO 229-SC02			17 59.6
ESO 231-SC30			19 16.9
ESO 236-SC07			21 21.5
ESO 245-SC09			01 53.7
ESO 252-SC14			05 16.0
ESO 258-SC01			07 45.8
ESO 260-SC6			08 46 15
ESO 260-SC7			08 48 00
ESO 260-SC17			09 04.8
ESO 261-SC03			09 11.4
ESO 261-SC07			09 24.3
ESO 265-SC01			11 01.0
ESO 275-SC01			15 55.1
ESO 277-SC04			16 40 33.3
ESO 278-SC02			17 06 06.4
ESO 280-SC06		g	18 09 07
ESO 281-SC24			18 40.0
ESO 282-SC26			19 13.9
ESO 309-SC03			06 50.7
ESO 311-SC14			07 49.4
ESO 311-SC21			08 01.7

Table D.3: Cluster Cross-Reference

Name	Look Under	GX	2000.0 RA
ESO 312-SC03			08 24.5
ESO 312-SC04			08 26.9
ESO 313-SC03			08 31.7
ESO 313-SC11			08 43.7
ESO 313-SC12			08 43.9
ESO 314-SC14			09 19.7
ESO 315-SC14			09 35.4
ESO 324-SC15			13 23.7
ESO 329-SC02			15 27.5
ESO 332-SC8			16 54 43
ESO 332-SC20			17 04.9
ESO 332-SC22			17 07.5
ESO 334-SC02			17 36.9
ESO 335-SC05			18 16 12
ESO 337-SC23			19 19.2
ESO 363-SC05	NGC 1963		05 32 10.8
ESO 367-SC10			07 17.1
ESO 368-SC7	AM 2		07 38 44
ESO 368-SC11			07 44.4
ESO 368-SC14			07 47.0
ESO 370-SC13			08 27.2
ESO 370-SC17			08 31.8
ESO 371-SC25			08 53.0
ESO 383-SC10			13 31.5
ESO 385-SC39	IC 1023		14 32 25
ESO 389-**05			15 57 50.2
ESO 392-SC13			17 26 52
ESO 393-9	Trumpler 27		17 36 12.7
ESO 393-SC12			17 38.7
ESO 393-SC15			17 43 35.2
ESO 397-SC01			19 04.1
ESO 424-SC25			05 49.8
ESO 425-SC06			06 04.8
ESO 425-SC15			06 14.6
ESO 426-SC26			06 36.3
ESO 427-SC32			07 06.2
ESO 429-SC02			07 33.4
ESO 429-SC05			07 37.0
ESO 429-SC13			07 41.1
ESO 430-SC09			08 02.4
ESO 430-SC14			08 03.6
ESO 430-SC18			08 06.9
ESO 432-SC03			08 42.9
ESO 435-SC09			09 55.5
ESO 435-SC17			09 58.8
ESO 435-SC33			10 03.9
ESO 435-SC48			10 09.6
ESO 436-SC02			10 14.0
ESO 437-SC61			10 48.0
ESO 442-SC04			12 34.1
ESO 445-SC74			13 54 38.1
ESO 447-SC29			14 37.4
ESO 452-11	ESO 452-SC11	g	16 39 25
ESO 452-SC11		g	16 39 25
ESO 455-23	Terzan 1	g	17 35 47.0
ESO 456-SC05	AL 2		17 53.0
ESO 456-SC09			17 53.9
ESO 456-SC29			17 58.6
ESO 456-SC38		g	18 01 49.1
ESO 456-SC38	ESO 456-SC38	g	18 01 49.1

Table D.3: Cluster Cross-Reference

Name	Look Under	GX	2000.0 RA
ESO 456-SC72			18 12.5
ESO 461-SC38			20 04.9
ESO 464-SC09			20 59.6
ESO 485-SC20			04 50 04.3
ESO 486-SC45			05 16.7
ESO 486-SC54			05 20.2
ESO 489-SC01			06 05.0
ESO 493-SC03			07 39.7
ESO 494-SC09			07 59.3
ESO 502-SC19			11 08.1
ESO 518-SC03			16 47.1
ESO 520-21	Palomar 6	g	17 43 42.2
ESO 520-SC?20			17 43.6
ESO 521-SC38			18 09.4
ESO 522-SC05			18 12.9
ESO 522-SC16	AL 4		18 19 05.8
ESO 524-SC01			18 56 38.9
ESO 525-SC08			19 27.3
ESO 551-01	Eridanus	g	04 24 44.5
ESO 558-SC8	Auner 1		07 04 15.3
ESO 559-SC02			07 18.1
ESO 559-SC13			07 28.7
ESO 561-SC05			07 59.3
ESO 570-SC12			11 12.2
ESO 587-SC04			17 04 22.3
ESO 589-SC26			18 02.2
ESO 010219–7305.5	NGC 376	S	01 03 53.5
ESO 011316–7332.3	NGC 460	S	01 14 37.9
ESO 053212–6446.2	[H60b] 4	L	05 32 25.4
Espin 6	IC 1310		20 10 01
Eta Carinae cluster	Trumpler 16		10 45 10
Eta Cha cl			08 42.2
[FD70] S34	NGC 1835	L	05 05 06.6
Feinstein 1			11 06.0
Fleming 86	IC 2114	L	04 54 24.7
Fleming 89	IC 2117	L	04 57 14.5
Fleming 90	IC 2126	L	05 21 49.7
Fleming 91	IC 2127		05 21 58.7
[FM80] 1			07 30 12
Fornax 1		F	02 37 02
Fornax 2		F	02 38 44
Fornax 3	NGC 1049	F	02 39 48
Fornax 4		F	02 40 07.7
Fornax 5		F	02 42 21
Fornax 6		F	02 40 06.8
Fornax C4	Fornax 4	F	02 40 07.7
French 1			21 07 22
Frolov 1			23 57 26.5
Frost 790	IC 2948		11 38 58
GAL 000.0+00.0	Central cluster		17 45 40.0
GAL 000.12+00.02	[NHS93] 17		17 45 50.5
GAL 000.121+00.017	[NHS93] 17		17 45 50.5
Galactic center	Central cluster		17 45 40.0
Gamma Vel cl			08 09 32.0
GC 133	NGC 248	S	00 45 24.1
GC 216	NGC 395	S	01 05 11
GC 231	NGC 422	S	01 09 25.4
GC 255	NGC 456	S	01 13 43.9
GC 1002	NGC 1785	L	04 58 45
GC 1104	NGC 1896		05 25 41.9

Table D.3: Cluster Cross-Reference

Name	Look Under	GX	2000.0 RA
GC 1438	NGC 2262		06 39 38.7
GC 2106	NGC 3247		10 24 01
GC 4229	NGC 6204		16 46 07.9
GC 4481	NGC 6774		19 16.3
GCl 4	Dejc 1		02 37 28.3
GCl 75	Palomar 6	g	17 43 42.2
GCl 102	NGC 6684		18 48 57.5
GCRV 7290	NGC 4147	g	12 10 06.2
GCRV 12241	NGC 6838	g	19 53 46.1
GCRV 13202	NGC 7006	g	21 01 29.5
Gingrich	IC 348		03 44 34
GJJC 1	IRAS 18333-2357		18 36 23.1
GLC 0435-59	Reticulum	L	04 36 11.3
GM 1-24	IRAS 17136-3617		17 17 02
Graff 1	IC 4756		18 38.9
Graff clus	IC 4756		18 38.9
Graham	Graham 1		10 56 32
Graham 1			10 56 32
Grasdalen	Grasdalen 1		16 23.8
Grasdalen 1			16 23.8
Gri 1			17 31 58
GRS 279.40_–31.70	NGC 2070	L	05 38 42.4
GT Car cl			10 59 00.6
GUM 11	NGC 2579		08 20 53
GUM 29	NGC 3247		10 24 01
GUM 30	NGC 3293		10 35 49
Gum 68	Antalova 1		17 28.9
GV 534	NGC 1835	L	05 05 06.6
h 22	NGC 110		00 27 25.4
h (147)	NGC 1785	L	04 58 45
h [162]	NGC 422	S	01 09 25.4
h 214	NGC 886		02 23 28.1
h 220	NGC 917		02 26 09
h 338	NGC 1707		04 58 21.1
h 353	NGC 1896		05 25 41.9
h (356)	NGC 1913	L	05 18 19.2
h (374)	NGC 1922	L	05 19 50.0
h 394	NGC 2250		06 33 47
h 400	NGC 2262		06 39 38.7
h 423	NGC 2319		07 00 37
h (456)	NGC 1967	L	05 26 44.6
h (579)	NGC 2033	L	05 34 29.8
h (608)	NGC 2044	L	05 36 06.4
h (642)	NGC 2060	L	05 37 48
h 704	NGC 3231		10 27 29
h 1999	NGC 6573		18 13 50
h 2034	NGC 6774		19 16.3
h 2040	NGC 6795		19 26 05.1
h 2071	NGC 6885		20 12 01
h 2091			20 54 43.1
h 2091	NGC 6991		20 54.9
h 2145	NGC 7193		22 02 59
h 2191			22 55.1
h 2344	NGC 248	S	00 45 24.1
h 2378	NGC 376	S	01 03 53.5
h 2379	NGC 395	S	01 05 11
h 2399	NGC 456	S	01 13 43.9
h 2581	NGC 1436		03 43 36.9
h 2582	NGC 1436		03 43 36.9
h 2656	NGC 1641	L	04 36 06

Table D.3: Cluster Cross-Reference

Name	Look Under	GX	2000.0 RA
h 2685	NGC 1712	L	04 50 57.1
h 2691	NGC 1731	L	04 53 30.4
h 2698	NGC 1737	L	04 53 58.8
h 2699	NGC 1743	L	04 54 03.4
h 2702	NGC 1745	L	04 54 20.9
h 2704	NGC 1748	L	04 54 24.7
h 2710	NGC 1761	L	04 56 34.4
h 2715	NGC 1770	L	04 57 16.8
h 2731	NGC 1787	L	05 00.0
h 2742	NGC 1804	L	05 01 05.1
h 2761	NGC 1828	L	05 04 21.0
h 2762	NGC 1830	L	05 04 39.5
h 2765	NGC 1833	L	05 04 22.3
h 2766	NGC 1836	L	05 05 35.6
h 2767	NGC 1838	L	05 06 34
h 2769	NGC 1837	L	05 04 56
h 2770	NGC 1845	L	05 05 12
h 2770a	SL 232	L	05 06 22.2
h 2775	NGC 1847	L	05 07 08.1
h 2780	NGC 1850	L	05 08 46.7
h 2782	NGC 1854	L	05 09 20.6
h 2783	NGC 1855	L	05 09 20.6
h 2791	NGC 1863	L	05 11 39.8
h 2799	NGC 1870	L	05 13 11.0
h 2808	NGC 1880	L	05 13 39.2
h 2825	NGC 1903	L	05 17 22.8
h 2830	NGC 1914	L	05 17 39.4
h 2837	NGC 1925	L	05 21 31
h 2841	NGC 1932	L	05 22 27.4
h 2841	NGC 1933	L	05 22 17.2
h 2842	NGC 1934	L	05 21 54.0
h 2845	NGC 1937	L	05 22 23.0
h 2855	NGC 1947		05 26 47.5
h 2859	NGC 1950	L	05 24 32.1
h 2861	NGC 1963		05 32 10.8
h 2865	NGC 1959	L	05 25 36.1
h 2866	NGC 1962	L	05 26 19.4
h 2869	NGC 1970	L	05 26 45.3
h 2872	NGC 1969	L	05 26 32.1
h 2875	NGC 1971	L	05 26 45.0
h 2876	NGC 1972	L	05 26 48.1
h 2877	NGC 1974	L	05 28 00.6
h 2884	NGC 1974	L	05 28 00.6
h 2887	NGC 1994	L	05 28 23.3
h 2897	NGC 2009	L	05 30 59.6
h 2901	NGC 2015	L	05 31 48
h 2912	NGC 2028	L	05 33 48.7
h 2922	NGC 2042	L	05 36 09.6
h 2925	NGC 2047	L	05 35 54.2
h 2939	NGC 2066	L	05 37 41.2
h 2947	NGC 2077	L	05 39 34.9
h 2950	NGC 2080	L	05 39 44.6
h 2954	NGC 2085	L	05 40 09.2
h 2981	NGC 2122	L	05 48 55
h 3140	NGC 2669		08 46 19
h 3154	NGC 2818		09 16 10
h 3189	NGC 2995		09 44.1
h 3250	NGC 3247		10 24 01
h 3301	NGC 3446		10 52 17
h 3314	NGC 3519		11 04 03

Table D.3: Cluster Cross-Reference

Name	Look Under	GX	2000.0 RA
h 3496	NGC 5120		13 25 39
h 3635	NGC 6167		16 34 35
h 3644	NGC 6204		16 46 07.9
h 3678	NGC 6334		17 20 58.3
h 3685	NGC 6360		17 25.4
h 3687	NGC 6383		17 34 42.2
h 3689	NGC 6383		17 34 42.2
h 3701'	NGC 6415		17 42 54
h 3702	NGC 6421		17 45 14
h 3706	NGC 6444		17 49.6
h 3712	NGC 6476		17 54 12
h 3722	NGC 6523		18 04 25
h 3725	NGC 6523		18 04 25
h Per			02 16 49
[H32] 3	Bol 307	A	00 39 18.6
[H32] 8	Bol 319	A	00 40 03.2
[H32] 10	Bol 316	A	00 39 53.8
[H32] 11		A	00 40 42.5
[H32] 13		A	00 40 42.0
[H32] 17	Bol 18	A	00 40 49.6
[H32] 20	Bol 40	A	00 41 39.0
[H32] 22	SKHB 99	A	00 41 36.3
[H32] 24	Bol 49	A	00 41 45.8
[H32] 25	Bol 100	A	00 42 29.1
[H32] 28	SKHB 100	A	00 41 37.9
[H32] 31		A	00 41 12.2
[H32] 40	Bol 67	A	00 42 03.4
[H32] 41	Bol 60	A	00 41 57.1
[H32] 45	Bol 70	A	00 42 06.9
[H32] 47	Bol 55	A	00 41 50.5
[H32] 48	Bol 125	A	00 42 42.4
[H32] 51	Bol 41	A	00 41 41.1
[H32] 52	Bol 108	A	00 42 31.3
[H32] 53	Bol 99	A	00 42 27.6
[H32] 54	Bol 13	A	00 40 38.8
[H32] 60	Bol 123	A	00 42 40.9
[H32] 63	Bol 140	A	00 42 58.8
[H32] 68	Bol 80	A	00 42 12.5
[H32] 69	Bol 194	A	00 43 45.3
[H32] 71	Bol 134	A	00 42 51.7
[H32] 72	Bol 157	A	00 43 14.1
[H32] 78	Bol 96	A	00 42 26.2
[H32] 85	Bol 69	A	00 42 05.7
[H32] 96	Bol 222	A	00 44 25.5
[H32] 104	Bol 187	A	00 43 38.8
[H32] 109	Bol 190	A	00 43 43.5
[H32] 110	Bol 203	A	00 43 56.0
[H32] 111	Bol 237	A	00 45 09.5
[H32] 113	Bol 189	A	00 43 42.5
[H32] 122	Bol 371	A	00 45 27.4
[H32] 123	Bol 368	A	00 44 48.1
[H32] 127		A	00 45 45.7
[H32] 128		A	00 44 56.2
[H32] 132	Bol 378	A	00 45 57.4
[H32] 137	Bol 380	A	00 46 06.4
[H32] 138	Bol 392	A	00 47 00.8
[H32] 139	Bol 97	A	00 42 27.5
[H32] V	Bol 324	A	00 40 20.8
[H60b] 1		L	05 16.0
[H60b] 2		L	05 17.9

Table D.3: Cluster Cross-Reference

Name	Look Under	GX	2000.0 RA
[H60b] 3		L	05 29.2
[H60b] 4		L	05 32 25.4
[H60b] 5		L	05 39 56.7
[H60b] 6		L	05 42 27.4
[H60b] 7		L	05 50 03.2
[H60b] 8		L	05 54.0
[H60b] 9		L	05 56 01.3
[H60b] 10		L	05 57.7
[H60b] 11		L	06 14 23.4
[H60b] 14		L	05 28 38.6
[H81]B- 451	NBol 97	A	00 42 55.8
[H85] 2	NGC 220	S	00 40 30.6
[H85] 2	NGC 222	S	00 40 44.1
[H85] 2	NGC 231	S	00 41 06.2
[H85] 62	NGC 460	S	01 14 37.9
[H86] 35		S	00 36 38.4
[H86] 55		S	00 39 25.6
[H86] 60		S	00 40 44.3
[H86] 62		S	00 40 47.6
[H86] 64		S	00 40 59.2
[H86] 70		S	00 43 44.4
[H86] 74		S	00 45 13.9
[H86] 76		S	00 46 01.7
[H86] 78		S	00 46 12.3
[H86] 80		S	00 46 11.2
[H86] 83		S	00 46 33.7
[H86] 84		S	00 46 34.1
[H86] 85		S	00 46 56.3
[H86] 86		S	00 47 01.2
[H86] 89		S	00 47 03.7
[H86] 93		S	00 47 24.4
[H86] 97		S	00 47 52.4
[H86] 98		S	00 47 54.3
[H86] 99		S	00 48 13.2
[H86] 100		S	00 48 20.2
[H86] 103		S	00 49 04.8
[H86] 104		S	00 49 12.2
[H86] 107		S	00 50 00.3
[H86] 109		S	00 49 45.5
[H86] 112		S	00 50 07.5
[H86] 115		S	00 50 36.9
[H86] 116		S	00 50 39.6
[H86] 116	Lindsay 40	S	00 50 38.5
[H86] 121		S	00 51 21.4
[H86] 123		S	00 51 44.4
[H86] 124		S	00 51 31.3
[H86] 125		S	00 52 16.8
[H86] 126		S	00 51 54.3
[H86] 127		S	00 51 48.8
[H86] 129		S	00 52 12.5
[H86] 130		S	00 52 16.6
[H86] 132		S	00 52 31.5
[H86] 133		S	00 52 33.7
[H86] 134		S	00 52 48.3
[H86] 135		S	00 52 48.2
[H86] 138		S	00 53 09.6
[H86] 140		S	00 53 40.1
[H86] 143		S	00 53 31.3
[H86] 147		S	00 53 50.2
[H86] 152		S	00 54 22.8

Table D.3: Cluster Cross-Reference

Name	Look Under	GX	2000.0 RA
[H86] 155		S	00 55 11.7
[H86] 158		S	00 55 08.6
[H86] 159		S	00 55 12.1
[H86] 165		S	00 55 43.0
[H86] 172		S	00 56 34.5
[H86] 174		S	00 57 17.8
[H86] 175		S	00 57 50.3
[H86] 177		S	00 57 49.8
[H86] 178		S	00 57 46.2
[H86] 179		S	00 57 57.2
[H86] 181		S	00 58 19.4
[H86] 183		S	00 58 33.7
[H86] 186		S	00 59 56.9
[H86] 188		S	01 00 13.1
[H86] 189		S	01 00 33.1
[H86] 191		S	01 00 58.2
[H86] 192	Lindsay 65	S	01 01 02.0
[H86] 193		S	01 01 17.8
Haffner 1	Tombaugh 1		07 00 27
Haffner 2	Tombaugh 2		07 03 06
Haffner 3			07 04 08
Haffner 4			07 06 04
Haffner 5			07 18.1
Haffner 6			07 20 01
Haffner 7			07 22 54
Haffner 8			07 23 03
Haffner 9			07 24 42
Haffner 10			07 28 36
Haffner 11			07 35 22
Haffner 12	NGC 2425		07 38 18
Haffner 13			07 40 26
Haffner 14			07 44 48
Haffner 15			07 45 30
Haffner 16			07 50 21
Haffner 17			07 51 36
Haffner 18			07 52 44
Haffner 18	Haffner 18a		07 52 38.2
Haffner 18	Haffner 18ab		07 52 39
Haffner 18	Haffner 18b		07 52 43
Haffner 18	Haffner 18c		07 52 48
Haffner 18a			07 52 38.2
Haffner 18a	Haffner 18		07 52 44
Haffner 18a	Haffner 18ab		07 52 39
Haffner 18ab			07 52 39
Haffner 18ab	Haffner 18		07 52 44
Haffner 18b			07 52 43
Haffner 18b	Haffner 18		07 52 44
Haffner 18b	Haffner 18ab		07 52 39
Haffner 18c			07 52 48
Haffner 18c	Haffner 18		07 52 44
Haffner 19			07 52 46
Haffner 20			07 56 15
Haffner 21			08 01 11
Haffner 22			08 12.6
Haffner 23			07 09.5
Haffner 24			07 28.8
Haffner 25			07 48 40
Haffner 26			08 15.4
Harvard 1	Trumpler 3		03 12 00
Harvard 2	Trumpler 9		07 55 40

Table D.3: Cluster Cross-Reference

Name	Look Under	GX	2000.0 RA
Harvard 3			08 46.5
Harvard 4	NGC 3330		10 38 48
Harvard 5			12 27 16.3
Harvard 6			12 37 54
Harvard 7	Trumpler 20		12 39 32
Harvard 8			13 18 12
Harvard 9			15 33.8
Harvard 10			16 19.9
Harvard 11	NGC 6167		16 34 35
Harvard 12	Trumpler 24		16 57.0
Harvard 13			17 03 57
Harvard 14	Trumpler 25		17 24 30.3
Harvard 15	Trumpler 26		17 28 29.9
Harvard 16			17 31 03
Harvard 17	Trumpler 29		17 41 36.4
Harvard 18	Trumpler 30		17 56.4
Harvard 19	Trumpler 32		18 17 10.4
Harvard 20			19 53 10.3
Harvard 21			23 54 17.6
Haute Provence 1		g	17 31 05.2
Haute Provence 2	Terzan 1	g	17 35 47.0
Haute Provence 3	Terzan 2	g	17 27 33.4
Haute Provence 4	Terzan 4	g	17 30 38.9
Haute Provence 5	Terzan 6	g	17 50 46.4
Havlen-Moffat	Havlen-Moffat 1		17 19 00.5
Havlen-Moffat 1			17 19 00.5
[HB90] 1		S	00 43 37.6
[HB90] 1	NGC 242	S	00 43 33.9
HBK 0-1	[ME53] II	A	00 32 46.9
[HC69] 44	NGC 6823		19 43 10
HD 4852	Bruck 49	S	00 48 55.7
HD 31947	NGC 1743	L	04 54 03.4
HD 269016	NGC 1835	L	05 05 06.6
HD 271203	NGC 1932	L	05 22 27.4
HEAO 0346+24	Pleiades		03 47 29
Henize N 4	NGC 1731	L	04 53 30.4
Henize N 57	NGC 2014	L	05 32 21.7
Henize N 59B	NGC 2040	L	05 36 06.1
Henize N 61	LH 83	L	05 35.8
Henize N 74	LH 116	L	05 45.0
Henize N 75B	LH 122	L	05 55 55
Henize N 83		L	04 54.2
Henize N 83	Henize N 83	L	04 54.2
Henize N 83	Henize N 83A	L	04 54 03.4
Henize N 83	Henize N 83B	L	04 53 58.8
Henize N 83	Henize N 83D	L	04 54 10
Henize N 83	IC 2114	L	04 54 24.7
Henize N 83	LH 5	L	04 54.2
Henize N 83A		L	04 54 03.4
Henize N 83A	NGC 1743	L	04 54 03.4
Henize N 83B		L	04 53 58.8
Henize N 83B	NGC 1737	L	04 53 58.8
Henize N 83C	IC 2114	L	04 54 24.7
Henize N 83D		L	04 54 10
Henize N 84A	NGC 460	S	01 14 37.9
Henize N 160A	NGC 2080	L	05 39 44.6
Henize N 190	NGC 1833	L	05 04 22.3
Henize N 199	LH 50	L	05 23.7
Henize N 200	LH 50	L	05 23.7
Herbig-Haro 7	[LAL96] 1		03 28.9
Herbig-Haro 8	[LAL96] 1		03 28.9
Herbig-Haro 9	[LAL96] 1		03 28.9
Herbig-Haro 10	[LAL96] 1		03 28.9
Herbig-Haro 11	[LAL96] 1		03 28.9
Herbig-Haro 12	[LAL96] 2		03 29.2
Herschel's Jewel Box	NGC 4755		12 53 38
Hodge 88 159		L	05 08 46.8
Hodge 88 266		L	05 18 09.5
Hodge 88 267		L	05 18 15.2
Hogg 1			09 40 33
Hogg 2			09 51.5
Hogg 3			09 57 40
Hogg 4			09 57 53
Hogg 5			10 06 09
Hogg 6			10 06 28
Hogg 7			10 29.1
Hogg 8			10 29 09
Hogg 9			10 58 22
Hogg 10			11 10 42.1
Hogg 10	Collinder 240		11 11 40.2
Hogg 11			11 11 32.6
Hogg 11	Collinder 240		11 11 40.2
Hogg 12			11 12 15
Hogg 13			11 16.3
Hogg 14			12 28 39
Hogg 15			12 43 36
Hogg 16			13 29 11
Hogg 17			14 33 50.4
Hogg 18			14 50 41.4
Hogg 19			16 28 51.7
Hogg 20			16 44.4
Hogg 21			16 45 36.9
Hogg 22			16 46 35
Hogg 23			12 28 31.6
[HR91] 1			20 27 24
[HS66] 8		L	04 30 38.1
[HS66] 13		L	04 35 27.8
[HS66] 23		L	04 42 54.1
[HS66] 24	SL 23	L	04 43 38.0
[HS66] 26		L	04 46 04.6
[HS66] 27		L	04 47 27.8
[HS66] 28		L	04 48 04.2
[HS66] 30		L	04 48 27.4
[HS66] 31		L	04 48 56.2
[HS66] 32		L	04 48 41.1
[HS66] 33		L	04 49 16.5
[HS66] 35		L	04 49 33.7
[HS66] 36		L	04 49 33.6
[HS66] 37		L	04 50 28.2
[HS66] 38		L	04 51 11.4
[HS66] 39		L	04 51 03.6
[HS66] 40		L	04 51 11.9
[HS66] 41		L	04 51 31.1
[HS66] 43		L	04 51 40.6
[HS66] 44		L	04 51 37.7
[HS66] 46		L	04 52 19.1
[HS66] 48		L	04 52 08.4
[HS66] 50		L	04 52 45.9
[HS66] 51		L	04 52 44.9
[HS66] 51	NGC 1731	L	04 53 30.4
[HS66] 52		L	04 52 43.0
[HS66] 56		L	04 53 37.4
[HS66] 58		L	04 54 13.3
[HS66] 59		L	04 54 37.2
[HS66] 60		L	04 54 44.1
[HS66] 61		L	04 55 11.3
[HS66] 62		L	04 54 54
[HS66] 63		L	04 55 01.0
[HS66] 64		L	04 55 13.4
[HS66] 65		L	04 55 30.5
[HS66] 66		L	04 55 21.0
[HS66] 67		L	04 55 27.7
[HS66] 68		L	04 56 06.5
[HS66] 70		L	04 56 07.3
[HS66] 72		L	04 56 54.1
[HS66] 73		L	04 57 06.1
[HS66] 74		L	04 57 11.6
[HS66] 75		L	04 56 49.8
[HS66] 76		L	04 58 09.9
[HS66] 77		L	04 58 28.8
[HS66] 78		L	04 59 35.2
[HS66] 80		L	04 59 49.0
[HS66] 81		L	04 59 59.1
[HS66] 82		L	04 59 52.4
[HS66] 83		L	05 00 26.1
[HS66] 84		L	05 00 52.0
[HS66] 84	NGC 1787	L	05 00.0
[HS66] 85		L	05 00 50.7
[HS66] 86		L	05 01 01.7
[HS66] 88		L	05 01 04.1
[HS66] 90		L	05 00 57.4
[HS66] 91		L	05 01 42.5
[HS66] 92		L	05 02 18.4
[HS66] 93		L	05 02 30.2
[HS66] 94		L	05 02 29.1
[HS66] 96		L	05 03 22.8
[HS66] 98		L	05 03 28.3
[HS66] 99		L	05 03 14.1
[HS66] 100		L	05 03 25.8
[HS66] 101		L	05 03 27.7
[HS66] 103		L	05 03 58.5
[HS66] 104		L	05 04 02.6
[HS66] 104	LH 24	L	05 05 09
[HS66] 104	NGC 1845	L	05 05 12
[HS66] 105		L	05 04 43.4
[HS66] 106		L	05 04 55.6
[HS66] 108		L	05 05 49.3
[HS66] 110		L	05 05 51.0
[HS66] 113		L	05 05 54.8
[HS66] 114		L	05 06 02.7
[HS66] 115		L	05 05 53.6
[HS66] 116		L	05 06 12.5
[HS66] 120		L	05 07 01.9
[HS66] 121		L	05 07 46.5
[HS66] 124		L	05 08 18.0
[HS66] 125		L	05 08 25.7
[HS66] 129		L	05 09 03.7
[HS66] 130		L	05 09 15.5
[HS66] 132		L	05 09 28.7
[HS66] 135		L	05 09 58.3

Table D.3: Cluster Cross-Reference

Name	Look Under	GX	2000.0 RA
[HS66] 137		L	05 09 43.3
[HS66] 138		L	05 09 57.3
[HS66] 139		L	05 09 45.3
[HS66] 140		L	05 09 40.5
[HS66] 143		L	05 10 12.0
[HS66] 144		L	05 09 57
[HS66] 148		L	05 09 48.5
[HS66] 149		L	05 10 36.3
[HS66] 153		L	05 10 30
[HS66] 154		L	05 10 56.8
[HS66] 156		L	05 11 10.8
[HS66] 157		L	05 11 05.5
[HS66] 162		L	05 12 06.2
[HS66] 164		L	05 12 27.3
[HS66] 168		L	05 12 35.0
[HS66] 173		L	05 12 52.6
[HS66] 178		L	05 13 48.4
[HS66] 184		L	05 14 10.2
[HS66] 185		L	05 14 47.4
[HS66] 186		L	05 14 49.0
[HS66] 187		L	05 14 45.8
[HS66] 193		L	05 15 21.6
[HS66] 194		L	05 15 37.8
[HS66] 195		L	05 15 06.9
[HS66] 196		L	05 15 42.4
[HS66] 199		L	05 15 30.9
[HS66] 202		L	05 16 03.8
[HS66] 206		L	05 17 11.6
[HS66] 207		L	05 17 17.5
[HS66] 208		L	05 17 30.9
[HS66] 210		L	05 17 22.5
[HS66] 212		L	05 18 02.1
[HS66] 214		L	05 17 49.4
[HS66] 215		L	05 18 18.0
[HS66] 217		L	05 18 40.1
[HS66] 223	LH 42	L	05 19 17.5
[HS66] 224		L	05 19 14.9
[HS66] 225		L	05 19 23.4
[HS66] 226		L	05 19 23.4
[HS66] 229		L	05 19 42.7
[HS66] 230		L	05 19 53.5
[HS66] 231		L	05 19 55.0
[HS66] 232		L	05 20 36.8
[HS66] 233		L	05 20 09.4
[HS66] 234		L	05 20 09.7
[HS66] 235		L	05 20 03.5
[HS66] 236		L	05 20 15.7
[HS66] 237		L	05 20 30.7
[HS66] 239		L	05 19 22
[HS66] 240		L	05 21 00.7
[HS66] 254		L	05 22 33.8
[HS66] 255		L	05 22 26
[HS66] 256		L	05 22 36
[HS66] 258		L	05 23 10.6
[HS66] 260		L	05 23 13.7
[HS66] 262		L	05 22 57.1
[HS66] 264		L	05 23 11.8
[HS66] 267		L	05 23 19.8
[HS66] 269		L	05 24 07.0
[HS66] 270		L	05 23 52.1

Table D.3: Cluster Cross-Reference

Name	Look Under	GX	2000.0 RA
[HS66] 272		L	05 24 12.6
[HS66] 274		L	05 24 06.2
[HS66] 277		L	05 24 48.5
[HS66] 284		L	05 25 24.2
[HS66] 287		L	05 26 00.7
[HS66] 288		L	05 26 01.3
[HS66] 289		L	05 26 07.7
[HS66] 294		L	05 26 23.2
[HS66] 299		L	05 26 38.2
[HS66] 299	LH 55	L	05 26.4
[HS66] 301A		L	05 26 39.4
[HS66] 302		L	05 27 09.7
[HS66] 303		L	05 27 22.6
[HS66] 304		L	05 27 15.5
[HS66] 305		L	05 27 54.0
[HS66] 307		L	05 27 38.0
[HS66] 309		L	05 28 17.4
[HS66] 311		L	05 28 01.0
[HS66] 313		L	05 28 25.4
[HS66] 314		L	05 28 26.5
[HS66] 315		L	05 28 17.8
[HS66] 317		L	05 29 01.9
[HS66] 318		L	05 28 44.2
[HS66] 319		L	05 28 47
[HS66] 322		L	05 29 20.9
[HS66] 324		L	05 28 56.0
[HS66] 325		L	05 29 36.6
[HS66] 326		L	05 29 39.2
[HS66] 329		L	05 29 46.3
[HS66] 330		L	05 29 57.6
[HS66] 333	LH 67	L	05 31 09
[HS66] 334		L	05 31 02.1
[HS66] 337		L	05 31 40.1
[HS66] 338		L	05 31 45.3
[HS66] 341		L	05 31 59.8
[HS66] 342		L	05 31 45
[HS66] 343		L	05 32 07.0
[HS66] 345		L	05 31 50
[HS66] 348		L	05 32 15.5
[HS66] 354		L	05 34 03.9
[HS66] 355		L	05 33 47.0
[HS66] 356			05 33 59.6
[HS66] 357		L	05 34 30.9
[HS66] 358		L	05 34 35.2
[HS66] 360		L	05 34 33.5
[HS66] 361		L	05 34 56.5
[HS66] 363		L	05 35 29.1
[HS66] 365		L	05 36 21.6
[HS66] 366		L	05 37 04.7
[HS66] 367		L	05 37 03.8
[HS66] 368		L	05 37 14.1
[HS66] 370		L	05 36 46
[HS66] 370	LH 96	L	05 37.0
[HS66] 370	NGC 2055	L	05 37 08
[HS66] 371		L	05 37 45
[HS66] 371	LH 97	L	05 37.6
[HS66] 372		L	05 37 46.4
[HS66] 373		L	05 38 16.8
[HS66] 374		L	05 38 17.6
[HS66] 375		L	05 38 14.5

Table D.3: Cluster Cross-Reference

Name	Look Under	GX	2000.0 RA
[HS66] 376		L	05 38 49.3
[HS66] 377		L	05 39 20.7
[HS66] 378		L	05 39 13.7
[HS66] 379		L	05 38 55.5
[HS66] 380		L	05 40 02.0
[HS66] 381		L	05 39 43.7
[HS66] 382		L	05 40 36.1
[HS66] 383		L	05 40 14.2
[HS66] 385		L	05 40 47.5
[HS66] 386		L	05 40 57.4
[HS66] 387		L	05 41 08.3
[HS66] 390		L	05 41 30.6
[HS66] 391		L	05 41 28.8
[HS66] 393		L	05 41 57.2
[HS66] 395		L	05 42 03.5
[HS66] 396		L	05 42 28.2
[HS66] 397		L	05 42 17.3
[HS66] 397A		L	05 42 42.0
[HS66] 398		L	05 42 42.0
[HS66] 399		L	05 43 06.1
[HS66] 400		L	05 43 06.5
[HS66] 401		L	05 43 07.6
[HS66] 402		L	05 44 07.5
[HS66] 403		L	05 43 59.9
[HS66] 404		L	05 44 24.2
[HS66] 404	LH 116	L	05 45.0
[HS66] 405		L	05 44 12.7
[HS66] 406		L	05 44 46.1
[HS66] 407		L	05 44 44.7
[HS66] 408		L	05 45 06.8
[HS66] 409		L	05 44 56.4
[HS66] 410		L	05 45 31.0
[HS66] 411		L	05 45 50.0
[HS66] 412		L	05 45 56.4
[HS66] 413		L	05 46 22.3
[HS66] 414		L	05 46 41.0
[HS66] 415		L	05 47 00.1
[HS66] 416		L	05 47 01.9
[HS66] 417		L	05 47 10.2
[HS66] 419		L	05 48 19.7
[HS66] 420		L	05 48 28.9
[HS66] 421		L	05 48 56.2
[HS66] 422		L	05 49 14.2
[HS66] 423	LH 118	L	05 49.8
[HS66] 424		L	05 49 35.9
[HS66] 425		L	05 50 02.1
[HS66] 426		L	05 50 25.2
[HS66] 427		L	05 50 17.6
[HS66] 428		L	05 50 50.3
[HS66] 429		L	05 50 52.6
[HS66] 430		L	05 50 48.4
[HS66] 431		L	05 51 12.1
[HS66] 432		L	05 51 03.5
[HS66] 433		L	05 51 47.3
[HS66] 434		L	05 51 36.6
[HS66] 435		L	05 51 35.9
[HS66] 436		L	05 51 47.8
[HS66] 437		L	05 52 15.5
[HS66] 438		L	05 51 53.1
[HS66] 439		L	05 52 07.1

Table D.3: Cluster Cross-Reference

Name	Look Under	GX	2000.0 RA
[HS66] 440		L	05 52 35.7
[HS66] 441		L	05 52 37.8
[HS66] 442		L	05 53 04.6
[HS66] 443		L	05 52 53.5
[HS66] 444		L	05 53 39.5
[HS66] 445		L	05 53 50.2
[HS66] 446		L	05 54 38.5
[HS66] 447		L	05 54 58.5
[HS66] 448		L	05 54 54.0
[HS66] 450		L	06 03 20.5
HW 1		S	00 18 25.7
HW 2		S	00 28 01.1
HW 3		S	00 29 54.9
HW 4		S	00 30 32.3
HW 5		S	00 31 02.5
HW 6		S	00 33 10.5
HW 7		S	00 33 37.3
HW 8		S	00 33 46.5
HW 9		S	00 36 31.3
HW 10		S	00 36 31.9
HW 11		S	00 37 33.1
HW 12		S	00 38 51.3
HW 13		S	00 39 30.4
HW 14		S	00 40 15.3
HW 15		S	00 40 47.6
HW 16		S	00 42 22.4
HW 17		S	00 42 17.7
HW 18		S	00 42 59.5
HW 19		S	00 43 28.3
HW 20		S	00 44 48.1
HW 21		S	00 45 39.6
HW 22		S	00 46 44.5
HW 23		S	00 46 42.1
HW 24		S	00 47 29.3
HW 25		S	00 48 44.5
HW 26		S	00 49 42.3
HW 27		S	00 50 32.8
HW 28		S	00 50 40.2
HW 29		S	00 53 49.4
HW 30		S	00 54 28.3
HW 31		S	00 55 33.9
HW 32		S	00 57 20.8
HW 33		S	00 57 23.6
HW 34		S	00 57 52.1
HW 35		S	00 58 42.4
HW 36		S	00 59 03.7
HW 37		S	00 59 15.4
HW 38		S	00 59 26.1
HW 39		S	00 59 30.9
HW 40		S	01 00 25.6
HW 41		S	01 00 35.8
HW 42		S	01 01 08.7
HW 43		S	01 01 08.2
HW 44		S	01 01 22.5
HW 45		S	01 03 49.2
HW 46		S	01 03 59.7
HW 47		S	01 04 04.4
HW 48		S	01 04 58.8
HW 49		S	01 05 56.9
HW 50		S	01 06 03.5
HW 51		S	01 06 18.3
HW 52		S	01 06 57.3
HW 53		S	01 06 59.0
HW 54		S	01 07 16.0
HW 55		S	01 07 20.0
HW 56		S	01 07 42.1
HW 57		S	01 07 44.0
HW 58		S	01 08 05.6
HW 59		S	01 08 53.9
HW 60			01 09 27.6
HW 61		S	01 09 42.8
HW 62		S	01 09 39.1
HW 63		S	01 10 12.7
HW 64		S	01 10 45.5
HW 65		S	01 11 58.5
HW 66		S	01 12 04.8
HW 67		S	01 13 01.9
HW 68		S	01 13 52.6
HW 69		S	01 14 16.3
HW 70		S	01 14 56.1
HW 71		S	01 15 32.7
HW 72		S	01 15 41.9
HW 73		S	01 16 25.0
HW 74		S	01 16 48.3
HW 75		S	01 17 29.7
HW 76		S	01 17 35.1
HW 77		S	01 20.0
HW 78		S	01 21 20.9
HW 79		S	01 22 45.0
HW 80		S	01 23 26.3
HW 81		S	01 24 10.3
HW 82		S	01 24 28.1
HW 83		S	01 38 36.8
HW 84		S	01 41 41.4
HW 85		S	01 42 28.1
HW 86		S	01 42 22.2
Hyades			04 26.9
IC 166			01 52 22
IC 348			03 44 34
IC 361			04 18 51
IC 410			05 22.0
IC 410	NGC 1893		05 22 46
IC 417	Stock 8		05 28 07
IC 444	Collinder 89		06 18.0
IC 1023			14 32 25
IC 1257		g	17 27 08
IC 1276		g	18 10 44.2
IC 1283	Collinder 371		18 17 16
IC 1284	Collinder 371		18 17 16
IC 1310			20 10 01
IC 1311			20 10 47
IC 1369			21 12 07
IC 1396			21 39.0
IC 1434			22 10.5
IC 1442			22 15 59
IC 1590			00 52 49
IC 1611		S	00 59 48.1
IC 1612		S	01 00 01.4
IC 1624		S	01 05 21.5
IC 1626		S	01 06 13.8
IC 1655		S	01 11 54.4
IC 1660		S	01 12 38.4
IC 1662		S	01 12 33.4
IC 1805			02 32 42
IC 1848			02 51 11
IC 2091			04 46 40.1
IC 2107	NGC 1707		04 58 21.1
IC 2111		L	04 51 53.0
IC 2111	KMHK 173	L	04 51 53.0
IC 2111	NGC 1722	L	04 51 51.5
IC 2114		L	04 54 24.7
IC 2114	NGC 1748	L	04 54 24.7
IC 2117		L	04 57 14.5
IC 2126		L	05 21 49.7
IC 2127			05 21 58.7
IC 2134		L	05 23 06.6
IC 2140		L	05 33 22.2
IC 2145		L	05 40 24
IC 2146		L	05 37 47.4
IC 2148		L	05 39 12.1
IC 2156			06 04 50.6
IC 2157			06 04 49.8
IC 2161		L	05 57 25.5
IC 2391			08 40.3
IC 2395			08 42 31
IC 2488			09 27 27
IC 2581			10 27 27
IC 2602			10 42 57
IC 2714			11 17 18
IC 2944	Collinder 249		11 38 20.4
IC 2948			11 38 58
IC 4291			13 36 55
IC 4499		g	15 00 18.5
IC 4651			17 24.7
IC 4665			17 46.2
IC 4715			18 17
IC 4725			18 31 45
IC 4756			18 38.9
IC 4802			18 55 07.1
IC 4802	NGC 6717	g	18 55 06.2
IC 4954	Roslund 4		20 04 52
IC 4955	Roslund 4		20 04 52
IC 4996			20 16 31.7
IC 5076	NGC 6991		20 54.9
IC 5146	Collinder 470		21 53.5
II Zw 4	Dejc 1		02 37 28.3
III Zw 50	Dejc 1		02 37 28.3
IRAS 00302+6134	King 15		00 33 07
IRAS 00551+6812	Skiff J0058.4+6828		00 58 24
IRAS 01241−7332	Lindsay 103	S	01 25 48
IRAS 01259+6301	NGC 559		01 29 33
IRAS 03304+5114	NGC 1348		03 34 09
IRAS 04287+4344	NGC 1582		04 31 39
IRAS 04429+4437	Ruprecht 148		04 46 35
IRAS 05090−6849	NGC 1850	L	05 08 46.7
IRAS 05264−6347	NGC 1947		05 26 47.5
IRAS 05281+3412	NGC 1931		05 31 26
IRAS 05463+2853	Czernik 23		05 50 08
IRAS 06056+2131	[CSS95] Cl 4a		06 08 41
IRAS 06056+2131	[CSS95] Cl 4b		06 08 25

Table D.3: Cluster Cross-Reference

Name	Look Under	GX	2000.0 RA
IRAS 06057+1358	NGC 2169		06 08 25
IRAS 06058+2138	[CSS95] Cl 2		06 08 54
IRAS 06061+2151	[CSS95] Cl 1a		06 09 17
IRAS 06061+2151	[CSS95] Cl 1b		06 09 06
IRAS 06067+2138	[CSS95] Cl 3		06 09 50
IRAS 06108+1248	NGC 2194		06 13 46
IRAS 06204+0442	Dolidze 22		06 23.3
IRAS 06323+0527	NGC 2252		06 34 19.8
IRAS 06346+0600	Collinder 106		06 37.1
IRAS 06351–0055	Berkeley 24		06 37 47
IRAS 07020–1939	Auner 1		07 04 15.3
IRAS 07051–2042	Ruprecht 11		07 07 23
IRAS 07139+1351	NGC 2355		07 17 00
IRAS 07174–1935	Ruprecht 15		07 19 34
IRAS 07176–1304	Haffner 6		07 20 01
IRAS 07213–2307	Ruprecht 17		07 23 35
IRAS 07349–1159	Melotte 71		07 37 30
IRAS 07429–2523	Ruprecht 32		07 45 06
IRAS 07495–3142	Haffner 17		07 51 36
IRAS 07498–2220	Ruprecht 39		07 52 20
IRAS 07525–3809	Ruprecht 152		07 54 29
IRAS 08031–3151	Ruprecht 52		08 05.0
IRAS 08164–3029	NGC 2567		08 18 30
IRAS 08387–3752	Ruprecht 66		08 40 32
IRAS 08599–5041	Ruprecht 73		09 01 12
IRAS 09089–5605	vdB-Ha 58		09 10 28
IRAS 09183–4902	vdB-Ha 63		09 20 38
IRAS 09386–5006	NGC 2972		09 40 12
IRAS 09433–4354	Ruprecht 81		09 45 13
IRAS 09473–5420	Ruprecht 83		09 49 15
IRAS 10172–5609	vdB-Ha 92		10 19 04
IRAS 11038–5932	Feinstein 1		11 06.0
IRAS 12242–6350	vdB-Ha 132		12 26 58
IRAS 12498–6654	vdB-Ha 140		12 53.5
IRAS 13342–6307	vdB-Ha 150		13 38 02
IRAS 13417–6148	Loden 991		13 45.4
IRAS 13500–5928	Loden 1095		13 53.5
IRAS 13503–5929	Loden 1095		13 53.5
IRAS 13544–6132	Loden 1101		13 58 40.6
IRAS 13569–6156	Lynga 1		14 00 02
IRAS 14119–5855	Loden 1282		14 15.9
IRAS 14147–5841	Ruprecht 167		14 18.2
IRAS 14149–6112	Loden 1256		14 18.2
IRAS 14295–6111	Hogg 17		14 33 50.4
IRAS 15020–5525	NGC 5823		15 05 26
IRAS 15236–5421	NGC 5925		15 27.7
IRAS 15519–5718	NGC 6005		15 55 47.4
IRAS 16039–5355	NGC 6031		16 07 34.4
IRAS 16465–4408	vdB-Ha 200		16 50.0
IRAS 16513–4515	Lynga 14		16 55 05
IRAS 16545–4750	NGC 6250		16 57 55
IRAS 16592–3940	NGC 6268		17 02 04.1
IRAS 17015–4808	Harvard 13		17 03 57
IRAS 17126–3922	NGC 6318		17 16 13.4
IRAS 17136–3617			17 17 02
IRAS 17141–4256	NGC 6322		17 18.5
IRAS 17261–4030	Ruprecht 125		17 29.7
IRAS 17298–3329	Liller 1	g	17 33 24.5
IRAS 17301–2917			17 33 21.9
IRAS 17302–2919	IRAS 17301-2917		17 33 21.9

Table D.3: Cluster Cross-Reference

Name	Look Under	GX	2000.0 RA
IRAS 17302–3327	Liller 1	g	17 33 24.5
IRAS 17349–3730	Collinder 338		17 38.2
IRAS 17361–3315	NGC 6404		17 39.6
IRAS 17402–3412	ESO 393-SC15		17 43 35.2
IRAS 17412–3346	Collinder 345		17 44 35
IRAS 17430–2848	RAFGL 2004		17 46 13.9
IRAS 17437–3128	NGC 6425		17 46 53
IRAS 17437–3131	NGC 6425		17 46 53
IRAS 17460–3446	NGC 6444		17 49.6
IRAS 17495–2826	Ruprecht 168		17 52.8
IRAS 18111–2837	AL 3		18 14 05.7
IRAS 18141–1501	NGC 6605		18 16 06
IRAS 18143–1500	NGC 6605		18 16 06
IRAS 18185–3310	Ruprecht 140		18 21 49.8
IRAS 18274+0112			18 29 57
IRAS 18295–1216	Ruprecht 142		18 32 14
IRAS 18296–1210	Ruprecht 143		18 32 43
IRAS 18297–1207	Ruprecht 143		18 32 43
IRAS 18333–2357			18 36 23.1
IRAS 18378–0429	Dolidze 33		18 40.7
IRAS 18461+3647	Iskudarian 1		18 48.0
IRAS 18475–1809	Ruprecht 145		18 50 19.4
IRAS 19090+1301	Berkeley 82		19 11 20.3
IRAS 19580+3429	Berkeley 49		19 59 30.2
IRAS 20337–0447	NGC 6941		20 36 23.5
IRAS 21055+5040	NGC 7031		21 06 52
IRAS 22259+5203	NGC 7296		22 28 01
IRAS 22534+5653	NGC 7423		22 55 06.5
IRAS 23058+6032	PWM78 3		23 08 10.8
IRAS 23308+5811	King 20		23 33 14
IRAS 23310+6354	Berkeley 101		23 32 46.5
IRAS 23455+6819	King 11		23 47 36.6
Iskudarian 1			18 48.0
Isserstedt 206	Czernik 20		05 20 32.5
Isserstedt 274	P Cygni cluster		20 17 43.5
Isserstedt 662	NGC 6728		18 57 31.4
Isserstedt 690	Trumpler 32		18 17 10.4
JaFu 1			17 43 57.4
JaFu 1	Palomar 6	g	17 43 42.2
JaFu 2			17 50 10.8
JaFu 2	NGC 6441	g	17 50 12.9
Johansson 1			15 46 20
Kappa Crucis cluster	NGC 4755		12 53 38
Kara 781	Palomar 15	g	16 59 50.9
Kemble 1			03 57 25.3
Kemble 2			18 35.0
King 1			00 21 52
King 2			00 50 57
King 3	NGC 609		01 36 24
King 4			02 36 02
King 5			03 14 40
King 6			03 28 00
King 7			03 59 10
King 8			05 49 17
King 9			22 15 31
King 10			22 55.0
King 11			23 47 36.6
King 12			23 53.0
King 13			00 10 10
King 14			00 31.9

Table D.3: Cluster Cross-Reference

Name	Look Under	GX	2000.0 RA
King 15			00 33 07
King 16			00 43.7
King 17			05 08 24
King 18			22 52 08
King 19			23 08.3
King 20			23 33 14
King 21			23 49.9
King 22	Berkeley 18		05 22 12
King 23	Czernik 28		07 21.8
King 24	Czernik 32		07 50 28
King 25			19 24.5
King 26			19 29.0
King 27	Czernik 40		19 42 38
KMHK 1	NGC 1466	L	03 44 32.4
KMHK 2	SL 2	L	04 24 09.8
KMHK 3		L	04 29 35.1
KMHK 4	NGC 1629	L	04 29 36.3
KMHK 5	[HS66] 8	L	04 30 38.1
KMHK 6		L	04 32 48.2
KMHK 7	SL 4	L	04 32 38.6
KMHK 8	LW 5	L	04 33 52.1
KMHK 9		L	04 34 55.0
KMHK 10		L	04 36 09.9
KMHK 11	[HS66] 13	L	04 35 27.8
KMHK 12	LW 7	L	04 35 36.6
KMHK 13	LW 9	L	04 35 58.9
KMHK 14	SL 5	L	04 35 38.6
KMHK 15		L	04 36 19.8
KMHK 16		L	04 36 37.1
KMHK 17		L	04 37 11.4
KMHK 18	NGC 1644	L	04 37 39.4
KMHK 19		L	04 37 06.4
KMHK 20	NGC 1651	L	04 37 31.8
KMHK 21	SL 8	L	04 37 49.9
KMHK 22	NGC 1649	L	04 38 06.9
KMHK 23	NGC 1652	L	04 38 22.6
KMHK 24	SL 11	L	04 39 05.8
KMHK 25	LW 15	L	04 38 26.3
KMHK 26	SL 12	L	04 39 59.3
KMHK 27	LW 20	L	04 39 58.6
KMHK 28	SL 14	L	04 40 28.8
KMHK 29	SL 15	L	04 40 43.4
KMHK 30		L	04 39 43.7
KMHK 31	SL 13	L	04 39 42.9
KMHK 32		L	04 41 00.6
KMHK 33	LW 22	L	04 40 20.4
KMHK 34		L	04 41 50.7
KMHK 35	LW 24	L	04 41 07.8
KMHK 36		L	04 41 25.4
KMHK 37	LW 25	L	04 41 46.4
KMHK 38		L	04 41 54.3
KMHK 39	LW 27	L	04 41 33.6
KMHK 40	LW 28	L	04 42 11.0
KMHK 42	LW 30	L	04 42 51.2
KMHK 43	NGC 1673	L	04 42 39.2
KMHK 44		L	04 43 26.7
KMHK 45	[HS66] 23	L	04 42 54.1
KMHK 46		L	04 43 14.5
KMHK 47	SL 19	L	04 43 03.6
KMHK 48		L	04 43 14.5

Table D.3: Cluster Cross-Reference

Name	Look Under	GX	2000.0 RA
KMHK 49	SL 22	L	04 43 37.2
KMHK 50	SL 23	L	04 43 38.0
KMHK 51		L	04 43 31.7
KMHK 52	BRHT 23b	L	04 43 41.8
KMHK 53	NGC 1676	L	04 43 52.6
KMHK 54	LW 39	L	04 43 59.4
KMHK 55	SL 24	L	04 43 50.3
KMHK 56		L	04 43 44.9
KMHK 57		L	04 43 53.8
KMHK 58		L	04 43 14.8
KMHK 59	LW 41	L	04 44 11.5
KMHK 60	LW 44	L	04 44 37.4
KMHK 61		L	04 44 14.6
KMHK 62	LW 43	L	04 44 17.0
KMHK 63	LW 46	L	04 44 46.7
KMHK 64	SL 27	L	04 45 04.7
KMHK 65	SL 26	L	04 45 17.4
KMHK 66		L	04 44 46.6
KMHK 67		L	04 45 08.6
KMHK 68	LW 45	L	04 44 29.4
KMHK 69		L	04 45 50.0
KMHK 70		L	04 45 50.3
KMHK 71	SL 28	L	04 44 40.8
KMHK 72		L	04 46 05.2
KMHK 73	SL 30	L	04 46 02.7
KMHK 74		L	04 45 58.4
KMHK 75	SL 31	L	04 45 40.6
KMHK 76	LW 57	L	04 46 22.4
KMHK 77	[HS66] 26	L	04 46 04.6
KMHK 78		L	04 46 11.8
KMHK 79		L	04 46 24.7
KMHK 80		L	04 46 55.7
KMHK 81	SL 29	L	04 45 12.6
KMHK 82		L	04 46 36.7
KMHK 83	SL 33	L	04 45 53.5
KMHK 84	SL 35	L	04 46 40.7
KMHK 85		L	04 46 33.5
KMHK 86	SL 34	L	04 45 46.7
KMHK 87		L	04 46 46.8
KMHK 88		L	04 46 50.8
KMHK 89	LW 63	L	04 47 15.6
KMHK 90		L	04 47 16.2
KMHK 91		L	04 46 28.1
KMHK 92		L	04 47 34.1
KMHK 93		L	04 47 24.1
KMHK 94		L	04 47 18.3
KMHK 95		L	04 47 26.4
KMHK 96	LW 62	L	04 46 18.9
KMHK 97	SL 36	L	04 46 08.5
KMHK 98	SL 37	L	04 46 45.8
KMHK 99	[HS66] 27	L	04 47 27.8
KMHK 100	NGC 1693	L	04 47 39.9
KMHK 101	NGC 1695	L	04 47 44.8
KMHK 102	SL 42	L	04 48 08.2
KMHK 103		L	04 47 41.0
KMHK 104	[HS66] 28	L	04 48 04.2
KMHK 105	SL 41	L	04 47 30.9
KMHK 106		L	04 47 29.1
KMHK 107		L	04 47 27.1
KMHK 108	NGC 1696	L	04 48 29.8

Table D.3: Cluster Cross-Reference

Name	Look Under	GX	2000.0 RA
KMHK 109	[HS66] 30	L	04 48 27.4
KMHK 110	NGC 1697	L	04 48 37.0
KMHK 111	[HS66] 32	L	04 48 41.1
KMHK 112		L	04 49 08.0
KMHK 113	[HS66] 31	L	04 48 56.2
KMHK 114		L	04 49 10.2
KMHK 115	NGC 1698	L	04 49 04.0
KMHK 116		L	04 49 20.5
KMHK 117	SL 47	L	04 49 03.3
KMHK 118		L	04 49 20.3
KMHK 119	[HS66] 33	L	04 49 16.5
KMHK 120		L	04 49 03.2
KMHK 121		L	04 49 10.9
KMHK 122	NGC 1702	L	04 49 25.9
KMHK 123		L	04 49 00.0
KMHK 124	[HS66] 35	L	04 49 33.7
KMHK 125		L	04 49 52.0
KMHK 126	[HS66] 36	L	04 49 33.6
KMHK 127		L	04 49 39.6
KMHK 128		L	04 49 13.9
KMHK 129	LW 66	L	04 49 04.2
KMHK 130	NGC 1704	L	04 49 55.5
KMHK 131	SL 51	L	04 50 19.7
KMHK 132	LW 65	L	04 49 20.0
KMHK 133	SL 48	L	04 49 27.5
KMHK 134		L	04 50 06.2
KMHK 135		L	04 50 06.5
KMHK 136	SL 49	L	04 50 10.4
KMHK 137	LW 69	L	04 49 39.0
KMHK 138		L	04 50 42.8
KMHK 139	[HS66] 37	L	04 50 28.2
KMHK 140		L	04 50 36.0
KMHK 141	SL 52	L	04 50 07.0
KMHK 142	SL 56	L	04 50 32.1
KMHK 143		L	04 50 32.7
KMHK 144		L	04 50 43.6
KMHK 145	NGC 1711	L	04 50 37.4
KMHK 146	SL 57	L	04 51 13.2
KMHK 147		L	04 50 53.7
KMHK 148	[HS66] 38	L	04 51 11.4
KMHK 149		L	04 51 18.9
KMHK 150		L	04 51 08.0
KMHK 151		L	04 50 21.3
KMHK 152	LW 75	L	04 50 14.0
KMHK 153	SL 58	L	04 50 59.9
KMHK 154	[HS66] 39	L	04 51 03.6
KMHK 155	NGC 1712	L	04 50 57.1
KMHK 156		L	04 51 01.2
KMHK 157	LW 76	L	04 50 24.8
KMHK 158	[HS66] 41	L	04 51 31.1
KMHK 159	[HS66] 40	L	04 51 11.9
KMHK 160	SL 53	L	04 49 53.2
KMHK 161		L	04 51 23.9
KMHK 162	SL 54	L	04 50 48.7
KMHK 163		L	04 51 29.9
KMHK 164		L	04 51 23.9
KMHK 165	SL 62	L	04 52 03.2
KMHK 166		L	04 51 33.1
KMHK 167	[HS66] 43	L	04 51 40.6
KMHK 168	NGC 1714	L	04 52 06.6

Table D.3: Cluster Cross-Reference

Name	Look Under	GX	2000.0 RA
KMHK 169	[HS66] 44	L	04 51 37.7
KMHK 170		L	04 51 39.7
KMHK 171		L	04 51 53.0
KMHK 171	NGC 1722	L	04 51 51.5
KMHK 172		L	04 51 51.1
KMHK 173		L	04 51 53.0
KMHK 173	IC 2111	L	04 51 53.0
KMHK 173	NGC 1722	L	04 51 51.5
KMHK 174	[HS66] 46	L	04 52 19.1
KMHK 175	SL 63	L	04 52 25.7
KMHK 176		L	04 51 56.3
KMHK 177	[HS66] 48	L	04 52 08.4
KMHK 178	SL 61	L	04 50 44.9
KMHK 179		L	04 51 45.0
KMHK 180	SL 66	L	04 51 56.0
KMHK 181	NGC 1718	L	04 52 25.6
KMHK 182	NGC 1727	L	04 52 12.3
KMHK 183		L	04 51 42.5
KMHK 184		L	04 52 45.0
KMHK 185	[HS66] 50	L	04 52 45.9
KMHK 186		L	04 52 46.1
KMHK 187		L	04 52 23.7
KMHK 188		L	04 51 47.0
KMHK 189		L	04 52 29.3
KMHK 190	[HS66] 51	L	04 52 44.9
KMHK 191	SL 70	L	04 52 50.0
KMHK 192		L	04 52 29.5
KMHK 193	[HS66] 52	L	04 52 43.0
KMHK 194	SL 71	L	04 52 55.3
KMHK 195		L	04 53 04.6
KMHK 196		L	04 53 04.9
KMHK 197	LW 83	L	04 52 06.8
KMHK 198	SL 68	L	04 52 06.7
KMHK 199	SL 75	L	04 52 54.9
KMHK 200	NGC 1736	L	04 53 02.3
KMHK 201	SL 81	L	04 53 09.8
KMHK 202		L	04 52 54.3
KMHK 203		L	04 52 54.8
KMHK 204		L	04 52 59.8
KMHK 205		L	04 52 59.1
KMHK 206	SL 76	L	04 53 09.0
KMHK 207		L	04 53 00.1
KMHK 208		L	04 53 06.7
KMHK 209	NGC 1732	L	04 53 11.5
KMHK 210	SL 74	L	04 52 01.4
KMHK 211		L	04 53 30.4
KMHK 211	NGC 1731	L	04 53 30.4
KMHK 212		L	04 53 35.3
KMHK 212	NGC 1731	L	04 53 30.4
KMHK 213	SL 79	L	04 52 53.3
KMHK 214	LW 86	L	04 52 44.8
KMHK 215		L	04 53 44.4
KMHK 216		L	04 53 44.6
KMHK 217	LW 87	L	04 52 54.6
KMHK 218	[HS66] 56	L	04 53 37.4
KMHK 219		L	04 53 29.0
KMHK 220	SL 80	L	04 52 21.1
KMHK 221	NGC 1734	L	04 53 33.9
KMHK 222		L	04 53 49.2
KMHK 223		L	04 54 08.0

Table D.3: Cluster Cross-Reference

Name	Look Under	GX	2000.0 RA
KMHK 224	NGC 1733	L	04 54 04.9
KMHK 225		L	04 54 16.3
KMHK 226	[HS66] 58	L	04 54 13.3
KMHK 227		L	04 54 05.7
KMHK 228		L	04 52 56.7
KMHK 229		L	04 53 51.5
KMHK 230		L	04 54 00.6
KMHK 231	OHSC 1	L	04 52 42.4
KMHK 232	SL 84	L	04 52 46.0
KMHK 233		L	04 54 28.6
KMHK 234	NGC 1735	L	04 54 20.2
KMHK 235	NGC 1743	L	04 54 03.4
KMHK 236		L	04 54 25.6
KMHK 237		L	04 54 01.0
KMHK 238	OHSC 2	L	04 53 10.1
KMHK 239	NGC 1751	L	04 54 11.9
KMHK 240	SL 92	L	04 54 26.7
KMHK 241		L	04 54 09.4
KMHK 242		L	04 54 18.7
KMHK 243		L	04 54 52.0
KMHK 244		L	04 54 26.2
KMHK 245		L	04 54 27.2
KMHK 246		L	04 54 55.3
KMHK 247	NGC 1754	L	04 54 18.4
KMHK 248		L	04 54 56.5
KMHK 249	SL 88	L	04 54 15.5
KMHK 250	SL 90	L	04 54 30.2
KMHK 251		L	04 54 42.9
KMHK 252	[HS66] 60	L	04 54 44.1
KMHK 253	[HS66] 59	L	04 54 37.2
KMHK 254	NGC 1749	L	04 54 56.5
KMHK 255		L	04 54 57.5
KMHK 256	SL 96	L	04 55 01.9
KMHK 257	NGC 1756	L	04 54 49.9
KMHK 258		L	04 54 45.9
KMHK 259		L	04 54 39.7
KMHK 260		L	04 54 42.7
KMHK 261	SL 101	L	04 55 10.1
KMHK 262		L	04 54 37.6
KMHK 263		L	04 55 07.4
KMHK 264		L	04 54 41.9
KMHK 265	SL 100	L	04 54 45.8
KMHK 266	[HS66] 61	L	04 55 11.3
KMHK 267		L	04 55 19.6
KMHK 268		L	04 55 23.2
KMHK 269	SL 95	L	04 54 42.1
KMHK 270		L	04 55 05.7
KMHK 271		L	04 55 03.6
KMHK 272	NGC 1755	L	04 55 14.7
KMHK 273		L	04 55 24.7
KMHK 274	LW 91	L	04 54 22.8
KMHK 275	SL 102	L	04 54 56.4
KMHK 276	SL 106	L	04 55 06.4
KMHK 277	SL 103	L	04 54 53.7
KMHK 278	[HS66] 63	L	04 55 01.0
KMHK 279		L	04 55 08.0
KMHK 280	SL 105	L	04 55 24.5
KMHK 281	[HS66] 64	L	04 55 13.4
KMHK 282		L	04 55 28.2
KMHK 283	[HS66] 65	L	04 55 30.5

Table D.3: Cluster Cross-Reference

Name	Look Under	GX	2000.0 RA
KMHK 284	[HS66] 66	L	04 55 21.0
KMHK 285		L	04 55 39.5
KMHK 286		L	04 55 41.6
KMHK 287	SL 108	L	04 55 15.0
KMHK 288		L	04 55 24.1
KMHK 289		L	04 55 32.4
KMHK 290	SL 109	L	04 55 33.1
KMHK 291	SL 107	L	04 55 45.1
KMHK 292		L	04 55 35.4
KMHK 293		L	04 55 46.1
KMHK 294	SL 110	L	04 55 44.4
KMHK 295	[HS66] 68	L	04 56 06.5
KMHK 296	[HS66] 67	L	04 55 27.7
KMHK 297		L	04 55 23.1
KMHK 298		L	04 55 47.3
KMHK 299		L	04 55 32.3
KMHK 300		L	04 55 39.6
KMHK 301	SL 112	L	04 55 52.6
KMHK 302		L	04 56 21.5
KMHK 303	SL 111	L	04 55 42.3
KMHK 304	NGC 1766	L	04 55 57.7
KMHK 305	SL 114	L	04 56 07.8
KMHK 306		L	04 56 06.3
KMHK 307	NGC 1761	L	04 56 34.4
KMHK 308	NGC 1764	L	04 56 27.4
KMHK 309		L	04 56 25.5
KMHK 310		L	04 56 28.8
KMHK 311		L	04 56 35.1
KMHK 312		L	04 55 55.4
KMHK 313	[HS66] 70	L	04 56 07.3
KMHK 314	SL 117	L	04 56 22.4
KMHK 315	SL 116	L	04 56 24.8
KMHK 316	SL 119	L	04 56 37.4
KMHK 317		L	04 56 17.6
KMHK 318	NGC 1767	L	04 56 27.4
KMHK 319		L	04 56 39.1
KMHK 320	SL 123	L	04 56 33.3
KMHK 321		L	04 56 40.2
KMHK 322	SL 126	L	04 57 22.7
KMHK 323	SL 118	L	04 55 32.5
KMHK 324	SL 124	L	04 56 31.3
KMHK 325		L	04 57 04.9
KMHK 326	[HS66] 72	L	04 56 54.1
KMHK 327		L	04 56 35.7
KMHK 328	NGC 1777	L	04 55 48.5
KMHK 329		L	04 57 09.4
KMHK 330	[HS66] 73	L	04 57 06.1
KMHK 331	NGC 1768	L	04 57 02.7
KMHK 332		L	04 57 14.2
KMHK 333		L	04 57 08.0
KMHK 334	NGC 1772	L	04 56 53.9
KMHK 335		L	04 56 51.9
KMHK 336	SL 131	L	04 57 27.5
KMHK 337	SL 133	L	04 57 34.6
KMHK 338	NGC 1775	L	04 56 53.6
KMHK 339	[HS66] 74	L	04 57 11.6
KMHK 340		L	04 56 56.6
KMHK 341	IC 2117	L	04 57 14.5
KMHK 342	LW 100	L	04 57 35.5
KMHK 343		L	04 55 55.9

Table D.3: Cluster Cross-Reference

Name	Look Under	GX	2000.0 RA
KMHK 344	LW 95	L	04 55 57.9
KMHK 345	NGC 1770	L	04 57 16.8
KMHK 346		L	04 57 30.2
KMHK 347	[HS66] 75	L	04 56 49.8
KMHK 348	SL 132	L	04 57 26.9
KMHK 349	SL 134	L	04 57 30.4
KMHK 350	LW 102	L	04 57 52.3
KMHK 351	LW 98	L	04 56 50.9
KMHK 352	SL 136	L	04 57 30.4
KMHK 353	LW 103	L	04 57 55.3
KMHK 354	SL 138	L	04 57 54.7
KMHK 355		L	04 57 22.1
KMHK 356	SL 135	L	04 56 43.8
KMHK 357	SL 142	L	04 58 15.2
KMHK 358	SL 139	L	04 57 56.1
KMHK 359		L	04 57 54.7
KMHK 360	NGC 1774	L	04 58 06.2
KMHK 361	SL 137	L	04 57 10.2
KMHK 362	OHSC 3	L	04 56 36.7
KMHK 363	NGC 1782	L	04 57 51.5
KMHK 364	SL 143	L	04 58 17.0
KMHK 365		L	04 58 10.8
KMHK 366		L	04 58 19.2
KMHK 367		L	04 58 15.2
KMHK 368		L	04 57 56.1
KMHK 369		L	04 58 21.1
KMHK 370	[HS66] 76	L	04 58 09.9
KMHK 371		L	04 58 16.0
KMHK 372		L	04 58 07.5
KMHK 373	[HS66] 77	L	04 58 28.8
KMHK 374	NGC 1776	L	04 58 39.2
KMHK 375	NGC 1789	L	04 57 51.5
KMHK 376		L	04 58 08.3
KMHK 377	SL 146	L	04 58 17.8
KMHK 378		L	04 58 22.2
KMHK 379		L	04 58 30.7
KMHK 380	SL 147	L	04 58 59.5
KMHK 381		L	04 58 46.1
KMHK 382		L	04 58 36.0
KMHK 383	NGC 1783	L	04 59 08.7
KMHK 384	SL 152	L	04 59 19.7
KMHK 385	NGC 1786	L	04 59 07.8
KMHK 386	SL 150	L	04 58 56.5
KMHK 387	SL 153	L	04 59 20.6
KMHK 388	SL 151	L	04 58 51.3
KMHK 389		L	04 59 01.3
KMHK 390	SL 154	L	04 59 14.7
KMHK 391	NGC 1791	L	04 59 06.0
KMHK 392		L	04 59 18.8
KMHK 393		L	04 59 25.2
KMHK 394	SL 156	L	04 59 37.8
KMHK 395		L	04 58 58.9
KMHK 396	LW 107	L	04 58 15.6
KMHK 397	SL 158	L	04 59 14.0
KMHK 398	SL 157	L	04 58 53.6
KMHK 399	LW 106	L	04 58 06.5
KMHK 400	[HS66] 78	L	04 59 35.2
KMHK 401	SL 161	L	04 59 58.6
KMHK 402	SL 160	L	04 59 26.6
KMHK 403		L	04 59 48.3

Table D.3: Cluster Cross-Reference

Name	Look Under	GX	2000.0 RA
KMHK 404	LW 112	L	05 00 10.0
KMHK 405	NGC 1793	L	04 59 38.3
KMHK 406	SL 162	L	04 59 53.8
KMHK 407		L	05 00 07.0
KMHK 408	[HS66] 80	L	04 59 49.0
KMHK 409	SL 164	L	04 59 25.3
KMHK 410		L	05 00 19.0
KMHK 411	NGC 1795	L	04 59 46.8
KMHK 412		L	05 00 04.3
KMHK 413	[HS66] 82	L	04 59 52.4
KMHK 414	LW 110	L	04 58 46.3
KMHK 415	[HS66] 81	L	04 59 59.1
KMHK 416		L	05 00 01.9
KMHK 417		L	04 59 05.7
KMHK 418	SL 168	L	05 00 44.2
KMHK 419	SL 166	L	04 59 12.5
KMHK 420		L	04 59 57.7
KMHK 421	[HS66] 83	L	05 00 26.1
KMHK 422	SL 167	L	05 00 41.2
KMHK 423		L	05 00 28.2
KMHK 424		L	05 00 30.7
KMHK 425	[HS66] 84	L	05 00 52.0
KMHK 426	OHSC 4	L	04 59 13.7
KMHK 427	LW 115	L	05 01 10.0
KMHK 428	[HS66] 85	L	05 00 50.7
KMHK 429	NGC 1801	L	05 00 35.1
KMHK 430	SL 169	L	05 00 22.9
KMHK 431		L	05 00 16.8
KMHK 432		L	05 01 02.4
KMHK 433		L	05 00 56.2
KMHK 434	SL 171	L	05 00 32.9
KMHK 435	[HS66] 86	L	05 01 01.7
KMHK 436	[HS66] 88	L	05 01 04.1
KMHK 437		L	05 01 22.1
KMHK 438		L	05 01 13.6
KMHK 439	SL 174	L	05 01 11.6
KMHK 440	SL 173	L	05 01 21.9
KMHK 441	[HS66] 90	L	05 00 57.4
KMHK 442		L	05 01 05.6
KMHK 443		L	05 01 28.8
KMHK 444	SL 177	L	05 01 47.1
KMHK 445	SL 178	L	05 01 44.3
KMHK 446	[HS66] 91	L	05 01 42.5
KMHK 447		L	05 00 14.7
KMHK 448	SL 176	L	05 01 29.3
KMHK 449	SL 179	L	05 01 45.2
KMHK 450		L	05 01 54.1
KMHK 451		L	05 01 45.1
KMHK 452		L	05 01 48.9
KMHK 453		L	05 00 13.1
KMHK 454	SL 175	L	05 00 49.5
KMHK 455		L	05 02 03.5
KMHK 456		L	05 02 05.4
KMHK 457		L	05 01 54.1
KMHK 458		L	05 02 19.1
KMHK 459	NGC 1805	L	05 02 21.2
KMHK 460	SL 183	L	05 01 33.3
KMHK 461		L	05 01 51.4
KMHK 462	NGC 1806	L	05 02 11.3
KMHK 463	[HS66] 93	L	05 02 30.2

Table D.3: Cluster Cross-Reference

Name	Look Under	GX	2000.0 RA
KMHK 464		L	05 01 54.6
KMHK 465		L	05 01 25.1
KMHK 466		L	05 01 28.5
KMHK 467	[HS66] 92	L	05 02 18.4
KMHK 468	[HS66] 94	L	05 02 29.1
KMHK 469	NGC 1815	L	05 02 26.9
KMHK 470	SL 187	L	05 02 10.4
KMHK 471		L	05 02 13.0
KMHK 472	NGC 1813	L	05 02 40.8
KMHK 473	[HS66] 96	L	05 03 22.8
KMHK 474	SL 193	L	05 03 27.7
KMHK 475	NGC 1810	L	05 03 22.8
KMHK 476	SL 195	L	05 03 31.8
KMHK 477	[HS66] 101	L	05 03 27.7
KMHK 478	[HS66] 98	L	05 03 28.3
KMHK 479		L	05 02 57.1
KMHK 480	SL 196	L	05 03 35.0
KMHK 481	LW 124	L	05 03 38.2
KMHK 482	SL 197	L	05 03 33.5
KMHK 483	[HS66] 99	L	05 03 14.1
KMHK 484	NGC 1814	L	05 03 45.4
KMHK 485	[HS66] 100	L	05 03 25.8
KMHK 486	[HS66] 103	L	05 03 58.5
KMHK 487	NGC 1823	L	05 03 23.8
KMHK 488	NGC 1816	L	05 03 51.2
KMHK 489	SL 192	L	05 02 27.6
KMHK 490		L	05 04 01.5
KMHK 491	NGC 1818	L	05 04 12.9
KMHK 492	SL 200	L	05 03 45.7
KMHK 493		L	05 03 46.1
KMHK 494		L	05 03 50.4
KMHK 495		L	05 04 25.5
KMHK 496		L	05 04 34.6
KMHK 497	LW 126	L	05 04 41.4
KMHK 498		L	05 04 26.9
KMHK 499	[HS66] 104	L	05 04 02.6
KMHK 500	SL 204	L	05 04 42.6
KMHK 501	LW 129	L	05 04 42.9
KMHK 502		L	05 04 42.0
KMHK 503	[HS66] 105	L	05 04 43.4
KMHK 504	LW 127	L	05 04 52.7
KMHK 505		L	05 04 32.6
KMHK 506		L	05 04 29.7
KMHK 507	SL 205	L	05 04 45.5
KMHK 508		L	05 04 09.3
KMHK 509	[HS66] 106	L	05 04 55.6
KMHK 510	NGC 1833	L	05 04 22.3
KMHK 511		L	05 05 03.4
KMHK 512	SL 214	L	05 05 24.2
KMHK 513	NGC 1822	L	05 05 08.1
KMHK 514		L	05 04 36.2
KMHK 515	NGC 1829	L	05 04 58.5
KMHK 516		L	05 03 56.1
KMHK 517		L	05 05 08.9
KMHK 518	SL 209	L	05 04 37.7
KMHK 519		L	05 05 24.8
KMHK 520		L	05 05 24.1
KMHK 521	SL 216	L	05 04 57.4
KMHK 522	SL 222	L	05 05 26.2
KMHK 523	NGC 1837	L	05 04 56

Table D.3: Cluster Cross-Reference

Name	Look Under	GX	2000.0 RA
KMHK 524	NGC 1826	L	05 05 33.7
KMHK 525	SL 213	L	05 04 49.8
KMHK 526	SL 219	L	05 04 43.4
KMHK 527	[HS66] 110	L	05 05 51.0
KMHK 528	[HS66] 108	L	05 05 49.3
KMHK 529	NGC 1840	L	05 05 19.9
KMHK 530	NGC 1831	L	05 06 16.2
KMHK 531	[HS66] 113	L	05 05 54.8
KMHK 532	OHSC 6	L	05 04 39.0
KMHK 533	[HS66] 114	L	05 06 02.7
KMHK 534	SL 224	L	05 05 42.7
KMHK 535	LW 134	L	05 06 27.5
KMHK 536	[HS66] 116	L	05 06 12.5
KMHK 537	[HS66] 115	L	05 05 53.6
KMHK 538	SL 228	L	05 06 27.2
KMHK 539	LW 135	L	05 06 40.8
KMHK 540		L	05 06 09.5
KMHK 541		L	05 06 12.0
KMHK 542	LW 132	L	05 05 14.5
KMHK 543	SL 233	L	05 07 04.1
KMHK 544		L	05 06 42.2
KMHK 545	SL 232	L	05 06 22.2
KMHK 546		L	05 06 47.5
KMHK 547	LW 138	L	05 07 05.0
KMHK 548	SL 238	L	05 07 22.6
KMHK 549		L	05 06 58.9
KMHK 550	SL 239	L	05 07 09.9
KMHK 551	SL 235	L	05 06 29.3
KMHK 552	SL 236	L	05 06 22.6
KMHK 553	NGC 1842	L	05 07 18.4
KMHK 554		L	05 07 11.1
KMHK 555	[HS66] 120	L	05 07 01.9
KMHK 556	NGC 1844	L	05 07 30.4
KMHK 557	NGC 1846	L	05 07 33.9
KMHK 558	LW 137	L	05 06 03.3
KMHK 559	SL 245	L	05 07 46.1
KMHK 560	[HS66] 121	L	05 07 46.5
KMHK 561	SL 246	L	05 07 24.9
KMHK 562	SL 249	L	05 07 34.8
KMHK 563	[HS66] 125	L	05 08 25.7
KMHK 564	[HS66] 124	L	05 08 18.0
KMHK 565		L	05 07 36.7
KMHK 566	SL 253	L	05 08 22.8
KMHK 567		L	05 07 48.7
KMHK 568	SL 254	L	05 08 22.1
KMHK 569	LW 140	L	05 07 22.0
KMHK 570	SL 252	L	05 07 50.5
KMHK 571	SL 258	L	05 08 35.5
KMHK 572		L	05 07 55.4
KMHK 573	SL 255	L	05 07 56.7
KMHK 574	SL 251	L	05 07 59.9
KMHK 575	SL 263	L	05 08 32.2
KMHK 576	SL 257	L	05 08 40.1
KMHK 577	SL 259	L	05 08 51.6
KMHK 578	SL 248	L	05 06 52.1
KMHK 579		L	05 08 50.1
KMHK 580	SL 256	L	05 08 10.3
KMHK 581		L	05 08 18.2
KMHK 582	SL 262	L	05 09 21.2
KMHK 583		L	05 08 50.6

Table D.3: Cluster Cross-Reference

Name	Look Under	GX	2000.0 RA
KMHK 584	[HS66] 129	L	05 09 03.7
KMHK 585	LW 141	L	05 07 35.2
KMHK 586		L	05 08 51.7
KMHK 587		L	05 08 32.5
KMHK 588	[HS66] 130	L	05 09 15.5
KMHK 589	[HS66] 132	L	05 09 28.7
KMHK 590	LW 148	L	05 09 40.7
KMHK 591	LW 149	L	05 09 32.1
KMHK 592	SL 266	L	05 09 06.1
KMHK 593	NGC 1849	L	05 09 34.5
KMHK 594	NGC 1852	L	05 09 24.1
KMHK 595	[HS66] 137	L	05 09 43.3
KMHK 596	SL 270	L	05 09 09.6
KMHK 597	SL 273	L	05 10 03.7
KMHK 598	SL 269	L	05 09 35.6
KMHK 599	[HS66] 135	L	05 09 58.3
KMHK 600		L	05 09 19.5
KMHK 601	SL 272	L	05 09 01.6
KMHK 602	[HS66] 143	L	05 10 12.0
KMHK 603		L	05 09 22.3
KMHK 604	LW 147	L	05 08 34.9
KMHK 605	SL 275	L	05 10 15.2
KMHK 606		L	05 09 37.2
KMHK 607		L	05 10 17.7
KMHK 608	[HS66] 140	L	05 09 40.5
KMHK 609		L	05 10 02.4
KMHK 610		L	05 09 35.4
KMHK 611	[HS66] 148	L	05 09 48.5
KMHK 612		L	05 09 47.8
KMHK 613	[HS66] 149	L	05 10 36.3
KMHK 614		L	05 10 40.3
KMHK 615	SL 287	L	05 10 49.0
KMHK 616	SL 281	L	05 10 33.4
KMHK 617		L	05 10 41.9
KMHK 618	SL 283	L	05 10 44.7
KMHK 619	SL 282	L	05 10 10.4
KMHK 620		L	05 10 54.8
KMHK 621	NGC 1861	L	05 10 21.1
KMHK 622		L	05 10 53.4
KMHK 623	SL 292	L	05 11 08.3
KMHK 624		L	05 10 02.6
KMHK 625	[HS66] 154	L	05 10 56.8
KMHK 626	SL 291	L	05 10 30.3
KMHK 627	SL 294	L	05 10 40.4
KMHK 628	SL 290	L	05 10 36.6
KMHK 629	SL 285	L	05 10 40.6
KMHK 630	SL 293	L	05 11 09.0
KMHK 631	[HS66] 157	L	05 11 05.5
KMHK 632	[HS66] 156	L	05 11 10.8
KMHK 633		L	05 10 37.4
KMHK 634		L	05 11 27.6
KMHK 635	NGC 1859	L	05 11 32.6
KMHK 636	SL 298	L	05 11 31.8
KMHK 637	LW 157	L	05 11 52.2
KMHK 638	SL 300	L	05 11 41.7
KMHK 639	SL 295	L	05 10 10.7
KMHK 640		L	05 11 10.0
KMHK 641	SL 301	L	05 12 04.7
KMHK 642	[HS66] 162	L	05 12 06.2
KMHK 643		L	05 11 35.6

Table D.3: Cluster Cross-Reference

Name	Look Under	GX	2000.0 RA
KMHK 644	SL 303	L	05 12 20.4
KMHK 645		L	05 11 58.7
KMHK 646	SL 302	L	05 11 44.0
KMHK 647	LW 155	L	05 10 32.0
KMHK 648	[HS66] 164	L	05 12 27.3
KMHK 649	[HS66] 168	L	05 12 35.0
KMHK 650	NGC 1862	L	05 12 33.6
KMHK 651		L	05 11 08.5
KMHK 652	SL 310	L	05 12 29.5
KMHK 653	SL 308	L	05 12 27.9
KMHK 654	[HS66] 173	L	05 12 52.6
KMHK 655		L	05 12 33.7
KMHK 656	NGC 1864	L	05 12 41.1
KMHK 657	SL 315	L	05 13 11.2
KMHK 658	SL 312	L	05 12 24.3
KMHK 659	LW 160	L	05 12 18.2
KMHK 660		L	05 13 26.1
KMHK 661	NGC 1878	L	05 12 49.7
KMHK 662		L	05 12 48.2
KMHK 663	SL 314	L	05 12 21.1
KMHK 664	NGC 1866	L	05 13 38.6
KMHK 665	NGC 1867	L	05 13 41.6
KMHK 666	SL 322	L	05 13 43.4
KMHK 667	[HS66] 178	L	05 13 48.4
KMHK 668	SL 329	L	05 14 11.8
KMHK 669	NGC 1871	L	05 13 52.4
KMHK 670	NGC 1873	L	05 14 01.7
KMHK 671	LH 37	L	05 13 53.6
KMHK 672		L	05 14 13.8
KMHK 673	LW 165	L	05 14 23.3
KMHK 674	NGC 1868	L	05 14 36.1
KMHK 675	LW 164	L	05 13 16.1
KMHK 676	SL 333	L	05 14 44.1
KMHK 677	[HS66] 185	L	05 14 47.4
KMHK 678	NGC 1890	L	05 13 47.2
KMHK 679	LW 171	L	05 14 46.3
KMHK 680		L	05 14 39.8
KMHK 681	[HS66] 184	L	05 14 10.2
KMHK 682	[HS66] 186	L	05 14 49.0
KMHK 683	SL 334	L	05 13 55.9
KMHK 684	SL 335	L	05 15 00.1
KMHK 685	[HS66] 187	L	05 14 45.8
KMHK 686		L	05 13 58.0
KMHK 687		L	05 14 38.3
KMHK 688	SL 336	L	05 14 28.8
KMHK 689	LW 174	L	05 15 26.6
KMHK 690	NGC 1882	L	05 15 32.8
KMHK 691	SL 339	L	05 15 17.9
KMHK 692	SL 337	L	05 14 30.0
KMHK 693	[HS66] 193	L	05 15 21.6
KMHK 694	[HS66] 194	L	05 15 37.8
KMHK 695	[HS66] 195	L	05 15 06.9
KMHK 696	[HS66] 196	L	05 15 42.4
KMHK 697		L	05 15 48.7
KMHK 698		L	05 15 40.2
KMHK 699	SL 345	L	05 16 17.1
KMHK 700	NGC 1887	L	05 16 05.3
KMHK 701	SL 342	L	05 15 32.6
KMHK 702	SL 346	L	05 16 28.4
KMHK 703	[HS66] 199	L	05 15 30.9

Table D.3: Cluster Cross-Reference

Name	Look Under	GX	2000.0 RA
KMHK 704		L	05 15 34.9
KMHK 705		L	05 16 42.7
KMHK 706	SL 347	L	05 16 25.7
KMHK 707		L	05 16 12.4
KMHK 708	OHSC 8	L	05 15 18.7
KMHK 709	[HS66] 202	L	05 16 03.8
KMHK 710		L	05 17 06.7
KMHK 711		L	05 17 01.6
KMHK 712	SL 354	L	05 17 30.9
KMHK 713	[HS66] 206	L	05 17 11.6
KMHK 714		L	05 17 13.8
KMHK 715	SL 352	L	05 16 40.7
KMHK 716	[HS66] 207	L	05 17 17.5
KMHK 717		L	05 17 29.5
KMHK 718		L	05 17 23.7
KMHK 719		L	05 16 59.2
KMHK 720		L	05 17 50.8
KMHK 721	[HS66] 208	L	05 17 30.9
KMHK 722	NGC 1897	L	05 17 31.6
KMHK 723		L	05 17 52.9
KMHK 724		L	05 17 00.1
KMHK 725	[HS66] 210	L	05 17 22.5
KMHK 726	[HS66] 212	L	05 18 02.1
KMHK 727	SL 359	L	05 17 49.7
KMHK 728	[HS66] 215	L	05 18 18.0
KMHK 729	SL 366	L	05 18 20.4
KMHK 730	SL 372	L	05 18 36.5
KMHK 731		L	05 17 44.9
KMHK 732	NGC 1914	L	05 17 39.4
KMHK 733	OHSC 9	L	05 16 21.9
KMHK 734	NGC 1902	L	05 18 18.3
KMHK 735		L	05 16 53.6
KMHK 736	SL 364	L	05 17 41.6
KMHK 737		L	05 18 15.0
KMHK 738	[HS66] 214	L	05 17 49.4
KMHK 739	NGC 1905	L	05 18 23.0
KMHK 740		L	05 17 47.5
KMHK 741	[HS66] 217	L	05 18 40.1
KMHK 742		L	05 18 30.7
KMHK 743		L	05 18 31.9
KMHK 744	SL 375	L	05 18 43.2
KMHK 745	LW 182	L	05 18 48.3
KMHK 746	NGC 1900	L	05 19 08.8
KMHK 747		L	05 18 05.4
KMHK 748	SL 377	L	05 19 00.6
KMHK 749		L	05 19 02.7
KMHK 750		L	05 18 18.2
KMHK 751		L	05 18 53.6
KMHK 752	SL 374	L	05 17 49.7
KMHK 753		L	05 18 46.3
KMHK 754		L	05 19 12.6
KMHK 755		L	05 18 56.7
KMHK 756	SL 378	L	05 18 57.9
KMHK 757	[HS66] 224	L	05 19 14.9
KMHK 758		L	05 19 11.9
KMHK 759		L	05 19 06.0
KMHK 760		L	05 19 14.9
KMHK 761	NGC 1915	L	05 19 28.1
KMHK 762	SL 382	L	05 19 25.5
KMHK 763	NGC 1911	L	05 19 25.2

Table D.3: Cluster Cross-Reference

Name	Look Under	GX	2000.0 RA
KMHK 764		L	05 18 51.8
KMHK 765	[HS66] 225	L	05 19 23.4
KMHK 766	[HS66] 226	L	05 19 23.4
KMHK 767	SL 380	L	05 18 46.5
KMHK 768	SL 384	L	05 19 44.5
KMHK 769	[HS66] 229	L	05 19 42.7
KMHK 770	SL 386	L	05 19 51.3
KMHK 771		L	05 19 42.8
KMHK 772		L	05 19 55.7
KMHK 773	SL 388	L	05 20 05.5
KMHK 774		L	05 19 44.5
KMHK 775	SL 383	L	05 19 33.2
KMHK 776	[HS66] 230	L	05 19 53.5
KMHK 777		L	05 20 05.6
KMHK 778	[HS66] 233	L	05 20 09.4
KMHK 779	[HS66] 231	L	05 19 55.0
KMHK 780	[HS66] 234	L	05 20 09.7
KMHK 781	[HS66] 236	L	05 20 15.7
KMHK 782	OHSC 10	L	05 20 38.2
KMHK 783	SL 389	L	05 19 36.4
KMHK 784	[HS66] 235	L	05 20 03.5
KMHK 785	[HS66] 237	L	05 20 30.7
KMHK 786	NGC 1919	L	05 20 17.1
KMHK 787		L	05 20 16.3
KMHK 788	SL 398	L	05 20 31.8
KMHK 789	SL 394	L	05 19 34.8
KMHK 790		L	05 20 34.3
KMHK 791	SL 401	L	05 20 50.2
KMHK 792	NGC 1920	L	05 20 32.1
KMHK 793	SL 395	L	05 19 59.0
KMHK 794		L	05 20 24.1
KMHK 795		L	05 20 00.0
KMHK 796	SL 396	L	05 19 36.3
KMHK 797	[HS66] 240	L	05 21 00.7
KMHK 798		L	05 20 41.2
KMHK 799	SL 399	L	05 20 20.4
KMHK 800		L	05 21 02.5
KMHK 801		L	05 20 27.7
KMHK 802		L	05 21 02.1
KMHK 803	OHSC 11	L	05 19 34.8
KMHK 804		L	05 20 58.0
KMHK 805	[HS66] 232	L	05 20 36.8
KMHK 806		L	05 21 04.6
KMHK 807	LW 191	L	05 20 27.4
KMHK 808	NGC 1923	L	05 21 34.5
KMHK 809	SL 400	L	05 19 38.7
KMHK 810	SL 407	L	05 21 15.5
KMHK 811	SL 409	L	05 21 37.9
KMHK 812		L	05 21 01.3
KMHK 813	SL 410	L	05 21 45.1
KMHK 814	SL 406	L	05 21 00.9
KMHK 815		L	05 21 59.4
KMHK 816		L	05 21 38.9
KMHK 817	SL 411	L	05 21 41.7
KMHK 818	SL 416	L	05 21 58.2
KMHK 819		L	05 21 20.9
KMHK 820		L	05 22 03.1
KMHK 821	LW 195	L	05 22 35.4
KMHK 822		L	05 21 56.8
KMHK 823		L	05 22 03.9

Table D.3: Cluster Cross-Reference

Name	Look Under	GX	2000.0 RA
KMHK 824		L	05 21 30.5
KMHK 825	NGC 1932	L	05 22 27.4
KMHK 826	LW 193	L	05 20 58.6
KMHK 827	SL 421	L	05 22 29.4
KMHK 828		L	05 22 31.2
KMHK 829		L	05 21 46.3
KMHK 830	OHSC 12	L	05 21 37.1
KMHK 831	SL 424	L	05 22 23.4
KMHK 832	[HS66] 254	L	05 22 33.8
KMHK 833	SL 428	L	05 22 52.1
KMHK 834	NGC 1940	L	05 22 44.2
KMHK 835		L	05 22 07.8
KMHK 836	NGC 1944	L	05 21 58.1
KMHK 837	[HS66] 258	L	05 23 10.6
KMHK 838		L	05 22 20.7
KMHK 839	NGC 1941	L	05 23 07.1
KMHK 840		L	05 22 54.8
KMHK 841	[HS66] 260	L	05 23 13.7
KMHK 842	SL 432	L	05 22 37.8
KMHK 843	SL 433	L	05 22 19.2
KMHK 844	[HS66] 262	L	05 22 57.1
KMHK 845	[HS66] 264	L	05 23 11.8
KMHK 846		L	05 23 02.1
KMHK 847	[HS66] 267	L	05 23 19.8
KMHK 848	LW 199	L	05 24 08.2
KMHK 849	[HS66] 269	L	05 24 07.0
KMHK 850	SL 440	L	05 24 12.6
KMHK 851	SL 438	L	05 24 10.6
KMHK 852		L	05 24 17.7
KMHK 853	SL 435	L	05 23 30.5
KMHK 854		L	05 24 40.2
KMHK 855	SL 441	L	05 23 42.1
KMHK 856	NGC 1942	L	05 24 42.7
KMHK 857	[HS66] 272	L	05 24 12.6
KMHK 858		L	05 24 28.0
KMHK 859	SL 448	L	05 24 59.4
KMHK 860	[HS66] 270	L	05 23 52.1
KMHK 861	SL 444	L	05 24 30.4
KMHK 862		L	05 24 52.4
KMHK 863		L	05 24 37.7
KMHK 864	IC 2134	L	05 23 06.6
KMHK 865	LW 201	L	05 23 23.2
KMHK 866	[HS66] 274	L	05 24 06.2
KMHK 867	[HS66] 277	L	05 24 48.5
KMHK 868	OHSC 14	L	05 23 29.3
KMHK 869	SL 446	L	05 24 47.8
KMHK 870	OHSC 15	L	05 23 59.3
KMHK 871	SL 452	L	05 25 10.0
KMHK 872		L	05 25 08.4
KMHK 873	LW 204	L	05 24 07.2
KMHK 874	NGC 1946	L	05 25 16.0
KMHK 875	NGC 1949	L	05 25 05.3
KMHK 876		L	05 25 03.9
KMHK 877	LW 209	L	05 25 44.4
KMHK 878		L	05 25 35.7
KMHK 879	SL 456	L	05 25 25.3
KMHK 880		L	05 25 09.8
KMHK 881	OHSC 16	L	05 24 20.8
KMHK 882	LW 212	L	05 26 08.4
KMHK 883	SL 451	L	05 24 13.4

Table D.3: Cluster Cross-Reference

Name	Look Under	GX	2000.0 RA
KMHK 884	[HS66] 287	L	05 26 00.7
KMHK 885	[HS66] 288	L	05 26 01.3
KMHK 886	NGC 1951	L	05 26 06.4
KMHK 887	SL 461	L	05 25 20.8
KMHK 888	NGC 1955	L	05 26 04.2
KMHK 889	SL 463	L	05 26 16.2
KMHK 890	[HS66] 284	L	05 25 24.2
KMHK 891	SL 455	L	05 24 17.2
KMHK 892	SL 465	L	05 26 13.7
KMHK 893		L	05 26 11.7
KMHK 894	SL 471	L	05 26 14.3
KMHK 895	[HS66] 289	L	05 26 07.7
KMHK 896	SL 470	L	05 26 25.7
KMHK 897		L	05 25 57.8
KMHK 898		L	05 26 23.9
KMHK 899		L	05 26 24.3
KMHK 900		L	05 26 29.5
KMHK 901	LW 211	L	05 25 28.0
KMHK 902	[HS66] 294	L	05 26 23.2
KMHK 903	LW 214	L	05 26 48.1
KMHK 904	SL 473	L	05 26 29.4
KMHK 905	[HS66] 299	L	05 26 38.2
KMHK 906	SL 472	L	05 26 14.4
KMHK 907		L	05 26 12.8
KMHK 908		L	05 27 02.0
KMHK 909	SL 474	L	05 26 08.5
KMHK 910		L	05 26 16.0
KMHK 911	SL 477	L	05 26 23.7
KMHK 912		L	05 27 14.7
KMHK 913	[HS66] 302	L	05 27 09.7
KMHK 914		L	05 26 59.1
KMHK 915	SL 482	L	05 27 18.3
KMHK 916	[HS66] 303	L	05 27 22.6
KMHK 917	[HS66] 301A	L	05 26 39.4
KMHK 918	SL 484	L	05 27 46.5
KMHK 919	LW 215	L	05 27 42.6
KMHK 920		L	05 27 35.4
KMHK 921	[HS66] 305	L	05 27 54.0
KMHK 922		L	05 27 44.3
KMHK 923	SL 485	L	05 27 50.0
KMHK 924	NGC 1968	L	05 27 39.7
KMHK 925	SL 487	L	05 27 08.2
KMHK 926	NGC 1987	L	05 27 16.4
KMHK 927	[HS66] 304	L	05 27 15.5
KMHK 928	SL 491	L	05 27 50.5
KMHK 929	NGC 1974	L	05 28 00.6
KMHK 930		L	05 28 13.2
KMHK 931	[HS66] 309	L	05 28 17.4
KMHK 932	NGC 2000	L	05 27 30.5
KMHK 933	SL 495	L	05 28 03.8
KMHK 934		L	05 27 37.7
KMHK 935	SL 496	L	05 28 32.6
KMHK 936		L	05 28 20.0
KMHK 937	SL 500	L	05 28 39.3
KMHK 938		L	05 28 43.7
KMHK 939	SL 490	L	05 27 18.4
KMHK 940	SL 497	L	05 28 23.9
KMHK 941		L	05 28 19.0
KMHK 942	[HS66] 313	L	05 28 25.4
KMHK 943	SL 498	L	05 28 35.1

Table D.3: Cluster Cross-Reference

Name	Look Under	GX	2000.0 RA
KMHK 944	NGC 1978	L	05 28 44.6
KMHK 945		L	05 28 27.8
KMHK 946	OHSC 17	L	05 29 04.3
KMHK 947	[HS66] 317	L	05 29 01.9
KMHK 948	[HS66] 318	L	05 28 44.2
KMHK 949	[HS66] 311	L	05 28 01.0
KMHK 950	[HS66] 315	L	05 28 17.8
KMHK 951	SL 502	L	05 29 11.5
KMHK 952	SL 503	L	05 28 59.6
KMHK 953		L	05 28 57.2
KMHK 954	[HS66] 322	L	05 29 20.9
KMHK 955	NGC 2001	L	05 29 08.2
KMHK 956		L	05 29 46.8
KMHK 957	SL 509	L	05 29 49.1
KMHK 958		L	05 29 23.9
KMHK 959	SL 511	L	05 29 49.0
KMHK 960	SL 505	L	05 28 49.7
KMHK 961	[HS66] 324	L	05 28 56.0
KMHK 962	[HS66] 326	L	05 29 39.2
KMHK 963	[HS66] 325	L	05 29 36.6
KMHK 964	OHSC 19	L	05 28 49.7
KMHK 965	SL 515	L	05 30 08.9
KMHK 966	SL 512	L	05 29 54.3
KMHK 967	[H60b] 14	L	05 28 38.6
KMHK 968	SL 510	L	05 29 21.1
KMHK 969		L	05 29 10.1
KMHK 970	SL 513	L	05 29 58.4
KMHK 971		L	05 29 55.2
KMHK 972	SL 516	L	05 30 00.1
KMHK 973	SL 525	L	05 30 23.4
KMHK 974		L	05 30 04.3
KMHK 975		L	05 29 59.4
KMHK 976		L	05 30 06.7
KMHK 977		L	05 30 10.4
KMHK 978	NGC 1997	L	05 30 34.9
KMHK 979		L	05 29 39.1
KMHK 980		L	05 30 11.5
KMHK 981	SL 521	L	05 30 26.1
KMHK 982	NGC 2002	L	05 30 21.4
KMHK 983		L	05 30 05.7
KMHK 984	[HS66] 329	L	05 29 46.3
KMHK 985		L	05 30 16.3
KMHK 986		L	05 30 35.6
KMHK 987		L	05 30 33.1
KMHK 988	SL 522	L	05 30 37.0
KMHK 989		L	05 30 46.6
KMHK 990	LW 228	L	05 30 52.7
KMHK 991	NGC 2004	L	05 30 40.9
KMHK 992	SL 529	L	05 31 06.8
KMHK 993		L	05 30 34.7
KMHK 994	SL 524	L	05 30 50.2
KMHK 995	SL 527	L	05 30 50.1
KMHK 996	[HS66] 330	L	05 29 57.6
KMHK 997		L	05 30 20.0
KMHK 998	NGC 2003	L	05 30 54.3
KMHK 999		L	05 30 12.7
KMHK 1000		L	05 31 05.0
KMHK 1001	NGC 2010	L	05 30 34.6
KMHK 1002		L	05 31 09.0
KMHK 1003	SL 540	L	05 31 33.9
KMHK 1004	SL 538	L	05 31 19.8
KMHK 1005	NGC 2006	L	05 31 19.9
KMHK 1006	SL 536	L	05 30 35.6
KMHK 1007		L	05 31 31.8
KMHK 1008	SL 539	L	05 30 56.4
KMHK 1009	SL 541	L	05 31 18.1
KMHK 1010	[HS66] 337	L	05 31 40.1
KMHK 1011		L	05 31 47.9
KMHK 1012		L	05 31 50.8
KMHK 1013	SL 549	L	05 32 03.6
KMHK 1014	[HS66] 334	L	05 31 02.1
KMHK 1015	[HS66] 338	L	05 31 45.3
KMHK 1016	SL 543	L	05 31 01.1
KMHK 1017	SL 550	L	05 31 55.1
KMHK 1018	NGC 2018	L	05 31 11.6
KMHK 1019		L	05 31 50.7
KMHK 1020		L	05 32 00.0
KMHK 1021		L	05 31 59.6
KMHK 1022	SL 545	L	05 31 08.1
KMHK 1023		L	05 31 46.0
KMHK 1024	SL 552	L	05 31 43.5
KMHK 1025		L	05 31 42.2
KMHK 1026	SL 546	L	05 31 02.5
KMHK 1027	SL 551	L	05 31 51.8
KMHK 1028	[HS66] 341	L	05 31 59.8
KMHK 1029		L	05 31 57.0
KMHK 1030	[HS66] 343	L	05 32 07.0
KMHK 1031	LW 231	L	05 30 27.8
KMHK 1032		L	05 31 58.9
KMHK 1033		L	05 31 54.5
KMHK 1034	[H60b] 4	L	05 32 25.4
KMHK 1035	SL 548	L	05 31 25.1
KMHK 1036		L	05 32 18.1
KMHK 1037		L	05 31 44.1
KMHK 1038		L	05 32 02.0
KMHK 1039	NGC 2011	L	05 32 19.8
KMHK 1040		L	05 32 20.2
KMHK 1041	SL 553	L	05 32 29.2
KMHK 1042	LW 234	L	05 30 59.8
KMHK 1043	NGC 2014	L	05 32 21.7
KMHK 1044	LW 238	L	05 32 54.0
KMHK 1045		L	05 32 23.7
KMHK 1046	SL 555	L	05 31 43.0
KMHK 1047		L	05 32 18.5
KMHK 1048	SL 561	L	05 32 04.9
KMHK 1049		L	05 32 40.4
KMHK 1050		L	05 32 36.5
KMHK 1051	[HS66] 348	L	05 32 15.5
KMHK 1052	SL 562	L	05 32 06.8
KMHK 1053		L	05 32 16.2
KMHK 1054	SL 564	L	05 32 49.6
KMHK 1055		L	05 33 01.5
KMHK 1056		L	05 32 30.0
KMHK 1057	NGC 2025	L	05 32 33.6
KMHK 1058	SL 565	L	05 32 48.9
KMHK 1059	SL 567	L	05 33 18.1
KMHK 1060		L	05 33 08.2
KMHK 1061	SL 566	L	05 32 50.3
KMHK 1062		L	05 32 37.4
KMHK 1063		L	05 33 37.2
KMHK 1064		L	05 32 39.8
KMHK 1065	SL 569	L	05 33 20.1
KMHK 1066	SL 573	L	05 33 44.8
KMHK 1067	NGC 2021	L	05 33 30.3
KMHK 1068	SL 568	L	05 33 03.4
KMHK 1069		L	05 33 26.8
KMHK 1070	OHSC 21	L	05 32 50.9
KMHK 1071		L	05 33 01.8
KMHK 1072	LW 243	L	05 32 41.0
KMHK 1073	SL 572	L	05 33 10.0
KMHK 1074		L	05 33 57.8
KMHK 1075		L	05 33 53.2
KMHK 1076		L	05 34 00.1
KMHK 1077		L	05 33 47.5
KMHK 1078	[HS66] 354	L	05 34 03.9
KMHK 1079		L	05 34 09.0
KMHK 1080	SL 578	L	05 34 19.5
KMHK 1081	LW 244	L	05 34 23.2
KMHK 1082		L	05 34 08.6
KMHK 1083		L	05 34 20.1
KMHK 1084	NGC 2031	L	05 33 41.3
KMHK 1085	SL 579	L	05 34 13.8
KMHK 1086	SL 580	L	05 34 11.1
KMHK 1087	[HS66] 355	L	05 33 47.0
KMHK 1088	SL 583	L	05 34 15.7
KMHK 1089	OHSC 22	L	05 34 50.8
KMHK 1090	[HS66] 358	L	05 34 35.2
KMHK 1091	SL 582	L	05 34 29.5
KMHK 1092	SL 576	L	05 33 14.2
KMHK 1093		L	05 34 41.7
KMHK 1094	SL 586	L	05 34 43.8
KMHK 1095		L	05 34 47.8
KMHK 1096	[HS66] 356		05 33 59.6
KMHK 1097	[HS66] 357	L	05 34 30.9
KMHK 1098		L	05 34 41.3
KMHK 1099	SL 585	L	05 34 30.8
KMHK 1100	SL 584	L	05 34 00.6
KMHK 1101	SL 588	L	05 34 39.3
KMHK 1102		L	05 34 04.2
KMHK 1103	LW 246	L	05 35 07.2
KMHK 1104	LW 245	L	05 35 06.8
KMHK 1105	NGC 2027	L	05 35 00.9
KMHK 1106	IC 2140	L	05 33 22.2
KMHK 1107		L	05 35 10.9
KMHK 1108	[HS66] 360	L	05 34 33.5
KMHK 1109		L	05 35 23.1
KMHK 1110	NGC 2038	L	05 34 42.4
KMHK 1111		L	05 34 54.3
KMHK 1112		L	05 35 15.2
KMHK 1113	NGC 2030	L	05 35 41.1
KMHK 1114	SL 593	L	05 35 08.1
KMHK 1115		L	05 35 41.7
KMHK 1116	[HS66] 361	L	05 34 56.5
KMHK 1117	SL 594	L	05 35 25.1
KMHK 1118		L	05 35 36.8
KMHK 1119		L	05 36 21.8
KMHK 1120		L	05 35 49.4
KMHK 1121	LW 247	L	05 34 59.1
KMHK 1122		L	05 35 38.6
KMHK 1123	SL 596	L	05 35 42.2

Table D.3: Cluster Cross-Reference

Name	Look Under	GX	2000.0 RA
KMHK 1124	[HS66] 363	L	05 35 29.1
KMHK 1125	NGC 2046	L	05 35 37.4
KMHK 1126	LW 248	L	05 36 24.5
KMHK 1127	SL 604	L	05 36 46.2
KMHK 1128		L	05 35 40.2
KMHK 1129	LW 250	L	05 36 38.2
KMHK 1130	SL 601	L	05 36 09.5
KMHK 1131		L	05 36 09.6
KMHK 1131	BRHT 16b	L	05 36 10.5
KMHK 1131	NGC 2042	L	05 36 09.6
KMHK 1132	NGC 2041	L	05 36 28.0
KMHK 1133		L	05 36 19.8
KMHK 1134		L	05 36 36.5
KMHK 1135	NGC 2051	L	05 36 07.5
KMHK 1136	SL 606	L	05 36 33.4
KMHK 1137	SL 607	L	05 36 31.7
KMHK 1138	[HS66] 365	L	05 36 21.6
KMHK 1139	[HS66] 367	L	05 37 03.8
KMHK 1140	NGC 2056	L	05 36 34.6
KMHK 1141	[HS66] 368	L	05 37 14.1
KMHK 1142	[HS66] 366	L	05 37 04.7
KMHK 1143	SL 615	L	05 36 56.1
KMHK 1144	SL 617	L	05 36 42.6
KMHK 1145	NGC 2057	L	05 36 55.1
KMHK 1146	SL 618	L	05 36 44.4
KMHK 1147		L	05 37 23.7
KMHK 1148	SL 612	L	05 36 21.5
KMHK 1149		L	05 37 44.2
KMHK 1150		L	05 37 19.8
KMHK 1151	SL 603	L	05 35 43.7
KMHK 1152	SL 619	L	05 36 46.5
KMHK 1153		L	05 37 44.2
KMHK 1154	NGC 2053	L	05 37 40.5
KMHK 1155	SL 620	L	05 36 28.4
KMHK 1156		L	05 37 12.1
KMHK 1157		L	05 37 16.2
KMHK 1158	SL 624	L	05 37 19.2
KMHK 1159		L	05 38 01.5
KMHK 1160	NGC 2065	L	05 37 35.9
KMHK 1161		L	05 38 11.9
KMHK 1162	SL 625	L	05 37 09.3
KMHK 1163	[HS66] 372	L	05 37 46.4
KMHK 1164	[HS66] 373	L	05 38 16.8
KMHK 1165	[HS66] 374	L	05 38 17.6
KMHK 1166	SL 628	L	05 38 30.1
KMHK 1167		L	05 38 23.0
KMHK 1168	LW 260	L	05 38 53.2
KMHK 1169	SL 629	L	05 38 21.5
KMHK 1170	NGC 2072	L	05 38 23.6
KMHK 1171	LW 261	L	05 39 11.0
KMHK 1172	[HS66] 375	L	05 38 14.5
KMHK 1173	NGC 2075	L	05 38 20.5
KMHK 1174		L	05 38 43.8
KMHK 1175		L	05 37 41.0
KMHK 1176	SL 635	L	05 39 08.6
KMHK 1177		L	05 38 26.6
KMHK 1178	IC 2146	L	05 37 47.4
KMHK 1179	SL 634	L	05 38 21.5
KMHK 1180	[HS66] 376	L	05 38 49.3
KMHK 1181		L	05 38 47.3
KMHK 1182	[HS66] 377	L	05 39 20.7
KMHK 1183	[HS66] 378	L	05 39 13.7
KMHK 1184	SL 638	L	05 39 37.1
KMHK 1185		L	05 39 03.1
KMHK 1186	[HS66] 379	L	05 38 55.5
KMHK 1187		L	05 38 57.7
KMHK 1188		L	05 39 29.9
KMHK 1189		L	05 39 49.3
KMHK 1190		L	05 39 49.8
KMHK 1191		L	05 39 10.1
KMHK 1192	[HS66] 380	L	05 40 02.0
KMHK 1193		L	05 39 27.9
KMHK 1194	NGC 2062	L	05 40 03.3
KMHK 1195		L	05 40 23.5
KMHK 1196		L	05 39 29.7
KMHK 1197		L	05 39 36.6
KMHK 1198	LW 266	L	05 40 30.7
KMHK 1199	[HS66] 381	L	05 39 43.7
KMHK 1200		L	05 39 39.3
KMHK 1201		L	05 40 02.8
KMHK 1202	SL 643	L	05 40 22.4
KMHK 1203		L	05 39 51.8
KMHK 1204		L	05 39 59.3
KMHK 1205	SL 646	L	05 39 53.9
KMHK 1206		L	05 40 33.6
KMHK 1207	SL 645	L	05 39 33.7
KMHK 1208	LW 263	L	05 39 08.4
KMHK 1209	[HS66] 382	L	05 40 36.1
KMHK 1210		L	05 40 07.8
KMHK 1211		L	05 40 40.6
KMHK 1212		L	05 40 40.7
KMHK 1213		L	05 40 02.8
KMHK 1214	SL 649	L	05 41 08.6
KMHK 1215	[HS66] 383	L	05 40 14.2
KMHK 1216	IC 2148	L	05 39 12.1
KMHK 1217		L	05 40 16.9
KMHK 1218	[HS66] 386	L	05 40 57.4
KMHK 1219	SL 648	L	05 40 10.4
KMHK 1220		L	05 40 12.7
KMHK 1221		L	05 41 04.6
KMHK 1222	SL 651	L	05 40 59.2
KMHK 1223	SL 647	L	05 39 34.7
KMHK 1224		L	05 41 08.1
KMHK 1225	SL 650	L	05 41 08.3
KMHK 1226	[HS66] 387	L	05 41 08.3
KMHK 1227	NGC 2088	L	05 40 59.7
KMHK 1228		L	05 40 39.3
KMHK 1229	NGC 2091	L	05 40 58.0
KMHK 1230		L	05 41 12.6
KMHK 1231	SL 654	L	05 41 10.3
KMHK 1232		L	05 41 01.9
KMHK 1233		L	05 41 42.1
KMHK 1234	SL 655	L	05 40 53.6
KMHK 1235	NGC 2092	L	05 41 22.2
KMHK 1236		L	05 40 37.8
KMHK 1237	SL 656	L	05 41 05.8
KMHK 1238		L	05 41 32.7
KMHK 1239	[HS66] 390	L	05 41 30.6
KMHK 1240		L	05 41 31.7
KMHK 1241	LW 272	L	05 42 25.7
KMHK 1242	[HS66] 391	L	05 41 28.8
KMHK 1243	LW 270	L	05 40 23.4
KMHK 1244		L	05 41 59.8
KMHK 1245	NGC 2093	L	05 41 49.1
KMHK 1246		L	05 42 01.4
KMHK 1247		L	05 42 01.6
KMHK 1248		L	05 41 58.9
KMHK 1249	SL 658	L	05 41 39.3
KMHK 1250	SL 663	L	05 42 29.5
KMHK 1251	NGC 2094	L	05 42 07.2
KMHK 1252	SL 661	L	05 41 41.3
KMHK 1253		L	05 42 21.1
KMHK 1254	SL 666	L	05 42 15.5
KMHK 1255		L	05 42 36.7
KMHK 1256		L	05 42 17.0
KMHK 1257	NGC 2100	L	05 42 08.3
KMHK 1258	[HS66] 396	L	05 42 28.2
KMHK 1259	NGC 2096	L	05 42 16.5
KMHK 1260		L	05 42 13.7
KMHK 1260	KMHK 1260	L	05 42 13.7
KMHK 1261	[HS66] 393	L	05 41 57.2
KMHK 1262		L	05 41 57.8
KMHK 1263	NGC 2098	L	05 42 29.8
KMHK 1264	NGC 2102	L	05 42 19.7
KMHK 1265	LW 278	L	05 43 11.9
KMHK 1266		L	05 42 03.0
KMHK 1267	[HS66] 395	L	05 42 03.5
KMHK 1268	SL 670	L	05 43 14.3
KMHK 1269	LW 276	L	05 43 11.9
KMHK 1270	[HS66] 397	L	05 42 17.3
KMHK 1271		L	05 42 45.5
KMHK 1272	NGC 2095	L	05 42 51.7
KMHK 1273		L	05 42 46.2
KMHK 1274	[HS66] 397A	L	05 42 42.0
KMHK 1275	SL 668	L	05 42 17.6
KMHK 1276	SL 671	L	05 42 57.3
KMHK 1277		L	05 42 36.7
KMHK 1278		L	05 43 28.0
KMHK 1279		L	05 42 51.2
KMHK 1280	[HS66] 398	L	05 42 42.0
KMHK 1281	SL 674	L	05 43 20.2
KMHK 1282	SL 675	L	05 43 15.6
KMHK 1283	SL 678	L	05 43 35.9
KMHK 1284	[HS66] 400	L	05 43 06.5
KMHK 1285	SL 672	L	05 42 41.7
KMHK 1286	SL 677	L	05 43 55.6
KMHK 1287	[HS66] 399	L	05 43 06.1
KMHK 1288	[HS66] 401	L	05 43 07.6
KMHK 1289	SL 676	L	05 43 08.8
KMHK 1290	SL 680	L	05 44 03.8
KMHK 1291	NGC 2107	L	05 43 11.9
KMHK 1292		L	05 43 44.8
KMHK 1293		L	05 43 44.9
KMHK 1294	NGC 2097	L	05 44 15.5
KMHK 1295		L	05 43 39.0
KMHK 1296		L	05 43 16.2
KMHK 1297		L	05 43 44.1
KMHK 1298	SL 685	L	05 44 15.1
KMHK 1299		L	05 43 33.9
KMHK 1300		L	05 44 03.5

Table D.3: Cluster Cross-Reference

Name	Look Under	GX	2000.0 RA
KMHK 1301		L	05 44 03.6
KMHK 1302	SL 684	L	05 43 37.8
KMHK 1303	SL 683	L	05 43 49.8
KMHK 1304	NGC 2108	L	05 43 56.9
KMHK 1305	[HS66] 402	L	05 44 07.5
KMHK 1306	NGC 2105	L	05 44 19.8
KMHK 1307		L	05 43 45.3
KMHK 1308	LW 285	L	05 44 35.4
KMHK 1309		L	05 44 09.2
KMHK 1310	SL 689	L	05 44 38.8
KMHK 1311	[HS66] 404	L	05 44 24.2
KMHK 1312	[HS66] 403	L	05 43 59.9
KMHK 1313		L	05 44 12.1
KMHK 1314	NGC 2109	L	05 44 22.7
KMHK 1315		L	05 44 26.5
KMHK 1316	SL 697	L	05 44 40.9
KMHK 1317		L	05 43 40.0
KMHK 1318	SL 694	L	05 45 06.5
KMHK 1319	SL 691	L	05 44 13.5
KMHK 1320	SL 692	L	05 44 13.7
KMHK 1321	[HS66] 405	L	05 44 12.7
KMHK 1322		L	05 45 09.2
KMHK 1323	SL 690	L	05 44 50.6
KMHK 1324	SL 696	L	05 45 14.1
KMHK 1325		L	05 44 48.0
KMHK 1326	SL 693	L	05 44 59.1
KMHK 1327	[HS66] 408	L	05 45 06.8
KMHK 1328	NGC 2111	L	05 44 32.5
KMHK 1329	SL 695	L	05 45 03.1
KMHK 1330	SL 701	L	05 45 32.7
KMHK 1331		L	05 44 45.9
KMHK 1332	[HS66] 406	L	05 44 46.1
KMHK 1333	SL 700	L	05 45 24.1
KMHK 1334	[HS66] 407	L	05 44 44.7
KMHK 1335	SL 698	L	05 45 12.6
KMHK 1336	[HS66] 409	L	05 44 56.4
KMHK 1337		L	05 44 57.7
KMHK 1338	OHSC 25	L	05 44 05.1
KMHK 1339	SL 702	L	05 45 06.4
KMHK 1340		L	05 44 27.3
KMHK 1341		L	05 44 54.5
KMHK 1342	NGC 2113	L	05 45 24.5
KMHK 1343	SL 704	L	05 45 24.3
KMHK 1344	[HS66] 410	L	05 45 31.0
KMHK 1345	[HS66] 411	L	05 45 50.0
KMHK 1346	SL 708	L	05 46 22.6
KMHK 1347	[HS66] 412	L	05 45 56.4
KMHK 1348		L	05 46 09.6
KMHK 1349		L	05 46 16.4
KMHK 1350	SL 709	L	05 46 14.7
KMHK 1351	NGC 2114	L	05 46 12.3
KMHK 1352	SL 703	L	05 44 54.3
KMHK 1353	SL 707	L	05 46 12.3
KMHK 1354		L	05 46 30.8
KMHK 1355		L	05 46 49.1
KMHK 1356	SL 710	L	05 46 58.1
KMHK 1357	LW 294	L	05 46 02.5
KMHK 1358	[HS66] 413	L	05 46 22.3
KMHK 1359	SL 711	L	05 46 55.0
KMHK 1360	SL 712	L	05 46 58.7

Table D.3: Cluster Cross-Reference

Name	Look Under	GX	2000.0 RA
KMHK 1361	[HS66] 415	L	05 47 00.1
KMHK 1362	SL 713	L	05 46 26.1
KMHK 1363		L	05 46 51.9
KMHK 1364		L	05 46 51.0
KMHK 1365	[HS66] 414	L	05 46 41.0
KMHK 1366	SL 714	L	05 47 17.0
KMHK 1367	SL 716	L	05 46 46.3
KMHK 1368	LW 295	L	05 46 18.7
KMHK 1369		L	05 47 12.6
KMHK 1370	NGC 2116	L	05 47 14.5
KMHK 1371	[HS66] 416	L	05 47 01.9
KMHK 1372	LW 297	L	05 46 07.5
KMHK 1373	SL 720	L	05 47 46.9
KMHK 1374	[HS66] 417	L	05 47 10.2
KMHK 1375		L	05 47 29.8
KMHK 1376		L	05 47 36.4
KMHK 1377	NGC 2117	L	05 47 47.2
KMHK 1378		L	05 47 53.6
KMHK 1379	SL 719	L	05 47 36.7
KMHK 1380	NGC 2118	L	05 47 39.6
KMHK 1381		L	05 48 21.4
KMHK 1382		L	05 47 37.7
KMHK 1383		L	05 47 33.2
KMHK 1384	SL 722	L	05 47 41.5
KMHK 1385	[HS66] 419	L	05 48 19.7
KMHK 1386		L	05 48 02.3
KMHK 1387	SL 721	L	05 47 30.9
KMHK 1388	SL 724	L	05 48 53.0
KMHK 1389		L	05 48 12.4
KMHK 1390	SL 726	L	05 48 59.4
KMHK 1391		L	05 49 01.8
KMHK 1392		L	05 48 15.4
KMHK 1393	SL 727	L	05 49 01.9
KMHK 1394	SL 723	L	05 47 44.8
KMHK 1395		L	05 48 52.6
KMHK 1396	LW 309	L	05 49 04.6
KMHK 1397	SL 728	L	05 49 02.7
KMHK 1398	NGC 2121	L	05 48 12.8
KMHK 1399	SL 729	L	05 49 20.6
KMHK 1400		L	05 48 59.5
KMHK 1401	[HS66] 421	L	05 48 56.2
KMHK 1402		L	05 49 09.5
KMHK 1403	[HS66] 420	L	05 48 28.9
KMHK 1404		L	05 49 04.6
KMHK 1405		L	05 48 15.6
KMHK 1406	[HS66] 422	L	05 49 14.2
KMHK 1407	SL 730	L	05 49 11.5
KMHK 1408		L	05 48 46.8
KMHK 1409		L	05 49 33.4
KMHK 1410		L	05 48 53.5
KMHK 1411		L	05 49 04.5
KMHK 1412	SL 733	L	05 48 44.7
KMHK 1413	SL 734	L	05 48 54.2
KMHK 1414	NGC 2122	L	05 48 55
KMHK 1415	SL 732	L	05 49 35.9
KMHK 1416		L	05 49 46.7
KMHK 1417	SL 738	L	05 50 08.2
KMHK 1418	SL 739	L	05 50 00.4
KMHK 1419		L	05 49 42.2
KMHK 1420	SL 736	L	05 49 16.6

Table D.3: Cluster Cross-Reference

Name	Look Under	GX	2000.0 RA
KMHK 1421		L	05 49 38.5
KMHK 1422		L	05 49 50.6
KMHK 1423		L	05 50 22.6
KMHK 1424	[H60b] 7	L	05 50 03.2
KMHK 1425	[HS66] 424	L	05 49 35.9
KMHK 1426	NGC 2120	L	05 50 34.8
KMHK 1427	SL 740	L	05 49 45.7
KMHK 1428		L	05 50 07.9
KMHK 1429	[HS66] 426	L	05 50 25.2
KMHK 1430	SL 743	L	05 50 23.7
KMHK 1431	[HS66] 425	L	05 50 02.1
KMHK 1432	SL 737	L	05 48 44.1
KMHK 1433	LW 318	L	05 50 43.0
KMHK 1434	SL 744	L	05 49 56.1
KMHK 1435		L	05 49 56.4
KMHK 1436		L	05 50 47.4
KMHK 1437	SL 748	L	05 50 15.5
KMHK 1438	SL 745	L	05 50 38.2
KMHK 1439	LW 319	L	05 51 06.1
KMHK 1440		L	05 50 44.1
KMHK 1441	SL 747	L	05 50 09.9
KMHK 1442	SL 746	L	05 50 45.3
KMHK 1443	[HS66] 427	L	05 50 17.6
KMHK 1444	[HS66] 428	L	05 50 50.3
KMHK 1445		L	05 50 45.1
KMHK 1446	LW 315	L	05 49 27.0
KMHK 1447	LW 320	L	05 51 21.2
KMHK 1448		L	05 50 28.2
KMHK 1449	SL 749	L	05 50 00.1
KMHK 1450	[HS66] 431	L	05 51 12.1
KMHK 1451	NGC 2125	L	05 50 53.0
KMHK 1452	LW 321	L	05 51 18.4
KMHK 1453	[HS66] 429	L	05 50 52.6
KMHK 1454		L	05 50 48.8
KMHK 1455	LW 323	L	05 51 45.9
KMHK 1456	[HS66] 430	L	05 50 48.4
KMHK 1457	[HS66] 432	L	05 51 03.5
KMHK 1458	NGC 2123	L	05 51 43.5
KMHK 1459		L	05 51 14.1
KMHK 1460		L	05 50 59.6
KMHK 1461	SL 753	L	05 51 48.8
KMHK 1462	NGC 2127	L	05 51 21.7
KMHK 1463	SL 752	L	05 51 37.3
KMHK 1464		L	05 50 36.0
KMHK 1465	[HS66] 433	L	05 51 47.3
KMHK 1466	[HS66] 434	L	05 51 36.6
KMHK 1467	SL 756	L	05 51 29.1
KMHK 1468		L	05 52 02.2
KMHK 1469	OHSC 27	L	05 52 29.7
KMHK 1470	[HS66] 436	L	05 51 47.8
KMHK 1471	NGC 2133	L	05 51 29.3
KMHK 1472	[HS66] 435	L	05 51 35.9
KMHK 1473	SL 754	L	05 50 35.6
KMHK 1474	[HS66] 437	L	05 52 15.5
KMHK 1475		L	05 52 07.4
KMHK 1476	NGC 2130	L	05 52 23.7
KMHK 1477	[HS66] 438	L	05 51 53.1
KMHK 1478	[HS66] 439	L	05 52 07.1
KMHK 1479	SL 759	L	05 52 09.4
KMHK 1480	NGC 2134	L	05 51 56.5

Table D.3: Cluster Cross-Reference

Name	Look Under	GX	2000.0 RA
KMHK 1481		L	05 52 32.0
KMHK 1482	SL 761	L	05 52 10.1
KMHK 1483	[HS66] 440	L	05 52 35.7
KMHK 1484		L	05 53 12.1
KMHK 1485	[HS66] 441	L	05 52 37.8
KMHK 1486		L	05 53 06.4
KMHK 1487	[HS66] 442	L	05 53 04.6
KMHK 1488	SL 763	L	05 52 53.7
KMHK 1489		L	05 52 57.3
KMHK 1490	NGC 2136	L	05 52 58.9
KMHK 1491		L	05 53 23.0
KMHK 1492	[HS66] 443	L	05 52 53.5
KMHK 1493	SL 768	L	05 53 54.5
KMHK 1494	SL 766	L	05 53 00.3
KMHK 1495	NGC 2137	L	05 53 11.9
KMHK 1496	NGC 2135	L	05 53 35.1
KMHK 1497	[HS66] 444	L	05 53 39.5
KMHK 1498	SL 767	L	05 53 12.2
KMHK 1499	SL 769	L	05 53 23.9
KMHK 1500		L	05 53 49.0
KMHK 1501		L	05 53 39.4
KMHK 1502	[HS66] 445	L	05 53 50.2
KMHK 1503	SL 770	L	05 53 42.8
KMHK 1504		L	05 53 15.7
KMHK 1505	SL 771	L	05 54 02.6
KMHK 1506	SL 775	L	05 53 27.0
KMHK 1507		L	05 53 28.2
KMHK 1508	SL 772	L	05 53 53.0
KMHK 1509	LW 329	L	05 54 37.6
KMHK 1510		L	05 54 33.9
KMHK 1511	NGC 2140	L	05 54 16.0
KMHK 1512	SL 774	L	05 54 14.6
KMHK 1513		L	05 54 30.5
KMHK 1514		L	05 54 06.5
KMHK 1515	SL 776	L	05 53 38.9
KMHK 1516	NGC 2138	L	05 54 49.7
KMHK 1517	SL 779	L	05 54 11.8
KMHK 1518	LW 332	L	05 55 08.1
KMHK 1519	SL 778	L	05 54 55.4
KMHK 1520	NGC 2145	L	05 54 22.6
KMHK 1521	[HS66] 447	L	05 54 58.5
KMHK 1522		L	05 55 10.7
KMHK 1523	[HS66] 446	L	05 54 38.5
KMHK 1524	SL 781	L	05 54 42.2
KMHK 1525	SL 782	L	05 55 09.1
KMHK 1526	[HS66] 448	L	05 54 54.0
KMHK 1527		L	05 55 40.6
KMHK 1528		L	05 54 57.7
KMHK 1529		L	05 55 33.2
KMHK 1530		L	05 56 08.6
KMHK 1531	NGC 2147	L	05 55 46.4
KMHK 1532	LW 335	L	05 55 57.1
KMHK 1533		L	05 55 52.6
KMHK 1534		L	05 55 54.2
KMHK 1535	SL 783	L	05 54 39.1
KMHK 1536	SL 788	L	05 55 45.8
KMHK 1537		L	05 56 06.4
KMHK 1538	SL 787	L	05 55 59.2
KMHK 1539		L	05 56 39.9
KMHK 1540	[H60b] 9	L	05 56 01.3

Table D.3: Cluster Cross-Reference

Name	Look Under	GX	2000.0 RA
KMHK 1541	NGC 2151	L	05 56 20.8
KMHK 1542		L	05 56 24.7
KMHK 1543		L	05 56 53.5
KMHK 1544	NGC 2161	L	05 55 42.3
KMHK 1545	SL 791	L	05 56 55.0
KMHK 1546		L	05 57 19.1
KMHK 1547		L	05 56 52.5
KMHK 1548		L	05 57 35.1
KMHK 1549		L	05 57 15.9
KMHK 1550		L	05 57 23.5
KMHK 1551	NGC 2154	L	05 57 38.5
KMHK 1552	SL 795	L	05 57 52.1
KMHK 1553		L	05 57 40.2
KMHK 1554		L	05 57 23.3
KMHK 1555	NGC 2153	L	05 57 52.3
KMHK 1556	SL 798	L	05 58 12.2
KMHK 1557	SL 797	L	05 57 23.1
KMHK 1558	NGC 2157	L	05 57 34.8
KMHK 1559		L	05 57 50.5
KMHK 1560	NGC 2156	L	05 57 50.0
KMHK 1561	NGC 2159	L	05 58 02.7
KMHK 1562	SL 800	L	05 58 20.2
KMHK 1563	NGC 2155	L	05 58 32.3
KMHK 1564	NGC 2160	L	05 58 13.0
KMHK 1565	SL 805	L	05 57 43.0
KMHK 1566		L	05 58 20.8
KMHK 1567	SL 806	L	05 58 49.9
KMHK 1568		L	05 58 46.9
KMHK 1569	SL 804	L	05 57 38.1
KMHK 1570	NGC 2173	L	05 57 58.0
KMHK 1571		L	05 58 26.2
KMHK 1572	IC 2161	L	05 57 25.5
KMHK 1573	NGC 2171	L	05 58 52.9
KMHK 1574	NGC 2164	L	05 58 55.6
KMHK 1575	SL 810	L	05 59 10.8
KMHK 1576	NGC 2166	L	05 59 33.0
KMHK 1577		L	05 59 50.2
KMHK 1578		L	05 59 58.9
KMHK 1579	NGC 2162	L	06 00 31.4
KMHK 1580	NGC 2172	L	06 00 05.6
KMHK 1581	LW 354	L	06 00 37.7
KMHK 1582	LW 352	L	06 00 19.7
KMHK 1583		L	06 00 16.0
KMHK 1584	SL 813	L	06 00 32.7
KMHK 1585		L	06 00 50.0
KMHK 1586		L	06 00 52.9
KMHK 1587		L	06 00 31.5
KMHK 1588	SL 817	L	06 00 37.9
KMHK 1589	NGC 2176	L	06 01 19.4
KMHK 1590	NGC 2177	L	06 01 15.7
KMHK 1591		L	06 02 02.6
KMHK 1592		L	06 01 30.3
KMHK 1593		L	06 01 52.4
KMHK 1594		L	06 01 25.9
KMHK 1595	SL 818	L	06 01 38.9
KMHK 1596	SL 823	L	06 02 18.1
KMHK 1597	LW 361	L	06 02 09.5
KMHK 1598	SL 822	L	06 02 06.9
KMHK 1599	SL 821	L	06 01 23.7
KMHK 1600	SL 824	L	06 02 28.4

Table D.3: Cluster Cross-Reference

Name	Look Under	GX	2000.0 RA
KMHK 1601	NGC 2190	L	06 01 02.3
KMHK 1602	NGC 2181	L	06 02 43.1
KMHK 1603		L	06 02 30.6
KMHK 1604	OHSC 29	L	06 01 12.3
KMHK 1605		L	06 02 28.9
KMHK 1606	SL 826	L	06 01 53.5
KMHK 1607		L	06 02 51.7
KMHK 1608	LW 360	L	06 01 30.0
KMHK 1609	SL 827	L	06 03 11.0
KMHK 1610	LW 368	L	06 03 02.0
KMHK 1611		L	06 03 20.7
KMHK 1612	SL 829	L	06 03 31.3
KMHK 1613	[HS66] 450	L	06 03 20.5
KMHK 1614		L	06 03 29.2
KMHK 1615		L	06 03 43.7
KMHK 1616	SL 828	L	06 02 13.6
KMHK 1617		L	06 03 43.8
KMHK 1618	LW 369	L	06 02 56.0
KMHK 1619		L	06 03 42.7
KMHK 1620	OHSC 30	L	06 02 31.5
KMHK 1621		L	06 03 30.1
KMHK 1622		L	06 03 54.3
KMHK 1623	SL 831	L	06 04 34.2
KMHK 1624	SL 830	L	06 04 13.0
KMHK 1625	LW 373	L	06 03 14.0
KMHK 1626		L	06 04 11.1
KMHK 1627	SL 833	L	06 05 03.6
KMHK 1628	SL 832	L	06 04 24.5
KMHK 1629	SL 837	L	06 05 52.2
KMHK 1630	LW 381	L	06 05 43.6
KMHK 1631	LW 383	L	06 05 38.7
KMHK 1632		L	06 05 56.2
KMHK 1633	NGC 2193	L	06 06 17.4
KMHK 1634		L	06 05 26.1
KMHK 1635	LW 386	L	06 06 17.5
KMHK 1636	NGC 2197	L	06 06 07.4
KMHK 1637		L	06 05 09.5
KMHK 1638	LW 384	L	06 05 35.4
KMHK 1639	NGC 2203	L	06 04 41.6
KMHK 1640	SL 835	L	06 04 48.1
KMHK 1641	LW 388	L	06 06 19.9
KMHK 1642	LW 390	L	06 06 26.9
KMHK 1643	LW 389	L	06 06 09.3
KMHK 1644	LW 392	L	06 07 00.9
KMHK 1645	SL 840	L	06 06 28.8
KMHK 1646		L	06 07 12.0
KMHK 1647	LW 395	L	06 07 30.7
KMHK 1648	LW 393	L	06 06 32.2
KMHK 1649		L	06 06 20.9
KMHK 1650		L	06 07 51.8
KMHK 1651	LW 394	L	06 07 00.3
KMHK 1652	SL 842	L	06 08 15.5
KMHK 1653	SL 841	L	06 08 01.6
KMHK 1654	SL 834	L	06 07 30.6
KMHK 1655	SL 843	L	06 08 08.5
KMHK 1656	SL 845	L	06 08 38.6
KMHK 1657	LW 397	L	06 07 28.9
KMHK 1658	SL 844	L	06 08 32.8
KMHK 1659	SL 846	L	06 08 39.2
KMHK 1660	LW 406	L	06 09 01.4

Table D.3: Cluster Cross-Reference

Name	Look Under	GX	2000.0 RA
KMHK 1661	LW 404	L	06 08 32.3
KMHK 1662	LW 407	L	06 08 58.3
KMHK 1663	LW 409	L	06 09 03.5
KMHK 1664	SL 848	L	06 08 17.5
KMHK 1665		L	06 09 25.0
KMHK 1666	LW 410	L	06 08 56.4
KMHK 1667	LW 411	L	06 09 30.1
KMHK 1668		L	06 08 53.1
KMHK 1669	NGC 2209	L	06 08 34.8
KMHK 1670		L	06 09 51.5
KMHK 1671	SL 850	L	06 10 12.7
KMHK 1672	LW 414	L	06 10 03.5
KMHK 1673	SL 852	L	06 10 21.5
KMHK 1674	SL 855	L	06 10 53.5
KMHK 1675	SL 853	L	06 10 11.0
KMHK 1676		L	06 09 46.4
KMHK 1677	SL 854	L	06 10 55.2
KMHK 1678		L	06 11 21.5
KMHK 1679	LW 421	L	06 10 53.8
KMHK 1680		L	06 11 28.7
KMHK 1681	NGC 2213	L	06 10 42.2
KMHK 1682	NGC 2210	L	06 11 31.3
KMHK 1683		L	06 11 45.2
KMHK 1684	LW 422	L	06 11 23.2
KMHK 1685	OHSC 31	L	06 11 16.8
KMHK 1686	SL 859	L	06 12 35.7
KMHK 1687	LW 425	L	06 12 45.1
KMHK 1688	NGC 2214	L	06 12 56.1
KMHK 1689	LW 427	L	06 13 07.1
KMHK 1690	LW 430	L	06 13 14.7
KMHK 1691	SL 861	L	06 13 16.6
KMHK 1692	SL 862	L	06 13 27.4
KMHK 1693	SL 863	L	06 13 57.6
KMHK 1694	SL 864	L	06 13 57.0
KMHK 1695		L	06 14 04.1
KMHK 1696	SL 865	L	06 14 07.8
KMHK 1697	LW 436	L	06 14 26.3
KMHK 1698	SL 866	L	06 14 32.4
KMHK 1699		L	06 14 40.9
KMHK 1700	SL 868	L	06 14 22.5
KMHK 1701	SL 867	L	06 14 03.6
KMHK 1702		L	06 13 56.2
KMHK 1703		L	06 14 03.5
KMHK 1704	SL 869	L	06 14 41.1
KMHK 1705	SL 870	L	06 14 28.5
KMHK 1706		L	06 14 44.8
KMHK 1707		L	06 14 28.8
KMHK 1708	SL 871	L	06 15 25.6
KMHK 1709	SL 872	L	06 15 02.1
KMHK 1710	LW 444	L	06 15 57.5
KMHK 1711		L	06 15 40.2
KMHK 1712	LW 445	L	06 15 47.3
KMHK 1713	SL 874	L	06 15 57.8
KMHK 1714	OHSC 33	L	06 15 17.1
KMHK 1715	SL 873	L	06 16 15.4
KMHK 1716	LW 448	L	06 16 36.2
KMHK 1717	LW 449	L	06 16 48.2
KMHK 1718		L	06 17 05.2
KMHK 1719		L	06 17 19.3
KMHK 1720	LW 451	L	06 17 44.2

Table D.3: Cluster Cross-Reference

Name	Look Under	GX	2000.0 RA
KMHK 1721	SL 876	L	06 18 07.9
KMHK 1722	LW 450	L	06 17 42.8
KMHK 1723	LW 454	L	06 18 11.1
KMHK 1724	SL 877	L	06 17 46.3
KMHK 1725	LW 458	L	06 19 11.2
KMHK 1726	SL 881	L	06 18 44.9
KMHK 1727	LW 459	L	06 19 17.6
KMHK 1728	SL 882	L	06 19 04.1
KMHK 1729		L	06 19 04.9
KMHK 1730	LW 460	L	06 19 15.2
KMHK 1731	SL 883	L	06 19 56.0
KMHK 1732		L	06 19 46.8
KMHK 1733	LW 463	L	06 19 46.4
KMHK 1734	LW 462	L	06 19 40.8
KMHK 1735		L	06 19 41.5
KMHK 1736		L	06 20 22.3
KMHK 1737	NGC 2231	L	06 20 43.7
KMHK 1738	SL 885	L	06 21 11.5
KMHK 1739		L	06 21 03.6
KMHK 1740	SL 886	L	06 21 26.3
KMHK 1741		L	06 21 33.6
KMHK 1742	LW 469	L	06 21 34.0
KMHK 1743	NGC 2241	L	06 22 52.0
KMHK 1744	LW 470	L	06 22 24.0
KMHK 1745		L	06 22 24.8
KMHK 1746	LW 472	L	06 23 11.8
KMHK 1747		L	06 23 34.4
KMHK 1748	LW 474	L	06 23 29.7
KMHK 1749	SL 890	L	06 23 02.9
KMHK 1750	LW 475	L	06 23 23.2
KMHK 1751	OHSC 34	L	06 24 28.7
KMHK 1752	SL 891	L	06 24 49.6
KMHK 1753	SL 892	L	06 25 16.0
KMHK 1754	OHSC 35	L	06 25 42.0
KMHK 1755	NGC 2249	L	06 25 49.5
KMHK 1756	NGC 2257	L	06 30 12.4
KMHK 1757	OHSC 36	L	06 29 41.9
KMHK 1758	SL 896	L	06 29 57.7
KMHK 1759	LW 482	L	06 32 23.6
KMHK 1760	SL 897	L	06 33 01.2
KMHK 1761		L	06 33 00.1
KMHK 1762	OHSC 37	L	07 07 39.9
Kod 1			18 15 07
KOHX 13	NGC 6624	g	18 23 40.5
Kron 1		S	00 21 26.7
Kron 2	NGC 121	S	00 26 48.7
Kron 3		S	00 24 46.4
Kron 4		S	00 23 03.5
Kron 5		S	00 24 42.8
Kron 6		S	00 25 26.3
Kron 7		S	00 27 45.1
Kron 8		S	00 28 01.9
Kron 9		S	00 30 00.7
Kron 10	NGC 152	S	00 32 55.5
Kron 11		S	00 36 27.9
Kron 12	NGC 176	S	00 35 58.6
Kron 13		S	00 35 41.4
Kron 14		S	00 37 21
Kron 15		S	00 40 13.3
Kron 16		S	00 40 33.8

Table D.3: Cluster Cross-Reference

Name	Look Under	GX	2000.0 RA
Kron 17		S	00 41 01.0
Kron 18	NGC 220	S	00 40 30.6
Kron 19	NGC 222	S	00 40 44.1
Kron 20	NGC 231	S	00 41 06.2
Kron 21		S	00 41 23.8
Kron 22	NGC 242	S	00 43 33.9
Kron 23	NGC 256	S	00 45 54.4
Kron 24	NGC 265	S	00 47 11.6
Kron 25		S	00 48 00.7
Kron 26	NGC 269	S	00 48 21.3
Kron 27		S	00 48 13.7
Kron 28		S	00 51 40.6
Kron 29		S	00 51 52.9
Kron 30		S	00 52 35.4
Kron 31		S	00 53 00.6
Kron 32	NGC 299	S	00 53 24.8
Kron 33	NGC 306	S	00 54 14.8
Kron 34		S	00 55 33.0
Kron 35	NGC 330	S	00 56 18.7
Kron 36	NGC 339	S	00 57 45.4
Kron 37		S	00 57 47.5
Kron 38		S	00 57 48.3
Kron 40	IC 1611	S	00 59 48.1
Kron 41	IC 1612	S	01 00 01.4
Kron 42		S	01 00 34.4
Kron 43		S	01 00 49.7
Kron 44		S	01 02 05.2
Kron 45		S	01 02 47.9
Kron 46	NGC 361	S	01 02 11.3
Kron 47		S	01 03 11.5
Kron 49	NGC 376	S	01 03 53.5
Kron 50		S	01 04 36.2
Kron 51	NGC 395	S	01 05 11
Kron 52	IC 1624	S	01 05 21.5
Kron 53	IC 1626	S	01 06 13.8
Kron 54		S	01 06 47.8
Kron 55		S	01 07 32.4
Kron 56		S	01 07 27.9
Kron 57		S	01 08 14.5
Kron 58	NGC 419	S	01 08 17.7
Kron 59	NGC 416	S	01 07 59.0
Kron 60	NGC 411	S	01 07 55.7
Kron 61		S	01 09 03.5
Kron 62	NGC 422	S	01 09 25.4
Kron 63		S	01 10 47.9
Kron 64	IC 1660	S	01 12 38.4
Kron 66	NGC 460	S	01 14 37.9
Kron 67	NGC 465	S	01 15 42.7
Kron 68		S	01 15 33.9
Kron 69	NGC 458	S	01 14 53.2
Ksi Tucanae	NGC 104	g	00 24 05.2
Lacaille II-6	Trumpler 10		08 47 45
Lacaille III-3	IC 2395		08 42 31
[LAL96] 1			03 28.9
[LAL96] 2			03 29.2
Lambda Centauri cl	Collinder 249		11 38 20.4
Lambda Orionis	Collinder 69		05 35.0
Latysev 1			02 52
Latysev 2			13 44.4
LBN 173.58-01.75	IC 410		05 22.0

Table D.3: Cluster Cross-Reference

Name	Look Under	GX	2000.0 RA
LBN 807	IC 410		05 22.0
LBN 809	Skiff J0507.2+3050		05 07 13.8
[LDEG91] 1			05 41 43
[LDEG91] 2			05 41 44
[LDEG91] 3			05 46 40
[LDEG91] 4			05 47 08
LDN 1630	[LDEG91] 1		05 41 43
LDN 1630	[LDEG91] 2		05 41 44
LDN 1630	[LDEG91] 3		05 46 40
LDN 1630	[LDEG91] 4		05 47 08
LDN 1680	Grasdalen 1		16 23.8
Lederman 1			02 27 18
LeDrew 1			00 53.3
LeDrew 2			20 44.0
LeDrew 3	Alessi J20046-1030		20 04.6
LeDrew 4			04 46.4
LeDrew 5			18 18.6
LeDrew 6			19 13.3
LeDrew 7			18 14.5
LeDrew 8			17 49.3
Leo B	Leo II		11 13 29.3
Leo I			10 08 27.5
Leo II			11 13 29.3
Levy-W. J1948.2+3743			19 48 12.1
Levy-W. J2108.8+0620			21 08 48.4
Levy-W. J2204.3+4508			22 04 23.3
Levy-W. J2340.6+5618			23 40 39.6
LH 1	NGC 1712	L	04 50 57.1
LH 4	NGC 1731	L	04 53 30.4
LH 5		L	04 54.2
LH 5	Henize N 83	L	04 54.2
LH 5	NGC 1737	L	04 53 58.8
LH 5	NGC 1743	L	04 54 03.4
LH 5	NGC 1745	L	04 54 20.9
LH 5	NGC 1748	L	04 54 24.7
LH 6		L	04 55 11.1
LH 7	SL 111	L	04 55 42.3
LH 11	[HS66] 74	L	04 57 11.6
LH 12		L	04 57.4
LH 13		L	04 57 44.1
LH 14	NGC 1776	L	04 58 39.2
LH 15	NGC 1787	L	05 00.0
LH 16		L	05 03 05.5
LH 17		L	05 03.7
LH 18	NGC 1823	L	05 03 23.8
LH 19	NGC 1814	L	05 03 45.4
LH 20		L	05 04.2
LH 21		L	05 04 27.5
LH 22		L	05 04.7
LH 23	SL 209	L	05 04 37.7
LH 24		L	05 05 09
LH 24	NGC 1833	L	05 04 22.3
LH 24	NGC 1837	L	05 04 56
LH 24	NGC 1845	L	05 05 12
LH 25		L	05 06 08.8
LH 26		L	05 05 57
LH 26	NGC 1845	L	05 05 12
LH 27		L	05 06 58.0
LH 28	SL 256	L	05 08 10.3
LH 29		L	05 07.9

Table D.3: Cluster Cross-Reference

Name	Look Under	GX	2000.0 RA
LH 30		L	05 08.2
LH 31		L	05 09 56.3
LH 32	SL 281	L	05 10 33.4
LH 33		L	05 11.2
LH 34	SL 310	L	05 12 29.5
LH 35		L	05 13.3
LH 36	NGC 1873	L	05 14 01.7
LH 37		L	05 13 53.6
LH 37	NGC 1869	L	05 13 53.6
LH 38	NGC 1871	L	05 13 52.4
LH 39		L	05 13.9
LH 40	NGC 1914	L	05 17 39.4
LH 41	NGC 1910	L	05 18 23.8
LH 42		L	05 19 17.5
LH 43	NGC 1923	L	05 21 34.5
LH 44		L	05 21.2
LH 46	NGC 1926	L	05 20 35.2
LH 47	IC 2126	L	05 21 49.7
LH 48	NGC 1937	L	05 22 23.0
LH 49		L	05 22 55
LH 50		L	05 23.7
LH 50	SL 435	L	05 23 30.5
LH 51	SL 456	L	05 25 25.3
LH 52		L	05 25.9
LH 53		L	05 26.1
LH 54	NGC 1955	L	05 26 04.2
LH 55		L	05 26.4
LH 56		L	05 26.2
LH 57		L	05 26 32
LH 59		L	05 26 42
LH 59	NGC 1969	L	05 26 32.1
LH 59	NGC 1971	L	05 26 45.0
LH 59	NGC 1972	L	05 26 48.1
LH 60	NGC 1968	L	05 27 39.7
LH 61		L	05 27 51
LH 62		L	05 27 46.4
LH 63	NGC 1974	L	05 28 00.6
LH 64		L	05 29.0
LH 65		L	05 30 04.1
LH 66		L	05 30.1
LH 67		L	05 31 09
LH 68	SL 541	L	05 31 18.1
LH 70	[HS66] 341	L	05 31 59.8
LH 71	SL 552	L	05 31 43.5
LH 72	SL 553	L	05 32 29.2
LH 73		L	05 31 55.6
LH 74	NGC 2015	L	05 31 48
LH 75	NGC 2011	L	05 32 19.8
LH 76	NGC 2014	L	05 32 21.7
LH 77		L	05 33 16
LH 78	SL 567	L	05 33 18.1
LH 79	NGC 2021	L	05 33 30.3
LH 80	NGC 2028	L	05 33 48.7
LH 81		L	05 34.6
LH 82		L	05 35 29
LH 83		L	05 35.8
LH 84	NGC 2027	L	05 35 00.9
LH 85		L	05 35.6
LH 86		L	05 35 54
LH 87		L	05 35 01

Table D.3: Cluster Cross-Reference

Name	Look Under	GX	2000.0 RA
LH 88	NGC 2040	L	05 36 06.1
LH 89		L	05 36.2
LH 89	NGC 2042	L	05 36 09.6
LH 90		L	05 36.1
LH 91		L	05 36.7
LH 92		L	05 36.7
LH 92	NGC 2055	L	05 37 08
LH 93	SL 609	L	05 36 40.0
LH 94	SL 610	L	05 36 42
LH 95	[HS66] 367	L	05 37 03.8
LH 96		L	05 37.0
LH 96	NGC 2055	L	05 37 08
LH 96	[HS66] 370	L	05 36 46
LH 97		L	05 37.6
LH 97	AH03 J0537.3-6919	L	05 37 22.8
LH 97	BRHT 54b	L	05 37 47
LH 97	LH 96	L	05 37.0
LH 97	NGC 2050	L	05 36 54
LH 97	[HS66] 371	L	05 37 45
LH 98	[HS66] 370	L	05 36 46
LH 99	NGC 2060	L	05 37 48
LH 100	NGC 2070	L	05 38 42.4
LH 101	NGC 2074	L	05 39 03
LH 102		L	05 40.0
LH 103		L	05 40 00
LH 105		L	05 39 54
LH 106		L	05 40.8
LH 107		L	05 40.7
LH 108		L	05 41.6
LH 109	NGC 2093	L	05 41 49.1
LH 110		L	05 41.7
LH 111		L	05 42 08.3
LH 112		L	05 42 29.1
LH 113	[HS66] 397A	L	05 42 42.0
LH 114		L	05 43 18
LH 115		L	05 44.1
LH 116		L	05 45.0
LH 116	SL 697	L	05 44 40.9
LH 116	[HS66] 404	L	05 44 24.2
LH 117		L	05 48 53.8
LH 118		L	05 49.8
LH 119		L	05 49 59.5
LH 120		L	05 50 31
LH 121	[HS66] 437	L	05 52 15.5
LH 122		L	05 55 55
LHA 115-N 66A	NGC 346	S	00 59.1
Liller 1		g	17 33 24.5
Liller I	Liller 1	g	17 33 24.5
Lindsay 1		S	00 03 53.2
Lindsay 2		S	00 12 56.1
Lindsay 3		S	00 18 25.3
Lindsay 4	Kron 1	S	00 21 26.7
Lindsay 5		S	00 22 41.1
Lindsay 6	Kron 4	S	00 23 03.5
Lindsay 7	Kron 5	S	00 24 42.8
Lindsay 8	Kron 3	S	00 24 46.4
Lindsay 9	Kron 6	S	00 25 26.3
Lindsay 10	NGC 121	S	00 26 48.7
Lindsay 11	Kron 7	S	00 27 45.1
Lindsay 12	Kron 8	S	00 28 01.9

Table D.3: Cluster Cross-Reference

Name	Look Under	GX	2000.0 RA
Lindsay 13	Kron 9	S	00 30 00.7
Lindsay 14		S	00 32 41.6
Lindsay 15	NGC 152	S	00 32 55.5
Lindsay 16	NGC 176	S	00 35 58.6
Lindsay 17	Kron 13	S	00 35 41.4
Lindsay 18	Kron 14	S	00 37 21
Lindsay 19		S	00 37 42.3
Lindsay 20	Kron 11	S	00 36 27.9
Lindsay 21	Kron 15	S	00 40 13.3
Lindsay 22	NGC 220	S	00 40 30.6
Lindsay 23	Kron 16	S	00 40 33.8
Lindsay 24	NGC 222	S	00 40 44.1
Lindsay 25	NGC 231	S	00 41 06.2
Lindsay 26	Kron 17	S	00 41 01.0
Lindsay 27	Kron 21	S	00 41 23.8
Lindsay 28		S	00 42 59.7
Lindsay 29	NGC 242	S	00 43 33.9
Lindsay 30	NGC 256	S	00 45 54.4
Lindsay 31		S	00 46 35.0
Lindsay 32		S	00 47 24.8
Lindsay 33		S	00 47 24.9
Lindsay 34	NGC 265	S	00 47 11.6
Lindsay 35	Kron 25	S	00 48 00.7
Lindsay 36	Kron 27	S	00 48 13.7
Lindsay 37	NGC 269	S	00 48 21.3
Lindsay 38		S	00 48 51.0
Lindsay 39		S	00 49 17.6
Lindsay 40		S	00 50 38.5
Lindsay 40	[H86] 116	S	00 50 39.6
Lindsay 41		S	00 50 55.6
Lindsay 42	NGC 290	S	00 51 14.2
Lindsay 43	Kron 28	S	00 51 40.6
Lindsay 44	Kron 29	S	00 51 52.9
Lindsay 45	Kron 30	S	00 52 35.4
Lindsay 46	Kron 31	S	00 53 00.6
Lindsay 47	NGC 294	S	00 53 05.6
Lindsay 48		S	00 53 27.9
Lindsay 49	NGC 299	S	00 53 24.8
Lindsay 50	NGC 306	S	00 54 14.8
Lindsay 51		S	00 54 54.8
Lindsay 52		S	00 55 17.7
Lindsay 53	Kron 34	S	00 55 33.0
Lindsay 54	NGC 330	S	00 56 18.7
Lindsay 55		S	00 56 44.8
Lindsay 56		S	00 57 29.8
Lindsay 57	Kron 38	S	00 57 48.3
Lindsay 58	Kron 37	S	00 57 47.5
Lindsay 59	NGC 339	S	00 57 45.4
Lindsay 60	NGC 346	S	00 59.1
Lindsay 61	IC 1611	S	00 59 48.1
Lindsay 62	IC 1612	S	01 00 01.4
Lindsay 63	Kron 42	S	01 00 34.4
Lindsay 64	Kron 43	S	01 00 49.7
Lindsay 65		S	01 01 02.0
Lindsay 66		S	01 01 45.1
Lindsay 67	NGC 361	S	01 02 11.3
Lindsay 68	Kron 44	S	01 02 05.2
Lindsay 69	Kron 45	S	01 02 47.9
Lindsay 70	Kron 47	S	01 03 11.5
Lindsay 71	NGC 371	S	01 03.3

Table D.3: Cluster Cross-Reference

Name	Look Under	GX	2000.0 RA
Lindsay 72	NGC 376	S	01 03 53.5
Lindsay 73		S	01 04 25.1
Lindsay 74	Kron 50	S	01 04 36.2
Lindsay 75	NGC 395	S	01 05 11
Lindsay 76	IC 1624	S	01 05 21.5
Lindsay 77	IC 1626	S	01 06 13.8
Lindsay 78		S	01 06 53.7
Lindsay 79	Kron 54	S	01 06 47.8
Lindsay 80		S	01 07 28.5
Lindsay 81	Kron 55	S	01 07 32.4
Lindsay 82	NGC 411	S	01 07 55.7
Lindsay 83	NGC 416	S	01 07 59.0
Lindsay 84		S	01 08 28.2
Lindsay 85	NGC 419	S	01 08 17.7
Lindsay 86	Kron 57	S	01 08 14.5
Lindsay 87	NGC 422	S	01 09 25.4
Lindsay 88	Kron 63	S	01 10 47.9
Lindsay 89	IC 1660	S	01 12 38.4
Lindsay 90	IC 1655	S	01 11 54.4
Lindsay 91		S	01 12 52.4
Lindsay 92	IC 1662	S	01 12 33.4
Lindsay 93		S	01 12 48.6
Lindsay 94	NGC 456	S	01 13 43.9
Lindsay 95		S	01 14 45.8
Lindsay 96	NGC 458	S	01 14 53.2
Lindsay 97	NGC 460	S	01 14 37.9
Lindsay 98	Kron 68	S	01 15 33.9
Lindsay 99	NGC 465	S	01 15 42.7
Lindsay 100		S	01 18 17.1
Lindsay 101		S	01 23 44.2
Lindsay 102		S	01 24 55.8
Lindsay 103		S	01 25 48
Lindsay 104		S	01 25 27.8
Lindsay 106		S	01 30 37.9
Lindsay 107		S	01 31.1
Lindsay 108		S	01 31 38.5
Lindsay 109		S	01 33 13.4
Lindsay 110		S	01 34 26.2
Lindsay 111	NGC 643	S	01 35 00.8
Lindsay 112		S	01 35 58.3
Lindsay 113		S	01 49 28.6
Lindsay 114		S	01 50 19.4
Lindsay 115	NGC 796	S	01 56 44.5
Lindsay 116		L	01 55 34.7
Lindsay [1961] 67	NGC 248	S	00 45 24.1
Lindsay [1961] 68		S	00 45 29.8
Lindsay [1961] 184		S	00 51 44.1
Lindsay [1961] 244		S	00 53 42.3
Lindsay [1961] 331		S	00 58 16.3
Lindsay [1961] 335		S	00 58 25.8
Lindsay [1961] 420		S	01 03 53.0
Lindsay [1961] 439		S	01 05 08.1
Lindsay [1961] 439	NGC 395	S	01 05 11
Ling 1			19 01 29
LkHA 101	Cl [BW88] 1		04 30 14.3
Loden 1			10 04 25
Loden 27			10 11.1
Loden 28			10 03 08.6
Loden 46			10 23 16
Loden 59			10 30 22

Table D.3: Cluster Cross-Reference

Name	Look Under	GX	2000.0 RA
Loden 89			10 28 47.6
Loden 112			10 32 40
Loden 143			10 28 44
Loden 153			10 34 46.7
Loden 153	NGC 3293		10 35 49
Loden 165			10 35 56
Loden 172			10 27 51
Loden 189			10 50
Loden 213			10 36 40
Loden 280			11 09.5
Loden 282	Basel 17		11 10 32.9
Loden 306			11 06 00.7
Loden 306	Shorlin 1		11 06 19
Loden 306	Shorlin 2		11 05 34
Loden 309			11 09.5
Loden 336			11 19.8
Loden 372			11 30 52
Loden 402			11 32 49
Loden 465	Stock 14		11 43 51
Loden 466	Stock 14		11 43 51
Loden 467	Stock 14		11 43 51
Loden 480			11 56 06
Loden 481			11 51 06.6
Loden 565			12 08 24.4
Loden 615			12 20 37.2
Loden 623	NGC 4439		12 28 27
Loden 624			12 28 25.7
Loden 670			12 42 48.6
Loden 682			12 47 19
Loden 694			12 53 31
Loden 757			13 12.4
Loden 807			13 24.9
Loden 821			13 23 39
Loden 848			13 33.1
Loden 894			13 39 44.3
Loden 915			13 33 44
Loden 991			13 45.4
Loden 995			13 52 21
Loden 1002			13 54.3
Loden 1010			13 45.4
Loden 1095			13 53.5
Loden 1101			13 58 40.6
Loden 1152			13 59.5
Loden 1171			13 59 31.4
Loden 1177			13 59.4
Loden 1194			14 05.8
Loden 1202			14 04.4
Loden 1225			14 09.2
Loden 1256			14 18.2
Loden 1282			14 15.9
Loden 1289			14 16 56.9
Loden 1296	Lynga 2		14 24 24
Loden 1339			14 33.5
Loden 1373			14 41.7
Loden 1375			14 44 33
Loden 1378			14 27 25
Loden 1409			14 44.7
Loden 2045			15 08 23.4
Loden 2104	NGC 5822		15 04 02.3
Loden 2115			15 05 53

Table D.3: Cluster Cross-Reference

Name	Look Under	GX	2000.0 RA
Loden 2158			15 33 05.9
Loden 2159			15 33 05.9
Loden 2313			15 40 44.5
Loden 2326			15 43 33
Loiano 1			19 58 14.4
Lund 3	Berkeley 59		00 02 10
Lund 4	Berkeley 104		00 03 27
Lund 6	Stock 19		00 04 39
Lund 7	Czernik 1		00 07 39
Lund 8	Berkeley 1		00 09 41
Lund 9	King 13		00 10 10
Lund 10	Berkeley 60		00 17 42
Lund 11	King 1		00 21 52
Lund 12	Berkeley 2		00 25 15
Lund 13	NGC 103		00 25 18
Lund 15	NGC 129		00 29 58
Lund 16	Stock 21		00 30 28
Lund 18	NGC 136		00 31 31
Lund 19	King 14		00 31.9
Lund 20	King 15		00 33 07
Lund 21	NGC 146		00 33.1
Lund 22	Stock 24		00 39 50
Lund 23	NGC 189		00 39 36
Lund 25	NGC 225		00 43 36
Lund 26	King 16		00 43.7
Lund 27	Czernik 2		00 43 39
Lund 28	NGC 188		00 47 30
Lund 29	Berkeley 4		00 45 13
Lund 31	Dolidze 13		00 50.0
Lund 32	King 2		00 50 57
Lund 34	IC 1590		00 52 49
Lund 35	Berkeley 62		01 01 12
Lund 36	Czernik 3		01 03 07
Lund 37	NGC 366		01 06 27
Lund 38	NGC 381		01 08 18
Lund 39	Stock 3		01 12 03
Lund 40	Basel 10		02 19 28
Lund 41	NGC 433		01 15 10
Lund 42	NGC 436		01 15 58
Lund 43	NGC 457		01 19 33
Lund 44	Stock 20		00 25 16
Lund 45	NGC 559		01 29 33
Lund 46	NGC 581		01 33 22
Lund 47	Czernik 4		01 35 36.4
Lund 48	Trumpler 1		01 35 40
Lund 50	NGC 609		01 36 24
Lund 51	NGC 637		01 43 04
Lund 52	NGC 657		01 43 29.8
Lund 53	NGC 654		01 44 00
Lund 54	NGC 659		01 44 24
Lund 55	NGC 663		01 46 17
Lund 57	Collinder 463		01 45 45
Lund 58	Collinder 21		01 50 12
Lund 59	Berkeley 6		01 51 12
Lund 60	IC 166		01 52 22
Lund 61	Stock 4		01 52.7
Lund 62	Berkeley 7		01 54 12
Lund 63	Czernik 5		01 55 40
Lund 64	NGC 752		01 57 35
Lund 65	NGC 744		01 58 30

Table D.3: Cluster Cross-Reference

Name	Look Under	GX	2000.0 RA
Lund 66	NGC 743		01 58 32
Lund 67	Berkeley 8		02 01 05
Lund 68	Czernik 6		02 02 08
Lund 69	Czernik 7		02 03 01
Lund 70	Stock 5		02 04.4
Lund 71	Stock 2		02 14 43
Lund 73	NGC 869		02 19 04
Lund 74	Berkeley 63		02 19 27
Lund 75	Berkeley 64		02 21 46
Lund 76	NGC 884		02 22 05
Lund 77	NGC 886		02 23 28.1
Lund 78	Tombaugh 4		02 29 10.7
Lund 79	Markarian 6		02 29 40
Lund 80	NGC 956		02 32 14.9
Lund 81	IC 1805		02 32 42
Lund 82	Czernik 8		02 32 58
Lund 83	Czernik 9		02 33.6
Lund 84	NGC 957		02 33 20
Lund 86	Czernik 11		02 36 36
Lund 87	King 4		02 36 02
Lund 88	Trumpler 2		02 36 53
Lund 89	Berkeley 65		02 39 06
Lund 90	Czernik 12		02 39 23
Lund 91	NGC 1039		02 42 08
Lund 92	NGC 1027		02 42 36
Lund 93	Czernik 13		02 44 27
Lund 95	IC 1848		02 51 11
Lund 96	IC 1848		02 51 11
Lund 97	Collinder 34		02 59 23.2
Lund 99	NGC 1193		03 05 56
Lund 100	NGC 1220		03 11 41
Lund 101	Trumpler 3		03 12 00
Lund 102	King 5		03 14 40
Lund 103	NGC 1245		03 14 42
Lund 104	Stock 23		03 16 10.8
Lund 105	Czernik 14		03 16 57
Lund 106	Melotte 20		03 24 19
Lund 107	Czernik 15		03 23 13
Lund 108	King 6		03 28 00
Lund 109	Czernik 16		03 31 02
Lund 110	NGC 1342		03 31 40
Lund 112	Bochum 3		07 03 28
Lund 112	NGC 1348		03 34 09
Lund 113	Berkeley 10		03 39 37
Lund 113	Bochum 15		07 40 15
Lund 115	NGC 2099		05 52 19
Lund 117	Pleiades		03 47 29
Lund 118	Tombaugh 5		03 47 44
Lund 119	NGC 1444		03 49 27
Lund 120	Czernik 17		03 52 20
Lund 121	King 7		03 59 10
Lund 122	NGC 1496		04 04 32
Lund 123	Dolidze 14		04 06 41
Lund 124	NGC 1502		04 07 50
Lund 125	NGC 1513		04 09 55
Lund 126	NGC 1528		04 15 19
Lund 127	IC 361		04 18 51
Lund 128	Hyades		04 26.9
Lund 129	Berkeley 11		04 20 27
Lund 131	NGC 1545		04 20 57

Table D.3: Cluster Cross-Reference

Name	Look Under	GX	2000.0 RA
Lund 132	Czernik 18		04 27 48
Lund 133	NGC 1582		04 31 39
Lund 134	NGC 1605		04 34 53
Lund 135	Berkeley 67		04 37 50
Lund 136	NGC 1624		04 40 37
Lund 137	Berkeley 68		04 44.5
Lund 138	Berkeley 12		04 44 24
Lund 139	NGC 1647		04 45 42.2
Lund 140	Ruprecht 148		04 46 35
Lund 141	NGC 1662		04 48 29
Lund 142	NGC 1663		04 49 24.3
Lund 143	NGC 1664		04 51 06
Lund 144	Berkeley 13		04 55 46.2
Lund 145	Czernik 19		04 56 56
Lund 146	Berkeley 14		04 59 44
Lund 147	Berkeley 15		05 02 05
Lund 148	NGC 1746		05 03.6
Lund 148	NGC 1750		05 03.9
Lund 150	NGC 1758		05 04.4
Lund 152	NGC 1778		05 08 06
Lund 153	King 17		05 08 24
Lund 154	NGC 1807		05 10 46
Lund 155	NGC 1798		05 11 40
Lund 156	NGC 1817		05 12 27
Lund 157	Dolidze 16		05 14.6
Lund 158	Czernik 20		05 20 32.5
Lund 159	NGC 1857		05 20 06
Lund 160	Berkeley 17		05 20 30
Lund 161	Collinder 62		05 20 53.0
Lund 162	Berkeley 18		05 22 12
Lund 164	Collinder 464		05 12 39.0
Lund 166	NGC 1893		05 22 46
Lund 168	Dolidze 19		05 23.7
Lund 169	DoDz 2		05 23.2
Lund 170	Dolidze 18		05 24 09
Lund 171	Berkeley 19		05 24 03
Lund 172	Berkeley 69		05 24 21
Lund 174	Collinder 65		05 26 05.7
Lund 175	NGC 1883		05 25 55
Lund 176	Czernik 21		05 26 40
Lund 177	Dolidze 21		05 27.4
Lund 178	Stock 8		05 28 07
Lund 179	NGC 1907		05 28 05
Lund 180	Dolidze 20		05 28 33
Lund 181	NGC 1912		05 28 43
Lund 182	NGC 1931		05 31 26
Lund 183	Berkeley 20		05 32 37
Lund 184	DoDz 3		05 33.5
Lund 185	Collinder 69		05 35.0
Lund 186	Collinder 70		05 35.6
Lund 187	NGC 1981		05 35.2
Lund 188	NGC 1976		05 35 16
Lund 189	NGC 1980		05 35 26
Lund 190	DoDz 4		05 35.9
Lund 191	NGC 1960		05 36 18
Lund 192	Stock 10		05 39.0
Lund 193	Berkeley 71		05 40 57
Lund 194	Basel 4		05 48 54
Lund 195	Collinder 74		05 48 40
Lund 196	King 8		05 49 17

Table D.3: Cluster Cross-Reference

Name	Look Under	GX	2000.0 RA
Lund 197	Czernik 23		05 50 08
Lund 198	Berkeley 72		05 50 12
Lund 199	Berkeley 21		05 51 46
Lund 200	Czernik 24		05 55 26
Lund 201	Berkeley 22		05 58 27
Lund 202	NGC 2126		06 02 34
Lund 203	NGC 2141		06 02 56
Lund 204	IC 2157		06 04 49.8
Lund 205	NGC 2158		06 07 26
Lund 206	NGC 2169		06 08 25
Lund 207	NGC 2168		06 09.0
Lund 208	Collinder 84		06 09 39
Lund 209	NGC 2186		06 12 08
Lund 210	Czernik 25		06 13 41
Lund 211	NGC 2194		06 13 46
Lund 212	NGC 2192		06 15 18
Lund 213	NGC 2204		06 15 33
Lund 214	Collinder 89		06 18.0
Lund 215	NGC 2215		06 20 50
Lund 216	Collinder 91		06 21 33
Lund 217	Berkeley 73		06 22 05
Lund 218	Collinder 92		06 22.9
Lund 219	Dolidze 22		06 23.3
Lund 220	NGC 2232		06 27 15
Lund 221	NGC 2236		06 29 40
Lund 222	NGC 2243		06 29 35
Lund 224	Collinder 96		06 30.3
Lund 225	Collinder 95		06 30 51.2
Lund 226	Czernik 26		06 30 58
Lund 227	NGC 2244		06 32 19
Lund 228	Collinder 97		06 30 58.1
Lund 229	NGC 2237		06 31 55.5
Lund 229	NGC 2244		06 32 19
Lund 231	Berkeley 23		06 33 15
Lund 232	NGC 2251		06 34 39
Lund 233	NGC 2252		06 34 19.8
Lund 234	NGC 2254		06 35 46.6
Lund 235	Collinder 104		06 36.5
Lund 236	Ruprecht 1		06 36.4
Lund 237	Trumpler 5		06 36 31
Lund 238	Cl vdB 1		06 37 05
Lund 239	Collinder 106		06 37.1
Lund 240	Collinder 107		06 37.7
Lund 241	Berkeley 24		06 37 47
Lund 242	NGC 2262		06 39 38.7
Lund 243	Collinder 110		06 38 39
Lund 244	NGC 2259		06 38 33.3
Lund 245	Collinder 111		06 38.7
Lund 246	NGC 2264		06 40 59
Lund 247	Berkeley 25		06 41 14
Lund 248	Ruprecht 2		06 41 01
Lund 249	Ruprecht 3		06 42 06
Lund 250	NGC 2266		06 43 20
Lund 251	Dolidze 23		06 43 05.7
Lund 252	NGC 2269		06 43 16.8
Lund 253	Dolidze 24		06 44 44
Lund 254	Dolidze 25		06 45.0
Lund 255	Collinder 115		06 46 40
Lund 256	NGC 2287		06 46.1
Lund 257	NGC 2286		06 47 41

Table D.3: Cluster Cross-Reference

Name	Look Under	GX	2000.0 RA
Lund 258	Ruprecht 4		06 48 57
Lund 259	NGC 2281		06 48 18
Lund 260	Berkeley 75		06 49 00
Lund 261	Biurakan 12		06 50 16
Lund 262	Biurakan 11		06 51 21
Lund 263	NGC 2301		06 51 46
Lund 264	NGC 2302		06 51 54
Lund 266	Ruprecht 149		06 52.2
Lund 267	Berkeley 29		06 53 04
Lund 268	Collinder 121		06 56 20.0
Lund 269	NGC 2304		06 55 12
Lund 270	Ruprecht 5		06 55 24
Lund 271	Ruprecht 6		06 56 05
Lund 272	NGC 2309		06 56 04
Lund 273	Biurakan 7		06 57 37
Lund 275	Ruprecht 7		06 57 50
Lund 276	NGC 2311		06 57 48
Lund 277	Biurakan 9		06 57 46
Lund 278	Biurakan 8		06 58 07
Lund 279	Tombaugh 1		07 00 27
Lund 280	Biurakan 13		07 00 22
Lund 281	Ruprecht 8		07 01 46
Lund 283	NGC 2323		07 02 47.8
Lund 284	Czernik 27		07 03 19
Lund 285	Tombaugh 2		07 03 06
Lund 286	Haffner 3		07 04 08
Lund 287	NGC 2324		07 04 08
Lund 288	Ruprecht 150		07 05 55
Lund 289	Haffner 4		07 06 04
Lund 290	Ruprecht 10		07 06 27.6
Lund 291	Berkeley 76		07 06 40
Lund 292	NGC 2335		07 06 50
Lund 293	NGC 2129		06 01 06
Lund 296	Collinder 466		07 06 56
Lund 297	Ruprecht 12		07 07 10
Lund 298	Ruprecht 11		07 07 23
Lund 299	Ruprecht 13		07 08.0
Lund 300	NGC 2343		07 08 07
Lund 301	NGC 2345		07 08 19
Lund 302	Haffner 23		07 09.5
Lund 304	NGC 6874		20 07.8
Lund 305	Berkeley 35		07 09 54
Lund 306	NGC 2354		07 14 16
Lund 307	Collinder 132		07 15 21.1
Lund 308	NGC 2353		07 14 31
Lund 309	Ruprecht 14		07 14 55
Lund 310	Berkeley 36		07 16 23
Lund 311	NGC 2355		07 17 00
Lund 312	Collinder 135		07 17 24.5
Lund 313	NGC 2360		07 17 44
Lund 314	Haffner 5		07 18.1
Lund 315	NGC 2362		07 18 42
Lund 316	Ruprecht 15		07 19 34
Lund 317	Haffner 6		07 20 01
Lund 318	NGC 2367		07 20 05
Lund 319	Berkeley 37		07 20 18
Lund 320	NGC 2368		07 21 02.2
Lund 321	Berkeley 77		07 21 28
Lund 322	Czernik 28		07 21.8
Lund 323	Haffner 7		07 22 54

Table D.3: Cluster Cross-Reference

Name	Look Under	GX	2000.0 RA
Lund 324	Ruprecht 16		07 23 09
Lund 325	Haffner 8		07 23 03
Lund 326	Ruprecht 17		07 23 35
Lund 327	Collinder 140		07 24 26.7
Lund 328	NGC 2374		07 23 57
Lund 329	Berkeley 78		07 23 38
Lund 330	Haffner 9		07 24 42
Lund 331	Ruprecht 18		07 24 39
Lund 332	NGC 2383		07 24 40
Lund 333	NGC 2384		07 25 12
Lund 334	Ruprecht 19		07 25.6
Lund 335	Trumpler 6		07 26 23
Lund 336	Melotte 66		07 26 19
Lund 337	Ruprecht 20		07 26 41
Lund 338	NGC 2395		07 27 13
Lund 339	Ruprecht 21		07 27.1
Lund 340	Trumpler 7		07 27 21
Lund 341	Czernik 29		07 28 24
Lund 342	Haffner 10		07 28 36
Lund 344	NGC 2396		07 28.0
Lund 345	Ruprecht 22		07 29 17
Lund 346	NGC 2401		07 29 25
Lund 347	Dolidze 26		07 30 02
Lund 348	Ruprecht 23		07 30 40
Lund 349	Czernik 30		07 31 11
Lund 350	Ruprecht 24		07 31 51
Lund 351	Haffner 15		07 45 30
Lund 352	NGC 2414		07 33 13
Lund 353	NGC 2483		07 55 39
Lund 354	Haffner 11		07 35 22
Lund 355	NGC 2421		07 36 12
Lund 356	NGC 2422		07 36 36
Lund 357	Ruprecht 25		07 36 47
Lund 358	Czernik 31		07 36 58
Lund 359	NGC 2423		07 37 07
Lund 360	Ruprecht 26		07 37 13
Lund 361	Ruprecht 27		07 37.6
Lund 362	Melotte 71		07 37 30
Lund 363	NGC 2425		07 38 18
Lund 364	NGC 2420		07 38 24
Lund 365	Melotte 72		07 38 29
Lund 366	Ruprecht 28		07 39 36
Lund 367	Melotte 72		07 38 29
Lund 368	Haffner 13		07 40 26
Lund 369	NGC 2432		07 40 54
Lund 370	NGC 2439		07 40 46
Lund 371	Ruprecht 29		07 41.1
Lund 372	Ruprecht 151		07 41.3
Lund 373	NGC 2437		07 41 47
Lund 374	Ruprecht 30		07 42 22
Lund 375	Ruprecht 31		07 43 00
Lund 376	NGC 2447		07 44 30
Lund 377	Haffner 14		07 44 48
Lund 378	Ruprecht 32		07 45 06
Lund 379	Auner 1		07 04 15.3
Lund 380	NGC 2451		07 45.4
Lund 381	Ruprecht 33		07 45.8
Lund 382	Ruprecht 34		07 45 54
Lund 383	Ruprecht 35		07 46 14
Lund 384	Berkeley 39		07 46 50

Table D.3: Cluster Cross-Reference

Name	Look Under	GX	2000.0 RA
Lund 385	NGC 2453		07 47 35
Lund 386	Ruprecht 36		07 48 24
Lund 387	Haffner 25		07 48 40
Lund 388	NGC 2455		07 48 59
Lund 389	Ruprecht 37		07 49 47
Lund 390	Haffner 16		07 50 21
Lund 391	Czernik 32		07 50 28
Lund 392	Ruprecht 38		07 50 31
Lund 393	Haffner 17		07 51 36
Lund 394	Ruprecht 39		07 52 20
Lund 395	NGC 2477		07 52 10
Lund 396	NGC 2467		07 52 30
Lund 398	Basel 8		06 34.2
Lund 400	Haffner 19		07 52 46
Lund 401	Ruprecht 40		07 33 27
Lund 402	Ruprecht 41		07 53 48
Lund 403	Ruprecht 152		07 54 29
Lund 404	DoDz 6		16 45 28.6
Lund 405	NGC 2482		07 55 10
Lund 406	NGC 2479		07 55 06
Lund 407	Trumpler 9		07 55 40
Lund 408	NGC 2489		07 56 16
Lund 409	Haffner 20		07 56 15
Lund 410	Ruprecht 42		07 57 37
Lund 411	NGC 2516		07 58.0
Lund 412	Ruprecht 43		07 58.8
Lund 413	Ruprecht 44		07 58 50
Lund 414	Ruprecht 45		07 59.6
Lund 415	NGC 2506		08 00 02
Lund 416	Ruprecht 153		08 00 18
Lund 417	NGC 2509		08 00 48
Lund 418	Haffner 21		08 01 11
Lund 419	Ruprecht 154		08 01.7
Lund 420	Ruprecht 46		08 02 10
Lund 421	Ruprecht 47		08 02 18
Lund 422	Ruprecht 48		08 02 42
Lund 423	Ruprecht 49		08 03 17
Lund 424	Collinder 173		08 03.5
Lund 425	Ruprecht 50		08 03.4
Lund 426	Ruprecht 51		08 03.6
Lund 427	Ruprecht 155		08 04.9
Lund 428	Ruprecht 52		08 05.0
Lund 429	NGC 2527		08 04 53
Lund 430	NGC 2533		08 07.0
Lund 432	NGC 2547		08 10 11
Lund 433	Ruprecht 53		08 10 50
Lund 434	Ruprecht 54		08 11 23
Lund 435	Ruprecht 55		08 12 19
Lund 436	NGC 2546		08 12.4
Lund 437	Haffner 22		08 12.6
Lund 438	Ruprecht 56		08 12.6
Lund 439	NGC 2548		08 13 44
Lund 440	Ruprecht 58		08 14 49
Lund 441	Ruprecht 57		08 14.8
Lund 442	Haffner 26		08 15.4
Lund 443	NGC 2568		08 18 19
Lund 445	NGC 2567		08 18 30
Lund 446	NGC 2571		08 18 57
Lund 447	Ruprecht 59		08 19 22.0
Lund 449	NGC 2579		08 20 53

Table D.3: Cluster Cross-Reference

Name	Look Under	GX	2000.0 RA
Lund 450	NGC 2580		08 21 28
Lund 451	Collinder 185		08 23 19
Lund 452	NGC 2588		08 23 10
Lund 453	NGC 2587		08 23 25
Lund 454	Collinder 187		08 24 12
Lund 455	Ruprecht 60		08 24 26
Lund 456	Ruprecht 61		08 25 15
Lund 457	Ruprecht 157		08 29 52
Lund 459	Ruprecht 63		08 32 40
Lund 460	Ruprecht 62		08 32 30
Lund 461	Pismis 4		08 34.6
Lund 462	NGC 2627		08 37 15
Lund 463	Ruprecht 64		08 37.4
Lund 464	Pismis 5		08 37 39
Lund 465	NGC 2635		08 38 27
Lund 466	Ruprecht 65		08 39 22
Lund 467	NGC 2645		08 39 04
Lund 468	NGC 2632		08 40 22
Lund 469	IC 2391		08 40.3
Lund 470	Ruprecht 66		08 40 32
Lund 471	Pismis 7		08 41 09
Lund 472	IC 2395		08 42 31
Lund 473	Pismis 8		08 41 35
Lund 474	Ruprecht 67		08 41 45
Lund 475	NGC 2660		08 42 39
Lund 476	NGC 2659		08 42 34
Lund 477	NGC 2658		08 43 28
Lund 478	Ruprecht 69		08 44 49.1
Lund 479	Collinder 197		08 44 40
Lund 480	Ruprecht 68		08 44.5
Lund 482	Collinder 196		08 45.1
Lund 484	NGC 2670		08 45 30
Lund 485	NGC 2671		08 46 12
Lund 486	Waterloo 6		08 40 20.7
Lund 487	Trumpler 10		08 47 45
Lund 488	Ruprecht 70		08 49.1
Lund 489	Ruprecht 71		08 49.5
Lund 490	NGC 2682		08 51 24
Lund 491	Ruprecht 72		08 52 05
Lund 492	Ruprecht 158		08 52 23
Lund 493	Markarian 18		09 00 31
Lund 495	Ruprecht 73		09 01 12
Lund 496	Muzzio 1		08 57.2
Lund 497	NGC 2818		09 16 10
Lund 498	Pismis 11		09 15 53
Lund 499	NGC 2849		09 19 23
Lund 500	Pismis 12		09 20 00
Lund 501	Ruprecht 159		09 20 08
Lund 502	Ruprecht 74		09 21.0
Lund 503	Ruprecht 75		09 21 54
Lund 504	Pismis 13		09 22 06.5
Lund 505	Ruprecht 76		09 24 18
Lund 506	Ruprecht 77		09 27 02
Lund 507	IC 2488		09 27 27
Lund 508	Ruprecht 78		09 29 07.9
Lund 509	Pismis 14		09 29.3
Lund 510	NGC 2910		09 30 30
Lund 511	NGC 2925		09 33 11
Lund 512	Pismis 15		09 34 45
Lund 513	NGC 2972		09 40 12

Table D.3: Cluster Cross-Reference

Name	Look Under	GX	2000.0 RA
Lund 515	Ruprecht 79		09 41 03
Lund 516	NGC 2982		09 42 01
Lund 517	Ruprecht 81		09 45 13
Lund 518	Ruprecht 82		09 45 49
Lund 519	NGC 3033		09 48 40
Lund 520	Ruprecht 83		09 49 15
Lund 521	Ruprecht 84		09 49 04
Lund 522	Pismis 16		09 51 14
Lund 523	Hogg 2		09 51.5
Lund 524	Collinder 213		09 55 00
Lund 525	Ruprecht 160		09 55.5
Lund 526	Hogg 3		09 57 40
Lund 527	Hogg 4		09 57 53
Lund 528	NGC 3105		10 00 40
Lund 529	Ruprecht 86		10 01 27.7
Lund 530	Ruprecht 85		10 01 26
Lund 531	NGC 3114		10 02.7
Lund 533	Hogg 5		10 06 09
Lund 534	Trumpler 12		10 06.5
Lund 535	Hogg 6		10 06 28
Lund 536	Ruprecht 161		10 08.8
Lund 537	Ruprecht 87		10 15 30
Lund 538	Ruprecht 88		10 18 48
Lund 539	NGC 3228		10 21 23
Lund 540	Berkeley 87		20 21 35
Lund 541	Trumpler 13		10 23 48
Lund 544	NGC 3255		10 26 32
Lund 545	IC 2581		10 27 27
Lund 546	Ruprecht 89		10 28.5
Lund 547	Hogg 7		10 29.1
Lund 549	Collinder 223		10 30.4
Lund 550	Ruprecht 90		10 31.0
Lund 551	NGC 3293		10 35 49
Lund 552	NGC 3324		10 37 19
Lund 553	NGC 3330		10 38 48
Lund 554	Melotte 101		10 42 00
Lund 555	Collinder 228		10 44 00
Lund 556	IC 2602		10 42 57
Lund 557	Trumpler 14		10 43 57
Lund 558	Trumpler 15		10 44 44
Lund 559	Collinder 232		10 44 39
Lund 560	Trumpler 16		10 45 10
Lund 562	Ruprecht 91		10 47 38.4
Lund 563	Ruprecht 162		10 53.0
Lund 564	Ruprecht 92		10 53 49
Lund 565	Trumpler 17		10 56 24
Lund 567	Hogg 9		10 58 22
Lund 568	NGC 3496		10 59 34
Lund 569	Sher 1		11 01 03
Lund 570	NGC 3503		11 01 18
Lund 571	NGC 3519		11 04 03
Lund 572	Ruprecht 163		11 04 47
Lund 573	Feinstein 1		11 06.0
Lund 574	NGC 3532		11 05.5
Lund 576	Hogg 10		11 10 42.1
Lund 578	Trumpler 18		11 11.4
Lund 579	Hogg 11		11 11 32.6
Lund 580	Hogg 12		11 12 15
Lund 581	NGC 3590		11 13 00
Lund 582	Stock 13		11 13.1

Table D.3: Cluster Cross-Reference

Name	Look Under	GX	2000.0 RA
Lund 583	Trumpler 19		11 14.3
Lund 584	NGC 3603		11 15 07
Lund 585	Hogg 13		11 16.3
Lund 586	IC 2714		11 17 18
Lund 587	Melotte 105		11 19 41
Lund 588	NGC 3680		11 25 38
Lund 589	Ruprecht 94		11 30.4
Lund 590	Ruprecht 164		11 31.1
Lund 591	NGC 3766		11 36 15
Lund 592	Collinder 249		11 38 20.4
Lund 594	Ruprecht 95		11 43 40
Lund 595	Stock 14		11 43 51
Lund 596	DoDz 1		02 47 27
Lund 597	NGC 3960		11 50 34
Lund 598	Ruprecht 96		11 50 53
Lund 599	Ruprecht 97		11 57 23
Lund 601	NGC 4052		12 02 01
Lund 602	Ruprecht 99		12 03 20
Lund 603	Ruprecht 100		12 05.7
Lund 604	NGC 4103		12 06 40
Lund 605	Stock 15		12 10.5
Lund 606	Ruprecht 101		12 09 40
Lund 607	NGC 4184		12 13.6
Lund 608	Ruprecht 103		12 15.9
Lund 609	NGC 4230		12 17 16
Lund 610	NGC 4337		12 24 04
Lund 611	NGC 4349		12 24 07
Lund 613	Melotte 111		12 25.1
Lund 614	Basel 13		21 13 11
Lund 615	Harvard 5		12 27 16.3
Lund 616	NGC 4439		12 28 27
Lund 617	Hogg 14		12 28 39
Lund 618	Ruprecht 165		12 28.6
Lund 619	NGC 4463		12 29 56
Lund 620	Ruprecht 105		12 34.0
Lund 621	Upgren 1		12 35 00
Lund 622	Harvard 6		12 37 54
Lund 623	Ruprecht 106	g	12 38 40.2
Lund 624	Trumpler 20		12 39 32
Lund 625	NGC 4609		12 42 20
Lund 626	Hogg 15		12 43 36
Lund 627	NGC 4755		12 53 38
Lund 628	NGC 4815		12 57 59
Lund 629	NGC 4852		13 00 05
Lund 631	Harvard 8		13 18 12
Lund 632	Stock 16		13 18 38.4
Lund 633	Ruprecht 107		13 19 46
Lund 635	NGC 5120		13 25 39
Lund 636	NGC 5138		13 27 16
Lund 637	Hogg 16		13 29 11
Lund 638	Collinder 271		13 30.0
Lund 639	Collinder 272		13 30.5
Lund 640	NGC 5168		13 31 08
Lund 641	Ruprecht 108		13 32 12
Lund 642	Trumpler 21		13 32 14
Lund 643	Collinder 275		13 35.4
Lund 644	IC 4291		13 36 55
Lund 645	NGC 5281		13 46 36.7
Lund 647	Collinder 277		13 48.4
Lund 648	NGC 5288		13 48 45.6

Table D.3: Cluster Cross-Reference

Name	Look Under	GX	2000.0 RA
Lund 649	NGC 5316		13 54.0
Lund 650	Lynga 1		14 00 02
Lund 651	NGC 5381		14 00.6
Lund 653	NGC 5460		14 07.6
Lund 654	Ruprecht 167		14 18.2
Lund 655	Lynga 2		14 24 24
Lund 656	NGC 5593		14 25 40
Lund 657	NGC 5606		14 27.8
Lund 658	NGC 5617		14 29.7
Lund 659	Pismis 19		14 30 43
Lund 660	Trumpler 22		14 31.2
Lund 661	Hogg 17		14 33 50.4
Lund 663	Ruprecht 111		14 35.8
Lund 664	Collinder 285		14 40.9
Lund 665	NGC 5715		14 43 39.0
Lund 666	NGC 5749		14 48 48.8
Lund 667	Hogg 18		14 50 41.4
Lund 668	NGC 5764		14 53 31.8
Lund 669	Ruprecht 112		14 57.0
Lund 670	NGC 5822		15 04 02.3
Lund 671	NGC 5823		15 05 26
Lund 672	Pismis 20		15 15 23.1
Lund 673	Pismis 21		15 16 47.7
Lund 674	Lynga 3		15 16 47
Lund 675	NGC 5925		15 27.7
Lund 676	Lynga 4		15 33 20
Lund 677	Harvard 9		15 33.8
Lund 678	Lynga 5		15 41 57.1
Lund 679	Collinder 292		15 50.8
Lund 680	NGC 5999		15 52 14
Lund 681	NGC 6005		15 55 47.4
Lund 682	Ruprecht 113		15 57.2
Lund 683	Trumpler 23		16 00 50.7
Lund 684	NGC 6025		16 03 18
Lund 685	Lynga 6		16 04 51
Lund 686	Ruprecht 114		16 06 31
Lund 687	NGC 6031		16 07 34.4
Lund 688	Ruprecht 115		16 12 51.1
Lund 689	Lynga 7	g	16 11 03.0
Lund 690	NGC 6067		16 13 09
Lund 691	Pismis 22		16 14 07.9
Lund 693	NGC 6087		16 18 51.8
Lund 694	Lynga 8		16 22 57.0
Lund 695	Harvard 10		16 19.9
Lund 696	Lynga 9		16 20 39
Lund 698	Ruprecht 117		16 23 30.7
Lund 699	Pismis 23		16 23 58
Lund 700	NGC 6115		16 24 26.8
Lund 701	NGC 6124		16 25 17.2
Lund 702	Collinder 302		16 26.0
Lund 703	NGC 6134		16 27 43.6
Lund 704	Ruprecht 119		16 28 09.3
Lund 705	Hogg 19		16 28 51.7
Lund 706	NGC 6152		16 32.7
Lund 707	NGC 6169		16 34 05.0
Lund 708	NGC 6167		16 34 35
Lund 709	Collinder 307		16 35.3
Lund 710	Ruprecht 120		16 35 12.2
Lund 712	NGC 6178		16 35 50.8
Lund 713	Dolidze 27		16 36.5

Table D.3: Cluster Cross-Reference

Name	Look Under	GX	2000.0 RA
Lund 714	Lynga 11		16 38 10
Lund 715	NGC 6192		16 40 20.8
Lund 716	NGC 6193		16 41 20.3
Lund 717	Ruprecht 121		16 41 47.6
Lund 718	NGC 6200		16 44 08.6
Lund 719	Hogg 20		16 44.4
Lund 721	Hogg 21		16 45 36.9
Lund 722	Lynga 12		16 46 03
Lund 723	NGC 6204		16 46 07.9
Lund 724	Westerlund 1		16 47 04
Lund 725	Lynga 13		16 48 54
Lund 726	NGC 6216		16 49 23.6
Lund 727	NGC 6208		16 49 25.8
Lund 728	NGC 6222		16 50.7
Lund 729	NGC 6231		16 54 09.8
Lund 730	Lynga 14		16 55 05
Lund 731	Collinder 316		16 55.5
Lund 732	NGC 6242		16 55 30.6
Lund 734	NGC 6249		16 57 41.7
Lund 735	NGC 6250		16 57 55
Lund 736	NGC 6253		16 59 06.1
Lund 737	NGC 6259		17 00.7
Lund 738	NGC 6268		17 02 04.1
Lund 739	NGC 6281		17 04 47.2
Lund 740	Harvard 13		17 03 57
Lund 741	DoDz 7		17 11 23
Lund 742	NGC 6318		17 16 13.4
Lund 743	NGC 6322		17 18.5
Lund 744	Ruprecht 123		17 23.4
Lund 745	NGC 2669		08 46 19
Lund 746	IC 4651		17 24.7
Lund 747	Harvard 3		08 46.5
Lund 747	Trumpler 25		17 24 30.3
Lund 748	Pismis 24		17 24 43.4
Lund 750	DoDz 8		17 26 24
Lund 751	IC 1257	g	17 27 08
Lund 752	Ruprecht 124		17 27 55.9
Lund 753	Trumpler 26		17 28 29.9
Lund 754	Ruprecht 125		17 29.7
Lund 755	Collinder 332		17 30.8
Lund 755	Harvard 16		17 31 03
Lund 756	Collinder 333		17 31 31.3
Lund 757	Harvard 16		17 31 03
Lund 759	NGC 6383		17 34 42.2
Lund 760	Ruprecht 126		17 35 04.4
Lund 762	Trumpler 28		17 36 59
Lund 763	Ruprecht 127		17 37 50.4
Lund 764	Collinder 338		17 38.2
Lund 765	NGC 6396		17 37 38
Lund 766	NGC 6404		17 39.6
Lund 767	NGC 6400		17 40 10
Lund 768	Trumpler 29		17 41 36.4
Lund 769	NGC 6405		17 40 17
Lund 770	Ruprecht 128		17 44 19.3
Lund 771	NGC 6416		17 44.3
Lund 772	Collinder 345		17 44 35
Lund 774	IC 4665		17 46.2
Lund 775	Ruprecht 130		17 47 32
Lund 776	Collinder 347		17 46 18.9
Lund 777	NGC 6425		17 46 53

Table D.3: Cluster Cross-Reference

Name	Look Under	GX	2000.0 RA
Lund 778	Ruprecht 129		17 47 08.2
Lund 779	Collinder 350		17 48.2
Lund 780	Ruprecht 131		17 49 06.9
Lund 781	Collinder 351		17 49 51
Lund 782	NGC 6444		17 49.6
Lund 783	NGC 6451		17 50 41
Lund 785	Basel 5		17 52 28.4
Lund 786	Ruprecht 133		17 52 34.1
Lund 787	Ruprecht 134		17 52.8
Lund 788	NGC 6469		17 52 56.5
Lund 789	Ruprecht 168		17 52.8
Lund 790	Czernik 37		17 53 16.4
Lund 791	NGC 6475		17 53 46
Lund 792	Trumpler 30		17 56.4
Lund 793	NGC 6494		17 56 56
Lund 794	Ruprecht 135		17 58 03.3
Lund 795	Ruprecht 136		17 59 17.8
Lund 796	Ruprecht 169		17 59.5
Lund 797	NGC 6507		17 59 50
Lund 798	Trumpler 31		17 59.8
Lund 799	Ruprecht 137		17 59.9
Lund 800	Ruprecht 138		17 59.9
Lund 801	Melotte 186		18 01.1
Lund 802	Ruprecht 139		18 01.2
Lund 803	NGC 6514		18 02 31
Lund 805	NGC 6520		18 03 25
Lund 806	NGC 6531		18 04 13
Lund 807	NGC 6523		18 04 25
Lund 808	NGC 6540	g	18 06 08.6
Lund 809	Collinder 468		18 06 35
Lund 810	NGC 6546		18 07.2
Lund 812	DoDz 9		18 08.8
Lund 813	Collinder 367		18 09 51
Lund 815	NGC 6568		18 12 45
Lund 816	Markarian 38		18 15 16.6
Lund 817	NGC 6583		18 15 50
Lund 818	Collinder 469		18 16 33.7
Lund 819	Collinder 371		18 17 16
Lund 820	NGC 6605		18 16 06
Lund 821	NGC 6596		18 17.5
Lund 822	Trumpler 32		18 17 10.4
Lund 823	NGC 6604		18 18.1
Lund 824	NGC 6603		18 18 28
Lund 825	NGC 6611		18 18 45
Lund 826	NGC 6613		18 20 00
Lund 827	NGC 6618		18 21 09
Lund 829	NGC 6625		18 23 12.8
Lund 830	Trumpler 33		18 24 38.8
Lund 831	Ruprecht 170		18 25 10.7
Lund 832	Dolidze 28		18 25 30.0
Lund 833	NGC 6631		18 27 09.5
Lund 834	NGC 6633		18 27 15
Lund 836	Ruprecht 141		18 31.3
Lund 837	Dolidze 29		18 31.4
Lund 838	NGC 6647		18 31.5
Lund 839	IC 4725		18 31 45
Lund 841	Ruprecht 142		18 32 14
Lund 842	Ruprecht 171		18 32 00.7
Lund 843	Ruprecht 143		18 32 43
Lund 844	NGC 6645		18 32 38
Lund 846	Ruprecht 144		18 33 32.7
Lund 847	NGC 6649		18 33 28.3
Lund 850	NGC 6664		18 36 30.6
Lund 851	IC 4756		18 38.9
Lund 852	Trumpler 34		18 39.8
Lund 853	Dolidze 32		18 40.5
Lund 854	Dolidze 33		18 40.7
Lund 855	Dolidze 34		18 42 03.1
Lund 856	NGC 6683		18 42 12.7
Lund 857	Trumpler 35		18 43 00.5
Lund 858	NGC 6694		18 45 15
Lund 859	Berkeley 79		18 44 57.5
Lund 860	Iskudarian 1		18 48.0
Lund 861	Apriamasvili 1		18 48.1
Lund 862	Czernik 38		18 49 47.0
Lund 863	Ruprecht 145		18 50 19.4
Lund 864	NGC 6704		18 50 45.8
Lund 865	NGC 6705		18 51 04
Lund 866	NGC 6709		18 51.5
Lund 867	Ruprecht 146		18 52 30
Lund 869	Collinder 394		18 52 16.3
Lund 870	Stephenson 1		18 54 30.6
Lund 871	Berkeley 80		18 54 20.6
Lund 872	NGC 6716		18 54 34
Lund 874	NGC 6738		19 01.4
Lund 875	Berkeley 81		19 01 39.7
Lund 876	NGC 6749	g	19 05 15.3
Lund 877	NGC 6755		19 07 49
Lund 878	NGC 6755		19 07 49
Lund 879	NGC 6756		19 08 43
Lund 880	Berkeley 82		19 11 20.3
Lund 882	Berkeley 43		19 15 30
Lund 883	NGC 6774		19 16.3
Lund 884	Berkeley 44		19 17 17
Lund 885	Berkeley 45		19 19 06
Lund 886	NGC 6791		19 20 52.7
Lund 887	NGC 6793		19 23 12.6
Lund 889	King 25		19 24.5
Lund 890	Collinder 399		19 26 12
Lund 891	Dolidze 35		19 25 24
Lund 892	NGC 6800		19 27 00
Lund 893	Berkeley 47		19 28 27.3
Lund 894	King 26		19 29.0
Lund 895	NGC 6802		19 30 35
Lund 896	Stock 1		19 35 47
Lund 897	NGC 6811		19 37 09.6
Lund 898	Collinder 401		19 38 21.7
Lund 900	NGC 6819		19 41.3
Lund 901	Czernik 40		19 42 38
Lund 903	NGC 6823		19 43 10
Lund 904	Roslund 1		19 45 06
Lund 905	Roslund 2		19 45 24.4
Lund 906	NGC 6827		19 48 53.2
Lund 907	Czernik 41		19 50 50.8
Lund 908	NGC 6830		19 51 00
Lund 909	NGC 6834		19 52 13
Lund 910	Harvard 20		19 53 10.3
Lund 912	NGC 6846		19 56 28.1
Lund 914	Berkeley 49		19 59 30.2
Lund 915	Berkeley 83		20 01 25.1
Lund 917	NGC 6866		20 03 55
Lund 920	DoDz 10		20 05 35
Lund 921	NGC 6871		20 06 27
Lund 922	Biurakan 1		20 07.5
Lund 923	Dolidze 1		20 08.2
Lund 924	Biurakan 2		20 09 14.3
Lund 925	Dolidze 2		20 09.9
Lund 926	Roslund 5		20 10.0
Lund 927	IC 1310		20 10 01
Lund 928	IC 1311		20 10 47
Lund 929	NGC 6883		20 11.3
Lund 930	Ruprecht 172		20 11 34
Lund 932	Berkeley 51		20 11 53
Lund 933	NGC 6885		20 12 01
Lund 934	Melotte 227		20 15 18
Lund 936	Dolidze 3		20 15 27
Lund 937	Dolidze 39		20 16 12
Lund 938	IC 4996		20 16 31.7
Lund 939	Dolidze 4		20 17 46.6
Lund 940	Collinder 419		20 18 07.0
Lund 941	Dolidze 40		20 18.2
Lund 942	Berkeley 85		20 18 47
Lund 943	Dolidze 41		20 19.2
Lund 944	Dolidze 42		20 19 39.7
Lund 945	Berkeley 86		20 20 21.2
Lund 946	Dolidze 5		20 20 29
Lund 947	Dolidze 6		20 20 38.0
Lund 948	Berkeley 88		20 21 16
Lund 950	NGC 6910		20 23 12
Lund 951	Collinder 421		20 23.3
Lund 952	NGC 6913		20 24 06
Lund 953	Dolidze 8		20 24.4
Lund 954	Berkeley 89		20 24 28.4
Lund 955	Dolidze 9		20 25 33.4
Lund 956	Dolidze 10		20 26.3
Lund 957	Dolidze 11		20 26 24.7
Lund 958	Roslund 6		20 28 49
Lund 959	Dolidze 44		20 29.7
Lund 960	NGC 6939		20 31 30
Lund 961	NGC 6940		20 34 32.3
Lund 962	Berkeley 90		20 35 16
Lund 963	Ruprecht 173		20 41 41.2
Lund 964	Ruprecht 174		20 43 28.3
Lund 965	Ruprecht 175		20 45 24
Lund 966	DoDz 11		20 51 04
Lund 967	Roslund 7		20 52 08.5
Lund 968	Baractova 1		20 53.7
Lund 969	h 2091		20 54 43.1
Lund 970	NGC 6997		20 56.5
Lund 971	Berkeley 53		20 55 59
Lund 972	NGC 6994		20 58 56
Lund 973	Collinder 427		21 00 36.6
Lund 974	Collinder 429		21 01 35.8
Lund 975	Collinder 428		21 03.2
Lund 977	Berkeley 54		21 03 00
Lund 978	Berkeley 84		20 04 42.2
Lund 979	NGC 7031		21 06 52
Lund 980	Dolidze 45		21 09.0
Lund 981	NGC 7039		21 11.2
Lund 982	Berkeley 91		21 10 51

Table D.3: Cluster Cross-Reference

Name	Look Under	GX	2000.0 RA
Lund 983	IC 1369		21 12 07
Lund 984	NGC 7044		21 13 08
Lund 985	Berkeley 52		20 14 30
Lund 986	Berkeley 55		21 16 57
Lund 987	Berkeley 56		21 17 34.5
Lund 988	NGC 7062		21 23 27
Lund 989	NGC 7067		21 24 12.3
Lund 990	NGC 7063		21 24.5
Lund 991	Berkeley 92		21 24 46.3
Lund 992	NGC 7082		21 29 19
Lund 993	NGC 7086		21 30 28
Lund 994	NGC 7092		21 31 52
Lund 995	IC 1396		21 39.0
Lund 996	NGC 7129		21 42 59
Lund 997	NGC 7127		21 43 52.9
Lund 998	NGC 7128		21 43 58
Lund 999	Baractova 2		21 43 38
Lund 1000	NGC 7142		21 45 09
Lund 1001	Collinder 470		21 53.5
Lund 1002	NGC 7160		21 53 40
Lund 1003	Berkeley 93		21 55 29
Lund 1004	NGC 7209		22 05 08
Lund 1005	Collinder 471		22 07.1
Lund 1006	IC 1434		22 10.5
Lund 1007	NGC 7226		22 10 26
Lund 1008	NGC 7235		22 12 24
Lund 1009	NGC 7243		22 15 09
Lund 1010	NGC 7245		22 15 16
Lund 1011	King 9		22 15 31
Lund 1012	IC 1442		22 15 59
Lund 1013	NGC 7261		22 20 10
Lund 1014	Berkeley 94		22 22 53
Lund 1015	NGC 7281		22 24 55.7
Lund 1016	NGC 7296		22 28 01
Lund 1017	Berkeley 95		22 28.3
Lund 1018	Berkeley 96		22 29 51.2
Lund 1019	Berkeley 97		22 39 22.2
Lund 1020	Czernik 42		22 39 35
Lund 1021	Berkeley 98		22 42 39.2
Lund 1022	NGC 7380		22 47 21
Lund 1023	King 18		22 52 08
Lund 1024	NGC 7419		22 54 17
Lund 1025	King 10		22 55.0
Lund 1026	NGC 7423		22 55 06.5
Lund 1027	NGC 7429		22 55.9
Lund 1028	King 19		23 08.3
Lund 1030	NGC 7510		23 11 04.2
Lund 1031	Markarian 50		23 15 14
Lund 1032	Berkeley 99		23 21 16.9
Lund 1034	NGC 7654		23 24 51
Lund 1036	Berkeley 100		23 25 58
Lund 1037	NGC 7686		23 30 07
Lund 1039	King 20		23 33 14
Lund 1040	Czernik 44		23 33 33
Lund 1041	Berkeley 101		23 32 46.5
Lund 1042	Stock 12		23 36 20
Lund 1043	Berkeley 102		23 38.7
Lund 1044	Berkeley 103		23 45.2
Lund 1045	Stock 17		23 43 47.0
Lund 1046	King 11		23 47 36.6

Table D.3: Cluster Cross-Reference

Name	Look Under	GX	2000.0 RA
Lund 1047	NGC 7762		23 49.9
Lund 1048	King 21		23 49.9
Lund 1055	vdB-Ha 4		07 37 45
Lund 1056	vdB-Ha 19		08 07 04.0
Lund 1057	vdB-Ha 23		08 14.4
Lund 1058	vdB-Ha 34		08 31 12
Lund 1059	vdB-Ha 37		08 35 48
Lund 1060	IC 2395		08 42 31
Lund 1062	vdB-Ha 54		08 49 41
Lund 1063	vdB-Ha 55		08 56 10.9
Lund 1064	vdB-Ha 56		08 57 08
Lund 1065	vdB-Ha 58		09 10 28
Lund 1066	Pismis 11		09 15 53
Lund 1067	vdB-Ha 63		09 20 38
Lund 1068	vdB-Ha 66		09 25 16
Lund 1069	vdB-Ha 67		09 26 43
Lund 1070	vdB-Ha 72		09 31 23
Lund 1071	vdB-Ha 73		09 31 56
Lund 1072	vdB-Ha 75		09 34 42
Lund 1073	vdB-Ha 78		09 43 48
Lund 1074	vdB-Ha 79		09 44.1
Lund 1075	vdB-Ha 84		10 01 19
Lund 1076	vdB-Ha 85		10 02.0
Lund 1077	vdB-Ha 87		10 04 34
Lund 1078	vdB-Ha 88		10 06 15
Lund 1079	vdB-Ha 90		10 12 10
Lund 1080	vdB-Ha 91		10 17.3
Lund 1081	vdB-Ha 92		10 19 04
Lund 1082	vdB-Ha 99		10 38 45.0
Lund 1084	vdB-Ha 106		10 52 38.6
Lund 1085	vdB-Ha 110		11 07.3
Lund 1086	vdB-Ha 111		11 09.5
Lund 1087	vdB-Ha 118		11 22.9
Lund 1088	Collinder 249		11 38 20.4
Lund 1089	vdB-Ha 131		12 26 25.7
Lund 1090	vdB-Ha 132		12 26 58
Lund 1091	Harvard 5		12 27 16.3
Lund 1092	vdB-Ha 140		12 53.5
Lund 1093	AL 1		13 15 16
Lund 1094	vdB-Ha 150		13 38 02
Lund 1095	vdB-Ha 151		13 40 12
Lund 1096	vdB-Ha 155		13 57.5
Lund 1097	vdB-Ha 164		14 44.1
Lund 1100	vdB-Ha 197		16 46 30.3
Lund 1101	vdB-Ha 200		16 50.0
Lund 1102	Ruprecht 122		16 55 08.3
Lund 1103	NGC 6318		17 16 13.4
Lund 1103	vdB-Ha 205		16 56 11.3
Lund 1104	NGC 6256	g	16 59 32.6
Lund 1105	vdB-Ha 211		17 02 07.9
Lund 1106	vdB-Ha 214		17 05 50.3
Lund 1107	vdB-Ha 217		17 16 20.4
Lund 1109	Basel 12		21 10.5
Lund 1110	vdB-Ha 221		17 18 34
Lund 1111	vdB-Ha 222		17 18 47.1
Lund 1112	vdB-Ha 223		17 20 42
Lund 1113	Terzan 2	g	17 27 33.4
Lund 1114	vdB-Ha 231		17 31 55.7
Lund 1116	vdB-Ha 245		17 46 14.4
Lund 1117	Terzan 6	g	17 50 46.4

Table D.3: Cluster Cross-Reference

Name	Look Under	GX	2000.0 RA
Lund 1118	AL 3		18 14 05.7
Lund 1119	Ruprecht 140		18 21 49.8
Lund 1121	NGC 1724		05 03 33
Lund 1122	NGC 2112		05 53 46
Lund 1123	Bochum 14		18 02.0
Lund 1124	Bochum 1		06 25 24.9
Lund 1125	Basel 7		06 36 19
Lund 1126	Bochum 2		06 48 50
Lund 1128	NGC 2409		07 31 37
Lund 1129	Bochum 5		07 32.1
Lund 1130	Bochum 6		07 31 45.1
Lund 1131	Bochum 7		08 44.8
Lund 1133	Basel 15		21 15.9
Lund 1134	Basel 14		21 21 14.0
Lund 1135	Bochum 11		10 47 12
Lund 1136	Bochum 12		10 57 18
Lund 1137	Basel 18		13 27 49
Lund 1139	Bochum 13		17 17 20.7
Lund 1140	Antalova 2		17 29.7
Lund 1141	Moffat 1		16 01 36.1
Lund 1142	Havlen-Moffat 1		17 19 00.5
Lund 1146	Bochum 9		10 35.5
Lund 1147	Bochum 10		10 42 08
Lund 1148	Cl vdB 113		18 08.6
Lund 1149	NGC 6837		19 53.5
Lund 1150	Cl vdB 130		20 17 42.2
Lund 1151	Dolidze 47		20 41 44.2
Lund 1152	Cl vdB 152		22 13 24.5
Lund 1153	Aveni-Hunter 1		23 37 47
Lund 1154	Cl vdB 150		22 12 52.8
Lund 1155	Mayer 1		00 21 54
Lund 1156	Mayer 2		04 19 51
Lund 1158	Sigma Ori		05 38 45
Lund 1159	NGC 1977		05 35.3
Lund 1160	Cl vdB 85		06 46 52
Lund 1162	Cl vdB 92		07 03 55
Lund 1163	Basel 11a		07 17 08
Lund 1164	Mayer 3		07 30 04
Lund 1165	Cl vdB 83		06 40.0
Lund 1166	NGC 1901		05 17.8
Lund 1167	Loden 27		10 11.1
Lund 1168	Loden 59		10 30 22
Lund 1169	Loden 112		10 32 40
Lund 1170	Loden 143		10 28 44
Lund 1172	Loden 165		10 35 56
Lund 1173	Loden 280		11 09.5
Lund 1174	Basel 17		11 10 32.9
Lund 1175	Graham 1		10 56 32
Lund 1176	Loden 309		11 09.5
Lund 1177	Loden 336		11 19.8
Lund 1178	Loden 372		11 30 52
Lund 1179	Loden 480		11 56 06
Lund 1180	Loden 565		12 08 24.4
Lund 1181	Loden 615		12 20 37.2
Lund 1182	NGC 2175.1		06 10 53
Lund 1183	Hogg 23		12 28 31.6
Lund 1184	Loden 757		13 12.4
Lund 1185	Loden 807		13 24.9
Lund 1186	Loden 848		13 33.1
Lund 1187	Loden 894		13 39 44.3

Table D.3: Cluster Cross-Reference

Name	Look Under	GX	2000.0 RA
Lund 1188	Loden 991		13 45.4
Lund 1189	Loden 1002		13 54.3
Lund 1190	Loden 1010		13 45.4
Lund 1191	Loden 1095		13 53.5
Lund 1192	Loden 1101		13 58 40.6
Lund 1193	Loden 1152		13 59.5
Lund 1194	Loden 1171		13 59 31.4
Lund 1195	Loden 1177		13 59.4
Lund 1196	Loden 1194		14 05.8
Lund 1197	Loden 1202		14 04.4
Lund 1198	Loden 1225		14 09.2
Lund 1199	Loden 1282		14 15.9
Lund 1200	Loden 1289		14 16 56.9
Lund 1201	Loden 1256		14 18.2
Lund 1202	Loden 1339		14 33.5
Lund 1203	Loden 1373		14 41.7
Lund 1204	Loden 1375		14 44 33
Lund 1205	Loden 1409		14 44.7
Lund 1206	Ruprecht 176		16 14 45
Lund 1209	Basel 11b		05 58 10
Lund 1210	Schuster 1		10 04 39.0
Lund 1211	Danks 1		13 12 26.8
Lund 1212	Danks 2		13 12 53.8
LW 1	NGC 1466	L	03 44 32.4
LW 5		L	04 33 52.1
LW 7		L	04 35 36.6
LW 9		L	04 35 58.9
LW 15		L	04 38 26.3
LW 17	SL 13	L	04 39 42.9
LW 20		L	04 39 58.6
LW 22		L	04 40 20.4
LW 24		L	04 41 07.8
LW 25		L	04 41 46.4
LW 27		L	04 41 33.6
LW 28		L	04 42 11.0
LW 30		L	04 42 51.2
LW 36	SL 23	L	04 43 38.0
LW 38	SL 24	L	04 43 50.3
LW 39		L	04 43 59.4
LW 41		L	04 44 11.5
LW 43		L	04 44 17.0
LW 44		L	04 44 37.4
LW 45		L	04 44 29.4
LW 46		L	04 44 46.7
LW 47	SL 28	L	04 44 40.8
LW 50	SL 29	L	04 45 12.6
LW 53	SL 31	L	04 45 40.6
LW 55		L	04 45 47.3
LW 56	SL 33	L	04 45 53.5
LW 57		L	04 46 22.4
LW 60	SL 36	L	04 46 08.5
LW 62		L	04 46 18.9
LW 63		L	04 47 15.6
LW 65		L	04 49 20.0
LW 66		L	04 49 04.2
LW 69		L	04 49 39.0
LW 73	SL 53	L	04 49 53.2
LW 75		L	04 50 14.0
LW 75	SL 59	L	04 50 20.2
LW 76		L	04 50 24.8

Table D.3: Cluster Cross-Reference

Name	Look Under	GX	2000.0 RA
LW 76	SL 59	L	04 50 20.2
LW 78	SL 54	L	04 50 48.7
LW 83		L	04 52 06.8
LW 86		L	04 52 44.8
LW 87		L	04 52 54.6
LW 88	SL 80	L	04 52 21.1
LW 91		L	04 54 22.8
LW 94	SL 118	L	04 55 32.5
LW 95		L	04 55 57.9
LW 96	NGC 1777	L	04 55 48.5
LW 98		L	04 56 50.9
LW 100		L	04 57 35.5
LW 100	NGC 1787	L	05 00.0
LW 102		L	04 57 52.3
LW 103		L	04 57 55.3
LW 106		L	04 58 06.5
LW 107		L	04 58 15.6
LW 110		L	04 58 46.3
LW 111	SL 166	L	04 59 12.5
LW 112		L	05 00 10.0
LW 115		L	05 01 10.0
LW 121	SL 192	L	05 02 27.6
LW 124		L	05 03 38.2
LW 126		L	05 04 41.4
LW 127		L	05 04 52.7
LW 129		L	05 04 42.9
LW 132		L	05 05 14.5
LW 133	NGC 1831	L	05 06 16.2
LW 134		L	05 06 27.5
LW 135		L	05 06 40.8
LW 137		L	05 06 03.3
LW 138		L	05 07 05.0
LW 140		L	05 07 22.0
LW 141		L	05 07 35.2
LW 145	SL 259	L	05 08 51.6
LW 146	SL 262	L	05 09 21.2
LW 147		L	05 08 34.9
LW 148		L	05 09 40.7
LW 149		L	05 09 32.1
LW 153	SL 295	L	05 10 10.7
LW 155		L	05 10 32.0
LW 157		L	05 11 52.2
LW 159		L	05 12 24.9
LW 160		L	05 12 18.2
LW 163	NGC 1866	L	05 13 38.6
LW 164		L	05 13 16.1
LW 165		L	05 14 23.3
LW 169	NGC 1868	L	05 14 36.1
LW 171		L	05 14 46.3
LW 174		L	05 15 26.6
LW 177	SL 354	L	05 17 30.9
LW 182		L	05 18 48.3
LW 184	NGC 1900	L	05 19 08.8
LW 186	SL 388	L	05 20 05.5
LW 188	SL 400	L	05 19 38.7
LW 190	SL 401	L	05 20 50.2
LW 191		L	05 20 27.4
LW 193		L	05 20 58.6
LW 195		L	05 22 35.4
LW 197	SL 433	L	05 22 19.2

Table D.3: Cluster Cross-Reference

Name	Look Under	GX	2000.0 RA
LW 198	IC 2134	L	05 23 06.6
LW 199		L	05 24 08.2
LW 201		L	05 23 23.2
LW 203	NGC 1942	L	05 24 42.7
LW 204		L	05 24 07.2
LW 206	SL 451	L	05 24 13.4
LW 207	SL 455	L	05 24 17.2
LW 209		L	05 25 44.4
LW 210		L	05 25 07.0
LW 211		L	05 25 28.0
LW 212		L	05 26 08.4
LW 214		L	05 26 48.1
LW 215		L	05 27 42.6
LW 217	SL 490	L	05 27 18.4
LW 220	[H60b] 14	L	05 28 38.6
LW 225	SL 525	L	05 30 23.4
LW 228		L	05 30 52.7
LW 230		L	05 31 23.2
LW 231		L	05 30 27.8
LW 232	SL 540	L	05 31 33.9
LW 233	SL 546	L	05 31 02.5
LW 234		L	05 30 59.8
LW 237	[H60b] 4	L	05 32 25.4
LW 238		L	05 32 54.0
LW 239	SL 576	L	05 33 14.2
LW 243		L	05 32 41.0
LW 244		L	05 34 23.2
LW 245		L	05 35 06.8
LW 246		L	05 35 07.2
LW 247		L	05 34 59.1
LW 248		L	05 36 24.5
LW 249	SL 603	L	05 35 43.7
LW 250		L	05 36 38.2
LW 251	SL 604	L	05 36 46.2
LW 255	SL 620	L	05 36 28.4
LW 258	IC 2146	L	05 37 47.4
LW 260		L	05 38 53.2
LW 261		L	05 39 11.0
LW 263		L	05 39 08.4
LW 266		L	05 40 30.7
LW 267	SL 647	L	05 39 34.7
LW 269	SL 649	L	05 41 08.6
LW 270		L	05 40 23.4
LW 272		L	05 42 25.7
LW 276		L	05 43 11.9
LW 277	SL 670	L	05 43 14.3
LW 278		L	05 43 11.9
LW 280	SL 677	L	05 43 55.6
LW 281	SL 680	L	05 44 03.8
LW 282	NGC 2097	L	05 44 15.5
LW 285		L	05 44 35.4
LW 287	SL 694	L	05 45 06.5
LW 289	SL 701	L	05 45 32.7
LW 290	SL 703	L	05 44 54.3
LW 294		L	05 46 02.5
LW 295		L	05 46 18.7
LW 297		L	05 46 07.5
LW 298	SL 710	L	05 46 58.1
LW 309		L	05 49 04.6
LW 311	SL 729	L	05 49 20.6

Table D.3: Cluster Cross-Reference

Name	Look Under	GX	2000.0 RA
LW 312	SL 737	L	05 48 44.1
LW 315		L	05 49 27.0
LW 316	NGC 2120	L	05 50 34.8
LW 318		L	05 50 43.0
LW 319		L	05 51 06.1
LW 320		L	05 51 21.2
LW 321		L	05 51 18.4
LW 322	SL 754	L	05 50 35.6
LW 323		L	05 51 45.9
LW 326	SL 768	L	05 53 54.5
LW 329		L	05 54 37.6
LW 332		L	05 55 08.1
LW 333	SL 783	L	05 54 39.1
LW 335		L	05 55 57.1
LW 337	NGC 2161	L	05 55 42.3
LW 346	SL 804	L	05 57 38.1
LW 348	NGC 2173	L	05 57 58.0
LW 352		L	06 00 19.7
LW 354		L	06 00 37.7
LW 357	NGC 2190	L	06 01 02.3
LW 360		L	06 01 30.0
LW 361		L	06 02 09.5
LW 367		L	06 02 14.3
LW 368		L	06 03 02.0
LW 369		L	06 02 56.0
LW 373		L	06 03 14.0
LW 379	SL 835	L	06 04 48.1
LW 380	NGC 2203	L	06 04 41.6
LW 381		L	06 05 43.6
LW 383		L	06 05 38.7
LW 384		L	06 05 35.4
LW 386		L	06 06 17.5
LW 388		L	06 06 19.9
LW 389		L	06 06 09.3
LW 390		L	06 06 26.9
LW 392		L	06 07 00.9
LW 393		L	06 06 32.2
LW 394		L	06 07 00.3
LW 395		L	06 07 30.7
LW 397		L	06 07 28.9
LW 399		L	06 08 15.7
LW 404		L	06 08 32.3
LW 405	SL 848	L	06 08 17.5
LW 406		L	06 09 01.4
LW 407		L	06 08 58.3
LW 408	NGC 2209	L	06 08 34.8
LW 409		L	06 09 03.5
LW 410		L	06 08 56.4
LW 411		L	06 09 30.1
LW 414		L	06 10 03.5
LW 421		L	06 10 53.8
LW 422		L	06 11 23.2
LW 423	NGC 2210	L	06 11 31.3
LW 425		L	06 12 45.1
LW 426	NGC 2214	L	06 12 56.1
LW 427		L	06 13 07.1
LW 430		L	06 13 14.7
LW 436		L	06 14 26.3
LW 444		L	06 15 57.5
LW 445		L	06 15 47.3

Table D.3: Cluster Cross-Reference

Name	Look Under	GX	2000.0 RA
LW 448		L	06 16 36.2
LW 449		L	06 16 48.2
LW 450		L	06 17 42.8
LW 451		L	06 17 44.2
LW 454		L	06 18 11.1
LW 458		L	06 19 11.2
LW 459		L	06 19 17.6
LW 460		L	06 19 15.2
LW 462		L	06 19 40.8
LW 463		L	06 19 46.4
LW 469		L	06 21 34.0
LW 470		L	06 22 24.0
LW 472		L	06 23 11.8
LW 474		L	06 23 29.7
LW 475		L	06 23 23.2
LW 479	NGC 2249	L	06 25 49.5
LW 480	SL 896	L	06 29 57.7
LW 481	NGC 2257	L	06 30 12.4
LW 482		L	06 32 23.6
Lynds 810	Turner 8		19 45 16
Lynga 1			14 00 02
Lynga 2			14 24 24
Lynga 3			15 16 47
Lynga 4			15 33 20
Lynga 5			15 41 57.1
Lynga 6			16 04 51
Lynga 7		g	16 11 03.0
Lynga 8			16 22 57.0
Lynga 9			16 20 39
Lynga 10	Pismis 23		16 23 58
Lynga 11			16 38 10
Lynga 12			16 46 03
Lynga 13			16 48 54
Lynga 14			16 55 05
Lynga 15			11 42.4
M 2	NGC 7089	g	21 33 27.0
M 3	NGC 5272	g	13 42 11.2
M 4	NGC 6121	g	16 23 35.5
M 5	NGC 5904	g	15 18 33.8
M 6	NGC 6405		17 40 17
M 7	NGC 6475		17 53 46
M 8	NGC 6523		18 04 25
M 9	NGC 6333	g	17 19 11.8
M 10	NGC 6254	g	16 57 08.9
M 11	NGC 6705		18 51 04
M 12	NGC 6218	g	16 47 14.5
M 13	NGC 6205	g	16 41 41.5
M 14	NGC 6402	g	17 37 36.1
M 15	NGC 7078	g	21 29 58.3
M 16	NGC 6611		18 18 45
M 17	NGC 6618		18 21 09
M 18	NGC 6613		18 20 00
M 19	NGC 6273	g	17 02 37.7
M 20	NGC 6514		18 02 31
M 21	NGC 6531		18 04 13
M 22	NGC 6656	g	18 36 24.2
M 23	NGC 6494		17 56 56
M 24	IC 4715		18 17
M 24	NGC 6603		18 18 28
M 25	IC 4725		18 31 45

Table D.3: Cluster Cross-Reference

Name	Look Under	GX	2000.0 RA
M 26	NGC 6694		18 45 15
M 28	NGC 6626	g	18 24 32.9
M 29	NGC 6913		20 24 06
M 30	NGC 7099	g	21 40 22.0
M 34	NGC 1039		02 42 08
M 35	NGC 2168		06 09.0
M 36	NGC 1960		05 36 18
M 37	NGC 2099		05 52 19
M 38	NGC 1912		05 28 43
M 39	NGC 7092		21 31 52
M 41	NGC 2287		06 46.1
M 42	NGC 1976		05 35 16
M 44	NGC 2632		08 40 22
M 45	Pleiades		03 47 29
M 46	NGC 2437		07 41 47
M 47	NGC 2422		07 36 36
M 48	NGC 2548		08 13 44
M 50	NGC 2323		07 02 47.8
M 52	NGC 7654		23 24 51
M 53	NGC 5024	g	13 12 55.3
M 54	NGC 6715	g	18 55 03.3
M 55	NGC 6809	g	19 39 59.4
M 56	NGC 6779	g	19 16 35.5
M 62	NGC 6266	g	17 01 12.6
M 67	NGC 2682		08 51 24
M 68	NGC 4590	g	12 39 28.0
M 69	NGC 6637	g	18 31 23.2
M 70	NGC 6681	g	18 43 12.7
M 71	NGC 6838	g	19 53 46.1
M 72	NGC 6981	g	20 53 27.9
M 73	NGC 6994		20 58 56
M 75	NGC 6864	g	20 06 04.8
M 79	NGC 1904	g	05 24 10.6
M 80	NGC 6093	g	16 17 02.5
M 92	NGC 6341	g	17 17 07.3
M 93	NGC 2447		07 44 30
M 103	NGC 581		01 33 22
M 107	NGC 6171	g	16 32 31.9
Mackie 1			18 41 52
Maffei 1	Czernik 11		02 36 36
Mandushev 1			19 43 30
Markarian 1	IC 1590		00 52 49
Markarian 2	NGC 366		01 06 27
Markarian 3	Trumpler 1		01 35 40
Markarian 4	NGC 869		02 19 04
Markarian 5	NGC 884		02 22 05
Markarian 6			02 29 40
Markarian 7	IC 1805		02 32 42
Markarian 8	IC 1848		02 51 11
Markarian 9	NGC 1444		03 49 27
Markarian 10	NGC 1502		04 07 50
Markarian 11	NGC 1624		04 40 37
Markarian 12	Collinder 69		05 35.0
Markarian 13	Collinder 70		05 35.6
Markarian 14	NGC 1976		05 35 16
Markarian 15	NGC 2244		06 32 19
Markarian 16	NGC 2264		06 40 59
Markarian 17	NGC 2362		07 18 42
Markarian 18			09 00 31
Markarian 19	NGC 3293		10 35 49

Table D.3: Cluster Cross-Reference

Name	Look Under	GX	2000.0 RA
Markarian 20	IC 2602		10 42 57
Markarian 21	Trumpler 14		10 43 57
Markarian 22	Trumpler 15		10 44 44
Markarian 23	Trumpler 16		10 45 10
Markarian 24	NGC 3590		11 13 00
Markarian 25	NGC 3766		11 36 15
Markarian 26	NGC 4463		12 29 56
Markarian 27	NGC 4815		12 57 59
Markarian 28	NGC 5168		13 31 08
Markarian 29	NGC 6169		16 34 05.0
Markarian 30	NGC 6193		16 41 20.3
Markarian 31	NGC 6231		16 54 09.8
Markarian 32	Trumpler 24		16 57.0
Markarian 33	NGC 6383		17 34 42.2
Markarian 34	NGC 6514		18 02 31
Markarian 35	NGC 6520		18 03 25
Markarian 36	NGC 6523		18 04 25
Markarian 37	NGC 6531		18 04 13
Markarian 38			18 15 16.6
Markarian 39	NGC 6604		18 18.1
Markarian 40	NGC 6611		18 18 45
Markarian 41	NGC 6618		18 21 09
Markarian 42	NGC 6823		19 43 10
Markarian 43	NGC 6871		20 06 27
Markarian 44	IC 4996		20 16 31.7
Markarian 45	NGC 6910		20 23 12
Markarian 46	NGC 6913		20 24 06
Markarian 47	IC 1396		21 39.0
Markarian 48	NGC 7380		22 47 21
Markarian 49	NGC 7510		23 11 04.2
Markarian 50			23 15 14
Markov 1			17 57.2
Mayall II	[ME53] II	A	00 32 46.9
Mayer 1			00 21 54
Mayer 2			04 19 51
Mayer 3			07 30 04
[MBB72] 57	NGC 2014	L	05 32 21.7
[MBB72] 76	NGC 2080	L	05 39 44.6
MC 76	NGC 2080	L	05 39 44.6
MCG +00-26-017	Palomar 3	g	10 05 31.4
MCG +00-39-016	Palomar 5	g	15 16 05.3
MCG +00-43-006	Palomar 15	g	16 59 50.9
MCG +02-26-027	Leo I		10 08 27.5
MCG +03-18-002	Berkeley 29		06 53 04
MCG +04-27-005	Leo II		11 13 29.3
MCG +05-12-001	Palomar 2	g	04 46 05.9
MCG −01-32-037	NGC 4604		12 40 45.1
MCG −02-29-029	NGC 3676		11 25 37.5
MCG −04-51-013	Palomar 12	g	21 46 38.8
MCG −06-06-016	Fornax 2	F	02 38 44
MCG −06-06-017	NGC 1049	F	02 39 48
MCG −06-07-002	Fornax 5	F	02 42 21
[ME53] II		A	00 32 46.9
Melotte 1	NGC 104	g	00 24 05.2
Melotte 2	NGC 188		00 47 30
Melotte 3	NGC 288	g	00 52 45.5
Melotte 4	NGC 362	g	01 03 14.3
Melotte 5	NGC 371	S	01 03.3
Melotte 6	NGC 436		01 15 58
Melotte 7	NGC 457		01 19 33

Table D.3: Cluster Cross-Reference

Name	Look Under	GX	2000.0 RA
Melotte 8	NGC 581		01 33 22
Melotte 9	NGC 654		01 44 00
Melotte 10	NGC 659		01 44 24
Melotte 11	NGC 663		01 46 17
Melotte 12	NGC 752		01 57 35
Melotte 13	NGC 869		02 19 04
Melotte 14	NGC 884		02 22 05
Melotte 15	IC 1805		02 32 42
Melotte 16	NGC 1027		02 42 36
Melotte 17	NGC 1039		02 42 08
Melotte 18	NGC 1245		03 14 42
Melotte 19	NGC 1261	g	03 12 15.3
Melotte 20			03 24 19
Melotte 21	NGC 1342		03 31 40
Melotte 22	Pleiades		03 47 29
Melotte 23	NGC 1528		04 15 19
Melotte 24	IC 361		04 18 51
Melotte 25	Hyades		04 26.9
Melotte 26	NGC 1647		04 45 42.2
Melotte 27	NGC 1664		04 51 06
Melotte 28	NGC 1746		05 03.6
Melotte 28	NGC 1750		05 03.9
Melotte 29	NGC 1807		05 10 46
Melotte 31			05 18 10.5
Melotte 32	NGC 1857		05 20 06
Melotte 33	NGC 1893		05 22 46
Melotte 34	NGC 1904	g	05 24 10.6
Melotte 35	NGC 1907		05 28 05
Melotte 36	NGC 1912		05 28 43
Melotte 37	NGC 1960		05 36 18
Melotte 38	NGC 2099		05 52 19
Melotte 39	NGC 2126		06 02 34
Melotte 40	NGC 2158		06 07 26
Melotte 41	NGC 2168		06 09.0
Melotte 42	NGC 2192		06 15 18
Melotte 43	NGC 2194		06 13 46
Melotte 44	NGC 2204		06 15 33
Melotte 45	NGC 2215		06 20 50
Melotte 46	NGC 2243		06 29 35
Melotte 47	NGC 2237		06 31 55.5
Melotte 47	NGC 2244		06 32 19
Melotte 48	NGC 2259		06 38 33.3
Melotte 49	NGC 2264		06 40 59
Melotte 50	NGC 2266		06 43 20
Melotte 51	NGC 2281		06 48 18
Melotte 52	NGC 2287		06 46.1
Melotte 54	NGC 2301		06 51 46
Melotte 55	NGC 2304		06 55 12
Melotte 56	NGC 2309		06 56 04
Melotte 57	NGC 2314		07 10 32.4
Melotte 58	NGC 2323		07 02 47.8
Melotte 59	NGC 2324		07 04 08
Melotte 60	NGC 2335		07 06 50
Melotte 61	NGC 2345		07 08 19
Melotte 62	NGC 2353		07 14 31
Melotte 63	NGC 2355		07 17 00
Melotte 64	NGC 2360		07 17 44
Melotte 65	NGC 2362		07 18 42
Melotte 66			07 26 19
Melotte 67	NGC 2421		07 36 12

Table D.3: Cluster Cross-Reference

Name	Look Under	GX	2000.0 RA
Melotte 68	NGC 2422		07 36 36
Melotte 69	NGC 2420		07 38 24
Melotte 70	NGC 2423		07 37 07
Melotte 71			07 37 30
Melotte 72			07 38 29
Melotte 73	NGC 2432		07 40 54
Melotte 74	NGC 2439		07 40 46
Melotte 75	NGC 2437		07 41 47
Melotte 76	NGC 2447		07 44 30
Melotte 77	NGC 2455		07 48 59
Melotte 78	NGC 2477		07 52 10
Melotte 79	NGC 2489		07 56 16
Melotte 80	NGC 2506		08 00 02
Melotte 81	NGC 2509		08 00 48
Melotte 82	NGC 2516		07 58.0
Melotte 83	NGC 2539		08 10 38
Melotte 84	NGC 2547		08 10 11
Melotte 85	NGC 2548		08 13 44
Melotte 86	NGC 2567		08 18 30
Melotte 87	NGC 2627		08 37 15
Melotte 88	NGC 2632		08 40 22
Melotte 89	NGC 2635		08 38 27
Melotte 90	NGC 2658		08 43 28
Melotte 91	NGC 2659		08 42 34
Melotte 92	NGC 2660		08 42 39
Melotte 93	NGC 2670		08 45 30
Melotte 94	NGC 2682		08 51 24
Melotte 96	NGC 2818		09 16 10
Melotte 97	IC 2488		09 27 27
Melotte 98	NGC 3114		10 02.7
Melotte 99	NGC 3201	g	10 17 36.8
Melotte 100	NGC 3293		10 35 49
Melotte 101			10 42 00
Melotte 102	IC 2602		10 42 57
Melotte 103	NGC 3532		11 05.5
Melotte 104	IC 2714		11 17 18
Melotte 105			11 19 41
Melotte 106	NGC 3680		11 25 38
Melotte 107	NGC 3766		11 36 15
Melotte 108	NGC 3960		11 50 34
Melotte 109	NGC 4103		12 06 40
Melotte 110	NGC 4349		12 24 07
Melotte 111			12 25.1
Melotte 112	NGC 4372	g	12 25 45.4
Melotte 113	NGC 4590	g	12 39 28.0
Melotte 114	NGC 4755		12 53 38
Melotte 115	NGC 4833	g	12 59 35.0
Melotte 116	NGC 4852		13 00 05
Melotte 117	NGC 5024	g	13 12 55.3
Melotte 118	NGC 5139	g	13 26 45.9
Melotte 119	NGC 5272	g	13 42 11.2
Melotte 120	NGC 5281		13 46 36.7
Melotte 121	NGC 5286	g	13 46 26.5
Melotte 122	NGC 5316		13 54.0
Melotte 123	NGC 5460		14 07.6
Melotte 124	NGC 5466	g	14 05 27.3
Melotte 125	NGC 5617		14 29.7
Melotte 126	NGC 5634	g	14 29 37.3
Melotte 127	NGC 5662		14 35 30.8
Melotte 128	NGC 5715		14 43 39.0

Table D.3: Cluster Cross-Reference

Name	Look Under	GX	2000.0 RA
Melotte 129	IC 4499	g	15 00 18.5
Melotte 130	NGC 5822		15 04 02.3
Melotte 131	NGC 5823		15 05 26
Melotte 132	NGC 5897	g	15 17 24.5
Melotte 133	NGC 5904	g	15 18 33.8
Melotte 134	NGC 5927	g	15 28 00.5
Melotte 135	NGC 5946	g	15 35 28.5
Melotte 136	NGC 5986	g	15 46 03.5
Melotte 137	NGC 5999		15 52 14
Melotte 138	NGC 6005		15 55 47.4
Melotte 139	NGC 6025		16 03 18
Melotte 140	NGC 6067		16 13 09
Melotte 141	NGC 6087		16 18 51.8
Melotte 142	NGC 6093	g	16 17 02.5
Melotte 143	NGC 6101	g	16 25 48.6
Melotte 144	NGC 6121	g	16 23 35.5
Melotte 145	NGC 6124		16 25 17.2
Melotte 146	NGC 6134		16 27 43.6
Melotte 147	NGC 6144	g	16 27 14.1
Melotte 148	NGC 6171	g	16 32 31.9
Melotte 149	NGC 6192		16 40 20.8
Melotte 150	NGC 6205	g	16 41 41.5
Melotte 151	NGC 6218	g	16 47 14.5
Melotte 152	NGC 6216		16 49 23.6
Melotte 153	NGC 6231		16 54 09.8
Melotte 154	NGC 6235	g	16 53 25.4
Melotte 155	NGC 6242		16 55 30.6
Melotte 156	NGC 6253		16 59 06.1
Melotte 157	NGC 6254	g	16 57 08.9
Melotte 158	NGC 6259		17 00.7
Melotte 159	NGC 6266	g	17 01 12.6
Melotte 160	NGC 6273	g	17 02 37.7
Melotte 161	NGC 6281		17 04 47.2
Melotte 162	NGC 6284	g	17 04 28.8
Melotte 163	NGC 6287	g	17 05 09.4
Melotte 164	NGC 6293	g	17 10 10.4
Melotte 165	NGC 6304	g	17 14 32.5
Melotte 166	NGC 6318		17 16 13.4
Melotte 167	NGC 6333	g	17 19 11.8
Melotte 168	NGC 6341	g	17 17 07.3
Melotte 169	IC 4651		17 24.7
Melotte 170	NGC 6352	g	17 25 29.2
Melotte 171	NGC 6356	g	17 23 35.0
Melotte 172	NGC 6362	g	17 31 54.8
Melotte 173	NGC 6366	g	17 27 44.3
Melotte 174	NGC 6388	g	17 36 17.0
Melotte 175	NGC 6402	g	17 37 36.1
Melotte 176	NGC 6397	g	17 40 41.3
Melotte 177	NGC 6400		17 40 10
Melotte 178	NGC 6405		17 40 17
Melotte 179	IC 4665		17 46.2
Melotte 180	NGC 6441	g	17 50 12.9
Melotte 181	NGC 6451		17 50 41
Melotte 182	NGC 6469		17 52 56.5
Melotte 183	NGC 6475		17 53 46
Melotte 184	NGC 6494		17 56 56
Melotte 185	NGC 6496	g	17 59 02.0
Melotte 186			18 01.1
Melotte 187	NGC 6520		18 03 25
Melotte 188	NGC 6531		18 04 13

Table D.3: Cluster Cross-Reference

Name	Look Under	GX	2000.0 RA
Melotte 189	NGC 6535	g	18 03 50.7
Melotte 190	NGC 6539	g	18 04 49.8
Melotte 191	NGC 6541	g	18 08 02.2
Melotte 192	NGC 6544	g	18 07 20.6
Melotte 193	NGC 6553	g	18 09 17.3
Melotte 194	NGC 6558	g	18 10 17.6
Melotte 195	NGC 6569	g	18 13 38.9
Melotte 196	NGC 6584	g	18 18 37.7
Melotte 197	NGC 6603		18 18 28
Melotte 198	NGC 6611		18 18 45
Melotte 199	NGC 6624	g	18 23 40.5
Melotte 200	NGC 6626	g	18 24 32.9
Melotte 201	NGC 6633		18 27 15
Melotte 202	NGC 6637	g	18 31 23.2
Melotte 203	NGC 6642	g	18 31 54.3
Melotte 204	IC 4725		18 31 45
Melotte 205	NGC 6645		18 32 38
Melotte 206	NGC 6649		18 33 28.3
Melotte 207	NGC 6652	g	18 35 45.7
Melotte 208	NGC 6656	g	18 36 24.2
Melotte 209	NGC 6664		18 36 30.6
Melotte 210	IC 4756		18 38.9
Melotte 211	NGC 6681	g	18 43 12.7
Melotte 212	NGC 6694		18 45 15
Melotte 213	NGC 6705		18 51 04
Melotte 214	NGC 6709		18 51.5
Melotte 215	NGC 6712	g	18 53 04.3
Melotte 216	NGC 6715	g	18 55 03.3
Melotte 217	NGC 6723	g	18 59 33.2
Melotte 218	NGC 6752	g	19 10 51.8
Melotte 219	NGC 6760	g	19 11 12.1
Melotte 220	NGC 6779	g	19 16 35.5
Melotte 221	NGC 6809	g	19 39 59.4
Melotte 222	NGC 6811		19 37 09.6
Melotte 223	NGC 6819		19 41.3
Melotte 224	NGC 6830		19 51 00
Melotte 225	NGC 6834		19 52 13
Melotte 226	NGC 6838	g	19 53 46.1
Melotte 227			20 15 18
Melotte 228	NGC 6864	g	20 06 04.8
Melotte 229	NGC 6866		20 03 55
Melotte 230	NGC 6934	g	20 34 11.6
Melotte 231	NGC 6939		20 31 30
Melotte 232	NGC 6940		20 34 32.3
Melotte 233	NGC 6981	g	20 53 27.9
Melotte 234	NGC 7078	g	21 29 58.3
Melotte 235	NGC 7089	g	21 33 27.0
Melotte 236	NGC 7092		21 31 52
Melotte 237	NGC 7099	g	21 40 22.0
Melotte 238	NGC 7209		22 05 08
Melotte 239	IC 1434		22 10.5
Melotte 240	NGC 7243		22 15 09
Melotte 241	NGC 7245		22 15 16
Melotte 242	NGC 7492	g	23 08 26.7
Melotte 243	NGC 7654		23 24 51
Melotte 244	NGC 7762		23 49.9
Melotte 245	NGC 7789		23 57 28.6
MGM 5	RAFGL 2004		17 46 13.9
Min 2- 59	IC 410		05 22.0
MKN 369	Dejc 1		02 37 28.3

Table D.3: Cluster Cross-Reference

Name	Look Under	GX	2000.0 RA
MLA 303	[V62] 211	A	00 41 02.1
MLA 1186	Bol D268	A	00 45 44.1
Moffat	Moffat 1		16 01 36.1
Moffat 1			16 01 36.1
Mu Normae cluster	NGC 6169		16 34 05.0
Muzzio 1			08 57.2
NBol 2	Bol 96	A	00 42 26.2
NBol 5	Bol 104	A	00 42 30.0
NBol 6	Bol 118	A	00 42 35.6
NBol 10	Bol 124	A	00 42 41.1
NBol 13	Bol 134	A	00 42 51.7
NBol 14	Bol 119	A	00 42 36.2
NBol 15	Bol 132	A	00 42 51.4
NBol 16		A	00 42 33.2
NBol 17	[WSB85] W 4	A	00 42 34.5
NBol 18		A	00 42 47.2
NBol 19	Bol 264	A	00 42 53.2
NBol 20	Bol D53	A	00 42 24.8
NBol 21	[WSB85] W 7	A	00 42 38.0
NBol 23		A	00 42 26.7
NBol 25		A	00 42 39.4
NBol 29		A	00 42 35.4
NBol 34	ACH 15	A	00 42 58.5
NBol 35	ACH 4	A	00 42 34.5
NBol 38		A	00 42 37.6
NBol 39	ACH 6	A	00 42 48.4
NBol 42		A	00 42 47.0
NBol 45	ACH 9	A	00 42 49.5
NBol 47	ACH 3	A	00 42 33.9
NBol 53		A	00 42 35.3
NBol 57		A	00 42 36.2
NBol 58		A	00 42 42.1
NBol 60	NBol 23	A	00 42 26.7
NBol 61		A	00 42 31.7
NBol 63		A	00 42 31.3
NBol 65		A	00 42 29.7
NBol 67	ACH 13	A	00 42 34.2
NBol 68		A	00 42 37.5
NBol 70		A	00 42 30.2
NBol 72	Bol 261	A	00 42 36.1
NBol 74		A	00 42 38.5
NBol 75		A	00 42 33.2
NBol 81		A	00 42 31.5
NBol 83		A	00 42 26.9
NBol 87		A	00 42 45.6
NBol 89		A	00 42 44.7
NBol 91		A	00 42 39.7
NBol 93	Bol D80	A	00 42 54.2
NBol 94		A	00 42 49.4
NBol 95		A	00 42 47.9
NBol 97		A	00 42 55.8
NGC 32			00 10 53.2
NGC 103			00 25 18
NGC 104		g	00 24 05.2
NGC 110			00 27 25.4
NGC 121		S	00 26 48.7
NGC 129			00 29 58
NGC 133			00 31 18
NGC 136			00 31 31
NGC 146			00 33.1

Table D.3: Cluster Cross-Reference

Name	Look Under	GX	2000.0 RA
NGC 152		S	00 32 55.5
NGC 176		S	00 35 58.6
NGC 188			00 47 30
NGC 189			00 39 36
NGC 220		S	00 40 30.6
NGC 222		S	00 40 44.1
NGC 225			00 43 36
NGC 231		S	00 41 06.2
NGC 241		S	00 43 28.5
NGC 242		S	00 43 33.9
NGC 242	OGLE-CL SMC0017	S	00 43 32.8
NGC 242	[HB90] 1	S	00 43 37.6
NGC 248		S	00 45 24.1
NGC 256		S	00 45 54.4
NGC 261		S	00 46 33.0
NGC 265		S	00 47 11.6
NGC 269		S	00 48 21.3
NGC 272			00 51 26
NGC 281	IC 1590		00 52 49
NGC 288		g	00 52 45.5
NGC 290		S	00 51 14.2
NGC 294		S	00 53 05.6
NGC 299		S	00 53 24.8
NGC 305			00 56 21
NGC 306		S	00 54 14.8
NGC 330		S	00 56 18.7
NGC 339		S	00 57 45.4
NGC 346		S	00 59.1
NGC 358			01 05 11
NGC 361		S	01 02 11.3
NGC 362		g	01 03 14.3
NGC 366			01 06 27
NGC 371		S	01 03.3
NGC 376		S	01 03 53.5
NGC 381			01 08 18
NGC 395		S	01 05 11
NGC 395	Lindsay [1961] 439	S	01 05 08.1
NGC 411		S	01 07 55.7
NGC 416		S	01 07 59.0
NGC 419		S	01 08 17.7
NGC 422		S	01 09 25.4
NGC 433			01 15 10
NGC 436			01 15 58
NGC 456		S	01 13 43.9
NGC 457			01 19 33
NGC 458		S	01 14 53.2
NGC 460		S	01 14 37.9
NGC 465		S	01 15 42.7
NGC 559			01 29 33
NGC 581			01 33 22
NGC 603			01 34 44
NGC 609			01 36 24
NGC 629			01 39 02.1
NGC 637			01 43 04
NGC 643		S	01 35 00.8
NGC 654			01 44 00
NGC 657			01 43 29.8
NGC 659			01 44 24
NGC 663			01 46 17
NGC 743			01 58 32
NGC 744			01 58 30
NGC 752			01 57 35
NGC 796		S	01 56 44.5
NGC 843			02 11 08
NGC 869			02 19 04
NGC 869	Double Cluster		02 20 40.6
NGC 884			02 22 05
NGC 884	Double Cluster		02 20 40.6
NGC 886			02 23 28.1
NGC 917			02 26 09
NGC 956			02 32 14.9
NGC 957			02 33 20
NGC 1027			02 42 36
NGC 1039			02 42 08
NGC 1049		F	02 39 48
NGC 1146			02 57 38
NGC 1193			03 05 56
NGC 1220			03 11 41
NGC 1245			03 14 42
NGC 1252			03 10 56
NGC 1261		g	03 12 15.3
NGC 1333	[LAL96] 1		03 28.9
NGC 1333	[LAL96] 2		03 29.2
NGC 1342			03 31 40
NGC 1348			03 34 09
NGC 1436			03 43 36.9
NGC 1437	NGC 1436		03 43 36.9
NGC 1444			03 49 27
NGC 1466		L	03 44 32.4
NGC 1496			04 04 32
NGC 1498			04 00 19
NGC 1502			04 07 50
NGC 1513			04 09 55
NGC 1520			03 57 51.1
NGC 1528			04 15 19
NGC 1545			04 20 57
NGC 1547			04 17 12.4
NGC 1548			04 21 20
NGC 1557			04 12 55
NGC 1579	Cl [BW88] 1		04 30 14.3
NGC 1582			04 31 39
NGC 1605			04 34 53
NGC 1624			04 40 37
NGC 1629		L	04 29 36.3
NGC 1641		L	04 36 06
NGC 1641	SL 6		04 36 09.5
NGC 1644		L	04 37 39.4
NGC 1647			04 45 42.2
NGC 1649		L	04 38 06.9
NGC 1651		L	04 37 31.8
NGC 1652		L	04 38 22.6
NGC 1662			04 48 29
NGC 1663			04 49 24.3
NGC 1664			04 51 06
NGC 1673		L	04 42 39.2
NGC 1676		L	04 43 52.6
NGC 1693		L	04 47 39.9
NGC 1695		L	04 47 44.8
NGC 1696		L	04 48 29.8
NGC 1697		L	04 48 37.0
NGC 1698		L	04 49 04.0
NGC 1702		L	04 49 25.9
NGC 1704		L	04 49 55.5
NGC 1707			04 58 21.1
NGC 1708			05 03 28
NGC 1711		L	04 50 37.4
NGC 1712		L	04 50 57.1
NGC 1714		L	04 52 06.6
NGC 1718		L	04 52 25.6
NGC 1722		L	04 51 51.5
NGC 1722	IC 2111	L	04 51 53.0
NGC 1722	KMHK 171	L	04 51 53.0
NGC 1722	KMHK 173	L	04 51 53.0
NGC 1724			05 03 33
NGC 1727		L	04 52 12.3
NGC 1731		L	04 53 30.4
NGC 1731	KMHK 211	L	04 53 30.4
NGC 1731	KMHK 212	L	04 53 35.3
NGC 1731	[HS66] 51	L	04 52 44.9
NGC 1732		L	04 53 11.5
NGC 1733		L	04 54 04.9
NGC 1734		L	04 53 33.9
NGC 1735		L	04 54 20.2
NGC 1736		L	04 53 02.3
NGC 1737		L	04 53 58.8
NGC 1737	Henize N 83B	L	04 53 58.8
NGC 1737	LH 5	L	04 54.2
NGC 1743		L	04 54 03.4
NGC 1743	Henize N 83A	L	04 54 03.4
NGC 1743	LH 5	L	04 54.2
NGC 1745		L	04 54 20.9
NGC 1745	LH 5	L	04 54.2
NGC 1746			05 03.6
NGC 1748		L	04 54 24.7
NGC 1748	IC 2114	L	04 54 24.7
NGC 1748	LH 5	L	04 54.2
NGC 1749		L	04 54 56.5
NGC 1750			05 03.9
NGC 1750	NGC 1746		05 03.6
NGC 1751		L	04 54 11.9
NGC 1754		L	04 54 18.4
NGC 1755		L	04 55 14.7
NGC 1756		L	04 54 49.9
NGC 1758			05 04.4
NGC 1758	NGC 1746		05 03.6
NGC 1761		L	04 56 34.4
NGC 1764		L	04 56 27.4
NGC 1766		L	04 55 57.7
NGC 1767		L	04 56 27.4
NGC 1768		L	04 57 02.7
NGC 1770		L	04 57 16.8
NGC 1772		L	04 56 53.9
NGC 1774		L	04 58 06.2
NGC 1775		L	04 56 53.6
NGC 1776		L	04 58 39.2
NGC 1777		L	04 55 48.5
NGC 1778			05 08 06
NGC 1782		L	04 57 51.5
NGC 1783		L	04 59 08.7
NGC 1783	NGC 1787	L	05 00.0

Table D.3: Cluster Cross-Reference

Name	Look Under	GX	2000.0 RA
NGC 1785		L	04 58 45
NGC 1786		L	04 59 07.8
NGC 1787		L	05 00.0
NGC 1787	NGC 1783	L	04 59 08.7
NGC 1787	SL 178	L	05 01 44.3
NGC 1789		L	04 57 51.5
NGC 1790			05 11 02
NGC 1791		L	04 59 06.0
NGC 1793		L	04 59 38.3
NGC 1795		L	04 59 46.8
NGC 1798			05 11 40
NGC 1801		L	05 00 35.1
NGC 1802			05 10 13
NGC 1804		L	05 01 05.1
NGC 1805		L	05 02 21.2
NGC 1806		L	05 02 11.3
NGC 1807			05 10 46
NGC 1810		L	05 03 22.8
NGC 1813		L	05 02 40.8
NGC 1814		L	05 03 45.4
NGC 1815		L	05 02 26.9
NGC 1816		L	05 03 51.2
NGC 1817			05 12 27
NGC 1818		L	05 04 12.9
NGC 1820		L	05 04.1
NGC 1822		L	05 05 08.1
NGC 1823		L	05 03 23.8
NGC 1825		L	05 04.1
NGC 1826		L	05 05 33.7
NGC 1828		L	05 04 21.0
NGC 1829		L	05 04 58.5
NGC 1830		L	05 04 39.5
NGC 1831		L	05 06 16.2
NGC 1833		L	05 04 22.3
NGC 1833	LH 24	L	05 05 09
NGC 1833	NGC 1845	L	05 05 12
NGC 1835		L	05 05 06.6
NGC 1836		L	05 05 35.6
NGC 1837		L	05 04 56
NGC 1837	LH 24	L	05 05 09
NGC 1837	NGC 1845	L	05 05 12
NGC 1838		L	05 06 34
NGC 1838	SL 225	L	05 06 08.3
NGC 1840		L	05 05 19.9
NGC 1841		L	04 45 24.2
NGC 1842		L	05 07 18.4
NGC 1844		L	05 07 30.4
NGC 1845		L	05 05 12
NGC 1845	LH 24	L	05 05 09
NGC 1845	LH 26	L	05 05 57
NGC 1845	NGC 1833	L	05 04 22.3
NGC 1845	NGC 1837	L	05 04 56
NGC 1845	SL 232	L	05 06 22.2
NGC 1846		L	05 07 33.9
NGC 1847		L	05 07 08.1
NGC 1848	SL 256	L	05 08 10.3
NGC 1849		L	05 09 34.5
NGC 1850		L	05 08 46.7
NGC 1851		g	05 14 06.3
NGC 1852		L	05 09 24.1

Table D.3: Cluster Cross-Reference

Name	Look Under	GX	2000.0 RA
NGC 1854		L	05 09 20.6
NGC 1854	NGC 1855	L	05 09 20.6
NGC 1855		L	05 09 20.6
NGC 1855	NGC 1854	L	05 09 20.6
NGC 1856		L	05 09 30.6
NGC 1857			05 20 06
NGC 1857	Czernik 20		05 20 32.5
NGC 1859		L	05 11 32.6
NGC 1860		L	05 10 39.5
NGC 1861		L	05 10 21.1
NGC 1862		L	05 12 33.6
NGC 1863		L	05 11 39.8
NGC 1864		L	05 12 41.1
NGC 1865		L	05 12 25.4
NGC 1866		L	05 13 38.6
NGC 1867		L	05 13 41.6
NGC 1868		L	05 14 36.1
NGC 1869		L	05 13 53.6
NGC 1869	LH 37	L	05 13 53.6
NGC 1869	NGC 1871	L	05 13 52.4
NGC 1869	NGC 1873	L	05 14 01.7
NGC 1870		L	05 13 11.0
NGC 1871		L	05 13 52.4
NGC 1871	NGC 1869	L	05 13 53.6
NGC 1872		L	05 13 11.5
NGC 1873		L	05 14 01.7
NGC 1873	NGC 1869	L	05 13 53.6
NGC 1874		L	05 13 11
NGC 1874	BRHT 7b	L	05 13 11.5
NGC 1878		L	05 12 49.7
NGC 1880		L	05 13 39.2
NGC 1881		L	05 13.6
NGC 1882		L	05 15 32.8
NGC 1883			05 25 55
NGC 1885		L	05 15 06.9
NGC 1887		L	05 16 05.3
NGC 1890		L	05 13 47.2
NGC 1891			05 21.3
NGC 1893			05 22 46
NGC 1893	IC 410		05 22.0
NGC 1894		L	05 15 51.4
NGC 1896			05 25 41.9
NGC 1897		L	05 17 31.6
NGC 1898		L	05 16 42
NGC 1900		L	05 19 08.8
NGC 1901			05 17.8
NGC 1902		L	05 18 18.3
NGC 1903		L	05 17 22.8
NGC 1904		g	05 24 10.6
NGC 1905		L	05 18 23.0
NGC 1907			05 28 05
NGC 1910		L	05 18 23.8
NGC 1910	SL 360	L	05 18 11.1
NGC 1911		L	05 19 25.2
NGC 1912			05 28 43
NGC 1913		L	05 18 19.2
NGC 1914		L	05 17 39.4
NGC 1915		L	05 19 28.1
NGC 1916		L	05 17 26.7
NGC 1919		L	05 20 17.1

Table D.3: Cluster Cross-Reference

Name	Look Under	GX	2000.0 RA
NGC 1920		L	05 20 32.1
NGC 1922		L	05 19 50.0
NGC 1923		L	05 21 34.5
NGC 1925		L	05 21 31
NGC 1925	SL 415	L	05 22 01.9
NGC 1926		L	05 20 35.2
NGC 1928		L	05 20 57.2
NGC 1931			05 31 26
NGC 1932		L	05 22 27.4
NGC 1933		L	05 22 17.2
NGC 1934		L	05 21 54.0
NGC 1937		L	05 22 23.0
NGC 1938		L	05 21 27.1
NGC 1939		L	05 21 24.3
NGC 1940		L	05 22 44.2
NGC 1941		L	05 23 07.1
NGC 1942		L	05 24 42.7
NGC 1944		L	05 21 58.1
NGC 1946		L	05 25 16.0
NGC 1947			05 26 47.5
NGC 1949		L	05 25 05.3
NGC 1950		L	05 24 32.1
NGC 1951		L	05 26 06.4
NGC 1955		L	05 26 04.2
NGC 1958		L	05 25 30.3
NGC 1959		L	05 25 36.1
NGC 1960			05 36 18
NGC 1962		L	05 26 19.4
NGC 1963			05 32 10.8
NGC 1965		L	05 26 29.6
NGC 1967		L	05 26 44.6
NGC 1968		L	05 27 39.7
NGC 1969		L	05 26 32.1
NGC 1969	LH 59	L	05 26 42
NGC 1970		L	05 26 45.3
NGC 1971		L	05 26 45.0
NGC 1971	LH 59	L	05 26 42
NGC 1972		L	05 26 48.1
NGC 1972	LH 59	L	05 26 42
NGC 1974		L	05 28 00.6
NGC 1976			05 35 16
NGC 1977			05 35.3
NGC 1978		L	05 28 44.6
NGC 1980			05 35 26
NGC 1981			05 35.2
NGC 1986		L	05 27 37.9
NGC 1987		L	05 27 16.4
NGC 1991	NGC 1974	L	05 28 00.6
NGC 1994		L	05 28 23.3
NGC 1996			05 38.2
NGC 1997		L	05 30 34.9
NGC 2000		L	05 27 30.5
NGC 2001		L	05 29 08.2
NGC 2002		L	05 30 21.4
NGC 2003		L	05 30 54.3
NGC 2004		L	05 30 40.9
NGC 2005		L	05 30 10.3
NGC 2006		L	05 31 19.9
NGC 2009		L	05 30 59.6
NGC 2010		L	05 30 34.6

Table D.3: Cluster Cross-Reference

Name	Look Under	GX	2000.0 RA
NGC 2011		L	05 32 19.8
NGC 2013			05 44.4
NGC 2014		L	05 32 21.7
NGC 2015		L	05 31 48
NGC 2015	BRHT 15b	L	05 32 17.8
NGC 2015	SL 557	L	05 32 06.8
NGC 2016		L	05 31.5
NGC 2017			05 39 16
NGC 2018		L	05 31 11.6
NGC 2019		L	05 31 57
NGC 2021		L	05 33 30.3
NGC 2023	[LDEG91] 1		05 41 43
NGC 2024	[LDEG91] 2		05 41 44
NGC 2025		L	05 32 33.6
NGC 2026			05 43 08
NGC 2027		L	05 35 00.9
NGC 2028		L	05 33 48.7
NGC 2030		L	05 35 41.1
NGC 2031		L	05 33 41.3
NGC 2033		L	05 34 29.8
NGC 2036		L	05 34 32.1
NGC 2037		L	05 34 40.1
NGC 2038		L	05 34 42.4
NGC 2039			05 46 13
NGC 2040		L	05 36 06.1
NGC 2041		L	05 36 28.0
NGC 2042		L	05 36 09.6
NGC 2042	KMHK 1131	L	05 36 09.6
NGC 2044		L	05 36 06.4
NGC 2044	AH03 J0536.1-6912	L	05 36 06.4
NGC 2044	BRHT 17a	L	05 36 11.9
NGC 2044	SL 602	L	05 35 59.6
NGC 2046		L	05 35 37.4
NGC 2047		L	05 35 54.2
NGC 2050		L	05 36 54
NGC 2050	LH 96	L	05 37.0
NGC 2050	NGC 2055	L	05 37 08
NGC 2050	SL 609	L	05 36 40.0
NGC 2051		L	05 36 07.5
NGC 2053		L	05 37 40.5
NGC 2055		L	05 37 08
NGC 2055	LH 92	L	05 36.7
NGC 2055	LH 97	L	05 37.6
NGC 2055	NGC 2050	L	05 36 54
NGC 2055	SL 610	L	05 36 42
NGC 2056		L	05 36 34.6
NGC 2057		L	05 36 55.1
NGC 2058		L	05 36 54.7
NGC 2059		L	05 37 00.8
NGC 2060		L	05 37 48
NGC 2061			05 44 06
NGC 2062		L	05 40 03.3
NGC 2063			05 43 55
NGC 2065		L	05 37 35.9
NGC 2066		L	05 37 41.2
NGC 2068	[LDEG91] 3		05 46 40
NGC 2070		L	05 38 42.4
NGC 2071	[LDEG91] 4		05 47 08
NGC 2072		L	05 38 23.6
NGC 2074		L	05 39 03

Table D.3: Cluster Cross-Reference

Name	Look Under	GX	2000.0 RA
NGC 2075		L	05 38 20.5
NGC 2077		L	05 39 34.9
NGC 2080		L	05 39 44.6
NGC 2085		L	05 40 09.2
NGC 2088		L	05 40 59.7
NGC 2091		L	05 40 58.0
NGC 2092		L	05 41 22.2
NGC 2093		L	05 41 49.1
NGC 2094		L	05 42 07.2
NGC 2095		L	05 42 51.7
NGC 2096		L	05 42 16.5
NGC 2097		L	05 44 15.5
NGC 2098		L	05 42 29.8
NGC 2099			05 52 19
NGC 2100		L	05 42 08.3
NGC 2100	NGC 2092	L	05 41 22.2
NGC 2102		L	05 42 19.7
NGC 2105		L	05 44 19.8
NGC 2107		L	05 43 11.9
NGC 2108		L	05 43 56.9
NGC 2109		L	05 44 22.7
NGC 2111		L	05 44 32.5
NGC 2112			05 53 46
NGC 2113		L	05 45 24.5
NGC 2114		L	05 46 12.3
NGC 2116		L	05 47 14.5
NGC 2117		L	05 47 47.2
NGC 2118		L	05 47 39.6
NGC 2120		L	05 50 34.8
NGC 2121		L	05 48 12.8
NGC 2122		L	05 48 55
NGC 2123		L	05 51 43.5
NGC 2125		L	05 50 53.0
NGC 2126			06 02 34
NGC 2127		L	05 51 21.7
NGC 2129			06 01 06
NGC 2130		L	05 52 23.7
NGC 2132			05 55 09.1
NGC 2133		L	05 51 29.3
NGC 2134		L	05 51 56.5
NGC 2135		L	05 53 35.1
NGC 2136		L	05 52 58.9
NGC 2137		L	05 53 11.9
NGC 2138		L	05 54 49.7
NGC 2140		L	05 54 16.0
NGC 2141			06 02 56
NGC 2143			06 03 07.4
NGC 2145		L	05 54 22.6
NGC 2147		L	05 55 46.4
NGC 2151		L	05 56 20.8
NGC 2153		L	05 57 52.3
NGC 2154		L	05 57 38.5
NGC 2155		L	05 58 32.3
NGC 2156		L	05 57 50.0
NGC 2157		L	05 57 34.8
NGC 2158			06 07 26
NGC 2159		L	05 58 02.7
NGC 2160		L	05 58 13.0
NGC 2161		L	05 55 42.3
NGC 2162		L	06 00 31.4

Table D.3: Cluster Cross-Reference

Name	Look Under	GX	2000.0 RA
NGC 2164		L	05 58 55.6
NGC 2165			06 11 05
NGC 2166		L	05 59 33.0
NGC 2168			06 09.0
NGC 2169			06 08 25
NGC 2171		L	05 58 52.9
NGC 2172		L	06 00 05.6
NGC 2173		L	05 57 58.0
NGC 2175	Collinder 84		06 09 39
NGC 2175.1			06 10 53
NGC 2175s	NGC 2175.1		06 10 53
NGC 2176		L	06 01 19.4
NGC 2177		L	06 01 15.7
NGC 2180			06 09 37
NGC 2181		L	06 02 43.1
NGC 2184			06 11 41
NGC 2186			06 12 08
NGC 2189			06 12.3
NGC 2190		L	06 01 02.3
NGC 2192			06 15 18
NGC 2193		L	06 06 17.4
NGC 2194			06 13 46
NGC 2197		L	06 06 07.4
NGC 2198			06 13.9
NGC 2202			06 16 51
NGC 2203		L	06 04 41.6
NGC 2204			06 15 33
NGC 2209		L	06 08 34.8
NGC 2210		L	06 11 31.3
NGC 2213		L	06 10 42.2
NGC 2214		L	06 12 56.1
NGC 2215			06 20 50
NGC 2218			06 24 28
NGC 2219			06 23 42
NGC 2220			06 20 35
NGC 2224			06 27 32.0
NGC 2225			06 26 37
NGC 2225	NGC 2226		06 26 37
NGC 2226			06 26 37
NGC 2231		L	06 20 43.7
NGC 2232			06 27 15
NGC 2234			06 29 29.2
NGC 2236			06 29 40
NGC 2237			06 31 55.5
NGC 2237	NGC 2244		06 32 19
NGC 2239	NGC 2237		06 31 55.5
NGC 2239	NGC 2244		06 32 19
NGC 2240			06 33 11
NGC 2241		L	06 22 52.0
NGC 2243			06 29 35
NGC 2244			06 32 19
NGC 2244	NGC 2237		06 31 55.5
NGC 2248			06 34.6
NGC 2249		L	06 25 49.5
NGC 2250			06 33 47
NGC 2251			06 34 39
NGC 2252			06 34 19.8
NGC 2253			06 42.6
NGC 2254			06 35 46.6
NGC 2257		L	06 30 12.4

Table D.3: Cluster Cross-Reference

Name	Look Under	GX	2000.0 RA
NGC 2259			06 38 33.3
NGC 2260			06 38 04
NGC 2262			06 39 38.7
NGC 2264			06 40 59
NGC 2265			06 41.5
NGC 2266			06 43 20
NGC 2269			06 43 16.8
NGC 2270			06 43.9
NGC 2277			06 47.8
NGC 2281			06 48 18
NGC 2282	Cl vdB 85		06 46 52
NGC 2284			06 49.1
NGC 2285			06 49.4
NGC 2286			06 47 41
NGC 2287			06 46.1
NGC 2298		g	06 48 59.2
NGC 2299			06 51.1
NGC 2301			06 51 46
NGC 2302			06 51 54
NGC 2304			06 55 12
NGC 2306			06 54.6
NGC 2309			06 56 04
NGC 2311			06 57 48
NGC 2312			06 58 48
NGC 2314			07 10 32.4
NGC 2318			06 59 28
NGC 2319			07 00 37
NGC 2323			07 02 47.8
NGC 2324			07 04 08
NGC 2331			07 07 01
NGC 2335			07 06 50
NGC 2338			07 07 48
NGC 2343			07 08 07
NGC 2345			07 08 19
NGC 2348			07 03 02.7
NGC 2349			07 10.0
NGC 2351			07 13.5
NGC 2352			07 13.6
NGC 2353			07 14 31
NGC 2354			07 14 16
NGC 2355			07 17 00
NGC 2356			07 17.2
NGC 2358			07 16.8
NGC 2360			07 17 44
NGC 2362			07 18 42
NGC 2364			07 20 47
NGC 2367			07 20 05
NGC 2368			07 21 02.2
NGC 2374			07 23 57
NGC 2383			07 24 40
NGC 2384			07 25 12
NGC 2394			07 28 37
NGC 2395			07 27 13
NGC 2396			07 28.0
NGC 2399			07 29.9
NGC 2400			07 30.0
NGC 2401			07 29 25
NGC 2408			07 40.5
NGC 2409			07 31 37
NGC 2413			07 33 19.0

Table D.3: Cluster Cross-Reference

Name	Look Under	GX	2000.0 RA
NGC 2414			07 33 13
NGC 2419		g	07 38 08.5
NGC 2420			07 38 24
NGC 2421			07 36 12
NGC 2422			07 36 36
NGC 2423			07 37 07
NGC 2425			07 38 18
NGC 2428			07 39 18
NGC 2430			07 39 30
NGC 2432			07 40 54
NGC 2437			07 41 47
NGC 2439			07 40 46
NGC 2447			07 44 30
NGC 2448			07 44 34
NGC 2451			07 45.4
NGC 2451B	PMG 1		07 45.4
NGC 2453			07 47 35
NGC 2455			07 48 59
NGC 2459			07 52 02
NGC 2464			07 57.3
NGC 2467			07 52 30
NGC 2477			07 52 10
NGC 2478	NGC 2422		07 36 36
NGC 2479			07 55 06
NGC 2482			07 55 10
NGC 2483			07 55 39
NGC 2489			07 56 16
NGC 2506			08 00 02
NGC 2509			08 00 48
NGC 2516			07 58.0
NGC 2520	NGC 2527		08 04 53
NGC 2527			08 04 53
NGC 2533			08 07.0
NGC 2539			08 10 38
NGC 2546			08 12.4
NGC 2547			08 10 11
NGC 2548			08 13 44
NGC 2567			08 18 30
NGC 2568			08 18 19
NGC 2571			08 18 57
NGC 2579			08 20 53
NGC 2580			08 21 28
NGC 2587			08 23 25
NGC 2588			08 23 10
NGC 2609			08 29 30
NGC 2627			08 37 15
NGC 2632			08 40 22
NGC 2635			08 38 27
NGC 2645			08 39 04
NGC 2653			08 55.6
NGC 2658			08 43 28
NGC 2659			08 42 34
NGC 2660			08 42 39
NGC 2664			08 47 08
NGC 2666			08 50.0
NGC 2669			08 46 19
NGC 2670			08 45 30
NGC 2671			08 46 12
NGC 2678			08 50 03
NGC 2682			08 51 24

Table D.3: Cluster Cross-Reference

Name	Look Under	GX	2000.0 RA
NGC 2808		g	09 12 02.6
NGC 2818			09 16 10
NGC 2846			09 19.9
NGC 2847			09 20 08.7
NGC 2849			09 19 23
NGC 2866			09 22 06.5
NGC 2866	Pismis 13		09 22 06.5
NGC 2901			09 32.4
NGC 2910			09 30 30
NGC 2925			09 33 11
NGC 2932			09 35.3
NGC 2972			09 40 12
NGC 2982			09 42 01
NGC 2995			09 44.1
NGC 2999			09 45.2
NGC 3033			09 48 40
NGC 3036			09 49 16
NGC 3105			10 00 40
NGC 3114			10 02.7
NGC 3123			10 07.0
NGC 3167			10 14.6
NGC 3201		g	10 17 36.8
NGC 3218			10 26.5
NGC 3228			10 21 23
NGC 3231			10 27 29
NGC 3247			10 24 01
NGC 3255			10 26 32
NGC 3293			10 35 49
NGC 3324			10 37 19
NGC 3330			10 38 48
NGC 3382			10 48.5
NGC 3446			10 52 17
NGC 3484			11 03.0
NGC 3496			10 59 34
NGC 3503			11 01 18
NGC 3519			11 04 03
NGC 3520			11 05 30
NGC 3532			11 05.5
NGC 3572			11 10 26.6
NGC 3572	Collinder 240		11 11 40.2
NGC 3572a	Collinder 240		11 11 40.2
NGC 3572b	NGC 3572		11 10 26.6
NGC 3578			11 12.8
NGC 3590			11 13 00
NGC 3603			11 15 07
NGC 3676			11 25 37.5
NGC 3680			11 25 38
NGC 3766			11 36 15
NGC 3909			11 49 30
NGC 3960			11 50 34
NGC 4052			12 02 01
NGC 4103			12 06 40
NGC 4147		g	12 10 06.2
NGC 4182			12 13.4
NGC 4184			12 13.6
NGC 4230			12 17 16
NGC 4337			12 24 04
NGC 4347			12 23.9
NGC 4349			12 24 07
NGC 4372		g	12 25 45.4

Table D.3: Cluster Cross-Reference

Name	Look Under	GX	2000.0 RA
NGC 4409			12 26 58.6
NGC 4420	NGC 4409		12 26 58.6
NGC 4426			12 27 10
NGC 4427	NGC 4426		12 27 10
NGC 4439			12 28 27
NGC 4463			12 29 56
NGC 4505			12 32.3
NGC 4590		g	12 39 28.0
NGC 4604			12 40 45.1
NGC 4609			12 42 20
NGC 4755			12 53 38
NGC 4815			12 57 59
NGC 4833		g	12 59 35.0
NGC 4852			13 00 05
NGC 5024		g	13 12 55.3
NGC 5043			13 16 40
NGC 5045			13 17.0
NGC 5053		g	13 16 27.0
NGC 5120			13 25 39
NGC 5138			13 27 16
NGC 5139		g	13 26 45.9
NGC 5155			13 29.6
NGC 5168			13 31 08
NGC 5269			13 44 45
NGC 5272		g	13 42 11.2
NGC 5281			13 46 36.7
NGC 5284			13 47.1
NGC 5286		g	13 46 26.5
NGC 5288			13 48 45.6
NGC 5299			13 50.4
NGC 5316			13 54.0
NGC 5359			13 59.8
NGC 5381			14 00.6
NGC 5385			13 52.4
NGC 5460			14 07.6
NGC 5466		g	14 05 27.3
NGC 5571			14 19 31.8
NGC 5593			14 25 40
NGC 5606			14 27.8
NGC 5617			14 29.7
NGC 5621			14 27.8
NGC 5634		g	14 29 37.3
NGC 5662			14 35 30.8
NGC 5662	Turner 7		14 32 33
NGC 5694		g	14 39 36.5
NGC 5715			14 43 39.0
NGC 5749			14 48 48.8
NGC 5764			14 53 31.8
NGC 5800			15 02.0
NGC 5822			15 04 02.3
NGC 5823			15 05 26
NGC 5824		g	15 03 58.5
NGC 5897		g	15 17 24.5
NGC 5904		g	15 18 33.8
NGC 5925			15 27.7
NGC 5927		g	15 28 00.5
NGC 5946		g	15 35 28.5
NGC 5986		g	15 46 03.5
NGC 5998			15 49 28
NGC 5999			15 52 14

Table D.3: Cluster Cross-Reference

Name	Look Under	GX	2000.0 RA
NGC 6005			15 55 47.4
NGC 6025			16 03 18
NGC 6031			16 07 34.4
NGC 6067			16 13 09
NGC 6087			16 18 51.8
NGC 6093		g	16 17 02.5
NGC 6101		g	16 25 48.6
NGC 6115			16 24 26.8
NGC 6121		g	16 23 35.5
NGC 6124			16 25 17.2
NGC 6134			16 27 43.6
NGC 6139		g	16 27 40.4
NGC 6144		g	16 27 14.1
NGC 6152			16 32.7
NGC 6167			16 34 35
NGC 6169			16 34 05.0
NGC 6171		g	16 32 31.9
NGC 6178			16 35 50.8
NGC 6192			16 40 20.8
NGC 6193			16 41 20.3
NGC 6200			16 44 08.6
NGC 6204			16 46 07.9
NGC 6205		g	16 41 41.5
NGC 6208			16 49 25.8
NGC 6216			16 49 23.6
NGC 6218		g	16 47 14.5
NGC 6222			16 50.7
NGC 6227			16 51.5
NGC 6229		g	16 46 58.9
NGC 6231			16 54 09.8
NGC 6235		g	16 53 25.4
NGC 6242			16 55 30.6
NGC 6249			16 57 41.7
NGC 6250			16 57 55
NGC 6253			16 59 06.1
NGC 6254		g	16 57 08.9
NGC 6256		g	16 59 32.6
NGC 6259			17 00.7
NGC 6266		g	17 01 12.6
NGC 6268			17 02 04.1
NGC 6273		g	17 02 37.7
NGC 6281			17 04 47.2
NGC 6284		g	17 04 28.8
NGC 6287		g	17 05 09.4
NGC 6293		g	17 10 10.4
NGC 6304		g	17 14 32.5
NGC 6316		g	17 16 37.4
NGC 6318			17 16 13.4
NGC 6322			17 18.5
NGC 6325		g	17 17 59.2
NGC 6328			17 23 41.2
NGC 6333		g	17 19 11.8
NGC 6334			17 20 58.3
NGC 6341		g	17 17 07.3
NGC 6342		g	17 21 10.2
NGC 6352		g	17 25 29.2
NGC 6355		g	17 23 58.6
NGC 6356		g	17 23 35.0
NGC 6357	Pismis 24		17 24 43.4
NGC 6360			17 25.4

Table D.3: Cluster Cross-Reference

Name	Look Under	GX	2000.0 RA
NGC 6362		g	17 31 54.8
NGC 6366		g	17 27 44.3
NGC 6374	NGC 6383		17 34 42.2
NGC 6380		g	17 34 28.0
NGC 6383			17 34 42.2
NGC 6388		g	17 36 17.0
NGC 6396			17 37 38
NGC 6397		g	17 40 41.3
NGC 6400			17 40 10
NGC 6401		g	17 38 36.9
NGC 6402		g	17 37 36.1
NGC 6403			17 43 23.6
NGC 6404			17 39.6
NGC 6405			17 40 17
NGC 6415			17 42 54
NGC 6416			17 44.3
NGC 6421			17 45 14
NGC 6425			17 46 53
NGC 6426		g	17 44 54.7
NGC 6432			17 47 22.3
NGC 6437			17 49 00
NGC 6440		g	17 48 52.6
NGC 6441		g	17 50 12.9
NGC 6441	JaFu 2		17 50 10.8
NGC 6444			17 49.6
NGC 6451			17 50 41
NGC 6453		g	17 50 51.8
NGC 6455			17 51 48
NGC 6469			17 52 56.5
NGC 6475			17 53 46
NGC 6476			17 54 12
NGC 6480			17 54 34.7
NGC 6494			17 56 56
NGC 6496		g	17 59 02.0
NGC 6506			17 59.8
NGC 6507			17 59 50
NGC 6514			18 02 31
NGC 6517		g	18 01 50.6
NGC 6520			18 03 25
NGC 6522		g	18 03 35.0
NGC 6523			18 04 25
NGC 6525			18 02.1
NGC 6528		g	18 04 49.6
NGC 6529			18 05.5
NGC 6530	NGC 6523		18 04 25
NGC 6531			18 04 13
NGC 6533	NGC 6523		18 04 25
NGC 6535		g	18 03 50.7
NGC 6539		g	18 04 49.8
NGC 6540		g	18 06 08.6
NGC 6541		g	18 08 02.2
NGC 6544		g	18 07 20.6
NGC 6546			18 07.2
NGC 6553		g	18 09 17.3
NGC 6554			18 08 55
NGC 6558		g	18 10 17.6
NGC 6561			18 10 25
NGC 6568			18 12 45
NGC 6569		g	18 13 38.9
NGC 6573			18 13 50

Table D.3: Cluster Cross-Reference

Name	Look Under	GX	2000.0 RA
NGC 6583			18 15 50
NGC 6584		g	18 18 37.7
NGC 6589	Collinder 371		18 17 16
NGC 6595	Collinder 371		18 17 16
NGC 6596			18 17.5
NGC 6603			18 18 28
NGC 6604			18 18.1
NGC 6605			18 16 06
NGC 6611			18 18 45
NGC 6613			18 20 00
NGC 6618			18 21 09
NGC 6624		g	18 23 40.5
NGC 6625			18 23 12.8
NGC 6626		g	18 24 32.9
NGC 6631			18 27 09.5
NGC 6633			18 27 15
NGC 6634	NGC 6637	g	18 31 23.2
NGC 6637		g	18 31 23.2
NGC 6638		g	18 30 56.2
NGC 6639			18 30 57.8
NGC 6642		g	18 31 54.3
NGC 6645			18 32 38
NGC 6647			18 31.5
NGC 6649			18 33 28.3
NGC 6652		g	18 35 45.7
NGC 6656		g	18 36 24.2
NGC 6656	IRAS 18333-2357		18 36 23.1
NGC 6659			18 33 55.8
NGC 6664			18 36 30.6
NGC 6681		g	18 43 12.7
NGC 6682			18 39.6
NGC 6683			18 42 12.7
NGC 6684			18 48 57.5
NGC 6694			18 45 15
NGC 6698			18 48.2
NGC 6704			18 50 45.8
NGC 6705			18 51 04
NGC 6709			18 51.5
NGC 6712		g	18 53 04.3
NGC 6715		g	18 55 03.3
NGC 6716			18 54 34
NGC 6717		g	18 55 06.2
NGC 6717	IC 4802		18 55 07.1
NGC 6723		g	18 59 33.2
NGC 6724			18 56 45
NGC 6728			18 57 31.4
NGC 6735			19 00 45.3
NGC 6737			19 02 10.0
NGC 6738			19 01.4
NGC 6743			19 01 26.7
NGC 6749		g	19 05 15.3
NGC 6752		g	19 10 51.8
NGC 6755			19 07 49
NGC 6756			19 08 43
NGC 6760		g	19 11 12.1
NGC 6773			19 15.0
NGC 6774			19 16.3
NGC 6775			19 16 30
NGC 6779		g	19 16 35.5
NGC 6791			19 20 52.7

Table D.3: Cluster Cross-Reference

Name	Look Under	GX	2000.0 RA
NGC 6793			19 23 12.6
NGC 6795			19 26 05.1
NGC 6800			19 27 00
NGC 6802			19 30 35
NGC 6809		g	19 39 59.4
NGC 6811			19 37 09.6
NGC 6815			19 40.9
NGC 6819			19 41.3
NGC 6820	Collinder 404		19 42 28
NGC 6823			19 43 10
NGC 6827			19 48 53.2
NGC 6828			19 50.4
NGC 6830			19 51 00
NGC 6832			19 48 15.5
NGC 6834			19 52 13
NGC 6837			19 53.5
NGC 6838		g	19 53 46.1
NGC 6839			19 54 19
NGC 6840			19 55 16
NGC 6843			19 56.1
NGC 6846			19 56 28.1
NGC 6847			19 57.0
NGC 6856			19 59.3
NGC 6858			20 03.1
NGC 6859			20 03 49.5
NGC 6863			20 05 07.4
NGC 6864		g	20 06 04.8
NGC 6866			20 03 55
NGC 6871			20 06 27
NGC 6873			20 07 44
NGC 6874			20 07.8
NGC 6882	NGC 6885		20 12 01
NGC 6883			20 11.3
NGC 6885			20 12 01
NGC 6892			20 16 57.2
NGC 6895			20 16.4
NGC 6896			20 18.0
NGC 6904			20 21 48.3
NGC 6910			20 23 12
NGC 6913			20 24 06
NGC 6934		g	20 34 11.6
NGC 6938			20 34 46
NGC 6939			20 31 30
NGC 6940			20 34 32.3
NGC 6941			20 36 23.5
NGC 6950			20 41 10.5
NGC 6973			20 52.1
NGC 6980			20 52.8
NGC 6981		g	20 53 27.9
NGC 6989			20 54.1
NGC 6991			20 54.9
NGC 6991	h 2091		20 54 43.1
NGC 6994			20 58 56
NGC 6996			20 56.4
NGC 6997			20 56.5
NGC 7005			21 01 56.0
NGC 7006		g	21 01 29.5
NGC 7011			21 01 45
NGC 7023			21 01 35.8
NGC 7023	Collinder 429		21 01 35.8

Table D.3: Cluster Cross-Reference

Name	Look Under	GX	2000.0 RA
NGC 7024			21 06 04.8
NGC 7025	French 1		21 07 22
NGC 7031			21 06 52
NGC 7036			21 10 12
NGC 7037			21 10 57
NGC 7039			21 11.2
NGC 7044			21 13 08
NGC 7050			21 15 16.8
NGC 7055			21 19 25.8
NGC 7058			21 21 48.3
NGC 7062			21 23 27
NGC 7063			21 24.5
NGC 7067			21 24 12.3
NGC 7071			21 26 40
NGC 7078		g	21 29 58.3
NGC 7082			21 29 19
NGC 7084			21 32 33
NGC 7086			21 30 28
NGC 7089		g	21 33 27.0
NGC 7092			21 31 52
NGC 7093			21 34 35.8
NGC 7099		g	21 40 22.0
NGC 7122			21 45 47.8
NGC 7127			21 43 52.9
NGC 7128			21 43 58
NGC 7129			21 42 59
NGC 7134			21 48 56
NGC 7142			21 45 09
NGC 7150			21 50.4
NGC 7160			21 53 40
NGC 7161			21 57.0
NGC 7175			21 58 51.6
NGC 7193			22 02 59
NGC 7209			22 05 08
NGC 7226			22 10 26
NGC 7234			22 12 28
NGC 7235			22 12 24
NGC 7243			22 15 09
NGC 7245			22 15 16
NGC 7261			22 20 10
NGC 7281			22 24 55.7
NGC 7295			22 27 52
NGC 7296			22 28 01
NGC 7352			22 39 44.2
NGC 7380			22 47 21
NGC 7394			22 50 24
NGC 7419			22 54 17
NGC 7423			22 55 06.5
NGC 7429			22 55.9
NGC 7438			22 57 03
NGC 7453			23 01 25.4
NGC 7492		g	23 08 26.7
NGC 7510			23 11 04.2
NGC 7654			23 24 51
NGC 7686			23 30 07
NGC 7708			23 36 30
NGC 7762			23 49.9
NGC 7772			23 51.8
NGC 7788			23 56 44
NGC 7789			23 57 28.6

Table D.3: Cluster Cross-Reference

Name	Look Under	GX	2000.0 RA
NGC 7790			23 58 24
NGC 7795			23 57 34.5
NGC 7801			00 00 23
NGC 7826			00 05 15
NGC 7833			00 06 32.6
[NHS93] 17			17 45 50.5
NRL 15	IC 1805		02 32 42
NRL 17	NGC 6604		18 18.1
OCISM 43	Collinder 470		21 53.5
OCISM 50	Collinder 427		21 00 36.6
OCISM 53	PMH79 1		22 19 00
OCISM 99	IC 348		03 44 34
OCISM 106	Collinder 84		06 09 39
OCl 1	Ruprecht 140		18 21 49.8
OCl 2	Ruprecht 131		17 49 06.9
OCl 3	NGC 6558	g	18 10 17.6
OCl 4	Ruprecht 134		17 52.8
OCl 5	Collinder 351		17 49 51
OCl 6	Ruprecht 133		17 52 34.1
OCl 7	Ruprecht 168		17 52.8
OCl 8	Czernik 37		17 53 16.4
OCl 9	Trumpler 31		17 59.8
OCl 9.0	Trumpler 31		17 59.8
OCl 10	NGC 6520		18 03 25
OCl 11	NGC 6540	g	18 06 08.6
OCl 12	Collinder 468		18 06 35
OCl 13	Ruprecht 137		17 59.9
OCl 14	Ruprecht 169		17 59.5
OCl 15	Ruprecht 136		17 59 17.8
OCl 16	Ruprecht 138		17 59.9
OCl 17	NGC 6544	g	18 07 20.6
OCl 18	NGC 6523		18 04 25
OCl 19	NGC 6523		18 04 25
OCl 20	Ruprecht 139		18 01.2
OCl 21	NGC 6469		17 52 56.5
OCl 22	Collinder 367		18 09 51
OCl 22.0	Collinder 367		18 09 51
OCl 23	NGC 6514		18 02 31
OCl 24	NGC 6546		18 07.2
OCl 25	Dolidze 27		16 36.5
OCl 26	NGC 6531		18 04 13
OCl 26.0	NGC 6531		18 04 13
OCl 26.1	Cl vdB 113		18 08.6
OCl 27	NGC 6583		18 15 50
OCl 28	NGC 6568		18 12 45
OCl 28.0	NGC 6568		18 12 45
OCl 29	NGC 6642	g	18 31 54.3
OCl 30	NGC 6494		17 56 56
OCl 31	Collinder 371		18 17 16
OCl 32	NGC 6507		17 59 50
OCl 32.0	NGC 6507		17 59 50
OCl 33	Markarian 38		18 15 16.6
OCl 34	Trumpler 33		18 24 38.8
OCl 35	Collinder 469		18 16 33.7
OCl 36	NGC 6603		18 18 28
OCl 37	NGC 6717	g	18 55 06.2
OCl 38	IC 4725		18 31 45
OCl 39	Ruprecht 146		18 52 30
OCl 40	NGC 6613		18 20 00
OCl 41	NGC 6596		18 17.5

Table D.3: Cluster Cross-Reference

Name	Look Under	GX	2000.0 RA
OCl 42	Collinder 394		18 52 16.3
OCl 42.0	Collinder 394		18 52 16.3
OCl 44	NGC 6618		18 21 09
OCl 45	NGC 6647		18 31.5
OCl 46	NGC 6716		18 54 34
OCl 47	NGC 6605		18 16 06
OCl 48	NGC 6645		18 32 38
OCl 49	Ruprecht 135		17 58 03.3
OCl 50	Ruprecht 171		18 32 00.7
OCl 51	IC 1257	g	17 27 08
OCl 52	Ruprecht 145		18 50 19.4
OCl 52.0	Ruprecht 145		18 50 19.4
OCl 53	Dolidze 28		18 25 30.0
OCl 54	NGC 6611		18 18 45
OCl 55	Trumpler 32		18 17 10.4
OCl 56	NGC 6604		18 18.1
OCl 57	NGC 6639		18 30 57.8
OCl 58	NGC 6625		18 23 12.8
OCl 59	NGC 6631		18 27 09.5
OCl 59.0	NGC 6631		18 27 09.5
OCl 60	Ruprecht 141		18 31.3
OCl 61	Ruprecht 142		18 32 14
OCl 62	Ruprecht 143		18 32 43
OCl 63	Ruprecht 144		18 33 32.7
OCl 64	Ruprecht 170		18 25 10.7
OCl 65	NGC 6774		19 16.3
OCl 65.0	NGC 6774		19 16.3
OCl 66	NGC 6649		18 33 28.3
OCl 67	NGC 6694		18 45 15
OCl 67.0	NGC 6694		18 45 15
OCl 68	NGC 6664		18 36 30.6
OCl 68.0	NGC 6664		18 36 30.6
OCl 69	Trumpler 34		18 39.8
OCl 70	Dolidze 29		18 31.4
OCl 71	Dolidze 31		18 34.9
OCl 72	NGC 6712	g	18 53 04.3
OCl 72.0	NGC 6712	g	18 53 04.3
OCl 73	Dolidze 30		18 32.9
OCl 73.0	Dolidze 30		18 32.9
OCl 74	NGC 6683		18 42 12.7
OCl 74.0	NGC 6683		18 42 12.7
OCl 75	Collinder 350		17 48.2
OCl 76	NGC 6705		18 51 04
OCl 76.0	NGC 6705		18 51 04
OCl 77.0	Apriamasvili 1		18 48.1
OCl 78	Dolidze 34		18 42 03.1
OCl 79	Dolidze 33		18 40.7
OCl 80	Dolidze 32		18 40.5
OCl 81	NGC 6426	g	17 44 54.7
OCl 82	NGC 6704		18 50 45.8
OCl 82.0	NGC 6704		18 50 45.8
OCl 83	Trumpler 35		18 43 00.5
OCl 84	Melotte 186		18 01.1
OCl 84.0	Melotte 186		18 01.1
OCl 85	IC 4665		17 46.2
OCl 85.0	IC 4665		17 46.2
OCl 86	Berkeley 79		18 44 57.5
OCl 87	Berkeley 80		18 54 20.6
OCl 88	Berkeley 81		19 01 39.7
OCl 89	NGC 6994		20 58 56

Table D.3: Cluster Cross-Reference

Name	Look Under	GX	2000.0 RA
OCl 90	NGC 6633		18 27 15
OCl 91	NGC 6749	g	19 05 15.3
OCl 92	NGC 6760	g	19 11 12.1
OCl 93	DoDz 7		17 11 23
OCl 94	IC 4756		18 38.9
OCl 95	Czernik 38		18 49 47.0
OCl 96	NGC 6755		19 07 49
OCl 97	NGC 6755		19 07 49
OCl 98	Collinder 401		19 38 21.7
OCl 99	NGC 6756		19 08 43
OCl 100	NGC 6709		18 51.5
OCl 100.0	NGC 6709		18 51.5
OCl 101	NGC 6738		19 01.4
OCl 101.0	NGC 6738		19 01.4
OCl 102	Berkeley 43		19 15 30
OCl 103	Berkeley 82		19 11 20.3
OCl 104	DoDz 8		17 26 24
OCl 105	Dolidze 35		19 25 24
OCl 106	King 25		19 24.5
OCl 107	Berkeley 45		19 19 06
OCl 108	King 26		19 29.0
OCl 108.1	NGC 6837		19 53.5
OCl 109	Berkeley 47		19 28 27.3
OCl 110	Berkeley 44		19 17 17
OCl 111	NGC 7492	g	23 08 26.7
OCl 112	Roslund 1		19 45 06
OCl 113	Collinder 399		19 26 12
OCl 113.0	Collinder 399		19 26 12
OCl 114	NGC 6802		19 30 35
OCl 115	NGC 6793		19 23 12.6
OCl 116	Harvard 20		19 53 10.3
OCl 116.0	Harvard 20		19 53 10.3
OCl 117	NGC 6838	g	19 53 46.1
OCl 118	Czernik 40		19 42 38
OCl 119	DoDz 9		18 08.8
OCl 119.0	DoDz 9		18 08.8
OCl 120	NGC 6827		19 48 53.2
OCl 121	Roslund 3		19 58 41.1
OCl 122	Collinder 404		19 42 28
OCl 123	NGC 6800		19 27 00
OCl 124	NGC 6823		19 43 10
OCl 124.0	NGC 6823		19 43 10
OCl 125	NGC 6830		19 51 00
OCl 126	Roslund 2		19 45 24.4
OCl 127	Stock 1		19 35 47
OCl 127.0	Stock 1		19 35 47
OCl 128	DoDz 5		16 27.4
OCl 129	DoDz 6		16 45 28.6
OCl 129.0	DoDz 6		16 45 28.6
OCl 130	Czernik 41		19 50 50.8
OCl 131	NGC 6815		19 40.9
OCl 132	NGC 6885		20 12 01
OCl 132.0	NGC 6885		20 12 01
OCl 133	Collinder 416		20 11 35
OCl 134	NGC 6834		19 52 13
OCl 135	Berkeley 83		20 01 25.1
OCl 136	Iskudarian 1		18 48.0
OCl 136.0	Iskudarian 1		18 48.0
OCl 137	Stephenson 1		18 54 30.6
OCl 137.0	Stephenson 1		18 54 30.6

Table D.3: Cluster Cross-Reference

Name	Look Under	GX	2000.0 RA
OCl 139	NGC 6846		19 56 28.1
OCl 140	Berkeley 52		20 14 30
OCl 141	NGC 6940		20 34 32.3
OCl 141.0	NGC 6940		20 34 32.3
OCl 142	NGC 6791		19 20 52.7
OCl 142.0	NGC 6791		19 20 52.7
OCl 143	Berkeley 84		20 04 42.2
OCl 144	Berkeley 49		19 59 30.2
OCl 145	Roslund 5		20 10.0
OCl 146	Berkeley 51		20 11 53
OCl 147	IC 1310		20 10 01
OCl 148	NGC 6871		20 06 27
OCl 148.0	NGC 6871		20 06 27
OCl 149	Biurakan 1		20 07.5
OCl 149.0	Biurakan 1		20 07.5
OCl 150.0	Biurakan 2		20 09 14.3
OCl 151	Ruprecht 172		20 11 34
OCl 152	NGC 6883		20 11.3
OCl 152.0	NGC 6883		20 11.3
OCl 153	Dolidze 1		20 08.2
OCl 154	Dolidze 37		20 03.0
OCl 155	NGC 6819		19 41.3
OCl 156	Dolidze 3		20 15 27
OCl 156.0	Dolidze 3		20 15 27
OCl 157	Dolidze 4		20 17 46.6
OCl 157.1	NGC 6874		20 07.8
OCl 158	IC 4996		20 16 31.7
OCl 158.0	IC 4996		20 16 31.7
OCl 159	Dolidze 39		20 16 12
OCl 159.0	Dolidze 39		20 16 12
OCl 160	Berkeley 85		20 18 47
OCl 160.0	Berkeley 85		20 18 47
OCl 161	Berkeley 87		20 21 35
OCl 162	Dolidze 40		20 18.2
OCl 163	Dolidze 41		20 19.2
OCl 164	Dolidze 42		20 19 39.7
OCl 164.0	Dolidze 42		20 19 39.7
OCl 165	Ruprecht 173		20 41 41.2
OCl 165.0	Ruprecht 173		20 41 41.2
OCl 166	DoDz 10		20 05 35
OCl 166.0	DoDz 10		20 05 35
OCl 167	Berkeley 86		20 20 21.2
OCl 167.0	Berkeley 86		20 20 21.2
OCl 167.1	Cl vdB 130		20 17 42.2
OCl 168	NGC 6913		20 24 06
OCl 169	Ruprecht 175		20 45 24
OCl 170	Dolidze 38		20 06 04
OCl 170.0	Dolidze 38		20 06 04
OCl 171	Dolidze 5		20 20 29
OCl 171.0	Dolidze 5		20 20 29
OCl 171.1	Dolidze 47		20 41 44.2
OCl 172	Dolidze 36		20 02.5
OCl 173	IC 1311		20 10 47
OCl 173.0	IC 1311		20 10 47
OCl 174	Dolidze 2		20 09.9
OCl 174.0	Dolidze 2		20 09.9
OCl 175	Dolidze 43		20 21.7
OCl 175.0	Dolidze 43		20 21.7
OCl 176	Ruprecht 174		20 43 28.3
OCl 177	Collinder 419		20 18 07.0

Table D.3: Cluster Cross-Reference

Name	Look Under	GX	2000.0 RA
OCl 178	Roslund 6		20 28 49
OCl 179	DoDz 11		20 51 04
OCl 179.0	DoDz 11		20 51 04
OCl 180	Dolidze 10		20 26.3
OCl 180.0	Dolidze 10		20 26.3
OCl 181	NGC 6910		20 23 12
OCl 181.1	Dolidze 6		20 20 38.0
OCl 182	Dolidze 6		20 20 38.0
OCl 183	NGC 6866		20 03 55
OCl 184	Collinder 421		20 23.3
OCl 184.0	Collinder 421		20 23.3
OCl 185	NGC 6811		19 37 09.6
OCl 186	Dolidze 11		20 26 24.7
OCl 187	Roslund 7		20 52 08.5
OCl 188	Dolidze 9		20 25 33.4
OCl 189	Dolidze 8		20 24.4
OCl 190	Dolidze 44		20 29.7
OCl 191	Dolidze 45		21 09.0
OCl 191.0	Dolidze 45		21 09.0
OCl 192	NGC 7063		21 24.5
OCl 193	Berkeley 89		20 24 28.4
OCl 194	Berkeley 54		21 03 00
OCl 195	Berkeley 88		20 21 16
OCl 196	Berkeley 90		20 35 16
OCl 197	NGC 6997		20 56.5
OCl 198	NGC 7044		21 13 08
OCl 199	Berkeley 56		21 17 34.5
OCl 200	Baractova 1		20 53.7
OCl 200.0	Baractova 1		20 53.7
OCl 201	Collinder 428		21 03.2
OCl 202	h 2091		20 54 43.1
OCl 203	NGC 7039		21 11.2
OCl 203.0	NGC 7039		21 11.2
OCl 204	IC 1369		21 12 07
OCl 205	NGC 7062		21 23 27
OCl 205.0	NGC 7062		21 23 27
OCl 206	Berkeley 91		21 10 51
OCl 207	Berkeley 53		20 55 59
OCl 208	NGC 7067		21 24 12.3
OCl 208.0	NGC 7067		21 24 12.3
OCl 209	NGC 7082		21 29 19
OCl 209.0	NGC 7082		21 29 19
OCl 210	NGC 7031		21 06 52
OCl 211	NGC 7092		21 31 52
OCl 211.0	NGC 7092		21 31 52
OCl 212	Berkeley 55		21 16 57
OCl 213	Collinder 470		21 53.5
OCl 214	NGC 7086		21 30 28
OCl 215	NGC 7209		22 05 08
OCl 215.0	NGC 7209		22 05 08
OCl 216	Baractova 2		21 43 38
OCl 217	NGC 6939		20 31 30
OCl 218	NGC 7128		21 43 58
OCl 219	NGC 7127		21 43 52.9
OCl 220	Berkeley 92		21 24 46.3
OCl 221	NGC 7243		22 15 09
OCl 221.0	NGC 7243		22 15 09
OCl 222	IC 1396		21 39.0
OCl 222.0	IC 1396		21 39.0
OCl 223	IC 1434		22 10.5

Table D.3: Cluster Cross-Reference

Name	Look Under	GX	2000.0 RA
OCl 223.0	IC 1434		22 10.5
OCl 224	IC 1442		22 15 59
OCl 225	NGC 7245		22 15 16
OCl 225.0	NGC 7245		22 15 16
OCl 226	NGC 7226		22 10 26
OCl 227	King 9		22 15 31
OCl 228	NGC 7296		22 28 01
OCl 228.0	NGC 7296		22 28 01
OCl 229	NGC 7235		22 12 24
OCl 231	Berkeley 94		22 22 53
OCl 232	Berkeley 96		22 29 51.2
OCl 233	Collinder 427		21 00 36.6
OCl 234	Berkeley 98		22 42 39.2
OCl 235	Collinder 429		21 01 35.8
OCl 236	NGC 7160		21 53 40
OCl 236.0	NGC 7160		21 53 40
OCl 237	NGC 7261		22 20 10
OCl 238	NGC 7281		22 24 55.7
OCl 239	Berkeley 93		21 55 29
OCl 240	NGC 7129		21 42 59
OCl 241	NGC 7142		21 45 09
OCl 242	Berkeley 95		22 28.3
OCl 243	Berkeley 97		22 39 22.2
OCl 244	NGC 7380		22 47 21
OCl 244.0	NGC 7380		22 47 21
OCl 245	Czernik 42		22 39 35
OCl 246	NGC 7423		22 55 06.5
OCl 247	King 18		22 52 08
OCl 248	King 10		22 55.0
OCl 249	NGC 7429		22 55.9
OCl 250	NGC 7419		22 54 17
OCl 251	NGC 7686		23 30 07
OCl 252	Collinder 285		14 40.9
OCl 252.1	Cl vdB 152		22 13 24.5
OCl 252.2	Aveni-Hunter 1		23 37 47
OCl 253	Dolidze 46		23 21.9
OCl 254	King 19		23 08.3
OCl 255	Collinder 471		22 07.1
OCl 256	NGC 7510		23 11 04.2
OCl 257	Markarian 50		23 15 14
OCl 258	Stock 12		23 36 20
OCl 259	Stock 11		23 30 55
OCl 259.1	Cl vdB 150		22 12 52.8
OCl 260	NGC 7654		23 24 51
OCl 260.0	NGC 7654		23 24 51
OCl 261	Czernik 43		23 25.8
OCl 261.0	Czernik 43		23 25.8
OCl 262	King 20		23 33 14
OCl 263	Berkeley 102		23 38.7
OCl 264	Berkeley 100		23 25 58
OCl 265	Czernik 44		23 33 33
OCl 266	Berkeley 103		23 45.2
OCl 267	Berkeley 101		23 32 46.5
OCl 268	Stock 17		23 43 47.0
OCl 269.0	NGC 7789		23 57 28.6
OCl 270	King 21		23 49.9
OCl 271	Berkeley 99		23 21 16.9
OCl 274	Stock 19		00 04 39
OCl 275.0	NGC 7788		23 56 44
OCl 276.0	NGC 7790		23 58 24

Table D.3: Cluster Cross-Reference

Name	Look Under	GX	2000.0 RA
OCl 277.0	Berkeley 58		00 00 12
OCl 279	King 11		23 47 36.6
OCl 280	NGC 7762		23 49.9
OCl 282	Berkeley 104		00 03 27
OCl 283	Czernik 1		00 07 39
OCl 284	Berkeley 1		00 09 41
OCl 285	King 13		00 10 10
OCl 286	Berkeley 59		00 02 10
OCl 286.0	Berkeley 59		00 02 10
OCl 287	DoDz 1		02 47 27
OCl 288	Berkeley 60		00 17 42
OCl 288.1	Mayer 1		00 21 54
OCl 289	Berkeley 2		00 25 15
OCl 290	King 1		00 21 52
OCl 291	NGC 103		00 25 18
OCl 291.0	NGC 103		00 25 18
OCl 292	Stock 20		00 25 16
OCl 293	Stock 21		00 30 28
OCl 294	NGC 129		00 29 58
OCl 295	NGC 136		00 31 31
OCl 296	NGC 133		00 31 18
OCl 297	King 14		00 31.9
OCl 298	King 15		00 33 07
OCl 299	NGC 146		00 33.1
OCl 301	NGC 189		00 39 36
OCl 302	Stock 24		00 39 50
OCl 303	Dolidze 12		00 40.8
OCl 303.0	Dolidze 12		00 40.8
OCl 304	Czernik 2		00 43 39
OCl 304.0	Czernik 2		00 43 39
OCl 305	NGC 225		00 43 36
OCl 306	King 16		00 43.7
OCl 307	Berkeley 4		00 45 13
OCl 308	Berkeley 61		00 48 10
OCl 309	NGC 188		00 47 30
OCl 309.0	NGC 188		00 47 30
OCl 310	Dolidze 13		00 50.0
OCl 311	King 2		00 50 57
OCl 312	NGC 272		00 51 26
OCl 313	IC 1590		00 52 49
OCl 313.0	IC 1590		00 52 49
OCl 314	Berkeley 62		01 01 12
OCl 314.0	Berkeley 62		01 01 12
OCl 315	Czernik 3		01 03 07
OCl 316	NGC 366		01 06 27
OCl 317	NGC 381		01 08 18
OCl 317.0	NGC 381		01 08 18
OCl 318	Stock 3		01 12 03
OCl 319	NGC 433		01 15 10
OCl 319.0	NGC 433		01 15 10
OCl 320	NGC 436		01 15 58
OCl 321	NGC 457		01 19 33
OCl 321.0	NGC 457		01 19 33
OCl 322	NGC 559		01 29 33
OCl 323	-Berkeley 8		02 01 05
OCl 324	Collinder 463		01 45 45
OCl 324.0	Collinder 463		01 45 45
OCl 325	NGC 609		01 36 24
OCl 326	NGC 581		01 33 22
OCl 327	Czernik 4		01 35 36.4
OCl 328	Trumpler 1		01 35 40
OCl 329	NGC 637		01 43 04
OCl 330	NGC 654		01 44 00
OCl 330.0	NGC 654		01 44 00
OCl 331	Berkeley 5		01 47 44
OCl 332	NGC 659		01 44 24
OCl 332.0	NGC 659		01 44 24
OCl 333	NGC 663		01 46 17
OCl 333.0	NGC 663		01 46 17
OCl 334	IC 166		01 52 22
OCl 335	Berkeley 6		01 51 12
OCl 336	Berkeley 7		01 54 12
OCl 337	NGC 657		01 43 29.8
OCl 338	Czernik 5		01 55 40
OCl 339	Stock 5		02 04.4
OCl 339.0	Stock 5		02 04.4
OCl 340	Czernik 6		02 02 08
OCl 341	Czernik 7		02 03 01
OCl 342	Stock 4		01 52.7
OCl 342.0	Stock 4		01 52.7
OCl 343	NGC 743		01 58 32
OCl 344	Berkeley 64		02 21 46
OCl 345	NGC 744		01 58 30
OCl 345.0	NGC 744		01 58 30
OCl 346	Berkeley 63		02 19 27
OCl 347	NGC 886		02 23 28.1
OCl 348	Stock 2		02 14 43
OCl 348.0	Stock 2		02 14 43
OCl 349	Tombaugh 4		02 29 10.7
OCl 349.1	Basel 10		02 19 28
OCl 350	NGC 869		02 19 04
OCl 350.0	NGC 869		02 19 04
OCl 351	Markarian 6		02 29 40
OCl 352	IC 1805		02 32 42
OCl 353	NGC 884		02 22 05
OCl 353.0	NGC 884		02 22 05
OCl 354	Czernik 10		02 33 55
OCl 355	Czernik 9		02 33.6
OCl 356	Czernik 13		02 44 27
OCl 357	NGC 1027		02 42 36
OCl 358	Czernik 11		02 36 36
OCl 359	Czernik 8		02 32 58
OCl 360	Berkeley 65		02 39 06
OCl 361	King 4		02 36 02
OCl 362	NGC 957		02 33 20
OCl 362.0	NGC 957		02 33 20
OCl 363	NGC 752		01 57 35
OCl 364	IC 1848		02 51 11
OCl 364.0	IC 1848		02 51 11
OCl 365	Trumpler 2		02 36 53
OCl 365.0	Trumpler 2		02 36 53
OCl 366	Trumpler 3		03 12 00
OCl 367	Czernik 12		02 39 23
OCl 368	IC 1848		02 51 11
OCl 368.0	IC 1848		02 51 11
OCl 369	Collinder 34		02 59 23.2
OCl 369.0	Collinder 34		02 59 23.2
OCl 370	Berkeley 10		03 39 37
OCl 371	Collinder 21		01 50 12
OCl 372	Collinder 464		05 12 39.0
OCl 372.0	Collinder 464		05 12 39.0
OCl 373	Berkeley 66		03 04 05
OCl 374	NGC 2314		07 10 32.4
OCl 375	Stock 23		03 16 10.8
OCl 375.0	Stock 23		03 16 10.8
OCl 376	Czernik 14		03 16 57
OCl 377	NGC 956		02 32 14.9
OCl 378	Czernik 17		03 52 20
OCl 379	Upgren 1		12 35 00
OCl 380	NGC 1220		03 11 41
OCl 381	King 6		03 28 00
OCl 382	NGC 1039		02 42 08
OCl 383	NGC 1502		04 07 50
OCl 383.0	NGC 1502		04 07 50
OCl 384	King 5		03 14 40
OCl 385	Tombaugh 5		03 47 44
OCl 386	Czernik 15		03 23 13
OCl 387	Czernik 16		03 31 02
OCl 388	Berkeley 9		03 32 38
OCl 389	NGC 1245		03 14 42
OCl 390	NGC 1193		03 05 56
OCl 391	NGC 1348		03 34 09
OCl 392	Melotte 20		03 24 19
OCl 392.0	Melotte 20		03 24 19
OCl 393	IC 361		04 18 51
OCl 394	NGC 1444		03 49 27
OCl 394.0	NGC 1444		03 49 27
OCl 395	King 7		03 59 10
OCl 396	NGC 1496		04 04 32
OCl 396.1	Mayer 2		04 19 51
OCl 397	NGC 1528		04 15 19
OCl 397.0	NGC 1528		04 15 19
OCl 398	NGC 1513		04 09 55
OCl 399	NGC 1545		04 20 57
OCl 399.0	NGC 1545		04 20 57
OCl 400	Berkeley 67		04 37 50
OCl 401	NGC 1342		03 31 40
OCl 402	Berkeley 13		04 55 46.2
OCl 403	NGC 1624		04 40 37
OCl 403.0	NGC 1624		04 40 37
OCl 404	Berkeley 11		04 20 27
OCl 404.0	Berkeley 11		04 20 27
OCl 405	NGC 1724		05 03 33
OCl 406	NGC 1605		04 34 53
OCl 406.0	NGC 1605		04 34 53
OCl 407	NGC 1582		04 31 39
OCl 407.0	NGC 1582		04 31 39
OCl 408	Ruprecht 148		04 46 35
OCl 409	IC 348		03 44 34
OCl 409.0	IC 348		03 44 34
OCl 410	NGC 1798		05 11 40
OCl 411	NGC 1664		04 51 06
OCl 411.0	NGC 1664		04 51 06
OCl 412	Berkeley 12		04 44 24
OCl 413	Berkeley 68		04 44.5
OCl 414	Berkeley 15		05 02 05
OCl 415	NGC 1548		04 21 20
OCl 416	Berkeley 14		04 59 44
OCl 417	NGC 1883		05 25 55
OCl 418	NGC 2126		06 02 34

Table D.3: Cluster Cross-Reference

Name	Look Under	GX	2000.0 RA
OCl 419	Berkeley 18		05 22 12
OCl 420	Berkeley 18		05 22 12
OCl 421	Pleiades		03 47 29
OCl 422	Berkeley 70		05 25 48
OCl 423	Collinder 62		05 20 53.0
OCl 423.0	Collinder 62		05 20 53.0
OCl 424	King 17		05 08 24
OCl 425	Dolidze 14		04 06 41
OCl 425.0	Dolidze 14		04 06 41
OCl 426	Czernik 18		04 27 48
OCl 427	Czernik 20		05 20 32.5
OCl 427.0	Czernik 20		05 20 32.5
OCl 428	NGC 1857		05 20 06
OCl 428.0	NGC 1857		05 20 06
OCl 429	NGC 1778		05 08 06
OCl 429.0	NGC 1778		05 08 06
OCl 430	Dolidze 15		05 04.6
OCl 430.0	Dolidze 15		05 04.6
OCl 431	Stock 10		05 39.0
OCl 432	Czernik 21		05 26 40
OCl 433	NGC 1912		05 28 43
OCl 433.0	NGC 1912		05 28 43
OCl 434	NGC 1907		05 28 05
OCl 435	Dolidze 16		05 14.6
OCl 435.0	Dolidze 16		05 14.6
OCl 436	Stock 8		05 28 07
OCl 437	NGC 2192		06 15 18
OCl 438.0	IC 410		05 22.0
OCl 439	NGC 1893		05 22 46
OCl 439.0	NGC 1893		05 22 46
OCl 440	Dolidze 18		05 24 09
OCl 441	NGC 1931		05 31 26
OCl 441.0	NGC 1931		05 31 26
OCl 442	Dolidze 20		05 28 33
OCl 443	Czernik 19		04 56 56
OCl 444	Berkeley 69		05 24 21
OCl 445	NGC 1960		05 36 18
OCl 446	NGC 2281		06 48 18
OCl 447	Berkeley 17		05 20 30
OCl 448	King 8		05 49 17
OCl 449	Berkeley 71		05 40 57
OCl 450	Berkeley 19		05 24 03
OCl 451	NGC 2099		05 52 19
OCl 452	NGC 1746		05 03.6
OCl 452	NGC 1750		05 03.9
OCl 453	NGC 1758		05 04.4
OCl 454	NGC 1746		05 03.6
OCl 454	NGC 1750		05 03.9
OCl 455	Basel 4		05 48 54
OCl 456	Hyades		04 26.9
OCl 456.0	Hyades		04 26.9
OCl 457	NGC 1647		04 45 42.2
OCl 457.0	NGC 1647		04 45 42.2
OCl 458	Czernik 23		05 50 08
OCl 458.0	Czernik 23		05 50 08
OCl 459	DoDz 3		05 33.5
OCl 459.0	DoDz 3		05 33.5
OCl 460	DoDz 4		05 35.9
OCl 460.0	DoDz 4		05 35.9
OCl 461	NGC 1663		04 49 24.3

Table D.3: Cluster Cross-Reference

Name	Look Under	GX	2000.0 RA
OCl 462	NGC 1807		05 10 46
OCl 463	NGC 1817		05 12 27
OCl 464	Berkeley 72		05 50 12
OCl 465	IC 2157		06 04 49.8
OCl 466	NGC 2168		06 09.0
OCl 466.0	NGC 2168		06 09.0
OCl 467	NGC 2129		06 01 06
OCl 467.0	NGC 2129		06 01 06
OCl 468	NGC 2158		06 07 26
OCl 469.1	Basel 11b		05 58 10
OCl 470	NGC 1662		04 48 29
OCl 471	NGC 2266		06 43 20
OCl 472	Czernik 24		05 55 26
OCl 473	Collinder 89		06 18.0
OCl 473.0	Collinder 89		06 18.0
OCl 474	Collinder 65		05 26 05.7
OCl 474.0	Collinder 65		05 26 05.7
OCl 475	NGC 2331		07 07 01
OCl 475.1	NGC 2175.1		06 10 53
OCl 476	Collinder 84		06 09 39
OCl 477	DoDz 2		05 23.2
OCl 478	Berkeley 23		06 33 15
OCl 479	Collinder 69		05 35.0
OCl 479.0	Collinder 69		05 35.0
OCl 480	Dolidze 19		05 23.7
OCl 481	NGC 2169		06 08 25
OCl 481.0	NGC 2169		06 08 25
OCl 482	Dolidze 17		05 22.4
OCl 483	Dolidze 21		05 27.4
OCl 484	NGC 2304		06 55 12
OCl 485	NGC 2194		06 13 46
OCl 486	Berkeley 29		06 53 04
OCl 487	NGC 2141		06 02 56
OCl 488	NGC 2420		07 38 24
OCl 489	Collinder 74		05 48 40
OCl 490	Berkeley 22		05 58 27
OCl 491	Collinder 95		06 30 51.2
OCl 491.0	Collinder 95		06 30 51.2
OCl 492	NGC 2259		06 38 33.3
OCl 493	Czernik 25		06 13 41
OCl 494	Trumpler 5		06 36 31
OCl 495	NGC 2264		06 40 59
OCl 496	NGC 2355		07 17 00
OCl 497	Berkeley 20		05 32 37
OCl 498	NGC 2186		06 12 08
OCl 499	NGC 2251		06 34 39
OCl 499.1	Basel 8		06 34.2
OCl 499.2	Basel 7		06 36 19
OCl 500	NGC 2254		06 35 46.6
OCl 501	NGC 2236		06 29 40
OCl 501.0	NGC 2236		06 29 40
OCl 502	NGC 2395		07 27 13
OCl 503	Collinder 70		05 35.6
OCl 503.0	Collinder 70		05 35.6
OCl 504	Collinder 92		06 22.9
OCl 505	Collinder 111		06 38.7
OCl 506	Collinder 97		06 30 58.1
OCl 506.0	Collinder 97		06 30 58.1
OCl 507	NGC 2632		08 40 22
OCl 507.0	NGC 2632		08 40 22

Table D.3: Cluster Cross-Reference

Name	Look Under	GX	2000.0 RA
OCl 508	Dolidze 22		06 23.3
OCl 509	NGC 2112		05 53 46
OCl 510	Collinder 106		06 37.1
OCl 511	NGC 2237		06 31 55.5
OCl 511.0	NGC 2237		06 31 55.5
OCl 512	NGC 2244		06 32 19
OCl 512.0	NGC 2244		06 32 19
OCl 513	Biurakan 7		06 57 37
OCl 514	NGC 2252		06 34 19.8
OCl 515	NGC 2237		06 31 55.5
OCl 515	NGC 2244		06 32 19
OCl 516	Dolidze 26		07 30 02
OCl 516.1	Sigma Ori		05 38 45
OCl 517	Collinder 104		06 36.5
OCl 517.0	Collinder 104		06 36.5
OCl 518	Collinder 107		06 37.7
OCl 518.0	Collinder 107		06 37.7
OCl 519	Collinder 91		06 21 33
OCl 520	Biurakan 12		06 50 16
OCl 521	Biurakan 11		06 51 21
OCl 522	Biurakan 8		06 58 07
OCl 523	Collinder 96		06 30.3
OCl 524	NGC 2269		06 43 16.8
OCl 525.0	NGC 1981		05 35.2
OCl 525.1	NGC 1977		05 35.3
OCl 526	Czernik 27		07 03 19
OCl 527	Cl vdB 1		06 37 05
OCl 528	NGC 1976		05 35 16
OCl 528.0	NGC 1976		05 35 16
OCl 529	NGC 1980		05 35 26
OCl 529.0	NGC 1980		05 35 26
OCl 530	Collinder 110		06 38 39
OCl 530.0	Collinder 110		06 38 39
OCl 531	NGC 2262		06 39 38.7
OCl 532	Biurakan 10		06 52 07
OCl 533	Dolidze 24		06 44 44
OCl 533.0	Dolidze 24		06 44 44
OCl 534	Biurakan 9		06 57 46
OCl 535	Collinder 115		06 46 40
OCl 535.1	Cl vdB 85		06 46 52
OCl 536	Berkeley 78		07 23 38
OCl 537	Dolidze 25		06 45.0
OCl 538	Dolidze 23		06 43 05.7
OCl 538.0	Dolidze 23		06 43 05.7
OCl 539	Berkeley 24		06 37 47
OCl 540	NGC 2301		06 51 46
OCl 540.0	NGC 2301		06 51 46
OCl 541	Berkeley 35		07 09 54
OCl 542	NGC 2324		07 04 08
OCl 543	Biurakan 13		07 00 22
OCl 544	Czernik 26		06 30 58
OCl 545	NGC 2232		06 27 15
OCl 546	Berkeley 73		06 22 05
OCl 548	NGC 2286		06 47 41
OCl 549	NGC 2682		08 51 24
OCl 549.0	NGC 2682		08 51 24
OCl 550	NGC 2215		06 20 50
OCl 551	Berkeley 37		07 20 18
OCl 552	Czernik 28		07 21.8
OCl 553	NGC 2311		06 57 48

Table D.3: Cluster Cross-Reference

Name	Look Under	GX	2000.0 RA
OCl 553.1	Cl vdB 80		06 30 50
OCl 554	NGC 2302		06 51 54
OCl 554.0	NGC 2302		06 51 54
OCl 555	Berkeley 77		07 21 28
OCl 556	Haffner 3		07 04 08
OCl 557	NGC 2309		06 56 04
OCl 558	Melotte 111		12 25.1
OCl 558.0	Melotte 111		12 25.1
OCl 559	NGC 2323		07 02 47.8
OCl 559.0	NGC 2323		07 02 47.8
OCl 560	Ruprecht 4		06 48 57
OCl 561	Berkeley 39		07 46 50
OCl 562	NGC 2335		07 06 50
OCl 563	Ruprecht 1		06 36.4
OCl 564	Collinder 465		07 06 52
OCl 565	NGC 2343		07 08 07
OCl 566	Collinder 466		07 06 56
OCl 566.1	Cl vdB 92		07 03 55
OCl 567	NGC 2353		07 14 31
OCl 567.0	NGC 2353		07 14 31
OCl 568	Berkeley 76		07 06 40
OCl 569	Ruprecht 6		06 56 05
OCl 570	Ruprecht 7		06 57 50
OCl 571	NGC 2368		07 21 02.2
OCl 572	NGC 2204		06 15 33
OCl 573	Ruprecht 8		07 01 46
OCl 574	Czernik 30		07 31 11
OCl 575	NGC 2345		07 08 19
OCl 575.0	NGC 2345		07 08 19
OCl 576	Berkeley 25		06 41 14
OCl 577	Berkeley 36		07 16 23
OCl 578	Haffner 8		07 23 03
OCl 579	NGC 2396		07 28.0
OCl 580	Melotte 72		07 38 29
OCl 581	Melotte 72		07 38 29
OCl 582	Haffner 6		07 20 01
OCl 583	Haffner 4		07 06 04
OCl 584	NGC 2548		08 13 44
OCl 584.1	Basel 11a		07 17 08
OCl 585	NGC 2374		07 23 57
OCl 586	Ruprecht 24		07 31 51
OCl 587	Melotte 71		07 37 30
OCl 588	NGC 2401		07 29 25
OCl 589	NGC 2360		07 17 44
OCl 590	Haffner 23		07 09.5
OCl 591	Ruprecht 5		06 55 24
OCl 592	NGC 2423		07 37 07
OCl 593	NGC 2506		08 00 02
OCl 594	Haffner 10		07 28 36
OCl 595	Czernik 29		07 28 24
OCl 596	NGC 2422		07 36 36
OCl 596.0	NGC 2422		07 36 36
OCl 597	NGC 2287		06 46.1
OCl 597.0	NGC 2287		06 46.1
OCl 598	NGC 2414		07 33 13
OCl 599	NGC 2425		07 38 18
OCl 600	Haffner 9		07 24 42
OCl 601	NGC 2437		07 41 47
OCl 601.0	NGC 2437		07 41 47
OCl 602	Ruprecht 26		07 37 13
OCl 603	Tombaugh 1		07 00 27
OCl 604	Ruprecht 10		07 06 27.6
OCl 605	Tombaugh 2		07 03 06
OCl 606	Ruprecht 151		07 41.3
OCl 606.0	Ruprecht 151		07 41.3
OCl 607	Ruprecht 11		07 07 23
OCl 608	Haffner 24		07 28.8
OCl 609	Ruprecht 15		07 19 34
OCl 609.1	Mayer 3		07 30 04
OCl 610	Ruprecht 9		07 01.9
OCl 611	NGC 2539		08 10 38
OCl 612	Ruprecht 16		07 23 09
OCl 613	Ruprecht 149		06 52.2
OCl 614	Berkeley 75		06 49 00
OCl 615	Ruprecht 37		07 49 47
OCl 616	NGC 2383		07 24 40
OCl 617	Ruprecht 45		07 59.6
OCl 618	NGC 2384		07 25 12
OCl 619	Collinder 121		06 56 20.0
OCl 619.0	Collinder 121		06 56 20.0
OCl 620	NGC 2432		07 40 54
OCl 621	NGC 2367		07 20 05
OCl 622	Ruprecht 19		07 25.6
OCl 623	NGC 2479		07 55 06
OCl 624	Haffner 5		07 18.1
OCl 625	Czernik 31		07 36 58
OCl 626	NGC 2421		07 36 12
OCl 626.1	Cl vdB 83		06 40.0
OCl 627	Ruprecht 17		07 23 35
OCl 628	Ruprecht 34		07 45 54
OCl 629	Ruprecht 38		07 50 31
OCl 630	NGC 2509		08 00 48
OCl 631	Ruprecht 13		07 08.0
OCl 633	NGC 2362		07 18 42
OCl 633.0	NGC 2362		07 18 42
OCl 634	Ruprecht 40		07 33 27
OCl 635	Trumpler 7		07 27 21
OCl 636	NGC 2455		07 48 59
OCl 637	Ruprecht 46		08 02 10
OCl 638	Trumpler 6		07 26 23
OCl 639	NGC 2354		07 14 16
OCl 639.0	NGC 2354		07 14 16
OCl 640	Ruprecht 33		07 45.8
OCl 641	Ruprecht 25		07 36 47
OCl 642	Ruprecht 3		06 42 06
OCl 643	Ruprecht 2		06 41 01
OCl 644	NGC 2243		06 29 35
OCl 645	Ruprecht 39		07 52 20
OCl 646	Ruprecht 18		07 24 39
OCl 647	Ruprecht 12		07 07 10
OCl 648	Ruprecht 150		07 05 55
OCl 649	NGC 2447		07 44 30
OCl 649.0	NGC 2447		07 44 30
OCl 650	Ruprecht 29		07 41.1
OCl 651	Ruprecht 32		07 45 06
OCl 651.0	Ruprecht 32		07 45 06
OCl 652	Ruprecht 157		08 29 52
OCl 653	NGC 2482		07 55 10
OCl 653.0	NGC 2482		07 55 10
OCl 654	Ruprecht 27		07 37.6
OCl 654.0	Ruprecht 27		07 37.6
OCl 655	Haffner 16		07 50 21
OCl 656	Haffner 25		07 48 40
OCl 657	Haffner 11		07 35 22
OCl 658	Ruprecht 62		08 32 30
OCl 659	Ruprecht 20		07 26 41
OCl 661	Haffner 7		07 22 54
OCl 662	Haffner 19		07 52 46
OCl 663	Trumpler 9		07 55 40
OCl 664	Ruprecht 22		07 29 17
OCl 668	NGC 2467		07 52 30
OCl 668.0	NGC 2467		07 52 30
OCl 669	Ruprecht 42		07 57 37
OCl 670	NGC 2453		07 47 35
OCl 671	Collinder 132		07 15 21.1
OCl 672	Ruprecht 14		07 14 55
OCl 673	Ruprecht 41		07 53 48
OCl 674	Haffner 14		07 44 48
OCl 675	Ruprecht 21		07 27.1
OCl 676	Ruprecht 49		08 03 17
OCl 677	Haffner 21		08 01 11
OCl 677.1	NGC 2483		07 55 39
OCl 678	Haffner 13		07 40 26
OCl 679	Collinder 140		07 24 26.7
OCl 680	Ruprecht 28		07 39 36
OCl 681	Ruprecht 44		07 58 50
OCl 682	Ruprecht 53		08 10 50
OCl 683	Czernik 32		07 50 28
OCl 684	Ruprecht 43		07 58.8
OCl 685	NGC 2527		08 04 53
OCl 685.0	NGC 2527		08 04 53
OCl 686	Ruprecht 57		08 14.8
OCl 687	Ruprecht 30		07 42 22
OCl 688	NGC 2439		07 40 46
OCl 689	Ruprecht 35		07 46 14
OCl 690	NGC 2489		07 56 16
OCl 691	Haffner 22		08 12.6
OCl 692	Haffner 20		07 56 15
OCl 693	Ruprecht 153		08 00 18
OCl 694	Haffner 17		07 51 36
OCl 695	NGC 2533		08 07.0
OCl 696	Haffner 15		07 45 30
OCl 697	Ruprecht 51		08 03.6
OCl 698	Ruprecht 50		08 03.4
OCl 699	Ruprecht 47		08 02 18
OCl 700	Collinder 135		07 17 24.5
OCl 701	NGC 2571		08 18 57
OCl 702	Ruprecht 48		08 02 42
OCl 703	Ruprecht 155		08 04.9
OCl 704	Collinder 187		08 24 12
OCl 705	Ruprecht 52		08 05.0
OCl 706	NGC 2587		08 23 25
OCl 707	Haffner 26		08 15.4
OCl 708	NGC 2567		08 18 30
OCl 709	NGC 2580		08 21 28
OCl 710	Ruprecht 54		08 11 23
OCl 711	Ruprecht 31		07 43 00
OCl 712	Ruprecht 58		08 14 49
OCl 713	Ruprecht 55		08 12 19
OCl 714	NGC 2627		08 37 15

Table D.3: Cluster Cross-Reference

Name	Look Under	GX	2000.0 RA
OCI 715	NGC 2588		08 23 10
OCI 716	NGC 2451		07 45.4
OCI 717	Ruprecht 59		08 19 22.0
OCI 718	Ruprecht 61		08 25 15
OCI 719	Ruprecht 152		07 54 29
OCI 720	NGC 2477		07 52 10
OCI 721	Collinder 196		08 45.1
OCI 722	Collinder 198		08 45.4
OCI 723	NGC 2658		08 43 28
OCI 723.0	NGC 2658		08 43 28
OCI 724	NGC 2579		08 20 53
OCI 725	Collinder 185		08 23 19
OCI 726	NGC 2546		08 12.4
OCI 727	NGC 2568		08 18 19
OCI 728	NGC 2635		08 38 27
OCI 729	Ruprecht 68		08 44.5
OCI 730	Ruprecht 56		08 12.6
OCI 730.0	Ruprecht 56		08 12.6
OCI 731	Pismis 3		08 31 21
OCI 732	Ruprecht 66		08 40 32
OCI 733	Pismis 2		08 17 54
OCI 733.0	Pismis 2		08 17 54
OCI 734	Pismis 7		08 41 09
OCI 735	Pismis 5		08 37 39
OCI 735.0	Pismis 5		08 37 39
OCI 736	Ruprecht 158		08 52 23
OCI 737	Ruprecht 72		08 52 05
OCI 738	Ruprecht 154		08 01.7
OCI 739	Melotte 66		07 26 19
OCI 740	Ruprecht 64		08 37.4
OCI 740.0	Ruprecht 64		08 37.4
OCI 741	Collinder 173		08 03.5
OCI 741.0	Collinder 173		08 03.5
OCI 742	Collinder 197		08 44 40
OCI 743	NGC 2818		09 16 10
OCI 744	Ruprecht 156		08 19 28.8
OCI 745	NGC 2669		08 46 19
OCI 745	NGC 2671		08 46 12
OCI 746	Pismis 4		08 34.6
OCI 747	Trumpler 10		08 47 45
OCI 747.0	Trumpler 10		08 47 45
OCI 748	Ruprecht 67		08 41 45
OCI 749	Ruprecht 74		09 21.0
OCI 750	Ruprecht 65		08 39 22
OCI 750.0	Ruprecht 65		08 39 22
OCI 751	Ruprecht 60		08 24 26
OCI 752	NGC 2659		08 42 34
OCI 752.0	NGC 2659		08 42 34
OCI 753	NGC 2547		08 10 11
OCI 753.0	NGC 2547		08 10 11
OCI 754	NGC 2645		08 39 04
OCI 755	Pismis 8		08 41 35
OCI 756	NGC 2849		09 19 23
OCI 757	Pismis 10		09 02.6
OCI 758	Ruprecht 63		08 32 40
OCI 759	NGC 2660		08 42 39
OCI 760	Ruprecht 70		08 49.1
OCI 761	Ruprecht 71		08 49.5
OCI 762	Ruprecht 69		08 44 49.1
OCI 763	IC 2395		08 42 31

Table D.3: Cluster Cross-Reference

Name	Look Under	GX	2000.0 RA
OCI 764	NGC 2670		08 45 30
OCI 765	Pismis 12		09 20 00
OCI 766	Markarian 18		09 00 31
OCI 767	IC 2391		08 40.3
OCI 767.0	IC 2391		08 40.3
OCI 769	Ruprecht 73		09 01 12
OCI 770	NGC 2982		09 42 01
OCI 771	Ruprecht 81		09 45 13
OCI 772	Pismis 11		09 15 53
OCI 773	Pismis 15		09 34 45
OCI 774	Pismis 13		09 22 06.5
OCI 775	Ruprecht 76		09 24 18
OCI 776	NGC 2516		07 58.0
OCI 776.0	NGC 2516		07 58.0
OCI 777	Ruprecht 160		09 55.5
OCI 778	NGC 2972		09 40 12
OCI 779	Hogg 1		09 40 33
OCI 780	Pismis 14		09 29.3
OCI 781	NGC 2910		09 30 30
OCI 782	Ruprecht 78		09 29 07.9
OCI 783	NGC 2925		09 33 11
OCI 783.0	NGC 2925		09 33 11
OCI 784	Ruprecht 77		09 27 02
OCI 785	Collinder 213		09 55 00
OCI 785.0	Collinder 213		09 55 00
OCI 786	Ruprecht 75		09 21 54
OCI 787	Ruprecht 79		09 41 03
OCI 788	Ruprecht 82		09 45 49
OCI 790	Pismis 16		09 51 14
OCI 791	Ruprecht 83		09 49 15
OCI 791.1	NGC 1901		05 17.8
OCI 792	Ruprecht 87		10 15 30
OCI 793	Hogg 4		09 57 53
OCI 794	Hogg 3		09 57 40
OCI 795	Ruprecht 159		09 20 08
OCI 797	Hogg 2		09 51.5
OCI 798	NGC 3105		10 00 40
OCI 799	Ruprecht 85		10 01 26
OCI 800	NGC 3228		10 21 23
OCI 800.1	Loden 27		10 11.1
OCI 801	Ruprecht 86		10 01 27.7
OCI 801.1	Loden 59		10 30 22
OCI 802	NGC 3114		10 02.7
OCI 802.0	NGC 3114		10 02.7
OCI 803	Trumpler 12		10 06.5
OCI 804	Hogg 5		10 06 09
OCI 805	Hogg 6		10 06 28
OCI 806	NGC 3330		10 38 48
OCI 807	NGC 3247		10 24 01
OCI 808	Trumpler 11		10 04.9
OCI 809	NGC 3247		10 24 01
OCI 810	Ruprecht 161		10 08.8
OCI 810.0	Ruprecht 161		10 08.8
OCI 811	IC 2581		10 27 27
OCI 811.0	IC 2581		10 27 27
OCI 811.1	Loden 112		10 32 40
OCI 812	Ruprecht 89		10 28.5
OCI 813	Ruprecht 90		10 31.0
OCI 814	Ruprecht 84		09 49 04
OCI 814.1	Loden 143		10 28 44

Table D.3: Cluster Cross-Reference

Name	Look Under	GX	2000.0 RA
OCI 815	Trumpler 13		10 23 48
OCI 815.1	Loden 153		10 34 46.7
OCI 816	NGC 3293		10 35 49
OCI 816.0	NGC 3293		10 35 49
OCI 816.1	Loden 165		10 35 56
OCI 817	NGC 3255		10 26 32
OCI 818	Collinder 223		10 30.4
OCI 819	NGC 3324		10 37 19
OCI 819.0	NGC 3324		10 37 19
OCI 820	Hogg 7		10 29.1
OCI 821	Hogg 8		10 29 09
OCI 822	Ruprecht 88		10 18 48
OCI 823	NGC 3680		11 25 38
OCI 824	Ruprecht 91		10 47 38.4
OCI 825	Trumpler 15		10 44 44
OCI 825.0	Trumpler 15		10 44 44
OCI 826	Trumpler 14		10 43 57
OCI 827	Collinder 232		10 44 39
OCI 828	Collinder 228		10 44 00
OCI 828.0	Collinder 228		10 44 00
OCI 829	Trumpler 16		10 45 10
OCI 829.0	Trumpler 16		10 45 10
OCI 830	Collinder 234		10 45 12.9
OCI 830.0	Collinder 234		10 45 12.9
OCI 831	Trumpler 17		10 56 24
OCI 832	Hogg 9		10 58 22
OCI 833	NGC 3503		11 01 18
OCI 834	Ruprecht 92		10 53 49
OCI 835	Collinder 236		10 57 00
OCI 835.0	Collinder 236		10 57 00
OCI 836	NGC 3496		10 59 34
OCI 837	Sher 1		11 01 03
OCI 838	IC 2602		10 42 57
OCI 838.0	IC 2602		10 42 57
OCI 839	NGC 3532		11 05.5
OCI 839.0	NGC 3532		11 05.5
OCI 840	Ruprecht 162		10 53.0
OCI 841	Melotte 101		10 42 00
OCI 842	Feinstein 1		11 06.0
OCI 842.1	Loden 280		11 09.5
OCI 843	Trumpler 19		11 14.3
OCI 843.0	Trumpler 19		11 14.3
OCI 843.1	Basel 17		11 10 32.9
OCI 843.2	Graham 1		10 56 32
OCI 844	NGC 3519		11 04 03
OCI 844.0	NGC 3519		11 04 03
OCI 845	Stock 13		11 13.1
OCI 845.1	Loden 309		11 09.5
OCI 846	NGC 3572		11 10 26.6
OCI 847	Hogg 10		11 10 42.1
OCI 848.0	Collinder 240		11 11 40.2
OCI 849	Hogg 11		11 11 32.6
OCI 850	Trumpler 18		11 11.4
OCI 850.0	Trumpler 18		11 11.4
OCI 851	Hogg 12		11 12 15
OCI 851.0	Hogg 12		11 12 15
OCI 852	NGC 3590		11 13 00
OCI 852.1	Loden 336		11 19.8
OCI 853	Hogg 13		11 16.3
OCI 853.1	Loden 372		11 30 52

Table D.3: Cluster Cross-Reference

Name	Look Under	GX	2000.0 RA
OCl 854	NGC 3603		11 15 07
OCl 855	IC 2714		11 17 18
OCl 856	Melotte 105		11 19 41
OCl 857	Ruprecht 163		11 04 47
OCl 858	Ruprecht 164		11 31.1
OCl 859	Ruprecht 94		11 30.4
OCl 860	NGC 3766		11 36 15
OCl 860.0	NGC 3766		11 36 15
OCl 861	NGC 3960		11 50 34
OCl 862	Collinder 249		11 38 20.4
OCl 862.0	Collinder 249		11 38 20.4
OCl 863	Ruprecht 95		11 43 40
OCl 864	IC 2948		11 38 58
OCl 864.0	IC 2948		11 38 58
OCl 865	Stock 14		11 43 51
OCl 865.3	Loden 480		11 56 06
OCl 866	Ruprecht 96		11 50 53
OCl 867	Ruprecht 97		11 57 23
OCl 868	Ruprecht 98		11 58.8
OCl 869	Stock 15		12 10.5
OCl 870	NGC 4052		12 02 01
OCl 870.0	NGC 4052		12 02 01
OCl 871	NGC 4103		12 06 40
OCl 871.0	NGC 4103		12 06 40
OCl 872	Ruprecht 99		12 03 20
OCl 873	Ruprecht 100		12 05.7
OCl 873.1	Loden 565		12 08 24.4
OCl 874	NGC 4230		12 17 16
OCl 875	Ruprecht 101		12 09 40
OCl 876	Ruprecht 103		12 15.9
OCl 876.0	Ruprecht 103		12 15.9
OCl 877	NGC 4184		12 13.6
OCl 877.0	NGC 4184		12 13.6
OCl 878	NGC 4337		12 24 04
OCl 879	Ruprecht 104		12 24 51
OCl 880	Harvard 5		12 27 16.3
OCl 881	Ruprecht 165		12 28.6
OCl 882	NGC 4349		12 24 07
OCl 882.0	NGC 4349		12 24 07
OCl 882.1	Loden 615		12 20 37.2
OCl 883	Hogg 14		12 28 39
OCl 884	NGC 4439		12 28 27
OCl 884.1	NGC 4439		12 28 27
OCl 884.2	Hogg 23		12 28 31.6
OCl 885	NGC 4463		12 29 56
OCl 886	Ruprecht 105		12 34.0
OCl 887	Ruprecht 106	g	12 38 40.2
OCl 888	Trumpler 20		12 39 32
OCl 889	Harvard 6		12 37 54
OCl 890	NGC 4609		12 42 20
OCl 891	Hogg 15		12 43 36
OCl 892	NGC 4755		12 53 38
OCl 893	NGC 4815		12 57 59
OCl 894	NGC 4852		13 00 05
OCl 894.1	Loden 757		13 12.4
OCl 895	Harvard 8		13 18 12
OCl 896	Ruprecht 107		13 19 46
OCl 897	Collinder 269		13 22.6
OCl 898	Stock 16		13 18 38.4
OCl 898.1	Loden 807		13 24.9

Table D.3: Cluster Cross-Reference

Name	Look Under	GX	2000.0 RA
OCl 899	NGC 5120		13 25 39
OCl 900	Collinder 271		13 30.0
OCl 901	Hogg 16		13 29 11
OCl 901.1	Loden 848		13 33.1
OCl 902	NGC 5138		13 27 16
OCl 902.0	NGC 5138		13 27 16
OCl 903	Trumpler 21		13 32 14
OCl 904	Collinder 272		13 30.5
OCl 905	NGC 5168		13 31 08
OCl 905.1	Loden 894		13 39 44.3
OCl 906	IC 4291		13 36 55
OCl 907	Ruprecht 108		13 32 12
OCl 907.0	Ruprecht 108		13 32 12
OCl 908	Collinder 275		13 35.4
OCl 909	Collinder 277		13 48.4
OCl 910	NGC 5288		13 48 45.6
OCl 911	NGC 5281		13 46 36.7
OCl 911.1	Loden 991		13 45.4
OCl 911.2	Loden 1002		13 54.3
OCl 911.3	Loden 1010		13 45.4
OCl 912	Ruprecht 110		14 06.5
OCl 913	NGC 5316		13 54.0
OCl 913.0	NGC 5316		13 54.0
OCl 913.1	Loden 1095		13 53.5
OCl 913.2	Loden 1101		13 58 40.6
OCl 914	Lynga 1		14 00 02
OCl 914.1	Loden 1152		13 59.5
OCl 915	NGC 5381		14 00.6
OCl 915.0	NGC 5381		14 00.6
OCl 915.1	Loden 1171		13 59 31.4
OCl 915.2	Loden 1177		13 59.4
OCl 915.3	Loden 1194		14 05.8
OCl 915.4	Loden 1202		14 04.4
OCl 915.5	Loden 1225		14 09.2
OCl 915.6	Loden 1256		14 18.2
OCl 915.7	Loden 1282		14 15.9
OCl 915.8	Loden 1289		14 16 56.9
OCl 916	Lynga 2		14 24 24
OCl 917	Ruprecht 167		14 18.2
OCl 917.0	Ruprecht 167		14 18.2
OCl 918	Melotte 227		20 15 18
OCl 918.0	Melotte 227		20 15 18
OCl 918.1	Loden 1339		14 33.5
OCl 919	NGC 5617		14 29.7
OCl 920	Trumpler 22		14 31.2
OCl 921	Pismis 19		14 30 43
OCl 922	NGC 5606		14 27.8
OCl 923	Hogg 17		14 33 50.4
OCl 923.1	Loden 1373		14 41.7
OCl 923.2	Loden 1375		14 44 33
OCl 924	Ruprecht 111		14 35.8
OCl 925	NGC 5460		14 07.6
OCl 925.0	NGC 5460		14 07.6
OCl 925.1	Loden 1409		14 44.7
OCl 926	NGC 5593		14 25 40
OCl 927	Ruprecht 112		14 57.0
OCl 928	NGC 5662		14 35 30.8
OCl 929	NGC 5715		14 43 39.0
OCl 930	NGC 5749		14 48 48.8
OCl 931	Pismis 21		15 16 47.7

Table D.3: Cluster Cross-Reference

Name	Look Under	GX	2000.0 RA
OCl 932	Pismis 20		15 15 23.1
OCl 933	Hogg 18		14 50 41.4
OCl 934	NGC 5764		14 53 31.8
OCl 935	Lynga 3		15 16 47
OCl 936	NGC 5823		15 05 26
OCl 937	NGC 5822		15 04 02.3
OCl 938	NGC 5925		15 27.7
OCl 939	NGC 6025		16 03 18
OCl 940	Ruprecht 113		15 57.2
OCl 940.0	Ruprecht 113		15 57.2
OCl 941	Lynga 4		15 33 20
OCl 942	Lynga 5		15 41 57.1
OCl 943	Collinder 292		15 50.8
OCl 944	Harvard 9		15 33.8
OCl 945	NGC 6005		15 55 47.4
OCl 946	NGC 5999		15 52 14
OCl 947	Ruprecht 114		16 06 31
OCl 948	NGC 6087		16 18 51.8
OCl 948.0	NGC 6087		16 18 51.8
OCl 949	Lynga 7	g	16 11 03.0
OCl 950	Trumpler 23		16 00 50.7
OCl 951	NGC 6031		16 07 34.4
OCl 952	Harvard 10		16 19.9
OCl 953	NGC 6067		16 13 09
OCl 954	Harvard 10		16 19.9
OCl 954.0	Hogg 10		11 10 42.1
OCl 955	Lynga 6		16 04 51
OCl 956	Ruprecht 115		16 12 51.1
OCl 957	Pismis 22		16 14 07.9
OCl 957.1	Ruprecht 176		16 14 45
OCl 958	Ruprecht 116		16 23 24.3
OCl 958.0	Ruprecht 116		16 23 24.3
OCl 959	Ruprecht 117		16 23 30.7
OCl 959.0	Ruprecht 117		16 23 30.7
OCl 960	NGC 6115		16 24 26.8
OCl 961	NGC 6152		16 32.7
OCl 961.0	NGC 6152		16 32.7
OCl 962	Lynga 8		16 22 57.0
OCl 963	Ruprecht 119		16 28 09.3
OCl 963.0	Ruprecht 119		16 28 09.3
OCl 964	NGC 6208		16 49 25.8
OCl 965	Collinder 307		16 35.3
OCl 966	Lynga 9		16 20 39
OCl 967	Pismis 23		16 23 58
OCl 968	NGC 6134		16 27 43.6
OCl 969	Hogg 19		16 28 51.7
OCl 970	NGC 5053	g	13 16 27.0
OCl 971	NGC 6167		16 34 35
OCl 972	NGC 6253		16 59 06.1
OCl 973	Lynga 12		16 46 03
OCl 974	Ruprecht 120		16 35 12.2
OCl 975	NGC 6193		16 41 20.3
OCl 976	Hogg 20		16 44.4
OCl 977	Hogg 21		16 45 36.9
OCl 978	NGC 6200		16 44 08.6
OCl 979	Lynga 11		16 38 10
OCl 980	NGC 6178		16 35 50.8
OCl 981	Hogg 22		16 46 35
OCl 982	NGC 6204		16 46 07.9
OCl 983	Ruprecht 121		16 41 47.6

Table D.3: Cluster Cross-Reference

Name	Look Under	GX	2000.0 RA
OCl 984	NGC 6169		16 34 05.0
OCl 985	Westerlund 1		16 47 04
OCl 986	Harvard 13		17 03 57
OCl 987	IC 4651		17 24.7
OCl 988	NGC 6192		16 40 20.8
OCl 989	NGC 6216		16 49 23.6
OCl 990	NGC 6124		16 25 17.2
OCl 991	NGC 6250		16 57 55
OCl 992	Lynga 14		16 55 05
OCl 993	NGC 6352	g	17 25 29.2
OCl 994	NGC 6249		16 57 41.7
OCl 995	Lynga 13		16 48 54
OCl 996	NGC 6259		17 00.7
OCl 997	NGC 6231		16 54 09.8
OCl 998	Collinder 316		16 55.5
OCl 998.0	Collinder 316		16 55.5
OCl 999	Trumpler 24		16 57.0
OCl 999.0	Trumpler 24		16 57.0
OCl 1000	NGC 6322		17 18.5
OCl 1001	NGC 6242		16 55 30.6
OCl 1002	NGC 6268		17 02 04.1
OCl 1003	NGC 6281		17 04 47.2
OCl 1004	NGC 6318		17 16 13.4
OCl 1005	Ruprecht 124		17 27 55.9
OCl 1006	Ruprecht 125		17 29.7
OCl 1006.0	Ruprecht 125		17 29.7
OCl 1007	Trumpler 25		17 24 30.3
OCl 1008	Ruprecht 123		17 23.4
OCl 1009	Trumpler 29		17 41 36.4
OCl 1009.0	Trumpler 29		17 41 36.4
OCl 1010	Collinder 332		17 30.8
OCl 1010	Harvard 16		17 31 03
OCl 1011	Collinder 302		16 26.0
OCl 1011.0	Collinder 302		16 26.0
OCl 1012	Harvard 16		17 31 03
OCl 1013	Collinder 338		17 38.2
OCl 1013.0	Collinder 338		17 38.2
OCl 1015	Ruprecht 127		17 37 50.4
OCl 1016	Pismis 24		17 24 43.4
OCl 1017	Collinder 333		17 31 31.3
OCl 1018	NGC 6396		17 37 38
OCl 1019	Ruprecht 126		17 35 04.4
OCl 1020	Ruprecht 128		17 44 19.3
OCl 1021	Trumpler 27		17 36 12.7
OCl 1021.1	Antalova 2		17 29.7
OCl 1022	NGC 6383		17 34 42.2
OCl 1023	NGC 6444		17 49.6
OCl 1024	NGC 6404		17 39.6
OCl 1025	Trumpler 30		17 56.4
OCl 1026	NGC 6383		17 34 42.2
OCl 1026.0	NGC 6383		17 34 42.2
OCl 1027	Collinder 345		17 44 35
OCl 1028	NGC 6475		17 53 46
OCl 1028.0	NGC 6475		17 53 46
OCl 1029	Trumpler 28		17 36 59
OCl 1030	NGC 6400		17 40 10
OCl 1030	NGC 6405		17 40 17
OCl 1030.0	NGC 6405		17 40 17
OCl 1031	NGC 6416		17 44.3
OCl 1031.0	NGC 6416		17 44.3

Table D.3: Cluster Cross-Reference

Name	Look Under	GX	2000.0 RA
OCl 1032	Trumpler 26		17 28 29.9
OCl 1033	NGC 6425		17 46 53
OCl 1034	Ruprecht 130		17 47 32
OCl 1035	NGC 6451		17 50 41
OCl 1036	NGC 6355	g	17 23 58.6
OCl 1037	Ruprecht 129		17 47 08.2
OCl 1038	Basel 5		17 52 28.4
OCl 1039	Collinder 347		17 46 18.9
OGLE-CL SMC0001	[H86] 35	S	00 36 38.4
OGLE-CL SMC0002	HW 11	S	00 37 33.1
OGLE-CL SMC0003	Lindsay 19	S	00 37 42.3
OGLE-CL SMC0004	Bruck 10	S	00 37 44.1
OGLE-CL SMC0005		S	00 39 21.7
OGLE-CL SMC0006		S	00 39 33.1
OGLE-CL SMC0007		S	00 40 30.5
OGLE-CL SMC0008	NGC 220	S	00 40 30.6
OGLE-CL SMC0009	NGC 222	S	00 40 44.1
OGLE-CL SMC0010	[H86] 62	S	00 40 47.6
OGLE-CL SMC0011	NGC 231	S	00 41 06.2
OGLE-CL SMC0012	Kron 21	S	00 41 23.8
OGLE-CL SMC0013	HW 16	S	00 42 22.4
OGLE-CL SMC0014		S	00 42 27.9
OGLE-CL SMC0015		S	00 42 54.2
OGLE-CL SMC0016	[BS95] 16	S	00 42 58.5
OGLE-CL SMC0017		S	00 43 32.8
OGLE-CL SMC0017	NGC 242	S	00 43 33.9
OGLE-CL SMC0018	[HB90] 1	S	00 43 37.6
OGLE-CL SMC0019	Bruck 31	S	00 43 37.6
OGLE-CL SMC0020	[BS95] 20	S	00 43 37.9
OGLE-CL SMC0021	[H86] 70	S	00 43 44.4
OGLE-CL SMC0022		S	00 43 58.0
OGLE-CL SMC0023	Bruck 33	S	00 44 12.6
OGLE-CL SMC0024		S	00 45 01.2
OGLE-CL SMC0025	[H86] 74	S	00 45 13.9
OGLE-CL SMC0026	NGC 248	S	00 45 24.1
OGLE-CL SMC0027	Bruck 39	S	00 45 25.7
OGLE-CL SMC0028		S	00 45 27.9
OGLE-CL SMC0029	Lindsay [1961] 68	S	00 45 29.8
OGLE-CL SMC0030		S	00 45 32.9
OGLE-CL SMC0031	Bruck 36	S	00 45 43.1
OGLE-CL SMC0032	NGC 256	S	00 45 54.4
OGLE-CL SMC0033	[H86] 78	S	00 46 12.3
OGLE-CL SMC0034	NGC 261	S	00 46 33.0
OGLE-CL SMC0035	[H86] 83	S	00 46 33.7
OGLE-CL SMC0036	Lindsay 31	S	00 46 35.0
OGLE-CL SMC0037		S	00 46 41.1
OGLE-CL SMC0038	[H86] 89	S	00 47 03.7
OGLE-CL SMC0039	NGC 265	S	00 47 11.6
OGLE-CL SMC0040	[H86] 86	S	00 47 01.2
OGLE-CL SMC0041	Lindsay 33	S	00 47 24.9
OGLE-CL SMC0042	[BS95] 35	S	00 47 49.7
OGLE-CL SMC0043	[H86] 97	S	00 47 52.4
OGLE-CL SMC0044	[H86] 98	S	00 47 54.3
OGLE-CL SMC0045	Kron 25	S	00 48 00.7
OGLE-CL SMC0046	NGC 269	S	00 48 21.3
OGLE-CL SMC0047		S	00 48 28.2
OGLE-CL SMC0048	Bruck 47	S	00 48 33.3
OGLE-CL SMC0049	Bruck 48	S	00 48 37.5
OGLE-CL SMC0050		S	00 48 59.0
OGLE-CL SMC0051	[H86] 103	S	00 49 04.8

Table D.3: Cluster Cross-Reference

Name	Look Under	GX	2000.0 RA
OGLE-CL SMC0052	[H86] 104	S	00 49 12.2
OGLE-CL SMC0053		S	00 49 17.5
OGLE-CL SMC0054	Lindsay 39	S	00 49 17.6
OGLE-CL SMC0055		S	00 49 21.3
OGLE-CL SMC0056		S	00 49 36.3
OGLE-CL SMC0057	Bruck 52	S	00 49 39.8
OGLE-CL SMC0058	[H86] 109	S	00 49 45.5
OGLE-CL SMC0059	[BS95] 45	S	00 50 16.1
OGLE-CL SMC0060	Bruck 55	S	00 50 22.0
OGLE-CL SMC0061	[H86] 107	S	00 50 00.3
OGLE-CL SMC0062	Bruck 54	S	00 50 28.1
OGLE-CL SMC0063	[H86] 115	S	00 50 36.9
OGLE-CL SMC0064	[H86] 116	S	00 50 39.6
OGLE-CL SMC0065		S	00 50 54.6
OGLE-CL SMC0066	Bruck 56	S	00 50 55.4
OGLE-CL SMC0067	Lindsay 41	S	00 50 55.6
OGLE-CL SMC0068	[BS95] 40	S	00 50 56.3
OGLE-CL SMC0069	NGC 290	S	00 51 14.2
OGLE-CL SMC0070	[BS95] 251	S	00 51 26.2
OGLE-CL SMC0071		S	00 51 31.8
OGLE-CL SMC0072		S	00 51 41.7
OGLE-CL SMC0073	Lindsay [1961] 184	S	00 51 44.1
OGLE-CL SMC0074	Kron 29	S	00 51 52.9
OGLE-CL SMC0075	[H86] 126	S	00 51 54.3
OGLE-CL SMC0076	[H86] 129	S	00 52 12.5
OGLE-CL SMC0077	[BS95] 56	S	00 52 13.4
OGLE-CL SMC0078	[H86] 130	S	00 52 16.6
OGLE-CL SMC0079	[H86] 125	S	00 52 16.8
OGLE-CL SMC0080	[H86] 132	S	00 52 31.5
OGLE-CL SMC0081	[H86] 133	S	00 52 33.7
OGLE-CL SMC0082	[BS95] 60	S	00 52 42.1
OGLE-CL SMC0083	Bruck 65	S	00 52 44.3
OGLE-CL SMC0084	[BS95] 63	S	00 52 46.7
OGLE-CL SMC0085	Bruck 66	S	00 52 47.7
OGLE-CL SMC0086	[H86] 135	S	00 52 48.2
OGLE-CL SMC0087	Bruck 67	S	00 52 49.0
OGLE-CL SMC0088	Kron 31	S	00 53 00.6
OGLE-CL SMC0089	Bruck 69	S	00 53 05.3
OGLE-CL SMC0090	NGC 294	S	00 53 05.6
OGLE-CL SMC0091	[H86] 138	S	00 53 09.6
OGLE-CL SMC0092	Bruck 71	S	00 53 17.9
OGLE-CL SMC0093	[H86] 143	S	00 53 31.3
OGLE-CL SMC0094	[H86] 140	S	00 53 40.1
OGLE-CL SMC0095	[BS95] 68	S	00 53 42.1
OGLE-CL SMC0096	Lindsay [1961] 244	S	00 53 42.3
OGLE-CL SMC0097	[BS95] 72	S	00 54 11.0
OGLE-CL SMC0098	Bruck 80	S	00 54 46.8
OGLE-CL SMC0099	Bruck 79	S	00 54 48.3
OGLE-CL SMC0100	[H86] 158	S	00 55 08.6
OGLE-CL SMC0101	[H86] 155	S	00 55 11.7
OGLE-CL SMC0102	[H86] 159	S	00 55 12.1
OGLE-CL SMC0103	Bruck 83	S	00 55 29.7
OGLE-CL SMC0104	Kron 34	S	00 55 33.0
OGLE-CL SMC0105	[H86] 165	S	00 55 43.0
OGLE-CL SMC0106		S	00 56 08.9
OGLE-CL SMC0107	NGC 330	S	00 56 18.7
OGLE-CL SMC0108	[H86] 172	S	00 56 34.5
OGLE-CL SMC0109	Lindsay 56	S	00 57 29.8
OGLE-CL SMC0110	[H86] 178	S	00 57 46.2
OGLE-CL SMC0111	[BS95] 88	S	00 57 50.3

Table D.3: Cluster Cross-Reference

Name	Look Under	GX	2000.0 RA
OGLE-CL SMC0112	[H86] 179	S	00 57 57.2
OGLE-CL SMC0113	Lindsay [1961] 331	S	00 58 16.3
OGLE-CL SMC0114	Lindsay [1961] 335	S	00 58 25.8
OGLE-CL SMC0115	[H86] 183	S	00 58 33.7
OGLE-CL SMC0116		S	00 59 04.6
OGLE-CL SMC0117	Bruck 96	S	00 59 13.9
OGLE-CL SMC0118	IC 1611	S	00 59 48.1
OGLE-CL SMC0119	[H86] 186	S	00 59 56.9
OGLE-CL SMC0120	IC 1612	S	01 00 01.4
OGLE-CL SMC0121	[H86] 188	S	01 00 13.1
OGLE-CL SMC0122	Bruck 99	S	01 00 26.8
OGLE-CL SMC0123	[H86] 189	S	01 00 33.1
OGLE-CL SMC0124	Kron 42	S	01 00 34.4
OGLE-CL SMC0125		S	01 00 46.8
OGLE-CL SMC0126	Lindsay 65	S	01 01 02.0
OGLE-CL SMC0127	[H86] 193	S	01 01 17.8
OGLE-CL SMC0128	Bruck 105	S	01 01 37.2
OGLE-CL SMC0129	Lindsay 66	S	01 01 45.1
OGLE-CL SMC0130	Bruck 108	S	01 01 52.3
OGLE-CL SMC0131		S	01 02 03.3
OGLE-CL SMC0132		S	01 02 13.2
OGLE-CL SMC0133		S	01 02 30.9
OGLE-CL SMC0134	Kron 47	S	01 03 11.5
OGLE-CL SMC0135		S	01 03 16.7
OGLE-CL SMC0136		S	01 03 22.1
OGLE-CL SMC0137		S	01 03 22.7
OGLE-CL SMC0138	Lindsay [1961] 420	S	01 03 53.0
OGLE-CL SMC0139	NGC 376	S	01 03 53.5
OGLE-CL SMC0140		S	01 04 14.1
OGLE-CL SMC0141	Bruck 121	S	01 04 30.2
OGLE-CL SMC0142	Kron 50	S	01 04 36.2
OGLE-CL SMC0143	[BS95] 125	S	01 04 39.6
OGLE-CL SMC0144		S	01 04 05.3
OGLE-CL SMC0145	Lindsay [1961] 439	S	01 05 08.1
OGLE-CL SMC0146		S	01 05 13.4
OGLE-CL SMC0147		S	01 05 08.0
OGLE-CL SMC0148		S	01 05 09.7
OGLE-CL SMC0149	IC 1624	S	01 05 21.5
OGLE-CL SMC0150	[BS95] 131	S	01 05 59.6
OGLE-CL SMC0151		S	01 06 12.6
OGLE-CL SMC0152		S	01 06 21.1
OGLE-CL SMC0153	Kron 54	S	01 06 47.8
OGLE-CL SMC0154	Bruck 129	S	01 07 02.3
OGLE-CL SMC0155	Kron 56	S	01 07 27.9
OGLE-CL SMC0156	Lindsay 80	S	01 07 28.5
OGLE-CL SMC0157	Kron 55	S	01 07 32.4
OGLE-CL SMC0158	NGC 416	S	01 07 59.0
OGLE-CL SMC0159	NGC 419	S	01 08 17.7
OGLE-CL SMC0160		S	01 08 37.5
OGLE-CL SMC0161	Kron 61	S	01 09 03.5
OGLE-CL SMC0162	Bruck 14	S	00 38 37.1
OGLE-CL SMC0163	HW 12	S	00 38 51.3
OGLE-CL SMC0164		S	00 38 55.6
OGLE-CL SMC0165		S	00 39 11.6
OGLE-CL SMC0166		S	00 41 56
OGLE-CL SMC0167	[H86] 55	S	00 39 25.6
OGLE-CL SMC0168		S	00 39 30.6
OGLE-CL SMC0169	Bruck 26	S	00 40 44.8
OGLE-CL SMC0170		S	00 40 55.5
OGLE-CL SMC0171	Bruck 21	S	00 41 15.3

Table D.3: Cluster Cross-Reference

Name	Look Under	GX	2000.0 RA
OGLE-CL SMC0172		S	00 41 48.4
OGLE-CL SMC0173		S	00 42 11.6
OGLE-CL SMC0174	[BS95] 17	S	00 43 14.3
OGLE-CL SMC0175	Bruck 31	S	00 43 37.6
OGLE-CL SMC0176	Bruck 34	S	00 44 51.6
OGLE-CL SMC0177	[BS95] 27	S	00 44 55.1
OGLE-CL SMC0178		S	00 45 10.9
OGLE-CL SMC0179		S	00 45 20.9
OGLE-CL SMC0180		S	00 45 23.1
OGLE-CL SMC0181		S	00 45 27.5
OGLE-CL SMC0182	[H86] 76	S	00 46 01.7
OGLE-CL SMC0183		S	00 46 10.4
OGLE-CL SMC0184	[H86] 80	S	00 46 11.2
OGLE-CL SMC0185	[H86] 84	S	00 46 34.1
OGLE-CL SMC0186	[H86] 85	S	00 46 56.3
OGLE-CL SMC0187		S	00 47 05.9
OGLE-CL SMC0188	[H86] 93	S	00 47 24.4
OGLE-CL SMC0189		S	00 48 09.1
OGLE-CL SMC0190	[H86] 99	S	00 48 13.2
OGLE-CL SMC0191	[H86] 100	S	00 48 20.2
OGLE-CL SMC0192		S	00 48 26.1
OGLE-CL SMC0193		S	00 48 36.6
OGLE-CL SMC0194	[BS95] 41	S	00 49 05.6
OGLE-CL SMC0195	[BS95] 42	S	00 49 16.5
OGLE-CL SMC0196		S	00 49 26.8
OGLE-CL SMC0197	Bruck 53	S	00 50 03.8
OGLE-CL SMC0198	[H86] 112	S	00 50 07.5
OGLE-CL SMC0199		S	00 50 15.1
OGLE-CL SMC0200	[BS95] 46	S	00 50 39.0
OGLE-CL SMC0201	[BS95] 48	S	00 50 42.5
OGLE-CL SMC0202		S	00 50 58.7
OGLE-CL SMC0203		S	00 51 10.3
OGLE-CL SMC0204	[H86] 121	S	00 51 21.4
OGLE-CL SMC0205	[H86] 124	S	00 51 31.3
OGLE-CL SMC0206	[H86] 123	S	00 51 44.4
OGLE-CL SMC0207	[H86] 127	S	00 51 48.8
OGLE-CL SMC0208		S	00 52 02.8
OGLE-CL SMC0209		S	00 52 15.3
OGLE-CL SMC0210	Bruck 64	S	00 52 30.3
OGLE-CL SMC0211	[BS95] 57	S	00 52 32.2
OGLE-CL SMC0212		S	00 52 44.5
OGLE-CL SMC0213	[H86] 134	S	00 52 48.3
OGLE-CL SMC0214		S	00 53 08.6
OGLE-CL SMC0215		S	00 53 16.9
OGLE-CL SMC0216	[H86] 147	S	00 53 50.2
OGLE-CL SMC0217	[BS95] 69	S	00 53 56.5
OGLE-CL SMC0218	[H86] 152	S	00 54 22.8
OGLE-CL SMC0219	Bruck 76	S	00 54 51.5
OGLE-CL SMC0220		S	00 55 14.1
OGLE-CL SMC0221		S	00 55 44.8
OGLE-CL SMC0222	Bruck 86	S	00 56 15.9
OGLE-CL SMC0223	[BS95] 81	S	00 56 25.6
OGLE-CL SMC0224		S	00 56 45.9
OGLE-CL SMC0225	[H86] 174	S	00 57 17.8
OGLE-CL SMC0226	[H86] 177	S	00 57 49.8
OGLE-CL SMC0227	[H86] 175	S	00 57 50.3
OGLE-CL SMC0228	[H86] 181	S	00 58 19.4
OGLE-CL SMC0229	[BS95] 272	S	00 58 38.1
OGLE-CL SMC0230		S	01 00 33.2
OGLE-CL SMC0231	[H86] 191	S	01 00 58.2

Table D.3: Cluster Cross-Reference

Name	Look Under	GX	2000.0 RA
OGLE-CL SMC0232		S	01 01 13.6
OGLE-CL SMC0233		S	01 02 40.0
OGLE-CL SMC0234		S	01 02 53.2
OGLE-CL SMC0235		S	01 03 59.0
OGLE-CL SMC0236	OGLE-CL SMC0144	S	01 04 05.3
OGLE-CL SMC0237		S	01 04 22.5
OGLE-CL SMC0238		S	01 07 52.3
OHSC 1		L	04 52 42.4
OHSC 2		L	04 53 10.1
OHSC 3		L	04 56 36.7
OHSC 4		L	04 59 13.7
OHSC 5		L	05 01 53.7
OHSC 6		L	05 04 39.0
OHSC 7		L	05 04 34.1
OHSC 8		L	05 15 18.7
OHSC 9		L	05 16 21.9
OHSC 10		L	05 20 38.2
OHSC 11		L	05 19 34.8
OHSC 12		L	05 21 37.1
OHSC 13		L	05 23 25.7
OHSC 14		L	05 23 29.3
OHSC 15		L	05 23 59.3
OHSC 16		L	05 24 20.8
OHSC 17		L	05 29 04.3
OHSC 18		L	05 29 30.3
OHSC 19		L	05 28 49.7
OHSC 20		L	05 31 20.1
OHSC 21		L	05 32 50.9
OHSC 22		L	05 34 50.8
OHSC 23		L	05 39 11.2
OHSC 24		L	05 40 38.7
OHSC 25		L	05 44 05.1
OHSC 26		L	05 47 23.6
OHSC 27		L	05 52 29.7
OHSC 28		L	05 55 35.4
OHSC 29		L	06 01 12.3
OHSC 30		L	06 02 31.5
OHSC 31		L	06 11 16.8
OHSC 32		L	06 14 21.9
OHSC 33		L	06 15 17.1
OHSC 34		L	06 24 28.7
OHSC 35		L	06 25 42.0
OHSC 36		L	06 29 41.9
OHSC 37		L	07 07 39.9
Om-2 Cygni group			20 15 08
Omega Centauri	NGC 5139	g	13 26 45.9
Omicron Velorum	IC 2391		08 40.3
Orion Belt Region	Collinder 70		05 35.6
Orion cluster	Collinder 69		05 35.0
P Cygni cluster			20 17 43.5
Palomar 1		g	03 33 20.8
Palomar 2		g	04 46 05.9
Palomar 3		g	10 05 31.4
Palomar 4		g	11 29 16.8
Palomar 5		g	15 16 05.3
Palomar 6		g	17 43 42.2
Palomar 6	JaFu 1		17 43 57.4
Palomar 7	IC 1276	g	18 10 44.2
Palomar 8		g	18 41 29.9
Palomar 9	NGC 6717	g	18 55 06.2

Table D.3: Cluster Cross-Reference

Name	Look Under	GX	2000.0 RA
Palomar 10		g	19 18 02.1
Palomar 11		g	19 45 14.4
Palomar 12		g	21 46 38.8
Palomar 13		g	23 06 44.4
Palomar 14		g	16 11 00.3
Palomar 15		g	16 59 50.9
[PAV78] 283	[V62] 211	A	00 41 02.1
[PAV78] 319	SKHB 83	A	00 41 08.8
[PAV78] 464	SKHB 137	A	00 42 09.5
[PAV78] 563	SKHB 253	A	00 43 56.0
Pazmino's cluster	Stock 23		03 16 10.8
Pease 1	NGC 7078	g	21 29 58.3
Peg gcl	Palomar 13	g	23 06 44.4
Per moving cluster	Melotte 20		03 24 19
[PFJ93] 8	Bol 78	A	00 42 12.4
[PFJ93] 23	Bol 96	A	00 42 26.2
[PFJ93] 51	Bol 128	A	00 42 47.8
[PFJ93] 62	Bol 138	A	00 42 55.7
[PFJ93] 67	Bol 144	A	00 42 59.9
PGC 9944	Dejc 1		02 37 28.3
PGC 15613	SL 6		04 36 09.5
PGC 15963	Palomar 2	g	04 46 05.9
PGC 17296	NGC 1947		05 26 47.5
PGC 20305	NGC 2314		07 10 32.4
PGC 29488	Leo I		10 08 27.5
PGC 34176	Leo II		11 13 29.3
PGC 42489	NGC 4604		12 40 45.1
PGC 59400	Palomar 15	g	16 59 50.9
PGC 62453	NGC 6684		18 48 57.5
PGC 65054	NGC 6941		20 36 23.5
Phoenix dwarf galaxy			01 51 06.3
Pismis	Haffner 16		07 50 21
Pismis 1	NGC 2568		08 18 19
Pismis 2			08 17 54
Pismis 3			08 31 21
Pismis 4			08 34.6
Pismis 5			08 37 39
Pismis 6	NGC 2645		08 39 04
Pismis 7			08 41 09
Pismis 8			08 41 35
Pismis 9	NGC 2659		08 42 34
Pismis 10			09 02.6
Pismis 11			09 15 53
Pismis 12			09 20 00
Pismis 13			09 22 06.5
Pismis 13	NGC 2866		09 22 06.5
Pismis 14			09 29.3
Pismis 15			09 34 45
Pismis 16			09 51 14
Pismis 17	NGC 3503		11 01 18
Pismis 18	IC 4291		13 36 55
Pismis 19			14 30 43
Pismis 20			15 15 23.1
Pismis 21			15 16 47.7
Pismis 22			16 14 07.9
Pismis 23			16 23 58
Pismis 24			17 24 43.4
Pismis 25	NGC 6380	g	17 34 28.0
Pismis 26	Tonantzintla 2	g	17 36 10.5
[PKL98] 1			01 13 50
[PKL98] 2			04 41 37
[PKL98] 4			05 07 22
[PKL98] 6			06 09 36
[PKL98] 8			06 15 26
[PKL98] 10	PMG 1		07 45.4
[PKL98] 11			09 09 30
[PKL98] 12			09 13 47
[PKL98] 15			13 43 28
[PKL98] 16			13 47 57
[PKL98] 17			13 51 44
Pleiades			03 47 29
PMG 1			07 45.4
PMG 2			07 45.4
PMH79 1			22 19 00
Poole J1855.0+1047			18 55 02.7
Poole J1855.8+1046			18 55 53
Poole J1857.0+1027			18 57 04
Poole J1857.0+1027	NGC 6724		18 56 45
Praesepe	NGC 2632		08 40 22
[PRT94] 1			11 11 58
[PTB93] 1			22 38.0
[PTB93] 2			22 24.9
[PTB93] 3			22 14.3
[PTB93] 4			23 17.7
[PTB93] 5			00 05.3
[PTB93] 6			23 52.9
[PTB93] 7			00 15.2
[PTB93] 8			00 04.2
[PTB93] 9			23 50.0
[PTB93] 10			01 58.7
PWM78 1			01 08 04.8
PWM78 2		g	17 58 39.4
PWM78 3			23 08 10.8
PWM78 4			23 50 53.0
Pyxis		g	09 07 57.8
Quintuple cluster	RAFGL 2004		17 46 13.9
Raab 1	NGC 188		00 47 30
Raab 2	NGC 436		01 15 58
Raab 3	NGC 457		01 19 33
Raab 4	NGC 581		01 33 22
Raab 5	NGC 654		01 44 00
Raab 6	NGC 659		01 44 24
Raab 7	NGC 663		01 46 17
Raab 8	NGC 752		01 57 35
Raab 9	NGC 869		02 19 04
Raab 10	NGC 884		02 22 05
Raab 11	IC 1805		02 32 42
Raab 12	NGC 1027		02 42 36
Raab 13	NGC 1039		02 42 08
Raab 14	NGC 1245		03 14 42
Raab 15	NGC 1342		03 31 40
Raab 16	NGC 1528		04 15 19
Raab 17	IC 361		04 18 51
Raab 18	NGC 1647		04 45 42.2
Raab 19	NGC 1664		04 51 06
Raab 20	NGC 1746		05 03.6
Raab 21	NGC 1807		05 10 46
Raab 22	NGC 1817		05 12 27
Raab 23	NGC 1857		05 20 06
Raab 24	NGC 1893		05 22 46
Raab 25	NGC 1907		05 28 05
Raab 26	NGC 1912		05 28 43
Raab 27	NGC 1960		05 36 18
Raab 28	NGC 2099		05 52 19
Raab 29	NGC 2126		06 02 31
Raab 30	NGC 2158		06 07 26
Raab 31	NGC 2168		06 09.0
Raab 32	NGC 2192		06 15 18
Raab 33	NGC 2194		06 13 46
Raab 34	NGC 2204		06 15 33
Raab 35	NGC 2215		06 20 50
Raab 36	NGC 2243		06 29 35
Raab 37	NGC 2259		06 38 33.3
Raab 38	NGC 2266		06 43 20
Raab 39	NGC 2281		06 48 18
Raab 40	NGC 2287		06 46.1
Raab 41	NGC 2301		06 51 46
Raab 42	NGC 2304		06 55 12
Raab 43	NGC 2309		06 56 04
Raab 44	NGC 2314		07 10 32.4
Raab 45	NGC 2323		07 02 47.8
Raab 46	NGC 2324		07 04 08
Raab 47	NGC 2335		07 06 50
Raab 48	NGC 2345		07 08 19
Raab 49	NGC 2353		07 14 31
Raab 50	NGC 2355		07 17 00
Raab 51	NGC 2360		07 17 44
Raab 52	NGC 2362		07 18 42
Raab 53	Melotte 66		07 26 19
Raab 54	NGC 2421		07 36 12
Raab 55	NGC 2422		07 36 36
Raab 56	NGC 2420		07 38 24
Raab 57	NGC 2423		07 37 07
Raab 58	Melotte 71		07 37 30
Raab 59	Melotte 72		07 38 29
Raab 60	NGC 2432		07 40 54
Raab 61	NGC 2439		07 40 46
Raab 62	NGC 2437		07 41 47
Raab 63	NGC 2447		07 44 30
Raab 64	NGC 2455		07 48 59
Raab 65	NGC 2477		07 52 10
Raab 66	NGC 2489		07 56 16
Raab 67	NGC 2506		08 00 02
Raab 68	NGC 2509		08 00 48
Raab 69	NGC 2516		07 58.0
Raab 70	NGC 2539		08 10 38
Raab 71	NGC 2547		08 10 11
Raab 72	NGC 2548		08 13 44
Raab 73	NGC 2567		08 18 30
Raab 74	NGC 2627		08 37 15
Raab 75	NGC 2632		08 40 22
Raab 76	NGC 2635		08 38 27
Raab 77	NGC 2658		08 43 28
Raab 78	NGC 2659		08 42 34
Raab 79	IC 2395		08 42 31
Raab 80	NGC 2670		08 45 30
Raab 81	NGC 2682		08 51 24
Raab 82	NGC 2818		09 16 10
Raab 83	IC 2488		09 27 27
Raab 84	NGC 3114		10 02.7

Table D.3: Cluster Cross-Reference

Name	Look Under	GX	2000.0 RA
Raab 85	NGC 3293		10 35 49
Raab 86	Melotte 101		10 42 00
Raab 87	IC 2602		10 42 57
Raab 88	NGC 3532		11 05.5
Raab 89	IC 2714		11 17 18
Raab 90	Melotte 105		11 19 41
Raab 91	NGC 3680		11 25 38
Raab 92	NGC 3766		11 36 15
Raab 93	NGC 3960		11 50 34
Raab 94	NGC 4103		12 06 40
Raab 95	NGC 4349		12 24 07
Raab 96	NGC 4755		12 53 38
Raab 97	NGC 4852		13 00 05
Raab 98	NGC 5281		13 46 36.7
Raab 99	NGC 5316		13 54.0
Raab 100	NGC 5460		14 07.6
Raab 101	NGC 5617		14 29.7
Raab 102	NGC 5662		14 35 30.8
Raab 103	NGC 5715		14 43 39.0
Raab 104	NGC 5822		15 04 02.3
Raab 105	NGC 5823		15 05 26
Raab 106	NGC 5999		15 52 14
Raab 107	NGC 6005		15 55 47.4
Raab 108	NGC 6025		16 03 18
Raab 109	NGC 6067		16 13 09
Raab 110	NGC 6087		16 18 51.8
Raab 111	NGC 6124		16 25 17.2
Raab 112	NGC 6134		16 27 43.6
Raab 113	NGC 6192		16 40 20.8
Raab 114	NGC 6216		16 49 23.6
Raab 115	NGC 6242		16 55 30.6
Raab 116	NGC 6253		16 59 06.1
Raab 117	NGC 6259		17 00.7
Raab 118	NGC 6281		17 04 47.2
Raab 119	NGC 6318		17 16 13.4
Raab 120	IC 4651		17 24.7
Raab 121	NGC 6400		17 40 10
Raab 122	NGC 6405		17 40 17
Raab 123	NGC 6451		17 50 41
Raab 124	NGC 6469		17 52 56.5
Raab 125	NGC 6475		17 53 46
Raab 126	NGC 6494		17 56 56
Raab 127	NGC 6520		18 03 25
Raab 128	NGC 6531		18 04 13
Raab 129	NGC 6603		18 18 28
Raab 130	NGC 6633		18 27 15
Raab 131	IC 4725		18 31 45
Raab 132	NGC 6645		18 32 38
Raab 133	NGC 6649		18 33 28.3
Raab 135	IC 4756		18 38.9
Raab 136	NGC 6694		18 45 15
Raab 137	NGC 6709		18 51.5
Raab 138	NGC 6811		19 37 09.6
Raab 139	NGC 6819		19 41.3
Raab 140	NGC 6823		19 43 10
Raab 141	NGC 6830		19 51 00
Raab 142	NGC 6834		19 52 13
Raab 143	NGC 6866		20 03 55
Raab 144	NGC 6939		20 31 30
Raab 145	NGC 6940		20 34 32.3

Table D.3: Cluster Cross-Reference

Name	Look Under	GX	2000.0 RA
Raab 146	NGC 7209		22 05 08
Raab 147	IC 1434		22 10.5
Raab 148	NGC 7243		22 15 09
Raab 149	NGC 7245		22 15 16
Raab 150	NGC 7654		23 24 51
Raab 151	NGC 7762		23 49.9
Raab 152	NGC 7789		23 57 28.6
RAFGL 333	IC 1805		02 32 42
RAFGL 2004			17 46 13.9
RAFGL 5144	NGC 1931		05 31 26
RC2 A1005+12	Leo I		10 08 27.5
RC2 A1110+22	Leo II		11 13 29.3
RC2 A2143–21	Palomar 12	g	21 46 38.8
RCW 51	NGC 3293		10 35 49
Reiland 1			23 04 45.3
Reticulum		L	04 36 11.3
Roslund 1			19 45 06
Roslund 2			19 45 24.4
Roslund 3			19 58 41.1
Roslund 4			20 04 52
Roslund 5			20 10.0
Roslund 6			20 28 49
Roslund 7			20 52 08.5
Ruprecht 1			06 36.4
Ruprecht 2			06 41 01
Ruprecht 3			06 42 06
Ruprecht 4			06 48 57
Ruprecht 5			06 55 24
Ruprecht 6			06 56 05
Ruprecht 7			06 57 50
Ruprecht 8			07 01 46
Ruprecht 9			07 01.9
Ruprecht 10			07 06 27.6
Ruprecht 11			07 07 23
Ruprecht 12			07 07 10
Ruprecht 13			07 08.0
Ruprecht 14			07 14 55
Ruprecht 15			07 19 34
Ruprecht 16			07 23 09
Ruprecht 17			07 23 35
Ruprecht 18			07 24 39
Ruprecht 19			07 25.6
Ruprecht 20			07 26 41
Ruprecht 21			07 27.1
Ruprecht 22			07 29 17
Ruprecht 23			07 30 40
Ruprecht 24			07 31 51
Ruprecht 25			07 36 47
Ruprecht 26			07 37 13
Ruprecht 27			07 37.6
Ruprecht 28			07 39 36
Ruprecht 29			07 41.1
Ruprecht 30			07 42 22
Ruprecht 31			07 43 00
Ruprecht 32			07 45 06
Ruprecht 33			07 45.8
Ruprecht 34			07 45 54
Ruprecht 35			07 46 14
Ruprecht 36			07 48 24
Ruprecht 37			07 49 47

Table D.3: Cluster Cross-Reference

Name	Look Under	GX	2000.0 RA
Ruprecht 38			07 50 31
Ruprecht 39			07 52 20
Ruprecht 40			07 33 27
Ruprecht 41			07 53 48
Ruprecht 42			07 57 37
Ruprecht 43			07 58.8
Ruprecht 44			07 58 50
Ruprecht 45			07 59.6
Ruprecht 46			08 02 10
Ruprecht 47			08 02 18
Ruprecht 48			08 02 42
Ruprecht 49			08 03 17
Ruprecht 50			08 03.4
Ruprecht 51			08 03.6
Ruprecht 52			08 05.0
Ruprecht 53			08 10 50
Ruprecht 54			08 11 23
Ruprecht 55			08 12 19
Ruprecht 56			08 12.6
Ruprecht 57			08 14.8
Ruprecht 58			08 14 49
Ruprecht 59			08 19 22.0
Ruprecht 60			08 24 26
Ruprecht 61			08 25 15
Ruprecht 62			08 32 30
Ruprecht 63			08 32 40
Ruprecht 64			08 37.4
Ruprecht 65			08 39 22
Ruprecht 66			08 40 32
Ruprecht 67			08 41 45
Ruprecht 68			08 44.5
Ruprecht 69			08 44 49.1
Ruprecht 70			08 49.1
Ruprecht 71			08 49.5
Ruprecht 72			08 52 05
Ruprecht 73			09 01 12
Ruprecht 74			09 21.0
Ruprecht 75			09 21 54
Ruprecht 76			09 24 18
Ruprecht 77			09 27 02
Ruprecht 78			09 29 07.9
Ruprecht 79			09 41 03
Ruprecht 80	NGC 2982		09 42 01
Ruprecht 81			09 45 13
Ruprecht 82			09 45 49
Ruprecht 83			09 49 15
Ruprecht 84			09 49 04
Ruprecht 85			10 01 26
Ruprecht 86			10 01 27.7
Ruprecht 87			10 15 30
Ruprecht 88			10 18 48
Ruprecht 89			10 28.5
Ruprecht 90			10 31.0
Ruprecht 91			10 47 38.4
Ruprecht 92			10 53 49
Ruprecht 93	NGC 3519		11 04 03
Ruprecht 94			11 30.4
Ruprecht 95			11 43 40
Ruprecht 96			11 50 53
Ruprecht 97			11 57 23

Table D.3: Cluster Cross-Reference

Name	Look Under	GX	2000.0 RA
Ruprecht 98			11 58.8
Ruprecht 99			12 03 20
Ruprecht 100			12 05.7
Ruprecht 101			12 09 40
Ruprecht 102	NGC 4184		12 13.6
Ruprecht 103			12 15.9
Ruprecht 104			12 24 51
Ruprecht 105			12 34.0
Ruprecht 106		g	12 38 40.2
Ruprecht 107			13 19 46
Ruprecht 108			13 32 12
Ruprecht 109	NGC 5381		14 00.6
Ruprecht 110			14 06.5
Ruprecht 111			14 35.8
Ruprecht 112			14 57.0
Ruprecht 113			15 57.2
Ruprecht 114			16 06 31
Ruprecht 115			16 12 51.1
Ruprecht 116			16 23 24.3
Ruprecht 117			16 23 30.7
Ruprecht 118	NGC 6115		16 24 26.8
Ruprecht 119			16 28 09.3
Ruprecht 120			16 35 12.2
Ruprecht 121			16 41 47.6
Ruprecht 122			16 55 08.3
Ruprecht 123			17 23.4
Ruprecht 124			17 27 55.9
Ruprecht 125			17 29.7
Ruprecht 126			17 35 04.4
Ruprecht 127			17 37 50.4
Ruprecht 128			17 44 19.3
Ruprecht 129			17 47 08.2
Ruprecht 130			17 47 32
Ruprecht 131			17 49 06.9
Ruprecht 132	NGC 6444		17 49.6
Ruprecht 133			17 52 34.1
Ruprecht 134			17 52.8
Ruprecht 135			17 58 03.3
Ruprecht 136			17 59 17.8
Ruprecht 137			17 59.9
Ruprecht 138			17 59.9
Ruprecht 139			18 01.2
Ruprecht 140			18 21 49.8
Ruprecht 141			18 31.3
Ruprecht 142			18 32 14
Ruprecht 143			18 32 43
Ruprecht 144			18 33 32.7
Ruprecht 145			18 50 19.4
Ruprecht 146			18 52 30
Ruprecht 147	NGC 6774		19 16.3
Ruprecht 148			04 46 35
Ruprecht 149			06 52.2
Ruprecht 150			07 05 55
Ruprecht 151			07 41.3
Ruprecht 152			07 54 29
Ruprecht 153			08 00 18
Ruprecht 154			08 01.7
Ruprecht 155			08 04.9
Ruprecht 156			08 19 28.8
Ruprecht 157			08 29 52

Table D.3: Cluster Cross-Reference

Name	Look Under	GX	2000.0 RA
Ruprecht 158			08 52 23
Ruprecht 159			09 20 08
Ruprecht 160			09 55.5
Ruprecht 161			10 08.8
Ruprecht 162			10 53.0
Ruprecht 163			11 04 47
Ruprecht 164			11 31.1
Ruprecht 165			12 28.6
Ruprecht 166	NGC 5120		13 25 39
Ruprecht 167			14 18.2
Ruprecht 168			17 52.8
Ruprecht 169			17 59.5
Ruprecht 170			18 25 10.7
Ruprecht 171			18 32 00.7
Ruprecht 172			20 11 34
Ruprecht 173			20 41 41.2
Ruprecht 173	Turner 11		20 43 24
Ruprecht 174			20 43 28.3
Ruprecht 175			20 45 24
Ruprecht 175	Turner 11		20 43 24
Ruprecht 176			16 14 45
S Nor cluster	NGC 6087		16 18 51.8
[S73] 1		A	00 32 41.3
[S73] 4	Bol 301	A	00 38 21.6
[S73] 5		A	00 38 55.2
[S73] 6		A	00 39 19.3
[S73] 7		A	00 39 37.7
[S73] 8		A	00 40 31.4
[S73] 9		A	00 41.4
[S73] 11		A	00 42.4
[S73] 12	SKHB 171	A	00 42 33.7
[S73] 14		A	00 44 14.8
[S73] 16	Bol 365	A	00 44 36.8
[S73] 17	Bol 237	A	00 45 09.5
[S73] 18		A	00 45 50.7
[S73] 19		A	00 45.9
[S73] 20		A	00 46 27.0
[S73] 21		A	00 46 32.4
[S73] 22	Bol 393	A	00 47 01.2
[S73] 23	Bol 401	A	00 48 08.5
[S73] 24		A	00 48 10.0
[S73] 25		A	00 51 58.6
Schuster	Schuster 1		10 04 39.0
Schuster 1			10 04 39.0
Schuster-West	Phoenix dwarf gal		01 51 06.3
Serpens Dwarf	Palomar 5	g	15 16 05.3
Sersic 40-3	Reticulum	L	04 36 11.3
Sersic cl	Reticulum	L	04 36 11.3
Sex C	Palomar 3	g	10 05 31.4
SGC 184402-6513.8	NGC 6684		18 48 57.5
SGR A*	Central cluster		17 45 40.0
Sh 2- 86	NGC 6823		19 43 10
Sh 2- 101	ADS 13292		20 02 23.6
Sh 2- 106	[HR91] 1		20 27 24
Sh 2- 140	PMH79 1		22 19 00
Sh 2- 184	IC 1590		00 52 49
Sh 2- 190	IC 1805		02 32 42
Sh 2- 199	IC 1848		02 51 11
Sh 2- 208	Waterloo 1		04 18 36.4
Sh 2- 237	NGC 1931		05 31 26

Table D.3: Cluster Cross-Reference

Name	Look Under	GX	2000.0 RA
Sh 2- 247	[CSS95] Cl 2		06 08 54
Sh 2- 247	[CSS95] Cl 3		06 09 50
Sh 2- 247	[CSS95] Cl 1a		06 09 17
Sh 2- 247	[CSS95] Cl 1b		06 09 06
Sh 2- 247	[CSS95] Cl 4a		06 08 41
Sh 2- 247	[CSS95] Cl 4b		06 08 25
Sh 2- 269	[EC95] 1		06 14 37.0
Sh 2- 311	NGC 2467		07 52 30
Shakhbazian 1			10 55 06.0
Sher 1			11 01 03
Shorlin 1			11 06 19
Shorlin 1	Loden 306		11 06 00.7
Shorlin 2			11 05 34
Shorlin 2	Loden 306		11 06 00.7
Sigma Ori			05 38 45
SKHB 1	[ME53] II	A	00 32 46.9
SKHB 2		A	00 33 33.9
SKHB 9	Bol 291	A	00 36 05.0
SKHB 10	Bol 292	A	00 36 16.7
SKHB 11	Bol 293	A	00 36 20.5
SKHB 12	Bol 294	A	00 36 33.0
SKHB 14	Bol 295	A	00 36 46.4
SKHB 18		A	00 37 18.5
SKHB 19	Bol 421	A	00 37 32.8
SKHB 20		A	00 37 58.1
SKHB 21	Bol 298	A	00 38 00.3
SKHB 22	Bol 301	A	00 38 21.6
SKHB 23	Bol 302	A	00 38 33.4
SKHB 24	Bol 429	A	00 38 38.6
SKHB 25	Bol 430	A	00 38 42.9
SKHB 26	Bol 303	A	00 38 50.5
SKHB 27	Bol 431	A	00 38 54.9
SKHB 28	Bol 304	A	00 38 56.8
SKHB 29	Bol 306	A	00 39 08.8
SKHB 30	Bol 307	A	00 39 18.6
SKHB 31	Bol 309	A	00 39 23.5
SKHB 32	Bol 310	A	00 39 25.8
SKHB 33	Bol 311	A	00 39 33.9
SKHB 34		A	00 39 40.1
SKHB 35	Bol 312	A	00 39 40.4
SKHB 36	Bol 313	A	00 39 44.5
SKHB 37	Bol 314	A	00 39 44.6
SKHB 38	Bol 315	A	00 39 48.6
SKHB 39	Bol 1	A	00 39 51.4
SKHB 40	Bol 316	A	00 39 53.8
SKHB 41	Bol 317	A	00 39 55.5
SKHB 42	Bol 318	A	00 40 01.0
SKHB 43	Bol 2	A	00 40 02.5
SKHB 44	Bol 319	A	00 40 03.2
SKHB 45	Bol 3	A	00 40 09.4
SKHB 46	Bol 321	A	00 40 15.3
SKHB 47		A	00 40 15.5
SKHB 48		A	00 40 16.9
SKHB 49	Bol 322	A	00 40 17.3
SKHB 50	Bol 4	A	00 40 18.4
SKHB 51	Bol 324	A	00 40 20.8
SKHB 52	Bol 5	A	00 40 20.6
SKHB 53	Bol 327	A	00 40 24.1
SKHB 54	Bol 328	A	00 40 24.9
SKHB 55		A	00 40 25.1

Table D.3: Cluster Cross-Reference

Name	Look Under	GX	2000.0 RA
SKHB 56	Bol 330	A	00 40 25.6
SKHB 57	Bol 331	A	00 40 26.4
SKHB 58	Bol 6	A	00 40 26.8
SKHB 59	Bol 7	A	00 40 27.6
SKHB 60	Bol 8	A	00 40 30.6
SKHB 61	Bol 9	A	00 40 31.2
SKHB 62	Bol 10	A	00 40 31.9
SKHB 63	Bol 11	A	00 40 32.6
SKHB 64	Bol 12	A	00 40 32.8
SKHB 65	Bol 13	A	00 40 38.8
SKHB 66	Bol 16	A	00 40 45.2
SKHB 67	Bol 336	A	00 40 47.7
SKHB 68	Bol 337	A	00 40 48.5
SKHB 69	Bol 452	A	00 40 48.3
SKHB 70	Bol 17	A	00 40 48.9
SKHB 71	Bol 18	A	00 40 49.6
SKHB 72	Bol 19	A	00 40 52.9
SKHB 73	Bol 20	A	00 40 55.6
SKHB 74	Bol 22	A	00 40 59.1
SKHB 75	Bol 21	A	00 40 59.1
SKHB 76	Bol 338	A	00 40 59.1
SKHB 77	Bol 339	A	00 41 00.6
SKHB 78	Bol 23	A	00 41 01.3
SKHB 80	Bol 455	A	00 41 05.7
SKHB 81	Bol 341	A	00 41 09.2
SKHB 82	Bol 24	A	00 41 12.1
SKHB 83		A	00 41 08.8
SKHB 84	Bol 25	A	00 41 12.7
SKHB 85	[V62] 15	A	00 41 12.8
SKHB 86	Bol 26	A	00 41 14.6
SKHB 87	Bol 27	A	00 41 14.6
SKHB 88	Bol 28	A	00 41 16.6
SKHB 89		A	00 41 17.4
SKHB 90	Bol 29	A	00 41 17.9
SKHB 91	Bol 30	A	00 41 19.0
SKHB 92	Bol 31	A	00 41 21.1
SKHB 93	Bol 32	A	00 41 21.7
SKHB 94	Bol 342	A	00 41 24.4
SKHB 95	Bol 33	A	00 41 26.4
SKHB 96	Bol 34	A	00 41 28.2
SKHB 97	Bol 457	A	00 41 29.2
SKHB 98	Bol 38	A	00 41 36.1
SKHB 99		A	00 41 36.3
SKHB 100		A	00 41 37.9
SKHB 101	Bol 39	A	00 41 38.1
SKHB 102	Bol 40	A	00 41 39.0
SKHB 103	Bol 41	A	00 41 41.1
SKHB 104	Bol 42	A	00 41 41.8
SKHB 105	Bol 343	A	00 41 42.2
SKHB 106	Bol 43	A	00 41 42.5
SKHB 107	Bol 44	A	00 41 42.9
SKHB 108	Bol 45	A	00 41 43.3
SKHB 109	Bol 46	A	00 41 45.0
SKHB 110	Bol 48	A	00 41 45.6
SKHB 111	Bol 47	A	00 41 45.7
SKHB 112	Bol 49	A	00 41 45.8
SKHB 113	Bol 50	A	00 41 46.4
SKHB 114	Bol 51	A	00 41 46.7
SKHB 115	Bol 54	A	00 41 47.9
SKHB 116	Bol 55	A	00 41 50.5

Table D.3: Cluster Cross-Reference

Name	Look Under	GX	2000.0 RA
SKHB 117	Bol 56	A	00 41 51.2
SKHB 118	Bol 57	A	00 41 53.0
SKHB 119	Bol 58	A	00 41 53.0
SKHB 120	Bol 59	A	00 41 54.3
SKHB 121	Bol 60	A	00 41 57.1
SKHB 122	Bol 61	A	00 42 00.2
SKHB 123	Bol 62	A	00 42 00.6
SKHB 124	Bol 63	A	00 42 00.8
SKHB 125	Bol 64	A	00 42 02.0
SKHB 126	Bol 65	A	00 42 02.1
SKHB 127	Bol 344	A	00 42 03.3
SKHB 128	Bol 66	A	00 42 03.1
SKHB 129	Bol 67	A	00 42 03.4
SKHB 130	Bol 68	A	00 42 03.3
SKHB 131	Bol 461	A	00 42 04.2
SKHB 132	Bol 69	A	00 42 05.7
SKHB 133	Bol 70	A	00 42 06.9
SKHB 134	Bol 73	A	00 42 07.4
SKHB 135	Bol 74	A	00 42 08.1
SKHB 136	Bol 75	A	00 42 09.0
SKHB 137		A	00 42 09.5
SKHB 138	Bol 76	A	00 42 10.2
SKHB 139	Bol 77	A	00 42 11.3
SKHB 140	Bol 78	A	00 42 12.4
SKHB 141	Bol 80	A	00 42 12.5
SKHB 142	Bol 81	A	00 42 13.6
SKHB 143	Bol 345	A	00 42 14.2
SKHB 144	Bol 82	A	00 42 15.8
SKHB 146	Bol 83	A	00 42 16.5
SKHB 147	Bol 85	A	00 42 18.4
SKHB 148	Bol 86	A	00 42 18.7
SKHB 149	Bol 346	A	00 42 20.2
SKHB 150	Bol 88	A	00 42 21.1
SKHB 151	Bol 91	A	00 42 22.0
SKHB 152	Bol 92	A	00 42 22.4
SKHB 153	Bol 348	A	00 42 23.0
SKHB 154	Bol 347	A	00 42 23.0
SKHB 155	Bol 93	A	00 42 23.2
SKHB 156	Bol 94	A	00 42 25.0
SKHB 157	Bol 95	A	00 42 25.9
SKHB 158	Bol 96	A	00 42 26.2
SKHB 159	Bol 97	A	00 42 27.5
SKHB 160	Bol 463	A	00 42 27.5
SKHB 161	Bol 99	A	00 42 27.6
SKHB 162	Bol 350	A	00 42 28.5
SKHB 163	Bol 100	A	00 42 29.1
SKHB 164	Bol 101	A	00 42 29.1
SKHB 165	Bol 103	A	00 42 29.8
SKHB 166	Bol 105	A	00 42 31.1
SKHB 167	Bol 108	A	00 42 31.3
SKHB 168	Bol 106	A	00 42 31.2
SKHB 169	Bol 107	A	00 42 31.3
SKHB 170	Bol 109	A	00 42 32.2
SKHB 171		A	00 42 33.7
SKHB 172	Bol 110	A	00 42 33.2
SKHB 173	Bol 111	A	00 42 33.4
SKHB 174	Bol 112	A	00 42 33.3
SKHB 175	Bol 114	A	00 42 34.4
SKHB 176	Bol 117	A	00 42 34.4
SKHB 177	Bol 115	A	00 42 34.5

Table D.3: Cluster Cross-Reference

Name	Look Under	GX	2000.0 RA
SKHB 178	Bol 116	A	00 42 34.7
SKHB 179	Bol 351	A	00 42 38.0
SKHB 180	Bol 352	A	00 42 38.3
SKHB 181	Bol 122	A	00 42 40.3
SKHB 182	Bol 123	A	00 42 40.9
SKHB 183	Bol 125	A	00 42 42.4
SKHB 184	Bol 126	A	00 42 43.8
SKHB 185	Bol 127	A	00 42 44.5
SKHB 186	Bol 354	A	00 42 47.6
SKHB 187	Bol 128	A	00 42 47.8
SKHB 188	Bol 130	A	00 42 48.9
SKHB 189	Bol 131	A	00 42 50.6
SKHB 190	Bol 134	A	00 42 51.7
SKHB 191	Bol 133	A	00 42 52.1
SKHB 192	Bol 135	A	00 42 52.1
SKHB 193	Bol 355	A	00 42 52.9
SKHB 194	Bol 136	A	00 42 53.7
SKHB 195	Bol 137	A	00 42 54.3
SKHB 196	Bol 140	A	00 42 58.8
SKHB 197	Bol 141	A	00 42 59.4
SKHB 198	Bol 143	A	00 42 59.7
SKHB 199	Bol 147	A	00 43 03.4
SKHB 200	Bol 148	A	00 43 03.9
SKHB 201	Bol 149	A	00 43 05.5
SKHB 202	Bol 467	A	00 43 06.5
SKHB 203	Bol 150	A	00 43 07.6
SKHB 204		A	00 43 08.1
SKHB 205	Bol 151	A	00 43 09.7
SKHB 206	Bol 356	A	00 43 10.3
SKHB 207	Bol 152	A	00 43 10.1
SKHB 208	Bol 154	A	00 43 12.5
SKHB 209	Bol 357	A	00 43 13.2
SKHB 210	Bol 155	A	00 43 13.6
SKHB 211	Bol 156	A	00 43 14.0
SKHB 212	Bol 157	A	00 43 14.1
SKHB 213	Bol 158	A	00 43 14.5
SKHB 214	Bol 160	A	00 43 15.2
SKHB 215	Bol 161	A	00 43 15.5
SKHB 216	Bol 162	A	00 43 16.5
SKHB 217	Bol 163	A	00 43 17.7
SKHB 218	Bol 165	A	00 43 18.3
SKHB 219	Bol 358	A	00 43 18.0
SKHB 220	Bol 469	A	00 43 19.4
SKHB 221	Bol 170	A	00 43 23.5
SKHB 222	Bol 171	A	00 43 25.7
SKHB 223	Bol 172	A	00 43 26.1
SKHB 224	Bol 173	A	00 43 28.9
SKHB 226	Bol 174	A	00 43 30.4
SKHB 227	Bol 176	A	00 43 30.6
SKHB 228	Bol 177	A	00 43 30.8
SKHB 229	Bol 178	A	00 43 31.0
SKHB 230	Bol 179	A	00 43 31.2
SKHB 231	Bol 180	A	00 43 31.9
SKHB 232	Bol 181	A	00 43 32.7
SKHB 233	Bol 182	A	00 43 36.8
SKHB 234	Bol 183	A	00 43 37.1
SKHB 235	Bol 185	A	00 43 37.4
SKHB 236	Bol 184	A	00 43 37.8
SKHB 237	Bol 187	A	00 43 38.8
SKHB 238	Bol 471	A	00 43 41.7

Table D.3: Cluster Cross-Reference

Name	Look Under	GX	2000.0 RA
SKHB 239	Bol 188	A	00 43 41.6
SKHB 240	Bol 189	A	00 43 42.5
SKHB 241	Bol 190	A	00 43 43.5
SKHB 242	Bol 192	A	00 43 44.5
SKHB 243	Bol 194	A	00 43 45.3
SKHB 244	Bol 193	A	00 43 45.7
SKHB 245		A	00 43 47.8
SKHB 246	Bol 196	A	00 43 48.6
SKHB 247	Bol 197	A	00 43 50.0
SKHB 248	Bol 199	A	00 43 49.9
SKHB 249	Bol 198	A	00 43 50.4
SKHB 250	Bol 201	A	00 43 53.1
SKHB 251	Bol 202	A	00 43 54.7
SKHB 252	Bol 203	A	00 43 56.0
SKHB 253		A	00 43 56.0
SKHB 254	Bol 204	A	00 43 56.6
SKHB 255	Bol 361	A	00 43 57.2
SKHB 256	Bol 205	A	00 43 58.3
SKHB 257	Bol 206	A	00 43 58.7
SKHB 258	Bol 207	A	00 43 59.7
SKHB 259	Bol 208	A	00 44 00.4
SKHB 260		A	00 44 00.9
SKHB 261	Bol 209	A	00 44 02.8
SKHB 262	Bol 211	A	00 44 03.2
SKHB 263	Bol 212	A	00 44 03.3
SKHB 264	Bol 213	A	00 44 03.6
SKHB 265	Bol 214	A	00 44 04.1
SKHB 266	Bol 215	A	00 44 06.5
SKHB 267	Bol 216	A	00 44 09.0
SKHB 268		A	00 44 10.1
SKHB 269	Bol 217	A	00 44 10.6
SKHB 270		A	00 44 12.0
SKHB 271	Bol 219	A	00 44 15.2
SKHB 272	Bol 218	A	00 44 14.5
SKHB 274	Bol 363	A	00 44 17.2
SKHB 275	Bol 220	A	00 44 19.5
SKHB 276	Bol 221	A	00 44 23.1
SKHB 277	Bol 222	A	00 44 25.5
SKHB 278	Bol 223	A	00 44 27.1
SKHB 279	Bol 224	A	00 44 27.2
SKHB 280	Bol 225	A	00 44 29.8
SKHB 281	Bol 228	A	00 44 33.2
SKHB 282	Bol 229	A	00 44 33.8
SKHB 283	Bol 230	A	00 44 35.4
SKHB 284	Bol 365	A	00 44 36.8
SKHB 285	Bol 231	A	00 44 38.7
SKHB 286	Bol 232	A	00 44 40.5
SKHB 287	Bol 233	A	00 44 42.0
SKHB 288	Bol 281	A	00 44 43.1
SKHB 289		A	00 44 45.7
SKHB 290	Bol 234	A	00 44 46.5
SKHB 291	Bol 366	A	00 44 46.9
SKHB 292	Bol 367	A	00 44 47.5
SKHB 293	Bol 368	A	00 44 48.1
SKHB 295		A	00 44 52.6
SKHB 296	Bol 283	A	00 44 55.4
SKHB 297	Bol 235	A	00 44 58.2
SKHB 298	Bol 236	A	00 45 08.9
SKHB 299	Bol 237	A	00 45 09.5
SKHB 300	Bol 370	A	00 45 14.6

Table D.3: Cluster Cross-Reference

Name	Look Under	GX	2000.0 RA
SKHB 301	Bol 238	A	00 45 15.0
SKHB 302	Bol 240	A	00 45 25.2
SKHB 303	Bol 371	A	00 45 27.4
SKHB 304	Bol 372	A	00 45 33.5
SKHB 305	Bol 373	A	00 45 42.1
SKHB 306	Bol 374	A	00 45 44.5
SKHB 307	Bol 375	A	00 45 45.6
SKHB 308	Bol 377	A	00 45 48.2
SKHB 309	Bol 376	A	00 45 48.7
SKHB 310	Bol 484	A	00 45 53.9
SKHB 311	Bol 378	A	00 45 57.4
SKHB 312	Bol 379	A	00 45 58.8
SKHB 313	Bol 380	A	00 46 06.4
SKHB 315	Bol 381	A	00 46 07.3
SKHB 316	Bol 486	A	00 46 08.5
SKHB 317	Bol 382	A	00 46 10.3
SKHB 318	Bol 383	A	00 46 11.9
SKHB 319	Bol 384	A	00 46 22.1
SKHB 321	Bol 385	A	00 46 25.0
SKHB 322	Bol 386	A	00 46 27.2
SKHB 323	Bol 387	A	00 46 33.7
SKHB 325		A	00 46 41.2
SKHB 326	Bol 389	A	00 46 43.8
SKHB 327		A	00 46 49.5
SKHB 328	Bol 391	A	00 46 58.1
SKHB 329	Bol 392	A	00 47 00.8
SKHB 330	Bol 393	A	00 47 01.2
SKHB 332	Bol 395	A	00 47 06.2
SKHB 333	Bol 494	A	00 47 20.5
SKHB 334	Bol 495	A	00 47 24.8
SKHB 335	Bol 396	A	00 47 25.2
SKHB 336	Bol 397	A	00 47 27.5
SKHB 337		A	00 47 29.7
SKHB 339		A	00 47 49.0
SKHB 341	Bol 398	A	00 47 57.9
SKHB 342	Bol 399	A	00 47 59.6
SKHB 343	Bol 400	A	00 48 01.3
SKHB 344	Bol 401	A	00 48 08.5
SKHB 346	Bol 402	A	00 48 36.1
SKHB 348	Bol 403	A	00 49 18.0
SKHB 350	Bol 404	A	00 49 32.6
SKHB 351	Bol 405	A	00 49 39.7
SKHB 352	Bol 407	A	00 50 10.1
SKHB 353		A	00 50 18.2
Skiff J0058.4+6828			00 58 24
Skiff J0458.2+4301			04 58 11
Skiff J0507.2+3050			05 07 13.8
Skiff J0614.8+1252			06 14 49
Skiff J0619.3+1832			06 19 22
Skiff J1942.3+3839			19 42 24
Skiff J2330.2+6015			23 30 12
SL 1	NGC 1466	L	03 44 32.4
SL 2		L	04 24 09.8
SL 4		L	04 32 38.6
SL 5		L	04 35 38.6
SL 6			04 36 09.5
SL 6	NGC 1641	L	04 36 06
SL 8		L	04 37 49.9
SL 11		L	04 39 05.8
SL 12		L	04 39 59.3

Table D.3: Cluster Cross-Reference

Name	Look Under	GX	2000.0 RA
SL 13		L	04 39 42.9
SL 14		L	04 40 28.8
SL 15		L	04 40 43.4
SL 16		L	04 42 59.1
SL 19		L	04 43 03.6
SL 22		L	04 43 37.2
SL 23		L	04 43 38.0
SL 24		L	04 43 50.3
SL 26		L	04 45 17.4
SL 27		L	04 45 04.7
SL 28		L	04 44 40.8
SL 29		L	04 45 12.6
SL 30		L	04 46 02.7
SL 31		L	04 45 40.6
SL 33		L	04 45 53.5
SL 34		L	04 45 46.7
SL 35		L	04 46 40.7
SL 36		L	04 46 08.5
SL 37		L	04 46 45.8
SL 41		L	04 47 30.9
SL 42		L	04 48 08.2
SL 47		L	04 49 03.3
SL 48		L	04 49 27.5
SL 49		L	04 50 10.4
SL 51		L	04 50 19.7
SL 52		L	04 50 07.0
SL 53		L	04 49 53.2
SL 54		L	04 50 48.7
SL 55	NGC 1711	L	04 50 37.4
SL 56		L	04 50 32.1
SL 57		L	04 51 13.2
SL 58		L	04 50 59.9
SL 59		L	04 50 20.2
SL 59	LW 75	L	04 50 14.0
SL 59	LW 76	L	04 50 24.8
SL 61		L	04 50 44.9
SL 62		L	04 52 03.2
SL 63		L	04 52 25.7
SL 64	NGC 1714	L	04 52 06.6
SL 66		L	04 51 56.0
SL 68		L	04 52 06.7
SL 70		L	04 52 50.0
SL 71		L	04 52 55.3
SL 72		L	04 52 33.8
SL 74		L	04 52 01.4
SL 75		L	04 52 54.9
SL 76		L	04 53 09.0
SL 79		L	04 52 53.3
SL 80		L	04 52 21.1
SL 81		L	04 53 09.8
SL 84		L	04 52 46.0
SL 87	NGC 1743	L	04 54 03.4
SL 88		L	04 54 15.5
SL 90		L	04 54 30.2
SL 92		L	04 54 26.7
SL 94	NGC 1756	L	04 54 49.9
SL 95		L	04 54 42.1
SL 96		L	04 55 01.9
SL 99	NGC 1755	L	04 55 14.7
SL 100		L	04 54 45.8

Table D.3: Cluster Cross-Reference

Name	Look Under	GX	2000.0 RA
SL 101		L	04 55 10.1
SL 102		L	04 54 56.4
SL 103		L	04 54 53.7
SL 105		L	04 55 24.5
SL 106		L	04 55 06.4
SL 107		L	04 55 45.1
SL 108		L	04 55 15.0
SL 109		L	04 55 33.1
SL 110		L	04 55 44.4
SL 111		L	04 55 42.3
SL 112		L	04 55 52.6
SL 114		L	04 56 07.8
SL 116		L	04 56 24.8
SL 117		L	04 56 22.4
SL 118		L	04 55 32.5
SL 119		L	04 56 37.4
SL 120	NGC 1767	L	04 56 27.4
SL 121	NGC 1777	L	04 55 48.5
SL 123		L	04 56 33.3
SL 124		L	04 56 31.3
SL 126		L	04 57 22.7
SL 131		L	04 57 27.5
SL 132		L	04 57 26.9
SL 133		L	04 57 34.6
SL 134		L	04 57 30.4
SL 135		L	04 56 43.8
SL 136		L	04 57 30.4
SL 137		L	04 57 10.2
SL 138		L	04 57 54.7
SL 139		L	04 57 56.1
SL 141	NGC 1774	L	04 58 06.2
SL 142		L	04 58 15.2
SL 143		L	04 58 17.0
SL 146		L	04 58 17.8
SL 147		L	04 58 59.5
SL 148	NGC 1783	L	04 59 08.7
SL 150		L	04 58 56.5
SL 151		L	04 58 51.3
SL 152		L	04 59 19.7
SL 152	NGC 1787	L	05 00.0
SL 153		L	04 59 20.6
SL 154		L	04 59 14.7
SL 156		L	04 59 37.8
SL 157		L	04 58 53.6
SL 158		L	04 59 14.0
SL 160		L	04 59 26.6
SL 161		L	04 59 58.6
SL 162		L	04 59 53.8
SL 164		L	04 59 25.3
SL 166		L	04 59 12.5
SL 167		L	05 00 41.2
SL 168		L	05 00 44.2
SL 169		L	05 00 22.9
SL 171		L	05 00 32.9
SL 173		L	05 01 21.9
SL 174		L	05 01 11.6
SL 175		L	05 00 49.5
SL 176		L	05 01 29.3
SL 177		L	05 01 47.1
SL 178		L	05 01 44.3
SL 178	NGC 1787	L	05 00.0
SL 179		L	05 01 45.2
SL 183		L	05 01 33.3
SL 184	NGC 1806	L	05 02 11.3
SL 187		L	05 02 10.4
SL 192		L	05 02 27.6
SL 193		L	05 03 27.7
SL 195		L	05 03 31.8
SL 196		L	05 03 35.0
SL 197		L	05 03 33.5
SL 200		L	05 03 45.7
SL 201	NGC 1818	L	05 04 12.9
SL 204		L	05 04 42.6
SL 205		L	05 04 45.5
SL 207	NGC 1830	L	05 04 39.5
SL 209		L	05 04 37.7
SL 211		L	05 05 02.7
SL 213		L	05 04 49.8
SL 214		L	05 05 24.2
SL 215	NGC 1835	L	05 05 06.6
SL 216		L	05 04 57.4
SL 219		L	05 04 43.4
SL 222		L	05 05 26.2
SL 223	NGC 1836	L	05 05 35.6
SL 224		L	05 05 42.7
SL 225		L	05 06 08.3
SL 225	NGC 1838	L	05 06 34
SL 227	NGC 1831	L	05 06 16.2
SL 228		L	05 06 27.2
SL 229		L	05 06 32.4
SL 230		L	05 06 34
SL 232		L	05 06 22.2
SL 232	LH 26	L	05 05 57
SL 232	NGC 1845	L	05 05 12
SL 233		L	05 07 04.1
SL 235		L	05 06 29.3
SL 236		L	05 06 22.6
SL 238		L	05 07 22.6
SL 239		L	05 07 09.9
SL 243	NGC 1846	L	05 07 33.9
SL 245		L	05 07 46.1
SL 246		L	05 07 24.9
SL 248		L	05 06 52.1
SL 249		L	05 07 34.8
SL 251		L	05 07 59.9
SL 252		L	05 07 50.5
SL 253		L	05 08 22.8
SL 254		L	05 08 22.1
SL 255		L	05 07 56.7
SL 256		L	05 08 10.3
SL 257		L	05 08 40.1
SL 258		L	05 08 35.5
SL 259		L	05 08 51.6
SL 261	NGC 1850	L	05 08 46.7
SL 262		L	05 09 21.2
SL 263		L	05 08 32.2
SL 266		L	05 09 06.1
SL 269		L	05 09 35.6
SL 270		L	05 09 09.6
SL 271	NGC 1856	L	05 09 30.6
SL 272		L	05 09 01.6
SL 273		L	05 10 03.7
SL 275		L	05 10 15.2
SL 278		L	05 10 16.3
SL 281		L	05 10 33.4
SL 282		L	05 10 10.4
SL 283		L	05 10 44.7
SL 285		L	05 10 40.6
SL 287		L	05 10 49.0
SL 290		L	05 10 36.6
SL 291		L	05 10 30.3
SL 292		L	05 11 08.3
SL 293		L	05 11 09.0
SL 294		L	05 10 40.4
SL 295		L	05 10 10.7
SL 298		L	05 11 31.8
SL 300		L	05 11 41.7
SL 301		L	05 12 04.7
SL 302		L	05 11 44.0
SL 303		L	05 12 20.4
SL 305	LW 159	L	05 12 24.9
SL 308		L	05 12 27.9
SL 310		L	05 12 29.5
SL 312		L	05 12 24.3
SL 314		L	05 12 21.1
SL 315		L	05 13 11.2
SL 317	NGC 1870	L	05 13 11.0
SL 318	NGC 1872	L	05 13 11.5
SL 319	NGC 1866	L	05 13 38.6
SL 320	BRHT 7b	L	05 13 11.5
SL 320	NGC 1874	L	05 13 11
SL 320	NGC 1880	L	05 13 39.2
SL 322		L	05 13 43.4
SL 328	LH 39	L	05 13.9
SL 329		L	05 14 11.8
SL 330	NGC 1868	L	05 14 36.1
SL 333		L	05 14 44.1
SL 334		L	05 13 55.9
SL 335		L	05 15 00.1
SL 336		L	05 14 28.8
SL 337		L	05 14 30.0
SL 339		L	05 15 17.9
SL 341		L	05 15 36
SL 342		L	05 15 32.6
SL 344	NGC 1894	L	05 15 51.4
SL 345		L	05 16 17.1
SL 346		L	05 16 28.4
SL 347		L	05 16 25.7
SL 349		L	05 16 54.6
SL 350	NGC 1898	L	05 16 42
SL 352		L	05 16 40.7
SL 353		L	05 17 10
SL 353	[H60b] 1	L	05 16.0
SL 354		L	05 17 30.9
SL 356	NGC 1903	L	05 17 22.8
SL 357		L	05 17 26.5
SL 357	SL 357	L	05 17 26.5
SL 359		L	05 17 49.7
SL 360		L	05 18 11.1
SL 360	NGC 1910	L	05 18 23.8

Table D.3: Cluster Cross-Reference

Name	Look Under	GX	2000.0 RA
SL 363	[H60b] 2	L	05 17.9
SL 364		L	05 17 41.6
SL 366		L	05 18 20.4
SL 372		L	05 18 36.5
SL 373	NGC 1913	L	05 18 19.2
SL 374		L	05 17 49.7
SL 375		L	05 18 43.2
SL 376	NGC 1900	L	05 19 08.8
SL 377		L	05 19 00.6
SL 378		L	05 18 57.9
SL 380		L	05 18 46.5
SL 382		L	05 19 25.5
SL 383		L	05 19 33.2
SL 384		L	05 19 44.5
SL 385		L	05 19 25.4
SL 386		L	05 19 51.3
SL 387		L	05 19 33
SL 388		L	05 20 05.5
SL 389		L	05 19 36.4
SL 394		L	05 19 34.8
SL 395		L	05 19 59.0
SL 396		L	05 19 36.3
SL 398		L	05 20 31.8
SL 399		L	05 20 20.4
SL 400		L	05 19 38.7
SL 401		L	05 20 50.2
SL 406		L	05 21 00.9
SL 407		L	05 21 15.5
SL 408	LH 44	L	05 21.2
SL 409		L	05 21 37.9
SL 410		L	05 21 45.1
SL 411		L	05 21 41.7
SL 413	NGC 1938	L	05 21 27.1
SL 414	NGC 1939	L	05 21 24.3
SL 415		L	05 22 01.9
SL 415	NGC 1925	L	05 21 31
SL 416		L	05 21 58.2
SL 420	NGC 1932	L	05 22 27.4
SL 421		L	05 22 29.4
SL 424		L	05 22 23.4
SL 428		L	05 22 52.1
SL 432		L	05 22 37.8
SL 433		L	05 22 19.2
SL 435		L	05 23 30.5
SL 435	LH 50	L	05 23.7
SL 437	IC 2134	L	05 23 06.6
SL 438		L	05 24 10.6
SL 440		L	05 24 12.6
SL 441		L	05 23 42.1
SL 444		L	05 24 30.4
SL 445	NGC 1942	L	05 24 42.7
SL 446		L	05 24 47.8
SL 448		L	05 24 59.4
SL 451		L	05 24 13.4
SL 452		L	05 25 10.0
SL 455		L	05 24 17.2
SL 456		L	05 25 25.3
SL 461		L	05 25 20.8
SL 463		L	05 26 16.2
SL 464	NGC 1951	L	05 26 06.4

Table D.3: Cluster Cross-Reference

Name	Look Under	GX	2000.0 RA
SL 465		L	05 26 13.7
SL 470		L	05 26 25.7
SL 471		L	05 26 14.3
SL 471	LH 55	L	05 26.4
SL 472		L	05 26 14.4
SL 473		L	05 26 29.4
SL 474		L	05 26 08.5
SL 476	NGC 1965	L	05 26 29.6
SL 476	NGC 1970	L	05 26 45.3
SL 477		L	05 26 23.7
SL 478	NGC 1967	L	05 26 44.6
SL 480	NGC 1972	L	05 26 48.1
SL 481	NGC 1971	L	05 26 45.0
SL 482		L	05 27 18.3
SL 484		L	05 27 46.5
SL 485		L	05 27 50.0
SL 486	NGC 1987	L	05 27 16.4
SL 487		L	05 27 08.2
SL 490		L	05 27 18.4
SL 491		L	05 27 50.5
SL 495		L	05 28 03.8
SL 496		L	05 28 32.6
SL 497		L	05 28 23.9
SL 498		L	05 28 35.1
SL 499	NGC 1994	L	05 28 23.3
SL 500		L	05 28 39.3
SL 501	NGC 1978	L	05 28 44.6
SL 502		L	05 29 11.5
SL 503		L	05 28 59.6
SL 505		L	05 28 49.7
SL 506	[H60b] 14	L	05 28 38.6
SL 509		L	05 29 49.1
SL 510		L	05 29 21.1
SL 511		L	05 29 49.0
SL 512		L	05 29 54.3
SL 513		L	05 29 58.4
SL 515		L	05 30 08.9
SL 516		L	05 30 00.1
SL 521		L	05 30 26.1
SL 522		L	05 30 37.0
SL 523	NGC 2004	L	05 30 40.9
SL 524		L	05 30 50.2
SL 525		L	05 30 23.4
SL 527		L	05 30 50.1
SL 529		L	05 31 06.8
SL 536		L	05 30 35.6
SL 537	NGC 2006	L	05 31 19.9
SL 538		L	05 31 19.8
SL 539		L	05 30 56.4
SL 540		L	05 31 33.9
SL 541		L	05 31 18.1
SL 543		L	05 31 01.1
SL 545		L	05 31 08.1
SL 546		L	05 31 02.5
SL 548		L	05 31 25.1
SL 549		L	05 32 03.6
SL 550		L	05 31 55.1
SL 551		L	05 31 51.8
SL 552		L	05 31 43.5
SL 553		L	05 32 29.2

Table D.3: Cluster Cross-Reference

Name	Look Under	GX	2000.0 RA
SL 554	NGC 2019	L	05 31 57
SL 555		L	05 31 43.0
SL 556	[H60b] 4	L	05 32 25.4
SL 557		L	05 32 06.8
SL 557	NGC 2015	L	05 31 48
SL 559	NGC 2011	L	05 32 19.8
SL 560	NGC 2014	L	05 32 21.7
SL 561		L	05 32 04.9
SL 562		L	05 32 06.8
SL 564		L	05 32 49.6
SL 565		L	05 32 48.9
SL 566		L	05 32 50.3
SL 567		L	05 33 18.1
SL 568		L	05 33 03.4
SL 569		L	05 33 20.1
SL 570	NGC 2021	L	05 33 30.3
SL 572		L	05 33 10.0
SL 573		L	05 33 44.8
SL 575	NGC 2028	L	05 33 48.7
SL 576		L	05 33 14.2
SL 578		L	05 34 19.5
SL 579		L	05 34 13.8
SL 580		L	05 34 11.1
SL 582		L	05 34 29.5
SL 583		L	05 34 15.7
SL 584		L	05 34 00.6
SL 585		L	05 34 30.8
SL 586		L	05 34 43.8
SL 588		L	05 34 39.3
SL 593		L	05 35 08.1
SL 594		L	05 35 25.1
SL 596		L	05 35 42.2
SL 601		L	05 36 09.5
SL 601	NGC 2042	L	05 36 09.6
SL 602		L	05 35 59.6
SL 602	LH 90	L	05 36.1
SL 603		L	05 35 43.7
SL 604		L	05 36 46.2
SL 605	NGC 2041	L	05 36 28.0
SL 606		L	05 36 33.4
SL 607		L	05 36 31.7
SL 609		L	05 36 40.0
SL 609	NGC 2050	L	05 36 54
SL 610		L	05 36 42
SL 610	NGC 2055	L	05 37 08
SL 612		L	05 36 21.5
SL 615		L	05 36 56.1
SL 617		L	05 36 42.6
SL 618		L	05 36 44.4
SL 619		L	05 36 46.5
SL 620		L	05 36 28.4
SL 624		L	05 37 19.2
SL 625		L	05 37 09.3
SL 628		L	05 38 30.1
SL 629		L	05 38 21.5
SL 632	IC 2146	L	05 37 47.4
SL 633	NGC 2070	L	05 38 42.4
SL 634		L	05 38 21.5
SL 635		L	05 39 08.6
SL 638		L	05 39 37.1

Table D.3: Cluster Cross-Reference

Name	Look Under	GX	2000.0 RA
SL 643		L	05 40 22.4
SL 645		L	05 39 33.7
SL 646		L	05 39 53.9
SL 647		L	05 39 34.7
SL 648		L	05 40 10.4
SL 649		L	05 41 08.6
SL 650		L	05 41 08.3
SL 651		L	05 40 59.2
SL 653	NGC 2091	L	05 40 58.0
SL 654		L	05 41 10.3
SL 655		L	05 40 53.6
SL 656		L	05 41 05.8
SL 658		L	05 41 39.3
SL 661		L	05 41 41.3
SL 662	NGC 2092	L	05 41 22.2
SL 663		L	05 42 29.5
SL 665	NGC 2102	L	05 42 19.7
SL 666		L	05 42 15.5
SL 668		L	05 42 17.6
SL 670		L	05 43 14.3
SL 671		L	05 42 57.3
SL 672		L	05 42 41.7
SL 674		L	05 43 20.2
SL 675		L	05 43 15.6
SL 676		L	05 43 08.8
SL 677		L	05 43 55.6
SL 678		L	05 43 35.9
SL 679	NGC 2107	L	05 43 11.9
SL 680		L	05 44 03.8
SL 682	NGC 2097	L	05 44 15.5
SL 683		L	05 43 49.8
SL 684		L	05 43 37.8
SL 685		L	05 44 15.1
SL 686	NGC 2108	L	05 43 56.9
SL 687	NGC 2105	L	05 44 19.8
SL 689		L	05 44 38.8
SL 690		L	05 44 50.6
SL 691		L	05 44 13.5
SL 692		L	05 44 13.7
SL 693		L	05 44 59.1
SL 694		L	05 45 06.5
SL 695		L	05 45 03.1
SL 696		L	05 45 14.1
SL 697		L	05 44 40.9
SL 697	LH 116	L	05 45.0
SL 698		L	05 45 12.6
SL 700		L	05 45 24.1
SL 701		L	05 45 32.7
SL 702		L	05 45 06.4
SL 703		L	05 44 54.3
SL 704		L	05 45 24.3
SL 707		L	05 46 12.3
SL 708		L	05 46 22.6
SL 709		L	05 46 14.7
SL 710		L	05 46 58.1
SL 711		L	05 46 55.0
SL 712		L	05 46 58.7
SL 713		L	05 46 26.1
SL 714		L	05 47 17.0
SL 716		L	05 46 46.3

Table D.3: Cluster Cross-Reference

Name	Look Under	GX	2000.0 RA
SL 719		L	05 47 36.7
SL 720		L	05 47 46.9
SL 721		L	05 47 30.9
SL 722		L	05 47 41.5
SL 723		L	05 47 44.8
SL 724		L	05 48 53.0
SL 726		L	05 48 59.4
SL 727		L	05 49 01.9
SL 728		L	05 49 02.7
SL 729		L	05 49 20.6
SL 730		L	05 49 11.5
SL 732		L	05 49 35.9
SL 733		L	05 48 44.7
SL 734		L	05 48 54.2
SL 735	[H60b] 7	L	05 50 03.2
SL 736		L	05 49 16.6
SL 737		L	05 48 44.1
SL 738		L	05 50 08.2
SL 739		L	05 50 00.4
SL 740		L	05 49 45.7
SL 742	NGC 2120	L	05 50 34.8
SL 743		L	05 50 23.7
SL 744		L	05 49 56.1
SL 745		L	05 50 38.2
SL 746		L	05 50 45.3
SL 747		L	05 50 09.9
SL 748		L	05 50 15.5
SL 749		L	05 50 00.1
SL 752		L	05 51 37.3
SL 753		L	05 51 48.8
SL 754		L	05 50 35.6
SL 756		L	05 51 29.1
SL 757	NGC 2133	L	05 51 29.3
SL 759		L	05 52 09.4
SL 760	NGC 2134	L	05 51 56.5
SL 761		L	05 52 10.1
SL 762	NGC 2136	L	05 52 58.9
SL 763		L	05 52 53.7
SL 764	NGC 2137	L	05 53 11.9
SL 766		L	05 53 00.3
SL 767		L	05 53 12.2
SL 768		L	05 53 54.5
SL 769		L	05 53 23.9
SL 770		L	05 53 42.8
SL 771		L	05 54 02.6
SL 772		L	05 53 53.0
SL 774		L	05 54 14.6
SL 775		L	05 53 27.0
SL 776		L	05 53 38.9
SL 778		L	05 54 55.4
SL 779		L	05 54 11.8
SL 781		L	05 54 42.2
SL 782		L	05 55 09.1
SL 783		L	05 54 39.1
SL 787		L	05 55 59.2
SL 788		L	05 55 45.8
SL 789	NGC 2161	L	05 55 42.3
SL 790	[H60b] 9	L	05 56 01.3
SL 791		L	05 56 55.0
SL 794	NGC 2157	L	05 57 34.8

Table D.3: Cluster Cross-Reference

Name	Look Under	GX	2000.0 RA
SL 795		L	05 57 52.1
SL 797		L	05 57 23.1
SL 798		L	05 58 12.2
SL 800		L	05 58 20.2
SL 804		L	05 57 38.1
SL 805		L	05 57 43.0
SL 806		L	05 58 49.9
SL 807	NGC 2173	L	05 57 58.0
SL 808	NGC 2164	L	05 58 55.6
SL 810		L	05 59 10.8
SL 813		L	06 00 32.7
SL 817		L	06 00 37.9
SL 818		L	06 01 38.9
SL 819	NGC 2190	L	06 01 02.3
SL 821		L	06 01 23.7
SL 822		L	06 02 06.9
SL 823		L	06 02 18.1
SL 824		L	06 02 28.4
SL 826		L	06 01 53.5
SL 827		L	06 03 11.0
SL 828		L	06 02 13.6
SL 829		L	06 03 31.3
SL 830		L	06 04 13.0
SL 831		L	06 04 34.2
SL 832		L	06 04 24.5
SL 833		L	06 05 03.6
SL 834		L	06 07 30.6
SL 835		L	06 04 48.1
SL 836	NGC 2203	L	06 04 41.6
SL 837		L	06 05 52.2
SL 840		L	06 06 28.8
SL 841		L	06 08 01.6
SL 842		L	06 08 15.5
SL 843		L	06 08 08.5
SL 844		L	06 08 32.8
SL 845		L	06 08 38.6
SL 846		L	06 08 39.2
SL 848		L	06 08 17.5
SL 849	NGC 2209	L	06 08 34.8
SL 850		L	06 10 12.7
SL 852		L	06 10 21.5
SL 853		L	06 10 11.0
SL 854		L	06 10 55.2
SL 855		L	06 10 53.5
SL 858	NGC 2210	L	06 11 31.3
SL 859		L	06 12 35.7
SL 860	NGC 2214	L	06 12 56.1
SL 861		L	06 13 16.6
SL 862		L	06 13 27.4
SL 863		L	06 13 57.6
SL 864		L	06 13 57.0
SL 865		L	06 14 07.8
SL 866		L	06 14 32.4
SL 867		L	06 14 03.6
SL 868		L	06 14 22.5
SL 869		L	06 14 41.1
SL 870		L	06 14 28.5
SL 871		L	06 15 25.6
SL 872		L	06 15 02.1
SL 873		L	06 16 15.4

Table D.3: Cluster Cross-Reference

Name	Look Under	GX	2000.0 RA
SL 874		L	06 15 57.8
SL 876		L	06 18 07.9
SL 877		L	06 17 46.3
SL 881		L	06 18 44.9
SL 882		L	06 19 04.1
SL 883		L	06 19 56.0
SL 885		L	06 21 11.5
SL 886		L	06 21 26.3
SL 890		L	06 23 02.9
SL 891		L	06 24 49.6
SL 892		L	06 25 16.0
SL 893	NGC 2249	L	06 25 49.5
SL 895	NGC 2257	L	06 30 12.4
SL 896		L	06 29 57.7
SL 897		L	06 33 01.2
SSWZ94 1			07 20 56.3
SSWZ94 2			08 25 25.2
SSWZ94 3			10 41 25.5
SSWZ94 4			12 14 03
SSWZ94 5			19 39 31.2
SSWZ94 6			19 51 01.9
Steine 1			20 35 13
Stephenson 1			18 54 30.6
Stephenson 2			18 36 39.6
Stock 1			19 35 47
Stock 2			02 14 43
Stock 3			01 12 03
Stock 4			01 52.7
Stock 5			02 04.4
Stock 6	NGC 886		02 23 28.1
Stock 7	Markarian 6		02 29 40
Stock 8			05 28 07
Stock 9	NGC 1931		05 31 26
Stock 10			05 39.0
Stock 11			23 30 55
Stock 12			23 36 20
Stock 13			11 13.1
Stock 14			11 43 51
Stock 15			12 10.5
Stock 16			13 18 38.4
Stock 17			23 43 47.0
Stock 18			00 01 35
Stock 19			00 04 39
Stock 20			00 25 16
Stock 21			00 30 28
Stock 22	NGC 433		01 15 10
Stock 23			03 16 10.8
Stock 24			00 39 50
Struve 2	NGC 629		01 39 02.1
Struve 748	NGC 1976		05 35 16
Struve 2631	NGC 6873		20 07 44
Struve 2637	Theta Sge group		20 10 05
SU Cygni			19 44 48.6
Tar neb cl	NGC 2070	L	05 38 42.4
Tau CMa cluster	NGC 2362		07 18 42
Taurus cluster	Hyades		04 26.9
Terzan 1		g	17 35 47.0
Terzan 2		g	17 27 33.4
Terzan 3		g	16 28 40.1
Terzan 4		g	17 30 38.9

Table D.3: Cluster Cross-Reference

Name	Look Under	GX	2000.0 RA
Terzan 5		g	17 48 04.9
Terzan 6		g	17 50 46.4
Terzan 7		g	19 17 43.7
Terzan 8		g	19 41 45.0
Terzan 9		g	18 01 38.8
Terzan 10		g	18 02 58
Terzan 11		g	18 12 15.8
Terzan 11	Terzan 5	g	17 48 04.9
Terzan 12	Terzan 11	g	18 12 15.8
Terzan N 5			17 11 15
Terzan N 15			17 18 31
Terzan N 16			17 18 29
Terzan N 17			17 18 41
Terzan N 20			17 33.5
Terzan N 23			17 45 11
Terzan N 33			17 12 36.2
Terzan N 34			17 13 15.4
Terzan N 35			17 14 01.5
Teutsch J0121.3+2507			01 21 18
Teutsch J0416.8+4103			04 16 50
Teutsch J0438.2+4317			04 38 15
Teutsch J0443.8+3603			04 43 52
Teutsch J0455.7+3647			04 55 43
Teutsch J0508.2+4951			05 08 16
Teutsch J0524.2+3329			05 24 17
Teutsch J0536.8+3112			05 36 49
Teutsch J0539.4+3320			05 39 29
Teutsch J0541.3+3914			05 41 22
Teutsch J0544.3+2848			05 44 23
Teutsch J0547.0-0506			05 47 00
Teutsch J0548.8+0930			05 48 49
Teutsch J0550.3+4142			05 50 23
Teutsch J0552.4+2954			05 52 24
Teutsch J0608.9+2615			06 08 56
Teutsch J0609.3+3113			06 09 20
Teutsch J0616.3+3621			06 16 22
Teutsch J0625.4+1351			06 25 24
Teutsch J0625.6+1336			06 25 40
Teutsch J0628.8+1455			06 28 50
Teutsch J0631.9+1151			06 31 54
Teutsch J0643.9+0123			06 43 55
Teutsch J1714.3+1718			17 14 20
Teutsch J1817.1+0722			18 17 07
Teutsch J1803.5-2207			18 03 30
Teutsch J1837.1-1014			18 37 07
Teutsch J1942.4+3839	Skiff J1942.3+3839		19 42 24
Teutsch J1947.7+2415			19 47 43
Teutsch J2002.3+3518	ADS 13292		20 02 23.6
Teutsch J2130.9+5249			21 30 59
Teutsch J2006.8+3518			20 06 53
TF 26	Bol 96	A	00 42 26.2
TF 45	Bol 124	A	00 42 41.1
TF 77	Bol 144	A	00 42 59.9
Theta Sge group			20 10 05
Theta-1 Orionis	NGC 1976		05 35 16
Toadstool	French 1		21 07 22
Tombaugh 1			07 00 27
Tombaugh 2			07 03 06
Tombaugh 3	IC 166		01 52 22
Tombaugh 4			02 29 10.7

Table D.3: Cluster Cross-Reference

Name	Look Under	GX	2000.0 RA
Tombaugh 5			03 47 44
Tonantzintla 1	NGC 6380	g	17 34 28.0
Tonantzintla 2		g	17 36 10.5
Trapezium	NGC 1976		05 35 16
Trifid nebula cl	NGC 6514		18 02 31
Trumpler 1			01 35 40
Trumpler 2			02 36 53
Trumpler 3			03 12 00
Trumpler 4	IC 2157		06 04 49.8
Trumpler 5			06 36 31
Trumpler 6			07 26 23
Trumpler 7			07 27 21
Trumpler 8	NGC 2479		07 55 06
Trumpler 9			07 55 40
Trumpler 10			08 47 45
Trumpler 11			10 04.9
Trumpler 12			10 06.5
Trumpler 13			10 23 48
Trumpler 14			10 43 57
Trumpler 15			10 44 44
Trumpler 16			10 45 10
Trumpler 16	Collinder 234		10 45 12.9
Trumpler 17			10 56 24
Trumpler 18			11 11.4
Trumpler 19			11 14.3
Trumpler 20			12 39 32
Trumpler 21			13 32 14
Trumpler 22			14 31.2
Trumpler 23			16 00 50.7
Trumpler 24			16 57.0
Trumpler 25			17 24 30.3
Trumpler 26			17 28 29.9
Trumpler 27			17 36 12.7
Trumpler 28			17 36 59
Trumpler 29			17 41 36.4
Trumpler 30			17 56.4
Trumpler 31			17 59.8
Trumpler 32			18 17 10.4
Trumpler 33			18 24 38.8
Trumpler 34			18 39.8
Trumpler 35			18 43 00.5
Trumpler 36	IC 1311		20 10 47
Trumpler 37	IC 1396		21 39.0
Turner 1	C1947+272		19 49 04
Turner 3	C1814-191b		18 17 24.6
Turner 4	C1814-190		18 16 51
Turner 5			09 33 50.9
Turner 6	GT Car cl		10 59 00.6
Turner 7			14 32 33
Turner 7	NGC 5662		14 35 30.8
Turner 8			19 45 16
Turner 9	SU Cygni		19 44 48.6
Turner 11			20 43 24
Turner 11	Ruprecht 173		20 41 41.2
Turner 11	Ruprecht 175		20 45 24
TXS 2033-047	NGC 6941		20 36 23.5
UGC 3583	Berkeley 29		06 53 04
UGC 3677	NGC 2314		07 10 32.4
UGC 5439	Palomar 3	g	10 05 31.4
UGC 5470	Leo I		10 08 27.5

Table D.3: Cluster Cross-Reference

Name	Look Under	GX	2000.0 RA
UGC 6253	Leo II		11 13 29.3
UGC 9792	Palomar 5	g	15 16 05.3
UGC 10642	Palomar 15	g	16 59 50.9
UGCA 91	Eridanus	g	04 24 44.5
UKS 1		g	17 54 27.2
UKS 2	vdB-Ha 66		09 25 16
UKS 0923-54.5	vdB-Ha 66		09 25 16
UKS 1751-24.1	UKS 1	g	17 54 27.2
UMa Cluster	Collinder 285		14 40.9
UMa glb	Palomar 4	g	11 29 16.8
Upgren 1			12 35 00
[V62] 0	Cl vdB 0	A	00 40 29.4
[V62] 3	Bol 307	A	00 39 18.6
[V62] 8	Bol 319	A	00 40 03.2
[V62] 10	Bol 316	A	00 39 53.8
[V62] 11	[H32] 11	A	00 40 42.5
[V62] 13	[H32] 13	A	00 40 42.0
[V62] 15		A	00 41 12.8
[V62] 17	Bol 18	A	00 40 49.6
[V62] 20	Bol 40	A	00 41 39.0
[V62] 22	SKHB 99	A	00 41 36.3
[V62] 24	Bol 49	A	00 41 45.8
[V62] 25	Bol 100	A	00 42 29.1
[V62] 28	SKHB 100	A	00 41 37.9
[V62] 31	[H32] 31	A	00 41 12.2
[V62] 40	Bol 67	A	00 42 03.4
[V62] 41	Bol 60	A	00 41 57.1
[V62] 45	Bol 70	A	00 42 06.9
[V62] 47	Bol 55	A	00 41 50.5
[V62] 48	Bol 125	A	00 42 42.4
[V62] 51	Bol 41	A	00 41 41.1
[V62] 52	Bol 108	A	00 42 31.3
[V62] 53	Bol 99	A	00 42 27.6
[V62] 54	Bol 13	A	00 40 38.8
[V62] 60	Bol 123	A	00 42 40.9
[V62] 63	Bol 140	A	00 42 58.8
[V62] 68	Bol 80	A	00 42 12.5
[V62] 69	Bol 194	A	00 43 45.3
[V62] 71	Bol 134	A	00 42 51.7
[V62] 72	Bol 157	A	00 43 14.1
[V62] 78	Bol 96	A	00 42 26.2
[V62] 85	Bol 69	A	00 42 05.7
[V62] 96	Bol 222	A	00 44 25.5
[V62] 104	Bol 187	A	00 43 38.8
[V62] 109	Bol 190	A	00 43 43.5
[V62] 110	Bol 203	A	00 43 56.0
[V62] 111	Bol 237	A	00 45 09.5
[V62] 113	Bol 189	A	00 43 42.5
[V62] 122	Bol 371	A	00 45 27.4
[V62] 123	Bol 368	A	00 44 48.1
[V62] 127	[H32] 127	A	00 45 45.7
[V62] 128	[H32] 128	A	00 44 56.2
[V62] 132	Bol 378	A	00 45 57.4
[V62] 137	Bol 380	A	00 46 06.4
[V62] 138	Bol 392	A	00 47 00.8
[V62] 139	Bol 97	A	00 42 27.5
[V62] 199	Bol 343	A	00 41 42.2
[V62] 205	Bol 81	A	00 42 13.6
[V62] 206	Bol 57	A	00 41 53.0
[V62] 207	Bol 30	A	00 41 19.0
[V62] 208	Bol 31	A	00 41 21.1
[V62] 209	Bol 28	A	00 41 16.6
[V62] 210	Bol 25	A	00 41 12.7
[V62] 211		A	00 41 02.1
[V62] 214	Bol 21	A	00 40 59.1
[V62] 215	Bol 33	A	00 41 26.4
[V62] 218	Bol 56	A	00 41 51.2
[V62] 220	Bol 54	A	00 41 47.9
[V62] 221	SKHB 89	A	00 41 17.4
[V62] 224	Bol 8	A	00 40 30.6
[V62] 225	SKHB 83	A	00 41 08.8
[V62] 229		A	00 42 34.6
[V62] 230	Bol 111	A	00 42 33.4
[V62] 234		A	00 42 30.1
[V62] 235	Bol 77	A	00 42 11.3
[V62] 236	Bol 59	A	00 41 54.3
[V62] 237	Bol 32	A	00 41 21.7
[V62] 238	Bol 7	A	00 40 27.6
[V62] 240	Bol 101	A	00 42 29.1
[V62] 241	Bol 156	A	00 43 14.0
[V62] 242	Bol 160	A	00 43 15.2
[V62] 243	Bol 155	A	00 43 13.6
[V62] 247	Bol 78	A	00 42 12.4
[V62] 248	Bol 177	A	00 43 30.8
[V62] 250	Bol 75	A	00 42 09.0
[V62] 251	Bol 91	A	00 42 22.0
[V62] 253	[V62] B25	A	00 43 18.2
[V62] 256	Bol 150	A	00 43 07.6
[V62] 260	Bol 50	A	00 41 46.4
[V62] 261	Bol 105	A	00 42 31.1
[V62] 262	Bol 130	A	00 42 48.9
[V62] 263	Bol 172	A	00 43 26.1
[V62] 264	Bol 173	A	00 43 28.9
[V62] 265	Bol 162	A	00 43 16.5
[V62] 267	Bol 62	A	00 42 00.6
[V62] 273	Bol 137	A	00 42 54.3
[V62] 274	Bol 122	A	00 42 40.3
[V62] 276	Bol 208	A	00 44 00.4
[V62] 277	Bol 188	A	00 43 41.6
[V62] 278	Bol 141	A	00 42 59.4
[V62] 279	Bol 149	A	00 43 05.5
[V62] 283	Bol 281	A	00 44 43.1
[V62] 286	Bol 214	A	00 44 04.1
[V62] 287	SKHB 245	A	00 43 47.8
[V62] 289	Bol 181	A	00 43 32.7
[V62] 290	Bol 197	A	00 43 50.0
[V62] 291	Bol 198	A	00 43 50.4
[V62] 293	Bol 184	A	00 43 37.8
[V62] 297	Bol 234	A	00 44 46.5
[V62] B20		A	00 40 45.1
[V62] B21		A	00 41 34.5
[V62] B21		A	00 41 34.6
[V62] B22		A	00 40 38.8
[V62] B22		A	00 42 07.3
[V62] B24		A	00 42 06.8
[V62] B25		A	00 43 18.2
[V62] B26		A	00 41 47.3
[V62] B29		A	00 43 25.8
[V62] B29		A	00 43 59.5
[V62] B32		A	00 41 35.0
[V64] 2	Bol 124	A	00 42 41.1
[V64] 5	Bol 118	A	00 42 35.6
vdB-Ha 1	Haffner 7		07 22 54
vdB-Ha 2	Collinder 140		07 24 26.7
vdB-Ha 3	Haffner 11		07 35 22
vdB-Ha 4			07 37 45
vdB-Ha 5	Haffner 13		07 40 26
vdB-Ha 6	NGC 2439		07 40 46
vdB-Ha 7	Haffner 14		07 44 48
vdB-Ha 8	Haffner 15		07 45 30
vdB-Ha 9	NGC 2451		07 45.4
vdB-Ha 10	Ruprecht 35		07 46 14
vdB-Ha 11	Czernik 32		07 50 28
vdB-Ha 12	Haffner 17		07 51 36
vdB-Ha 13	NGC 2477		07 52 10
vdB-Ha 14	Ruprecht 152		07 54 29
vdB-Ha 15	NGC 2489		07 56 16
vdB-Ha 16	Haffner 20		07 56 15
vdB-Ha 17	Ruprecht 50		08 03.4
vdB-Ha 18	NGC 2533		08 07.0
vdB-Ha 19			08 07 04.0
vdB-Ha 20	Ruprecht 54		08 11 23
vdB-Ha 21	Haffner 22		08 12.6
vdB-Ha 22	NGC 2546		08 12.4
vdB-Ha 23			08 14.4
vdB-Ha 24	NGC 2568		08 18 19
vdB-Ha 25	Pismis 2		08 17 54
vdB-Ha 26	NGC 2567		08 18 30
vdB-Ha 27	NGC 2571		08 18 57
vdB-Ha 28	NGC 2580		08 21 28
vdB-Ha 29	NGC 2588		08 23 10
vdB-Ha 30	NGC 2587		08 23 25
vdB-Ha 31	Ruprecht 60		08 24 26
vdB-Ha 32	Ruprecht 61		08 25 15
vdB-Ha 33	Pismis 3		08 31 21
vdB-Ha 34			08 31 12
vdB-Ha 35	Ruprecht 63		08 32 40
vdB-Ha 36	Pismis 4		08 34.6
vdB-Ha 37			08 35 48
vdB-Ha 38	NGC 2627		08 37 15
vdB-Ha 39	NGC 2635		08 38 27
vdB-Ha 40	NGC 2645		08 39 04
vdB-Ha 41	Ruprecht 66		08 40 32
vdB-Ha 42	IC 2391		08 40.3
vdB-Ha 43	Pismis 7		08 41 09
vdB-Ha 44	Pismis 8		08 41 35
vdB-Ha 45	NGC 2660		08 42 39
vdB-Ha 46	NGC 2659		08 42 34
vdB-Ha 47	IC 2395		08 42 31
vdB-Ha 48	NGC 2658		08 43 28
vdB-Ha 49	Ruprecht 68		08 44.5
vdB-Ha 50	NGC 2670		08 45 30
vdB-Ha 51	NGC 2671		08 46 12
vdB-Ha 52	Harvard 3		08 46.5
vdB-Ha 53	Trumpler 10		08 47 45
vdB-Ha 54			08 49 41
vdB-Ha 55			08 56 10.9
vdB-Ha 56			08 57 08
vdB-Ha 57	Markarian 18		09 00 31
vdB-Ha 58			09 10 28

Table D.3: Cluster Cross-Reference

Name	Look Under	GX	2000.0 RA
vdB-Ha 59	NGC 2818		09 16 10
vdB-Ha 60	Pismis 11		09 15 53
vdB-Ha 61	NGC 2849		09 19 23
vdB-Ha 62	Pismis 12		09 20 00
vdB-Ha 63			09 20 38
vdB-Ha 64	Pismis 13		09 22 06.5
vdB-Ha 65	Ruprecht 75		09 21 54
vdB-Ha 66			09 25 16
vdB-Ha 67			09 26 43
vdB-Ha 68	Ruprecht 77		09 27 02
vdB-Ha 69	IC 2488		09 27 27
vdB-Ha 70	Ruprecht 78		09 29 07.9
vdB-Ha 71	NGC 2910		09 30 30
vdB-Ha 72			09 31 23
vdB-Ha 73			09 31 56
vdB-Ha 74	Pismis 15		09 34 45
vdB-Ha 75			09 34 42
vdB-Ha 76	NGC 2972		09 40 12
vdB-Ha 77	Ruprecht 79		09 41 03
vdB-Ha 78			09 43 48
vdB-Ha 79			09 44.1
vdB-Ha 80	Ruprecht 83		09 49 15
vdB-Ha 81	Pismis 16		09 51 14
vdB-Ha 82	NGC 3105		10 00 40
vdB-Ha 83	Ruprecht 85		10 01 26
vdB-Ha 84			10 01 19
vdB-Ha 85			10 02.0
vdB-Ha 86	NGC 3114		10 02.7
vdB-Ha 87			10 04 34
vdB-Ha 88			10 06 15
vdB-Ha 89	Trumpler 12		10 06.5
vdB-Ha 90			10 12 10
vdB-Ha 91			10 17.3
vdB-Ha 92			10 19 04
vdB-Ha 93	NGC 3228		10 21 23
vdB-Ha 94	Trumpler 13		10 23 48
vdB-Ha 95	NGC 3247		10 24 01
vdB-Ha 96	NGC 3255		10 26 32
vdB-Ha 97	IC 2581		10 27 27
vdB-Ha 98	NGC 3293		10 35 49
vdB-Ha 99			10 38 45.0
vdB-Ha 100	NGC 3330		10 38 48
vdB-Ha 101	Melotte 101		10 42 00
vdB-Ha 102	Trumpler 14		10 43 57
vdB-Ha 103	IC 2602		10 42 57
vdB-Ha 104	Trumpler 15		10 44 44
vdB-Ha 105	Trumpler 16		10 45 10
vdB-Ha 106			10 52 38.6
vdB-Ha 107	Trumpler 17		10 56 24
vdB-Ha 108	NGC 3496		10 59 34
vdB-Ha 109	NGC 3532		11 05.5
vdB-Ha 110			11 07.3
vdB-Ha 111			11 09.5
vdB-Ha 112	NGC 3572		11 10 26.6
vdB-Ha 113	Trumpler 18		11 11.4
vdB-Ha 114	NGC 3590		11 13 00
vdB-Ha 115	NGC 3603		11 15 07
vdB-Ha 116	IC 2714		11 17 18
vdB-Ha 117	Melotte 105		11 19 41
vdB-Ha 118			11 22.9

Table D.3: Cluster Cross-Reference

Name	Look Under	GX	2000.0 RA
vdB-Ha 119	Ruprecht 164		11 31.1
vdB-Ha 120	NGC 3766		11 36 15
vdB-Ha 121	Collinder 249		11 38 20.4
vdB-Ha 122	IC 2948		11 38 58
vdB-Ha 123	NGC 3960		11 50 34
vdB-Ha 124	Ruprecht 97		11 57 23
vdB-Ha 125	Ruprecht 98		11 58.8
vdB-Ha 126	NGC 4052		12 02 01
vdB-Ha 127	NGC 4103		12 06 40
vdB-Ha 128	NGC 4184		12 13.6
vdB-Ha 129	NGC 4337		12 24 04
vdB-Ha 130	NGC 4349		12 24 07
vdB-Ha 131			12 26 25.7
vdB-Ha 132			12 26 58
vdB-Ha 133	Harvard 5		12 27 16.3
vdB-Ha 134	NGC 4439		12 28 27
vdB-Ha 135	NGC 4463		12 29 56
vdB-Ha 136	Harvard 6		12 37 54
vdB-Ha 137	Trumpler 20		12 39 32
vdB-Ha 138	NGC 4609		12 42 20
vdB-Ha 139	Hogg 15		12 43 36
vdB-Ha 140			12 53.5
vdB-Ha 141	NGC 4755		12 53 38
vdB-Ha 142	NGC 4815		12 57 59
vdB-Ha 143	NGC 4852		13 00 05
vdB-Ha 144	AL 1		13 15 16
vdB-Ha 145	Harvard 8		13 18 12
vdB-Ha 146	Ruprecht 107		13 19 46
vdB-Ha 147	NGC 5168		13 31 08
vdB-Ha 148	Trumpler 21		13 32 14
vdB-Ha 149	IC 4291		13 36 55
vdB-Ha 150			13 38 02
vdB-Ha 151			13 40 12
vdB-Ha 152	NGC 5281		13 46 36.7
vdB-Ha 153	NGC 5288		13 48 45.6
vdB-Ha 154	NGC 5316		13 54.0
vdB-Ha 155			13 57.5
vdB-Ha 156	NGC 5381		14 00.6
vdB-Ha 157	Lynga 2		14 24 24
vdB-Ha 158	NGC 5606		14 27.8
vdB-Ha 159	NGC 5617		14 29.7
vdB-Ha 160	Pismis 19		14 30 43
vdB-Ha 161	Trumpler 22		14 31.2
vdB-Ha 162	NGC 5662		14 35 30.8
vdB-Ha 163	NGC 5715		14 43 39.0
vdB-Ha 164			14 44.1
vdB-Ha 165	NGC 5749		14 48 48.8
vdB-Ha 166	Hogg 18		14 50 41.4
vdB-Ha 167	NGC 5764		14 53 31.8
vdB-Ha 168	NGC 5822		15 04 02.3
vdB-Ha 169	NGC 5823		15 05 26
vdB-Ha 170	Pismis 20		15 15 23.1
vdB-Ha 171	Pismis 21		15 16 47.7
vdB-Ha 172	NGC 5925		15 27.7
vdB-Ha 173	NGC 5927	g	15 28 00.5
vdB-Ha 174	Lynga 4		15 33 20
vdB-Ha 175	NGC 5946	g	15 35 28.5
vdB-Ha 176		g	15 39 07.3
vdB-Ha 177	Lynga 5		15 41 57.1
vdB-Ha 178	NGC 5999		15 52 14

Table D.3: Cluster Cross-Reference

Name	Look Under	GX	2000.0 RA
vdB-Ha 179	NGC 6005		15 55 47.4
vdB-Ha 180	Trumpler 23		16 00 50.7
vdB-Ha 181	NGC 6025		16 03 18
vdB-Ha 182	Lynga 6		16 04 51
vdB-Ha 183	NGC 6031		16 07 34.4
vdB-Ha 184	Lynga 7	g	16 11 03.0
vdB-Ha 185	Ruprecht 115		16 12 51.1
vdB-Ha 186	NGC 6067		16 13 09
vdB-Ha 187	Pismis 22		16 14 07.9
vdB-Ha 188	NGC 6087		16 18 51.8
vdB-Ha 189	Lynga 9		16 20 39
vdB-Ha 190	Pismis 23		16 23 58
vdB-Ha 191	NGC 6134		16 27 43.6
vdB-Ha 192	NGC 6167		16 34 35
vdB-Ha 193	Collinder 307		16 35.3
vdB-Ha 194	NGC 6192		16 40 20.8
vdB-Ha 195	NGC 6193		16 41 20.3
vdB-Ha 196	NGC 6204		16 46 07.9
vdB-Ha 197			16 46 30.3
vdB-Ha 198	NGC 6208		16 49 25.8
vdB-Ha 199	NGC 6216		16 49 23.6
vdB-Ha 200			16 50.0
vdB-Ha 201	NGC 6231		16 54 09.8
vdB-Ha 202	Ruprecht 122		16 55 08.3
vdB-Ha 203	Collinder 316		16 55.5
vdB-Ha 204	NGC 6242		16 55 30.6
vdB-Ha 205			16 56 11.3
vdB-Ha 206	NGC 6250		16 57 55
vdB-Ha 207	NGC 6253		16 59 06.1
vdB-Ha 208	NGC 6256	g	16 59 32.6
vdB-Ha 209	NGC 6259		17 00.7
vdB-Ha 210	NGC 6266	g	17 01 12.6
vdB-Ha 211			17 02 07.9
vdB-Ha 212	NGC 6268		17 02 04.1
vdB-Ha 213	NGC 6281		17 04 47.2
vdB-Ha 214			17 05 50.3
vdB-Ha 215	NGC 6293	g	17 10 10.4
vdB-Ha 216	NGC 6304	g	17 14 32.5
vdB-Ha 217			17 16 20.4
vdB-Ha 218	NGC 6318		17 16 13.4
vdB-Ha 219	NGC 6316	g	17 16 37.4
vdB-Ha 220	NGC 6322		17 18.5
vdB-Ha 221			17 18 34
vdB-Ha 222			17 18 47.1
vdB-Ha 223			17 20 42
vdB-Ha 224	IC 4651		17 24.7
vdB-Ha 225	Trumpler 25		17 24 30.3
vdB-Ha 226	NGC 6352	g	17 25 29.2
vdB-Ha 227	Pismis 24		17 24 43.4
vdB-Ha 228	Terzan 2	g	17 27 33.4
vdB-Ha 229	Haute Provence 1	g	17 31 05.2
vdB-Ha 230	Harvard 16		17 31 03
vdB-Ha 231			17 31 55.7
vdB-Ha 232	NGC 6383		17 34 42.2
vdB-Ha 233	NGC 6380	g	17 34 28.0
vdB-Ha 234	NGC 6388	g	17 36 17.0
vdB-Ha 235	Terzan 1	g	17 35 47.0
vdB-Ha 236	Tonantzintla 2	g	17 36 10.5
vdB-Ha 237	Trumpler 27		17 36 12.7
vdB-Ha 238	Trumpler 28		17 36 59

Table D.3: Cluster Cross-Reference

Name	Look Under	GX	2000.0 RA
vdB-Ha 239	NGC 6396		17 37 38
vdB-Ha 240	NGC 6404		17 39.6
vdB-Ha 241	NGC 6400		17 40 10
vdB-Ha 242	NGC 6405		17 40 17
vdB-Ha 243	Ruprecht 128		17 44 19.3
vdB-Ha 244	Collinder 347		17 46 18.9
vdB-Ha 245			17 46 14.4
vdB-Ha 246	NGC 6425		17 46 53
vdB-Ha 247	Ruprecht 130		17 47 32
vdB-Ha 248	NGC 6441	g	17 50 12.9
vdB-Ha 249	Terzan 6	g	17 50 46.4
vdB-Ha 250	NGC 6451		17 50 41
vdB-Ha 251	NGC 6453	g	17 50 51.8
vdB-Ha 252	Ruprecht 134		17 52.8
vdB-Ha 253	Czernik 37		17 53 16.4
vdB-Ha 254	NGC 6475		17 53 46
vdB-Ha 255	NGC 6520		18 03 25
vdB-Ha 256	NGC 6522	g	18 03 35.0
vdB-Ha 257	NGC 6528	g	18 04 49.6
vdB-Ha 259	NGC 6558	g	18 10 17.6
vdB-Ha 260	NGC 6569	g	18 13 38.9
vdB-Ha 261	AL 3		18 14 05.7
vdB-Ha 262	NGC 6624	g	18 23 40.5
VII Zwicky 7	Palomar 1	g	03 33 20.8
W 5	IC 1848		02 51 11
W 55	NGC 6823		19 43 10
W. Herschel V.13	NGC 6523		18 04 25
W. Herschel VII.37	NGC 2262		06 39 38.7
W. Herschel VIII.1B	NGC 2319		07 00 37
W. Herschel VIII.4	NGC 1896		05 25 41.9
W. Herschel VIII.7	NGC 1663		04 49 24.3
W. Herschel VIII.20	NGC 6885		20 12 01
W. Herschel VIII.22	NGC 6885		20 12 01
W. Herschel VIII.41	NGC 1802		05 10 13
W. Herschel VIII.43	NGC 1750		05 03.9
W. Herschel VIII.46	NGC 2430		07 39 30
W. Herschel VIII.47	NGC 2428		07 39 18
W. Herschel VIII.76	NGC 6991		20 54.9
[W95] 3	Pyxis	g	09 07 57.8
Waterloo 1			04 18 36.4
Waterloo 2			05 28 01
Waterloo 3			07 55 06.4
Waterloo 6			08 40 20.7
Waterloo 7			07 26 08.0
Waterloo 8	[FM80] 1		07 30 12
[WB89] 220	NGC 7423		22 55 06.5
[WB89] 653	NGC 1931		05 31 26
[WB89] 751	NGC 2169		06 08 25
[WB89] 846	Collinder 106		06 37.1
[WB89] 848	Berkeley 24		06 37 47
[WB89] 1049	Ruprecht 32		07 45 06
Westerlund 1			16 47 04
Westerlund 2	NGC 3247		10 24 01
Westerlund 3	Pismis 22		16 14 07.9
[WG71] Cl* 1		S	01 42 52.9
[WG71] Cl* 2		S	01 45 14.6
[WG71] Cl* 3		S	01 49 43.0
[WG71] Cl* 4	Lindsay 114	S	01 50 19.4
[WG71] Cl* 5		S	01 50 51.6
[WG71] Cl* 6		S	01 53 13.1
[WG71] Cl* 7		S	01 53 34.3
[WG71] Cl* 8		S	01 56 35.5
[WG71] Cl* 9	NGC 796	S	01 56 44.5
[WG71] Cl* 10		S	02 00 01.7
[WG71] Cl* 11		S	02 00 37.3
[WG71] Cl* 12		S	02 01 02.7
[WG71] Cl* 13		S	02 02 42.0
[WG71] Cl* 14		S	02 04 49.0
[WG71] Cl* 15		S	02 07 44.8
[WG71] Cl* 16		S	02 08 08.4
[WG71] Cl* 17		S	02 08 10.8
[WG71] Cl* 18		S	02 15 41.4
WHI B0200-03			02 02 56.8
Whiting 1	WHI B0200-03		02 02 56.8
Wilk's cluster	Melotte 71		07 37 30
[WSB85] C 11	ACH 6	A	00 42 48.4
[WSB85] C 14	ACH 7	A	00 42 48.6
[WSB85] C 19	Bol 132	A	00 42 51.4
[WSB85] W 4		A	00 42 34.5
[WSB85] W 5	Bol 261	A	00 42 36.1
[WSB85] W 6	Bol 119	A	00 42 36.2
[WSB85] W 7		A	00 42 38.0
WSTB 36W188	NBol 23	A	00 42 26.7
WSTB 37W125	NBol 23	A	00 42 26.7
WZ Sgr cl			18 16 59.6
Z 85 - 13	Berkeley 29		06 53 04
Z 0650.2+1659	Berkeley 29		06 53 04
Zet Scl	Blanco 1		00 04.2
Zeta Scl cluster	Blanco 1		00 04.2

Appendix E
World Wide Web and Postal Addresses

World Wide Web and postal addresses are given here for organizations, individuals, and information cited in the main text. Given the ephemeral nature of this information, we will attempt to maintain a current copy of it on the World Wide Web. This copy can be reached via the Willmann-Bell, Inc. web site at http://www.willbell.com/downloads.

2MASS or 2-Micron All Sky Survey:
http://www.ipac.caltech.edu/2mass/

2MASS-GC01 and 2MASS-GC02: See "amastro" message 2618 by B. Archinal, of 2000 June 20 at
http://groups.yahoo.com/group/amastro/message/2618.

Amateur Astronomy or "amastro" e-mail list:
See http://groups.yahoo.com/group/amastro/message, or write Jeff Medkeff (jeff@roboticobservatory.com) for information.

Archinal, Brent: barchinal@usgs.gov

Astronomical Data Center (ADC):
http://adc.gsfc.nasa.gov/. The ADC closed as of October 1, 2002. The web site is still available but frozen as of that date.

Astrophysics Data System (ADS):
http://adswww.harvard.edu/index.html

Canadian Astronomy Data Centre (DSS access):
Dominion Astrophysical Observatory,
Victoria, British Columbia
http://cadcwww.dao.nrc.ca/dss/

Centre de Données astronomiques de Strasbourg (CDS):
Observatoire de Strasbourg
11 rue de l'Université
67000 Strasbourg
France
http://cdsarc.u-strasbg.fr/
question@simbad.u-strasbg.fr

Common names for star clusters: See Saguaro Astronomy Club database, version 7.2 of the database is currently available at
http://www.saguaroastro.org/archive/sacdbs.htm.

Also used was "A Collection of Some Common Names for Deep Sky Objects." by H. Frommert, at
http://www.seds.org/messier/xtra/supp/d-names.html.
or
http://www.seds.org/messier/xtra/supp/d-names.txt
(plain text).

DeMary, T. [2002]: "Re: NGC 6222 identified?"—See "amastro" message 9025 of October 13, 2002 at:
http://groups.yahoo.com/group/amastro/message/9025

***Dictionary of Nomenclature of Celestial Objects*, maintained by the IAU:**
http://vizier.u-strasbg.fr/cgi-gin/Dic

Digitized Sky Survey:
http://archive.stsci.edu/dss/index.html
http://stdatu.stsci.edu/dss/dss_form

Drawings of M 13, M 20, and M 42. See "Harvard Annals" below.

Eicher, D. See "Goldstein, A" below.

ESA:
http://astro.estec.esa.nl/Hipparcos/movies/hyades.html.

ESO Online Digitized Sky Survey:
European Southern Observatory,
Garching, Germany
http://archive.eso.org/dss/dss/

Frommert, H.: See "Common names for star clusters" above.

George Observatory, in Brazos Bend State Park, Texas:
http://www.geocities.com/birdbarn2000/page11.html.

Goldstein, A. [1999]: See "amastro" message 1017 of November 3, 1999 at
http://groups.yahoo.com/group/amastro/message/1017.

Guide Star Catalogue (GSC) data system:
http://www-gsss.stsci.edu/gsc/GSChome.htm

Guide Star Catalogue (GSC) 2.2:

http://www-gsss.stsci.edu/gsc/gsc2/GSC2home.htm
http://www-gsss.stsci.edu/support/data_access.htm

Harris, W. 1999 Globular Cluster Catalog:
http://physun.physics.mcmaster.ca/Globular.html

Harvard Annals VIII, 1876, part 2, chapter 1. Drawings of M 13 (plate 15, top), M 20 (plates 10 and 32), and M 42 (plate 27):
http://ads.harvard.edu/books/hcoann/

Hipparcos and Tycho Catalogues [ESA, 1997]:
http://astro.estec.esa.nl/Hipparcos/
http://vizier.u-utrasbg-fs/viz-bin/VizeR

Hubble Space Telescope (HST) images:
http://oposite.stsci.edu/pubinfo/pictures.html

Hurt, Robert L., Tom H. Jarrett, J. Davy Kirkpatrick, and Roc M. Cutri [2000]. "Serendipitous 2MASS Discoveries Near the Galactic Plane: A Spiral Galaxy and Two Globular Clusters." See
http://xxx.lanl.gov/abs/astro-ph/0006262.

Hypersky: See
http://www.willbell.com/software/hypersky/ hypersky .htm

Lowell Observatory public ftp area:
For the globular cluster data table:
ftp://ftp.lowell.edu/pub/bas/deepsky/globulars.tab
For the list of references:
ftp://ftp.lowell.edu/pub/bas/deepsky/globulars.ref
For the open cluster data table:
ftp://ftp.lowell.edu/pub/bas/deepsky/ocpos.lis

Lund Catalogue: *Catalogue of Open Cluster Data,* Lyngå
Lund Observatory
Box 43,
S-221, 00 Lund
Sweden
Also available from
Stellar Data Centre (CDS)
or
Astronomical Data Center (ADS)
The catalog is also available via the World Wide Web from these two organizations, at
http://cdsweb.u-strasbg.fr/cgi-bin/Cat?VII/92A
and
ftp://adc.gsfc.nasa.gov/pub/adc/archives/catalogs/7/7092A/
respectively.

M 73: See NGC 6994 below.

Mackie, G. [2000]: See "amastro" message 2873 by A. Whitman of 2000 August 13 at:
http://groups.yahoo.com/group/amastro.message/2873
Also see reply by Archinal, message 2875 of 2000 August 14, at
http://www.egroups.com/message/amastro/message/2875.

Markov 1 : See Paul Markov's web page describing his discovery observation of this group at http://home.ica.net/~pmarkov/log.htm (click on "2000" and move down to "July 4/5"), and at http://home.ica.net/~pmarkov/markov1.htm.

McNeil, J. [1999]: See "amastro" message 1019 of November 3, 1999 at
http://groups.yahoo.com/group/amastro/message/1019.

Morel, M. [2002]: "NGC 6222 identified?"—See "amastro" message 9023 of October 12, 2002 at:
http://groups.yahoo.com/group/amastro/message/9023

MegaStar: See
http://www.willbell.com/software/megastar/index.htm.

NASA/GSFC SkyView:
http://skyview.gsfc.nasa.gov/

NASA Astronomical Data System (ADS):
http://adswww.harvard.edu/

The National Deep Sky Observers Society:
NDSOS
1607 Washington Blvd.
Louisville, KY 40242-3539
http://www.cismall.com/deepsky/

NASA Extragalactic Database (NED):
http://nedwww.ipac.caltech.edu

Netastrocatalog: http://www.visualdeepsky.org/

NGC/IC Project:
http://www.ngcic.org

NGC 6994 = M 73: See "amastro" message 6299 by B. Skiff of December 27, 2001 at
http://groups.yahoo.com/group/ amastro/message/6299.

Pensack, D. [1999]: See "amastro" message 1018 of November 4, 1999 at
http://groups.yahoo.com/group/amastro/message/1018.

"RealSky" from the Astronomical Society of the Pacific:
http://www.aspsky.org/realsky.html

Saguaro Astronomy Club database: See "Common names for star clusters" above.

SAOimage software:
http://tdc-www.harvard.edu/software/saoimage.html

SIMBAD:
http://simbad.u-strasbg.fr/Simbad
http://cdsweb.u-strasbg.fr/Simbad.html.

Skiff information on Galactic Clusters and Asterisms: (see section 4.2.4):
ftp://www.lowell.edu/pub/bas/deepsky/ocpos.lis

Skiff information on Galactic Globular Clusters: (see section 4.2.7):
ftp://www.lowell.edu/pub/bas/deepsky/globulars.tab
ftp://www.lowell.edu/pub/bas/deepsky/globulars.ref

Skiff J0058.4+6828: See message from B. Skiff of September 24, 1999, posted at:
http://groups.yahoo.com/group/amastro/message/832.

SkyEye:
Instituto di Radioastronomia
Bologna, Italy
http://www.ira.bo.cnr.it/avo/

SkyView Utility:
http://skyview.gsfc.nasa.gov/

Sloan Digital Sky Survey (SDSS):
http://www.apo.nmsu.edu/sdsshome.html.

Steine, Mikkel: See http://Messier45.com

STScI Digitized Sky Survey:
Space Telescope Science Institute, Baltimore, Maryland.
http://archive.stsci.edu/dss/index.html

Tycho-2 Catalogue:
http://adc.gsfc.nasa.gov/adc-cgi/cat.pl?/catalogs/1/259/

USNO, recommended star catalogs:
http://ad.usno.navy.mil/star/star_cats_rec.shtml

USNO-B1.0: http://www.nofs.navy.mil/projects/pmm

***VizieR* catalog viewing facility of the Centre de Donées Stellaires:**
http://vizier.u-strasbg.fr/

Washington Visual Double Star Catalogue 1996.0: Available from the ADC at:
http://adc.gsfc.nasa.gov/adc-cgi/cat.pl?/catalogs/1/1237/
and the current version from the USNO at:
http://ad.usno.navy.mil/wds/.

WEBDA—"A Site Devoted to Stellar Clusters". Open cluster database maintained by J.-C. Mermilliod:
http://obswww.unige.ch/webda/

Whitman, A. [2000]: See Mackie, G., above.

Willmann-Bell, Inc. P.O. Box 35025,
Richmond, Virginia 23235, USA
http://www.willbell.com

Wilson, B. [1998]: "Obscure Globular Clusters of the Milky Way: Terzan Clusters and the Faintest Globular UKS 1," *The Deep-Sky Observer, The Quarterly Journal of the Webb Society*, no. 114, October, 8-16. See
http://www.angelfire.com/id/jsredshift/obscure.htm
for a revised copy of this article.

The Webb Society:
c/o Don Miles
96 Marmion Road,
Southsea,
Hants PO5 2BB,
U.K.
don@webbsoc.demon.co.uk
http://www.webbsociety.freeserve.co.uk/

References

Generally accepted abbreviations for various catalogs and atlases are listed in brackets following the entries as appropriate.

Abell, G. 1955. "Globular Clusters and Planetary Nebulae discovered on the National Geographic Society-Palomar Observatory Sky Survey." *P.A.S.P.* 67: 258–261.

Abell, G. 1958. "The distribution of rich clusters of galaxies." *Ap.J.* Supp. 3: 211-288. [Abell]

Abell G., H. Corwin Jr., and R. Olowin. 1989. "A catalog of rich clusters of galaxies." *Ap.J.* Supp. 70: 1–138. [ACO]

Abt, H., C. Perry, E. Olsen, and A. Grauer. 1980. "A small cluster near IC 1805." *P.A.S.P.* 92: 60. [Abt 1 = Mrk 6]

Acker, A., F. Ochsenbein, B. Stenholm, R. Tylenda, J. Marcout, and C. Schohn. 1992. *Strasbourg-ESO Catalogue of Galactic Planetary Nebulae.* Garching bei München, Germany: European Southern Observatory. [PN]

Adams, M. T., K. Strom, and S. Strom. 1983. "The star-forming history of the young cluster NGC 2264." *Ap. J. Supp.* 53 (Dec): 893–936.

Adams, S., C. J. Penn, and M.J. Seaton. 1980. "Where Exactly is the Planetary Nebula in M15?" *The Observatory* 100: 209.

Agekyan, T. A., and V.V. Orlov. 1984. "Moving-cluster Membership of Solar-Neighborhood Stars." *Astron. Zh.* 61 (Jan.–Feb.): 60–65. Trans. in *Soviet Astronomy* 28, no. 1: 36–39. [AO84]

Aitken, R.G. 1932. *New General Catalogue of Double Stars Within 120° of the North Pole.* 2 vols. Washington, D.C.: Carnegie Inst. Publ. No. 417. [ADS]

Alcaino, G. 1971. "The globular cluster NGC 4833." *Astron. Astrophys.* 13: 287–292.

Alcaino, G. 1974. *Atlas of Galactic Globular Clusters with Colour Magnitude Diagrams.* Chile: Ediciones Nueva Universidad, Universidad Católica de Chile.

Alcaino, G. 1975a. "M4–The closest globular cluster." *Astron. Astrophys.* Supp. Ser. 21: 5–14.

Alcaino, G. 1975b. "The globular cluster NGC 288." *Astron. Astrophys.* Supp. Ser. 21: 15–24.

Alcaino, G. 1976. "The Globular Cluster NGC 3201." *Astron. Astrophys.* Supp. Ser. 26: 251–259.

Alcaino, G. 1977. "The metal-poor globular cluster NGC 6656." *Astron. Astrophys.* Supp. Ser. 29 (Sep.): 383–395.

Alcaino, G. and W. Liller. 1980. "The Main Sequence of the Globular Cluster NGC 288." *Astron. J.* 85: 1592–1603.

Alcaino, G. and W. Liller. 1981. "The main sequence of the globular cluster NGC 3201." *Astron. J.* 86 (Oct.): 1480–1499.

Alcaino, G. and W. Liller. 1983. "The Main Sequence of the Globular Cluster M22." *Astron. J.* 88: 1330.

Alcaino, G. and W. Liller. 1984. "BVRI main-sequence photometry of the globular cluster M4." *Ap.J.* Supp. Ser. 56 (Sep.): 19–65.

Alcaino, G., W. Liller, and F. Alvarado. 1988. "BVI CCD photometry of the globular cluster M4." *Ap. J.* 330 (July 15): 569–578.

Alcaino, G., W. Liller, and F. Alvarado. 1989. "BVRI CCD photometry of the globular cluster NGC 3201." *Astron. Astrophys.* 216 (June): 68–79.

Allen, R. H. 1962. *Star Names, Their Lore and Meaning.* New York: Dover Publications, Inc.

Alter, G., B. Balazs, and J. Ruprecht. 1970. *Catalogue of Star Clusters and Associations.* Budapest: Akadémiai Kiado.

Alter, G., *et al.*, 1959. *Bull. Astr. Inst. Czech.* 10, No.3, Appendix.

Alter, G., *et al.*, 1960. *Bull. Astr. Inst. Czech.* 11, No.1, Appendix.

Alter, G., *et al.*, 1961. *Bull. Astr. Inst. Czech.* 12, No.1, Appendix. [Ruprecht 1 to 147].

Alter, G., *et al.*, 1962. *Bull. Astr. Inst. Czech.* 13, No.1, Appendix.

Alter, G., *et al.*, 1963. *Bull. Astr. Inst. Czech.* 14, No.1, Appendix.

Alter, G., *et al.*, 1964. *Bull. Astr. Inst. Czech.* 15, No.1, Appendix.

Alter, G., *et al.*, 1965. *Bull. Astr. Inst. Czech.* 16, No.1, Appendix.

Alter, G., *et al.*, 1966. *Bull. Astr. Inst. Czech.* 17, No.1, Appendix. [Ruprecht 148 to 175].

Alter, G., J. Ruprecht, V. Vanysek. 1958. *Catalogue of Star Clusters and Associations.* Prague: Publishing House of the Czechoslovak Academy of Sciences.

Ambartsumian, V. A. 1938. *Ann. Len. State Univ.* 22, nos. 4, 19. (English translation in *The Dynamics of Star Clusters.* Ed. J. Goodman & P.Hut, 1985. Dordrecht: Reidel)

Andrews, A. D., and E. M. Lindsay. 1967. "New Southern Clusters and Nebulous Ovals." *Irish Astron. J.* 8: 126-127, plates 7 and 8. [AL]

Antalová, A. 1972. "UBV Photographic Photometry of Stars in the Region AR_{1950}: 17^h03^m–17^h41^m $Decl_{1950}$: −28.8° to −33.4° III. The Catalogue and Identification Maps of Open Star Clusters: NGC 6405, NGC 6383, "NGC 6374", Av 2, NGC 6416 and H. Alpha Emission Regions: Gum 67 (Av 3), Gum 68 (Av 2 [sic, Av 1]). *Bulletin of the Astronomical Society of Czechoslovakia* 23, no. 2:126–139. [Ant 1 to 3]

Aparicio, A., B. Bertelli., C. Chiosi., and J. Garcia-Pelayo 1991. "CCD UBVR photometry of two old open clusters: King 11 and Be42—Comparison with theoretical models." *Astronomy and Astrophysics* Supplement Series 88: 155–175.

Apriamasvili, S.P. 1964. "On a New Open Cluster in Scutum." *Astr. Cirk.* 280: 1–2. [Apr 1]

Archinal, Brent A. 1993. *The "Non-Existent" Star Clusters of the RNGC.* Southsea, Hants, England: The Webb Society

Archinal, Brent A. 1994. Letter to the editor. *Webb Society Quarterly Journal* 97 (July): 39–41.

Argelander, F. 1903. *Bonner Durchmusterung Des nördlichen Himmels.* Rev. F. Küstner. Bonn, Germany: Marcus and Weber's Verlag. [BD (north)]

Argyle, R. W. 1986. *Webb Society Deep-Sky Observer's Handbook.* 2nd ed. Vol. 1, *Double Stars.* Short Hills, NJ: Enslow Pub. Inc.

Armandroff, T. E. 1989a. "The properties of the disk system of globular clusters." *Astron. J.* 97(Feb.): 375–389.

Armandroff, T. E. 1989b. "ERRATUM—The properties of the disk system of globular clusters." *Astron. J.* 97 (May): 1532.

Arp, H. C. and B.F. Madore. 1987. *A Catalogue of Southern Peculiar Galaxies and Associations.* 2 vols. Cambridge: Cambridge University Press. [AM 0430–392, AM 1353–265, AM 2346–731]

Arp, H. C. and C.T. van Sant. 1958. "Southern hemisphere photometry IV: The galactic cluster NGC 4755." *Astron. J.* 63: 341.

Arp, H., and S. van den Bergh. 1960. "A New Faint Globular Cluster." *P.A.S.P.* 72, no. 424 (Feb.): 48 and plate I. [Palomar 14 = Arp 1 = AvdB]

Arp, H. C. and F. D. A. Hartwick. 1971. "A photometric study of the metal-rich globular cluster M71." *Ap.J.* 167: 499–509.

Arp, H. C. and W. G. Melbourne. 1959. "Color-Magnitude Diagram for the Globular Cluster M22." *Astron. J.* 64: 28–32.

Ashman, K. M., and S. E. Zepf. 1992. "The formation of globular clusters in merging and interacting galaxies." *Ap. J.* part 1, 384: 50—61.

Astronomer Royal [Sir Frank Dyson]. 1911. "Observations of Nebulae Made at the Royal Observatory, Greenwich." *MNRAS* 71: 509–511.

Astronomer Royal, 1915. "Stellar Photographs by the late John Franklin-Adams." *Mem. Royal Ast. Soc.* 60: 141–144, plates 4–14.

Auner, G., J. Dengel, H. Hartl, and R. Weinberger. 1980. "A Ghost Image of Sirius as a Hiding Place for a New Star Cluster." *P.A.S.P.* 92: 422–425. [Auner 1]

AURA. 1995. *The STScI Digitized Sky Survey.* Association of Universities for Research in Astronomy. [DSS]

Aurière M., G. Coupinot, and J. Hecquet. 1992. "New Globular Clusters in the Bulge of M31." *Astron. Astrophys.* 256: 95–103. [ACH]

Auwers, A. 1862. "Verzeichniss neuer Nebelflecke." *Astronomische Beobachtungen auf der Königlichen Universitäts-Sternwarte zu Königsberg.* Ed. E. Luther. Königsberg, Germany: E.J. Dalkowski.

Aveni, A. F. and J. Hunter Jr. 1969. "Observational Studies Relating to Star Formation II." *Astron. J.* 74, no. 8 (October): 1021–1023, [Aveni-Hunter 1]

Baade, W. 1944. "The Resolution of Messier 32, NGC 205, and the Central Region of the Andromeda Nebula." *Ap. J.* 100: 137–146.

Baade, W.; ed. by C. Payne-Gaposchkin. 1963. *Evolution of Stars and Galaxies.* Cambridge, Mass.: Harvard University Press.

Baade, W., and H. C. Arp. 1964. "Positions of emission nebulae in M 31." *Ap.J.* 139: 1027–1044. [BA]

Bailey, S. I. 1902. "A discussion of variable stars in the cluster omega Centauri." *Harvard Annals* 38: 1–252.

Bailey, S. 1908. "Catalogue of Bright Clusters and Nebulae." *Ann. Harv. Coll. Obs.* 60, No. 8.

Balona, L. A. C.D. Laney. 1995. "CCD Strömgren photometry of NGC 6231." *M.N.R.A.S.* 276: 627–634.

Barker, E. S. 1980. *Deep-Sky Observer's Handbook* Vol. 3, *Open and Globular Star Clusters.* Ed. K. Glyn Jones. Hillside, NJ: Enslow Publishers.

Barkhatova, K. A. 1958a. "Ucenye zapiski Ural'skogo Gosudarstvennogo Universiteta." no. 22. Obtained via loan from the University of Arizona library. Photocopy now available in the U. S. Naval Observatory library.

Barkhatova, K. A. 1958b. "Clusters in the region of the North American Nebula."*Soviet Astronomy* 2, 3:410–419. [Barkhatova 1]

Barmby, P., J. P. Huchra, J. P. Brodie, D. A. Forbes, L. L. Schroder, and C. J. Grillmair. 2000. "M31 Globular Clusters: Colors and Metallicities." *Astron. J.,* 119: 727–747. [BHB2000]

Barnard, E. E. 1927. *A Photographic Atlas of Selected Regions of the Milky Way.* Washington,. D.C.: Carnegie Institution of Washington.

Barnard, E. E., 1889. "The Cluster G.C. 1420 and the Nebula N.G.C. 2237." *Astronomische Nachrichten* no. 2918 (August 24):253–254 and insert.

Bassino, L. P. and J. C. Muzzio. 1995. "Is M54 the Nucleus of the Sagittarius Galaxy?" *The Observatory* 115, no. 1128 (Oct.): 256–257.

Battinelli, P., A. Brandimarti, and R. Capuzzo-Dolcetta. 1994. "Integrated photometric properties of open clusters." *Astron. Astrophys.* Supp. Ser. 104 (May 1): 379–390.

Battistini, P., F. Bonoli, A. Braccesi, F. Fusi Pecci, M. Malagnini, and B. Marano. 1980. "Search for (globular) clusters in M31. I: Candidates in a 70′ square field centered on M31." *Astron. Astrophys.* Suppl. Ser. 42: 357–374. [Bol 1 to Bol 288; Bol D1 to Bol D132]

Battistini, P., F. Bonoli, A. Braccesi, L. Federici, F. Fusi Pecci, B. Marano, and F. Borngen. 1987. "Search for (globular) clusters in M31. IV: Candidates in a 3x3° square field centered on M31." *Astron. Astrophys.* Supp. Ser. 67: 447–482. [Bol 289 to Bol 513; Bol D133 to Bol D350]

Battistini, P., F. Bonoli, M. Casavecchia, L. Ciotti, L. Federici, and F. Fusi Pecci. 1993. "New globular cluster candidates in the inner regions of M31 and the projected density profile of the cluster system." *Astron. Astrophys.* 272: 77–97. [NBol]

Baumgardner, J. and M. Mendillo. 1993. "If Galileo Had Owned a CCD." *Sky & Telescope* 85, no. 6 (June): 19–21.

Beasley, M. A., and R. M. Sharples. 2000. "Spectroscopy of globular cluster candidates in the Sculptor group galaxies NGC 253 and 55." *M.N.R.A.S.* 311: 673–682.

Becker, R., and R. White. 1988. "LkHα 101: The Stellar Wind, the Surrounding Nebula and an Associated Radio Star Cluster." *Astrophys. J.* 324 (Jan. 15): 893–898, plates 2–3. [Cl BW 88]

Becker, W., and R. Fenkart. 1971. "A catalogue of galactic star clusters observed in three colours." *Astron. Astrophys.* Supp. Ser. 4: 241–252. [Basel 1 to 6]

Benedict, G, J. Higdon, W. Jefferys, R. Duncombe, P. Hemenway, P. Shelus, A. Whipple, E. Nelan, D. Story, B. McArthur, J. McCartney, O. Franz, L. Fredrick, & W. Van Altena [1993]. 'NGC 4314. II. Hubble Space Telescope I-band surface photometry of the nuclear region.' Astron. J., 105, pp. 1369–1377. [HJD93]

Bernabei, S., and V. F. Polcaro. 2001. "A search for peculiar objects in young open clusters. II. A new Be star, the optical counterpart of IRAS 19564+3224 and a new open cluster in Vulpecula." Astron. Astrophys. 371: 123–132. [Loiano 1]

Berry, R. 1994. "Image processing in astronomy." *Sky & Telescope* 87, no. 4 (April): 30–36.

Becvar, A. 1962. *Atlas of the Heavens—Atlas Coeli 1950.0.* Prague: Publishing House of the Czechoslovak Academy of Sciences.

Becvar, A. 1964. *Atlas of the Heavens—II Catalogue 1950.0.* Prague: Publishing House of the Czechoslovak Academy of Sciences.

Bhatia, R. K., M. A. Read, D. Hatzidimitriou, & S. Tritton [1991]. "A catalogue of binary star cluster candidates in the Large Magellanic Cloud." Astron. Astrophys. Supp. Ser., 87, pp. 335–352. [BRHT]

Bica, E. 1994. "Discovery of an obscured globular cluster candidate in the bulge." *Astron. Astrophys.* 285: 868–870.

Bica, E. L. D., and H. R. Schmitt [1995]. "Revised and Extended Catalog of Magellanic System Clusters, Associations, and Emission Nebulae. I. Small Magellanic Cloud and Bridge." *Astrophysical Journal Supplement* 101 (November):41–85. [[BS95]]

Bica, E., J. J. Clariá, Ch. Bonatto, A. E. Piatti, S. Ortolani, and B. Barbuy. 1995. "Three globular cluster candidates in the direction of the bulge shown to be small emission nebulae." *Astron. Astrophys.* 303: 747–752.

Bica, E., J. J. Clariá, H. Dottori, J. F. C. Santos, Jr., and A. E. Piatti. 1996. "Integrated *UBV* Photometry of 624 Star Clusters and Associations in the Large Magellanic Cloud." *Ap. J.* Supp. Ser. 102 (Jan.): 57–73.

Bica, E., S. Ortolani, and B. Barbuy. 1993. "NGC 6603: a young rich open cluster towards the bulge." *Astron. Astrophys.* 270: 117–121.

Bica, E., S. Ortolani, and B. Barbury. 1994 "The globular cluster NGC 6540." *Astron. Astrophys.* 283: 67–75.

Bica, E., S. Ortolani, and B. Barbuy. 1999. "The nature of the star clusters ESO 93–SC08 and ESO 452–SC11." *Astron. Astrophys.* Supp. Ser. 136: 363–372.

Bica, E., and C. M. Dutra. 2002. "Updating the Census of Star Clusters in the Small Magellanic Cloud." *Astron. J.,* 119, no. 3: 1214–1224. March.

Bigourdan, M. 1887. "Nébuleuses nouvelles, découvertes à l'observatoire de Paris." *Comptes Rendus* (December 5): 1116–1119.

Bigourdan, M. G. 1899–1917. Observations de Nébuleuses et D'Amas Stellaires. Extract of *Annales de l'Observatoire de Paris.* 5 vols. Paris: Gauthier-Villars, Imprimeur-Libraire de l'Observatoire de Paris.

Blanco, V. M. 1949. "A new galactic star cluster in Sculptor." *P.A.S.P.* 61: 183–184. [Blanco 1]

Blitz, L., M. Fitch, and A. A. Stark. 1982. "Catalogue of CO radial velocities toward galactic H II regions." *Ap.J. Supp.* 49: 183–206. [BFS]

Böhlin, K. 1909. "On the Galactic System, with Regard to its Structure, Origin and Relations in Space." *Kungl. Svenska Vetenskapsakademiens Handlinger* 43, no. 10.

Bok, B. F., P. F. Bok, and J. A. Graham. 1966. "A photometric study of the I Scorpii Association." *M.N.R.A.S.* 131: 247–252.

Bok, B. J. and C. S. Cordwell. 1973. *Molecules in the Galactic Environment.* Ed. M. A. Gordon and L. E. Snyder, 53. New York: Wiley.

Bond, G. P. 1863. "List of New Nebula seen at the Observatory of Harvard College." *Astronomische Nachrichten* 1453 (Dec. 18): 193–198.

Bònoli, E., L. Federici, and F. Pecci. 1988. "The nature of the most distant M31 globular cluster candidate." *Astron. Astrophys.* 205: 6–8.

Braes, L. L. E. 1961. "Three-colour photometry of IC 2602." *M.N.A.S.S.A.* 20: 7.

Brand J., L. Blitz, and J. Wouterloot. 1986. "Catalogue of the optical nebulae in the longitude range 230° to 305°." *Astron. Astrophys.* Supp. Ser. 65: 537–550. [BRAN]

Brandt, J. C., T. P. Stecher, D. L. Crawford, and S. P. Maran. 1971. "The GUM Nebula: Fossil Strömgren Sphere of the VELA X Supernova." *Astrophys. J.*, 163 (February 1): L99–L104. [Gam Vel cluster]

Bratolyubova-Tsulukidze, L., M. Kudryavtsev, A. Melioranskii, I. Savenko and B. Yushkov. 1976. "Correlation of hard X-ray source positions with globular clusters." *Soviet Astronomy Letters* 2: 71–72. [KOHX]

Braun, R. 1990. "The interstellar medium of M31. II. A survey of 20 centimeter continuum emission." *Ap.J. Supp.* 72: 761–775. [[B90]]

Brewer, J. P., G. G. Fahlman, H. B. Richer, L. Searle, and I. Thompson. 1993. "CCD photometry in the globular cluster NGC 3201." *Astron. J.* 105: 2158–2171.

Brocato, E., V. Castellani, and A. Digiorgio. 1993. "The intermediate age galactic cluster M11." *Astron. J.* 105, no.6: 2192–2198, 2372.

Brodie, J. P. and J. P. Huchra. 1991. "Extragalactic globular clusters. III—Metallicity comparisons and anomalies." *Ap.J.* 379 (Sep. 20): 157–167.

Brown, A. G. A., M. A. C. Perryman, J. Kovalevsky, N. Robichon, C. Turon, and J. C. Mermillod. 1997. "The Hyades: Distance Structure and Dynamics." *Proc. of the Hipparcos Venice '97 Symposium.* Nordwijk, Netherlands: ESA Publications Division. Pp. 681–686. ESA SP–402.

Brück, M. T. 1976. "Star Clusters in the Small Magellanic Cloud." *Occasional Reports of the Royal Observatory, Edinburgh*, 1. [Brück]

Brüggemann, H. 1937. *Astr. Abhand. d. Hamburger Sternw. Bergedorf* 4, no. 7.

Buonanno, R., C. E. Corse, F. Fusi Pecci, G. G. Fahlman, and H. B. Richer. 1994. "Two young Galactic globular clusters: Terzan 7 and Arp 2." *Ap. J.* 430, no. 2, pt. 2: L121–124.

Buonanno, R., C. E. Corsi, and F. Fusi Pecci. 1989. "The ages of globular clusters and the Sandage period-shift effect." *Astron. Astrophys.* 216: 80–108.

Burnham, R. 1978 (1966–1978). *Burnham's Celestial Handbook.* 3 Vols. New York: Dover Publications Inc.

Bystedt J. E. V., E. Brinks, A. G. De Bruyn, F. P. Isreal, P. B. W. Schwering, W. W. Shane, and R. A. M. Walterbos. 1984. "A high resolution radio continuum survey of Messier 31. I. Observations at 610 MHz, data reduction, and the 36W catalogue of radio sources." *Astron. Astrophys.* Suppl. Ser. 56: 245–280. [WSTB 36W]

Cacciari, C. 1984a. "BV photometry of RR Lyrae variables in the globular cluster NGC 3201." *Astron. J.* 89 (Feb.): 231–262.

Cacciari, C. 1984b. "ERRATUM—BV photometry of RR Lyrae variables in the globular cluster NGC 3201." *Astron J.* 89 (July):1082.

Canali, E. 1997. "An Interesting Asterism in Corvus." *The Guide Star: Newsletter of the Amateur Astronomers Association of Pittsburgh, Inc.* 31, no. 2 (May): 7–8. [Canali]

Cannon, A. J. 1925. "The Henry Draper Extension." *Ann. Astron. Obs. Harvard Coll.* 100: 17. [HDE (partial)]

Cannon, A. J. and E. C. Pickering. 1918–1924. *Ann. Astron. Obs. Harvard Coll.* 91–99. [HD]

Cannon, A. J. and M. W. Mayall. 1949. "The Henry Draper Extension. II." *Ann. Astron. Obs. Harvard Coll.* 112: 1–295. [HDE (partial)]

Cannon, R. D. 1974. "Photometry of southern globular clusters. III. Bright stars in 47 Tucanae, NGC 6397, and NGC 288." *M.N.R.A.S.* 167: 551–580.

Cannon, R. D. and Stobie, R. S. 1973. "Photometry of Southern Globular Clusters—I. Bright Stars in ω Centauri." *M.N.R.A.S.* 162: 207–225.

Canterna, R. and P. J. Flower [1977]. "A New Dwarf Irregular Galaxy in the Constellation Phoenix." *Astrophysical Journal* 212 (March 1):L57–L58. [Phoenix dwarf (name)].

Canterna, R., D. L. Crawford, and C. L. Perry. 1979. "Multicolor photometry of the galactic cluster NGC 1039 (M34)." *P.A.S.P.* 91 (June): 263–270.

Caputo, F. 1987. "Observational tests for stellar evolution and pulsation theory. I—The globular clusters M 4 and M 15." *Astron. Astrophys.* 172: 67–73.

Carlson, D. 1940. "Some Corrections to Dreyer's Catalogues of Nebulae and Clusters." *Astrophysical Journal* 91: 350–359. Also available as *Contributions from the Mount Wilson Observatory* 626, 1939.

Carney, B. W., J. Storm, and C. Williams. 1993. "BV photometry of V9, the only RR Lyrae variable in the globular cluster 47 Tucanae." *P.A.S.P.* 105: 294–300.

Carpenter, J., R. Snell, and F. Schloerb. 1995. "Star formation in the Gemini OB1 molecular cloud complex." *Ap.J.* 450: 201–216. [C.95 or CSS95]]

Cederblad, Sven. 1946. "Studies of the Bright Diffuse Galactic Nebulae with special regard to their spatial distribution." *Meddelande Frn Lunds Astronomiska Observatorium* ser. II, no. 119. Lund, Sweden: Lund Observatory.

Cesarsky, D. A., S. Laustsen, J. Lequeux, H. E. Schuster, and R. M. West [1977]. "Two New Faint Stellar Systems Discovered on ESO Schmidt Plates." *Astron. Astrophys.* 61:L31–L33. [Eridanus; SagDIG]

Cester, B., G. Guircin, F. Mardirossian, and M. Pucillo. 1977. "Photoelectric photometry of the open cluster M34." *Astron. Astrophys.* Supp. Ser. 30: 227.

Chaboyer, B. 1995. "Absolute ages of globular clusters and the age of the universe." *Ap.J.* 444, no. 1: L9–L12.

Chapman, A. 1998. *The Victorian Amateur Astronomer.* Chichester, U. K.: Wiley-Praxis.

Chernoff, D. F. and S. L. Shapiro. 1988. "Tidal heating of globular clusters." In *The Harlow-Shapley Symposium on Globular Cluster Systems in Galaxies.* IAU Symp. 126: 283–296. Dordrecht: Kluwer Academic Publishers.

Chevalier, C. and S. A. Ilovaisky. 1991. "Cousins BVRI CCD photometry of stars in the M 67 'dipper asterism.'" *Astron. Astrophys.* Supp. Ser. 90: 225–229.

Chun, M. S. 1976. Thesis. Melbourne: Australian National University.

Chupina, N. and S. Vereshchagin. 1998. "Stellar clumps within the corona in the open cluster M 67." *Astron. Astrophys.*, 334: 552–557. June. [{[CV98]}]

Clariá, J. J. 1971. "Photometric Study of the Galactic Cluster NGC 5460." *Astron. J.* 76: 639–644.

Clariá, J. J., E. Lapasset, and M. A. Bosio. 1993. "Further observations of stars in the open cluster NGC 5460." *Astron. Astrophys.* Supp. Ser. 99: 1–10.

Cohen, J. G. 1981. "Abundance in globular cluster red giants. IV—M22 and Omega Centauri." *Ap.J.* 247 (Aug 1): 869–878.

Collinder, Per. 1931. "On Structural Properties of Open Galactic Clusters and their Spatial Distribution." Dissertation. *Annals of the Observatory of Lund* no. 2.

Comeron, F., G. H. Reike, A Burrows, and M. J. Reike. 1993. "The Stellar Population in the ρ Ophiuchi Cluster." *Astrophys. J.* 416 (Oct. 10): 185–203.

Cooper, E. J. 1854. *Catalogue of Stars Near the Ecliptic Observed at Markree, During the Years 1852, 1853, & 1854, and Whose Places are Supposed to be Hitherto Unpublished.* Vol. 3. Dublin: Alex Thom and Sons, Printers and Publishers. [NGC 2218]

Corsi, C. E., R. Buonanno, F. Fusi Pecci, F. R. Ferraro, V. Testa, L. Greggio. 1994. "Globular clusters in the Magellanic Clouds—I. BV CCD photometry for 11 clusters." *M.N.R.A.S.* 271: 385–420.

Corwin, H. G., Jr. 1970a. "Observational Notes on Nebulae in Cygnus." *The Griffith Observer.* (September): 197–199.

Corwin, H. G., Jr. 1970b. "Observational Notes on Clusters in Cygnus." *The Griffith Observer,* (October): 216–218.

Corwin, Harold G., Jr., Antoinette de Vaucouleurs, and Gerard de Vaucouleurs. 1985. "Southern Galaxy Catalogue—A Catalogue of 5481 Galaxies South of Declination –17 Degrees Found on 1.2-m U. K. Schmidt IIIa-J Plates." *University of Texas Monographs in Astronomy,* no. 4, February. [SGC]

Coulson, I. M. and J. A. R. Caldwell. 1985. "The Cepheid HD 144972 and the problematic distance to the open cluster NGC 6067." *M.N.R.A.S.* 216: 671–678.

Couteau, P. 1981. *Observing Visual Double Stars.* Cambridge: MIT Press.

Cox, A. N. 1954. "A Study of the Galactic Cluster NGC 2287." *Ap.J.* 119: 188–196.

Cragin, Murray, James Lucyk, and Barry Rappaport. 1993. *The Deep Sky Field Guide to Uranometria 2000.0*, Richmond, VA: Willmann-Bell Inc. [DSFG or *DSFG1e*]

Cragin, Murray and Emil Bonanno. 2001. *Uranometria 2000.0 Volume 3: Deep Sky Field Guide*, Richmond, VA: Willmann-Bell Inc. [DSFG2e]

Crampton, D., A. Cowley, D. Schade, and P. Chayer. 1985. "The M31 globular cluster system." *Ap.J.* 288: 494–513.

Crampton, D., A. Cowley, J. Hutchings, D. Schade, and L. van Speybroeck. 1984. "Optical counterparts for X-ray sources in M31." *Ap.J.* 284: 663–669. [C84]

Cudworth, K. and D. G. Monet. 1979. "Astrometry in the globular cluster M13. I—New proper motions and membership probabilities." *Astron. J.* 84 (June): 744–782.

Cudworth, K. M. 1985. "Photometry, proper motions and membership in the globular cluster M71." *Astron. J.* 90: 65.

Cudworth, K. M. 1986. "Proper motions, membership and photometry in the globular cluster M22." *Astron. J.* 92: 348–357.

Cudworth, K. M. 1990. "Further observations of the planetary nebula in the globular cluster M22." *Astron. J.* 99: 1863.

Curtis, H. D., 1915. "Search for Faint Members of the Taurus Cluster." *P.A.S.P.* 27 (Dec.): 243.

Czernik, M. 1966. "New Open Star Clusters." *Acta Astronomica* 16, no. 1:93–94. [Czernik]

Dachs, J. and D. Kaiser. 1984. "UBV Photometry of the southern galactic cluster NGC 4755." *Astron. Astrophys.* Supp. Ser. 58: 411–429.

Danks, A., M. Dennefield, W. Wamsteker, and P. Shaver. 1983. "Near infrared spectroscopy and infrared photometry of a new WC9 star." *Astron. Astrophys.* 118: 301–305. [Danks (discovery)]

Danks, A., W. Wamsteker, P. Shaver, and D. Retallack. 1984. "A near-infrared study of the region $l = 305°$." *Astron. Astrophys.* 132: 301–311.

Dawson, D. and P. Ianna. 1998. "Collinder 110: An Old Open Cluster in Monoceros." *Astron. J.* 115: 1076–1082.

De la Fuente Marcos, R. 1998. "Searching for Open Cluster Remnants." *Astron. Astrophys.* 333: L27–L30.

de Vaucouleurs, G., A. de Vaucouleurs, and H. Corwin, Jr. 1976. *Second Reference Catalogue of Bright Galaxies.* The University of Texas Monographs in Astronomy 2. Austin: University of Texas Press. [RC2]

de Vaucouleurs, G., A. DeVaucouleurs, H. G. Corwin, Jr., R. J. Buta, G. Paturel, and P. Foque. 1991. *Third Reference Catalogue of Bright Galaxies.* New York: Springer-Verlag. [RC3]

Dejc [or Dejch, or Deutsch], A. N. 1963. "New intergalactic globular cluster?" *Astr. Cirk.* 259: 1-2. [Dejc 1]

Delporte, E. 1930. *Delimitation Scientifique Des Constellations.* Cambridge: Cambridge University Press.

Demers, S. and A. Wehlau. 1977. "Variable stars of NGC 4833." *Astron. J.* 82 (Aug.): 620–625.

Demers, S., P. Battinelli, M. J. Irwin, and W. E. Kunkel. 1995. "A search for stellar aggregates in dwarf spheroidal galaxies." *M.N.R.A.S* 274 (no. 2): 491–498.

Detweiler, H., K Yoss, R. Radick, and S. Becker. 1984. "The radial velocity of the Hyades cluster." *Astron. J.* 89 (July): 1038–1049.

Dias, W., B. Alessi, A. Moitinho, and J. Lépine. 2002. "New catalogue of optically visible open clusters and candidates." *Astron. Astrophys.* 389: 871–873. [Alessi]

di Cicco, D. 1992. "The ST-6 CCD Image Camera." *Sky & Telescope.* 84, no. 4 (Oct.): 395–401.

di Cicco, D. 1997. "The Missing Mushroom." in Observer's Notebook. *Sky & Telescope* 94, no. 3 (Sept.): 104.

Dickens, R. J. and R. Woolley. 1967. "Studies of the globular cluster ω Centauri. V." *Royal Obs. Bull.* 6, no. 128: E255–E331.

Dixon, R. S. and G. Sonneborn [1980]. *A Master List Of Nonstellar Optical Astronomical Objects,* Columbus, OH: Ohio State University Press. [MOL]

Djorgovski, S. 1987. "Discovery of three obscured globular clusters." Part 2, Letters to the Editor. *Ap. J.* 317 (June 1): L13, L14. [Djorg 1,2, and 3]

Djorgovski, S. and G. Meylan. 1993. "The Galactic Globular Cluster System: A List of the Known Clusters and Their Positions." *Structure and Dynamics of Globular Clusters.* Astronomical Society of the Pacific Conference Series, vol. 50. San Francisco: ASP. 325–336.

Djorgovski, S., D. J. Thompson, R. R. De Carvalho, and J. R. Mould. 1990. "A rich, nearby galaxy cluster in Sagittarius." *Astron. J.* 100: 599.

Dolidze, M. V. 1961a. "On the Star Cluster near γ Cyg." *Astr. Cirk.* 223: 11–12. [Dolidze 1 to 11]

Dolidze, M. V 1961b. "Some Data of the Nebulae and Star Clusters." *Astr. Cirk.* 224: 18–22. [Dolidze 12 to 46]

Dolidze, M. V. and G. Dzimselejsvili [or Jimsheleishvili]. 1966. "New Possible Star Clusters." *Astr. Cirk.* 382: 7–8. [Do-Dz]

Douglas, J. N., F. N. Bash, F. A. Bozyan, G. W. Torrence, and C. Wolfe. 1996. "The Texas Survey of radio sources covering $-35.5° < \delta < 71.5°$ at 365 MHz." *Astron. J.* 111: 1945–1963. [TXS]

Dreyer, J. L. E. 1879. *A Supplement to Sir John Herschel's "General Catalogue of Nebulae and Clusters of Stars."* Transactions of the Royal Irish Academy 26: 381–426. [GC 5080 to 6251]

Dreyer, J. L. E. 1888. *A New General Catalogue of Nebulae and Clusters of Stars.* Mem. Roy. Astron. Soc. 49, part 1, no. 212. [NGC]

Dreyer, J. L. E. 1895. *Index Catalogue of Nebulae Found in the Years 1888 to 1894.* Mem. Roy. Astron. Soc. 51, no. 185. [First IC]

Dreyer, J. L. E. 1908. *Second Index Catalogue of Nebulae and Clusters of Stars.* Mem. Roy. Astron. Soc. 59, no. 105. [Second IC]

Dreyer, J. L. E. 1912. *The Scientific Papers of Sir William Herschel.* 2 vols. Ed. by a joint committee [mostly Dreyer] of the R.S. and R.A.S. London: Royal Society and Royal Astronomical Society.

Dubath, P., G. Meylan, D. Queloz, and M. Mayor. 1993. "Probing the kinematics in the core of the globular cluster M15 with EMMI at the NTT." *ESO Messenger* no. 74: 23–26.

Dutra, C. M., E. Bica, J. Claria, and A. Piatti. 1999. "Spectroscopic analysis of the candidate globular clusters NGC 1928 and 1939 in the Large Magellanic Cloud." *M.N.R.A.S.* 305, no. 2 (April): 373–379.

Dutra, M. and E. Bica. 2000. "New star clusters projected close to the Galactic Centre." *Astron. Astrophys.* 359: L9–L12. [[DB00]]

Dutra, M. and E. Bica. 2001. "New infrared star clusters and candidates in the Galaxy detected with 2MASS." Astron. Astrophys. 376: 434–400. [[DB01]].

Dufour, R. J. 1984. "The unique planetary nebula NGC 2818." *Astrophys. J.* 287 (Dec 1): 341–352.

Dunlop, J. 1828. "A catalogue of nebulae and clusters of stars in the southern hemisphere, observed at Paramatta in New South Wales, by James Dunlop, Esq." *Phil. Trans.*: 118:113–151 and 9 plates. [Δ]

Edmonds, P. D. and R. L. Gilliland. 1996. "K Giants in 47 Tucanae: Detection of a New Class of Variable Stars." *Ap.J.* 464: L157–160.

Eggen, O. 1959. "The gamma Leo group of high velocity stars." *The Observatory* 79: 88–97.

Eggen, O. J. 1980. "A Cepheid Variable in NGC 6067." *IBVS* 1853: 1.

Eggen, O. J 1981. "The region of NGC 2287 and CR 121." *Astrophys. J.* 247 (July 15): 507–521.

Eggen, O. J 1983. "NGC 6067 and three cepheids." *Astron. J.* 88 (March): 379.

Eggen, O. J 1984. "TW Horologii and NGC 1252. A Rebuttal." *P.A.S.P.* 96 (Jan.): 70–71.

Eggen, O. J 1991. "The IC 2391 Supercluster." *Astron. J.* 102: 2028–2040.

Eggen, O. J 1992. "The Hyades Supercluster in the FK5." *Astron. J.* 104: 1482–1492.

Eggen, O. J. and A. R. Sandage. 1964."New photoelectric observations of stars in the old galactic cluster M 67." *Astron. J.* 140: 130–143.

Eggen, O. J., D. Lynden-Bell, and A. R. Sandage. 1962. "Evidence from the motions of old stars that the Galaxy collapsed." *Ap.J.* 136: 748–766.

Egret, D. and C. Fabricius. 1997. "The Tycho Catalogue: Stellar Content, 31." Proc. of the Hipparcos Venice '97 Symposium. Noordwijk: ESA.

Egret, D., M. Wenger, and P. Dubois. 1991. "The SIMBAD Astronomical Database." In *Databases and On-line Data in Astronomy*, M. A. Albrecht and D. Egret, Eds, 79-88. Dordrecht: Kluwer Academic Publishers.

Eiroa, C. and M. Casali. 1992. "Near-infrared images of the Serpens cloud core: the stellar cluster." *Astron. Astrophys.* 262: 468–482. [IRAS 18274–0112]

Eiroa, C. and M. Casali. 1995. "The S 269 stellar cluster." *Astron. Astrophys.* 303: 87–94. [[EC95 1]]

Elvis M., D. Plummer, J. Schachter, and G. Fabbiano. 1992. "The Einstein Slew Survey." *Ap.J.* Supp. 80: 257–303. [1ES]

ESA. 1997. *The Hipparcos and Tycho Catalogues.* SP-1200. Noordwijk, Netherlands: ESA Publications Division.

Espin, T. E. 1894. "Some Nebulous Objects not in the New General Catalogue of Nebulae." *M.N.R.A.S.* 54 (no. 5, March 9):327–328. [IC 1299, 1304–1307, 1310, 1311, 1314, 1363, 1369, 1378, 1400, 1402, 1434, and 1442]

Espin, T. E. 1900. "Stars with Remarkable Spectra." *Astronomische Nachrichten* 152, no. 3633: 135–141. [IC 2156, IC 2157, IC 5146]

Evans, D. S. 1992. *Lacaille: Astronomer, Traveler—With a New Translation of His Journal.* Tucson, AZ: Pachart Publishing House.

Evans, L. T. 1975. "Near-Infrared Photometry of Globular Clusters—IV: The Metal Poor Cluster NGC 6656 (M22)." *M.N.R.A.S.* 171: 647–657.

Fahlman, G. G., H. B. Richer, and D. A. Vandenberg. 1985. "Deep CCD photometry in globular clusters. III-M15." *Ap.J.* Supp. 58 (June): 225–254.

Fall, S. M. and M. J. Rees. 1977. "Survival and disruption of galactic substructure." *M.N.R.A.S.* 181: 37P–42P.

Feast, M. W. 1963. "The galactic cluster NGC 4755 (kappa Crucis)." *M.N.R.A.S.* 126: 11–28.

Feder, Toni. 1998. "'Two Surveys Begin to Map the Universe in Three Dimensions." *Physics Today* 51, no. 2 (Feb.): 61–62.

Feibelman, Walter A. 1995. "P Cygni and Its Cluster." *J. Roy. Astron. Soc. Can.* 89, 1 (February): cover, 3–5. [P Cygni cluster]

Feinstein, A. 1964. "A Group of Stars Around the Helium star HD 96446." *The Observatory* 84 (June): 111–117. [Feinstein 1]

Feinstein, A. 1966. "The open cluster NGC 2451." *P.A.S.P.* 78: 301.

Feinstein, A 1967. "Collinder 121, a young Southern open cluster similar to h and chi Per." *Astrophys. J.* 149: 107.

Feinstein, A., A. Cabrera, and J. J. Clariá. 1978. "Multicolor Photometry of the Open Cluster NGC 2287." *Astron. Astrophys.* Supp. Ser. 34: 241–248.

Fenkart, R. P. and A. Schröder. A. Carbresn, and J. J. Clariá. 1985. "UBV three-colour photometric parameters of four galactic clusters near Cassiopeia." *Astron. Astrophys.* Supp. Ser. 59: 83.

Ferraro, F. R. and F. Paresce. 1993. "Candidate Blue Stragglers in the core of M15 from UV CMDs obtained with HST." In *Structure and Dynamics of Globular Clusters.* Ed. S. G. Djorgovski and G. Meylan. A.S.P. Conference Series, vol. 50: 301.

Ferraro, F. R., F. Fusi Pecci, M. D. Guarnieri, A. Moneti, L. Origlia, and V. Testa. 1994. "CCD and IR-array photometry of Galactic globular clusters—I. *BJVK* photometry of M69." *M.N.R.A.S.* 266: 829–845.

Figer, D. F., S. S. Kim, M. Morris, and E. Serabyn. 1999. "Super star clusters in the Galactic Center as revealed by HST-NICMOS." in K. A. van der Hucht, G. Koenigsberger, and P. R. J. Eenens, eds., *Wolf-Rayet Phenomena in Massive Stars and Starburst Galaxies, Proceedings IAU Symposium No. 193.* Astronomical Soc. of the Pacific. San Francisco: ASP.

FitzGerald, M. P. and A. F. J. Moffat. 1980. "Luminous stars beyond the solar circle: Investigation of a galactic field at l = 231°." *M.N.R.A.S.* 193: 761–774. [Waterloo 7; [FM80]1]

FitzGerald, M. P., R. Hurkens, and A. F. J. Moffat. 1976. "Bochum 15, a New Young Stellar Aggregate in Puppis." *Astron. & Astrophys.* 46: 287–291. [Bochum 15]

Fitzsimmons, A. 1993. "CCD Strömgren uvby photometry of the young clusters NGC 1893, NGC 457, Berkeley 94 and Bochum 1." *Astron. Astrophys.* Supp. Ser. 99: 15–29.

Forbes, D. A., J. P. Brodie, and C. J. Grillmair, 1996a. "On the Origin of Globular Clusters in Elliptical and cD Galaxies." *Astron. J.* 113: 1652–1665.

Forbes, D. A., J. P. Brodie, and J. Huchra. 1996b. "Globular Cluster Luminosity Functions and the Hubble Constant from WFPC2 Imaging: The Dominant Group Elliptical NGC 5846." *Astron. J.* 112: 2448–2453, plate 102.

Forbes, D. A., C. J. Grillmair, and C. R. Smith. 1997. "Globular Clusters in the Sombrero Galaxy (NGC 4594)." *Astron. J.* 113: 1648–1651.

Ford, H., G. Jacoby, and D. Jenner. 1977. "Planetary nebulae in local group galaxies. IV. Identifications, positions and radial velocities of nebulae in NGC 147 and NGC 185." *Ap.J.* 213: 18-26. [FJJ NGC 147 and FJJ NGC 185]]

Forte, J. C. and M. Mendez. 1988. "Dust within globular clusters." *Astron.J.* 95 (Feb.): 500–509.

Forte, J. C. and M. Mendez. 1989. "Dust Clouds within Globular Clusters: Polarization." *Ap.J.* 345: 222–229.

Francic, S. P. 1989. "Mass functions for eight nearby galactic clusters." *Astron. J.* 98 (Sept.): 888–925.

Freedman, W. L., B. F. Madore, B. K. Gibson, L. Ferrarese, D. D. Kelson, S. Sakai, J. R. Mould, R. C. Kennicutt, Jr., H. C. Ford, J. A. Graham, J. P. Huchra, S. M. G. Hughes, G. D. Illingworth, L. M. Macri, and P. B. Stetson. 2001. "Final Results from the Hubble Space Telescope Key Project to Measure the Hubble Constant." *Astrophys. J.* 553 (no. 1): 47–72.

Freeman, K. C. 1990. "Our Fossil Galaxy." In *Dynamics and Interactions of Galaxies*. Ed. R. Wielen. pp. 36–47. Berlin: Springer-Verlag.

French, S. C. 1997. "The Dolphin's Deep-Sky Delights." *Sky & Telescope* 93, no. 12 (June): 106–108. [French 1]

Fricke, W., *et al.*, 1988. *Fifth Fundamental Catalogue*. Part I, *The Basic Fundamental Stars*. Heidelberg: Astron. Rechen-Institut Heidelberg, no. 32.

Friel, E. D. and K. A. Janes. 1991. In *The Formation and Evolution of Star Clusters*. Ed. K. Janes. A.S.P. Conference Series vol. 13: 569-571.

Frolov, V. N. 1977. "Photometry and proper motions of stars of four galactic clusters in Cassiopeia." *Izv. Glav. Astron. Obs.* 195: 80–97. [Frolov]

Fusi Pecci, F. and G. Clementini. 1995. "The Stellar Population of a typical Globular Cluster." In *Stellar Populations*. Ed. P.C. van der Kruit and G. Gilmore. IAU Symp. No. 164: 67–73.

Fusi Pecci, F., C. Cacciari, F. R. Ferraro, R. Gratton, and L. Origlia. 1994. "Globular Clusters with the VLT." *ESO Messenger* 77: 14–20.

Gascoigne, S. and G. E. Kron. 1952. "Colors and Magnitudes of Some Star Clusters in the Magellanic Clouds." *P.A.S.P.* 64 (Aug.): 196–200.

Gascoigne, S. C. B. and E. J. Burr. 1956. "Surface Photometry of the Globular Clusters 47 Tucanae and Omega Centauri." *M.N.R.A.S.* 116: 570–582.

Gatewood, G., J. K. De Jonge, M. Castelaz, I. Han, T. Persinger, J. Prosser T. Reiland, and J. Stein. 1988. "A study of Upgren 1." *Astrophys. J.* 332: 917–920.

Geffert, M., P. Bonnefond, G. Maintz, and J. Guibert. 1996. "The Astrometric Accuracy of the 'Carte du Ciel' Plates and Proper Motions in the Field of the Open Cluster NGC 1647." *Astron. Astrophys.* Supp. Ser. 118 (Aug.): 277–282.

Geisler, D., D. Minniti, and J. J. Clariá. 1992. "Washington photometry of globular cluster giants—The most metal-poor clusters." *Astron. J.* 104 (Aug.): 627–644.

Geisler, D., J. J. Clariá, and D. Minniti. 1992. "Washington photometry of open cluster giants—nine old disk clusters in the third Galactic quadrant." *Astron. J.* 104 (Nov.): 1892–1905.

Geyer, E. H. 1967. "Eine Dreifarbenphotometrie von Omega Centauri (NGC 5139)." *Zh. Astrophys.* 66: 16–32.

Gieren, W. P. and P. Fouqué. 1993. "Comparison of the Open Cluster and Surface-Brightness Distance Scales for Galactic Classical Cepheids." *Astron. J.* 106, no. 2 (Aug.): 734–739. [C1814–191a]

Gill, D. 1902. "Notes on Nebulae observed at the Royal Observatory, Cape of Good Hope." *M.N.R.A.S.* 42, no. 6 (April 11): 468–470. [IC 4291]

Gill, D. 1903. "Revision of the Cape Photographic Durchmusterung for the equinox 1875." *Ann. Cape Obs.* Edinburgh, IX. [CPD, partial]

Gill, D. and J. C. Kapteyn. 1896. "Cape Photographic Durchmusterung for the equinox 1875 (–18° to –37°)." *Ann. Cape Obs.*, London, 3. [CPD, partial]

Gill, D. and J. C. Kapteyn. 1897. "Cape Photographic Durchmusterung for the equinox 1875 (–38° to –52°)." *Ann. Cape Obs.*, London, 4. [CPD, partial]

Gill, D. and J. C. Kapteyn. 1900. "Cape Photographic Durchmusterung for the equinox 1875 (–53° to –89°)." *Ann. Cape Obs.*, Edinburgh, 5. [CPD, partial]

Gillett, F. C., G. H. Jacoby, R. R. Joyce J. G. Cohen, G. Neugebauer, B. T. Soiffer, T. Nakajima, and K. Matthews. 1989. "The Optical/Infrared Counterpart(s) of IRAS 18333–2357." *Astrophys. J.* 338 (March 15): 862–874.

Gilliland, R. L., T. M. Brown, D. K. Duncan, N. B. Suntzeff, G. W. Lockwood, D. T. Thompson, R. E. Schild, W. A. Jeffrey, and B. E. Penprase. 1991. "Time-resolved CCD photometry of an ensemble of stars in the open cluster M67." *Astron. J.*, 101: 541–561.

Gingerich, O. 1960. "Abbé Lacaille's List of Clusters and Nebulae." *Sky & Telescope* 19, no. 4 (Feb.): 206–208

Gingerich, O. 1982. "Astronomical Scrapbook—The Great Comet and the Carte." *Sky & Telescope* 64, no. 3 (Sept.): 237–239.

Gingrich, C. H. 1922. "Parallaxes of Stars in the Region of B.D. +31°643." *Astrophys. J.* 56: 139–144. Also available as *Contributions from the Mount Wilson Observatory* no. 239. [Gingrich]

Gliese, W. 1969. "Catalogue of Nearby Stars." *Veröff. Astron. Rechen-Inst. Heidelberg* no. 22. [GJ]

Gliese, W. and H. Jahreiss. 1979. "Nearby Star Data Published 1969–1978." *Astron. Astrophys.* Supp. Ser. 38: 423–448. [GJ, continued]

Glyn Jones, K. 1968. *Messier's Nebulae and Clusters*. London: Faber. Revised edition, Cambridge: Cambridge Univ. Press.

Glyn Jones, K. 1975. *The Search for the Nebulae*. Giles, U.K: Alpha Academic.

Glyn Jones, K. 1986. "The First Deep-Sky Observer?" *W.S.Q.J.* 63: 21–27.

Glyn Jones, K. 1991. *Messier's Nebulae & Star Clusters*. 2d ed. Cambridge: Cambridge University Press.

Goldstein, Alan. 1981. "National Coordinator's Letter." *Betelgeuse* 6, 2 (March–April): 1–2. [NGC 2169 as "37"cluster.]

Graff, K. 1922. "Photographische Helligkeiten und Farben in der zerstreuten Sterngruppe bei 18h 30m +5.° 5 (1855)." *Astronomische Nachrichten* 5198 (November 25): 311–314. [Graff 1 (= IC 4756)]

Graham, J. 1970. "The Space Distribution of the OB Stars in Car." *Astron. J.* 75: 703–717. [Graham 1]

Grasdalen, G., K. Strom, and S. Strom. 1973. "A 2-Micron Map of the Ophiuchus Dark-Cloud Region." *Ap.J.* 184 (September 1): L53-L57, plate L1. [Grasdalen 1]

Greenstein, J. L. 1939. "Magnitudes and colors in the globular cluster Messier 4." *Ap.J.* 90: 387–413.

Grindlay, J. E. and P. Hertz. 1981. "Discovery of an obscured globular cluster associated with GX 354+0(=4U/MXB 1728–34)." *Astrophys. J.* 247: L17. [Grindlay 1]

Grubissich, C. 1973. "The Stellar Group Basel 11 [sic] in Taurus." *Astron. Astrophys.* Supp. Ser. 11: 283–286. [Basel 11b]

Guarnieri, M. D., A. Bragaglia, and F. Fusi Pecci. 1993. "Colour Magnitude Diagram for the globular cluster M 13." *Astron. Astrophys.* Supp. Ser. 102: 397–400.

Gum, C. S. 1955. "A survey of southern H II regions." *Memoirs of the Royal Astronomical Society* 67: 155–177. [GUM]

Gunn, J. E. and R. F. Griffin. 1979. "Dynamical studies of globular clusters based on photoelectric radial velocities of individual stars. I. M3" *Astron. J.* 84: 752.

Gyulbudaghian, A. and T. Maghakian. 1977a. "New Cometary Nebulae." *Soviet Astron. Lett.* 3: 58–60. [GM 1-]

Gyulbudaghian, A. and T. Maghakian. 1977b. "*Erratum*: New Cometary Nebulae." *Soviet Astron. Lett.* 3: 261

Haddock, F., C. Mayer, and R. Sloanaker. 1954. "Radio observations of ionized hydrogen nebulae and other discrete sources at a wavelength of 9.4 cm." *Nature* 174: 176–177. [NRL]

Haffner, H. 1957. "Neue galaktische Sternhaufen in der südlichen Milchstrasse." *Z. Astrophys.* 43: 89–94. [Haf]

Hall, Douglas S. and F. G. van Landingham. 1970. "The Nearby Poor Cluster Collinder 399." *P.A.S.P.* 82: 640.

Halley, E. 1715. "An Account of Several Nebulae or lucid Spots like Clouds, lately discovered among the Fixt Stars by help of the Telescope." *Phil. Trans.* No. 347 (Jan.–Mar.): 390–392.

Hanson, R. B. 1980. "The Hyades cluster distance." In *Star Clusters*. E. Hesser, ed. IAU Symposium No. 85. Dordrecht: D. Reidel Publ. Co.

Harrington, P. 1984. "Summertime's Swan Song." *Deep Sky* 7, 2, no. 2 (Summer): 7–15.

Harrington, P. 1985. "Deep Sky Objects in Auriga & Gemini." *Deep Sky* 13, 3, no. 4 (Winter): 6–13.

Harrington, P. 1986. "On the Trail of Halley." *Deep Sky* 14, 4, no. 1 (Spring): 6–11.

Harrington, P. 1987. "Treasures of the Unicorn." *Deep Sky* 21, 5, no. 4 (Winter): 14–20.

Harrington, P. 1988. "Deep Sky Wonders in Ophiuchus, Serpens, and-Scutum." *Deep Sky* 23, 6, no. 2, (Summer): 24–29.

Harrington, P. 1990. *Touring the Universe Through Binoculars.* New York: Wiley Science Editions

Harris, D. E., W. Forman, I. M. Gioa, J. A. Hale, F. R. Harnden Jr., C. Jones, T. Karakashian, T. Maccacaro, J. D. McSweeney, F. A. Primnini, J. Schwarz, H. D. Tananbaum, and J. Thurman. 1994. *EINSTEIN Observatory catalog of IPC X-ray sources.* SAO HEAD CD-ROM Series I (Einstein), Nos 18–36. Cambridge:Smithsonian Astrophysical Observatory. [2E]

Harris, H. C. and W. E. Harris. 2000. "Star Clusters." chapter 22 (pp. 545–568) of *Astrophysical Quantities*, 4th edition, ed. A. N. Cox. Heidelberg: Springer Verlag.

Harris, W. E., R. L. Phelps, B. F. Madore, O. Pevunova, B. A. Skiff, C. Crute, B. Wilson, and B. A. Archinal. 1997. "IC 1257: A New Globular Cluster in the Galactic Halo." *Astron. J.* 113, no. 2: 688–691.

Harris, W. E. 1977. "Photometric calibration in the metal-rich globular cluster M69." *P.A.S.P.* 89: 482–484.

Harris, W. E. 1991. "CCD photometry of the outer-halo cluster Palomar 15." *Astron. J.* 102: 1348–1357.

Harris, W. E. 1996. "A Catalog of Parameters for Globular Clusters in the Milky Way." *Astron. J.* 112 (Oct.): 1487–1488.

Harris, W. E. and R. Racine. 1979. "Globular clusters in galaxies." *Ann. Rev. Astron. Astrophys.* 17: 241–274.

Harris, W. E. and S. van den Bergh. 1984. "The distant globular clusters Palomar 14 and Palomar 15." *Astron. J.* 89: 1816–1821.

Harris, W. E., P. R. Durrell, G. R. Petitpas, T. M. Webb, and S. C. Woodworth. 1997. "Unveiling Palomar 2: The Most Obscure Globular Cluster in the Outer Halo." *Astron. J.* 114: 1043–1050.

Hartung, E. J. 1984. *Astronomical Objects for Southern Telescopes.* Cambridge: Cambridge University Press.

Hartwick, F. D. A. and A. Sandage. 1968. "The Color-Magnitude Diagram for the abnormally strong-line globular cluster M69." *Ap.J.* 153: 715–722.

Harvard College Observatory. 1908. "Nebulae Discovered at the Harvard College Observatory." *Harvard Annals* 60, no. 6: 148–194. [Frost, pp. 179–192; HN (e.g. Fleming), pp. 149–150]

Hassan, M. 1976. "UBV Photometry of the galactic cluster Mel 71" *Astron. Astrophys.* Supp. Ser. 26: 9–12.

Hatzidimitriou, D. and R. K. Bhatia [1990]. "Cluster Pairs in the Small Magellanic Cloud." *Astron. Astrophys.* 230:11–15. [[HB90] 1]

Havlen, R. and A. Moffat. 1977. "A new cluster containing 2 Wolf-Rayet stars and 2 Of stars." *Astron. Astrophys.* 58: 351–356. [HM 1]

Henize, K. 1956. "Catalogues of Ha emission stars and nebulae in the Magellanic Clouds." *Ap.J.* Supp. 2: 315–344. [Henize N or LHA 120-N, LHA 115-N]

Hénon, M. 1961. "Sur l'Évolution Dynamique des Amas Globulaires." *Ann. d'Astrophys.* 24, no. 5: 369–419.

Herbig, G. H. 1956. "The Source of Illumination of NGC 1579." *P.A.S.P.* 68, No. 403 (Aug.): 353–356. [LkHα 101]

Herbig, G. H. 1974. "Draft Catalog of Herbig-Haro Objects." Lick Obs. Bull. 658. [HH]

Herschel, J. F. W. 1833. *Observations of Nebulae and Clusters of Stars, made at Slough, with a Twenty-feet Reflector, between the years 1825 and 1833.* Phil. Trans. for the year 1833, part II: 359–505, plates 9–16.

Herschel, J. F. W. 1847. *Results of Astronomical Observations Made During the Years 1834, 5, 6, 7, 8, at the Cape of Good Hope; Being the Completion of a Telescopic Survey of the Whole Surface of the Visible Heavens, Commenced in 1825.* Cornhill, London: Smith, Elder and Co.

Herschel, J. F. W. 1864. *A General Catalogue of Nebulae and Clusters of Stars, Arranged in Order of Right Ascension and Reduced to the Common Epoch 1860.0 (With Precessions Computed for the Epoch 1880.0)* London: Taylor and Francis. [GC 1 to 5079]

Herschel, J. F. W. 1871. *Seventh Catalogue of Double Stars, observed at Slough, in the years 1822–1828 inclusive, with the 20-feet Reflector; 84 of which have not been previously described.* Mem. R.A.S. 38: 1–16. [ADS 6366 cluster].

Herschel, W. 1785. "On the Construction of the Heavens." *Phil. Trans.* 75: 213–266.

Herschel, W. 1786. "Catalogue of One Thousand new Nebulae and Clusters of Stars." *Phil. Trans.* 76: 457–499.

Herschel, W. 1788. "Catalogue of a second Thousand of new Nebulae and Clusters of Stars; with a few introductory Remarks on the Construction of the Heavens." *Phil. Trans.* 79: 212–255.

Herschel, W. 1814. "Astronomical Observations relating to the sidereal part of the Heavens, and its Connection with the nebulous part: arranged for the purpose of a critical Examination. *Phil. Trans.* 104:248–284.

Heske, A. and H. J. Wendker. 1984. "Photometry and spectroscopy in the young cluster region Tr 24/Sco OB 1." *Astron. Astrophys.* Supp. Ser. 57: 205.

Heske, A. and H. J. Wendker. 1985. "Further photometry and spectroscopy in the young cluster region Tr 24/Sco OB 1." *Astron. Astrophys.* 151: 309–314.

Hesser, J. E. and S. J. Shawl. 1985. "Integrated spectral types from image-tube spectra for 90 Galactic globular clusters." *P.A.S.P.* 97: 465–518.

Hesser, J. E., W. E. Harris, D. A. Vandenberg, J. W. B. Alwright, P Shott, and B. Stetson. 1987. "A CCD color-magnitude study of 47 Tucanae." *P.A.S.P.* 99 (Aug.): 739–808.

Hill, G. and C. L. Perry. 1969. "Photometric Studies of Southern Galactic Clusters. II. IC 2602." *Astron. J.* 74: 1011.

Hirshfeld, A. and R. W. Sinnott. 1985. *Sky Catalogue 2000.0.* Vol. 2, *Double Stars, Variable Stars and Nonstellar Objects.* Cambridge, MA: Sky Publishing Corporation.

Hoag, A. A., H. L. Johnson, B. Iriarte, R. I. Mitchell, K. L. Hallam, and S. Sharpless. 1961. "Photometry of stars in galactic cluster fields." *Publ. U.S.N.O.* Second series, 17: 343–542.

Hodapp, K. and J. Rayner. 1991. "The S106 Star-forming Region." *Astron. J.* 102 (September): 1108–1117. [[HR 91] 1]

Hodder, P. J. C., J. M. Nemec, H. B. Richer, and G. G. Fahlman. 1992. "Deep CCD photometry and variable stars in the metal-rich globular cluster M71." *Astron. J.* 103 (Feb.): 460–479.

Hodge, P. 1985. "The Stellar Associations of the Small Magellanic Cloud." *P.A.S.P.* 97 (June): 1065–1070. [H85]

Hodge, P. and F. Wright. 1967. *The Large Magellanic Cloud.* Washington, D.C.: Smithsonian Press Publication 4699.

Hodge, P. and F. Wright. 1974. "Catalog of 86 new star clusters in the Small Magellanic Cloud." *Astron. J.* 79: 858–859. [HW]

Hodge, P. W. and J. Sexton. 1966. "457 new star clusters of the Large Magellanic Cloud." *Astron. J.* 71:363–358. [[HS66]]

Hodge, P. W. 1960. "Studies of the Large Magellanic Cloud. I. The red globular clusters." *Ap. J.* 131:351–357 [[H60b]]

Hodge, P. W. 1981. *Atlas of the Andromeda Galaxy.* Seattle: Univ. of Washington Press. [[H81] B-]

Hodge, P. W. 1985. "The Stellar Associations of the Small Magellanic Cloud." *P.A.S.P.* 97 (June): 530–536. [[H85]]

Hodge, P. W. 1986. "Clusters of the Small Magellanic Cloud. I. A Catalogue of 213 New Clusters." *P.A.S.P.* 98: 1113–1122. [[H86]]

Hodge, P. W. 1988. "A catalog of 255 new clusters in the Large Magellanic Cloud." *P.A.S.P.* 100: 1051–1070. [[H88]]

Hodge, P. W. and G. Wallerstein. 1966. "A suggested revision in the Distance to the Hyades and its Implications." *P.A.S.P.* 78: 411.

Høg E., C. Fabricius, V. V. Makarov, S. Urban, T. Corbin, G. Wycoff, U. Bastian, P. Schwekendiek, and A. Wicenec. 2000. "The Tycho-2 Catalogue of the 2.5 Million Brightest Stars." *Astron. Astrophys.* 355: L27. [Tycho-2]

Hogg, A. R. 1965. "Catalogue of Open Clusters South of –45° Declination" *Memoirs of the Mount Stromlo Observatory* 4, no. 17. [Hogg]

Hogg, A. R. and G. E. Kron. 1955. "The galactic cluster IC 4665." *Astron. J.* 60 (Nov.): 365–370.

Hogg, H. S. 1958. "Globular Star Clusters." *J.R.A.S.C* 52 (no.3): 97–108.

Hogg, H. S. 1959a. "Star Clusters". In *Handbuch der Physik, Band LIII, Astrophysik IV: Sternsysteme*. Ed. S. Flügge. Berlin: Springer-Verlag.

Hogg, H. S., 1959b. "The Differences Among Globular Clusters: The areas of difference among globular clusters." *Astron. J.* 64: 425–428.

Holden, D., and J. Caswell. 1969. "178 MHz observations of galactic radio sources." *M.N.R.A.S.* 143: 407–435. [[HC69]]

Holtzman, J. A., S. M. Faber, E. J. Shaya, T. R. Lauer, J. Grothe, D. A. Hunter, W. A. Baum, S. P. Ewald, J. F. Hester, R. M. Light, C. R. Lynds, E. J. O'Neil, Jr., and J. A. Westphal. 1992. "Planetary Camera observations of NGC 1275—Discovery of a central population of compact massive blue star clusters." *Astron. J.* 103 (Mar.): 691–702, 1020–1023.

Hoogerwerf, R., J. H. J. De Bruijne, A. G. A. Brown, J. Lub, A. Blaauw, and P. T. De Zeeuw. 1997. "New Results for Three Nearby OB Associations." Proc. of the Hipparcos Venice '97 Symp. Noordwijk, Netherlands: ESA Publications Division. Pp. 571–574. ESA SP-402.

Houston, W. S. 1974. "Deep-Sky Wonders." *Sky and Telescope* 47, no. 2 (Feb.): 133.

Houston, W. S. 1975a. "Deep-Sky Wonders." *Sky & Telescope* 50, 3 (September): 200.

Houston, W. S. 1975b. "Four Neglected Deep-Sky Wonders." *Sky and Telescope* 50, no. 6 (December): 420–421.

Houston, W. S. 1976. "Deep-Sky Wonders." *Sky and Telescope* 51, no. 1 (Jan.): 68–69.

Houston, W. S. 1977. "Deep-Sky Wonders." *Sky and Telescope* 54, no. 2 (Aug.): 155.

Houston, W. S. 1978. "Pazmino's Cluster." *Sky & Telescope* 55, no. 3 (March): 275–276. [Pazmino's cluster = Stock 23].

Houston, W. S. 1979. "Deep-Sky Wonders." *Sky and Telescope* 58, no. 3 (Sept.): 289–290.

Houston, W. S. 1980. "Deep-Sky Wonders." *Sky & Telescope* 60, no. 6 (Dec.): 546–547. [Kemble 1 (Kemble's Cascade)]

Houston, W. S. 1982. "Deep-Sky Wonders." *Sky and Telescope* 63, no. 2 (Feb.): 211–213.

Houston, W. S. 1983. "Deep-Sky Wonders." *Sky and Telescope* 66, no. 1 (Jan.): 82–83.

Houston, W. S. 1984. "Deep-Sky Wonders."' *Sky & Telescope* 67, no. 3 (March): 287–289. [Kemble 1 (Kemble's Cascade)]

Houston, W. S. 1985. "Deep-Sky Wonders." *Sky and Telescope* 69, no. 6 (June): 574–577.

Houston, W. S. 1988a. "Deep-Sky Wonders." *Sky and Telescope* 75, no. 2 (Feb.): 227–228.

Houston, W. S. 1988b. "Deep-Sky Wonders." *Sky & Telescope* 76, no. 5 (Nov.): 582–583. [Reiland 1 (Reiland's Nebulous Cluster)]

Houston, W. S. 1989. "Deep-Sky Wonders." *Sky and Telescope* 78, no. 3 (Sept.): 330–332.

Hubble, E. 1932. "Nebulous objects in Messier 31 Provisionally Identified as Globular Clusters." *Ap.J.* 76: 44–69. [[H32]]

Huchra, J., J. Brodie, and S. Kent. 1991. "Extragalactic globular clusters. II. The M31 globular cluster system." *Ap.J.* 370: 495–504. ("GS-SET" [name only] originates from Table 2; [HBK])

Hynes, S. J. 1986a. "Southern Sky Section Report." *Webb Society Quarterly Journal* 65 (July): 45–46.

Hynes, S. J. 1986b. "Southern Sky Section Report." *Webb Society Quarterly Journal* 66 (Oct.): 37–39.

Hynes, S. J. 1987. "Some Galactic Clusters containing Cepheid variables." *W.S.Q.J.*70: 1–11.

Hynes, S. J. 1987. *Webb Society Deep-Sky Observer's Handbook.* Vol. 7, *The Southern Sky.* Ed. K. Glyn Jones. Short Hills, NJ: Enslow Publishers Inc.

Hynes, S. J. 1994. "Nebulae & Clusters Section." *The Webb Society Observing Section Reports* 12, (January): 23–34. Includes observations by Randall M. Poole: 27–30.

Ianna, P. A. and D. M. Schlemmer. 1993. "Membership in the Galactic Open Cluster NGC 1039 (M34)." *Astron. J.* 105: 209–219.

Ibata, R. A., G. Gilmore, and M. J. Irwin. 1994. "A dwarf satellite galaxy in Sagittarius." *Nature* 370: 194–195. [Sagittarius Dwarf Galaxy]

Illingworth, G. 1975. "Dynamical Masses and Mass-To Ratios for Globular Clusters." In *Dynamics of Stellar Systems*, IAU Symp. 69, A. Hayli, ed. pp. 151–157, Dordrecht: D. Reidel.

Illingworth, G. and I.R. King. 1977. "Dynamical models for M15 without a black hole." *Ap. J.* 218 (Dec. 15): L109–L112.

Irwin, M. J., S. Demers, and W. E. Kunkel. 1995. "The Pyxis Cluster: A Newly Identified Galactic Globular Cluster." *Astron. J.* 453: L21–L24, plate L3.

Iskudarian, S. G. 1959. [Title unknown.] Proc. Of Armenian Academy of Sciences, 29 (no. 5). [Biurakan 1 to 6]

Iskudarian, S. G. 1960. "Five New Open Clusters." *Soobshch. Byurakan Obs.* 28: 43–49. [Biurakan 7 to 11]

Iskudarian, S. G. and K.A. Saakian. 1961. "The Cluster of White Dwarfs in Lyrae [sic]." *Astron. Cirk.* 221: 6–9. [Iskudarian 1]

Isles, J. E. 1990. *Webb Society Deep-Sky Observer's Handbook.* Vol. 8, *Variable Stars.* Short Hills, NJ: Enslow Pub. Inc.

Israel, F. P. 1978. "HII regions and CO clouds—The blister model." *Astron. Astrophys.* 70, no 6 (Dec.): 769–775.

Isserstedt, J. 1970. "Optische Spiralarmindikatoren und galaktische Struktur (Optical Spiral Tracers and Galactic Structure)." *Astron. Astrophys.* 9, 70–78. [Iss 1003 to 1067].

Isserstedt, J. and T. Schmidt-Kaler. 1968. *Veröffentlichungen des Astronomischen Instituts der Ruhr-Universität Bochum* 1. Bochum: Astronomisches Institut. [Iss 1 to 1002].

Isserstedt, J. and T. Schmidt-Kaler. 1973. "Der Offene Sternhaufen Collinder 107 und ein Sternring in Monoceros [The Open Cluster Collinder 107 and a Stellar Ring in Monoceros]." *Astron. Astrophys.* Supp. Ser. 10: 365-383.

Ivanov, G. 1992. "Nonstellar objects in M33." *Astrophys. Lett.* 28: 281–289. [I92a]

Ivanov, G.R. 1992. "Stellar Associations in M81." *M.N.R.A.S.* 257: 119–124.

Jacoby, G. H., J. A. Morse, L. K. Fullton, K. B. Kwitter, and R. B. C. Henry. 1997. "Planetary Nebulae in the Globular Clusters Pal 6 and NGC 6441." *Astron. J.* 114, no. 6, December: 2611–2625. [JaFu 1 and 2]

Jakiel, R. 1997. "Taking the Big Test." *Astronomy* 25, no.10 (Oct.) 98–101.

Jakiel, R. 1998. "The *Ultimate* Deep Sky Challenge?" *The Deep-Sky Observer, Quarterly Journal of the Webb Society* no. 112 (April): 24–26.

Janes, K. A., C. Tilley, and G. Lyngå. 1988. "Properties of the Open Cluster System." *Astron. J.* 95: 771–784.

Jaschek, C., and J.-C. Pecker. 1979. "A Meeting on the Nomenclature of Astronomical Objects." *CDS Bulletin*, no. 16 (January): 57–70.

Jimenez, R. and P. Padoan. 1996. "A New Self-consistency Check on the Ages of Globular Clusters." *Ap.J.* 463: L17–L20.

Johansson, K. 1980. "Colour excess and stellar distribution in five selected directions of the Milky Way in Carina, Crux, Centaurus and Norma." *Astron. Astrophys.* Supp. Ser, 41 (July): 43–66. [Johansson]

Johansson, K. 1981. "A Study of a Small Cluster Candidate in Norma." *Astron. Astrophys.* Supp. Ser., 44 (April): 127–129. [Lodén 2326]

Johnson, H. L. 1954. "Magnitudes and colors in M 34." *Astrophys. J.* 119: 185.

Johnson, H. L., A.R. Sandage, and H.D. Wahlquist. 1956. "The galactic cluster M11." *Astrophys. J.* 124: 81.

Johnson, H. L., and A. R. Sandage. 1955. "The galactic cluster M67 and its significance in stellar evolution." *Astrophys. J.* 121: 616.

Joint IRAS Science Working Group. 1988. *Infrared Astronomical Satellite (IRAS), Catalogs and Atlases.* Washington, D.C.: U. S. Government Printing Office. NASA RP-1190, v. 2-6. [IRAS]

Jones, J. H. 1993. "CCD photometry of Andromeda IV: dwarf irregular galaxy or M31 open cluster?" *Astron.J.* 105: 933–937.

Jones, K. L. and A. A. Page. 1991. "Search for Southern Open Cluster Flare stars: M7, IC 2602, IC 2391 and NGC 2516." Proc. ASA 9(**2**): 277–278.

Joshi, U. C. and R. Sagar. 1977. "Photoelectric photometry of the Open Cluster Tr 1." *Astrophys & Sp. Sci.* 48: 225–230.

JRASC. 1994a. "Notes." *J. Roy. Astron. Soc. Can.* 88, no. 3: 171.

JRASC. 1994b. "Notes." *J. Roy. Astron. Soc. Can.* 88, no. 4: 275–276. [SU Cygni group]

Jung, J., M. Bischoff. and F. Ochsenbein. 1973. "The Catalogue of Stellar Identifications (CSI). A progress report II." *Bull. Inf. CDS* 4: 27–34. [CSI]

Kaluzny, J. 1997. "CCD Photometry of Distant Open Clusters: III. Berkeley 18." *Astron. Astrophys.* Supp. Ser. 121: 455–460.

Kaluzny, J. and M. J. Shara. 1987. "Discovery of six new short-period variables in the old Open Cluster NGC 188." *Ap.J.* 314: 585–593.

Kaluzny, J. and T. Richtler. 1989. "CCD BV Photometry of the Old Open Cluster Berkeley 39." *Acta Astronomica* 39: 139–151.

Kaluzny, J., B. Mazur, W. Krzeminski. 1993 "Discovery of 12 short-period eclipsing binaries in the old open cluster Berkeley 39." *M.N.R.A.S.* 262: 49–56.

Kaluzny, J., B. Mazur, W. Krzeminski. 1996. "Variable Stars in the Field of the Old Open Cluster NGC 2243." *Astron. Astrophys.* Supp. Ser. 118 (Aug.): 303–310

Kanagy, S. P. and S. P. Wyatt. 1978. "Dust patches in globular clusters." *Astron. J.* 83 (July): 779–784.

Kanatas, I., W. K. Griffiths, R.J. Dickens, and A.J. Penny. 1995. "CCD photometry in the globular cluster M4." *M.N.R.A.S.* 272: 265–290.

Karachentseva, V. E. 1973. "The catalogue of isolated galaxies." *Soob. Spets. Astrofiz. Obs. Akad. Nauk. SSSR* 8: 3–72. [Kara]

Karimova, D. K. and P. N. Kholopov. 1963. "A.N. Deutsch's Object." *Astr. Cirk.* 259: 2.

Kassis, M., E. Friel, and R. Phelps. 1996. "CCD Photometry of the Old Open Cluster 092-SC18 [sic]." *Astron. J.* 111 no. 2 (Feb.): 820–827.

Keeler, James E., 1908. "Photographs of Nebulae and Clusters made with the Crossley Reflector." *Pub. of Lick Obs.* 8.

Kemble, Lucian. 1995. "The Jewels of the Dragon." Unpublished (?) manuscript copy provided by A. Moland.

Kepple, G. and G. W. Sanner, eds. 1987. "An Observer's Guide to Ophiuchus & Serpens Cauda." *The Observer's Guide* 2 (May and June): 12-26.

Kepple, G. R., and G. W. Scanner. 1998. *The Night Sky Observer's Guide, Volume 1, Autumn & Winter.* Richmond: Willmann-Bell, Inc.

Kepple, G. R., and G. W. Scanner. 1998. *The Night Sky Observer's Guide, Volume 2, Spring and Summer.* Richmond: Willmann-Bell, Inc.

Kharchenko, N. and E. Schilbach. 1995. "Schmidt plate survey in the galactic centre direction. 1. Investigation of open clusters in the Sagittarius-Carina arm." *Astron. Nachr.* 316, No. 2: 91–104. [C1819–146 and C1820–146].

Kholopov, P. N., ed. 1985–87. *General Catalogue of Variable Stars.* 4th ed. Moscow: Nauka.

Kholopov, P. N., N. N. Samus, M. S. Frolov, V. P. Goranskij, N. A. Gorynya, E. A. Karitskaya, E. V. Kazarovets, N. N. Kireeva, N. P. Kukarkina, N. E. Kurochkin, G. I. Medvedeva, E. N. Pastukhova, N. B. Perova, A. S. Rastorguev, and S. Yu. Shugarov. 1998. *General Catalogue of Variable Stars 4th Edition, Volumes I–III,* Moscow: Sternberg Astronomical Institute and Institute of Astronomy (Russian Acad. Sci.).

Kim, S., M. Morris, and H. M. Lee. 1999. "Evaporation of Compact Young Clusters Near the Galactic Center." *Ap. J.* 525 (November 1): 228–239.

King, I. R. 1949. "Some New Galactic Clusters." *Harvard Bull.* 919: 41–42. [King 1 to 21].

King, I. R. 1961. "A New Galactic Cluster." *PASP* 73, no. 431 (April): 163–164. [King 22]

King, I. R. 1966. "Five New Open Clusters." *PASP* 78, no. 460 (Feb.): 81–82. [King 23 to 27]

King, I. R. 1972. "The Identity and Aliases of the Stellar System Terzan 5." *Astron. Astrophys.* 19: 166.

Kinman, T. D. 1959. "Globular clusters. II. The spectral types of individual stars and of the integrated light." *M.N.R.A.S.* 119: 538–558.

Kinman, T. D. and L. Rosino. 1961. "Notes on Faint Star Clusters." *P.A.S.P.* 74 (Dec.): 499–506.

Knoechel, G. and A.F.J. Moffat. 1982. "Mass Loss, Linear Polarization Variability, and Duplicity of the Luminous B2 Supergiant HD 80077." *Astron. Astrophys.* 110: 263–271.

Knödlseder, J. 2000. "Cygnus OB2—a young globular cluster in the Milky Way." *Astron. Astrophys.* 360: 539–548.

Kodaira, K., T. Greene, and A. Tokunaga. 1995. "On the Stellar Nature of an Infrared Object, Kodaira 1." *Publ. Astro. Soc. Japan* 47: 27–29.

Kontizas, M., D. H. Morgan, D. Hatzidimitriou, and E. Kontizas. 1990. "The Cluster System of the Large Magellanic Cloud." *Astron. Astrophys.* Supplement Series 84: 527. [KMHK or KMH90]

Kravtsov, V. V., N. N. Samus, G. Alcaino, and W. Liller. 1994. "New Variable Stars in the Globular Cluster M 22 = NGC 6656." *Astron. Lett.* 20, no. 3: 339–342.

Kron, G. E. and N. U. Mayall. 1960. "Photoelectric photometry of galactic and extragalactic star clusters." *Astron. J.* 65: 581.

Kron, G. E. 1956. "Star clusters in the Small Magellanic Cloud. I. Identification of 69 clusters." *P.A.S.P.* 68: 125–130. [Kron]

Kukarkin, B. V. 1974. *The Globular Star Clusters.* Moscow: Nauka.

Kurtz, S., E. Churchwell, and D. Wood. 1994. "Ultracompact H II regions. II. New high-resolution radio images." *Ap.J. Supp.* 91: 659–712. [[KCW94]]

Küstner, F. 1921. "Der kugelförmige Sternhaufen Messier 15." *Veröff. Univ.-Sternw. Bonn.* 15. [Küstner]

Lada, C. and E. 1991. The Nature, Origin and Evolution of Embedded Star Clusters. In *The Formation and Evolution of Star Clusters.* ASP Conference Series vol. 13, Ed. K. Janes: 3–22.

Lada, C., J. Alves, and E. Lada. 1996. "Near-Infrared Imaging of Embedded Clusters: NGC 1333." *Astron. J.* 111, no. 3 (May): 1964–1976. [[LAL96]]

Lada, E., D. DePay, N. Evans II, and I. Gatley. 1991. "A 2.2-Micron Survey in the L1620 Molecular Cloud." *Ap.J.* 371: 171–182, plate 8. [[LDEG91]]

Larsen, S. S. and J. P. Brodie. 2000. "Hubble Space Telescope Observations of Star Clusters in NGC 1023: Evidence for Three Cluster Populations?" *Astron. J.* 120: 2938–2949.

Lasker, B., C. Sturch, B. McLean, J. Russell, H. Jenkner, and M. Shara, 1990. "The Guide Star Catalog. I. Astronomical foundations and image processing." *Astron. J.* 99: 2019–2058, 2173–2178. [GSC]

Latyshev, I. N. 1972. "Possibly near-by Open Clusters." *Astron. Tsirk.* 631: 2–4. [Latyshev 1]

Latyshev, I. N. 1977. "Possibly near-by Open Clusters." *Astron. Tsirk.* 969: 7–8. [Latyshev 2]

Lauberts, A. 1976. "Three distant stellar clusters found on ESO blue survey plates." *Astron. Astrophys.* 52: 309–311. [E 1, E 2, E 3].

Lauberts, A. 1982. *The ESO/Uppsala Survey of the ESO (B) Atlas*, Garching bei München, Germany: European Southern Observatory. [ESO]

Lauer, T. R., J. A. Holtzman, S. M. Faber, W. A. Baum, D.G. Currie, S. P. Ewald, E. J. Groth, J. J. Hester, T. Kelsall, R. M. Light, R. C. Lynds, E. J. O'Neil, Jr., D. P. Schneider, E. J. Shaya, and J. A. Westphal. 1991. "The postcollapse core of M15 images with the *HST* planetary camera." *Ap.J.* 369 (Mar 10): L45–L49.

Laustsen, S., C. Madsen, and R. M. West. 1987. *Exploring the Southern Sky. A Pictorial Atlas from the European Southern Observatory (ESO).* Berlin: Springer-Verlag.

Lederman, R. D. and S. Gottlieb. 1996. "If You Don't See it … Maybe it Isn't There." *W.S.Q.J.* 105 (July): 25–31.

LeDrew, Glenn. 2001. "Discovery of an old Open Cluster in Cassiopeia." Unpublished. [LeDrew 1]

Leisawitz, D. 1988. *Catalog of Open Clusters and Associated Interstellar Matter.* Washington, D.C.: NASA Ref. Publ. 1202 (June). [OCISM]

Leonard, P. J. T., H. B. Richter, and G. G. Fahlman. 1992. "The mass and stellar content of the globular cluster M13." *Astron. J.* 104: 2104–2111.

Levato, H. and S. Malaroda. 1975. "Spectral Types in the Open Cluster NGC 2451." *P.A.S.P.* 87: 823–825.

Levy, David H. 2001. "My Favorite Deep-Sky Wonders." *Sky and Telescope* 101, no. 4 (April): 113–117. [Levy-Wallach J2204.4+4509]

Lewin, W. H. G. 1976. "X-Ray Bursts." *IAU Circ.* 2922.

Lewin, W. H. G. and P.C. Joss. 1981. "X-ray bursters and the X-ray sources of the galactic bulge." *Space Sci. Rev.* 28: 3–87.

Lieske, J. H., Lederle, T., Fricke, W. & Morando, B. [1977]. "Expressions for the Precession Quantities Based upon the IAU (1976) System of Astronomical Constants." Astron. Astrophys., 58, pp. 1-16.

Liller, W. 1977. "Searches for the optical counterparts of the X-ray burst sources MXB 1728-34 and MXB 1730-33." *Ap.J.* 213: L21–L23. [Liller 1]

Liller, W. and G. Alcaino. 1983a. "A search for globular clusters around the edge-on spiral galaxy NGC 55." *Ap. J.* part 1, 264: 53–55, 57–58.

Liller, W. and G. Alcaino. 1983b. "A search for globular clusters around the edge-on late-type spiral galaxy NGC 253." *Ap. J.* part 1, 265: 166–175.

Lindroos, K. P. 1985. "A Study of visual double stars with early type primaries. IV. Astrophysical data." *Astron. Astrophys.* Supp. Ser. 60: 183–211.

Lindsay, E. M. 1958. "The cluster system of the Small Magellanic Cloud." *M.N.R.A.S.* 118: 172–182. [Lindsay]

Lindsay, E. M. 1961. "A New Catalogue of Emission-Line Stars and Planetary Nebulae in the Small Magellanic Cloud." *Astronomical Journal* 66 (no. 4, May):169–185. [L61]

Lindsay, E. M. 1963. "Note on NGC and IC Objects in the Small Magellanic Cloud." Irish *Ast. J.* 6 (no. 1, March): 2–3.

Ling A. 1987. "Nonexistence at the Edge of the Scutum Star Cloud." *Deep Sky* 5, no. 3 (Fall): 16.

Ling, A. 1984. "Clusters in Cygnus." *Betelgeuse* 9, no. 4 (July–Aug.): 2.

Ling, A. 1986. "Open Clusters in Aquila." *Betelgeuse* 11, no. 4 (July–Aug.): 3.

Liu, T., I. McLean, and E. Becklin. 1994. In *Infrared Astronomy with Arrays.* Ed. I. McLean. Dordrecht: Kluwer.

Lloyd Evans, T. 1974. "Near-infrared photometry of globular clusters. II. The metal-rich cluster 47 Tucanae (NGC 104)." *M.N.R.A.S.* 167: 393–491.

Lloyd Evans, T. 1977. "Near infrared photometry of globular clusters-VI. The moderately metal-poor cluster NGC 6121 (M4)." *M.N.R.A.S.* 178: 353–367.

Lodén, L. O. 1973. "A List of Suspected Clusters in the Southern Milky Way." *Astron. Astrophys.* Supp. Ser. 10:125–133. [Lodén, initial paper, 44? objects]

Lodén, L. O. 1977. "A study of some loose clustering in the southern Milky Way." *Astron. Astrophys.* Supp. Ser. 29:31–50, plates 1 to 9. [Lodén, continued]

Lodén, L. O. 1979a. "Photometry of loose clusterings in the Southern Milky Way." *Astron. Astrophys.* Supp. Ser. 36:83–93. [Lodén, continued]

Lodén, L. O. 1979b. "Continued Studies of Loose Clusterings in the Southern Milky Way." *Astron. Astrophys.* Supp. Ser. 38:355–365. [Lodén, continued]

Lodén, L. O. 1980. "Concluding observations of Loose Clusterings in the Southern Milky Way." *Astron. Astrophys.* Supp. Ser. 41:173–181. [Lodén, continued]

Lodén, L. O. 1981. "A photometric study of two stellar clusterings in the Southern Milky Way (and a general consideration on previous and present data concerning galactic clusterings)." *Astron. Astrophys.* Supp. Ser. 44:155–158. [Lodén, continued, fields 28 and 915.]

Lortet, M. C. 1985. "Nomenclature for Objects in the Galaxy M33." *Astron. Astrophys.* Supp. Ser. 64, no. 2 (May): 325–328.

Lortet, M. C., G. Testor, and V. Niemela. 1984. "Optical study of the galactic nebula NGC 6357 and of its stellar content, Pis 24 and the WC 6 star HD 157504." *Astron. Astrophys.* 140: 24–32.

Lozinskaya, T. A., T. J. Sitnik, and A. I. Lomovski. 1986. "Nebular Complex in the region of Cas OB2 Association—Ring Nebula Sh 157." *Astrophys & Sp. Sci.* 121: 357–385.

Lucke, P. B. and P. W. Hodge. 1970. "A Catalogue of Stellar Associations in the Large Magellanic Cloud." *Astron. J.* 75, no. 2 (March): 171–175. [LH]

Luginbuhl, C. B. and B. A. Skiff. 1990. *Observing Handbook and Catalogue of Deep-Sky Objects.* Cambridge: Cambridge University Press. [Skiff J0614.8+1252]

Lundström, I. and B. Stenholm. 1984. "Wolf-Rayet stars in open clusters and associations." *Astron. Astrophys.* Supp. Ser. 58: 163–192. [Danks (naming)]

Lupton, R. H., J. E. Gunn, R. F. Griffin. 1987. "Dynamical studies of globular clusters based on photoelectric radial velocities of individual stars and on the observed mass function. II. M13." *Astron. J.* 93 (May): 1114–1136.

Lynds, B. T. 1962. "Catalogue of dark nebulae." *Ap. J.* Supp. 7, no. 64: 1–52. [LDN]

Lynds, B. T. 1965. "Catalogue of bright nebulae." *Astrophys J.* Supp. Ser. 12, no. 105 (Aug.): 163–185. [LBN]

Lyngå, G. 1964. "Studies of the Milky Way from Centaurus to Norma. II. Open clusters." *Medd. Lunds* Ser. II, no. 140. [Lyngå 1 to 14]

Lyngå, G. 1981. *Catalogue of Open Cluster Data.* Sweden: Lund Observatory.

Lyngå, G. 1983. IAU Commission No. 37, IAU Numbers for Some Recently Discovered Clusters. *Bulletin d'Information du Centre de Données Stellaires* 24: 127.

Lyngå, G. 1987. *Catalogue of Open Cluster Data.* Lund, Sweden: Lund Observatory. [Lund Catalogue]

Lyngå, G. and B. E. Westerlund. 1963. "A catalogue of clusters in the outer parts of the Large Magellanic Cloud." *M.N.R.A.S.* 127: 31–36. [LW]

Lyngå, G. and N. Hansson. 1972. "Nebulae of the Southern Milky Way. An Atlas." *Astron. Astrophy. Suppl.* 6:327–414.

Ma, C., E. F. Arias, T. M. Eubanks, A. L. Fey, A. M. Gontier, C. S. Jacobs, O. J. Sovers, B. A. Archinal, and P. Charlot. 1998. "The International Celestial Reference Frame As Realized by Very Long Baseline Interferometry." *Astron J.* 116: 516–546.

Mackie, G. 2001. "The Mackie 1 Asterism." *J. Roy. Astron. Soc. Can.* 95, no. 2: 687. [Mackie 1]

Madore, B. and H. Arp. 1979. "Three new faint star clusters." Letters to the Editor. *Ap.J.* 227: L103–L104, plates L3–L6. [AM 1 to 3]

Madore, B. and H. Arp. 1982. "A distant star cluster in Hydra, AM-4." *P.A.S.P.* 94: 40–42. [AM 4]

Madore, B. F. 1980. "Terminology and fundamental data of globular clusters." In *Globular Clusters.* Ed. D. Hanes and B. Madore. Cambridge: Cambridge Univ. Press.

Madore, B. F. and S. van den Bergh. 1975. "UBV Photometry of the Cepheid V367 Scuti in the Open Cluster NGC 6649." *Ap.J.* 197: 55–65.

Maffei, P. 1968. "Infrared object in the region of IC 1805." *P.A.S.P.* 80: 618–621. [Maffei]

Malkan, M., D. Kleinmann, and J. Apt. 1980. "Infrared Studies of Globular Clusters Near the Galactic Center." *Ap.J.* 237: 432–437. [UKS 1 and vdB-Ha 66 = UKS 2]

Mallas, J. H., and E. Kreimer. 1978. *The Messier Album.* Cambridge, MA: Sky Publishing Corp.

Mamajek, E. E., W. A. Lawson, and E. D. Feigelson. 1999. "The η Chamaeleontis Cluster: A Remarkable New Nearby Young Open Cluster." *Ap. J.* 516: L77–L80, May 10. [η Cha cl]

Manchester, R. N., A. G. Lyne, C. Robinson, M. Bailes, and N. D'Amico. 1991. "Discovery of ten millisecond pulsars in the globular cluster 47 Tucanae." *Nature* 352 (July 18): 219–221.

Mandushev, G., A. Staneva, and N. Spasova. 1991. "Dynamical masses for Galactic globular clusters." *Astron. Astrophys.* 252 (Dec.): 94–99.

Markarian, B. and V. Lipovetskij. 1971. "Galaxies with ultraviolet continuum. IV." *Astrofizika* 7: 299–310. [MKN 303 to 401]

Markarian, B. E. 1951. "On the classification of open (galactic) stellar clusters. II. Preliminary list of open O-type star clusters." *Soob. Biurakan Obs.* 9. [Markarian]

Markov, P. 2001. "The 'Markov 1' Asterism in Hercules." *J. Roy. Astron. Soc. Can.* 95, no. 4: 689. [Markov 1]

Marshall, F., E. Boldt, S. Holt. R. Mushotzky, S. Pravdo, R. Rothschild, and P. Serlemitsos. 1979. "New hard X-ray sources observed with HEAO A-2." *Ap. J. Suppl.* 40: 657–665. [HEAO]

Martin, W. C. 1939. "Photographic Photometry of Variable Stars in the Globular Cluster ω Centauri, based on Plates Taken by H. van Gent with the Yale Refractor at Johannesburg, Measured by C.J. Kooreman and W. Chr. Martin." *Ann. Sterrew. Leiden* 17, part 2: 1–166, plates I–II.

Mathieu, R. D. 1984. "The structure and dynamics of the open cluster M11." *Astrophys. J.* 284 (Sept. 15): 643–662.

Mattison, A. M., and Elijah H. Burritt [1856a]. *The Geography of the Heavens and Class-Book of Astronomy, accompanied by a Celestial Atlas.* New York: Mason Brothers. [Arcturus group]

Mattison, A. M., and Elijah H. Burritt [1856b]. *Atlas designed to illustrate Burrutt's [sic] Geography of the heavens [sic].* New York: Mason Brothers.

Mayall, N. U. and L. H. Aller. 1942. "The Rotation of the Spiral Nebula Messier 33." *Ap.J.* 95: 5–23.

Mayall, N. U., and O. J. Eggen. 1953. "Four Nebulous Objects in the Outer Parts of the Andromeda Nebula." *P.A.S.P* 65: 24–29. [[ME53]; Mayall]

McGee, R., J. Brooks, and R. Batchelor. 1972. "The radio continuum of the Large Magellanic Cloud. I. The sources at 6 cm wavelength." *Austral. J. Phys.* 25: 581–597. [[MBB72]]

McMath, Robert R., 1942. "Heber Doust Curtis 1872–1942." *P.A.S.P.* 54: 69–71.

McNamara, B. J. and W. L. Sanders. 1977. "The internal motions of M 11." *Astron. Astrophys.* 54: 569–576.

Meketa, J. 1984. "20 'Nonexistent' Objects in Cygnus." *Deep Sky* 7, 2, no. 2 (Summer): 12.

Meketa, Jim. 1984. "The Ophiuchus Globulars." *Deep Sky* 7, 2, 2: 16–21.

Melnick, W. and S. D'Odorico. 1978. "Star Clusters in M33: I. Identification." *Astron. Astrophys.* Supp. Ser. 34: 249–252. [[MD78]].

Melotte, P. J. 1915a. "A Catalogue of Star Clusters shown on Franklin-Adams Chart Plates." *Mem. R. A. S.* 60: 175.

Melotte, P. J. 1915b. "The Distribution of Star Clusters." *J.B.A.S.* 25 (no. 7): 341–343.

Menzies, J. 1967. Thesis. Canberra: Australian National University.

Menzies 1972. "The Globular Cluster NGC 4833." *M.N.R.A.S.* 156: 207.

Messier, C. 1784. In the *Connaissance des Temps* for 1784.

Mermilliod, J.-C. 1996. "The Open Cluster Database." in E. Milone and J.-C. Mermilliod (eds.) "The Origins, Evolutions, and Destinies of Binary Stars in Clusters." *ASP Conference Series* 90: 475-483.

Meylan, G. 1988. "Studies of dynamical properties of globular clusters-IV. Detailed structure of 47 Tucanae." *Astron. Astrophys.* 191 (Feb.): 215–216.

Meylan, G., M. Mayor, and P. Dubath. 1994. "The jumbo galactic globular cluster." *Bull. Am. Astr. Soc.* 184, no. 58.16. Abstract only.

Meyssonnier, N., J. Lequeux, and M. Azzopardi. 1993. "An objective-prism survey of emission-line objects in M31." *Astron. Astrophys.* Supp. Ser. 102: 251–268. [MLA]

Minkowski, R. 1947. New Emission Nebulae (II)." *P.A.S.P.* 59, no. 350 (Oct): 257–259. [Min 2-]

Minniti, D., E. W. Olszewski, and M. Rieke. 1995. "IR Color-Magnitude Diagrams of 20 Galactic Globular Clusters and Bulge Fields." *Astron. J.* 110, no. 4: 1686–1698.

Moffat, A. F. J. 1972. "Photometry of 11 young open star clusters." *Astron. Astrophys.* Supp. Ser. 7: 355.

Moffat, A. F. J. 1976. "Mass Loss from the M3 Supergiant HD 143183 in a Young Compact Star Cluster in Norma." *Astron. Astrophys.* 50: 429–434. [Moffat 1]

Moffat, A. F. J. and Fitzgerald, M. P. 1977. "Some very luminous supergiants associated with compact groups of luminous OB stars." *Astron. Astrophys.* 54: 263–268.

Moffat, A. F. J., M. P. FitzGerald, and P. D. Jackson. 1979. "The Rotation and Structure of the Galaxy Beyond the Solar Circle. I. Photometry and Spectroscopy of 276 Stars in 45 HII Regions and Other Young Stellar Groups Toward the Galactic Anticentre." *Astron. Astrophys.* Supp. Ser. 38: 197–225. [Waterloo 1, 2, 3]

Moffat, A. F. J., and N. Vogt. 1975a. "Southern Open Star Clusters IV. UBV-Hβ Photometry of 26 Clusters from Monoceros to Vela." *Astron. Astrophys.* Suppl. Ser. 20: 85–124. [Bochum 1–7]

Moffat, A. F. J., and N. Vogt. 1975b. "Southern Open Star Clusters V. UBV-Hβ Photometry of 20 Clusters in Carina." *Astron. Astrophys.* Suppl. Ser., 20: 125–153. [Bochum 8–12]

Moffat, A. and N. Vogt. 1975c. "Southern Open Star Clusters VI. UBV-Hβ Photometry of 18 Clusters from Centaurus to Sagittarius." *Astron. Astrophys.* Supp. Ser. 20: 155–182. [Bochum 13 and 14]

Monet, D. G., S. E. Levine, B. Canzian, H. D. Ables, A. R. Bird, C. C. Dahn, H. H. Guetter, H. C. Harris, A. A. Henden, S. K. Leggett, H. F. Levison, C. B. Luginbuhl, J. Martini, A. K. B. Monet, J. A. Munn, J. R. Pier, A. R. Rhodes, B. Riepe, S. Sell, R. C. Stone, F. J. Vrba, R. L. Walker, G. Westerhout, R. J. Brucato, I. N. Reid, W. Schoening, M. Hartley, M. A. Read, and S. B. Tritton. 2003. "The USNO-B Catalog." *Astron. J.,* submitted.

Moneti, A., I. Glass, and A. Moorwood. 1992. "Infrared imaging of *IRAS* sources near the Galactic Centre." *M.N.R.A.S.* 258: 705–714. [MGM 1 to 7]

Moneti, A., I. Glass, and A. Moorwood. 1994. "Spectroscopy and further imaging of *IRAS* sources near the Galactic Centre." *M.N.R.A.S.*, 268: 194–202. [MGM 8]

Moore, P. and M. B. Pepin. 1995. "Beyond Messier: The Caldwell Catalog." *Sky and Telescope* 90, no. 6 (Dec.): 38–42. [Caldwell]

Morel, Mati. 1983. *A Visual Atlas of the Large Magellanic Cloud.* Rankin Park, Australia: Morel Astrographics.

Morel, Mati. 1989. *A Visual Atlas of the Small Magellanic Cloud.* Rankin Park, Australia: Morel Astrographics. (Morel Astrographics, 18 Elizabeth Cook Drive, Rankin Park, NSW, Australia).

Morel, Mati. 1990. *LMC Selected Areas.* Rankin Park, Australia: Morel Astrographics.

Morel, Mati. 1992. *Catalogue of LMC Clusters and Nebulae.* Preliminary version. Rankin Park, Australia: Morel Astrographics.

Morgan, W. W. 1956. "The integrated spectral types of globular clusters." *P.A.S.P.* 68: 509–516.

Morgan, W. W., G. Gonzales, and Z. Gonzales. 1953. "Blue Giants in the neighbourhood of NGC 6231." *Ap.J.* 118: 323–325.

Morgan, W. W., S. Sharpless, and D. Osterbrock. 1952. "Some features of galactic structure in the neighborhood of the Sun." *Astron. J.* 57: 3.

Morgan 1959. "The Differences Among Globular Clusters: The integrated spectra of globular clusters." *Astron. J.* 64: 432–436.

Nagata, T., A. R. Hyland, S. M. Straw, S. Sato, and K. Kawara. 1993. "Bright Near-Infrared Sources Within 1° of the Galactic Center. I. Survey and 1–20 Micron Photometry." *Ap. J.* 406 (April 1): 501–511. [[NHS93]]

Nagata, T., C. E. Woodward, M. Shure, and N. Kobayashi. 1995. "Object 17: Another Cluster of Emission-Line Stars Near the Galactic Center." *Astron. J.* 109, no. 4 (April): 1676–1681 and plate 64. [Arches Cluster]

Nagata, T., C. E. Woodward, M. Shure, J. L. Pipher, and H. Okuda. 1990. "AFGL 2004: An Infrared Quintuplet Near the Galactic Center." *Ap. J.* 351 (March 1): 83–88 and plates 4–6. [Quintuplet cluster (naming)]

Nakaya, H., M. Watanabe, M. Ando, T. Nagata, and S. Sato. 2001. "A Highly Reddened Star Cluster Embedded in the Galactic Plane." *Astron. J.* 122, August: 876–884.

National Geographic Society. 1955. *Palomar Observatory Sky Survey* Washington, D.C.: National Geographic Society. [POSS]

Neckel, T. 1984. "Polarimetric and new photometric observations in the NGC 6334/6357 region." *Astron. Astrophys.* 137: 58–62. ["unknown" cluster about G353.1+06]

Newell, B. and E. J. O'Neill, Jr. 1978. "The surface-brightness distribution of the globular cluster M15." *Ap.J. Supp.* 37 (May): 27–43.

Newell, B., G. S. Dacosta, and J. Norris. 1976. "Evidence for a central massive object in the X-ray cluster M15." *Ap.J.* 208 (Sep. 1): L55–L59.

Nilson, P. 1973. "Uppsala general catalogue of Galaxies. Data for 12921 galaxies north of Decl. = –2° 30′." *Uppsala Astr. Obs. Ann.* 6. [UGC]

Nilson, P. 1974. "Catalogue of Selected Non-UGC Galaxies." *Uppsala Astr. Obs. Rep.* no. 5. [UGCA]

Norton, A. P. 1973. *Norton's Star Atlas and Reference Handbook (epoch 1950.0).* Edinburgh: Gall & Inglis.

Odenkirchen, M. and C. Soubiran. 2002. "NGC 6994—clearly not a physical stellar ensemble." *Astron. Astrophys.* 383: 163–170.

Olszewski, E., H. Harris, R. Schommer, and R. Canterna. 1988. "A catalog of LMC star clusters outside the Hodge-Wright atlas." *Astron. J.* 95: 84–90. [OHSC]

O'Meara, S. J. 1994. "Dark Tales from Texas." Amateur Astronomers, *Sky & Telescope* 88, no. 4: 96–99.

O'Meara, S. J. 1998a. *The Messier Objects.* Cambridge: Cambridge University Press, Cambridge.

O'Meara, S. J. 1998b. "The Outer Limits." *Sky & Telescope* 96, no. 2, (August): 86–89.

O'Meara, S. J. 2002. *Deep-Sky Companions: The Caldwell Objects.* Cambridge, Mass.: Sky Publishing Corp.

O'Meara, S. J. and D. W. E. Green. 2003. "The Mystery of the Double Cluster." *Sky and Telescope*, 105, no. 2 (February): 116–119.

Ortolani S., E. Bica, and B. Barbuy 1994. "NTT observations of obscured globular clusters." *ESO Messenger* no. 75: 26–28.

Ortolani, S., E. Bica, and B. Barbuy. 1995. "BH 176 [vdB-Ha 176] and AM-2: globular or open clusters?" *Astron. Astrophys.* 300: 726–731.

Ortolani, S., E. Bica, and B. Barbuy. 1997. "V, I and Gunn z photometry of faint bulge globular clusters: Terzan 10, ESO 456-SC 38 and UKS 1." *Astron. Astrophys.* Supp. Ser. 126: 319–324.

Ortolani, S., E. Bica, and B. Barbuy. 2000. "ESO 280-SC06: a new globular cluster in the Galaxy." *Astron. Astrophys.* 361: L57–L59.

Osborn, W., Y. Sano, and R. Spalding. 2002. "The Neglected Open Cluster Stock 1." *P.A.S.P,* 114: 1382–1388, December.

Paresce, F., G. Meylan, M. Shara, D. Baxter, and P. Greenfield. 1991. "Blue stragglers in the core of the globular cluster 47 Tucanae." *Nature* 352 (July 25): 297–301.

Pasterfield, D. 1994. Letter to the editor. *Webb Society Quarterly Journal* 97 (July): 39.

Pasztor, L., L. Toth, and L. Balazs. 1993. "Searching for embedded clusters in the Cepheus-Cassiopeia region." *Astron. Astrophys.* 268: 108–115. [PTB93]

Paturel, G., P. Fouque, L. Bottinelli, and L. Gouguenheim. 1989. *Principal Galaxies Catalog, Monographies de la base de donnees extragalactiques* No. 1. [PGC]

Pavani, D. B., E. Bica, C. M. Dutra, H. Dottori, B. X. Santiago, G. Carranza, G., and R. J. Díaz. 2001. "Open clusters or their remnants: B and V photometry of NGC 1901 and NGC 1252." *Astron. Astrophys.* 374, p.554–563.

Pease, F. G. 1917. "Photographs of Nebulae with the 60-inch Reflector 1911-1916." *Contributions from the Mount Wilson Solar Observatory* 132. Reprinted from *Ap.J.* 46: 24–55, 1917.

Pease, F. G. 1928. "A Planetary Nebula in the Globular Cluster Messier 15." *P.A.S.P.* 40, no. 237 (Oct.): 342, plate 28b. [Küstner 648 = Pease 1]

Pedreros, M., B. F. Madore, and W. L. Freedman. 1984. "Photographic Photometry of the Open Cluster NGC 7790." *Ap. J.* 286 (Nov. 15): 563–572.

Pellet, A., N. Astier, A. Viale, G. Courtes, A. Maucherat, G. Monnet, and F. Simien. 1978. "A survey of HII regions in M31." *Astron. Astrophys.* Supp. Ser. 31: 439–461. [[PAV78]]

Peng, W. and J. C. Weisheit. 1991a. "Analysis of C IV absorption lines from clouds at high redshifts." *Ap.J.* 373 (June 1): 471–481.

Peng, W. and J. C. Weisheit. 1991b. "Young Globular Clusters?" *P.A.S.P.* 103: 891–893.

Pennington, H. 1998. *The Year-Round Messier Marathon Field Guide.* Richmond, VA: Willmann-Bell, Inc.

Penny, A. and B. Griffiths. 1991. "High Precision Stellar Photometry in M13." *GEMINI Newsletter, RGO* no. 33 (Sep.): 4–5

Perelmuter, J-M. and R. Racine. 1995. "The globular cluster system of M81." *Astron. J.* 109, no. 3: 1055–1070.

Perelmuter, J-M., Brodie, J., Huchra, J. 1995. "Kinematics and metallicity of 25 globular clusters in M81." *Astron. J.* 110: 620–627. [[P.95] or [PBH95]]

Perrine, C. D. 1932. "Cordoba Durchmusterung Declination –62° to –90°." *Results of National Argentine Obs.* 21, part 2:1–140. [CD, partial]

Perry, C. L. and G. Hill. 1969. "Photometric Studies of Southern Galactic Clusters. I. IC 2391." *Astron. J.* 74: 899–907.

Perry, C. L., C. B. Franklin, A. U. Landolt, and D. L. Crawford. 1976. "Multicolor photometry of the open cluster NGC 4755." *Astron. J.* 81: 632–637.

Perry, C. L., G. Hill, and D. M. Christodoulou. 1991. "A study of Sco OB1 and NGC 6231. II. A new analysis." *Astron. Astrophys.* Supp. Ser. 90 (Oct.): 195–223.

Perryman, M.A.C. 1997. "The Hipparcos Catalogue Contents." Proc. of the Hipparcos Venice '97 Symposium. ESA.

Persi, P., M. Roth, M. Tapia, M. Ferrari-Toniolo, and A. Marenzi. 1994. "The young stellar population associated with the HII region NGC 3576." *Astron. Astrophys.* 282: 474–484. [[PRT94] 1]

Pesch, P. 1959. "The Galactic Cluster NGC 457." *Ap.J.* 130: 764–768.

Peters, C. H. F. 1881. "Positions of Nebulae. Series I." *Copernicus* I: 51–54.

Peterson, C. J. 1986. "A bibliography of globular-cluster color-magnitude diagram studies." *P.A.S.P.* 98 (Dec.): 1258–1272.

Peterson, C. J. 1993. "Integrated Photometric Properties of Globular Clusters." pp. 337–345. In *Structure and Dynamics of Globular Clusters,* S. Djorgovski and G. Meylan. Astronomical Society of the Pacific Conference Series vol. 50. San Francisco: ASP.

Peterson, R. C. 1980. "Evidence for primordial inhomogeneities from abundance of giants in M5, M13, and M22." In *Star Clusters,* IAU Symp. no. 85, J.E. Hasser, ed., pp 461–464. Hingham, Mass.: Reidel.

Pfleiderer, J., R. Weinberger. and R. Mross. 1978. "Some New Possible Very Red and Faint Star Clusters." In *Star Cluster Symposium—Budapest 1977.* B.A. Balàzs, ed. Budapest: Roland Eötvös University. [PWM78 1 to 4]

Phelps, R. L., K. A. Janes, and K. A. Montgomery. 1994. "Development of the Galactic Disk: A Search for the oldest open clusters." *Astron. J.* 107, no. 103: 1079–1096.

Philip, A., P. Demarque, A. Sweigart, and R. Ciardullo. 1977. "A comparison of observations with main-sequence evolutionary models." *P.A.S.P.* 89: 554–556. [Bok 1]

Piatti, Andrés E., J. Santos Jr., J. Clariá, E. Bica, A. Sarajedini, and D. Geisler. 2001. "Ages and metallicities of five intermediate-age star clusters projected toward the Small Magellanic Cloud." *M.N.R.A.S.*, 325, no. 2, 1 August: 792.

Pickering, E. C. [1901]. "Objects Having Peculiar Spectra." *Harvard Circular* 60. [Fleming (some discoveries)]

Pickering, E. C. and M. Fleming. 1897. "Miscellaneous Investigations of the Henry Draper Memorial." *Ann. Harv. Coll. Obs.* 26, part II.

Pietrzyński, G., Udalski, M. Kubiak, M. Szymanski, P. Wozniak, and K. Zebrun [1998]. "Optical Gravitational Lensing Experiment. The Catalog of Clusters in the Small Magellanic Cloud." *Acta Astronomica* 48:175–268. [OGLE-CL]

Pilachowski, C., E. M. Leep, G. Wallerstein, and R.C. Peterson. 1982. "Abundances of the elements in six stars in the globular cluster M22." *Ap.J.* 263 (Dec. 1): 187–198.

Pismis, P. 1957. "Un Nuevo Cumulo Galactico En Puppis." *Boletin de Los Observatorios Tonantzintla y Tacubaya* 16 (June): 37–38. [Haffner 16 = Pismis cluster]

Pismis, P. 1959. "Nuevos Cumulos Estelares En Regiones Del Sur." *Boletin de Los Observatorios Tonantzintla y Tacubaya* 18 (Aug.): 37–38. [Pismis 1 to 24; Ton 1 = Pismis 25; Ton 2 = Pismis 26]

Pismis, P., M. A. Moreno, and I. Hasse. 1979. "Internal Motions in H II Regions. VI. S 140 and the Associated CO Cloud." *Revista Mexicana de Astronomia y Astrofisca* 4, no. 4 (Aug.): 331–335, plate 5. [PMH79 1]

Platais, I. 1979. "BD +48° 3398 = SVS 2299: A New Classical Cepheid—A Possible Member of an Anonymous Galactic Cluster." *Astron. Tsirk.* 1049. [Anon Platais]

Platais, I. 1986. "On the Reality of an Anonymous Galactic Cluster." *Naucnye Informacii* 61: 89–94.

Platais, I., V. Kozhurina-Platais, and F. van Leeuwen. 1998. "A Search for Star Clusters from the *HIPPARCOS* Data." *Astron. J.*, 116: 2423–2430. [[PKL98]]

Pommier, Rod [2000]. "Seeking Star Clusters." *Astronomy* 28, no. 5 (May):84–89.

Poole, R. M. 1993. "Credulous Clusters." *Betelgeuse* 18, No. 2 (Summer): 3–4. [Poole]

Pothier, Y. and B. Archinal. 1998. "The Displaced Cluster Barkhatova 2." The Deep-Sky Observer. *Webb Society Quarterly Journal* 113 (July): 11–14.

Pound, M. W. and K. A. Janes. 1986. "The intermediate-age Open Cluster Mel 71." *P.A.S.P.* 98: 210–217.

Price, S. and R. Walker. 1983. "The Revised Air Force Geophysics Laboratory (AFGL) infrared sky survey catalog." AFGL-TR-83-0161. Hanscom AFB, Mass: Airforce Geophysics Laboratory. [RAFGL]

Primini, F., F. Forman, and C. Jones. 1993. "High-resolution X-ray observations of the central region of M31 with the ROSAT satellite." *Ap.J.*, 410: 615–625. [[PFJ93]]

Prosser, C. F. 1993. "The Open Cluster IC 4665." *Astron. J.* 105: 1441–1454.

Pryor, C. and Meylan, G. 1993. "Velocity Dispersions for Galactic Globular Clusters." In *Structure and Dynamics of Globular Clusters,* S. Djorgovski and G. Meylan. Astronomical Society of the Pacific Conference Series, vol. 50: 337–345. San Francisco: ASP.

Puche, D. 1986. Master Thesis, Université de Montréal.

Pulkova. 1955. *Izvestiya Glavnoj Astronomicheskoj Observatorii v Pulkove* 154: 14.

Raab, S. 1922. "A research on open clusters." *Lund Medd. Astron. Obs.* Ser. II, no. 28. [Raab]

Racine, R. 1980. "Globular Cluster Systems in Galaxies." In *Star Clusters.* IAU Symp. No. 85, J.E. Hesser, ed. Pp. 369–383. Hingham, Mass: Reidel.

RAS. 1936. *The Franklin-Adams Chart, 3rd ed.* London: Royal Astronomical Society.

Rasmuson, N. H. 1921. *Lund Medd.* Ser. 2: 26.

Reed, L., G. L. Harris, and W. E. Harris. 1992. "Integrated BVR photometry of halo globular clusters in M31." *Astron. J.* 103 (March): 824–839.

Reinmuth, K. 1926. "Die Herschel-Nebel nach Aufnahmen der Königstuhl-Sternwarte." *Veröffentlichungen der Badischen Sternwarte zu Heidelberg (Königstuhl)* 9. Berlin: De Gruyter.

Richer, H. B., D. R. Crabtree, A. C. Fabian, and D. N. C. Lin. 1993. "Star and cluster formation in NGC 1275." *Astron. J.* 105, no. 3 (Mar.): 877–885.

Richer, H. B., G. G. Fahlman, R. A. Ibata, P. B. Stetson, R. A. Bell, M. Bolte, H. E. Bond, W. E. Harris, J. E. Hesser, G. Mandushev, C. Pryor, and D. A. Vandenberg. 1995. "Hubble Space Telescope observations of white dwarfs in the globular cluster M4." *Ap.J.* 451: L17–L20.

Richer, H. B. and G. G. Fahlman. 1988. "Deep CCD photometry in globular clusters. VI. White dwarfs, cataclysmic variables and binary stars in M71." *Ap.J.* 325: 218–224.

Richtler, T. 1995. "CCD photometry of the globular clusters NGC 6496, NGC 6624 and NGC 6637." *Astron. Astrophys.* Supp. Ser. 109: 1–7.

Richtler, T., E. K. Grebel, and W. Seggewiss. 1994. "The cases of the 'disk' globular clusters NGC 6496, NGC 6624, and NGC 6637." *Astron. Astrophys.* 290: 412–420.

Roberts, M. S. 1960. "Dust and glass in Globular Clusters." *Astron. J.* 65 (Oct.): 457–466.

Roberts, M. S. 1988. "Interstellar Matter in Globular Clusters." In *Globular Cluster Systems in Galaxies.* IAU Symposium No. 126: 411

Robinson, B. J. and R. McGee. 1970. "OH Absorbtion at 1667 MHz Near the Galactic Centre." *Aust. J. Phys.* 23, no 3 (June): 405–423.

Rodgers, A., C. Campbell, and J. Whiteoak. 1960. "A catalogue of Hα emission regions in the southern milky way." *M.N.R.A.S.* 121: 103–110. [RCW]

Rolleston, W. R. J. and P. B. Byrne. 1997. "Photometrically determined membership of the young open cluster IC 2391." *Astron. Astrophys.* Supp. Ser. 126: 357–364.

Rosenberg, A., G. Piotto, I. Saviane, A Aparicio, and S. Zaggia. 1998b. "The Metallicity of Palomar 1." *Astron. J.* 115 (Feb.): 658–665.

Rosenberg, A., I. Saviane, G. Piotto, A. Aparicio, and S. Zaggia. 1998a. "Palomar 1: Another Young Galactic Halo Globular Cluster?" *Astron. J.* 115 (Feb.): 648–657.

Röser, S. and U. Bastian. 1989. *Positions and Proper Motions of 181,731 Stars North of −2°.5 Declination for Equinox and Epoch J2000.0.* Heidelberg: Astronomisches Rechen-Institut.

Röser, S. and U. Bastian. 1994. "NGC 2451—What is it?" *Astron. Astrophys.* 285: 875–879. [Puppis Moving Group 1 and 2]

Rosino, L., A. Bianchini and D. Martino. 1976. "The Milky Way field around NGC 7635 in Cas." *Astron. Astrophys.* Supp. Ser. 24: 1–27. [V582 Cas]

Rosino, L., S. Ortolani, B. Barbuy, and B. Bica. 1997. "NGC 6749: A Metal-Poor Halo Globular Cluster in a Disc Field Rich in Mira Variables." *Monthly Notices of the Royal Astronomical Society* 289 (August 11): 745–752.

Roslund, C. 1960. "Remarks on some new and some known galactic clusters." *P.A.S.P.* 72: 205–207. [Ro or Roslund]

Roslund, C. and W. Pretorius. 1963. "Note on a possible Cepheid variable in NGC 6649." *Ark. f. Astr.* 3, no. 17: 201–202.

Royal Obs. 1966. "Studies of the Globular Cluster ω Centauri." *Royal Obs. Ann.* no. 2. London: Her Majestiy's Stationary Office.

Ruprecht, J. 1966. "Classification of Open Star Clusters." *Bulletin of the Astronomical Society of Czechoslovakia* 17: 33–44.

Ruprecht, J., B. Balàzs and R. E. White. 1981. *Catalogue of Star Clusters and Associations* Supp. I. Budapest: Akadèmiai Kiadò.

Safford, T. H. 1887. "Nebulae Found at the Dearborn Observatory, 1866–8." *Annual Reports of the Board of Directors of the Chicago Astronomical Society, together with the Report of the Director of the Dearborn Observatory, for 1885 and 1886.* Appendix C, pp. 37–41. [IC 348]

Sagar, R. and R. D. Cannon. 1995. "A deep UBVRI CCD photometric study of the moderately young southern open star cluster NGC 4755." *Astron. Astrophys.* Supp. Ser. 111: 75–84.

Sagar, R. and W. K. Griffiths. 1991. "CCD photometry of the distant young open cluster NGC 7510." *M.N.R.A.S.* 250: 683–691.

Samus, N., V Kravtsov, M. Pavlov, G. Alciano, and W. Liller. 1995a. "A new photographic C-M diagram for NGC 4833." *Astron. Astrophys.* Supp. Ser. 109 (Mar): 479–486.

Samus, N., V Kravtsov, M. Pavlov, G. Alciano, and W. Liller. 1995b. "A new photographic color-magnitude study of M 22 = NGC 6656." *Astron. Astrophys.* Supp. Ser. 109: 487–499.

Sandage, A. 1958. "Cepheids in Galactic Clusters. I. CF Cas in NGC 7790." *Ap.J.* 128: 150–160.

Sandage, A. 1970. "Main Sequence photometry, Colour-Magnitude Diagrams, and Ages for the Globular Clusters M3, M13, M15 and M92." *Ap.J.* 162: 841.

Sandage, A. and B. Katem. 1977. "Faint photometry in M15: The intrinsic width of the main sequence, the luminosity function, and the density gradient of faint field stars." *Ap.J.* 215 (July 1): 62–73.

Sandage, A. and H. Arp. 1957. *Mt. Wilson & Palomar Obs. Report.*

Sandage, A. R. 1953. "The Color-Magnitude Diagram for the Globular Cluster M3." *Astron. J.* 58: 61.

Sarajedini, A. and A. C. Layden. 1995. "A Photometric Study of the Globular Cluster M54 and the Sagittarius Dwarf Galaxy: Evidence for Three Distinct Populations." *Astron. J.* 109: 1086–1094, plates 30, 31.

Sargent, W., C. Kowal, F. Hartwick, and S. van den Bergh. 1977. "Search for globular clusters in M31. I. The disk and the minor axis." *Astron. J.* 82: 947–953, plates III to XV. [SKHB and vdB]

Saurer, W., R. Seeberger, R. Weinberger and R. Ziener. 1994. "Berkeley 93: A Distant Star Cluster Nestled in a Dust Cloud." *Astron. J.* 107, no. 6 (June): 2101–2107. [SSWZ94]

Sawyer Hogg, H. B. 1973. *Catalogue of Variable Stars in Globular Clusters Comprising 2119 Entries.* Toronto: University of Toronto Press.

Schild, R. E., W. A. Hiltner, and N. Sanduleak. 1969. "A spectroscopic study of the association Scorpius OB1." *Ap.J.* 156: 609–615.

Schmidt, E. G. 1984. "The luminosity scale of Cepheid variable stars." *Ap.J.* 285: 501–514.

Schönfeld, E. 1886. *Bonner Durchmusterung des südlichen Himmels.* Bonn, Germany: A. Marcus. [BD (south)]

Schüller, Fr. [1931]. "Clusters and Nebula in Orion and Puppis." *Bureau Central Astronomique Circulaire* (i.e., *IAU Circular*), no. 316, March 11. [Cr 467, Wilk's cluster]

Schuster, H. E. and R. M. West [1976]. "A Very Distant Globular Cluster?" *Astron. Astrophys.* 49:129-131. [Phoenix dwarf (discovery)]

Schwan, H. 1991. "The distance and main sequence of the Hyades cluster based on 145 stars with highly accurate proper motions obtained from work on the catalogues FK5 and PPM." *Astron. Astrophys.* 243: 386–400.

Seggewiss, W. 1971. "Photoelectric Observations of Stars in the Southern Open Clusters NGC 2335, NGC 2343, NGC 2453, NGC 4439 and H5." *Veröffentlichungen der Astronomischen Institute Bonn.*

Seitzer, P. and B. W. Carney. 1990. "The obscure globular cluster Palomar 15." *Astron. J.* 99: 229–239.

SERC/PPARC (Particle Physics and Astronomy Research Council, formerly Science and Engineering Research Council) and Anglo-Australian Observatory Board. 1993–5. *Second Epoch Survey and Equatorial Red Atlas.* Part of the *Digitized Sky Survey* (DSS). Edinburgh: Royal Observatory.

Serio, G. F., L. Indorato, and P. Natasi. 1985. "G.B. Hodierna's Observations of Nebulae and His Cosmology." *J.H.A.* 16, no. 1: 1–36.

Sérsic, J. L. 1974. "A List of Peculiar Galaxies, Interacting Pairs, Groups and Clusters South of Declination –43°." *Astrophys. & Sp. Sci.* 28: 365–373. [Reticulum = Sérsic cluster]

Setteducati, A. F. and H. F. Weaver. 1960. "Newly Found Star Clusters." Berkeley, CA: Radio Astronomy Laboratory. (We have been unable to locate a copy of this publication. It is cited in the Lund Catalogue (with a publication date of 1962) and Ruprecht, *et al.*, [1981](with a publication date of 1960, assumed here).) [Berkeley or Be]

Shakhbazian, R. K. 1957. "On a stellar [sic, galaxy] cluster in Ursa Major." *Astr. Tsirk.* 177: 11–12. [Shk 1]

Shapley, H. 1915. "Studies Based on the Colors and Magnitudes in Stellar Clusters." Cont. from *Mt. Wilson Solar Observatory* no. 115. Washington, D.C.: Carnegie Inst.

Shapley, H. 1918a. "Globular Clusters and the Structure of the Galactic System." *P.A.S.P.* 30 (Feb.): 42–54.

Shapley, H. 1918b. "Studies based on the colors and magnitudes in stellar clusters. VI. On the determination of the distances of globular clusters." *Ap.J.* 48: 89–124.

Shapley, H. 1930. *Star Clusters.* Harvard Observatory Monographs no. 2. New York: McGraw-Hill Book Co. [Harvard]

Shapley, H. 1943. *Galaxies*. Philadelphia: Blakiston.

Shapley, H. 1944. "Galactic and Extragalactic Studies, XVII. Revision of the Distances of Thirty High Latitude Globular Clusters." *Harvard Reprint* no. 257. Reprinted from the *Proceedings of the National Academy of Sciences* 30, no. 3 (Mar.): 61–68. See p. 69, footnote 7.

Shapley, H. 1969. *Through Rugged Ways to the Stars.* New York: Scribner.

Shapley, H. and E. Lindsay. 1963. "A Catalogue of Clusters in the Large Magellanic Cloud." *Irish Astron. J.* 6: 74–91. [SL]

Shapley, H. and H. B. Sawyer. 1927. *Harvard Obs. Bull* 824.

Shapley, H. and H. H. Wilson 1925. "The Magellanic Clouds, V. The Absolute Magnitudes and Linear Diameters of 108 Diffuse Nebulae." *Harvard College Observatory Circular* no. 275.

Sharov, A. 1973. "Possible new globular clusters in the Andromeda Nebula." *Soviet Astronomy* 17: 174–178. [[S73]].

Sharov, A. S., V. M. Lyutyi, and V. F. Esipov. 1995. "Photoelectric Photometry of Globular Clusters in the Andromeda Galaxy." *Astron. Lett.* 21, no. 2: 240–243.

Sharpless, S. 1953. "A Catalogue of Emission Nebula Near the Galactic Plane." *Ap. J.* 118:362–369. [Sh 1–]

Sharpless, S. 1959. "A catalogue of HII regions." *Ap.J.* Supp. 4 (Dec): 257–279. [Sh 2-] (Also available as U.S. Naval Observatory Reprint No. 7).

Sher, D. 1964. "A search for star clusters listed near η Carinae." *The Observatory* 84: 263–266 and Plate IX. [Sher 1].

Sinnott, R., M. Perryman, E. Høg, and H. Schrijver. 1997. *Millennium Star Atlas: An All-Sky Atlas Comprising One Million Stars to Visual Magnitude Eleven from the Hipparcos and Tycho Catalogues and Ten Thousand Nonstellar Objects.* Cambridge, Mass.: Sky Publishing Corp.

Sinnott, R. W., ed. 1988. *NGC 2000.0*. Cambridge, MA: Sky Publishing Corporation.

Skiff, B. 1981. "The Scutum Starcloud—Star Trails." *Deep Sky Monthly* 50 (July): 4–9.

Skiff, B. 1982. "Auriga West—Star Trails." *Deep Sky Monthly* 56 (Jan.): 8–9, 11.

Skiff, B. 1983. "Exploring Open Clusters in Canis Major and Puppis. At the Eyepiece." *Deep Sky* 2, 1, (Spring): 17–21.

Skiff, B. 1988. "Uranometria 2000.0: Limited by Its Sources." in Astronomy Reviews. *Astronomy* 16, no. 2 (Feb.): 72–73, 75.

Skiff, B. 1990. "Double Stars—Sagitta and Vulpecula." *Deep Sky* 31, 8, n. 3 (Summer): 46–47.

Skiff, B. 1992. "The Planetary Nebula in Messier 15." *Webb Society Quarterly Journal* 88 (April): 30–34.

Skiff, B. 1994. "Photometry of the Stellar Group Dolidze-Dzimsheleshvili 8." *Webb Society Quarterly Journal* 98 (Oct.): 1–4.

Skiff, B. 1995a. "Observational Data for Galactic Globular Clusters." *W.S.Q.J.* 99 (Jan.): 7–23.

Skiff, B. 1995b. "A Galaxy Behind the Milky Way, and Other CCD Catches." *CCD Astronomy* 2, no. 1 (Winter): 40–43. [Skiff J0458.2+4301]

Skiff, B. 1998a "Brocchi's Cluster Revealed." *Sky & Telescope* 95, no. 1: 65–67.

Skiff, B. 1998b. "Photometry and Astrometry of the Stellar Grouping Collinder 21." Unpublished.

Skrutskie, M. F., S. E. Schneider, R. Stiening, S. E. Strom, M. D. Weinberg, C. Beichman, T. Chester, R. Cutri, C. Lonsdale, J. Elias, R. Elston, R. Capps, J. Carpenter, J. Huchra, J. Liebert, D. Monet, S. Price, and P. Seitzer. 1997. "The Two Micron All Sky Survey (2MASS): Overview and Status." In *The Impact of Large Scale Near-IR Sky Surveys*, F. Garzon, *et al.*, eds., Dordrecht: Kluwer Academic Publishing Company, p. 25.

Skuljan, J., P. L. Cottrell, and J. B. Hearnshaw. 1997. "Eggen's Moving Groups: Fact or Fiction?" Proc. of the Hipparcos Venice '97 Symp. Noordwijk, The Netherlands: ESA Publications Division. Pp. 525–530. ESA SP-402.

Sky & Telescope. 1967. "Astronomical Notes from Prague—Stellar Rings. *Sky & Telescope* 34 (Nov.): 299.

Sky & Telescope. 1994. "Needle in a Haystack." *Sky & Telescope* 88, no. 2 (Aug.):12.

Smyth, W. H. 1844. *A Cycle of Celestial Objects: Volume 2, The Bedford Catalogue*. Reprinted 1986, Richmond: Willmann-Bell, Inc.

Solomon, P. M., and D. B. Sanders. 1980. "Giant molecular clouds as the dominant component of interstellar matter in the Galaxy."In *Giant molecular clouds in the Galaxy; Proceedings of the Third Gregynog Astrophysics Workshop.* P. M. Solomon and M. G. Edmunds, eds. Oxford: Pergamon Press. Pp. 41–73.

Solomon, S. J. and B. J. McNamara. 1980. "M11—A study of its inner and outer regions." *Astron. J.* 85 (April): 432–437.

Spergel, D.N. 1991. "Evacuation of gas from globular clusters by winds from millisecond pulsars." *Nature* 352 (July 18): 221–222.

Spitaler, R. 1890. "Beobachtungen von Cometen and Nebeln." *Astr. Nachr.* 125, no. 2993: 281–286.

Spitzer, L. 1940. "The Stability of Isolated Clusters." *M.N.R.A.S.* 100, no. 5: 397–413.

Steemers, W. J. G. and A. M. van Genderen. 1986. "VBLUW photometry of two hypergiants HD 80077 and HD 74180 and of the open cluster Pismis 11." *Astron. Astrophys.* 154: 308–312.

Stefanik, R., J. Caruso, G. Torres, S. Jha, and D. Latham. 1997. "The Membership of Upgren 1." *Baltic Astronomy* 6 (July):137–140.

Stéphan, M. 1873. "Nebulae discovered and observed at the observatory of Marseilles." *M.N.R.A.S.* 34 (Dec.): 75–76. [NGC 6846]

Stéphan, M. 1874. "Nébuleuses découvertes et observées à l'observatoire de Marseille par E. Stéphan." *Astronomische Nachrichten* 1972 (Jan. 28): 51–54. [This is apparently the same as the previous publication.]

Stephenson, C. and N. Sanduleak. 1971. "Luminous Stars in the Southern Milky Way." *Publications of the Warner and Swasey Observatory, Case Western Reserve University* 1, no. 1. [LS]

Stephenson, C. B. 1959. "A possible new galactic cluster involving Delta Lyrae." *P.A.S.P.* 71: 145–151. [Stephenson 1]

Stephenson, C. B. 1990. "A Possible New and Very Remote Galactic Cluster." *Astron. J.* 99, no. 6 (June): 1867–1868. [Stephenson 2]

Steppe, H. 1974. "RGU Photometry of the Open Clusters NGC 581 (= M103), Tr 1 and NGC 659." *Astron. Astrophys.* Supp. Ser. 15: 91–105.

Steppe, H. 1977. "*RGU* photometry of 8 open clusters near η Car: NGC 3572, NGC 3590, Tr 18, Tr 17, Ru 92, Stock 13 and Ba 17." *Astron. Astrophys.* Supp. Ser. 27: 415–427. [Basel 17]

Stock, J. 1956. "Magnitudes and Colors for Stars in Two New Galactic Clusters." *Ap.J.* 123: 258–265. [Stock 1 and 2]

Struve, F. G. W. 1827. *Catalogus Novus Stellarum Duplicium et Multiplicium: Maxima ex Parte in Specula Universitatis Caesarea Dorpatensis per Magnum Telescopium Achromaticum Fraunhoferi Detectarum.* Dorpati, Estonia: J. C. Schuenmanni, typographi academici. [STF or Σ]

Sulentic, J. W. and W. G. Tifft. 1973. *The Revised New General Catalogue of Nonstellar Astronomical Objects*. 4th printing, 1977. Tucson, AZ: The University of Arizona Press. [RNGC]

Suntzeff, Nicholas B. 1992. "Population II in the Milky Way Galaxy and the LMC." in Barbuy and Renzini (eds.) *The Stellar Populations of Galaxies, IAU Symposium 149.* Dordrecht: Kluwer. 23–28.

Tammann, G. A. 1969. "Die Lichtelemente eines anonymen Cepheiden und über seine warscheinliche Zugehörigkeit zu dem offenen Sternhaufen NGC 6649." *Astron. Astrophys.* 3: 308–315.

Tapia, M., M. Roth, J. López, M. Rubio, P. Persi, and M. Ferrari-Toniolo. 1991a. "Infrared and optical CCD images of the young cluster associated with GM 24." *Astron. Astrophys.* 242: 388–396. [IRAS 17136–3617 cluster].

Tapia, M., M. Roth, J. López, M. Rubio, P. Persi, and M. Ferrari-Toniolo. 1991b. "*Erratum* Infrared and optical CCD images of the young cluster associated with GM 24." *Astron. Astrophys.* 250: 292.

Tavarez, M. and E. Friel. 1995. "Lyngå 7: Old Open Cluster or Globular Cluster?" *Astron. J.* 110: 223–227.

Tayler, R. J. and P. R. Wood. 1975. "The Gas and Horizontal Branch Star Content of Globular Clusters." *M.N.R.A.S.* 171: 467–474.

Tennyson, Alfred Lord. 1842. *Poems*. Boston, MA: W. D. Ticknor.

Terzan, A. 1966. "Un nouvel amas globulaire dans la region du centre de la Voie lactee." *C.R. Acad. Sci.* Ser. B, 263 (July 11): 221–222. [Terzan 1]

Terzan, A. 1967. "Un nouvel amas globularie dans la region centrale de la Galaxie." *C.R. Acad. Sci.* Ser. B, 265 (Sept. 25): 734–736. [Terzan 2]

Terzan, A. 1968. "Six nouveaux amas stellaires (Terzan 3-8) dans la region du centre de la Voie lactee et les constellations du Scorpion et du Sagittaire." *C.R. Acad. Sci.* Ser. B, 267 (Nov. 25): 1245–1248. [Terzan 3 to 8]

Terzan, A. 1971a. "Quatre nouveaux amas stellaires dans la direction de la région centrale de la Galaxie." *Astron. Astrophys.* 12: 477–481. [Terzan 9, 10, 11, 12]

Terzan, A. 1971b. "Erratum: Four New Star Clusters in the Direction of the Central Area of the Galaxy." *Astron. Astrophys.* 15: 336. [Terzan 12/ Terzan 11]

Terzan, A. and K. H. Ju. 1980. "A Photometric Study of the Bright Cloud B in Sagittarius: III." *ESO Messenger* 20: 6–7. [Terz N 1 to 24]

Terzan, A. 1985. "A Photometric Study of the Bright Cloud B in Sagittarius: IV. 17 New Diffuse Objects." *ESO Messenger* 42 (Dec.): 4–6. [Terz N 25 to 41]

Thé, P. S. and C. Roslund. 1963. "Photometry of the galactic cluster NGC 6649." *Contr. Bosscha Obs.* 19.

Thome, J. M. 1892. "Cordoba Durchmusterung Declination –22° to –32°." *Results of National Argentine Obs.*, 16:1–604. [CD, partial]

Thome, J. M. 1894. "Cordoba Durchmusterung Declination –32° to –42°." *Results of National Argentine Obs.* 17: 1–541. [CD, partial]

Thome, J. M. 1900. "Cordoba Durchmusterung Declination –42° to –52°." *Results of National Argentine Obs.* 18: 1–502. [CD, partial]

Thome, J. M. 1914. "Cordoba Durchmusterung Declination –52° to –62°." *Results of National Argentine Obs.* 21, part 1: 1–305. [CD, partial]

Tifft, W.G., L.P. Conolly, and D. F. Webb. 1972. "NGC 2818, an open cluster containing a planetary nebula." *M.N.R.A.S.* 158: 47–62.

Tirion, W., B. Rappaport, and G. Lovi. 1988a. *Uranometria 2000.0* Volume I: The Northern Hemisphere to −6°. Richmond, VA: Willmann-Bell Inc.

Tirion, W., B. Rappaport, and G. Lovi. 1988b. *Uranometria 2000.0.* Vol. II, *The Southern Hemisphere to* +6°. Richmond, VA: Willmann-Bell Inc.

Tirion, W., B. Rappaport, and W. Remaklus. 2001a. *Uranometria 2000.0* Deep Sky Atlas Volume I: The Northern Hemisphere to −6°. Richmond, VA: Willmann-Bell Inc.

Tirion, W., B. Rappaport, and W. Remaklus. 20001b. *Uranometria 2000.0* Deep Sky Atlas Volume II: The Southern Hemisphere to +6°. Richmond, VA: Willmann-Bell Inc.

Tirion, Wil. 1981. *Sky Atlas 2000.0: 26 Star Charts, Covering Both Hemispheres*. Cambridge, MA: Sky Publishing Corporation.

Tombaugh, C. 1938. "Two new faint galactic star clusters." *P.A.S.P.* 50: 171. [Tombaugh 1 and 2]

Tombaugh, C. 1941. "Three more new galactic star clusters." *P.A.S.P.* 53: 219–221. [Tombaugh 3 to 5]

Toomre, A., and J. Toomre. 1972. "Galactic Bridges and Tails." *Astrophys. J.* 178: 623–666.

Topaktas, L. and R. P. Fenkert. 1982. "Photographic RGU photometry of five southern open clusters in Vela II. *Astron. Astrophys.* Supp. Ser. 49: 475–482. [Basel 20]

Trager, S. C., I. R. King, S. Djorgovski. 1995a. "Catalogue of Galactic Globular-Cluster Surface-Brightness Profiles." *Astronomical Journal* 109, no. 1 (Jan.): 218–241.

Trager, S. C., I. R. King, S. Djorgovski. 1995b. "Erratum: Catalogue of Galactic Globular-Cluster Surface-Brightness Profiles (Astron. J. 109, 218 [1995])." *Astronomical Journal* 109, no. 4 (April): 1912.

Trinchieri, G. and G. Fabbiano. 1991. "The discrete X-ray source population in M31." *Ap.J.* 382: 82. [TF]

Trumpler, R. J. 1930. "Preliminary Results on the Distances, Dimensions and Space Distribution of Open Star Clusters." *Lick Observatory Bulletin* 14, no. 420: 154–188.

Turner, D. G. 1982. "On the possibility of cluster membership for the cepheid V Centauri." *P.A.S.P.*, 94: 1003–1007, December. [Turner 7]

Turner, D. G. 1984. "The Optical Companions of the Long-Period Cepheid WZ Sagittarii—Remains of an Open Cluster?" *P.A.S.P.* 96 (June): 422–428. [C1814-190]

Turner, D. G. 1985a. "The reddening (and distance?) of P Cygni." *Astron. Astrophys.* 144: 241–244.

Turner, D. G. 1985b. "A Newly-Discovered Open Cluster Surrounding the 681-Day Cepheid S Vulpeculae." *J. Roy. Astron. Soc. Can.* 79, no. 4: 175–179. [C1947+272 = Turner 1].

Turner, D. G. 1986a. "Variable Stars in LYNDS 810." *Info. Bull. on Var. Stars*, 2874: 1.

Turner, D. G. 1986b. "The large globule LYNDS 810 as a possible member of the Vulpecula OB1 complex." *Astron. Astrophys.*, 167 (October): 157–160.

Turner, D. G. 1992. "Galactic Clusters with Associated Cepheid Variables. III, NGC 1647 with SZ Tauri." *Astron. J.* 104: 1865–1875.

Turner, D. G. 1998. "A Search for Stars Physically Associated with the 16 Day Cepheid X Cygni. II. Clusters in the Field." *Astron. J.*, 116 (July): 274–283. [Turner 11].

Turner, D. G. 1999. "A Distance Calibrating Cluster in Carina." *J.R.A.S.C.*, 93 (April): 64–65, [Shorlin]

Turner, D. G., G. I. Mandushev, and D. Forbes. 1994. "Galactic Cluster with Associated Cepheid Variables. IV. C2128+488 (Anon. Platais) and V1726 Cygni." *Astron. J.* 107, no. 5 (May): 1796–1805.

Turner, D. G., G. I. Mandushev, and G. A. Welch. 1997. "Galactic Clusters with Associated Cepheid Variables. V. The Case of SU Cygni." *Astron. J.* 113, no. 6 (June): 2104–2115.

Turner, D. G., and L. N. Berdnikov. 2002. "T Antliae, a Newly Discovered Cluster Cepheid Studied Using Archival Data." *Bull. Am. Ast. Soc.,* 200: #07.03. [Turner 5]

Turner, D. G., M. A. Ibrahimov, G. I. Mandushev, L. N. Berdnikov, and A. J. Horsford. 1998. "A Search for the Parent Cluster of the Cepheid SU Cygni." *J.R.A.S.C.*, 92 (June): 145–152. [Mandushev 1]

Turner, D. G., P. J. T. Leonard, and B.F. Madore. 1986. "Photometry of the S Vul Cluster." *J. Roy. Astron. Soc. Can.* 80, no. 4: 166–179.

Turner, D. G., S. van den Bergh, P. F. Younger, T. A. Danks, and D. Forbes. 1993. "A Search for OB Associations Near Southern Long Period Cepheids. IV. XY Carinae, GT Carinae, WZ Sagittarii, and SW Velorum." *Astrophys. J.* Supp. Ser. 85 (March): 119–136. [WZ Sgr cl = C1814–191a; C1814–191b]

Upgren, A. and V. Rubin. 1965. "An old open cluster near the North Galactic Pole." *P.A.S.P.* 77: 355–358. [Upgren 1]

Urban, S. E. and T. E. Corbin. 1998. "The Astrographic Catalogue—A Century of Work Pays Off." *Sky & Telescope* 6 (June): 40–44.

USNO and RGO. 1999. *The Astronomical Almanac for the Year 2000.* Washington, D.C.: U.S. Government Printing Office. Pp. H56–H58.

Vaiana, G. S., J. P. Cassinelli, G. Fabiano, R. Giacconi, L. Golub, P. Gorenstein, B. M. Haisch, F. R. Harnden, Jr., H. M. Johnson, J. L. Linsky, C. W. Maxson, R. Mewe, R. Rosner, F. Seward, K. Topka, and C. Zwaan. 1981. "Results from an extensive Einstein stellar survey." *Ap.J.* 245: 163–182. [1E]

Van Albada, T.S. 1968. "Numerical Integrations of the *N*-Body Problem." *Bull. Astron. Inst. Neth.* 19: 479–499.

Van Bueren, H. G. 1952. "On the structure of the Hyades cluster." *Bull. Astr. Inst. Neth.* 11:385–403.

van den Bergh, S. 1957. "A search for Cepheids in galactic clusters." *Astrophys. J.* 126: 323. [Cl vdB 1]

van den Bergh, S. 1959. "A catalogue of dwarf galaxies." Richmond Hill, Ontario: *Publ. David Dunlap Obs.* 2: 145–156. [DDO]

van den Bergh, S. 1964. "Stellar associations in the Andromeda nebula." *Ap.J.* Supp. Ser. 9: 65–80. [[V64]]

van den Bergh, S. 1966. "A study of reflection nebulae." *Astron. J.* 71, no. 10 (Dec.): 990–998. [Cl vdB 80, 83, 85, 92, 130, 150, 152]

van den Bergh, S. 1969. "Photometric and Spectroscopic Observations of Globular Clusters in the Andromeda Nebula." *Ap.J. Supp.* 171, no. 171: 145–174. [Cl vdB 0]

van den Bergh, S. 1972. "Search for faint companions to M31." *Ap.J.* 171: L31–L33. [And I –IV]

van den Bergh, S. 1981. "UBV observations of globular clusters in the Magellanic Clouds." *Astron. Astrophys.* Supp. Ser. 46: 79–87.

van den Bergh, S. 1991. "Star Clusters in the Magellanic Clouds." In *The Magellanic Clouds.* IAU Symp. 148, R. Haynes and D. Milne, eds. Dordrecht: Kluwer, pp. 161–164.

van den Bergh, S. 1999. "The local group of galaxies." *Astron. Astrophys. Rev.* 9: 372–318.

van den Bergh, S. and G. L. Hagen. 1975. "Uniform survey of clusters in the southern Milky Way." *Astron. J.* 80, no. 1 (Jan.): 11–16. [vdB-Ha]

van den Bergh, S., C. Morbey, and J. Pazder. 1991. "Diameters of Galactic Globular Clusters." *Astrophysical Journal* 375 (July 10): 595–599.

van der Hucht, K. A., P. S. Conti, I. Lundstrom, and B. Stenholm. 1981. "The Sixth Catalogue of galactic Wolf-Rayet stars, their past and present." *Space Sci. Rev.* 28: 277–306. [WR]

van Genderen, A. M., W. Bijlevald, and E. Van Groningen. 1984. "VBLUW photometry of the associations Sco OB1 (containing the open cluster NGC 6231)—A discussion on the evolutionary status of the hypergiant Zeta (1) Sco (B1Ia+)." *Astron. Astrophys.* Supp. Ser. 58: 537–548.

van Paradijs, J. and R. Isaacman. 1989. "An Infrared Search for obscured globular clusters associated with X-ray sources." *Astron. Astrophys.* 222 (Sept.): 129–131.

Vasilevskis, S. 1955. "Positions and proper motions of stars in the region of the galactic cluster IC 4665." *Astron. J.* 60: 384.

Vetesnik, M. 1962. "Photographic photometry of star clusters in galaxy M31." *Bull. Astron. Inst. Czech.* 13: 180. [[V62]]

Vickers, J. C. 1994a. *Deep Space CCD Atlas: North* Duxbury, MA: John C. Vickers, Back River Observatory, P.O. Box 1292, Duxbury, MA 02331).

Vickers, J.C. 1994b. *Deep Space CCD Atlas: South.* Duxbury, MA: John C. Vickers, Back River Observatory.

Vorontsov-Vel'yaminov, B. & Krasnogorskaia, A. 1962. "Morphological catalogue of galaxies. Part I. Catalogue of 7200 galaxies between declinations +90° and +45°." *Trudy Gos. Astr. Inst.* Sternberg, 32. [MCG 1]

Vorontsov-Vel'yaminov, B. and V. Arkhipova. 1963. "Morphological catalogue of galaxies. Part III. Catalogue of 6740 galaxies between declinations +15° and –9°." *Trudy Gos. Astr. Inst.* Sternberg, 33. [MCG 3]

Vorontsov-Vel'yaminov, B. and V. Arkhipova. 1964. "Morphological catalogue of galaxies. Part II. Catalogue of 9650 galaxies between declinations +45° and +15°." *Trudy Gos. Astr. Inst.* Sternberg, 34. [MCG 2]

Vorontsov-Vel'yaminov, B. and V. Arkhipova. 1968. "Morphological catalogue of galaxies. Part IV. Catalogue of 5410 galaxies between declinations –9° and –33°." *Trudy Gos. Astr. Inst.* Sternberg, 38. [MCG 4]

Vorontsov-Vel'yaminov, B. and V. Arkhipova. 1974. "Morphological catalogue of galaxies." Part V. *Trudy Gos. Astr. Inst.* Sternberg, 46. [MCG 5]

Walker, A. R. 1985. "CCD Photometry of Galactic Clusters containing Cepheid variables –I. Lyngå 6." *M.N.R.A.S.* 213: 889–897.

Walker, A. R. 1992. "The LMC Cluster GLC 0435-59 (Reticulum): Photometry of the RR Lyraes, and a Color-Magnitude Diagram." *Astron. J.* 103, no. 4 (April): 1166–1204.

Walterbos R. A. M., E. Brinks, and W. W. Shane. 1985. "A high resolution radio continuum survey of Messier 31. II. Observations at 1412 MHz, data reduction and the 37W catalogue of radio sources." *Astron. Astrophys.* Suppl. Ser. 61: 451–471. [WSTB 37W]

Warner, B. and N. Warner. 1984. *Maclear & Herschel—Letters & Diaries at the Cape of Good Hope 1834–1838.* Cape Town, South Africa: A. A. Balkema.

Wayman, P. A., L. Symms, and K. Blackwell. 1965. "Proper motions and radial velocities of Hyades stars." Royal Obs. Bull. 98, Series E:33–62.

Weaver, H. and P. Weaver. 1957. "Robert Julius Trumpler 1886–1956." *P.A.S.P.* 69 (August): 304–307.

Webb, T. W. 1962. *Celestial Objects for Common Telescopes.* Vol. 2, *The Stars.* Ed. and rev. by M. W. Mayall. New York: Dover Publications.

Weinberger, R. 1995. "New Interesting Objects Discovered in Optical Sky Surveys." *P.A.S.P.* 107 (Jan.): 58–61. [[W95]]

Welch, D. L. 1991. "Accurate Positions for SMC Clusters." *Astron. J.* 101, no. 2, February: 538–540.

Westerhout, G. 1958. "A survey of the continuous radiation from the galactic system at a frequency of 1390 Mc/s." *Bull. Astron. Inst. Netherlands* 14: 215–260. [W]

Westerlund, B. 1960. "On the identification of a radio source in Carina." *Arkiv för Astronomi* 2, no.39. [We 2]

Westerlund, B. 1961. "A Heavily Reddened Cluster in Ara." *P.A.S.P.* 73 (no. 430): 51–55. [We 1]

Westerlund, B. 1968. "On the extended infrared source in Ara." *Ap. J. Lett.* 154: L67–L68, plate L1.

Westerlund, B. 1969. "OB Stars near the Supernova Remnant RCW 103 and the Galactic Structure in Norma." *Astron. J.*, 74, no. 7 (September):882–890 and plates IV–VIII. [We 3]

Westerlund, B. and J. Glaspey. 1971. "On the structure of the wing of the Small Magellanic Cloud." *Astron. Astrophys.* Supp. Ser. 10: 1–7. [WG71]

White, R. E. and S. J. Shawl. 1987. "Axial ratios and orientations for 100 Galactic globular star clusters." *Ap. J.* 317 (June 1): 246–263.

White, R.E. and T. T. Kraft. 1972. "Pseudo color-magnitude diagrams for three southern hemispheric globular star clusters." *P.A.S.P.* 84: 298.

Whiteoak, J. B. 1961. "A Study of the Galactic Cluster IC 2602." *M.N.R.A.S.* 123: 245–256.

Whiting, A. B., G. K. T. Hau, and M. Irwin. 2002. "The Southern Dwarf Hunt: Local Group Dwarf Candidates in the Southern Sky." *Astrophys. J.* Supp. Ser., 141 (July): 123–146. [WHI]

Whitman, Alan, and Guy Mackie. 2000. "MKSP 2000: Reports." *Focus, Newsletter of the Okanagan Centre of the RASC* 5, no. 7, October: 1, 5–6. [Mackie 1]

Wielen, R. 1975. "Dynamics of Star Clusters: Comparison of Theory with Observations and Simulations." In *Dynamics of Stellar Systems*, 119–131. A. Hayli, ed. Dordrecht: Reidel.

Williams, P. M. 1966. "Photometry of NGC 2451." *M.N.A.S.S.A.* 25, no. 10 (Oct. 31): 122–131.

Williams, P. M. 1967a. "Photoelectric Photometry of NGC 2451." *M.N.A.S.S.A.* 26: 30–39.

Williams, P. M. 1967b. "The Open Cluster NGC 2451." *M.N.A.S.S.A.* 26, no. 10 (Nov. 15): 139–143.

Wilson, B. [1998]. "Obscure Globular Clusters of the Milky Way: Terzan Clusters and the Faintest Globular UKS 1." *The Deep-Sky Observer, The Quarterly Journal of the Webb Society*, no. 114 (October):8–16.

Wilson, O. C. and M. K. V. Bappu. 1957. "H and K emission in late-type stars: dependence of line width on luminosity and related topics." *Ap. J.* 125: 661–688.

Wilson, R. 1953. *General catalogue of stellar radial velocities.* Washington, D.C.: Carnegie Inst. Publication 601. [GCRV]

Wilson, R. and J. Bolton. 1960. "A survey of galactic radiation at 960 MC/S [MHz]." *P.A.S.P.* 72: 331–347. [CTB]

Wirth, A., L. L. Smarr, and T. L. Bruno. 1985. "The missing bulge globular clusters in M31—New optical candidates." *Astrophys. J.* 290: 140–153. [WSB85]

Wolf, M. 1892. "Photographische Aufnahmen der Nova Aurigae und einiger neuer ausgedehnter Nebelflecke." *Astronomische Nachrichten* 3130 (Nov. 26): 157–160. [IC 410]

Wolf, Max. 1904. "A Remarkable Nebula in Cygnus connected with Starless Regions." *M.N.R.A.S.* 64, no. 9: 838–840. [IC 5146]

Wolf, Max. 1926. "Die Herschel-Nebel nach Aufnahmen der Königstuhl-Sternwarte." *Veröffentlichungen der Badischen Sternwarte zu Heidelberg (Königstuhl)*, 2d ser., vol. 9. Berlin: Walter de Gruytar & Co.

Worley, C. and G. Douglass. 1996. *The Washington Visual Double Star Catalogue 1996.0.* Washington, D.C.: U. S. Naval Observatory.

Wouterloot, J. and J. Brand. 1989. "IRAS sources beyond the solar circle. I. CO observations." *Astron. Astrophys.* Supp. Ser. 80: pp. 149–187. [WB89]

Yanny, B., P. Guhathakurta, D. P. Schneider, and J. N. Bachall. 1993. "HST observations of globular cluster cores." In *Structure and Dynamics of Globular Clusters.* S. G. Djorgovski and G. Meylan, eds., A.S.P. Conference Series 50: 275–283.

Zacharias, N, M. I. Zacharias, G. Douglass, and G. L. Wycoff. 1996. "The Twin Astrographic Catalog (TAC) Version 1.0." *Astron. J.* 112: 2336.

Zinn, R. 1980. "The dwarf spheroidal galaxies." In *Globular Clusters.* D. Hanes and B. Madore, eds. Cambridge: Cambridge University Press. Pp. 191–192

Zinn, R. 1985. "The globular cluster system of the galaxy. IV—The halo and disk subsystems." *Ap. J.* 293 (June 15): 424–444.

Zinnecker, H., C. J. Keable, J. S. Dunlop, R. D. Cannon, and W. K. Griffiths. 1988. "The Nuclei of Nucleated Dwarf Elliptical Galaxies—Are they Globular Clusters?" In *The Harlow Shapley Symposium on Globular Cluster Systems in Galaxies.* IAU Symp. 126, J. E. Grindlay and A. G. Davis Phillip, eds. Pp. 603–604. Dordrecht: Kluwer.

Zuckerman, B. 1973. "A Model of the Orion Nebula." *Ap. J.* 183: 863–870.

Zuckerman, B. and P. Palmer. 1974. "Radio radiation from interstellar molecules." *Ann. Rev. Astron. Astrophys.* 12: 279–313.

Zwicky, F. 1959. "Galaxies—The Local Group." *Carnegie Institute Yearbook* 58: 60–61. [Palomar 15 = Zwicky 1]

Zwicky, F. and C. Kowal. 1968. *Catalogue of galaxies and of clusters of galaxies.* Vol. VI. Pasadena, CA: California Institute of Technology. [CGCG]

Zwicky, F. and E. Herzog. 1963. *Catalogue of galaxies and of clusters of galaxies.* Vol. II. Pasadena, CA: California Institute of Technology. [CGCG]

Zwicky F. and E. Herzog. 1966. *Catalogue of galaxies and of clusters of galaxies.* Vol. III. Pasadena, CA: California Institute of Technology. [CGCG]

Zwicky F. and E. Herzog. 1968. *Catalogue of galaxies and of clusters of galaxies.* Vol. IV. Pasadena, CA: California Institute of Technology.

Zwicky F., E. Herzog, and P. Wild. 1960. *Catalogue of galaxies and of clusters of galaxies.* Vol. I. Pasadena, CA: California Institute of Technology. [CGCG]

Zwicky F., M. Karpowicz, and C. Kowal. 1965. *Catalogue of galaxies and of clusters of galaxies.* Vol. V. Pasadena, CA: California Institute of Technology. [CGCG]

Zwicky, F. and M. Zwicky. 1971. *Catalogue of selected compact galaxies and of post-eruptive galaxies.* Guemligen, Switzerland: F. Zwicky. [II Zw and III Zw]

Bibliography

Observational

Barker, E. S. *Webb Society Deep-Sky Observer's Handbook.* Vol. 3, *Open and Globular Clusters.* Ed. K. Glyn Jones. Springfield, NJ: Enslow Publishers Inc., 1980.

Burnham, R., Jr. *Burnham's Celestial Handbook.* Vols. 1–3. New York: Dover Publ. Inc., 1978.

Clark, R. N. *Visual Astronomy of the Deep-Sky,* Cambridge: Cambridge University Press, 1990.

Crossen, C. and W. Tirion. *Binocular Astronomy.* Richmond, VA: Willmann-Bell, Inc., 1993.

Cragin, M., J. Lucyk, and B. Rappaport. *The Deep Sky Field Guide to Uranometria 2000.0.* Richmond, VA: Willmann-Bell, Inc., 1993.

Cragin, M. and E. Bonanno. *Uranometria 2000.0 Volume 3: Deep Sky Field Guide.* Richmond, VA: Willmann-Bell Inc., 2001.

Hartung, E. J. *Astronomical Objects for Southern Telescopes.* Cambridge: Cambridge University Press, 1968 and 1984.

Hirshfeld, A., R. W. Sinnott, and F. Ochsenbein. *Sky Catalogue 2000.0.* 2d ed. Vol. 1. Cambridge: Cambridge University Press and Sky Publishing Corp., 1991.

Hirshfeld, A. and R. W. Sinnott. *Sky Catalogue 2000.0.* Vol. 2. Cambridge: Cambridge University Press and Sky Publishing Corp., 1985.

Houston, W. and S. O'Meara. *Deep-Sky Wonders.* Cambridge: Mass.: Sky Publishing Corp., 1999.

Luginbuhl, C. and B. Skiff. *Observing Handbook and Catalogue of Deep-Sky Objects.* Cambridge: Cambridge University Press, 1990.

O'Meara, S. *The Messier Objects.* Cambridge: Mass.: Sky Publishing Corporation and Cambridge University Press, 1998.

Sinnott, R. (ed.). *NGC 2000.0.* Cambridge: Cambridge University Press, 1988.

Astrophotography & CCD Imaging

Berry, R. *Introduction to Astronomical Image Processing.* Richmond, VA: Willmann-Bell Inc., 1991.

Berry, R. *Choosing and Using a CCD Camera.* Richmond, VA: Willmann-Bell Inc., 1993.

Berry, R. and J. Burnell, *The Handbook of Astronomical Image Processing,* Richmond, VA: Willmann-Bell, Inc. 2000

Berry, R., V. Kanto, and J. Munger. *The CCD Camera Cookbook.* Richmond, VA: Willmann-Bell Inc., 1994.

Budding, E. *An Introduction to Astronomical Photometry,* Cambridge: Cambridge University Press, 1993.

Buil, C. *CCD Astronomy.* Richmond, VA: Willmann-Bell Inc., 1991.

Covington, M. *Astrophotography for the Amateur.* Cambridge: Cambridge University Press, 1985.

Liller, W. *The Cambridge Astronomy Guide,* Cambridge: Cambridge University Press, 1985.

Reeves, R. *Wide-Field Astrophotography,* Richmond, VA: Willmann-Bell, Inc. 1999

Reference

Alter, G., J. Ruprecht, and V. Vanysek. *Catalogue of Star Clusters and Associations,* Prague: Academia, 1958. 2nd Edition. Budapest: Akademiai Kiado, 1970.

Archinal, B. A. *The "Non-Existent" Star Clusters of the RNGC.* Webb Society Monograph No. 1. Portsmouth, England: The Webb Society, 1993.

Kepple, G. R. and G. W. Scanner. 1998. *The Night Sky Observer's Guide, Volume 1, Autumn and Winter.* Richmond: Willmann-Bell, Inc.

Kepple, G. R. and G. W. Scanner. 1998. *The Night Sky Observer's Guide, Volume 2, Spring & Summer.* Richmond: Willmann-Bell, Inc.

Lyngå, G. *Lund Catalogue of Open Cluster Data.* 5th Ed. Sweden: Lund Observatory, 1987.

Pennington, H. *The Year-Round Messier Marathon Field Guide.* Richmond, VA: Willmann-Bell, Inc., 1997.

Ruprecht, J., B. Balazs, and R.E. White. *Catalogue of Clusters and Associations.* Supplement 1. Budapest: Akademiai Kiado, 1981.

Ruprecht, J., B. Balazs, and R.E. White. *Catalogue of Clusters and Associations.* Vol. 2, *Globular Clusters.* Budapest: Akademiai Kiado, 1981.

Sulentic, J. and W. Tifft. *The Revised New General Catalogue of Nonstellar Astronomical Objects.* Tucson: University of Arizona Press, 1973.

Tirion, W., B. Rappaport, and W. Remaklus. *Uranometria 2000.0 Deep Sky Atlas* Volume 1: The Northern Hemisphere to -6°. Richmond, VA: Willmann-Bell Inc., 2001.

Tirion, W., B. Rappaport, and W. Remaklus. *Uranometria 2000.0 Deep Sky Atlas* Volume 2: The Southern Hemisphere to +6°. Richmond, VA: Willmann-Bell Inc., 2001.

Tirion, W. and B. Skiff. *Bright Star Atlas 2000.0.* Richmond, VA: Willmann-Bell Inc., 2001.

Technical

Djorgovski, S. G. and G. Meylan, eds. *Structure and Dynamics of Globular Clusters.* ASP Conference Series, vol. 50. San Francisco: Astronomical Society of the Pacific, 1993.

Falgarone, E. *et al.,* eds. *Fragmentation of Molecular Clouds and Star Formation.* IAU Symposium No. 147. Dordrecht: Kluwer Academic Publ., 1991.

Goodman, J. and P. Hut, eds. *Dynamics of Star Clusters.* Proceedings of the 13th Symposium of the IAU. Dordrecht: Kluwer Academic Publ., 1985.

Grindlay, J. E. and A. G. Davis Philip, eds. *The Harlow Shapley Symposium on Globular Cluster Systems in Galaxies.* IAU Symposium No. 126. Dordrecht: Kluwer Academic Pub., 1988.

Hanes, D. and B. Madore, eds. *Globular Clusters.* Cambridge: Cambridge University Press, 1980.

Hesser, J., ed. *Star Clusters.* IAU Symposium No. 85. Dordrecht: D. Reidel Publ. Co., 1980.

Janes, K., ed. *The Formation and Evolution of Star Clusters.* ASP Conference Series, Vol. 13, San Francisco: Astronomical Society of the Pacific, 1991.

Madore, B. F., ed. *Cepheids: Theory and Observations.* IAU Colloquium No. 82. Cambridge: Cambridge University Press, 1985.

Smith, G. H. and J. P. Brodie, eds. *The Globular Cluster-Galaxy Connection.* ASP Conference Series, Vol. 48. Astronomical Society of the Pacific, 1993.

Solomon, P. M. and M. G. Edmunds, eds. *Giant Molecular Clouds in the Galaxy.* Oxford: Pergamon Press, 1980.

Tenorio-Tagle, G., M. Prieto, and F. Sanchez, eds. *Star Formation in Stellar*

Systems. Proceedings of the Third Canary Islands Winter School of Astrophysics. Cambridge: Cambridge University Press, 1992.

Van der Kruit, P.C. G. Gilmore, eds. *Stellar Populations*. IAU Symposium No. 164. Dordrecht: Kluwer Academic Publishers, 1995.

General

Cohen, M. *In Darkness Born*. Cambridge: Cambridge University Press, 1988.

Glyn Jones, K. *The Search for the Nebulae*. Giles, U.K.: Alpha Academic Press, 1975.

Hearnshaw, J. B. *The Analysis of Starlight*. Cambridge: Cambridge University Press, 1990.

Jaschek, C. and M. Jaschek. *The Classification of Stars*. Cambridge: Cambridge University Press, 1990.

Kaler, J. B. *Stars and their Spectra*. Cambridge: Cambridge University Press, 1989.

Malin, D. and P. Murdin. *Colors of the Stars*. Cambridge: Cambridge University Press, 1984.

Maran, S., ed. *The Astronomy and Astrophysics Encyclopedia*. Cambridge: Cambridge University Press, 1992.

Murdin, P. and D. A. Allen. *Catalogue of the Universe*. Cambridge: Cambridge University Press, 1979.

Payne-Gaposchkin, C. *Stars and Clusters*. Cambridge: Harvard University Press, 1979.

Shapley, H. *Star Clusters*. Harvard Observatory Monograph No. 2. Cambridge: Harvard University Press, 1930.

Whitney, C.A. *The Discovery of Our Galaxy*, New York: Knopf, 1971.

Index

This index is drawn from the text. It does not index the contents of the tables and Appendix A which comprise a significant fraction of this work. Objects contained in Tables 4.1, 7.1, C1, C.2, and C.3 are arranged in right ascension order. Objects in Tables D.1, and D.2 are arranged in order of name. Finally, Table D.3 lists all objects cataloged in this work in order of name which is cross-referenced to right ascension and enables entry by name in those tables ordered by right ascension.

Symbols

Numerics

A

B

C

O

P